Rod Machado's Instrument Pilot's Handbook

Written by
Rod Machado

Published by The Aviation Speakers Bureau

Rod Machado's Instrument Pilot's Handbook

ISBN 978 09712015-6-9 55995

Please visit (and *bookmark*) our web site for any additional book updates:
www.rodmachado.com

Published by:
The Aviation Speakers Bureau, P.O. Box 6030, San Clemente, CA 92674-6030.

Cover layout by Rod Machado
Front cover artwork created by Rod Machado
All material created, written and produced by Rod Machado
All illustrations designed and drawn by Rod Machado (QuarkXPress, Corel, Photoshop)
Photographs (unless marked otherwise or in the public domain) by Rod Machado
Copyright 2007 by Rod Machado

First Edition
10 9 8 7 6 5 4 3 2 1

Contents

CONTENTS

Acknowledgments

The author wishes to acknowledge the help and or support of the following individuals, companies or groups:

Aviation Supplies and Academics (ASA)

Brian Weiss of WORD'SWORTH, Santa Monica, CA.

Diane Titterington of The Aviation Speakers Bureau, San Clemente, CA.

The New Piper Aircraft Corporation. Charts and graphs provided by Piper are to be used for information purposes only. A Pilot Operating Handbook is the only true source of information.

The Cessna Aircraft Corporation. Cessna authorized the use of their materials with the understanding that they are to be used for training purposes only, not the actual operation of an aircraft.

Aircraft Owners and Pilots Association for permission to use their flight planning software.

All the folks at ASRS, Moffett Field, CA

Captain Ralph Butcher

Gene Croxton

Rick Crose

Bill Cox

Captain John Dill

Bridgette Doremire

Don Eick

Captain Al Englehardt

Skip Forster

Fred L Gibbs

Captain Dave Gwinn

Meg Godlewski

Garmin

Phil Hewitt

Dan Hofert

Captain James P. Johnson of James Johnson Associates

John Moore

Danny Mortensen, President of Airline Ground Schools

Tim Peterson

Steve Pelissier

Linda Pendelton

Jason Randal

Captain Wally Roberts

Eric Secretan and his fine staff at NACO

Hank Smith

Summit, CD

Max Trescott

Celia Vanderpool

Bruce Williams of BruceAir.com

Greg Yamamoto

Clipart from the following companies may have been used: 3G Graphics, Archive Arts, BBL Typographic, Cartesia Software, Image Club Graphics Inc., Management Graphics Ltd., One Mile Up Inc., Studio Piazza Xilo Inc., Techpool Studios Inc., Totem Graphics Inc., TNT Designs, SmartPics.

And the many others that I may have forgotten. I'll place your name here on the next printing. Please forgive me.

Updating Your Book

Because the world of instrument flying changes quickly, you should make it a regular practice to update your book by visiting my web site located at:

http://www.rodmachado.com

Visit the Book/Slide update page for any changes that may affect this text or changes in the FAA Knowledge exam.

Author's Note

Any errors found in this book are solely the responsibility of the author, Rod Machado.

Bruce Williams

I've known Rod Machado for a long time (in pilot years). We've often worked the same gigs on the aviation trade-show circuit (but his crowds are always much bigger), and I count signing him as the official flight instructor for *Microsoft Flight Simulator* as one of the best deals I made when I worked on that product.

Of course, lots of people "know" Rod in the way that they "know," say, TV news anchors. They see Rod at aviation seminars, always impeccably pressed, with coiffed hair that could lead even a televangelist down the path to Deadly Sin #6. (If you sense that I've already succumbed to Envy, you're right—my hair went gray a long time—and many fewer students—ago. And I never had to ride with "Bob," Rod's archetypical "challenged" student, who apparently suffers from Aviation Deficit Hypocognitive Disorder.)

The man is unflappable, even in front of a crowd. He epitomizes the old joke about flight instructors being trained to perspire only on the right side of their faces. Interrupted by roaring jets at EAA AirVenture or heckling trivia-meisters at AOPA Expo, he just picks up the tune, and with his inexhaustible supply of puns and anecdotes, he effortlessly guides the audience back to the subject at hand. His handkerchief is just a pocket square. He never has to dab his brow.

And, oh, those puns. Rod revels in wordplay with the glee of a five-year-old who's just discovered "knock-knock" jokes. I know this because I've read this entire book. Every word of it.

I also know that Rod knows that some people buy his books expecting to sample a two-star, typical suburban, medium-spicy stir-fry only to discover that the cook has kicked things up several stars. They dive in. They laugh. And occasionally they groan—especially at Rod's takeoffs on take-out.

But Rod's readers also *remember*. You may not be able to cite chapter and verse of the FARs, but like earworms, Rod's turns of phrase stick with you. ("Mandy," anyone?)

Now, I'm the kind of guy who reads manuals. In fact, in a former life, I wrote and edited wobbly stacks of them, back when big software companies published user guides. And I've been poring over aviation handbooks since, as a boy, I sneaked off with my father's very official U.S. Air Force binders for the C-54. Before I read this book, I thought I'd absorbed a lot of esoterica about instrument flying.

Cont.

FOREWORD (Cont.)

But turning its pages, I quickly discovered that I still had much to learn. I was reminded—again—that while Rod has an unlimited supply of puns always ready to deploy, he also possesses an encyclopedic knowledge of aviation, and he's acquired that wisdom both through formal study and that invaluable study hall—real flying and teaching experience.

Today, you can find many authoritative sources of aviation information, even on the Web. The trouble is, those sources (e.g., the FAA's own classic *Instrument Flying Handbook*) usually are written by the authorities, with all the verve that, after many meetings and deliberations, a blue-ribbon commission can muster, and in a style for which the "executive summary" was mercifully invented.

So here's my advice: Enjoy this five-star stir-fry. If necessary, keep a supply of icy beverages readily at hand. After laughing—and, yes, occasionally groaning—your way through to Chapter 17, you'll discover that you're well on your way to mastering a daunting body of aviation-related knowledge. And, no matter how much power you've diverted to your information-deflecting shields, you'll discover that you also know more than just a collection of facts—you'll understand why those obscure details matter to you as an instrument pilot.

Bruce Williams

Seattle, June 2007

Bruce Williams worked on six different versions of the Microsoft Flight Simulator program during his 15 years at Microsoft. He is a certified flight instructor and an industry expert on simulated flight. He currently teaches aerobatics and gives seminars on the use of Microsoft Flight Simulator in flight and ground training through his company BruceAir LLC. Bruce is the author of "Microsoft Simulator as a Training Aid." Visit his web site at www.bruceair.com.

DEDICATION

This book is dedicated to three individuals who've helped me understand the details of instrument flying and convective weather in ways that are nearly impossible to measure. My feeble attempts to express the deep gratitude I have for their aviation professionalism, wisdom and enthusiasm always seems to fall hopelessly short of the mark. Each of these gentlemen is not only a personal friend, but an outstanding instructor and pilot (I've flown with each of them). Their guidance and wisdom through the years have helped me become a far better instructor than I would have been without them in my life. In my opinion, they are the wisest of men and the wisest of aviators. In appreciation for all they've done for me and for other pilots, I dedicate this book to:

Captain Ralph Butcher
Captain Dave Gwinn
Captain Wally Roberts

ABOUT THE AUTHOR

Rod Machado traded his motorcycle for flying lessons at the age of 16. His parents were delighted he gave up riding with the vegetarian motorcycle gang known as the *Sprouts*. Captured by the romance and adventure of flight in a Taylorcraft L-2 at Amelia Reid Aviation in San Jose, California, Rod has remained hooked ever since. In fact, he is one of the few airline-transport-rated pilots who still gets excited by a Cessna 150 fly-by.

Rod is a professional speaker who travels across the United States and Europe delighting his listeners with upbeat and lively presentations. Machado truly loves mixing it up with the audience. His unusual talent for simplifying the difficult and adding humor to make the lessons stick has made him a popular lecturer both in and out of aviation. Rod's presentations include topics as diverse as Risk Assessment, IFR charts, Aviation Weather, and Handling In-flight Emergencies. He is also known for his rapid fire, humorous banquet presentations.

Rod Machado

Rod is a National Aviation Safety Counselor with over 33 years experience in aviation and over 30 years of experience as a flight instructor. He has over 8,000 hours of flight experience earned the hard way—one CFI hour at a time. Since 1978, Rod has taught hundreds and hundreds of flight instructor revalidation clinics and safety seminars across the United States and Europe. He was named the 1991 Western Region Flight Instructor of the Year. You can read his monthly column, "License to Learn," in *AOPA Pilot* magazine as well as his monthly columns in *Flight Training Magazine*.

Rod's eclectic interests are reflected by his equally varied academic credentials. He holds a degree in aviation science and degrees in psychology from California State University at Long Beach.

Rod believes you must take time to exercise or you'll have to take time to be sick. Holding black belts in the Korean disciplines of Tae Kwon Do and Hapkido and ranking in Gracie Jujitsu, he gets his exercise from practicing and teaching martial arts. He also runs 20 miles a week and claims it's uphill both ways.

What the instrument rating is to a pilot, the black belt is to a martial artist. Let me elaborate.

Both the martial artist and instrument pilot are trained to handle challenging situations with skill and poise. It's their defensive skills that allow them to do the right thing if and when their environment turns bad. When the martial artist is asked whether or not he's ever had to use his training, he will often reply, "I use it every day." His training teaches him discipline and confidence, which is something he uses in all aspects of his life, not just in self-defense situations.

The instrument rating does something very similar in the life of a pilot, even when he's not flying instruments. How? His instrument training teaches him to fly precisely and to make maximum and optimal use of the ATC system. For this, and many other reasons, he's a far more capable pilot even when he's not flying in actual IFR conditions.

There's another parallel to consider, too. Both the instrument pilot and the martial artist learn to avoid whenever possible those situations where their defensive skills (avoiding blows from a fist or from a thunderstorm) might actually be needed. That's why I consider the instrument rating to be the martial arts equivalent of a first-degree black belt. I'm not pulling any punches when I tell you that to get the most out of your airplane, to fly it safely, to fly it confidently, you'll want to earn your instrument rating. Period.

I'm guessing you're already sold on that concept. If so, then this book provides the information you need to take the first step, which is passing the FAA instrument knowledge exam. But the goal is not just "minimally competent to pass the test." The goal is "maximally competent to fly the airplane," which is why you will find far more than the minimum information presented in these pages. You will emerge from the final page with not just answers to test questions, but the knowledge behind each answer.

For instance, good instrument pilots know how to gauge the thunderstorm potential of a cumulus cloud by estimating the rainfall rate. They understand how to scan their instruments in a way that provides maximum performance with minimum effort. They know that keeping the needle centered during an ILS or LPV approach is best done by using the sky pointer on the attitude indicator instead of staring at the heading indicator.

Whether you're an IFR-rating-seeker in training, or already rated and looking for a review of those instrument concepts you might have forgotten over the years, this book is for you.

Ultimately, by reading this book, you'll know what I know about instrument flying.

That's what I want for you. So have fun, learn and fly.

Rod Machado

Chapter 1
Starting Your Instrument Training

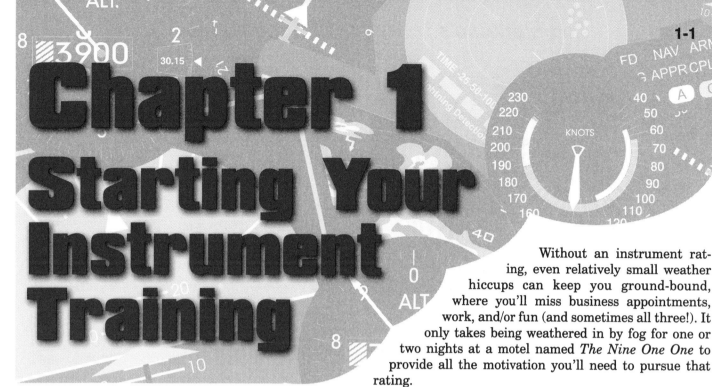

Without an instrument rating, even relatively small weather hiccups can keep you ground-bound, where you'll miss business appointments, work, and/or fun (and sometimes all three!). It only takes being weathered in by fog for one or two nights at a motel named *The Nine One One* to provide all the motivation you'll need to pursue that rating.

An Instrument Rating? Why Me?

There are a lot of things you really don't need as a pilot. I hate to disappoint you, but a big watch is one of them. Sorry, but someone had to tell you this.

On the other hand, one thing I absolutely know you can use is an instrument rating. It's a combination passport, insurance policy, and bragging-rights card, all rolled into one. It will enable you to leap tall buildings at a single bound, travel almost as fast as a speeding bullet, and do it all in conditions that appear to require X-ray vision. People will say, "Who was that hooded pilot?" and others will say, "I don't know, but he had an instrument rating." That makes it worth the effort.

Everyone I know who has an instrument rating feels it is was one of the most valuable aviation moves they ever made. An instrument rating (Figure 1) is one of your best aviation investments, because it lets you make the fullest possible use of your capability to fly. Think about it for a second. As a VFR-only pilot, you are not using the full potential of most airplanes, which are typically IFR capable. You pay the full rent (if a renter) or the full expenses (if an owner), but you can use only part of the possibilities! The only way to be PICE (pilot-in-command of everything) is to get your instrument rating.

Another and less obvious benefit of an instrument rating is the newfound confidence you will have in your ability to fly the airplane. You will learn to fly more capably, more competently, and more smoothly. You will navigate with more precision, and fly with the confidence that comes from knowing that if the weather is a bit less than perfect, you are not putting yourself and your passengers at risk. And on those weekend trips, you don't have to spend half your time worrying about whether the weather will be good enough to get home again in time for work on Monday morning.

The fact is that instrument training also makes you a better VFR pilot. Perhaps the biggest difference you'll notice is that you will fly with much greater VFR precision. You'll maintain altitude, hold headings and generally maneuver the airplane with much greater proficiency. You'll soon find it routine to be ahead of the airplane with the spinner at your back, instead of being behind it with tail feathers in your face.

Please don't let me (or anyone else) mislead you. The instrument rating will not be your unlimited license to fly fearlessly into raging hurricanes, towering thunderstorms, and not-so-heavenly hail. A big part of getting an IFR rating is learning when to say "No." In fact, having the instrument rating may make the go/no-go decision harder because you have more options from which to

Fig. 1

I UNITED STATES OF AMERICA XI
DEPARTMENT OF TRANSPORTATION • FEDERAL AVIATION ADMINISTRATION
IV NAME
ALBERT TIMETER
V ADDRESS 1498 MT. STANLEY
WESTLAKE, MI 91773-2451

VI NATIONALITY USA SEX HEIGHT WEIG
IVa D.O.B. 14 AUG 1972 M 68
IX HAS BEEN FOUND TO BE PROPERLY QUALIFIED TO
II PRIVATE PILOT
CERTIFICATE NUMB
DATE OF ISS

XII RATINGS
AIRPLANE SINGLE AND MULTIENGINE; INSTRUMENT AIRPLANE
XIII LIMITATIONS

Albert Timeter

VII SIGNATURE
OF HOLDER

Technically advanced aircraft (TAAs) are the newer generation of glass cockpit airplanes that are becoming very popular for instrument training.

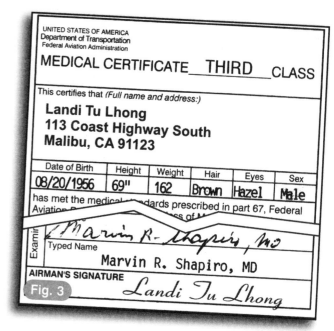

choose. Certain weather phenomena like thunderstorms and icing keep even the most experienced instrument rated pilots on the ground. Even big pilots in really BIG airplanes avoid, rather than challenge, the worst of the weather. The instrument rating extends, by a considerable number, your options to fly when the weather won't allow VFR operations. But it is not an unlimited extension. Knowing where to draw the line in the runway is one of the brain skills you will be acquiring.

I'm happy to play a part in helping you better understand what's required to obtain this rating. I know it will make you a better pilot if you are willing to work hard to gain this credential. In short, it makes you an overall better pilot even if you don't wear overalls when you fly.

Let's take a closer look at what you'll be doing to become an instrument rated pilot.

What It Takes to Obtain an Instrument Rating—Part 61

You can start working on your instrument rating as soon as you've earned your private pilot certificate. Yes, five minutes later is fine, and many people jump into formal instrument training immediately after passing the private checkride. There was a time when applicants for the instrument rating needed a certain minimum flight time (125 hours, for example) before they were eligible to take the instrument rating practical (flight) test. Not any more. The FAA, with help from the researchers in the aviation industry, finally concluded that minimum flight time wasn't a strong predictor of a person's readiness to be a good instrument pilot.

It goes without saying that you'll also need at least a third class medical certificate (Figure 3). Just thought I'd mention this in case you were under the impression that the medical standards, such as eyesight, cardiovascular health, and normal brain function, are suddenly suspended when you enter a cloud and no one can see you.

So, are you qualified to obtain an instrument rating? That depends. Can you read, speak, write, and understand English? You must at least be able to do this. Pig Latin and baby babble don't count. If you've gotten this far, you're probably qualified in the language department.

You'll need to pass a knowledge test for the instrument rating, and that's part of what this book is all about. In addition to providing you with the information necessary to pass the test, I'll also be discussing and dissecting much more material that's useful and practical for the instrument pilot in training. When we're finished, you will thoroughly understand the physical and mental skills involved in instrument flying.

The instrument knowledge exam consists of 60 multiple-choice questions. You're given 2 hours and 30 minutes to answer them, and you must obtain at least a 70% score to pass. Where can you take the test? Denny's? Sorry, but you'll have to visit one of the many FAA-approved test centers around the country. Don't worry. There's almost certainly one nearby. Ask your instructor. He or she will know. If not, you can fly to the nearest center with your instructor and log the time toward your rating!

In terms of aeronautical experience, you'll need at least 50 hours of cross-country flight time as pilot in command (PIC). At least 10 hours of this must be in an airplane. Of course, I'm assuming that you're working toward the airplane instrument rating here. Sorry, there is no instrument rating for hot air balloon pilots (but if there were, you certainly wouldn't have to worry about airframe icing, right?).

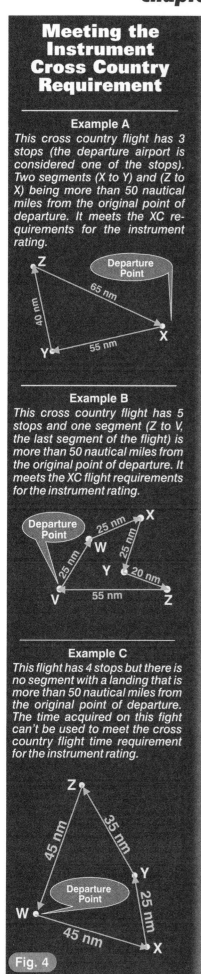

Meeting the Instrument Cross Country Requirement

Example A

This cross country flight has 3 stops (the departure airport is considered one of the stops). Two segments (X to Y) and (Z to X) being more than 50 nautical miles from the original point of departure. It meets the XC requirements for the instrument rating.

Example B

This cross country flight has 5 stops and one segment (Z to V, the last segment of the flight) is more than 50 nautical miles from the original point of departure. It meets the XC flight requirements for the instrument rating.

Example C

This flight has 4 stops but there is no segment with a landing that is more than 50 nautical miles from the original point of departure. The time acquired on this fight can't be used to meet the cross country flight time requirement for the instrument rating.

Fig. 4

In certain parts of the country (Southern California, for instance), early morning and late evening stratus clouds make it easy for instrument students to obtain actual instrument experience.

Fig. 5

To count as a cross-country flight, you must make a landing more than 50 nautical miles from the original point of departure as shown in Figure 4. Fortunately, the cross-country flights you made as a student pilot can be used to at least partially meet this requirement. Just to make things clear on the cross country issue, you can land at as many airports as you like on a cross-country flight. To count as a cross-country flight toward the instrument rating, one of the airports you land at must be more than 50 nautical miles from the original point of departure. Suppose you land at an airport that's 40 miles from the original point of departure, and then proceed to another that's 51 miles from the original point of departure. Does this count toward the instrument rating? You bet it does.

Granted, most applicants working on the instrument rating soon after obtaining their private pilot certificate will have to work hard to acquire the minimum cross-country flight time. Here's an idea that may help you clear this hurdle.

When you and your instructor begin the approach phase of your instrument training, you'll probably make instrument approaches to different airports. If so, elect to make some of these approaches to airports that are more than 50 nautical miles away. If your wheels touch down at those airports (you can do touch-and-goes, that's OK), then the entire flight counts toward the requirement for 50 hours of cross-country time as PIC. The reason you can do this is that it's legal to log PIC time as that time during which you're the sole manipulator of the controls of an aircraft for which you are rated. If you received your private pilot certificate in a single-engine land airplane, then you're rated to fly a single-engine land airplane. If you're taking your instrument training in a Cessna 172, for instance, then you're allowed to log the time as PIC when you are the sole manipulator of the controls, even if your instructor is on board. This doesn't necessarily make you the legal PIC, but it does allow you to log the time as PIC. You were the sole manipulator of the controls during the flight, weren't you?

Regarding the instrument training time, you'll need a minimum of 40 hours of actual or simulated instrument time. Let me explain what *instrument time* is for purposes of meeting this requirement. Whenever you are flying solely by reference to the instruments—in other words, without reference to the horizon outside—you are accumulating loggable instrument flight time.

Now, it would be great if nice, mild, real instrument conditions were always available close to the airport whenever you wanted to train (Figure 5). You'd get all the *actual* instrument conditions you could possibly desire. Very realistic. But not a very realistic possibility in some parts of the country, like Palm Springs, California, unless you want to spend about 40 years getting your 40 hours (but mostly getting a sunburn).

Conveniently, there is an alternative available. *Simulated* instrument time is logged whenever you are flying entirely by reference to the instruments with your

Why Have the IFR Rating? Stuck On Top, Perhaps?

In the aviation equivalent of painting oneself into a corner, this pilot left himself no way out. The decision to stay out of the clouds must be made early, while there are still viable options available.

The FSS said that there was a large band of rain showers and thunderstorms blocking my route. I called back an hour or more later and [FSS] said that the area of rain had passed and that I shouldn't have any trouble going VFR. Initially I was at 5,500 feet, but then I climbed to 7,500 feet to clear the hills and clouds. The farther north I went, the more marginal the weather became. I climbed again trying to maintain VMC. I was talking with several controllers advising them of my problem and requesting higher altitudes to clear the clouds. Eventually I was at 18,300 feet. A controller advised me that I had less than 15 minutes of consciousness at that altitude. I was aware of my bad situation, but I felt that I could not descend into the clouds as I did not have an artificial horizon and I am not instrument rated. I knew that an instrument rating is required at 18,000 feet and above, but I couldn't descend into instrument conditions. The plane got out of control twice and into a spin, but I was able to spot a cloud base for reference and recover.

NASA Callback Report

view of the outer world blocked by an elongated visor (generically referred to as a *hood)*, glasses that are opaque on the top part (*Foggles* is one popular brand), or a Klingon force field. Devices like these (shown in Figure 6) are designed by people who specialize in evading all provisions of the Geneva Conventions, and you will develop a deep and meaningful love/hate relationship with all forms of view-limiting devices as your training progresses. Using these contraptions will make you wish you had your head in the clouds.

Out of the 40 hours total instrument time required, a minimum of 15 hours must be given by an *instrument flight instructor*. Yes, there are certified flight instructors who only teach others to fly airplanes (called CFI-A, the *A* stands for *airplane*) and certified flight instructors who only teach instrument flying (CFI-I, the *I* stands for *instruments*). Of course, many instructors elect to obtain both ratings. We unofficially represent these ratings by the designation CFI-AI. You'll need to find at least a CFI-I (usually spoken as "C-F-double-I") to give you a minimum of 15 hours of flight training in preparation for the instrument rating. In all likelihood, you'll just train from beginning to end with an instrument flight instructor.

It's also likely that the 40 hours of minimum time will all be spent with the instructor, despite the regulations allowing you to acquire as many as 25 hours of instrument time alone. No, I don't mean flying solo while wearing some type of view limiting device! Anyone who'd even try such a thing should sign up to be the world's first living brain donor, because it's obvious that their brain isn't being used at all.

So how would you acquire instrument time while flying without an instructor? By having someone who is appropriately rated in the airplane sit in the right seat as a safety pilot, while you fly with a view limiting device (Figure 6). This is perfectly legal, and is, in fact, how many instrument-rated pilots meet their instrument currency requirements and keep their skills sharp. The simulated instrument flight time acquired while doing this counts toward the 40-hour minimum for the instrument rating.

If you decide to acquire instrument time with a safety pilot on board, you'll certainly want to discuss this plan with your prospective instrument flight instructor first. Don't, however, count on any instructor being too enthusiastic about your scheme if you intend to try to use it as a way of cutting the amount of time you'll spend with the instructor.

The fact is that most IFR students need *at least* 40 hours of dual instrument instruction to gain the required level of competence, and sometimes much more, particularly in major urban areas where the airspace is complex and congested. One study found that the national average was closer to 55 hours.

Like fine wine, there can be no instrument pilot before its time. Getting it right is a lot more important than getting it quickly. Take the long view, and be patient. An instrument rating will last a lifetime, so a few hours beyond the bare minimum shouldn't be viewed as a burden or imposition, but rather as an opportunity to hone your skills and elevate your confidence as well as your airplane.

In addition to the other requirements, you will need to make a long instrument cross-country flight with your instrument flight instructor. The FAA defines "long" as being a minimum of 250 nautical miles along airways or

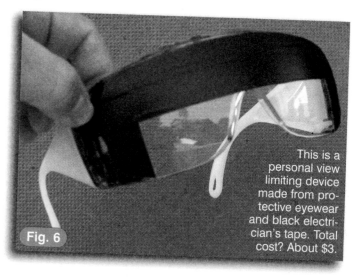

Fig. 6   This is a personal view limiting device made from protective eyewear and black electrician's tape. Total cost? About $3.

Courtesy NASA Collection
Fig. 7A

Courtesy Frasca Simulator
Fig. 7B

Fig. 7C

Flight training devices (FTDs) are often full motion devices that come very close to simulating reality (Figure 7A). In fact, it's possible to obtain a type rating for some airplanes by using these devices and never once having to fly the real airplane. Frasca's Piper Seminole FTD (Figure 7B) is a smaller version of these devices. Aviation Training Devices (ATDs) are often smaller desktop units, such as the one in Figure 7C, which is a sub-category of ATDs known as *basic ATD* or BATD.

via an ATC-directed routing, with at least one landing at an airport more than 50 nautical miles from the original point of departure. The purpose of this flight is to give you experience flying IFR over long distances. It's also helpful in getting you away from your home area, where you feel most comfortable because you have everything memorized. Part of IFR flying is being capable of coping with sudden changes and unfamiliar circumstances without getting rattled.

You'll be required to make an instrument approach at each airport on your long cross country, and to make at least three different kinds of instrument approaches (either a GPS, VOR, Localizer, LDA, SDF, NDB and/or an ILS approach. Don't worry. You'll learn about these abbreviations later). You aren't required to make approaches to three different airports (although this is certainly a good thing to do for the experience it offers). If you think about it, you must make approaches to a minimum of two airports, one of which may be your home airport. Getting an IFR rating is costly in both time and money, but invaluable in terms of what it gives you for the rest of your piloting life. And there is a way to help reduce the cost of this training and make it more effective in the process. This involves using something known as a simulator or a flight training device.

Aviation Training Devices (ATDs) & Flight Training Devices (FTDs)

The regulations allow you to obtain a maximum of 20 of the required hours "flying" one of two devices—a flight training device (FTD), or an aviation training device ATD)—to meet the 40 hour minimum instrument time requirement.

FTDs tend to be highly sophisticated units that simulate the cockpit environment (Figure 7A). These devices are often full-size aircraft cockpit mockups of specific aircraft. They often have three degrees of motion and use a visual presentation to provide a simulation that's almost like the real thing. So real and life-like is it that most airlines use them to train the pilots that carry passengers around the world. In fact, they're so real that pilots have actually had heart attacks in them during exhaustive training sessions. I guess you could also call them heart attack simulators, too (although I don't think the instructor's objective is to stop and engine and the pilot's heart at the same time).

The Frasca Piper Seminole simulator (Figure 7B) is a flight training devices (FTD). No an FTD is not a machine that gives you flowers when you push its buttons (that device is known as a *husband*). These machines are full size replicas of the instruments, equipment, panels, and controls of an aircraft, or set of aircraft, in an open flight deck area or in an enclosed cockpit, including the hardware and software for the systems installed, that is necessary to simulate the aircraft in ground and flight operations. It does not need to have a visual system or have any degree of motion (although on one occasion, I heard that a pilot leaned on the fixed box containing the panel mockup and tipped it over (thus simulating a hard landing on a wing).

It's possible that your flight school will have a FTD or ATD available for training purposes. What if they don't? You might consider purchasing your own Basic ATD to help you train at home.

The FAA's Ruling on the Long "250 Nautical Mile" Instrument Cross Country Flight

QUESTION: Do the approaches required under § 61.65(d)(2)(iii)(C) need to be completed at three different airports?

ANSWER: Ref. § 61.65(d)(2)(iii); No. Under § 61.65(d)(2)(iii), a pilot seeking an instrument-airplane rating must perform three different kinds of approaches with the use of navigation systems, but the approaches may be performed at one or more airports. In addition, in order to meet the aeronautical experience requirements under § 61.65(d)(2)(iii), the pilot also must (1) land at one or more airport(s), other than the airport of original departure, using an instrument approach; (2) return to the airport of original departure using an instrument approach; (3) travel a total distance of 250 nautical miles or greater along airways or ATC-directed routing; and (4) choose an airport for landing that is separated by a minimum straight line distance of more than 50 nautical miles from the airport of original departure (see § 61.1(b)(3)(ii)(B)). Given the requirement that the pilot land at a minimum of one airport other than the airport he or she originated from, it is most efficient if a different approach is used for each landing so the requirements under § 61.65(d)(2)(iii)(C) partially are met.

FAA Question & Answer Response

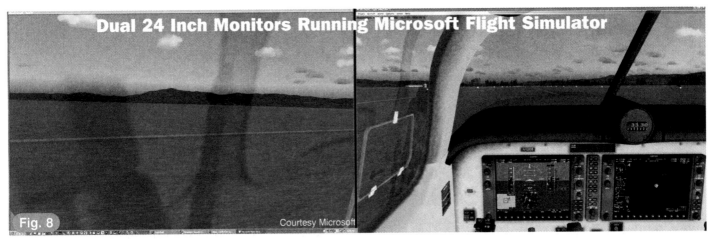

Dual 24 Inch Monitors Running Microsoft Flight Simulator

Fig. 8   Courtesy Microsoft

When it comes to desktop PC flight simulation, it's difficult to find a program as useful as Microsoft Flight Simulator. I know, since I wrote the flight lessons and am the instructor's voice in this program. What makes this simulator so useful is the ability to simulate not only IFR flight, but the VFR transitions so necessary for practical training.

A Basic ATD (Figure 7C) is nearly what it sounds like—a desktop computer flight simulation program with approved hardware (these units typically cost $3,000-$4,000). Hold on. Not so fast. This doesn't mean you can fire up your computer's Captain Galactic space fighter program and start clicking off those instrument hours. Sure, that would be nice, but you wouldn't learn to fly instruments as much as you would learn to make Romulans from Romulat go splat. A Basic ATD consists of flight simulation software and hardware which has been determined to meet specific instrument-realism requirements as approved by the FAA. So, any off-the-shelf computer simulator hardware/software combination isn't necessarily considered a BATD.

In either case, a FTD or an ATD (Basic ATD included in this category) can only be used to meet the experience requirements set forth in the FARs if that device has been approved by the FAA for such purposes. How would you know if it met these requirements? The easiest way to find out is ask the manufacturer of that equipment or the FAA.

To receive any instrument time credit for use of a FTD or ATD during instrument training, it must meet certain minimum FAA specifications. Your instructor can give you information on these programs. There is a catch, though (more of a limitation, really). Because a BATD isn't a sophisticated simulator or a flight training device, you can only count 10 hours of BATD time toward the 40 hour minimum instrument time requirement.

It's also important to note that if you are planning on counting any of these hours (regardless of whether they are in a FTD or ATD, you must be with an authorized instructor. That's right. No solo 2 a.m. PC flight sim sessions at home in bed while wearing your bunny slippers and clip-on aviator wings. You can't log these flight hours (in any simulator, FTD or ATD unless you're being given dual instruction from an authorized instructor, and if that's happening at home at 2 a.m. while you have your bunny slippers on, I sure hope you are married to the instructor and that both of you can keep a secret. Check with your local flight school to determine if they use a flight training device or an aviation training device in their training.

The big question is, if you don't want to spend the money for a Basic ATD, should you purchase an ordinary computer-based flight simulator instead? The answer is a resounding YES! I am a big fan of these *personal computer assisted training devices* (PCATD) as an aid to instrument training. Microsoft Flight Simulator (Figure 8) is a good example. Sure, you can't log flight hours with your CFI using this software, but that's irrelevant here. Many good things result from having access to a regular computer-based flight simulator, even if it's not approved as a Basic ATD.

For a software investment of around $100, you can practice your instrument flying skills at home, whenever you want, without having to have your instructor present. Yes, even in bed while wearing your funny bunny slippers

Assault and Battery of the Wind
William Butler Yeats

An air carrier Captain tells a harrowing tale of an encounter with wind shear, and extends thanks to quite a cast of behind-the-scenes actors:

We performed a normal takeoff. At approximately 800 feet AGL, our airspeed dropped rapidly. At the same time, the wind shear warning activated. I put my hand on the First Officer's hand and together we pushed the throttles all the way to the stops. Even with the engines giving us everything they were capable of, our airspeed hung at V2 plus 5 knots. We used our available energy to arrest the descent, and then evidently burst clear of the wind shear. The encounter lasted maybe 20-30 seconds. The remainder of the flight was uneventful.

The Flight Attendant did tell me she heard the wind shear warning from her jumpseat, and she thanked me for getting us out of the wind shear. It was not me that saved us. It was our team working together.

I am pleased with the training we have received on wind shear. I want to thank [everyone] who came up with the wind shear guidance equipment and the procedures to use it. I want to thank our ground instructors for teaching us and simulator instructors for testing us and refining our technique. It works.   **NASA Callback Report**

and tiny plastic wings, if you choose. Think of it this way. After spending time in the actual airplane, wouldn't it be nice to come home and review what you've learned? Or go over things that were giving you a problem, yet which could only be repeated once or twice, if at all, in the plane? That's just some of what a computer-based flight simulator can do for you.

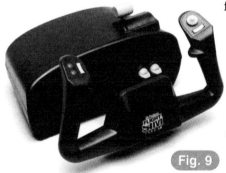

You can practice your instrument scan, VOR, ADF, GPS, Localizer and ILS navigation skills, flight planning, weather avoidance and a host of other useful things on these realistic devices. You can do things you could never do in a real airplane, such as pausing an approach or instantly returning to where an approach begins. A few of the computer-based flight simulator programs on the market today will even download the current weather from any one of several weather vendors (e.g., DUAT) and simulate it in the form of clouds, reduced visibility, turbulence, etc., in your computer-based flight program (Figure 8). Now that's high tech and real time.

Joystick or flight yoke? Which should you choose? At the private pilot level and beyond, it really doesn't matter all that much from a learning perspective.

You can even simulate flying the approach or approaches to an airport that you plan on going to later in the day. These are just a few of the great things these devices can do for you.

The big question for most pilots contemplating purchase of a PCATD is whether to acquire a joystick or flight yoke (Figure 9). You don't want to operate a simulator by use of a mouse or keyboard alone, since you're not likely to find either as a control device in a real airplane. At this stage of your training, it doesn't matter which of the alternatives you choose. Get what you can afford or what you feel most comfortable with. As an instrument student, you already have acquired well over 90% of all the motor (physical) skills you'll need to fly an airplane. What you're interested in learning are perceptual (sensing) and cognitive (thinking) skills. You can do this unhindered by the means you use to control the simulated airplane, as long as it's not a computer mouse. We don't fly airplanes with a mouse or keyboard, at least not yet. So if you have a mouse on board, make sure it's the type that spins a wheel as an alternate source of vacuum pressure (no, this "rat on a wheel" device isn't commonly found in rental airplanes, either).

What's the Difference Between a Part 141 and a Part 61 Flight School?

Part 141 is a section of the Federal Aviation Regulations (FARs) that describes a more structured and carefully monitored program of flight training compared to Part 61. This doesn't necessarily mean that a Part 141 school provides better training, but it doesn't exclude that possibility, either. After all, Part 141 training includes a structured curriculum, phase checks (Star Trek fans, sorry but this isn't where you check your phaser) with a chief instructor and carefully monitored flight instructors. Training under Part 61 may provide similar high quality training, too. To be frank, the type of training you receive basically depends on the flight instructor and the management of the flight school. If we assume the same instructor and management dedication in either a 141 or 61 flight school, what's the difference? Part 141 allows you to obtain the instrument rating with as little as 35 hours instrument time instead of Part 61's minimum of 40 hours. As I said above, the average is far higher than even the 40 hour minimum, so it's probably unrealistic to think in terms of 35 hours unless you are starting out with a *lot* of aviation time under your seatbelt, and perhaps a lot of informal or prior instrument training. Most all the other requirements for the instrument rating are the same with the exception of the allowable flight time for FTDs and ATDs. In the case of a Part 141 school, you may garner up to 40% or 50% (percentage depends on the type of device) of the total instrument flight training hour requirements in an FAA approved FTD or ATD.

I suggest you make finding a good instructor the most important criterion in your search for the best training available. NOTHING, I repeat, NOTHING else matters more!

Cirrus' SR22 is one of the newer cutting edge airplanes on the market today.   Fig. 10

A Plane of Fame in Which to Train?

What's the best type of airplane in which to take IFR training? The short answer is that it doesn't matter what airplane you use. That's the long answer, too.

That's right. There's no solid evidence indicating that flying one type of airplane versus another will make you a better instrument pilot. I am assuming, of course, that regardless of what airplane you choose, you'll have one with all the necessary instruments. I'm also assuming that it will have a cockpit, too, preferably closed. In other words, I hope you're not going to train in something like a Stearman (an open-cockpit biplane) or some type of ultralight, licensed as an experimental airplane. If you did, there's a good chance you wouldn't be able to keep your hood on and your hair will be a mess. Given these wild exceptions, find an airplane you like and can afford and train in it.

It might make a whole lot of sense to train in what you already know how to fly, so you aren't learning a new airplane and new IFR skills at the same time. If you do step up, make it a baby step, say Cessna 152 to Cessna 172, not Cessna 152 to Boeing 747.

I've taught many folks to fly IFR in a Cessna 152, which is so small that when a student sneezes we lose 15 knots. Most pilots, however, prefer to train in airplanes like the Cessna 172, Piper Warrior or Columbia or Cirrus aircraft (Figure 10). Airplanes like these make wonderful instrument training platforms. Being a little larger and heavier than the Cessna 152, these airplanes are a little more stable and comfortable to fly, and they often have the latest glass cockpit technology, too.

Treat with suspicion any comment that suggests flying a more difficult airplane will make you a better instrument pilot. It won't. It will most likely make you a more tired and frustrated pilot. There's no evidence that flying a more difficult airplane (say one that's less stable or one with more complex systems) makes you an overall better instrument pilot. If this were true, then taking your instrument training in a Boeing 747 would eventually elevate you to the proficiency of a Bob Hoover or Neil

If you can fly an approach at 600 mph, that means you'll spend less time shooting the approach and that means less time to make any mistakes! How can you lose on this one?

Rent Me! $2,000/Hr.

Rental Aircraft Cost

Armstrong. Well, it won't. All it will do is allow you to spend a gazillion dollars over a few years time, and you'll become good at flying a Boeing 747 on instruments and have a really hard time finding airports to practice your approaches. That's all.

Learning to fly instruments in a complex airplane (one having retractable gear, flaps and a controllable propeller) may not be in your best interests either (unless you

The Minimum Equipment You Need for IFR Training

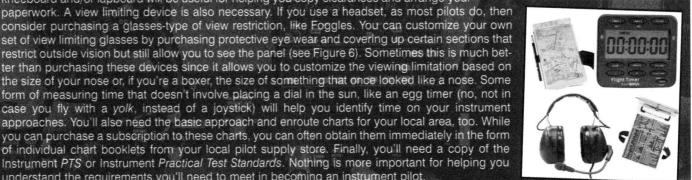

When you begin your instrument training your flight instructor will, no doubt, give you a list of goodies you'll need for training. Here are a few items you'll probably be asked to purchase.

First, you'll definitely need a good headset to go on your good head. A good kneeboard and/or lapboard will be useful for helping you copy clearances and arrange your paperwork. A view limiting device is also necessary. If you use a headset, as most pilots do, then consider purchasing a glasses-type of view restriction, like Foggles. You can customize your own set of view limiting glasses by purchasing protective eye wear and covering up certain sections that restrict outside vision but still allow you to see the panel (see Figure 6). Sometimes this is much better than purchasing these devices since it allows you to customize the viewing limitation based on the size of your nose or, if you're a boxer, the size of something that once looked like a nose. Some form of measuring time that doesn't involve placing a dial in the sun, like an egg timer (no, not in case you fly with a *yolk*, instead of a joystick) will help you identify time on your instrument approaches. You'll also need the basic approach and enroute charts for your local area, too. While you can purchase a subscription to these charts, you can often obtain them immediately in the form of individual chart booklets from your local pilot supply store. Finally, you'll need a copy of the Instrument *PTS* or Instrument *Practical Test Standards*. Nothing is more important for helping you understand the requirements you'll need to meet in becoming an instrument pilot.

already fly one of these airplanes regularly). The reason is that the first 10 to 15 hours of instrument training involve quite abrupt power changes. Jockeying the throttle in an airplane with a large engine can subject it to excessive thermal stress. That's why when a student shows up with a Cessna 210 or a Piper Malibu and wants me to teach him instruments in it, I recommend that we spend several hours in a smaller airplane or a flight training device before stepping up to the complex airplane. If he insists that we fly the larger airplane, then so be it. A good instructor can make this work and still prevent excessive engine shock cooling in the process.

It's been my experience that students find it easier to concentrate on the fundamentals of instrument training in a less complicated airplane rather than in a complex one. Of course, once the basics are mastered, then you can move up to a faster, more complex airplane if you wish. This makes sense in that once you start doing instrument approaches, there's no point in wasting time getting to an airport to shoot an approach if you don't have to. A faster airplane is practical for this portion of the training if flying one is within your budget. If not, be happy with a slower machine. You'll still learn the basics and not be worse off because of it.

Glass Cockpits vs. Analog Gauges?

Given how enthusiastic pilots are about an airplane's bells and whistles, it's quite possible that you might consider doing your instrument training in what has become known as a *glass cockpit* airplane (Figure 11). The question is, how does a glass cockpit compare to analog flight gauges for instrument training? Here are a few things to consider.

Training in a glass cockpit airplane will probably take more total flight time given that primary flight display (PFD) and multi-function displays (MFDs) are complex creatures to operate. Fortunately, there are many software simulation packages that allow you to learn how to operate this equipment on your personal computer. Additionally, given the complexity of glass cockpit equipment, you'll probably find that keeping proficient in the use of all these features will require more currency training on your part. While a pilot in an airplane with traditional gauges can go for months without forgetting how to set a VOR frequency into the navigation radio, you can't expect to remain as familiar and as comfortable with your PFDs and MFDs if you don't use them frequently. That's the down side (if you want to call it that), but there is an upside that makes this all worthwhile.

Courtesy Columbia Aircraft Co.   Fig. 11

Glass cockpit technology can provide the type of information that instrument pilots used to dream about. Weather, terrain and collision avoidance information and moving maps are but a few of the goodies available.

A fully equipped glass cockpit with primary and multi-function displays can provide you with information that instrument pilots only used to dream about. Weather, terrain, collision avoidance and moving map information are all on the short list of goodies found in many glass cockpit aircraft. If you're a serious IFR pilot (yes, they tell jokes, too) and plan on using the rating to meet a demanding travel schedule, then you'll most certainly find all this information extremely useful.

Overall, if you can afford it and you plan on making good use of your instrument rating, then learning in a glass-cockpit airplane might be the best bet for you. If this type of airplane is beyond your budget (because you're paid in stones, not cash), then learn in what you can afford. You can always move up to a glass cockpit airplane later on when you get more stones (just don't throw them around in a glass cockpit airplane).

We call this our all-weather instrument trainer because you can really feel "all" the weather when you fly IFR. And because the wind is always blowing on your charts, we can honestly say that it has a moving map display, too.

How Often Should You Train?

To get the best results, try to take two or three instrument lessons per week (Figure 12). This training ratio seems to produce the best results, all things considered. Use your desktop computer simulator to help reinforce what you learn in the air. Bring a tape recorder along on each lesson to record your ground discussions. You might even arrange to patch the recorder into the airplane's intercom system. This can provide you with an opportunity to study ATC communications as well as review the in-flight points your instructor provides during training.

One other strategic note here. I encourage you to figure out *before* you start how you are going to pay for all the expenses of getting your IFR rating. Time after time, I have seen people get part way into their training, then have to quit for long periods because they couldn't afford to continue. This is incredibly dispiriting. If and when they do return to it, they have to pretty much start over again, which is a sad and bad waste of time and money.

DATE 200X	AIRCRAFT TYPE	AIRCRAFT IDENT	ROUTE OF FLIGHT		NR INST APP.	REMARKS AND ENDORSEMENTS	NR LDG
			FROM	TO			
1-07	BE-36	N2132B	KSNA	KSNA	1	IFR Introduction	
1-10	BE-36	N2132B	KSNA	KSNA	0	Attitude Instrument Flying	
1-12	BE-36	N2132B	KSNA	KSNA	0	Charlie Pattern	Fig. 12

Training at least two or three days a week is a reasonable way to guarantee good progress toward your instrument rating. On those days when the airplane isn't available or the weather is just too severe to train, you can always spend time in an FTD or ATD.

The cost of your flight training is predictable. Know before you go. Start when you are completely ready, including financially. Don't count on winning the lottery or a rich uncle's timely demise to fund your flight training.

Is Quicker Any Slicker? Those Accelerated Instrument Rating Programs

Several accelerated-type instrument training programs exist. These schools offer a two week instrument training program for those who need or want to finish quickly, or who can't obtain capable instruction locally.

Most of these programs involve sending a professional flight instructor out to your home base (Figure 13). This portable pilot comes equipped with a desktop flight training device (often a computer-based flight simulator of some sort). You're trained for several hours daily, using this simulation device and an airplane that you provide. It's assumed that you will have passed the IFR knowledge exam before the training begins, so all the instructor needs to do is train and prepare you for the instrument practical test (the checkride).

Of course, you pay for not only the instructor's time, but also his or her travel and housing costs (and don't suggest the Greyhound bus or Moped, either), so this type of training isn't for those on the tightest of budgets. For some people, however, time is in shorter supply than money. For others, a hyper-concentrated approach suits their learning style better than dragging out training over a period of six months. If you fall into one of these categories, accelerated training may be the method of choice for you.

What do I think of such training? Over the years, I've had a chance to fly with many pilots who've been trained in this way. In my opinion, they fly as well as pilots who've taken the longer road to IFRdom.

Many of these people simply didn't have the time to train in the traditional manner. Some became frustrated trying to find a good instructor and enrolled in an accelerated program hoping that their instructor would be high quality. In almost all instances, they were not disappointed. In fact, if there's any single, compelling reason for enrolling in one of these programs, it's because you're pretty certain that a highly qualified and experienced instructor will show up at your door to train you. This, in itself, makes the program worthwhile, in my estimation. And the training will be highly standardized and structured, making maximum use of every second.

There are two caveats, however. The first is that if for any reason you don't hit it off personally with the instructor because he tries to hit you, you're pretty much stuck. Changing is not as easy as it would be at a local flight school, where you'd just say, "That one has big ears and I don't like big ears. Give me a different one."

The second caveat is that accelerated training makes it easier to lose confidence if there is a large gap in time

Professional Instrument Courses (PIC)   Fig. 13

Accelerated IFR training programs are often the most practical choice for those individuals who are too busy to extend their training over several months.

between obtaining the instrument rating and flying IFR. In other words, it's important for pilots who've been trained in an accelerated program to get out and fly IFR. If they don't, they'll find themselves becoming less and less sure of their instrument flying skills. Now, I'm not talking about the physical flying skills as much as I am thinking skills, which includes the ability to plot, plan and scheme your way through an instrument flight.

Why does confidence erode so quickly? Perhaps there just isn't enough time spent between lessons to give sufficient thought to important concepts. If you train two or three times a week, you have time between lessons to make more connections with the concepts you've learned. This means that you're a little more sure about the instrument world around you. You feel more confidence as a result. So if you're planning on taking accelerated training, make it a point to file and fly IFR as often as possible as soon as possible after completing your training. This will reinforce your level of confidence.

What's Ahead

Becoming a private pilot was without a doubt a significant and proud experience for you. You went from being a supervised student one day to being a fully licensed pilot the next. Oh, what a feeling that was.

Don't be surprised if you experience something similar after obtaining the instrument rating. While you'll have nothing tangible to show for your training except a fuller flight bag, you will have the confidence to better cope with Mother Nature if and when she ever attempts to ambush or outflank you. This alone makes the investment of time in acquiring an instrument rating worth every penny. Now it's time to get down to specifics. No plane, no gain. Let's plan to scan, and learn how pilots actually control their airplane solely by reference to instruments.

To Fly Glass, or Not to Fly Glass

Max Trescott

That is the question which you may be asking, and that Shakespeare would have asked if he were a pilot. Many pilots, when getting an instrument rating, wonder whether to learn in planes with round gauges or those equipped with modern glass cockpits, such as the Garmin G1000 (Cessna, Columbia, Diamond, etc) or Avidyne Entegra (Cirrus, etc). The answer, of course, depends upon your objective. For example, if you're aiming for an airline job, having some glass experience could help you get hired.

If your goal is to get an instrument rating at the lowest possible cost—and I hope it's not—then, of course, round gauge airplanes are less expensive to fly. While it's fine to shop for the rock bottom cost for many things in life, (especially those that can't kill you), consider that to some extent you get what you pay for, and you want the best instrument training you can get—not the cheapest. Frankly, getting the best training has more to do with the quality of instruction than the price of the airplane, so if you need to save a few bucks, use a round gauge airplane, but pay for a great instructor. Remember the life you save *will* be your own.

In general, it makes sense to learn in the type of plane in which you'll ultimately do your IFR flying. If your goal is to make IFR trips in the safest airplane, than I highly recommend you train in and fly glass cockpit aircraft. You may not perceive much benefit in flying one of these airplanes VFR for 40 miles to get a hamburger, however on longer cross countries and when flying IFR, these aircraft prove their worth.

One of the biggest advantages is improved positional awareness. With the large moving map, you'll always know exactly where you are. Try doing that with just two VOR needles, and you'll quickly appreciate the difference. Situational awareness is also improved. With terrain awareness capabilities, you'll never be in doubt about whether the rocks are in front of you or below you where they're supposed to be. Knowing this not only brings great peace of mind, but also keeps your mind in one piece!

Near, real-time data in the cockpit also makes a big difference. Traffic advisory systems help you spot traffic (when you're not in the clouds), Stormscopes provide lightning data and XM Satellite's aviation weather displays virtually the same graphical weather products that you're able to get sitting in front of your computer on the ground. Another benefit of glass cockpits is that the autopilot frees a pilot from the mundane task of keeping the wings level, so that he or she can concentrate on important decision making, such as evaluating changing weather, reviewing fuel consumption, and considering alternate plans.

Savvy readers may counter, "But Max, I can get all of these capabilities by adding new avionics to my older airplane." Yes grasshopper that is true, but what about when things start to fail? Most older aircraft have only a single electrical power source—the battery. Modern glass cockpits have at least two electrical sources and sometimes two separate power buses for even greater redundancy. Ironically, even though glass-cockpit aircraft are more dependent upon electricity than older aircraft, they still display far more information when equipment starts to fail. For my money, flying in the clouds is far more enjoyable when I'm behind a glass cockpit. And when equipment starts to fail, I pray that it's just a bad dream or that I'm flying glass.

Max Trescott is the author of *Max Trescott's G1000 Glass Cockpit Handbook*, which you can order at 800-247-6553. You can learn more about this and his other glass cockpit training materials at www.g1000book.com.

Max Trescott

Postflight Briefing #1-1

Using PC-Based Simulations: Learning, not Logging

Earning an IFR rating—at least the flying part of the training—ought to be easy. After all, by the time you start working on the instrument ticket, you already know how to fly, and IFR flying is series of basic maneuvers—mostly straight-and-level, with a few gentle turns and gradual climbs and descents. Of course, there's far more to the art of *operating* by reference to instruments, including working in the ATC system, managing complex avionics, and, most important, maintaining situational awareness and following detailed procedures that keep you safe when you can't see the ground.

Airlines and corporate aviation departments have long made extensive use of sophisticated flight simulators and training devices to get their pilots up to speed and maintain proficiency. The rapid development of personal computer hardware and simulation software has also made it possible to bring many benefits of virtual flying to small flight schools and individual pilots.

Bruce Williams

But while the aviation community often touts the benefits of using simulation in flight training—especially IFR training—many instructors and pilots still don't take full advantage of the technology, probably because too many instructors and students think of simulators only as substitutes for flying time or as tools for remedial training, not as opportunities to learn and practice new discrete, abstract skills.

For example, aviation forums on the Web burst with arguments about which software to use, what type of hardware makes for a realistic virtual cockpit, and how best to use PC-based simulations in a training/proficiency program. Unfortunately, most of those discussions generate more heat than light, largely because too many folks focus on flight models, cockpit layouts, and other issues that *seem* important but which really aren't the keys to making effective use of PC-based flight simulations.

With competent instruction, most instrument students adapt quickly to the basics of controlling an aircraft by reference to instruments. The hurdles that aviators must jump to become competent IFR pilots and then maintain IFR proficiency usually aren't "flying" problems per se. Instead, the obstacles involve understanding and applying abstract concepts and following complex procedures, such as entering and then running laps around holding patterns, tracking DME arcs, and flying instrument approaches, all the while juggling communications and checklists. That's a lot to handle, especially when the "crew" is one pilot. In other words, instrument students who have trouble holding altitude and heading under the hood often aren't sloppy flyers; they just aren't ready to juggle six balls simultaneously.

The primary benefit that PC-based simulations offer a typical general-aviation pilot is the ability to divide complex tasks into manageable pieces and isolate specific skills and tasks. And because today's PC-simulations are inexpensive and run on most late-model PCs and laptops, they make training as convenient as watching movies on DVD. You can use PC-based simulations at a flight school, like any other flight-training aid, but you can also practice at home (or even during a "break" at work). When you're learning (or refreshing) a specific skill, you can jump directly into a situation that focuses on a specific type of procedure or IFR-flying problem. If a given situation confuses you or if you get behind the airplane, you can stop, reset the situation, and try again until you've both absorbed the underlying concepts and gradually learned to apply them in practice. And at first you can even let the autopilot handle the basic flying chores while you grasp the gestalt of operating under IFR.

Perhaps most important, stop worrying about whether a particular PC-based simulation is "FAA approved" or if you can log time spent using a PC-based "simulator." In the first place, the FAA doesn't approve simulation *software*—it certifies *flight training devices* and *simulators*, which are expensive, purpose-built training gizmos that include both software and hardware. Second, remember that many instructional tools that we use every day (including DVDs, GPS simulators—even airplane models and white boards) aren't "FAA approved." But that doesn't mean they aren't useful—even indispensible—training aids.

Next, remember that whether you can enter the hours spent "flying" a PC simulation as "simulator time" has little to do with the value that such experience adds to the quality and efficiency of your training. An hour in an airplane isn't always an hour well-spent, especially if the goal of a lesson is frustrated by traffic-saturated ATC, weather, or other factors. If you and your instructor want to keep track of "dual" time spent using a PC-simulation as a training aid, log those hours as ground instruction. After all, "flying" *Microsoft Flight Simulator* with your instructor to learn about holding patterns is a great way to visualize and "chair-fly"—better than a white board and static diagrams. Even if you're "flying" solo at home, enjoy and benefit from the experience. It's no different (and probably more fun) than other solo (and not-loggable) "training" such as poring over books and taking practice tests.

With proper guidance, time spent "virtual flying" will help you climb over learning plateaus and make the time you spend in a real airplane more efficient and effective if you remember that earning a new certificate or rating ultimately is about learning, not logging.

Bruce Williams (BruceAir.com)

Microsoft Flight Simulator as a Training Aid: A Guide for Pilots, Instructors, and Virtual Aviators

Chapter 2
Your Flight Instruments: Behind the Panel

While phone solicitors dial for dollars, instrument pilots dive for dials. The information the instruments provide literally tell pilots flying in the clouds which end is up and keep them from ending up where they do not want to be.

This is why it's important for all instrument pilots to know the difference between a pitot and Pluto. Understanding what these pointers do is essential to keeping your airplane upright so you don't get uptight in the clouds. So come with me for a tour of what's happening *behind* the panel.

I'll show you how to scan the flight instruments in the next chapter, but first we'll learn all the neat little secrets about how these instruments work and what can keep them from working as intended. If you like Rube Goldberg devices, you are going to love what you're about to see. The most stalwart of aviation instruments often look like a senior engineering project gone wild, with a prize going to the most convoluted entry. Wheels, gears, bellows, discs, pumps—they're all there at work behind your panel.

The Six Basic Flight Instruments

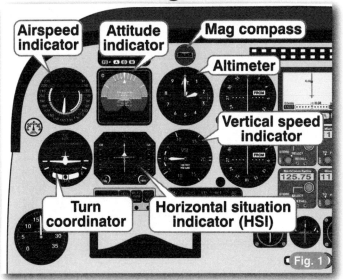

Fig. 1

As a commercial and/or instrument rated private pilot, you should know something about the more complex instruments found in today's modern airplanes, including multi-function displays (MFDs), primary flight displays (PFDs), autopilots and so on. Yet it's the Solid Six, the basic (round-dial) instruments shown in Figure 1, that remain the mainstay of every aviation panel. These six instruments are so important that you'll find a representation of them (or the information they

Primary Flight Display Instruments

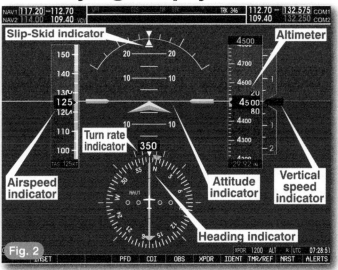

Fig. 2

The newest primary flight displays (PFDs) provide the same instrumentation as analog instruments. The main difference is how these instruments are interpreted.

covey) on even the most advanced *glass cockpit* instrument panels as shown in Figure 2. The methods and technology used by these instruments to generate their information has changed little over the years, perhaps because they do what they do so dependably. So let's start our tour at the starting line, with the six-pack of instruments found on virtually every instrument panel. Understanding what makes these instruments go will separate you by several flight levels from the average pilot. Keep in mind that when using a primary flight display (the display containing the flight instruments as shown in Figure 2), the flight instruments you see provide you with essentially the same information as round-dial or analog instruments. You might have to interpret the symbolic instrument presentation in a slightly different way, but the information is still the same. Learn round-dial instruments and you'll know how glass cockpit instruments work.

Fig. 3

Courtesy Wally Roberts

This is what the cockpit of the modern corporate aircraft can look like today. Beam me up Scotty!

Static Port

Fig. 5

Airplanes normally have static ports at locations where dynamic air pressure is at a minimum. It is not unusual for an airplane to have two static ports to help minimize variations in static pressure.

You're undoubtedly familiar with the basic flight instruments shown on the instrument panel in Figure 1. Virtually every general aviation airplane built in the last 25 years has these instruments laid out in about the same configuration. Clockwise from the top left-hand corner they are the airspeed indicator, attitude indicator, altimeter, vertical speed indicator, heading indicator (HSI or horizontal situation indicator), turn coordinator and the magnetic compass. This is what a typical instrument panel of a common instrument trainer looks like. A pilot's financial status permitting, this basic panel can morph into something more sophisticated than the deck of the Starship Enterprise (Figure 3), providing the aviation equivalent of bling-bling and causing one of aviation's major psychological ills, panel envy.

Without further ado, let's do, starting our tour in the upper left-hand corner with the airspeed indicator.

The Airspeed Indicator

At one of our local fast-food establishments, a fellow began his order by pointing to a framed picture on the wall and saying, "I'll have one of those." The cashier replied, "You can't have one of those. That's our employee of the month. He's not on the menu." Oh! You're not supposed to be able to meet your meat before you eat (cannibals, won't they ever learn?). Pointing to something is often considered rude (especially if you don't know our customs and intend to eat it). On the other hand, if it's the airspeed needle doing the pointing, manners don't matter, and you just have to read the speed. But if you're at all curious, you'll eventually wonder, "How does it *do* that?"

The airspeed indicator is actually a wind indicator. It provides you with an airspeed indication by mechanically measuring the difference between ram (moving) air pressure and static (not moving) air pressure. You may not need a weatherman to know which way the wind blows, but you do need an airspeed indicator to know precisely how fast you're flowing and going. Figure 4A and 4B show the mechanical process that yields this measurement.

Part of the airspeed indicator shown in Figure 4A is connected to the pitot tube, a narrow metallic wind scoop,

The Airspeed Indicator

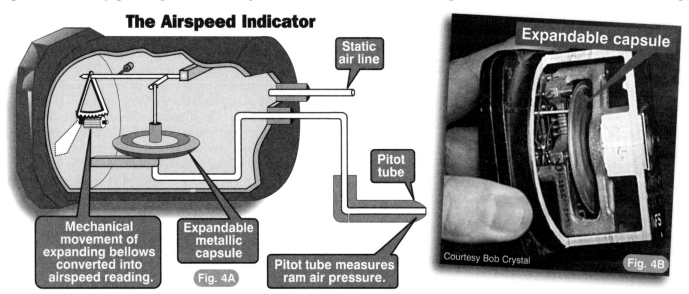

Static air line

Pitot tube

Mechanical movement of expanding bellows converted into airspeed reading.

Expandable metallic capsule

Fig. 4A

Pitot tube measures ram air pressure.

Expandable capsule

Courtesy Bob Crystal

Fig. 4B

Atmospheric Pressure Changes With Height

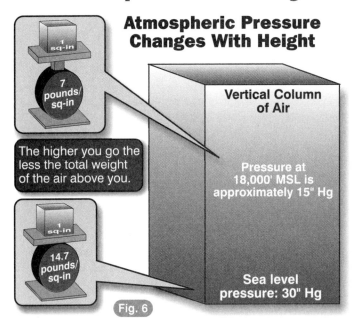

The higher you go the less the total weight of the air above you.

Vertical Column of Air

Pressure at 18,000' MSL is approximately 15" Hg

Sea level pressure: 30" Hg

Fig. 6

The Traditional Pitot Tube

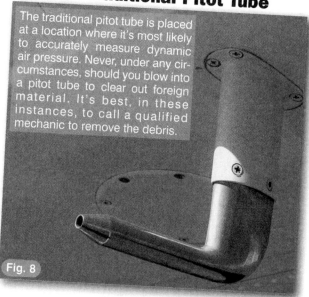

The traditional pitot tube is placed at a location where it's most likely to accurately measure dynamic air pressure. Never, under any circumstances, should you blow into a pitot tube to clear out foreign material. It's best, in these instances, to call a qualified mechanic to remove the debris.

Fig. 8

usually mounted under a wing, that collects moving, high velocity air. I once had a student who thought there had to be a sheep's horn mounted somewhere on the plane to collect ram air. I pointed out that the pitot tube was as close as he was going to get, which left him feeling kind of sheepish. The ram air pressure gathered by the pitot tube expands a metallic bellows located within the airspeed indicator's body. This is mechanically converted into movement of the airspeed needle via a gearing system (Figure 4A has been simplified because not everyone is an engineer. After all, not everyone likes to drive trains).

You can see that the container surrounding the bellows is connected to a static line which connects to a *static pressure* source. A static source (Figure 5) samples non-moving (static) air, allowing this to enter the airspeed container. Think of static air pressure as simply the natural

weight of the atmosphere, which we often refer to as *atmospheric pressure* (Figure 6). It's the Zero Zone, the pressure of standing still. The difference between dynamic air pressure and static air pressure is the amount of air pressure caused by the airplane speeding through the sky, and hence it gives us our indicated airspeed reading.

It takes two to tango, and a similar number to make an airspeed. If *either* of these two air sources (pitot or static sources) is blocked or plugged, the airspeed number will be wrong. That's why knowing how the indicated airspeed is derived is very important to an instrument pilot. You have to know what can go wrong so you'll know when everything's all right. Let's examine the pitot-static system and see the result if mischievous obstructions like ice or insects manage to block the pitot tube or static ports.

The Static Port—Measuring the Air That's There

Things aren't always what they appear to be, which may be why we don't get static from the static port.

Figure 5 shows a common variety of static port just sort of hanging out, which is what static ports do. Just as you might turn sideways to avoid having the wind blow in your face, the static port faces sideways to the air striking the plane as it moves. The static port lets the weight of the non-moving air (atmospheric pressure) enter through its opening. As shown in Figure 7, two other instruments (the *vertical speed indicator* and the *altimeter)* also require information from the static port in order to function. We'll visit these instruments a little later in our tour.

Pitot Tubes—Measuring Air on the Move

Figure 8 is the common variety of pitot tube that is found on many Cessna and Beechcraft airplanes.

The Pitot Tube and Static Port

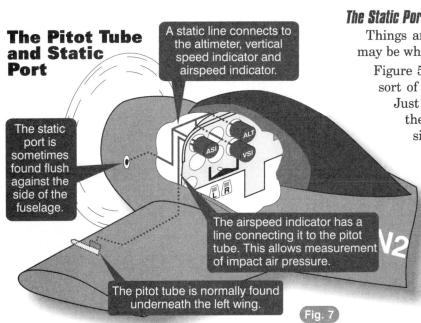

A static line connects to the altimeter, vertical speed indicator and airspeed indicator.

The static port is sometimes found flush against the side of the fuselage.

The airspeed indicator has a line connecting it to the pitot tube. This allows measurement of impact air pressure.

The pitot tube is normally found underneath the left wing.

Fig. 7

Static Display: Tape Placed Over Static Port

Flying the flags might have prevented another return-to-land incident, as reported by a corporate Captain:

Early morning departure from a dark ramp. I did not finish my walk-around inspection as I was interrupted by a passenger arriving early. I never resumed my normal routine. On takeoff, I heard the first officer call, "You've got no airspeed." I then called, "Say your airspeed." Came the reply, "I've got no airspeed either." By that time, we had considerable speed and I elected to continue takeoff. Once airborne, I got the "ADC (Air Data Computer) failure" light. We decided to dump fuel and return to base.

The aircraft had been inspected and washed the day before, and tape had been left on the static ports and pitot tubes. I had not seen it in the dark, and my preflight had been interrupted. No excuse! It was CAVU this time, but what if it had been 200 feet and half-mile visibility?

A "remove before flight" flag or long strip of "caution" tape attached to the tape covering the static ports and pitot tubes would have provided a visual warning to ground and flight crews.

NASA Callback Report

Figure 9 shows a pitot-static head that's a combination pitot tube and static port common to Piper airplanes. Impact pressure is sensed through the pitot opening on the front side (position A), while static pressure is sensed through two holes, one on the bottom (position B) of the scarf cut and the other at the rear of the device (position C). These two openings allow a balanced measure of static pressure. You might see an airplane with what appears to be a pitot tube protruding horizontally out the left side of the fuselage (Figure 10). This is the Piper Arrow ram-static pressure mast that's used in its automatic gear extension system.

Pitot tubes make really cozy homes for a variety of insects. The specific variety depends on where you live, but to avoid having the bugs bug you, the pitot tube generally has a cover that's placed over it between flights. Of course, for the pitot system to do its job, you need to *remove* the pitot tube cover before flight (Figure 11). Not doing so is like putting on a tie but forgetting the shirt. Both result in the formation of large crowds and lots of finger pointing. After all, if the air can't blow into the tube, then the airspeed needle won't move. The basic principle is, no blow, no go. Most pitot tube covers have a long and obvious red flag attached to them, in the hopes of flagging you down during the preflight.

Pitot Tube Cover

REMOVE BEFORE FLIGHT!

Fig. 11

A pitot tube found on Piper airplanes is co-located with its static source. Port A is the pitot opening; port B on the scarf cut and port C on the rear of the mast are used to provide a balanced measurement of static pressure.

A

B

C

Fig. 9

I know of one pilot who departed with a homemade, thin plastic pitot tube cover still attached. With the long red streamer dangling in the wind, the airplane lifted off while the airspeed read zero. Realizing his error, he tried a rather creative solution by turning on the pitot heat, hoping it would burn through the plastic. Nice try, but no meltdown, and no airspeed, either. If you need a good reason to do a thorough preflight, this is it. If you need a reason to get glasses to see pitot cover warning flags, this is it, too.

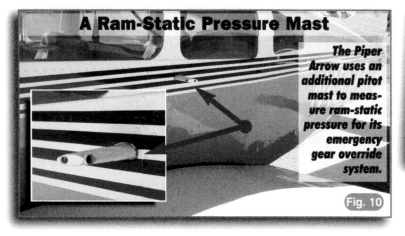

A Ram-Static Pressure Mast

The Piper Arrow uses an additional pitot mast to measure ram-static pressure for its emergency gear override system.

Fig. 10

Pitot Icing

Courtesy NASA

Fig. 12

Pitot ice, which may look like the ice shown here, can easily restrict the ram airflow into the pitot tube and render a "zero" airspeed reading.

Other things can block the pitot tube, reducing the airspeed reading to zero. If you don't have pitot heat (or didn't make sure it was working before flight), then any accumulation of ice can block the opening. Pitot tubes are efficient collectors of ice and can ingest ice crystals that accumulate and lead to a blockage even when no airframe icing is present. Figure 12 shows how rime and clear ice form on a surface and it's a good example of the type of ice that might form on an

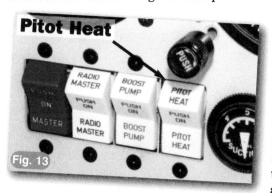

Fig. 13

unheated pitot tube. As pitot ice accumulates, the airspeed consequences are unpredictable, ranging from a gradual to a total reduction. A lot depends on just how and where the ice forms and how much of the tube is obstructed.

If you're airborne, an airspeed reading of zero doesn't mean your airplane isn't flying. It only means that you now have a less clear idea about how fast it's flying, and thus have to rely on other clues (i.e., power settings, pitch, etc.) to determine your approximate speed. If you find yourself flying with zero airspeed, it's Nature's way of telling you that either you left the pitot cover on or now would be a great time to activate the pitot heat (no, not to try and burn off the plastic cover, either).

I recommend activating the pitot heat (Figure 13) any time you expect to encounter visible moisture (a cloud) on an IFR flight, regardless of the outside air temperature. In other words, push the pitot heat switch if you're in clouds, even if it's not cold enough for ice to form. Ice works in mysterious ways, and often shows up when and where it's least expected, with little regard for what theory says it's supposed to do. That's why many commercial operators operate with the pitot heat on, regardless of the weather conditions (unless its operation is restricted by the manufacturer). If it's good enough for them, it's good enough for me. And you, too.

Pitot Tube: Waxing Eloquent

Here, we look at a case of malfunctioning instruments caused by the human touch. The Captain of a corporate jet reports:

During takeoff roll, passing through 100 knots, airspeed difference was noted between captain's and first officer's airspeed indicators. As airspeed increased, the difference between the two systems became larger. As the ADC (Air Data Computer) sensed the airspeed difference, the ADC miscompare alert illuminated, the yaw damper inop alert illuminated, the yaw damper disengaged, the elevator trim inop alert illuminated, and the elevator trim disengaged, along with the autothrottles disengaging. With all these cautions and their associated chimes, there was a great deal of activity, including IMC almost immediately after takeoff.

The SID calls for level-off at 2,000 feet and 200 knots airspeed. Well, we missed both of those. The airspeed difference remained for approximately 20 minutes, then went away, restoring all systems.

Cause: the aircraft had been waxed the day before, and burned wax residue was found in the Captain's pitot tube on postflight. **NASA Callback**

When You Just Can't Wait

A general aviation pilot debated filing an IFR flight plan for a pleasure flight in mixed VMC/IMC. The reporter even considered canceling the flight because of the weather, but admits that "my judgment was clouded by 'get-there-itis' combined with beckoning patches of blue sky."

"After considering the options, I decided that flying VFR would allow me the freedom to find a hole in the clouds and get on top in clear air. As we climbed toward the blue patches, it seemed harder and harder to find a hole large enough to climb through. Since it looked like we only needed to climb about another 100 feet to clear the tops, I decided that I would plow on through. Things got worse.

At first the sun poked through occasionally, beckoning us on. Then it started getting darker, and we picked up a trace of rime ice. Just as I was deciding that we would have to turn back, the engine started surging. I thought we had carb ice but carb heat didn't help. As I was trouble-shooting the engine, another aviation demon was sneaking up on us. It turned out that the pitot heat was inoperative, and the pitot tube [and its drain port] had frozen over. As we were climbing, the airspeed indicator was falsely reading a higher and higher air-
speed, and I was gradually compensating (unaware) to stay at Vx indicated airspeed. The plane then began to porpoise, indicating an imminent stall. Just as the stall broke hard, the scenario came together in my mind. We banked at least 90 degrees, and I pushed the yoke forward.... I pulled the throttle back to idle, and recovered from the stall in solid IMC. I did a 180 turn and headed for VMC. We broke out in a few minutes and landed VFR.

The pitot tube didn't thaw out until we got below the freezing level.... I am convinced that the surging engine was due to the high pitch attitude."

The reporter points out several lessons to be learned from this incident: Check the pitot heat before any flight which has the potential to be in IMC, and carefully monitor weight and balance for aft-of-limit conditions that may hamper stall recovery. Finally, avoid the beckoning lure of those "blue patches" between clouds.

NASA Callback Report

Get There Itis

Shields up! Phasers to stun. One to beam out!! Oh wait, that's next year's model.

Why the big deal about turning on the pitot heat? While a plugged pitot tube may be just annoying, a plugged pitot tube and pitot drain hole can be downright dangerous. This is the type of problem you don't want to have unless you're Superman. Then again, Superman doesn't need an airplane, does he? If, for some reason, both of these openings become blocked, you need to know how to detect and cope with the problem immediately.

Given how fast ice can accumulate, it's possible for the pitot tube and the pitot drain hole to immediately and simultaneously freeze over when pitot heat isn't used in icing conditions (I mean this can happen in a few seconds, literally!). Under these conditions, ram air pressure responsible for expanding the airspeed indicator's metallic bellows becomes trapped within the pitot lines. This leaves the airspeed indicator's metallic bellows expanded slightly but still surrounded by static air pressure (remember, the static line probably isn't plugged). The differential pressure between static air pressure and the air locked in the pitot lines causes the mechanical workings of the airspeed indicator to behave like an altimeter would, as shown in Figure 14.

Keep your eye on the principle here. Airspeed is measured by the difference between static and ram air pressure. If the airplane were in a climb when the double blockage occurred, then the static pressure surrounding the bellows would begin to decrease with an increase in altitude, *increasing* the difference in pressure between the static reading and the (sealed and inaccurate) ram reading. As a result, the bellows would expand as all sealed and flexible containers do when the pressure around them decreases. Mechanically speaking, this would result in the airspeed needle showing an increase in airspeed, despite the fact that the airplane really isn't going any faster! Holy Batmobile. A free ride.

A pilot who's unaware of what's happening might think he or she is in some peculiar type of updraft and pull back

Because he decided to forgo the pre-purchase inspection, Bob is not surprised when all his fake panel instruments slide away during a steep turn.

on the yoke to reduce the airspeed. Of course, this continues the climb, resulting in larger and larger indicated airspeed readings because (still watching that principle?) the pressure differential is increasing.

It's even possible that the pilot might reduce power in an attempt to reduce the airspeed in a climb. Can you see the problem here? The pilot, plane, and passengers are now in danger, just as if someone had slipped Kryptonite into Superman's Speedo. Under these conditions, if the pilot wasn't scanning or interpreting the other instruments properly (a good possibility because it's very easy to focus solely on the airspeed indicator's seemingly miraculous increase), the airplane could stall. Sadly, that's just what happened to the crew of a Boeing 727 in 1974, as discussed in the accompanying sidebar to the right.

On the other hand, if the double blockage occurred during a descent, exactly the opposite would happen. No matter what the pilot did, as atmospheric pressure increased, indicated airspeed would decrease. If the pilot didn't scan or properly interpret the other flight instruments on the panel, he or she might drive the airplane into the ground, all the while thinking that the aerial chariot was losing airspeed. In level flight at any given altitude, a similar blockage would result in the indicated airspeed remaining constant despite an actual change in airspeed.

Now you know why an instrument pilot must be skilled at instrument scanning, instrument interpretation and aircraft control. You also know why we check the pitot heat before every IFR flight. How do we do that? During the preflight, activate the master switch.

Airspeed Errors With Pitot Tube and Drain Hole Plugged

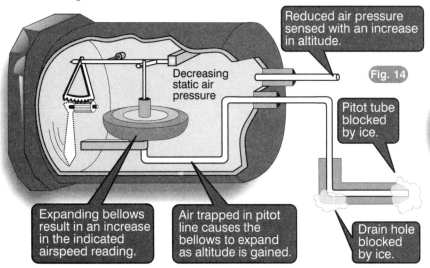

Reduced air pressure sensed with an increase in altitude.

Decreasing static air pressure

Fig. 14

Pitot tube blocked by ice.

Altitude Increasing

Expanding bellows result in an increase in the indicated airspeed reading.

Air trapped in pitot line causes the bellows to expand as altitude is gained.

Drain hole blocked by ice.

If the pitot tube and drain hole are covered with ice (because the pitot heat wasn't turned on), static air pressure can become trapped inside the pitot line and bellows. As altitude increases and static pressure decreases, the indicated airspeed will show an increase without the airplane actually increasing its speed. See The Impossible Climb, next page.

The Impossible Climb

The following is the sad story of what happened when three professional pilots failed to properly scan and interpret the flight instruments after experiencing a simultaneous freezing of the pitot head and pitot drain openings.

On the evening of December 1, 1974, a Boeing 727 climbing in instrument conditions stalled and crashed into Bear Mountain, in upstate New York. The only three people on board (the flight crew) were killed.

The airplane departed New York's Kennedy airport to Buffalo to pick up its chartered passengers (it's important to note that the airplane was lightly loaded, having only the flight crew on board at the time). Prior to departing into moderate to heavy rainshowers and frequent moderate icing, the first officer was inadvertently distracted and failed to activate the pitot head heater switches. A climb rate of 2,500 feet per minute was established while the airplane climbed through 13,000 feet to its assigned altitude of 31,000 feet. As the airplane climbed through 16,000 feet the indicated airspeed began to rise with no change in power setting. The following exchange occurred between crewmembers (as transcribed from the cockpit voice recorder):

First officer (who is flying at the time): *Do you realize we're going 340 knots and I'm climbing 3,000 feet per minute?*

Second officer: *That's because we're light.*

(The first officer continued to exert back pressure on the yoke. As the airplane passed though 23,000 feet it was climbing at more than 6,500 feet per minute. The indicated airspeed was 405 knots and an overspeed warning horn (which is linked to the airspeed indicator) sounded.)

Captain: *Would you believe that *#X?*

First officer: *I believe it. I just can't do anything about it.*

Captain: *Pull her back and let her climb.*

(The overspeed warning horn was heard again, followed 10 seconds later by the sound of the stall warning stick shaker, which is independent of the airspeed measuring system. The aircraft was now on the verge of a stall.)

First officer: *There's that Mach buffet, I guess we'll have to pull it up.*

Captain: *Pull it up.*

(Mach buffet is a vibration that takes place when an aircraft exceeds its critical Mach number. At 420 knots indicated air-

speed, both the first officer and captain mistook the stick shaker stall warning for Mach buffet. The landing gear warning horn then sounded, indicating that the throttles had been retarded with the gear up. Thirteen seconds after arriving at 24,800 feet, the airplane was falling at a rate of 15,000 feet per minute, turning rapidly to the right.)

Crew: *Mayday! Mayday!*

ATC: *Go ahead....*

Crew: *Roger, we're out of control... descending through 20,000 feet.... We're descending through 12,000 feet, we're in a stall!*

That was the last transmission from the crew.

It should be obvious that this crew became fixated on the airspeed indicator to the exclusion of the other flight instruments. No doubt, the attitude indicator showed a dramatic nose up attitude before the stall occurred, too. The fact that the airplane was light must have also led the crew to believe the airplane was initially behaving normally, at least until the stall occurred. All instrument pilots can learn from this tragic event.

Source: *FAA Aviation News*
Issue: February 1976

Then turn the pitot heat switch on and wait a moment for it to heat up. Now test it the same way you test an iron. Not a pitching wedge or a five iron, an ironing iron. No, don't lay the underside of your arm on it or you might yell out the name, Yoweee!—the deity in charge of pitot heat fire. Simply touch it lightly and quickly to see if it's warm. That'll do.

Reading in Color: The Airspeed Indicator's Face

General aviation airplanes have airspeed indicators that are color coded, and for a very good reason, too. Colors are symbols that provide information. Traffic lights, for example, do the same thing. Green means normal, yellow means caution, red means stop and white is the color of the policeman's flashlight that you stare at while trying to explain how the yellow should have lasted longer. These are also the four colors that you will find on the airspeed indicator in a single-engine airplane (Figure 15).

The airspeed indicator's white arc represents the airplane's flap operating range. The low speed end, or beginning of the white arc, is the power-off stall speed in the landing configuration (i.e.,

with flaps fully extended and gear down). This is called *Vso*. You can remember this by thinking of it as the velocity (V) of stall (s) with everything out (o). Of course, by *out* I mean flaps and gear fully extended (assuming, of course, it's a retractable-gear airplane).

According to our figure, at Vso the airplane needs a minimum of 54 knots of wind flowing over the wings to become (or remain) airborne. The assumption here is that the airplane is always at its maximum allowable landing weight, since the airplane is configured for landing (i.e., gear and flaps are down). Lighter weights reduce the stall

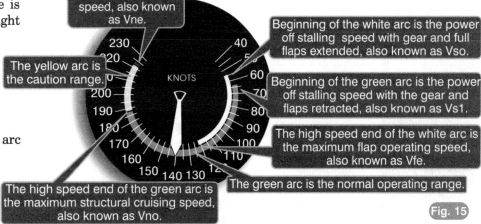

Airspeed Indicator Markings

The red line is the never to be exceeded speed, also known as Vne.

The yellow arc is the caution range.

Beginning of the white arc is the power off stalling speed with gear and full flaps extended, also known as Vso.

Beginning of the green arc is the power off stalling speed with the gear and flaps retracted, also known as Vs1.

The high speed end of the white arc is the maximum flap operating speed, also known as Vfe.

The green arc is the normal operating range.

The high speed end of the green arc is the maximum structural cruising speed, also known as Vno.

KNOTS

Fig. 15

Maneuvering Speed Truth

As you know by now, an airplane flown at or below its maneuvering speed in turbulence, will stall before exceeding its limit load factor (if you don't know this then please read Postflight Briefing #2-5 in *Rod Machado's Private Pilot Handbook* for a comprehensive and very different look at maneuvering speed). As a result, the airplane doesn't suffer structural damage. Yes, it may momentarily stall, but you probably never have to use standard stall recovery procedures as a result. You can't say the same about a doing something as positive when a wing comes off.

In strong turbulence, the only way to ensure that you won't exceed the airplane's structural limit is to fly a little below maneuvering speed, perhaps by 10-15 knots. Since maneuvering speed is an indicated airspeed, the horizontal component of a gust (which can cause a 10-25 knot airspeed change in moderate turbulence according to one British study) can temporarily increase your indicated airspeed many knots over Va.

Additionally, maneuvering speed is determined in a power-off condition by the manufacturer. Since you use power when you fly airplanes (you do, don't you?), the result is that the airplane stalls at a slightly slower speed. Why? Because some of that power is applied vertically, in the direction of lift, thus reducing the total amount of lift the wings need to produce for flight. Thus, the wings can fly at a slightly lower angle of attack for a given power condition. In cruise flight your wings are now slightly farther away from the angle of attack at which they will stall when a strong vertical gust is encountered. Those wings can now develop slightly more lift (perhaps more than they, or the airplane's fixed weight components, can withstand) before they stall if and when they encounter a strong enough vertical gust.

All this adds up to one important point. It's safer to fly a little less than the manufacturer's posted maneuvering speed for your airplane when in strong turbulence.

speed below the colored minimum. (For your information, the color coded stall speed can also be the minimum steady speed at which the airplane is controllable. Either definition is correct).

Moving in a clockwise direction and following the white arc, we come to its high-speed end. This represents the maximum airspeed at which you may fully extend the flaps or fly with them fully extended. Called *Vfe* or velocity (V) of flaps (f) extended (e), flaps may not be used above this speed for fear of structural damage (and the prime directive of any pilot is to avoid bending any or all parts of the airplane).

Most things that are green are good (especially vegetables, although my little nephew considers asparagus to be nothing more than spinach legs). That's why the green arc represents the normal operating range of the airplane. The beginning of the green arc represents the power-off stall speed or minimum steady flight speed in a specified configuration. For the airplanes we typically fly, this configuration occurs when the plane is at its maximum takeoff weight and the flaps and gear (if retractable) are up. This is called *Vs1* or velocity (V) of stall (s) with everything inside (1)—think of the *1* as the letter *i* representing gear and flaps up or *inside*. With flaps up, gear up, and power at idle, the beginning of the green arc in Figure 15 suggests this airplane needs a minimum of 64 knots of wind flowing over its wings before it starts flying. If you're flying an airplane with a primary flight display, Figure 16 shows how these airspeeds might be portrayed on these instruments (the display may vary between manufacturers).

The high speed end of the green arc is called *Vno* or the maximum structural cruising speed. Since the green arc is the airplane's normal operating range, think of the top of the green arc as the velocity (V) of normal (n) operation (o). At and below Vno, airplanes (certified on or after September 14, 1969) are certified to withstand substantial sharp-edge vertical gusts of 50 feet per second without experiencing structural damage (or sharp edge vertical gusts of 30 feet per second if the airplane was certified

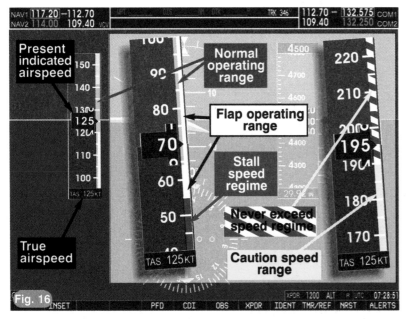

Fig. 16

Present indicated airspeed

Normal operating range

Flap operating range

Stall speed regime

Never exceed speed regime

Caution speed range

True airspeed

TAS 125KT

Digital Airspeed Readouts on PFDs

Primary flight displays provide digital airspeed readouts, as shown in Figure 16. The numerical airspeed tape moves vertically with airspeed change. The airplane's present airspeed is shown in the white-on-black box in the center of the tape. Notice that the yellow, green and white color codes correspond to the same color codes shown in Figure 15. On this primary flight display, the never-exceed speed region, is shown by a red striped line and the stall speed region is shown by a solid red color. PFD manufacturers may vary the color coding used for these airspeed regions.

Some PFDs provide you with trend lines (the magenta line, Figure 17, position Z) that show where your airspeed will be in six seconds. Best rate, angle and glide speeds may also be shown by thumbnail identifiers (position X).

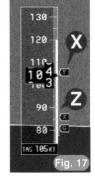

Fig. 17

How Strong Are Those Wings?

Looking at the Mooney airplane to the right, you're only seeing a portion of the force the wings on most small general aviation airplanes are safely capable of handling. As a matter of fact, it's rare for a wing to fail because it's over-stressed by turbulence. Most wing failures occur because the pilot was flying in or near IMC and lost control of the airplane, resulting in a dramatic increase in airspeed. Too much speed increases the likelihood of damage by flutter or excess stress caused by the pilot pulling too hard during a 200-300 mph recovery. Take comfort in knowing that you'll be lucky to find a single case of a wing breaking off an airplane flown at or below its Vo/Va.

Should we have told the FBO about this?

Naw!

Courtesy Mooney Aircraft Co.

before September 14, 1969). Operations above Vno within the yellow arc are allowed only in smooth air (and this means smooth air, not air that's less than the 30 or 50 FPS limit values, either). To learn more about these vertical gust values and how they may affect your airplane, you might want to read Chapter 21 of my *Instrument Pilot's Survival Manual* that covers this topic in much greater detail.

Your airplane has one speed that should never be exceeded. Coincidentally, it's called *Vne* or velocity (V) that you never (n) exceed (e). This is the red line on the airspeed indicator. It's also the maximum speed at which the airplane can be operated in smooth air and going above it means all bets are off, and if you go past it you're a bit off, too. Exceeding Vne can cause aerodynamic *flutter*, which, coincidentally, is something your heart valves also do if you experience flutter. Aerodynamic flutter is often an uncontrollable and destructive vibration of certain airfoil surfaces.

Dynamic divergence and *aileron reversal* are a couple of the other bad boys associated with exceeding *Vne*. Don't go there. Many unprepared pilots have lost control of their airplane in IMC (instrument meteorological conditions) and reached, then exceeded, *Vne*. Many have paid a hefty price for this error. Don't exceed this speed. Period. No exceptions and no excuses, unless you're a test pilot and getting test pilot pay, a bonus, and a free chocolate treat for bringing the plane back undamaged. Consider this your Surgeon General's warning to avoid flying above the airspeed indicator's redline.

Vne is 90% of the speed at which flutter occurs. Granted, Vne has a slight, built-in safety factor but who wants to count on that? General aviation flying isn't the test pilot business. If you're looking for thrills, try tightrope walking during bee season. Leave exploring the

far reaches of the airplane's envelope to folks who wear parachutes and are trained to do such things.

Three important speeds are *not* shown on the airspeed indicator: Va, Vlo and Vle. The first speed is called *maneuvering speed* or *Va*, otherwise remembered as velocity (V) of acceleration (a). In turbulence, you should be at or below maneuvering speed. (my preference in serious turbulence is to be below maneuvering speed, perhaps by 10–15 knots, since this is an indicated airspeed and a gust can increase your indicated airspeed many knots over Va).

Maneuvering speed is found well below Vno. Your Pilot's Operating Handbook or posted placards provide you with the airplane's maneuvering speed. Since Va is

technically defined at the airplane's maximum design weight and since maneuvering speed decreases with a decrease in weight, the FAA has added a new term referencing the maneuvering speeds associated with lighter weights. This term is called *Vo* or *operating maneuvering speed*. Some manufacturers provide one or more Vo's for weights less than max gross, as shown in Figure 18.

Divergent Flutter

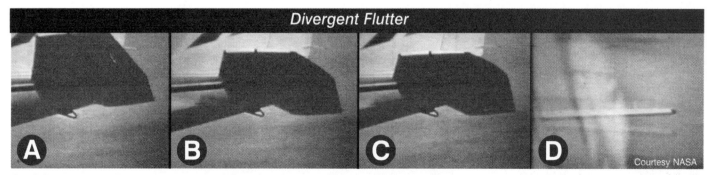

Courtesy NASA

The following video frame sequence (A to B to C) represents approximately one-fifth of a second in which the horizontal stabilizer and the elevator are in the throes of divergent flutter. The test pilot on this Twin Comanche induced flutter at high speed by pulsing the control wheel with his hand then, when flutter occurred, he immediately reduced power and applied some back pressure on the elevator. Frame D also shows the range of surface movement as captured by a camera inside the cockpit.

Gear Operating Speeds

SECTION 2 LIMITATIONS	PIPER AIRCRAFT CORPORATION PA-28RT-201T, TURBO ARROW IV	
SPEED	KIAS	KCAS
Maximum Flaps Extended Speed (VFE) - Do not exceed this speed with the flaps extended.	108	104
Maximum Landing Gear Extension Speed - Do not exceed this speed when extending the landing gear.	133	130
Maximum Landing Gear Retraction Speed - Do not exceed this speed when retracting the landing gear.	111	109
Maximum Landing Gear Extended Speed (VLE) - Do not exceed this speed with the landing gear extended.	133	130

Fig. 19

The other two speeds not shown on the airspeed indicator are *Vlo* and *Vle*. These speeds refer to operations of the airplane's retractable landing gear (if equipped with retractable gear, of course; please don't make yours retractable if it wasn't built that way). The velocity (V) of landing gear (l) operation (o) (Vlo) is the maximum speed at which the gear may be raised or lowered. The velocity (V) with the landing gear (l) extended (e) (Vle) is the maximum speed at which the airplane can be flown with the gear down.

When the gear is in transition, it's often more vulnerable to the effects of speed (often because of exposed and relatively delicate gear doors or the forces placed on the mechanisms used to extend or retract the gear). Once down and locked into position, the gear is able to resist a larger wind force. This is why Vlo is sometimes less than Vle rather than equal to it. Look in your Pilot's Operating Handbook or on the airplane's placards to find information on these speeds (Figure 19).

As a passing point, if you ever manage to extend your gear beyond Vlo or fly gear down beyond Vle, don't raise the gear again. Leave it down until you have a chance to check the gear doors for damage. Some gear doors can warp, bend, twist or even depart the airplane if excessive speeds are encountered. Don't be like the Air Force colonel departing in a T-28 with a young lieutenant in the rear seat. The colonel lifted off prematurely, retracted the gear, and the airplane began settling back to the runway. The prop dug out a few hundred chunks of asphalt from the landing surface before the airplane was once again airborne. The colonel continued flying, paying no attention to the matter. The lieutenant said, "Sir, shouldn't we return to land and check for damage?"

The colonel replies in a gruff voice, "Naw, let 'em check their own dang runway."

Should Turbulence Scare You? A Case for a G-Meter

I constantly marvel at the human reaction to in-flight turbulence on airliners. People scream, people cry, people pray. And that's just in the cockpit. Simply stated, we don't like turbulence because it's unpredictable. Many years ago, I sent a student pilot on a solo cross county flight to Palm Springs, CA. Several large mountains—aviation's biggest troublemakers—form the perimeter of the route to this desert airport. Given enough wind, these mountains often produce sheets of churning, bubbling air.

That day was forecast clear and smooth (ha!). My student departed, only to return four hours later, his face flushed free of all blood, color, and apparent life. He waved me over and told his tale. "It was the worst turbulence I've ever seen," he blurted. "It was so bad I thought I saw the Buddha."

Since he was in a Cessna 150 Aerobat (it had a G meter), I walked him over to the cockpit. We looked inside at the G meter (which stays pegged at the highest G-force encountered, until reset). I pointed to the instrument. It read 1.7 G's. I said, "You only pulled .7 more G's than you feel in straight-and-level, unaccelerated flight. In fact, you experience more G's (2 to be exact) in a 60 degree steep bank turn."

He looked puzzled, liked a baker who had never heard of yeast. I was waiting for him to admit that he really saw his friend Bubba, not the Buddha. In then end, he was simply amazed that the shellacking he took never exceeded even one-third of the airplane's limit load factor (aerobatic aircraft have a limit load factor of 6 G's positive). In other words, he was in a 6G airplane with a 1.7G triggered imagination. If anything, this should reinforce the point that it's not the G force that scares pilots, it's the unpredictability of the event. This is, however a good reason to install a G-meter in your airplane to help calibrate your "seat of the pants" reaction to turbulence.

On the other hand, how likely is the average airplane to reach or exceed this G force limit? On a rare occasion, it happens. When and where it happens is no real surprise.

A NASA study on gusts and maneuvering loads found that exceeding an airplane's limit load factor as a result of pilot-applied control inputs was primarily the province of aerobatic flight, aerial applications and instructional operations.

It's no surprise that an aerobatic pilot, confined to a designated cube of airspace, might yank and bank to keep the airplane within that cube. Aerial applicators are similarly self-restricted by the size of the field they're dusting. Both operations can lead to high load factors as pilots maneuver to remain within these self-imposed zones.

A Typical G-Meter

Students are no less likely to be rough on the flight controls, which is the primary reason instructional flights experience excessive load factors. This same NASA study concluded that commercial survey operations (e.g., forest and pipeline patrol airplanes) were most likely to experience turbulence or gust-induced forces outside the design flight envelope. This isn't surprising, because these folks constantly fly from 50 to 1,500 feet above the surface where mechanical turbulence is greatest.

Understanding the Airplane's Gust/Stress Envelope

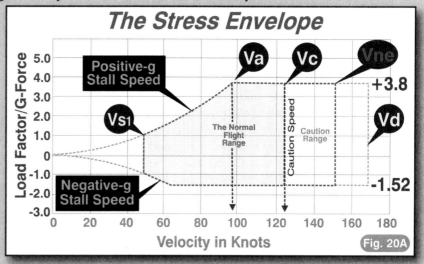

The stress envelope, sometimes known as the v-g (velocity-load factor) diagram provides you with a picture of an airplane's stress limits. Figure 20A shows the stress limits for a typical general aviation airplane. The borders of the stress envelope (the red dashed line) identify the operating limits of this airplane. The left upper border of the normal flight (green) envelope is the airplane's stall speed in the clean configuration (Vs1). The upward and downward curving lines represent the accelerated stall speed for a specific positive or negative load factor (remember, as the load factor increases [or decreases in the negative direction] the stall speed increases and this line represents that increase in stall speed). Va represents the airplane's maneuvering speed at the airplane's max certified gross weight. The far right vertical border of the caution range (yellow) envelope is the airplane's maximum allowable cruising speed (also known as Vne—never exceed velocity). Vd is the airplane's design dive speed. Beyond Vd the airplane may experience flutter and a bunch of other bad things I'd rather not talk about. Vne is designed to be no more than 90% of Vd. The top and bottom parts of the normal and caution regions represent the limit load factors for the airplane. In this instance, the airplane shown is certified as a normal category airplane (+3.8 G's, -1.52 G's).

The borders of the airplane's stress envelope are established by the physical limits of the airplane's accelerated stall speed (both in the positive-g and negative-g condition), by the the limit load factor (both in the positive-g and negative-g condition), by the stall speed (Vs1), and design dive speed (Vd).

The airplane's gust envelope in Figure 20B represents the gust limits of a typical general aviation airplane certified under the newer FAR Part 23 regulations (effective September 14, 1969).

These regulations require that an airplane be capable of withstanding a 50 FPS sharp-edge gust at Vc (the beginning the the yellow arc on most airspeed indicators) without exceeding its limit load factor. These regulations also require an airplane to withstand 25 FPS sharp-edge gusts at its design dive speed (Vd).

Looking at Figure 20B, the blue diagonal lines represent the effect of a 50 FPS sharp edge gust on the airplane. It's clear that a gust of this magnitude (or less) would not stress the airplane beyond its design limits (this envelope and all the others shown in this book are based on the airplane operating at maximum gross weight).

Airplanes certified under the the older Civil Air Regulations (CAR 3.201, pre-September 14, 1969) are only required to withstand 30 FPS and 15 FPS sharp-edge gusts, respectively, without exceeding their stress limits (Figure 20C). Beechcraft Bonanzas, for example, were certified under the older FAR Part 23.

As a point of curiosity, a sharp-edge gust is one that is expected to occur instantaneously instead of coming on slowly and peaking in intensity. Since most gusts aren't the theoretical sharp-edge type, it certainly works in your favor to expose the airplane to a little less overall stress.

If you'd like to learn more about how turbulence can affect your airplane, please read Postflight Briefing #9-3 on Page 9-64.

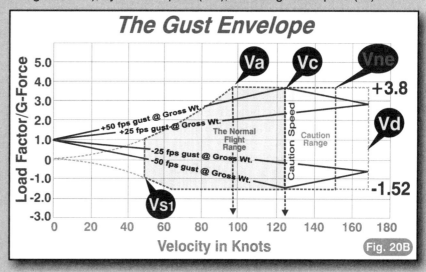

Airplane certificated on or after September 14th, 1969 were required to meet the stress standards of a design envelope based on a maximum sharp-edge gust of 50 feet per second.

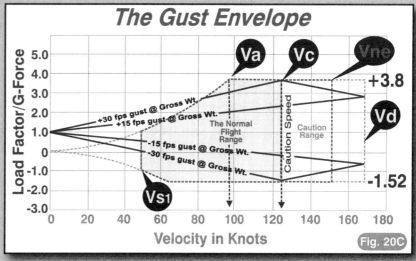

Airplane certificated prior to September 14th, 1969 were required to meet the stress standards of a design envelope based on a maximum sharp-edge gust of 30 feet per second.

An Indication of Airspeed

Sometimes there's a big difference between what you think you're doing and what you're actually doing. A fellow I read about said he was pulled over by the police for doing 60 mph (according to the radar gun) in a 45 mph zone. He politely told the officer that he was indicating 45 mph and that specific studies have shown that radar guns, when pointed at trees, sometimes show erroneous readings of 80 mph or more. The officer said, "That doesn't matter. If the gun shows you're speeding, you sign the ticket. If you don't do it, you go to jail." The guy didn't sign the ticket. He went to jail. He said it was very crowded there. Every time he turned around, he bumped into a tree.

Extended Pitot Mast Helps Sense Undisturbed Air

Courtesy NASA Collection

Fig. 21

You get the point, right? While our friend was indicating 45 mph, that wasn't the speed he was actually traveling. Keeping in mind that the airspeed indicator is really showing a difference between ram and static air pressure, anything affecting those pressures will affect the indicated airspeed. In an airplane, what you show is often not what you go.

Your *indicated airspeed (IAS)* is the number the airspeed needle points to. If the needle points to 100 knots, then 100 knots is the indicated airspeed. (Sounds too simple doesn't it? It's somewhat like the question, "What do you hear in the cone of silence?")

During an IFR flight, if a controller asks for your current airspeed, he or she expects to get back the indicated airspeed. Read what's on the dial. That's all the controller wants. Whatever you do, don't say, "100 knots. Manufactured in Thailand. Call Fred's Instrument Repair if you need service." Sometimes the pitot tube doesn't accurately sample the impact-air pressure. That's because there are always tradeoffs when it comes to placing the pitot tube on the airframe. Sometimes, there's just no good place or no reasonable way to connect the pitot tube to the airframe without it being affected by airframe aerodynamics or angle of attack. This is why some airplanes feature

Air Error

Pitot tubes are not always installed in such a way that they can accurately sample impact-air pressure. Flying at variable angles of attack, the airplane's pitot tube sometimes simply can't scoop up a sample of air which accurately reflects the airplane's speed (Figure 22). Sometimes the pitot tube scoops up less air than is actually striking it. Other times it scoops up air which has been artificially accelerated by a curved surface, giving a slightly higher than normal indicated airspeed reading. The net result is that the pitot pressure, and thus the indicated airspeed, aren't always an accurate reflection of the windspeed blowing on the airplane.

Once again, the engineers come through with an answer. In this case it's a chart which allows you to correct for such errors (Figure 23). This chart allows you to calibrate your indicated airspeed readings for accuracy. When this is done you have the more precise airspeed reading known as *calibrated airspeed*.

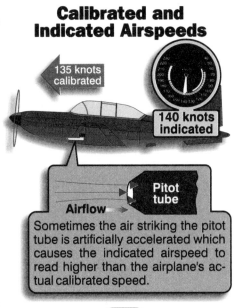

Calibrated and Indicated Airspeeds

135 knots calibrated

140 knots indicated

Airflow

Pitot tube

Sometimes the air striking the pitot tube is artificially accelerated which causes the indicated airspeed to read higher than the airplane's actual calibrated speed.

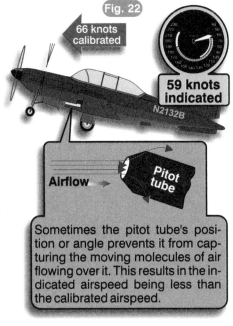

Fig. 22

66 knots calibrated

59 knots indicated

N2132B

Airflow

Pitot tube

Sometimes the pitot tube's position or angle prevents it from capturing the moving molecules of air flowing over it. This results in the indicated airspeed being less than the calibrated airspeed.

KIAS = Knots Indicated Air Speed/KCAS = Knots Calibrated Air Speed

AIRSPEED CALIBRATION CHART

FLAPS UP											
KIAS	50	60	70	80	90	100	110	120	130	140	150
KCAS	50	64	72	81	89	98	107	116	126	135	153

FLAPS 10°							
KIAS	40	50	60	70	80	90	100
KCAS	55	58	64	72	81	90	107

FLAPS 30°					
KIAS	40	50	60	70	80	85
KCAS	54	57	62	71	80	85

Fig. 23

Condition: Power required for level flight or maximum rated RPM dive

Speed Math

As a general rule, you'll find that for every thousand feet of altitude gain, true airspeed increases approximately 2% over indicated airspeed. Another way of saying this is that you are going 2% faster than what is shown on your airspeed indicator for every thousand feet of altitude gain.

At 10,000 feet above sea level, with an indicated airspeed of 100 knots, your true speed through the air is approximately 120 knots. For those who enjoy higher math, which all aviation calculations involve, you simply take 2% and multiply it by 10 (which is your altitude in thousands of feet above sea level). This equals 20%. Take 20% of 100 knots which equals 20 knots and add this onto 100. This totals to a true airspeed of 120 knots.

a pitot tube extended well ahead of the structure to which it's connected (Figure 21) in an attempt to minimize these problems (no, this isn't used to help the pilot keep fit by doing pullups, either). Flying at variable angles of attack, the airplane's pitot tube sometimes simply can't scoop up a sample of air that accurately reflects the airplane's speed (Figure 22). Sometimes the pitot tube scoops up less air than is actually striking it. Other times it scoops up air that has been artificially accelerated by a curved surface, giving a slightly higher than normal indicated airspeed reading. The net result is that the pitot pressure, and thus the indicated airspeed, isn't always an accurate reflection of the wind on the airplane.

Fortunately, crafty engineers came through with an answer. In this case it's a chart that allows you to correct for such errors (Figure 23). Printed at Houdini's Hideaway, this magic chart lets you calibrate your indicated airspeed readings to take account of the known errors. When this is done, you have the more precise airspeed reading known as *calibrated airspeed (CAS)*.

Calibrated Airspeed

Figure 23 shows the differences between the IAS and CAS. Notice that these differences are slightly larger at slower airspeeds, and with flaps extended, as well as at higher cruise speeds. It's important to note that most of the critical airspeeds you'll need are indicated airspeeds (Va, Vne, Vno, etc.). In other words, you don't need to look at any chart and convert IAS to CAS to use these speeds. So why bother with CAS at all? There *is* a case where knowing calibrated airspeed is useful, as you'll soon see. Calibrated airspeed, however, is not the airplane's *true* speed through the air.

True Airspeed, Honest

True airspeed (TAS) is exactly what the name suggests. It's the airplane's true speed through the air. While you may have a calibrated airspeed of 100 knots, that doesn't necessarily mean you're doing 100 knots. In all likelihood, you're going faster. Holly bat lips! For once you're getting more than you appear to be getting. Here's why.

Air at sea level is very dense. Drag is obviously quite high since air molecules are packed closer together. As the airplane ascends, it experiences less-dense air. This means less drag since fewer air molecules are around to resist the airplane's forward motion. Airplanes flying at higher altitudes can actually move faster through the air at a given power setting because of the decrease in density (Figure 24).

While the airplane goes faster through the thinner air, there are fewer air molecules striking the pitot tube and expanding the bellows of the airspeed indicator. The result is that at higher altitudes you are moving faster than your airspeed indicator shows. Therefore, as you gain altitude, your true airspeed increases faster than your indicated (or *calibrated*) airspeed—up to a point. Remember, in real life, you don't get something for nothing. That's why every day spent at the airport is like a day spent at a Disneyland theme park. Yep. While there's no Adventureland, Tomorrowland or Fantasyland, there's always a Realityland.

I'm sure you're thinking, "If I go faster by flying higher, why not fly really high?" Nice try, but no banana! Due to the perversity of nature and adversity of aviation, this logic can't hold water (or air). I said TAS increases with altitude for a given power setting. Pay close attention to the "for a given power setting" portion of the previous statement. This is the fine print you and I worry about on automobile rental contracts.

The ability of the engine to produce power decreases due to the reduced air density as you climb. The very thing which allows you to fly faster

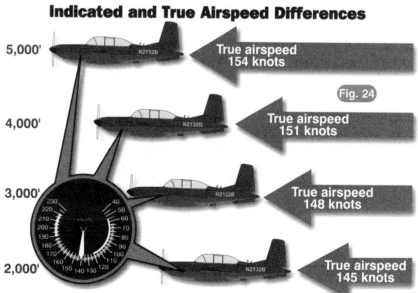

Indicated and True Airspeed Differences

Fig. 24

5,000' True airspeed 154 knots

4,000' True airspeed 151 knots

3,000' True airspeed 148 knots

2,000' True airspeed 145 knots

All airplanes have the same indicated airspeed of 140 Knots, but their true airspeed varies with altitude.

for a given amount of power (thinner air) limits the power you can produce! Welcome to Realityland! Turbocharging helps, but it too has limitations. Check your Pilot's Operating Handbook to identify the altitudes where you'll obtain the greatest gain in true airspeed for a given decrease in engine power. In most cases, you'll find that non-turbocharged airplanes tend to obtain the best true airspeed for the power produced at altitudes between 8,000 and 10,000 feet.

Two factors affect air density: *pressure* and *temperature*. Is there some way to precisely predict your true airspeed? Yes, and you don't have to be psychic to do so. That's *psychic*, not *psychotic*, and there's a big difference between the two. One knows the weather before it happens, the other doesn't know whether anything really happened. Fortunately, true airspeed predictions are easy to make.

You can find your true airspeed by using your flight computer (your E6-B or an electronic version). Figure 25 shows a computer with an outside air temperature of –12 degrees Celsius (Figure 25, position A) and a pressure altitude of 5,000 feet (Figure 25, position B). The true airspeed (TAS) is read on the outside scale (Figure 25, position C), opposite the calibrated airspeed (CAS) on the inside scale

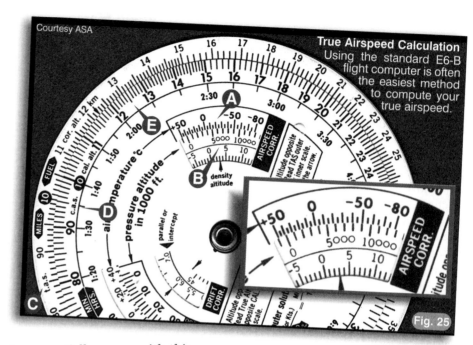

ing essentially wrong with this as long as the IAS-CAS error in cruise flight isn't excessive.

On the other hand, some PFDs provide you with an automatic calculation of true airspeed as shown in (Figure 26). The airplane's air data computer calculates the TAS based on the calibrated airspeed, pressure altitude, and outside air temperature (OAT).

High! The Altimeter

Moving right along in our behind-the-panel tour, we move over one slot and find ourselves up at the altimeter. There are lots of ways to get high in aviation (all perfectly legal and honest, honest!). In the next few minutes you will discover that there's altitude and then there's *altitude*. In fact, there are many altitudes. Knowing one from the other is crucial to your success as an instrument pilot, not to mention your long—as a person.

An altimeter (Figure 27) provides you with your height above sea level—otherwise known as your *true altitude*. Sea level is a worldwide standard. You'll seldom find anyone who

asks, "How high is sea level?" If you do, please loosen his tie because it's blocking a vital organ from getting

Some PFDs display your TAS which is automatically calculated by the airplane's air data computer.

(Figure 25, position D). A CAS of 125 knots as shown at Figure 25, position E, produces a TAS of 131 knots. Sure, during cruise flight it's often more convenient to use IAS instead of CAS to calculate your TAS. There's noth-

Mach Meter

General aviation airplanes are getting faster and faster. It won't be long before you'll own or rent an airplane capable of flying at Mach 1 (the speed of sound) and perhaps even beyond. Who knows, you many eventually hit Mach 2 and no one will be able to hear anything you say until two hours after you land. In the meantime, for those who are interested in fast airplanes, here's the skinny on Mach indicators.

The Mach number is the ratio of the true airspeed to the speed of sound (which, in turn, is determined by air density). It's calibrated by means of the measured pressure differential between static and impact air, with correction applied for temperature and altitude. Think of the Mach number as airspeed that's converted to a decimal fraction of the speed of sound. For instance, Mach .75 means that the airplane is flying at 75% of the speed of sound at the particular temperature and altitude conditions that exist. They typically don't put Mach indicators on airplanes that can't fly close to the speed of sound. That's why you're unlikely to hear a Cessna 152 report his speed at Mach .08.

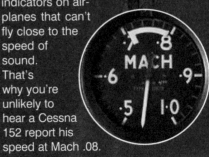

TAS & IAS While Approaching High Altitude Airports

The difference between true and indicated airspeed is very important for pilots making approaches to high altitude airports. Suppose you're on approach to an airport at 10,000 feet above sea level. Your indicated airspeed on approach is 80 knots. This means your true airspeed is 20% greater (or 96 knots). In other words, your wheels are going to touch down at 96 knots despite showing only 80 knots on the airspeed indicator. That runway is going to seem a lot shorter than it normally would. This is especially disconcerting if your mind was set for an 80 knot touchdown speed.

To lift off and accelerate for an 80 knot climb requires a longer-than-normal takeoff distance at high altitude airports. Your airplane must move along that runway a lot faster than 80 knots to generate an 80 knot indicated airspeed. In fact, at 10,000 feet, it must speed up to 96 knots to show only 80 knots on the airspeed indicator's face. What does that mean to you? It means high-altitude airports require longer takeoff runs and landing distances.

Does this mean, while on approach to a high altitude airport, you should slow the airplane down? No! That wouldn't be good at all. Approach at the same airspeed you always use. Think about it for a second. The wings need a certain number of molecules per minute flowing over them to maintain lift. Your job is supplying those molecules. In thinner air, you will be moving faster (higher TAS) to achieve the same *indicated* airspeed, but indicated airspeed (total number of air molecules arriving at the leading edge) is all the wing (and the pilot) really cares about. *The airplane stalls at the same indicated airspeed whether you're at 1,000 feet or 10,000 feet.* If the airplane requires 60 knots of wind blowing over its wing to keep from stalling, you need to keep the indicated airspeed above 60 knots. (Remember, for most approaches, you want to be at least 30% above the stall speed.)

Landing Distance and True Airspeed

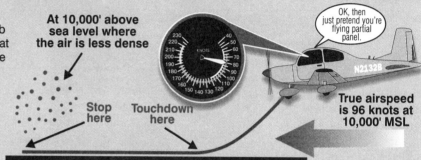

At sea level where the air is quite dense

Stop here   Touchdown here

Ouch! That thing just poked me in the eye!

True airspeed is 80 knots at sea level

Landing distances at sea level are shorter for a given indicated airspeed.

At 10,000' above sea level where the air is less dense

Stop here   Touchdown here

OK, then just pretend you're flying partial panel.

True airspeed is 96 knots at 10,000' MSL

Landing distances at 10,000' MSL are longer for a given indicated airspeed.

the oxygen it deserves. Sea level provides a consistent reference for altimeter measurement.

Your true altitude is how high you are above sea level, even if there isn't an ocean within a thousand miles. It says nothing about how high you are above the ground, though that is of course of great interest to you as a pilot. Pressure altimeters do not directly tell you your height above the ground. The ground, after all, isn't a consistent reference. Ground height varies dramatically. If you know how high you are above sea level, and you also know the ground's height above sea level (this is found on navigational charts), then finding your height above the ground is simply a "take-away" math problem. Height above ground is technically known as your *absolute altitude*.

Altimeters work by measuring the difference between sea level pressure and

The Altimeter

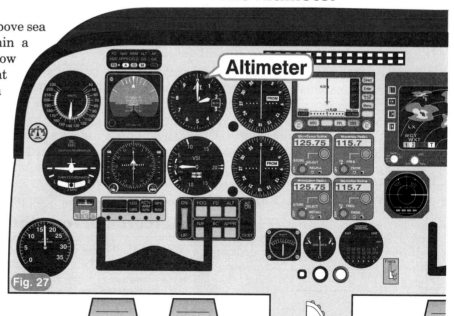

Altimeter

Fig. 27

Equivalent Airspeed

If you're flying airplanes that travel at speeds in excess of 200 knots, then you'll be interested in something known as *equivalent airspeed*. This is the calibrated airspeed of an aircraft corrected for adiabatic compressible flow for the particular altitude you're using. Equivalent airspeed is equal to calibrated airspeed in a standard atmosphere at sea level. Since equivalent airspeed is relatively unimportant to those of us who fly smaller airplanes, I won't use any of your brain's valuable hard disk space discussing this concept further. Just be aware it's out there.

Inside a Basic Altimeter

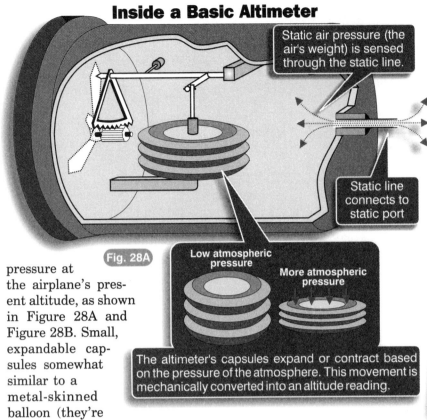

Static air pressure (the air's weight) is sensed through the static line.

Static line connects to static port

Fig. 28A

Low atmospheric pressure

More atmospheric pressure

The altimeter's capsules expand or contract based on the pressure of the atmosphere. This movement is mechanically converted into an altitude reading.

Inside an Actual Altimeter

Courtesy Bob Crystal

Fig. 28B

pressure at the airplane's present altitude, as shown in Figure 28A and Figure 28B. Small, expandable capsules somewhat similar to a metal-skinned balloon (they're called *aneroid wafers*) are located inside the altimeter. The expansion or contraction of the capsule is mechanically converted into a movement of altimeter hands, resulting in an altitude readout.

You'll notice that the altimeter's case is connected to the static port. This allows static air pressure to surround the capsule. Any change in static air pressure is then reflected by an expansion or contraction of the capsule, providing the altitude reading. To understand precisely how this process works, we need a clearer understanding of how atmospheric pressure changes with height.

Years ago, it was common to measure atmospheric pressure with a mercury barometer. A tube of the heavy liquid metal mercury (in today's world, ground up tuna or swordfish might also work) was filled and placed upside down in a vat of mercury (Figure 29A). The weight of the mercury inside the inverted tube created a small vacuum as the column of mercury attempted to sink out of the tube and into the vat. It's the vacuum that prevents the mercury from entirely sinking into the reservoir. The column finally stabilizes at a certain height (Figure 29B). Let's say the height is 30 inches of mercury (sometimes abbreviated Hg, which is the chemists' symbol for the element mercury). Decreasing the atmosphere's pressure on the reservoir surrounding the tube allows the column to decrease in height. Increasing atmospheric pressure pushes on the reservoir, moving the column upward into the tube and increasing its height (Figure 29C).

The changing height of the mercury column represents a change in atmospheric pressure in much the same way as the changing pitch of your voice represents the weight of the car that just parked on top your toe. In fact, after lots and lots of people made lots and lots of measurements at many elevations, spilling a lot of mercury along the way, we learned that atmospheric pressure changes the height of the column approximately one inch for every one thousand foot change in altitude (Figure 29D). This is the value that engineers use for altimeter calibration.

How a Mercurial Barometer Works

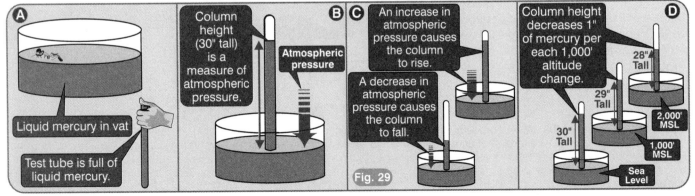

A

Liquid mercury in vat.

Test tube is full of liquid mercury.

Column height (30" tall) is a measure of atmospheric pressure.

Atmospheric pressure

B

C

An increase in atmospheric pressure causes the column to rise.

A decrease in atmospheric pressure causes the column to fall.

Fig. 29

Column height decreases 1" of mercury per each 1,000' altitude change.

D

28" Tall

29" Tall

2,000' MSL

30" Tall

1,000' MSL

Sea Level

Radar Altimeters

Unlike pressure altimeters, radar altimeters provide you with a continuous indication of your height above ground. Radar altimeters are sometimes known as radio altimeters (not the kind you can dance to, though, since radar doesn't have rhythm). This system looks downward and accurately measures the distance between the aircraft and the highest object on the terrain below. The system works by sending a radio signal earthward and receiving the reflected energy at the aircraft. The time interval between the transmitted and received radio signal is then automatically converted into an absolute altitude reading. The figure below shows a radar altimeter with a dial type readout. Other types have a digital presentation. Warning lights and aural tones are frequent enhancements. They help alert pilots when the aircraft reaches a preselected altitude.

There are three main functions associated with a radar altimeter. First, it serves as a ground proximity warning device. Second, it is an accurate cross-check for the barometric altimeter. Third, it gives the pilot a warning when reaching the minimum descent altitude (MDA) or decision altitude (DA) during instrument approaches. Radar altimeters operate on a radio frequency between 4,200 and 4,400 MHz.

Antenna located under fuselage.

RADAR ALTITUDE

Suppose we say that at sea level, under typical conditions, our column of mercury stands 30 inches tall (the real number is 29.92, for those made nervous by rounding off to simplify the math). We say the atmospheric pressure is 30 inches of mercury. At 1,000 feet mean sea level (MSL), the pressure decreases and the mercury column falls approximately one inch. It now stands 29 inches tall. The atmospheric pressure at 1,000 feet MSL is properly stated as 29 inches of mercury. Altitude measurement is based on the consistency of this known pressure change. Of course, the altimeter in your aircraft isn't a mercury barometer, because there might not be 30 inches of room from the seat to the ceiling for the device. Besides, it would make a real mess if the tube broke and would annoy the pilot if the tube kept poking him in the eye. But your altimeter is calibrated using the same pressure-change scale. Expansion or contraction of the small expandable capsules located within the altimeter is calibrated in inches of mercury. In other words, taken from sea level to 1,000 feet MSL, the capsule expands a small but predictable amount. Altimeter designers calibrate this change as equaling one inch on the mercury barometer, and cleverly work it out mechanically so it moves the altimeter hands exactly 1000 feet. That's basically how the altimeter works. Now let's look at how the altimeter determines your airplane's height above sea level.

Figure 30, position A shows an altimeter resting at sea level, where the pressure is 30″ of Hg. This is the pressure sensed through the airplane's static port, so the pressure surrounding the expandable capsule is also 30″ Hg. The pressure inside the capsule is also at 30″ Hg, because everyone agrees that's what sea level pressure is. The outside and inside pressures are the same. What's going to happen to the capsule? Nothing. With no pressure difference, the capsule doesn't expand (or contract) and the altimeter reads an altitude of zero feet.

Figure 30, position B shows an altimeter at 3,000 feet MSL. The static pressure at 3,000 MSL is 27″ Hg. The pressure inside the capsule, which is sealed, is still 30″ Hg. Something's got to give, and it's the capsule, which expands in proportion to this pressure differential. That expansion gets sent, through wheels and widgets, to the rotating pointers that are all you normally see of the altimeter.

The Air's Not Fair, The Pressure's Not Ready to Be Steady

If the pressure at sea level always remained constant at 30″ Hg, that would be the end of our altimeter story. Unfortunately, the pressure at sea level varies daily, hourly, and sometimes even minute-by-minute. The atmosphere actually changes weight slightly, causing air

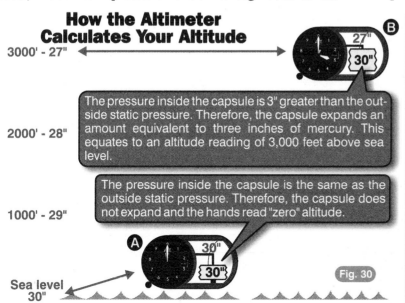

How the Altimeter Calculates Your Altitude

3000' - 27"

The pressure inside the capsule is 3" greater than the outside static pressure. Therefore, the capsule expands an amount equivalent to three inches of mercury. This equates to an altitude reading of 3,000 feet above sea level.

2000' - 28"

The pressure inside the capsule is the same as the outside static pressure. Therefore, the capsule does not expand and the hands read "zero" altitude.

1000' - 29"

Sea level 30"

Fig. 30

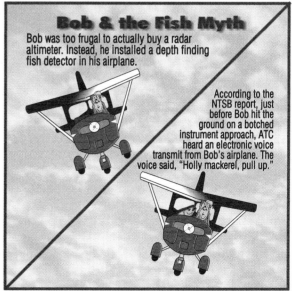

Bob & the Fish Myth

Bob was too frugal to actually buy a radar altimeter. Instead, he installed a depth finding fish detector in his airplane.

According to the NTSB report, just before Bob hit the ground on a botched instrument approach, ATC heard an electronic voice transmit from Bob's airplane. The voice said, "Holly mackerel, pull up."

to push down harder on different parts of the earth than others. You can count on the pressure at sea level changing about as often as the weight of someone on the South Beach Diet.

Remember, the air locked inside the aneroid is at *standard* sea level pressure. It's like carrying a sample of sea level aloft. All altitude measurements are based on the difference between that sample and what's outside the plane, which is great except that the sample has to reflect what's happening *now* at sea level. Since sea level pressure can change from hour to hour at any point on earth, think about how quickly it can change when moving across the country in your airplane. You obviously need some way

Fig. 31

Adjustment Knob

to keep your altimeter informed about the changing pressure at sea level. A small knob at the front of the altimeter (Figure 31) allows you to do just that.

By twisting this knob, the little numbers in the *Kollsman window* rotate as shown on the face of the altimeter in Figure 32. Rotating this knob is the pilot's way of telling the altimeter what the pressure is at sea level, and thus correcting for any variations from the standard sample carried in the aneroid wafer. Changing the numbers in the Kollsman window recalibrates the pressure inside the altimeter's expandable capsule. This is done mechanically by repositioning an internal linkage which gives the cap-

Who Is In the Kollsman Window?

The Kollsman window is named for the inventor of the barometric altimeter, Paul Kollsman. Prior to 1928, there were no reliable mechanical altimeters, because there was no way to adjust for the variations caused by changes in barometric pressure. You mostly figured out how high you were by looking out the window, a method subject to some pretty spectacular errors (not to mention spectacular tree top scenery).

It may be a physically small thing, but the Kollsman window was crucial to creation of the commercial aviation industry and the ability of pilots to fly "blind." It was aviation pioneer Jimmy Doolittle who used the Kollsman altimeter to make the first "blind flight," in 1929. It was probably the marketing department of the first passenger-carrying airline that renamed *blind flight* to *instrument flight*.

Originally, the entire altimeter was referred to as the Kollsman window, but today the term generally means the small window on the altimeter into which the pilot sets the correct, current barometric pressure.

sule a new starting point from which to begin measuring. Whatever pressure value you set in the Kollsman window, the altimeter assumes this is the new sea level pressure. Now the altimeter measures the difference between the pressure value set in the Kollsman window and the outside static pressure to obtain your height above sea level.

What Happens When You Change the Altimeter Setting

Rotating the altimeter's knob, changes the numbers in the Kollsman window. This mechanically repositions an internal linkage that changes the starting point from which the altimeter begins its measurement. It is, however, much easier to think of the pressure inside the sealed capsule changing to equal the barometric pressure value set in the Kollsman window (trust me! Think about it this way and you'll never have difficulty understanding how the altimeter works).

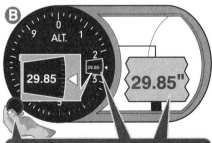

When the altimeter knob is rotated and 29.85" is set in the Kollsman window, the altimeter acts as if a pressure of 29.85" Hg has been set inside its sealed capsule.

Fig. 32

When 30.20″ Hg is set in the Kollsman window, for instance, the pressure inside the expandable capsule is recalibrated to 30.20″ Hg as shown in Figure 32A. Now the altimeter knows the pressure at sea level is 30.20″ Hg. Setting 29.85″ Hg in the Kollsman window tells the altimeter the pressure at sea level is 29.85″ Hg (Figure 32B).

Figure 33 shows how this process works. Airplane A is over San Diego (SAN) where the sea level pressure is 30.15″ Hg. This value is set in the Kollsman window. The difference between 30.15″ Hg and 27.15″ Hg is three inches of pressure or 3000 feet. The altimeter reads three thousand feet—the airplane's true altitude.* Airplane B is over Los Angeles (LAX) where the sea level pressure has lowered to 29.15″ Hg. The static pressure at Airplane B's altitude of 3,000 feet is 26.15″ Hg. The difference between these two is three inches. Therefore, the altimeter reads 3000 feet. (**As you'll soon see, to obtain true altitude, you also need to correct the altimeter for non-standard temperature variations. For now, we'll just assume that true altitude is obtained by correcting the altimeter for pressure changes.*)

The value you set in the Kollsman window is referred to as the *altimeter setting,* and is not to be confused with babysitting or record-setting. The altimeter setting can be obtained from several sources including air traffic control towers, flight service stations and automatic weather stations (ASOS, AWOS, AWSS). Ever wonder where *they* get it? I'll tell you in a few minutes, and you won't believe it.

What happens if you don't update the altimeter setting to the local altimeter setting, which (as a minimum) means updating your Kollsman window setting to a station along the route and within 100 nautical miles of the airplane (as you're required to do when flying IFR)? There's a good chance that at some point your altimeter will not be providing the correct information—you're not going to be at the altitude you think you're at. In IMC, this is a scary thought (it's even a scary thought on the ground!) and not having the current altimeter setting is downright dangerous. It's like being in the water, bleeding, with a great white shark nearby. You know something bad will happen, it's just a matter of time and appetite! For your information, the ocean makes me nervous. That's why I scream at the same pitch regardless of whether a shark's about to eat me or a piece of seaweed touches my toe.

How You Know Your Altitude

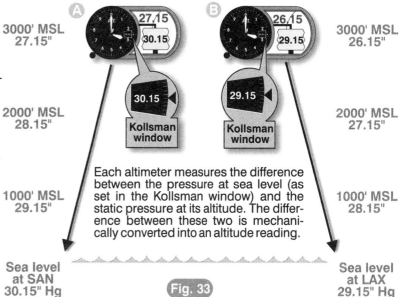

Each altimeter measures the difference between the pressure at sea level (as set in the Kollsman window) and the static pressure at its altitude. The difference between these two is mechanically converted into an altitude reading.

Fig. 33

How Sloping Pressure Levels Affect Your Altimeter

Altimeter C reads the correct altitude of 3,000' MSL. Altimeter D reads 3,000' MSL even though it's only 2,000' MSL. This occurs because its altimeter setting hasn't been updated to the current sea level pressure at LAX of 29.15".

Pressure level slopes from SAN to LAX

Pressure level slopes from SAN to LAX

Fig. 34

Figure 34 shows what can happen. Notice that at 1,000 feet MSL above SAN, the pressure is 29.15″ Hg (position A). This is the same as the sea level pressure at LAX (position B). Do you see how the 29.15″ pressure level gradually sloped from 1,000 feet MSL at position A down to the surface between SAN and LAX? It can be said that pressure levels drop when flying towards an area of lower pressure. If you're still with me on this flight, you realize that the altimeter is really a pressure measuring device. If you don't adjust for changes in the sea level pressure below the point you're at, flying a "level" altitude will mean you are really following a given pressure level—which might be far from level!

At 3,000 feet above SAN the static pressure is 27.15″ Hg (position C). Approaching LAX, the 27.15″ pressure level slopes downward to 2,000 feet above the surface (position D). With the SAN sea level pressure of 30.15″ Hg set in the Kollsman window, the altimeter indicates 3,000 feet as long as you stay at the level where the outside pressure is 27.15″ Hg, as shown by positions C and D. Can you see what's happening? The level where the pressure is 27.15″ Hg slopes downward, while the altimeter remains constant at 3,000 feet at position D. If we don't update the altimeter setting, the indicated altitude (what's shown on the altimeter's face) becomes different from our true altitude (our actual height above sea level).

Over LAX, our indicated altitude is 3,000 feet but our true altitude is only 2,000 MSL as shown in Figure 34, position D. Is this a problem? Yes! What happens if there is a mountain at 2,500 feet MSL along your path? (Figure 35A). Looking at the face of the altimeter (its *indicated* altitude), it appears you'll clear the mountain by 500 feet. In reality, you're 500 feet below the top of the mountain. Under these conditions, there's a good chance that your airplane's landing gear might knock a bald eagle out of its tree and this is one bird that doesn't want to fly around with tire tracks on its head. What a shock it would be if you were in IMC and you thought you would clear that 2,500 foot mountain by 500 feet (as you'll see in a upcoming chapter, some segments of an instrument approach may give you only a 500 foot clearance at distances of up to 15 miles from the airport). You might end up with the top of a pine tree poking through your cockpit. Now that's what I call an air freshener.

Let's say you're near LAX and suddenly you realize your mistake of not updating the altimeter setting given to you by the controller. You call LAX Approach Control and the controller tells you the altimeter setting is 29.15″ Hg (He or she will actually say "Altimeter setting is two-niner-one-five.") You set this in the Kollsman window. What will your altimeter read? The difference between the recalibrated pressure in the expandable capsule and static pressure is now two inches. Now the altimeter correctly shows an indicated and true altitude of 2,000 feet (Figure 35B), at which point you immediately begin climbing back to your previously

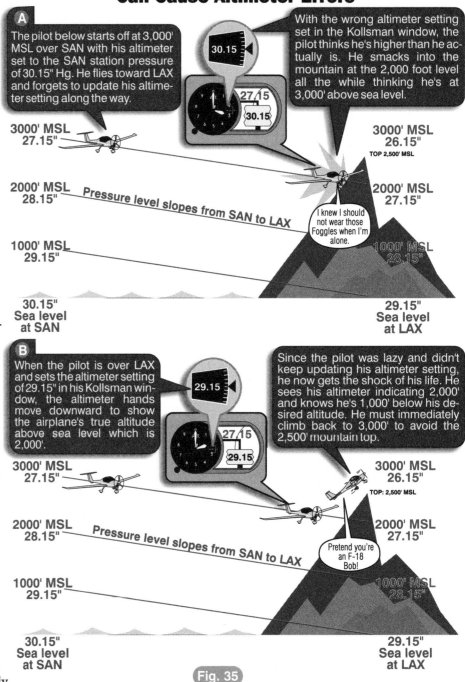

Failure to Update Your Altimeter Setting Can Cause Altimeter Errors

A The pilot below starts off at 3,000' MSL over SAN with his altimeter set to the SAN station pressure of 30.15" Hg. He flies toward LAX and forgets to update his altimeter setting along the way.

With the wrong altimeter setting set in the Kollsman window, the pilot thinks he's higher than he actually is. He smacks into the mountain at the 2,000 foot level all the while thinking he's at 3,000' above sea level.

3000' MSL 27.15"
2000' MSL 28.15"
Pressure level slopes from SAN to LAX
1000' MSL 29.15"
30.15" Sea level at SAN

3000' MSL 26.15" TOP 2,500' MSL
2000' MSL 27.15"
I knew I should not wear those Foggles when I'm alone.
1000' MSL 28.15"
29.15" Sea level at LAX

B When the pilot is over LAX and sets the altimeter setting of 29.15" in his Kollsman window, the altimeter hands move downward to show the airplane's true altitude above sea level which is 2,000'.

Since the pilot was lazy and didn't keep updating his altimeter setting, he now gets the shock of his life. He sees his altimeter indicating 2,000' and knows he's 1,000' below his desired altitude. He must immediately climb back to 3,000' to avoid the 2,500' mountain top.

3000' MSL 27.15"
2000' MSL 28.15"
Pressure level slopes from SAN to LAX
1000' MSL 29.15"
30.15" Sea level at SAN

3000' MSL 26.15" TOP: 2,500' MSL
2000' MSL 27.15"
Pretend you're an F-18 Bob!
1000' MSL 28.15"
29.15" Sea level at LAX

Fig. 35

selected altitude of 3,000 feet while trying to stick your eyeballs back in their sockets. Of course, this assumes that ATC doesn't notice your altitude deviation first, which they are most likely to do if you have an altitude encoder (as do most IFR-certified airplanes). You don't, however, want to count on ATC to catch your mistakes in these situations. After all, it could be tea time and someone could accidentally lay a crumpet down on your airplane's datablock.

As an IFR pilot (or soon to be one), make it a point to update your altimeter setting every time ATC offers one or at least keep it set to a station within 100 nautical miles of your airplane. There may be no free lunches, but you can always get a free altimeter setting.

In Figure 35B, did you notice that twisting the knob and moving the numbers down from 30.15″ Hg to 29.15″ Hg caused the hands to unwind 1,000 feet? This progression is shown in Figure 36. From a strictly mechanical point of view, whenever the numbers in the Kollsman window move downward (get smaller), the hands also move downward (read less). Changing the numbers one inch in the Kollsman window is worth a one thousand foot altitude change on the altimeter's face. Figure 36 shows what the altimeter hands do when rotating the knob to the current altimeter setting over LAX.

How a Changing Altimeter Setting Moves the Altimeter's Hands

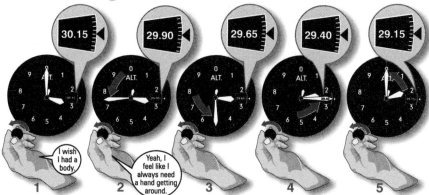

When you're over LAX and you rotate the numbers in the Kollsman window down from 30.15" to 29.15", (1" of Hg change) the indicated altitude moves down from 3,000 feet to 2,000 feet—which is now your true altitude over LAX. (Note: when the numbers go up or down, the hands also go up or down respectively. This is the way the mechanical linkage inside the altimeter works. Change the numbers 1" and the hands move 1,000', change them .5" and the hands move 500' or change them .1" and the hands move 100'.)

Fig. 36

There's a very important point to be made here. *When the altimeter is set too high, it reads too high in terms of altitude, and you will be **lower** than you think you are.* If the altimeter is set too low, the altimeter reads too low. Flying from SAN to LAX, toward an area of lower sea level pressure, and not updating the altimeter setting, meant the barometric pressure setting in the Kollsman window was too high. Therefore, the altimeter read too high. The indicated altitude (3,000 feet) was higher than our true altitude (2,000 feet), as shown in Figure 35A.

Figure 37 shows an airplane flying from a low pressure area toward a high pressure area (in the opposite direction of our flight from LAX to SAN). The airplane maintains a constant indicated altitude of 3,000 feet without updating its altimeter setting. The airplane follows the 26.15" pressure level, which slopes upward as the high pressure area over SAN is approached. With the altimeter set too low, it will read too low and you will be **higher** than you intend to be. The indicated altitude will be 3,000 feet but you will actually be 4,000 feet above sea level when over LAX.

If you had to pick the most dangerous flight scenario, it would probably be flying in IMC from *high* pressure to *low* pressure instead of low to high, though in IFR conditions it is never

Stranger Than Fiction

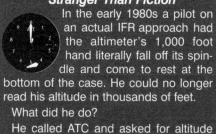

In the early 1980s a pilot on an actual IFR approach had the altimeter's 1,000 foot hand literally fall off its spindle and come to rest at the bottom of the case. He could no longer read his altitude in thousands of feet.
What did he do?
He called ATC and asked for altitude readouts from his Mode C transponder.

good to be at the wrong altitude, either high or low.

Cold Comfort and the Altimeter

Let me give you the good news first. The vast, vast majority of the time, temperature has so little effect on the altimeter that you can ignore it.

But not always. Under certain extremes, particularly extreme cold, the expansion and contraction of the atmosphere that accompany temperature change can affect altimeter readings by 500 feet or more. That can leave you facing a mountain face in a most inopportune way, which is why it's important to be aware of when you need to be aware of these extremes.

Most instrument rated pilots never experience these types of temperatures. But then again, I've been in Alaska in the winter and had my hair freeze. Of course, unless you are a TV evangelist, you probably won't worry about having your near-cryogenically frozen coiffure crack off. If it's that cold and hairy outside, though, you're going to have to make some adjustments. Let's find out how to identify these errors and correct for them.

Failure to Update Your Altimeter Setting When Flying From a Low to a High Pressure Area

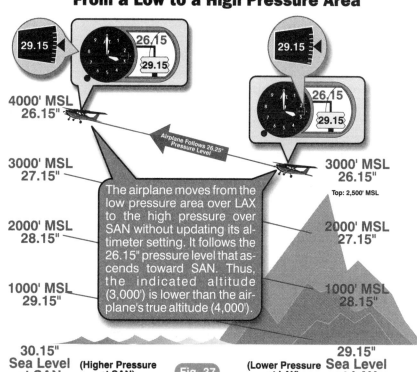

Fig. 37

Figure 38 depicts the effect of temperature on columns of air. When air is at standard or normal temperature (59°F/15°C at sea level), the altimeter experiences no temperature error. Airplane B, sitting on top of a column of normal temperature air, has an indicated altitude (4,000 feet) which is equal to its true altitude (4,000 feet).

Warmer temperatures result in expansion of the air. Airplane A rests atop an expanded layer of air. The air beneath Airplane A weighs the same as the air beneath Airplane B. The difference is that the warmer, expanded column of air is taller. This is comparable to a situation in which there are two guys both weighing 400 pounds, with one standing 6 feet tall and the other standing 4 feet tall. They both produce the same indication on a scale, but their weight is distributed differently in the vertical direction. In a similar manner, a mass of air having temperatures that vary from standard distributes its weight differently in the vertical direction.

Since the pressure levels are taller or expanded in warmer air, Airplane A's indicated altitude is 4,000 feet and its true altitude is 4,100 feet because its outside air temperature (OAT) is warmer than standard for this altitude. Colder air produces shorter or more closely spaced pressure levels. Airplane C's indicated altitude is 4,000 feet and its true altitude is 3,900 feet.

How Temperature Affects the Altimeter

Changes in temperature raise or lower the pressure levels of air. This causes slight differences between indicated altitude & true altitude.

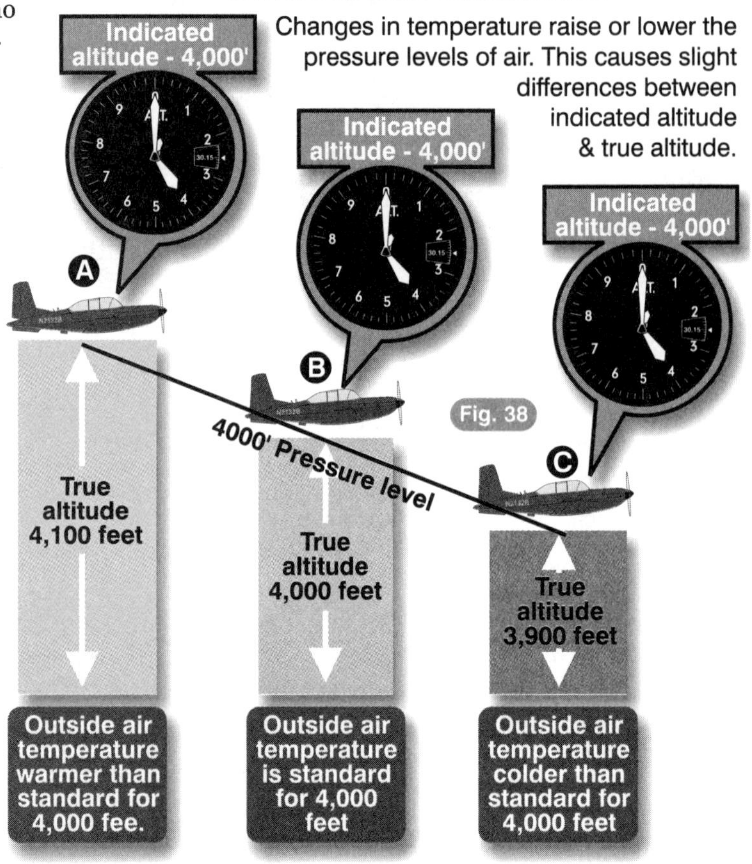

Indicated altitude - 4,000'

Indicated altitude - 4,000'

Indicated altitude - 4,000'

Fig. 38

4000' Pressure level

True altitude 4,100 feet

True altitude 4,000 feet

True altitude 3,900 feet

Outside air temperature warmer than standard for 4,000 fee.

Outside air temperature is standard for 4,000 feet

Outside air temperature colder than standard for 4,000 feet

It's best to think about this in the following way. Without correcting the altimeter for temperature variations by using your flight computer, if the temperature is going down, then the airplane is going down; if the temperature is going up, then the airplane is going up.

Here's an excellent memory aid to help keep both pressure and temperature altimeter errors straight. *When flying from high to low, look out below.* This rule assumes that you forgot to set the nearest altimeter setting or correct your altimeter for temperature extremes. You must *look out below* because you are not as high as you think you are. The statement *look out below* should be your danger cue. You are closer to sea level (and terrain) than your altimeter says you are.

What should you think if you're arriving or departing an airport under extremely cold temperatures? You should think, "If the temperature is cold, then the thermometer has gone down. Therefore, the airplane is going down." In other words, your airplane's true altitude is lower than the indicated altitude.

You already know how to correct for pressure variations during flight. But how do you make correction for variations in temperature? You can use your flight computer (mechanical or electronic) for these computations. Once again, we don't normally correct the altimeter for temperature variations unless the temperatures are extreme and we plan on crossing terrain at low altitudes (see sidebar next page).

So Sorry: Altimeter Setting Not Here

Let's assume you're departing an airport IFR from which no altimeter setting is available. Does this mean you must depart IFR without some means of establishing the correct setting for your altimeter? Not at all. Just work the problem backwards, starting with the one known quantity, which in this case is the airport elevation. Simply rotate the altimeter knob until the hands point to field elevation, as shown in Figure 39. This is what the hands would read if you had the current altimeter setting, isn't it? Now, in a backwards sort of way, the numbers in the Kollsman window give you a barometric pressure setting for the area. This allows you to start your IFR flight with a correct reading on the altimeter.

If you are given an altimeter setting over the radio while on the ground, you should cross check the altimeter setting by seeing if the elevation it yields is pretty close to the published elevation for the airport. If the altimeter indication varies by more than +/– 75 feet from the known field elevation, then it's time for a timeout, because the accuracy of your altimeter is questionable (this is a

When the Altimeter Setting Isn't Available

If the altimeter setting is not available while on the ground at an airport, simply rotate the knob until the altimeter hands indicate field elevation. The numbers in the Kollsman window would be your altimeter setting if it were available from attached.

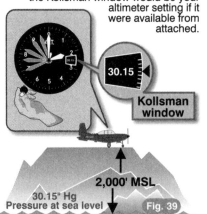

30.15

Kollsman window

2,000' MSL

30.15" Hg Pressure at sea level

Fig. 39

How Cold is Cold? A Temperature Induced Altimeter Error

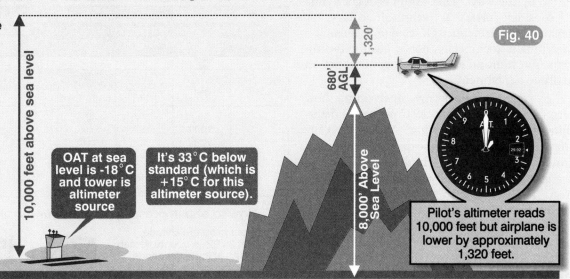

OAT at sea level is -18°C and tower is altimeter source

It's 33°C below standard (which is +15°C for this altimeter source).

Fig. 40

Pilot's altimeter reads 10,000 feet but airplane is lower by approximately 1,320 feet.

Recently, I read a story about a Chinese woman who was abducted by aliens, became pregnant and gave birth as a result of the extraterrestrial encounter. She named her child Sum Ting Wong. There's a good chance that you, too, will experience something wrong if you make IFR approaches to airports under extremely cold conditions. Here's a way to compensate for this.

The source for the altimeter setting (the tower, which is at sea level, in this instance) has an OAT that's 33 degrees Celsius below standard. Standard temperature at sea level is +15 degrees Celsius and the OAT at the tower is -18 degrees Celsius. This is a difference of 33 degrees Celsius. At four feet of error per thousand feet for each degree Celsius temperature difference, this results in an approximate altimeter error of 1,320 feet (4 x 33 x10 = 1,320). Instead of having the required 2,000 foot terrain clearance in mountainous terrain, this pilot is only 680 feet above the mountain top.

A good rule-of-thumb formula for making altimeter temperature corrections is the one used by the United States Air Force. It's based on the fact that the altimeter's temperature error is proportional to the difference between the actual and standard temperature and the height of the aircraft above the source of the altimeter setting. You can expect the error to be approximately four feet per thousand feet for each degree Celsius of temperature difference. A standard lapse rate is assumed. Here's how it would work. If the altimeter setting source is at sea level and it's -18° C at the surface, then it's 33° C below standard (which is +15° C) for that particular source. For an airplane flying at 10,000 feet MSL, the airplane would be (4 x 10) x (33) or 1,320 feet lower than the indicated altitude of 10,000 feet (Figure 40).

If you were to try working the same problem on the front side of your E6B computer, it would look like that shown in Figure 41. To solve the problem on the manual computer, you need to know what the non-standard outside air temperature is at your altitude. If the OAT at the altimeter source is -18 degrees Celsius and with a standard lapse rate of 2 degrees Celsius per thousand feet, this gives you an OAT of -38 degrees Celsius at a pressure altitude of 10,000 feet above the altimeter's source (we're assuming that our pressure altitude is 10,000 feet in this example). Setting 10,000 feet under an OAT of -38 degrees Celsius, and reading our true altitude above the indicated altitude of 10,000 feet, gives us a true altitude of approximately 8,770 MSL. This is close enough to our estimated answer above which places us at 8,680 feet MSL.

Obviously, the closer you get vertically to the altimeter reporting source (let's assume it's at the airport to which you're making the approach) the less the error becomes. Let's assume that you're at 200 feet MSL (which is 200 feet above this sea level airport having a -18 degree C surface temperature). Since this airport is the altimeter source and both are at sea level (I did it this way to make the math easier to calculate), what is the altimeter error? The answer is (4 x 200/1000) x 33 = 26.4 feet (remember, since the error is four feet per thousand feet, I needed to divide 200 by 1000 to get our altitude in fractions of a thousand feet). This isn't a bad error, but suppose we have an altimeter with an error of +/- 75 feet (the *maximum* acceptable amount before you should consider sending it to an instrument technician for repair or recalibration). If these errors are cumulative and all work against you, then you could have a 26+75 = 101 foot error. That's an error of half the height you can expect to be above the touchdown zone of the runway on an unrestricted Category 1 ILS approach (which is 200 feet above the touchdown zone of the runway). If I were certain of these errors, I might not descend as low on my instrument approach as a means of compensation.

The big problem, however, occurs when nearing the approach environment in mountainous areas from the enroute structure. This happened to an Air Force C-130 in Greenland in 1987 when it almost hit a mountain during radar vectors in extremely cold weather. Apparently the aircraft's altimeter was indicating the assigned minimum altitude, yet the aircraft's true altitude was actually much lower. This is why some pilots elect not to fly at the airway's lowest minimum enroute altitude (MEA) in mountainous areas when there are extremely cold temperatures present.

Now, just because it's cold doesn't mean it's cold enough to be a problem. If you know the temperature at the altimeter source, and this source is close enough to the airport, then this knowledge may help you better prepare yourself to make a safer approach to this airport under these conditions.

Courtesy ASA   Fig. 41

OAT -38C

True Alt. 8,770 feet

recommendation found in the AIM, not the FARs, by the way). This would be a good time to consider having a technician correct or repair the altimeter. (Of course I mean an instrument technician, not a beauty technician. You want an altitude adjustment, not an attitude adjustment.)

Do you remember my mentioning how amazed you'd be at how ATC personnel determine the altimeter setting? You're probably thinking they have a big, expensive, high tech, state-of-the-art device. Think again. Many of them do it with a small altimeter of their very own. They simply turn the knob until the altimeter reads the field elevation or elevation of the tower cab, then look at the numbers in the Kollsman window! That's the altimeter setting they issue (and you thought it was done with smoke, mirrors and controlled substances).

Pressure Altitude

There's no getting around the fact that nearly every family has an acquaintance named Fred. He's the type of guy who's just one cow short of a herd and always prone to exaggeration. One fellow I know named Fred would tell everyone that he lived on the Riviera. Finally, his friends discovered that he lived in his Buick Riviera. Fred would tell jokes that no one laughed at. Then he'd say, "Well, you're not looking at it the right way!" I suppose if everyone could look at it the right way, then everyone would understand his humor. In a similar way, before I can calculate my airplane's performance, I also need to look at the altimeter the right way, the way the engineers were looking at it when they originally computed the airplane's performance.

For the sake of discussion, let's assume that when the engineer computed the airplane's performance, he or she did so at sea level on what is called a *standard day*. A standard day has nothing to do with whether or not you got through the day with nothing unusual happening; an aviation standard day is when the temperature and pressure at sea level are 59°F (or 15°C) and 29.92″ Hg, respectively. Given these conditions, the engineer must have been looking at an altimeter whose Kollsman window was set to 29.92″ Hg when he measured the airplane's performance and created the performance charts. Therefore, to compute your performance accurately, you also need to be looking at an altimeter whose Kollsman window is also set to 29.92″ Hg.

How to Determine and Use Pressure Altitude

A Think of pressure altitude as the altitude the engineers were at when they created the airplane's performance charts. This is the altitude your altimeter reads when 29.92″ of Hg is set in your Kollsman window.

WEIGHT LBS	PRESS ALT FT	CLIMB SPEED KIAS	RATE OF CLIMB - FPM			
			-20°C	0°C	20°C	40°C
2550	S.L.	73	795	730	665	600
	2000	73	705	645	585	525
	4000	73	625	565	510	450
	6000	72	540	485	430	370
	8000	72	460	405	350	295
	10,000	72	380	325	275	
	12,000	72	300	250		

B **How to obtain pressure altitude for the chart above**

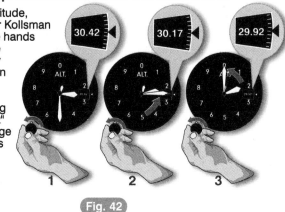

To find your pressure altitude, simply set 29.92″ in your Kollsman window. The altitude the hands point to is your pressure altitude. Once you know this, reset the numbers in the Kollsman window to the previous altimeter setting. Note that rotating the numbers from 30.42″ down to 29.92″ (a change of .5″) moves the hands down 500'. Therefore, the hands move from 2,500' down to 2,000'.

Fig. 42

Think of this problem as being similar to speaking to someone in a different time zone. You and this other person can't agree on what time it is unless you reset your watch to that person's time reference (his time zone). Similarly, you want to use the engineer's pressure reference when calculating your airplane's performance. So, set your altimeter to 29.92″ Hg, read the value indicated (the *indicated altitude*) which is also called the *pressure altitude*. Use the pressure altitude and the temperature (and whatever other variables the performance chart requires) to compute the airplane's performance.

Now, that was the simple explanation. In reality, when an engineer measures the airplane's performance, it's usually not done on a standard day, nor is it done at sea level. In fact, I have it on good authority that few people have ever actually seen a standard day. To compensate for this, the engineer often extrapolates the performance information he's obtained back to standard day values using computers, graphs, pencils, and strong cups of coffee (because addition and subtraction are involved in this process).

Figure 42A is a climb performance chart. It requires two variables—pressure altitude and temperature—to determine climb rate. Figure 42B shows how we obtain pressure altitude. In this example, let's assume that we're

---

Sensitive Altimeters

Modern altimeters are called *sensitive altimeters.* This is not because they take a bad sunset personally or weep over untied shoelaces.

Sensitive altimeters have adjustable barometric scales (a Kollsman window) that allow you to set the pressure reference from which altitude is measured. These altimeters often also have two or even three expandable capsules instead of one. This allows them greater precision or sensitivity in altitude measurement. It's possible to hold a sensitive altimeter in your hand, climb the stairs and observe an altitude change (if you aren't too exhausted to read it after the climb). Now that's sensitive!

sitting at an airport located at 2,500 feet MSL with a local altimeter setting of 30.42" Hg. Because the current altimeter setting is placed in the Kollsman window, the far left altimeter in Figure 42B reads field elevation (our *true altitude*). By placing 29.92" Hg in the Kollsman window, the altimeter's hands move down to a value of 2,000 feet. This is our pressure altitude. Using 2,000 feet and the outside air temperature, you can determine your airplane's performance on the rate of climb chart provided.

Once you've determined the pressure altitude, immediately reset the altimeter to the current local altimeter setting (30.42" Hg in this example). This keeps the altimeter reading the correct height above sea level (true altitude).

As a reminder, it's important to note what happened to the altimeter's hands when the numbers in the Kollsman window changed. Because of the way the mechanical linkage works, when the Kollsman numbers go down, the altimeter's hands go down. Numbers up, hands up. Since one inch of pressure change is worth 1,000 feet of altitude change, rotating the Kollsman numbers down .5" of Hg moves the hands down 500 feet. This works for other fractions of mercury change, too. If I move the Kollsman numbers up from 30.15 to 30.25 (a difference of .1" of Hg) the altimeter's hands will go up 100 feet.

Remember, pressure altitude is used for performance computations. It's the height above a *standard datum plane,* which is nothing more than a fancy phrase for an imaginary reference point. This reference point is what the engineer's altimeter would have read if temperature and pressure at sea level was 59°F and 29.92" Hg.

There are certain things you never want to hear on an airplane. The following exchange is one of them:

"Nice smoke system you've installed on this airplane."

"Ahh, this airplane doesn't have a smoke system."

And there's one thing you don't want to hear after a discussion of pressure altitude. This is, "I've got two more things I want to mention to you." I do. Don't worry. These items aren't too difficult, either.

Let's suppose ATC says that the altimeter setting is 29.92" Hg and the surface temperature is 59°F (or 15°C). Yes, it's one of those very rare days when it's actually a standard day at sea level. Under this condition, your altimeter would read true altitude as well as pressure altitude.

Altitude Encoders

Many airplanes now have automatic pressure altitude reporting equipment (either an *encoding altimeter* or a *blind encoder* [most common]) as shown below. Also referred to as Mode C capability, this equipment is similar to an altimeter. It sends encoded pressure information to ATC radar via the airplane's onboard transponder. The transponder is a device which makes the airplane appear as an electronic blip on radar. Airplanes with altitude encoding equipment have their altitude information shown as well as their horizontal position depicted next to the radar blip.

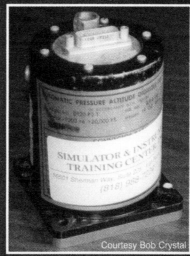
Courtesy Bob Crystal

Altitude encoding devices have their Kollsman windows permanently set to 29.92" Hg. They send pressure altitude pulses to ATC radar, where the computer automatically corrects this reading for local barometric pressure. This correction allows controllers to read the pilot's true altitude on the radar screen.

Some misinformed pilots, finding themselves several hundred feet off an assigned altitude while being radar tracked, reach up and turn the Kollsman window knob on their airplane's altimeter so that the altimeter hands read the proper height. They're hoping that ATC is seeing what the altimeter on the instrument panel is showing. Nice try, but no bueno. ATC is getting its lowdown from a higher source. The airplane's altitude encoder, which is typically hidden behind the instrument panel and totally invisible to the pilot, is telling tales on him. The visible altimeter talks only to you; the encoding altimeter device talks only to ATC. It's called a "blind" encoder because you can't see it, not because ATC can't see where you're at.

I mention this because when operating at or above 18,000 feet MSL (assuming you *can* operate at or above 18,000 feet MSL), you're required to set your altimeter to 29.92" Hg, not the local altimeter setting. Altitudes at and above 18,000 feet are referred to as *flight levels*. An altimeter that reads 20,000 feet with 29.92 set in the Kollsman window is referred to as *flight level two zero zero*

Troubles Come in 3's

A recent NASA Callback report from a captain (the pilot not flying in the incident reported) describes another kind of culture shock "the communications mix-ups" that can occur when experienced pilots are paired with newer flight deck crew:

Approaching [destination airport] from the east we were cleared to 11,000 feet/250 knots. We checked in with Approach at 11,000 feet with the ATIS information. When Approach acknowledged our check they issued a new altimeter setting of 30.00. We acknowledged the updated information. As I reset the two altimeters on the captain's side, I inadvertently said 3,000 (three thousand), referring to the altimeter setting rather than a more appropriate verbiage of 30.00 (three zero zero zero). No other conversation was ongoing at the time. We were both monitoring Approach Control and at the time I thought my meaning was clear. Several moments later I noticed we were descending out of 11,000 feet and 3,000 was set in the altitude window. We began a climb back to 11,000 as I reconfirmed our assigned altitude....

After landing we discussed the incident further and how a similar situation might be avoided in the future. The first officer is relatively new a month or two with the airline. I learned that he had misinterpreted my verbalization of the altimeter setting as a newly assigned altitude and thought, when I restated it, that I wanted him to reset the altitude select window. I explained that I would be more precise in the future. We also used this event as a basis for discussing why, per our [company] procedures, the pilot not flying always is the person to reset the assigned altitude and that it is verified by the pilot flying prior to any altitude changes.

NASA Callback Report

Different Types of Altimeter Displays

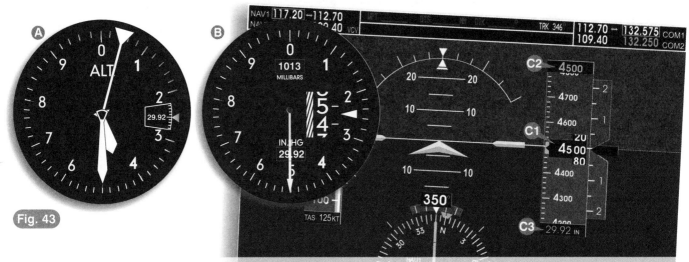

Fig. 43

As an instrument pilot, you're likely to encounter one of three types of altimeter displays. Altimeter A is your typical display with the standard 100 foot, 1,000 foot and 10,000 foot reference hands. Altimeter B is a drum type altimeter display. The single rotating hand indicates hundreds of feet in 20 foot increments. Thousand and ten-thousand foot values are read in the drum window. Primary flight displays (altimeter C) use a tape display of altitudes. Your present altitude is read in the white-on-black window (position C1). Position C2 represents the target altitude you may (or may not) have previously selected in the PFD. Position C3 represents the latest altimeter setting that you've dialed into the altimeter.

or FL200. Just add two zeros onto the value. FL350 is 35,000 feet and referred to as *flight level three five zero*. In the flight level altitudes, you're flying pressure altitudes, not true altitudes.

The reason we set the altimeter to 29.92 is that most airplanes flying at higher altitudes fly fast. Pilots of jet aircraft flying at hundreds of miles per hour would have to spend all their time resetting their altimeters instead of eating the box lunch. They'd be changing altimeter settings faster than teenagers channel surfing with the TV's remote control. To prevent this problem, it was decided that all pilots flying in Class A airspace would simply agree to use 29.92 as the altimeter setting and revert back to local station pressure when below 18,000 feet. At least everyone operating at and above 18,000 feet MSL is flying by the same altitude reference.

Finally, at this point in your flying development I hope you've heard of *density altitude*. Now, let's suppose that the temperature and pressure at sea level were standard. This means that if you were sitting in an airplane at sea level (hope it's a float plane), then you'd have 29.92 set in your Kollsman window and the outside air temperature would be 59 degrees F. In this instance your indicated altitude would also be your true altitude which would also be the pressure altitude. It would also be your density altitude, too. However, the moment the temperature changed, then your density altitude would also change since density altitude is pressure altitude corrected for variations from standard temperature. I mention this because these concepts often put a kink in a pilot's cerebellum during an oral or written exam. Hopefully, you'll remain unkinked if asked questions on these topics.

Reading the Altimeter

As you remember from your private pilot training, reading the altimeter is just like reading a watch that

uses hands instead of digital readouts. Figure 43 shows three basic types of altimeter displays you're likely to encounter in general aviation. Altimeter A has three hands and is found in most smaller airplanes. Altimeter B is known as a *drum type* altimeter, and this is more like reading a digital watch, with the altitude shown digitally on the altimeter's face. The drum provides you with altitude readings in thousands and hundreds of feet. The drum doesn't tell you your altitude in increments smaller than hundreds of feet. That's why a long hundred-foot hand is provided on these types of altimeters. You can read your altitude in thousands and hundreds of feet on the drum and in hundreds and tens of feet by using the long hundreds foot hand.

The hundreds foot hand also allows you to obtain a better estimate of the trend or change of your altitude. You can imagine how challenging it would be to trying holding altitude by use of the drum numbers only. To do so might have you flying to the beat of a different drummer.

Altimeter C is a typical presentation found on today's primary flight displays. As altitude changes, the numerical display tape of altitude moves up and down in the display window while the number values in the white-on-black window in the center of the display (position C1) change to reflect the airplane's current altitude. Reading the PFD's digital display is similar to reading a drum-type altimeter except that there is no mechanical altimeter hand present. Therefore, the 10,000 foot, 1,000 foot and 10 foot altitude values are read directly from the center window in position C1. Obviously you shouldn't need a hand reading this altimeter display, right?

As long as you recognize the different altimeter displays you shouldn't misinterpret your altitude. The last thing you want to do is misinterpret something, right? That could be dangerous. In Alaska, pilots are warned to

The Primary Flight Display's Trend Lines

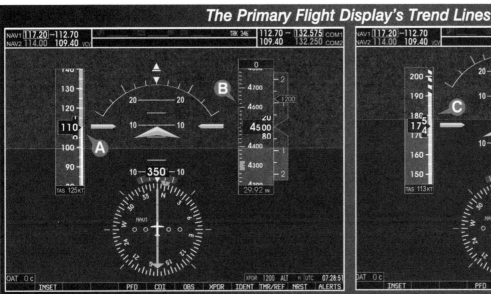
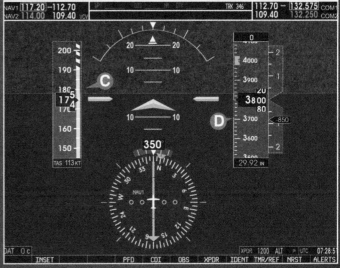

One of the very unique features of the primary flight display is the trend line. This is the magenta line in positions A, B, C and D that show where a particular airspeed and altitude value will be in the next six seconds based on the airplane's present pitch and power condition. For instance, the nose up attitude on the left PFD shows a decreasing airspeed and increasing altitude. The airspeed trend line in position A indicates that the airspeed and altitude will be at 107 knots and 4,630 feet in six seconds. The pitch down attitude shown on the PFD to the right has trend lines indicating that the airspeed and vertical speed will be 182 knots (position C) and 3,710 feet (position D) in six seconds. The wonderful thing about trend lines is that they help you anticipate airspeed and altitude targets. Anticipating trends with round-dial instruments was more a matter of feel and it took some time to develop this skill.

wear tiny bells on their clothing just in case they have to make a forced landing in the woods. Apparently, the bells warn away all but the grizzly bear, which is why you want to watch the ground for grizzly bear droppings. "Don't misinterpret these droppings," says an authority on bears. "If you see grizzly bear scat, then scat!" One can easily identify grizzly bear droppings because they have tiny bells in them.

The Vertical Speed Indicator (VSI)

Our magical panel tour isn't over, so let's move over and examine the *vertical speed indicator* (VSI, also known as the *vertical velocity indicator* or VVI), which is located on the bottom right-hand side of the instrument panel's six pack of instruments (Figure 44). Calibrated to read in feet per minute, the needle swings upward or downward reflecting the airplane's rate of climb or descent.

The Vertical Speed Indicator

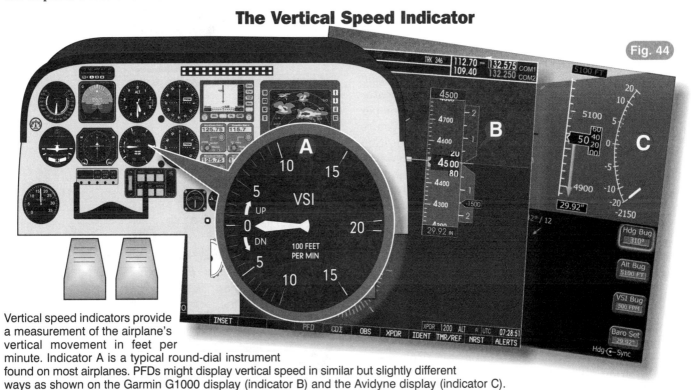

Fig. 44

Vertical speed indicators provide a measurement of the airplane's vertical movement in feet per minute. Indicator A is a typical round-dial instrument found on most airplanes. PFDs might display vertical speed in similar but slightly different ways as shown on the Garmin G1000 display (indicator B) and the Avidyne display (indicator C).

Figure 45A and B and C show the internal workings of the VSI. The case is vented to static pressure through an amazingly small opening called a *capillary tube* (also called an *airflow restrictor*). The expandable capsule connects to the static source via a normal size tube. At a constant altitude, the pressure in the case and the capsule are equal and no climb or descent rate is shown. During a climb, air pressure in the capsule decreases but air pressure in the case can't decrease as quickly because of the airflow restrictor. Therefore, pressure in the capsule is less than in the case, resulting in the capsule's *compression,* which is mechanically converted into a rate of climb indication. Just the opposite happens during a descent, when the capsule is at a greater pressure than the case, resulting in the capsule's expansion, which is mechanically converted into a rate of descent indication.

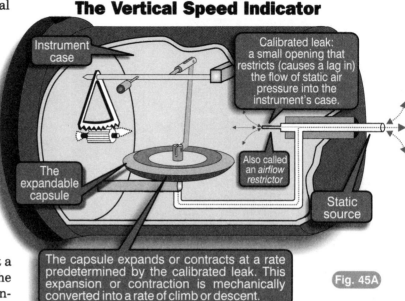

The Vertical Speed Indicator

Instrument case

Calibrated leak: a small opening that restricts (causes a lag in) the flow of static air pressure into the instrument's case.

The expandable capsule

Also called an *airflow restrictor*

Static source

The capsule expands or contracts at a rate predetermined by the calibrated leak. This expansion or contraction is mechanically converted into a rate of climb or descent.

Fig. 45A

You'll find the vertical speed indicator very useful in helping you plan climbs and descents. Suppose you're 10 nautical miles from an approach fix and traveling at two nautical miles per minute (a 120 knot ground speed). It takes five minutes to cover those 10 miles. If the airplane's altitude is 3,000 feet above the altitude at which you want to cross the fix, a descent rate of 600 feet per minute is required to reach the fix at the desired altitude. While this is only a rough estimate, it does aid in planning the descent.

This instrument is also useful for detecting trends away from an established pitch attitude. Frankly, I find the VSI much more useful than the altimeter for detecting small changes in airplane pitch. During a steep turn I'll include the VSI in my scan and watch for needle movement. Any deviation from a zero reading is quickly corrected by a change in elevator pressure. While the instrument does have a slight lag, it is hardly noticeable when small, smooth pitch changes are made.

There are times when you'll notice that, while sitting on the ground, the rate needle in the vertical speed indicator reads in error. It may, for instance, show a 100 foot per minute descent rate in the runup area. Hopefully you're not in a newly forming airport sinkhole. So the question is, can you fly still fly IFR with this error? The answer is yes, you can. The vertical speed indicator isn't a required instrument for IFR flight. Therefore, you can simply make a mental correction for this error in flight. This is important since ATC expects you to report your inability to climb or descend at 500 fpm to an assigned altitude when you're within 1,000 feet of that altitude.

Alternate Static Source

A pilot was flying IFR and had just switched sectors when the controller asked, "2132 Bravo, are you on frequency?" The pilot replied, "No, but I will be soon." Sometimes a pilot's brain is like an airplane's static source—it becomes clogged. Fortunately for airplanes, there's often an alternate source of static pressure in the event the primary source becomes plugged.

The Internal Workings of the Vertical Speed Indicator

Expandable capsule

To static source

My thumb (useful for preventing car doors from closing).

Tube connecting capsule to static source

Fig. 45B

Courtesy Bob Crystal

Fig. 45C

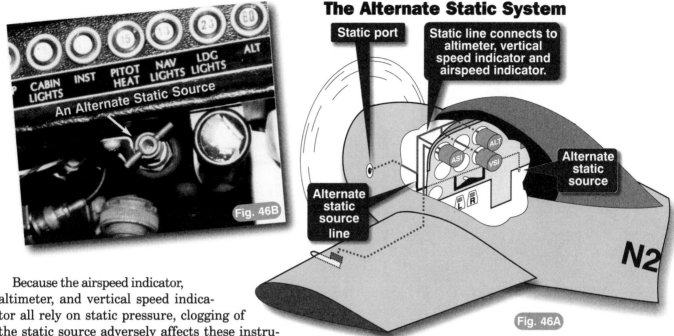

Fig. 46B

An Alternate Static Source

The Alternate Static System

Static port

Static line connects to altimeter, vertical speed indicator and airspeed indicator.

Alternate static source

Alternate static source line

Fig. 46A

Because the airspeed indicator, altimeter, and vertical speed indicator all rely on static pressure, clogging of the static source adversely affects these instruments. In fact, to be perfectly precise, a plugged static port will prevent any static air pressure change, causing the altimeter to freeze at its last indication and the VSI to read zero, regardless of altitude change. Fortunately, many airplanes have an alternate static source that provides a second chance at getting air.

The alternate static source for the airplane's three pressure instruments is shown in Figure 46A. If the primary static source becomes plugged, a little valve (normally located under the instrument panel above the pilot's or passenger's knee), can be opened (Figure 46B). Cabin static air pressure now becomes the pressure source for the airspeed indicator, altimeter and VSI. And be sure to let your passengers know you're reaching for the valve and not their knee caps.

Cabin static air pressure is slightly less than outside pressure, so selecting it will cause a slight, momentary climb on the VSI. The altimeter will usually read higher than the true altitude (usually less than 50 feet. FAR Part 23 requires a correction card in the cockpit if the altimeter changes by more than 50 feet when the alternate source is used). Because airspeed measurement is the difference between impact and static pressure, the airspeed indication will be slightly higher while using the alternate static source. This is a good reason to always be suspicious of an airplane salesperson who insists on showing you how fast the airplane flies but reaches under or below the panel while doing so. Of course, if there's no alternate static source there, then he's trying to grab your knee cap.

The Gyroscopic Instruments

If the first thing you think of when I say *gyros* is a Middle Eastern food, we need to talk.

The gyroscope is an amazing bit of technology, and it is the foundation of three major airplane instruments—the attitude indicator, the heading indicator, and the turn coordinator. Without gyros, we'd not only be hungry, but lost and upside down.

A gyroscope is essentially a spinning disc that's resistant to deflection as demonstrated by the spinning child's top shown in Figure 47. This resistance to deflection, sometimes known as *rigidity in space*, is based on Newton's three laws of motion. Simply stated, these laws say that a body at rest (or in motion) tends to remain at rest (or in motion). They also say that the deflection of a moving body is proportional to the force applied to it and inversely proportional to the body's weight and speed. It's these laws of motion that enable us to harness the gyroscope and put it to work telling us which way is up.

Gyroscopic Rigidity in Space

A child's toy top stays vertical or rigid in space when spun. When not spun, it easily falls to its side.

The same principle applies to modern day gyro instruments. A spinning gyro remains fixed in space allowing the airplane to rotate around it.

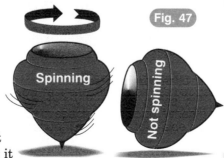

Fig. 47

Spinning

Not spinning

As we continue our behind-the-panel trek, we've arrived at the gyro section, led by the attitude indicator.

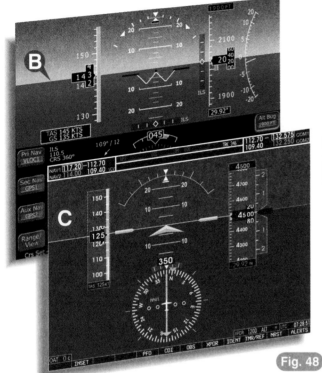

Fig. 48

The Attitude Indicator

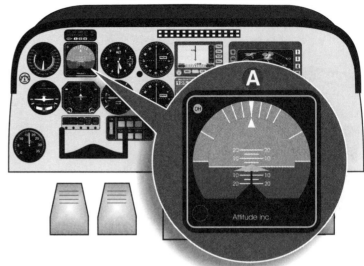

The attitude indicator is, essentially, a miniature horizon in your panel. The traditional attitude indicator presentation (position A) is found in most round-dial airplanes. Primary flight displays (positions B and C) present a larger sky-ground horizon picture making it much easier to identify the airplane's attitude even if you're sitting in the back seat (which you shouldn't be if you're acting as PIC).

The Attitude Indicator

One of the airplane's three gyroscopic instruments is called the *attitude indicator* or *artificial horizon*. The attitude indicator (Figure 48, position A) is located in the top middle of the panel's six primary instruments. In primary flight displays, the attitude indicator often fills the entire background of the glass instrument display (Figure 48, B and C). The attitude it indicates is the plane's, not the pilot's. If you want a pilot attitude indicator, buy one of those thingies that changes color with your emotional temperature, or consult your passengers.

When a hunter shoots a moose, he's often proud of his accomplishment and elects to mount the head over the top-middle of the fireplace so it's highly visible. Of course, the moose still has the last expression on its face before it

became an ornament. It's an expression that says, "What is that? A gun?" Well, that's why the attitude indicator is hung smack in the top-middle of the instrument panel, even though it's far from shot (we hope).

The attitude indicator is similar to the outside or visible horizon in the way it provides you with attitude information. Figure 49 shows how the attitude indicator presents its pitch and bank information. The basis of this presentation is a symbolic set of airplane wings resting over a moveable horizon card. Painted directly onto the horizon card is a white horizon line, a light colored area above the line representing the sky and a darker colored area below representing the ground (even in smoggy Los Angeles—which is a nice place to be if you're a muffler—these two colors shouldn't be reversed). Bank and pitch markings are also shown on the card.

The Attitude Indicator

Sky pointer

10° Bank lines

60° Bank line

DH

Bank pointer

Sky

20
10
10
20

Degrees pitch line

10   10
20   20

Ground

Fig. 49

Attitude Inc.

Airplane adjustment knob   Horizon line   Artificial airplane wing

Various Attitudes and Banks   Fig. 50

Straight & level A

Nose up pitch B

Nose down pitch C

Left turn at 30° of bank D

Right turn at 30° of bank E

Nose up pitch in a left turn at 30° of bank F

Nose up pitch in a right turn at 60° of bank G

Nose down pitch in a right turn at 20° of bank H

Attached to the instrument's case are the attitude indicator's symbolic wings (the yellow triangle in Figure 49), while the instrument's horizon card is free to rotate underneath them. Because the horizon card is mechanically attached to a stabilized gyro, it essentially remains fixed in space while the airplane rotates about it during flight. This gives the impression that the symbolic airplane wings are the things that move (they don't move, since they're attached to the instrument's case, which is bolted to the instrument panel).

Pitch Attitude and Flight Conditions

Variable attitude conditions on the face of the attitude indicator are shown in Figure 50. (Remember, in each case the airplane has pitched or rolled around the horizon card that's remaining stationary in space.) A straight and level pitch attitude is shown on attitude indicator A. The airplane is flying straight because the symbolic airplane wings are not banked and the airplane's nose is level with the horizon indicating it is probably holding its altitude (that's *probably,* since we'd need to look at the altimeter to be sure).

Attitude indicator B shows the airplane in straight flight with a nose-up pitch attitude. Attitude indicator C depicts straight flight with a nose down pitch attitude. The airplane's wings are level and the nose is pointed below the horizon.

Attitude indicator D depicts a left turn in a level pitch attitude. Sometimes it's a little difficult to determine which way the airplane is banked. Ask yourself, "Which wing is pointed toward the ground?" In this picture it's obvious that the left wing is pointed downward. The airplane must be in a left turn. This should be obvious to you by now (as obvious as a redneck pilot using a rag for gas cap). After all, if the left wing is pointed to the ground you should be making a left turn.

Another important question to ask is, "If I wanted to return to straight flight in attitude indicator D, which wing would I raise?" (You've got a 50–50 chance on this one.) Yes, the left wing. It's the one dipping toward the ground. During your first introduction to instrument training it's possible you might become a little confused about how to roll back to level flight. Just ask yourself which wing needs raising and raise it. Then keep the tip of the yellow triangle on the white horizon line to maintain a level pitch attitude. Keep in mind that we refer to straight flight as both wings being parallel with the horizon and level flight as the airplane's longitudinal axis being parallel with the horizon. Attitude indicator D shows the airplane in a level pitch attitude while in a bank.

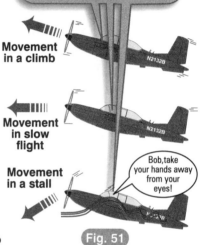

Movement in a climb

Movement in slow flight

Bob, take your hands away from your eyes!

Movement in a stall

Fig. 51

Looking at attitude indicator E, what type of turn does it show? Ask yourself, "Which wing is pointed toward the ground?" The answer is, the right wing. The airplane is in a right turn. The vertical indicator at the top of the instrument points to the 30° bank increment (each of the first three indices represent 10° of bank). Therefore the airplane is in a 30° right bank. If you wanted to return to straight and level flight, which way would you turn? You must turn the control wheel to the left to raise the right wing and return to straight flight.

An airplane in a nose-up pitch attitude while in a left 30° bank turn is shown by attitude indicator F. Attitude indicator G shows an airplane in a nose-up pitch attitude while in a right turn at a very steep 60° of bank. Finally, attitude indicator H shows an airplane in a nose-down pitch attitude while in a right turn at 20° of bank.

Have you noticed that I have not mentioned climbing or descending in reference to pitch attitude? Even though a nose up pitch attitude is normally associated with a climb, there are occasions where it's not. For instance, Figure 51 shows three different flight conditions associated with a nose-up pitch attitude. The airplane may either be climbing with full power, cruising with limited power, or stalling with no power. All these conditions are associated with a nose-up pitch attitude. When flying by reference to instruments, the only way you can be sure you know what the airplane is doing is to use all the information that's available. You can fly partial panel, but you shouldn't fly partial information. You will learn how to gather all the information a little later, in the next chapter on instrument scan.

The Gyrocompass

It was during the last decade of the 19th century that the application of the gyroscope found a place in the solution to real world problems. The increasing use of steel in ships brought about the need to overcome the unreliability of the magnetic compass when surrounded by large amounts of metal. In this age of Edison, Bell and the Wright brothers, two inventors, one on either side of the Atlantic, sought solutions to this problem. Dr. H. Anschutz of Germany and Elmer Sperry both built on the properties of the gyroscope; stability and precession. A gyroscope will always point to a fixed point in space if left undisturbed. If force is exerted upon it, it will react at right angles to the force applied. This characteristic of a gyro combined with other elements of precession, pendulocity and damping, will allow the gyro to settle toward true north. In 1908 Dr. Anschutz patented the first north seeking gyrocompass with the United Kingdom's Patent office. That same year, Elmer Sperry invented and introduced the first ballistic gyrocompass, which included vertical damping. Both of these first devices were of the single pendulum type.

Courtesy: Federal Aviation Administration

The Attitude Indicator

When the attitude indicator's gyro is spun by air, it remains rigid or fixed in space. The airplane rotates around the gyro and mechanically converts this movement into pitch and bank information on the face of the horizon card.

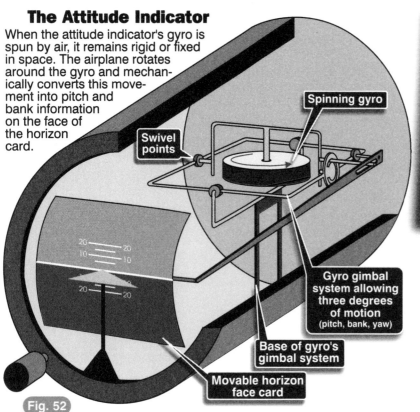

- Spinning gyro
- Swivel points
- Gyro gimbal system allowing three degrees of motion (pitch, bank, yaw)
- Base of gyro's gimbal system
- Movable horizon face card

Fig. 52

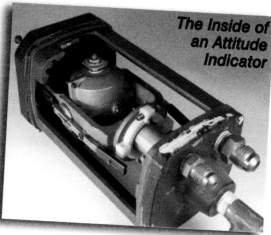

The Inside of an Attitude Indicator

Figure 52 displays the internal workings of the attitude indicator. While this is a highly simplified drawing, it does allow you to understand the principles on which the attitude indicator works. Notice the circular disk in the center of the instrument. This is the gyroscope. It is mechanically connected to the sky/ground horizon card on the face of the indicator. When spun, this disk takes on gyroscopic properties and maintains its position, fixed in space, relative to the earth. Thus, the horizon's face card, which is mechanically connected to the gyro, also remains fixed in space. From inside the airplane, the horizon face card accurately represents the real horizon in either a right or left hand turn as shown in Figure 53. As you can clearly see, the airplane rotates about the attitude indicator's gyro-stabilized (fixed) horizon card.

The attitude gyros in most light airplanes are spun by air pressure. A vacuum pump (Figure 54) sucks air through the instrument and over the gyro (Figure 55), spinning it at high velocity. This system is known as the vacuum system, but it comes without any fancy attachments for doing the blinds and is useless for cleaning your airplane. Typically both the attitude indicator and the heading indicator use gyroscopes that are spun by vacuum air pressure.

The Horizon Line

The attitude indicator's horizon line remains parallel to the earth's surface at all times and the sky pointer always points upward to the sky.

Right turn — Sky pointer

Left turn — Sky pointer

Fig. 53

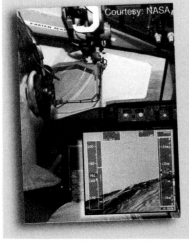

Courtesy: NASA

Synthetic Vision

There's nothing like seeing what you're not supposed to see. That's the promise of *synthetic vision* as shown from the cockpit of a NASA airplane to the left. What you're seeing is a computer generated presentation of terrain and obstacle information along with airplane attitude and performance information. This presentation is created through the use of WAAS GPS, solid state gyros, barometric pressure sensor, a battery backup and a terrain database. The result is a synthetic view of obstacles, terrain, and airport features on your cockpit's multi-function display or another display such as a laptop or tablet computer.

On many general aviation synthetic visions systems, the display will provide you with attitude and heading information, airspeed, altitude and other useful information. This information enhances your situational awareness in several ways. For instance, during IFR (or VFR) approaches to airports at night, day or in IMC, you'll have a clear 3D picture of the terrain surrounding an airport along with the runway and pertinent obstacles. Many synthetic vision systems allow other essential items to be overlaid on an MFD in 2D format, such as airport runway information, NEXRAD weather, approach charts and more.

Chapter 2 - Your Flight Instruments: Behind the Panel

2-33

Attitude Indicator Adjustment Knob

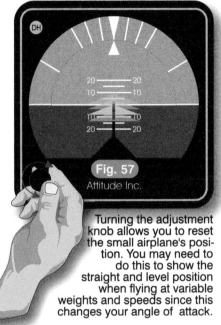

Fig. 57
Attitude Inc.

Turning the adjustment knob allows you to reset the small airplane's position. You may need to do this to show the straight and level position when flying at variable weights and speeds since this changes your angle of attack.

You may also come across an airplane with a heading indicator whose gyros are electrically spun in order to provide backup should the vacuum system take the afternoon off without prior permission. Either way, the spinning of a gyro allows these instruments to work their magic. This is why you'll always want to listen for unusual sounds coming from these gyros after the battery is turned on but before engine start. If they're spinning and they aren't in good working order you might hear a whine (unless you're sitting next to a pilot who made a bad landing) or some other strange sound that would deserve closer inspection.

No suction and you're out of luck-tion (OK, so I like poetry). When the airplane's air-spun gyro malfunctions, it's usually because the vacuum pump isn't providing sufficient vacuum pressure (like none, for instance). An airplane's vacuum gauge (Figure 56) keeps you informed about the amount of suction provided by the pump. Operations outside the normal range (green arc) on the gauge usually result in erroneous readings on the gyro instruments. On some airplanes, low power settings (such as a low engine idle before takeoff or long, low-power descents) produce insufficient vacuum for the instruments. Increasing power slightly usually takes care of the problem.

There are a few more things about the attitude indicator you should know. First, notice the little knob on the bottom left of the instrument in Figure 57. Rotating this knob moves the reference airplane up or down in the attitude indicator's window. This allows you to set the symbolic wings precisely on the horizon line before takeoff and in flight. It's sometimes necessary to adjust the symbolic wings since there are several variables that can change the attitude required for level flight. These variables might be either the weight of the airplane or the speed at which it is flown.

The Suction Gauge

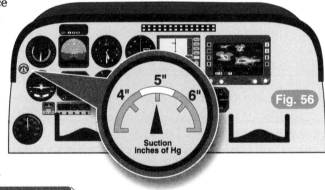

Fig. 56

5"
4" 6"
Suction inches of Hg

The Vacuum System

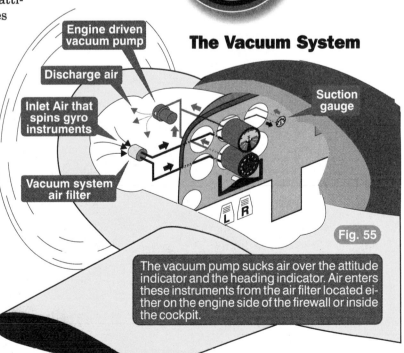

Engine driven vacuum pump

Discharge air

Inlet Air that spins gyro instruments

Vacuum system air filter

Suction gauge

L R

Fig. 55

The vacuum pump sucks air over the attitude indicator and the heading indicator. Air enters these instruments from the air filter located either on the engine side of the firewall or inside the cockpit.

The Airplane's Vacuum Pump System

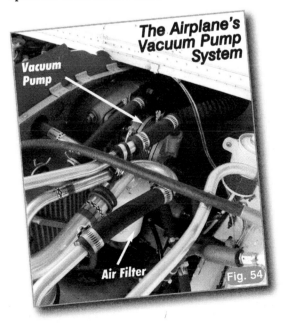

Vacuum Pump

Air Filter

Fig. 54

Attitude Indicator Errors

The attitude indicator has a self-erecting gyroscope that maintains a vertical spin axis relative to the earth's surface. Pretty snazzy, huh? Remember, a gyroscope resists movement *perpendicular* to its axis. So in this case, the attitude indicator's vertical axis allows the instrument to portray accurate attitude information because whatever the airplane does, the gyro stands up straight. You can tilt the plane, but the gyro resists going there. The plane rotates, the gyro doesn't, so if you realign the airplane with the gyro (which is what you're doing when you have a "straight and level" indication on the instrument), you are in fact flying straight and level.

Nothing's perfect, though. Sometimes the gyro is moved from the absolute vertical by internal friction and other minute forces, which displaces it from its vertical spin alignment. To compensate for these forces, gyroscopes operating on vacuum driven attitude indicators have a mechanism to help align a tilted axis back to the vertical. Here's how it works.

Figure 58 shows an internal view of the attitude indicator. Air is drawn through a passage in the attitude indicator's rear gimbal into a housing that surrounds the gyro, where it's directed against the gyro's peripheral

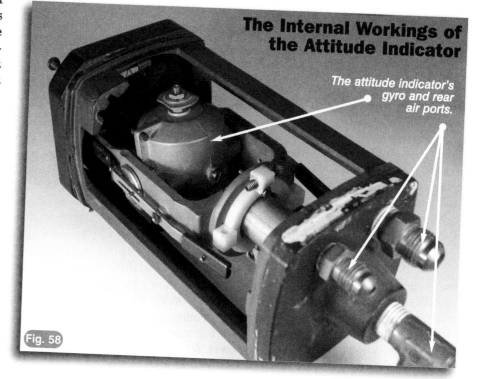

The Internal Workings of the Attitude Indicator

The attitude indicator's gyro and rear air ports.

Fig. 58

vanes, causing the gyro to spin (thus remaining rigid in space). Then the air is drawn downward below the spinning gyro where it passes through four exhaust ports that are equally spaced from each other at 90 degree angles (Figure 59). From here, the air is sucked into the vacuum pump, and then discharged.

Each of the four ports is partially covered by a pendulous vane arrangement. Thus, small but equal amounts of air are always partially escaping from each port. These vanes, however, can swing slightly like a clock's pendulum, thus varying the amount of air escaping from each port. As the amount of air varies, the force applied to the bottom of the gyroscope's housing changes. This is the heart of the attitude indicator's self-erecting mechanism.

If the gyro's axis tilts from the vertical (because of friction, for example), one air exhaust port of the opposing set of pendulous vanes (those across from each other) will be uncovered slightly (Figure 60A and B) while the other remains fully covered. The uncovered port allows more air to escape. The net result is that a tilted gyro experiences a *precessing* force (one that acts 90 degrees to the direction of the gyro's rotation) that helps return the gyro to a vertical position as shown by the sequence in Figure 61.

This assumes, of course, that the airplane's pitch and bank attitude don't exceed the limits beyond which the gyro will tumble. Older types of attitude indicators have bank limits somewhere around 100°–110° and pitch limits of 60°–70°. Exceeding these pitch limits prevents the gyro's self-erecting mechanism

The AI's Pendulous Vanes

One of the attitude gyro's four exhaust ports.

Pendulous Vanes

Fig. 59

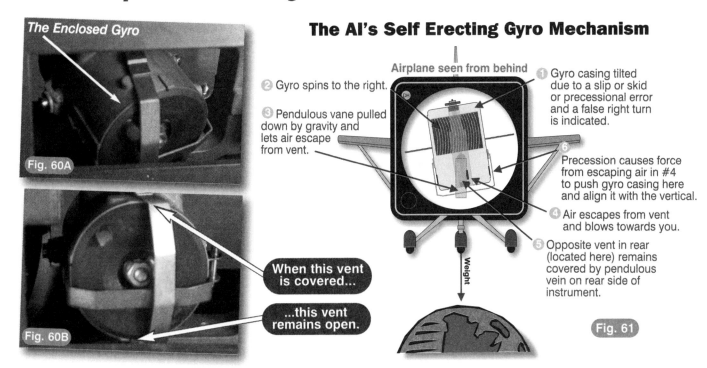

The Enclosed Gyro

Fig. 60A

Fig. 60B

When this vent is covered...

...this vent remains open.

The AI's Self Erecting Gyro Mechanism

Airplane seen from behind

② Gyro spins to the right.

③ Pendulous vane pulled down by gravity and lets air escape from vent.

① Gyro casing tilted due to a slip or skid or precessional error and a false right turn is indicated.

⑥ Precession causes force from escaping air in #4 to push gyro casing here and align it with the vertical.

④ Air escapes from vent and blows towards you.

⑤ Opposite vent in rear (located here) remains covered by pendulous vein on rear side of instrument.

Weight

Fig. 61

from working properly, resulting in the gyro tumbling. This also usually results in the pilot's brain tumbling and not working properly.

Banks in excess of the instrument's limits cause the gimbals to hit their stops, resulting in an abrupt precession of the gyro (and excessive wear on the gimbals, too). It may take several minutes for an attitude indicator to right itself after tumbling. It may take the pilot a lot longer. Until the gyro is fully upright, it's an unreliable source of attitude information. On the other hand, modern attitude indicators are less likely to tumble. Some can handle 360 degrees of pitch or 360 degrees of roll (maneuvers you shouldn't be doing in IMC even if your instrument instructor was named Evel Knievel).

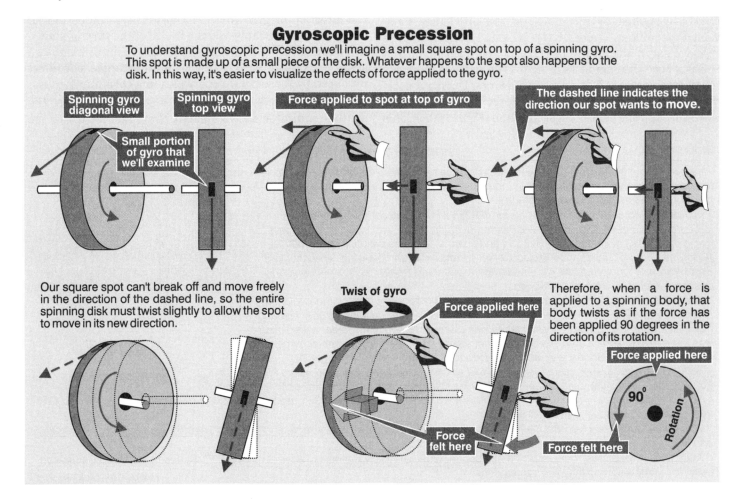

Gyroscopic Precession

To understand gyroscopic precession we'll imagine a small square spot on top of a spinning gyro. This spot is made up of a small piece of the disk. Whatever happens to the spot also happens to the disk. In this way, it's easier to visualize the effects of force applied to the gyro.

Spinning gyro diagonal view

Spinning gyro top view

Force applied to spot at top of gyro

The dashed line indicates the direction our spot wants to move.

Small portion of gyro that we'll examine

Our square spot can't break off and move freely in the direction of the dashed line, so the entire spinning disk must twist slightly to allow the spot to move in its new direction.

Twist of gyro

Force applied here

Therefore, when a force is applied to a spinning body, that body twists as if the force has been applied 90 degrees in the direction of its rotation.

Force applied here

Force felt here

Force applied here

Force felt here

90°

Rotation

Gyroscopic Precession in the Attitude Indicator

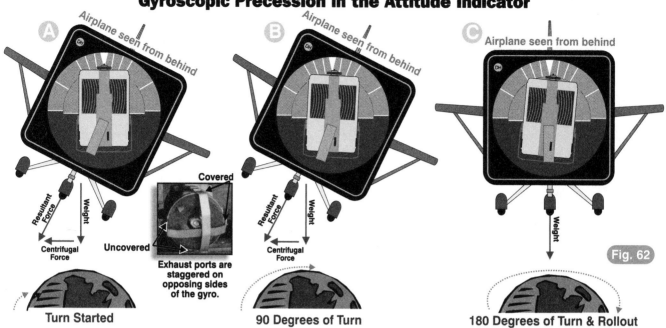

Turn Started   90 Degrees of Turn   180 Degrees of Turn & Rollout

Unfortunately, the gyroscope's self-erecting mechanism doesn't act immediately. The gyro may precess back to the horizontal plane at rates of approximately 8 degrees per minute, depending on the type of attitude indicator in use. This explains why the attitude indicator shows slightly erroneous readings during turns and changes in speed.

For instance, in straight and level flight the gyro's spin axis remains perpendicular with the earth's surface because of gravity. Any deviation of the spin axis from vertical is corrected by movement of the previously mentioned pendulous vanes. Keep in mind that airplanes spend most of their time in straight and level flight and this is where the engineers designed the attitude indicator to work with the fewest number of errors. During a coordinated turn, however, centrifugal force is directed downward through the center of the airplane (Figure 62A). This

causes centrifugal force to pull the pendulous vanes to the side of the gyro which simultaneously opens one exhaust port (the one facing you in Figure 62A while keeping the exhaust port on the opposite side of the gyro covered (the exhaust ports on opposing sides of the gyro are staggered slightly so that a moving pendulous vane allows only one port on opposing sides to be uncovered at any one time). As air exits the exhaust port of the spinning gyro (spinning to the right as you see it) feels a force applied 90 degrees in the direction of gyro rotation. This causes the bottom of the gyro to precess towards the inside of the turn as shown in Figure 62B (which means the attitude indicator shows a slight decrease in bank). This is an unfortunate side effect produced by these pendulous vanes in a turn.

When the airplane rolls out of a coordinated turn, the attitude indicator shows a slight climb and a turn in the

Forced to Fly in IMC

Instrument meteorological conditions (IMC) manage to sneak up on many pilots. This reporter hoped to avoid the forecast midday thunderstorms by departing in the early morning. Alas, the thunderstorms didn't read the forecast.

I called FSS to get a weather briefing for VFR flight. The forecast called for a cold front to be coming in quite fast and the weather to get much worse with thunderstorms developing by midday. I climbed to 12,500 feet and noted a solid overcast layer at 11,000 feet [along my route of flight]. I contacted Center to request flight following, and checked Flight Watch to confirm there were adequate broken and scattered holes in which to descend safely close to my destination.

The solid overcast layer began rising and quickly turned into cumulonimbus clouds, forcing me to climb. As I reached 14,500 feet, the clouds were developing very fast and rising all around me.... In a very short time I was close to 18,000 feet. Center asked me if I was IFR capable, and I stated, "Negative." They asked me if I had supplemental oxygen, and I stated, "Negative." Soon I was at 19,700 feet, and Center said I had to get back down to 12,500 feet. I was given a heading and was told to chop the power and keep wings level with a 500-600-foot-per-minute descent down through the clouds with reference to my artificial horizon. So I did as I was told...and I broke out of the clouds at 13,000 feet. I had a very bad headache and was disoriented. I was handed over to the tower [and landed uneventfully].

With 20/20 hindsight, I see that the rising cloud tops were extremely clear, strong STOP signs. I should have turned around when I confirmed the overcast layer was ascending.

Taking the conservative route—doing a 180 degree turn—is usually the better bet when facing IMC. Kudos to the sharp Center controller for safely resolving this pilot's emergency.

NASA Callback Report

The inside of an AHRS (Attitude and Heading Reference System)

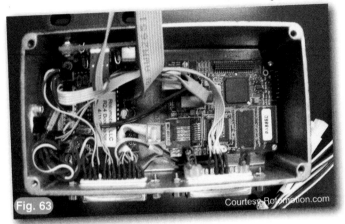

Fig. 63   Courtesy Rotomotion.com

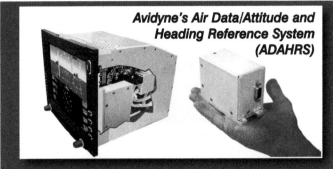

Avidyne's Air Data/Attitude and Heading Reference System (ADAHRS)

Avidyne's PFD uses an integrated air data computer and attitude and heading reference system (AHRS) in their single unit, otherwise known as the ADAHRS.

opposite direction (Figure 62C). The error (approximately 3 to 5 degrees) is greatest through 180 degrees of turn and is quickly corrected by the erecting mechanism. A 360 degree turn results in the precession error of the first 180 degree turn canceling out the precession error of the second 180 degree turn. Given this error, if you rolled out so that the attitude indicator showed straight and level flight *immediately* (*immediately* is the key word here) after a 180 degree turn, you'd be descending and still turning slightly in the previous direction of turn.

The attitude indicator is also susceptible to acceleration and deceleration errors. Accelerating causes the horizon bar to move down, indicating a climb attitude. Decelerating causes the horizon bar to move up, indicating a descending attitude. Here's a memory aid to help recall this error. Let the ornament on the front end of your car (the *hood*, which isn't a place where you live) represent the AI's small yellow triangle—the instrument's symbolic airplane. When you accelerate, the front of your car including the ornament rises slightly above the real horizon, thus pictorially representing a climb attitude. When you step on the brakes, the hood ornament dips below the horizon, thus pictorially representing a descent. Remember, this is just a memory aid, since it's really the attitude indicator's horizon bar that moves up or down. Of course, if you drive while fatigued, your car may not have a typical hood ornament. You may have a mailbox or the bumper of another car up there instead.

Knowing something about these errors is important. Here's why. If you follow the horizon bar with the minia-

ture airplane as you accelerate, the airplane will descend slightly. After all, if the horizon bar goes down and you follow it with the attitude indicator's miniature airplane, you'll end up in a slight descent. Attempting to do the same while decelerating will cause you to climb slightly.

There is really only one more error to consider regarding the attitude indicator. Skidding turns move the pendulous vanes from their vertical position and precess the gyro toward the inside of the turn. If you skid in a turn, then expect the attitude indicator to show a turn in the opposite direction of the skid after you return to straight and level flight.

At this point you're probably hoping that you kept the receipt for the attitude indicator in your airplane. With all its errors, taking it back to the store is looking like a good option. Never fear, these errors aren't all that large in the first place. I've flown many modern airplanes where I didn't even notice the attitude indicator's errors despite looking for them. On older airplanes with aged instrumentation, these errors can be a bit more noticeable. It's important to know about these errors because the attitude indicator is one of the most important instruments on the panel.

On the other hand, if you're using an airplane with a primary flight display like the Garmin G1000 or Avidyne's Entegra, then you won't experience any of the precessional errors we've just discussed. That's because these modern PFDs don't use spinning gyros. Instead, their attitude and heading data are provided by a unit called AHRS or the *attitude and heading reference system*, which is solid state and contains no moving parts (Figure 63).

Vacuum Pump Failure

While flying VFR with flight following, I experienced a vacuum pump failure. Conditions ahead appeared to require an IFR clearance, so I advised the controller that I had experienced a vacuum pump failure and therefore the heading and attitude indicators were inoperative. I also told him that conditions ahead appeared to require an IFR clearance. He asked if I preferred to land or file IFR. I indicated that, since I was having no problems, I would prefer to file IFR. He issued an IFR clearance and provided no-gyro vectors to the airport. I landed with no problems.

Since then I have learned that he probably should not have issued the clearance because you should not enter IFR conditions with an inoperative vacuum pump. He should have advised me of that.

It was the pilot's responsibility—not the controller's—to determine the legality of IFR flight. The situation could have been avoided if the reporter had executed a 180° turn at the first sign of deteriorating weather.

NASA Callback Report

In the Garmin G1000, the AHRS consists of three rate sensors, three accelerometers, and two two-axis tilt sensors. It uses inputs from the magnetometer (for heading information) and GPS (for track information). Air data computer inputs are used only when GPS and magnetometer info is unavailable.

So why should you learn anything about air-spun gyros if you're using a modern PFD? Well, most modern airplanes with PFDs also have round-dial backup instruments that still use round-dial technology for their operations. This, and this alone, is still sufficient reason to know about how these important backup instruments work on airplanes with modern PFDs.

As a final note, make sure that the attitude indicator is working properly before you depart IFR or at night. Do this by checking to see that the horizon bar is erect and stable within five minutes after engine start for instruments powered by vacuum pressure. For attitude indicators powered by electricity, the instrument should become stable within five minutes after electrical power is applied (most modern attitude indicators, vacuum or electric powered, will erect in just a minute or so). While taxiing, make sure the horizon bar doesn't exceed 5 degrees of bank when you turn. It's better to catch attitude indicator problems before you're in the soup. That's the last place you want this important instrument to roll over and play dead.

The Heading Indicator

When the gyro in the heading indicator spins, it remains rigid (fixed) in space. The airplane rotates about the gyro as it turns and a gearing system converts this movement into a heading change on the face of the indicator.

Gimbal system allowing two degrees of motion

Swivel points

Spinning gyro

Face card that rotates with fixed position of gyro

Fig. 65

The Heading Indicator

Figure 64 shows the airplane's *heading indicator,* which in many well equipped airplanes can also be part of the horizontal situation indicator (HSI). For now, let's discuss the ordinary, everyday vacuum-powered heading indicator, which is sometimes called the *directional gyro* or *DG.*

The heading indicator is a gyro instrument that provides the same information found on the magnetic compass—heading information. Why have two instruments to do one job? Because the magnetic compass is an instrument best read by one of those bobbing dolls you see on the back window shelf of cars. Like some passengers, the magnetic compass makes a poor candidate for air transport. The heading indicator attempts to remedy some of the ills of the magnetic compass, though the latter remains a key component in your pilot's instrument kit—without it, you wouldn't be able to set the heading indicator in the first place.

The Heading Indicator

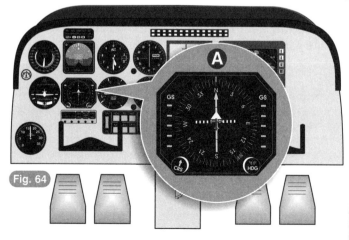

Fig. 64

The heading indicator in modern airplanes is often found in combination with an omni display (position A), known as the HSI or horizontal situation indicator or as part of the primary flight display (position B).

When looking at the heading indicator, you'll see the small outline of a stationary airplane centered in the display over a compass card that's free to rotate. The nose of the small outlined airplane always points straight up to a number which is your airplane's present heading. As the actual airplane turns, the compass card remains stabilized or fixed in space by an internal spinning gyro, as shown in Figure 65. The small outline airplane points to your airplane's magnetic heading. Figure 66 shows the internal workings of an actual heading indicator.

Before an IFR takeoff, after the gyros have had sufficient time to spin up (this usually takes about five minutes after engine start), set the heading indicator to the heading shown

The Inside of a Heading Indicator

Fig. 66

Courtesy Bob Crystal

on the magnetic compass. Do this by pushing and rotating the heading indicator's adjustment knob, as shown in Figure 67. Once the heading indicator is set to the compass' magnetic heading, it should provide accurate directional information for a reasonable period of time. It's wise to check the heading indicator while taxiing, making sure it continues to indicate the heading after turning.

Like a cautious parent, however, you need to check up on this child occasionally, lest it wander. In fact, you can be certain that the heading will wander. How much and when depends on how affected the heading indicator is by something known as *gyroscopic drift*.

Because of internal mechanical errors (bearing friction being the big problem) and/or the airplane's constantly changing position in space relative to the earth, it's possible for the heading indicator to experience gyroscopic heading drift. To compensate for this problem, the most important thing to remember is to keep checking or updating the reading on the heading indicator with the magnetic compass at least every 15 minutes. Make sure you're in straight and level, unaccelerated flight before taking a compass reading and resetting the heading indicator. Check for gyroscopic drift more often if your airplane's heading indicator has a history of wandering, which is also referred to as *precessing*. If precession isn't the cause of your wandering heading, you may be a disciple of the "two headings are better than one" school of flying.

Notice that the heading indicator in Figure 67 is calibrated in five-degree increments. Every 30°, starting from north, is referenced by printed letters or numerals that are sometimes called *cardinal numbers* (which is easier to say than *archbishop numbers*). Between the letters and numerals are slashes, calibrated to five- and ten-degree increments. The slashes at 10° increments are slightly larger, for easier identification.

In Figure 67, the heading indicator indicates that the airplane is presently heading north. This is called *360 degrees* or *zero* degrees, depending on who's talking. Either value is correct. The *E* represents east or 90°, *S* represents south or 180° and *W* represents west or 270°. Of course, real pros refer to these headings by their numerical values, not their numbers. If an IFR pilot referred to an easterly heading as *Eeeee*, you'd know he didn't have much experience. If he said, "My heading is *Eeeee*, no, wait, I was looking at the fuel gauge," then you'd know he didn't have much common sense, either.

Heading Indicator

The outline airplane's nose in the heading indicator points to the actual airplane's magnetic heading. As the airplane turns, the numbered disk rotates under the outline airplane allowing your new heading to appear on top.

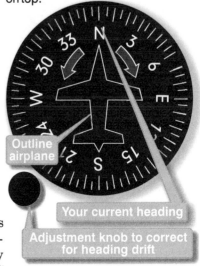

Outline airplane

Your current heading

Adjustment knob to correct for heading drift

Fig. 67

The Turn Coordinator

Fig. 68

An Oldie but a Goodie

You can still find them in older airplanes. They're called *turn and slip indicators* and they tell you something just a bit different from what you'd read on your *turn coordinator*.

A deflection of the vertical needle on the turn and slip indicator tells you the direction and rate the airplane's *heading* is changing. In other words, if the nose doesn't move laterally, then the turn and slip needle shouldn't move, either. Unlike the turn and slip indicator, the miniature airplane on the turn coordinator shows the direction and rate of *roll* and, when the bank is established, it shows the airplane's *rate* of turn. Because of the way the gyro in the turn and slip indicator is aligned, it is not capable of showing the rate and direction of roll.

The Turn Coordinator

In our family the turn coordinator was a distant and older relative who sat in the back seat of our family station wagon issuing instructions to the driver (which wouldn't have been so bad had he not had flashbacks of driving a tank in WWII, thus explaining his frequent use of the phrase, "Go over that car"). The turn coordinator (Figure 68) is actually a gyro instrument that provides information on your airplane's direction of roll, rate of heading change and whether the airplane is slipping or skidding in the turns (i.e., movement about its yaw and roll axes).

There are two instruments that actually make up the turn coordinator, a needle and an inclinometer (Figure 69) or a trend line and sliding trapezoid if you're using a PFD (Figure 70). Let's review the function of the inclinometer first.

The ball in the inclinometer tells you whether or not your turn is coordinated, thus whether rudder and aileron are applied in the proper proportion. Since the ball is free to roll right or left within the glass tube, any inappropriate rudder use (or lack of use) will force the ball sideways from

The PFD's Turn Rate and Coordination Information

Fig. 70

Turn Coordinator

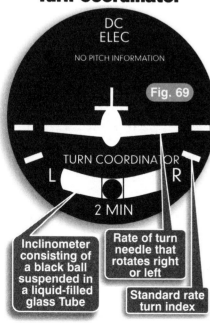

Fig. 69

Inclinometer consisting of a black ball suspended in a liquid-filled glass Tube

Rate of turn needle that rotates right or left

Standard rate turn index

On many PFDs, the right or left deflection of a magenta trend line (position A) shows what your heading will be in six seconds. The second hash mark (position B) to the left of the airplane's present heading is 18 degrees off center. When the trend line touches this point, the airplane is turning at 3 degrees per second and is making a standard rate turn (18 degree offset/6 second trend= 3 degrees per second). The inclinometer is represented by the bar under the trapezoid (position C). Movement right or left of the triangle indicates the degree of slipping or skidding (see Figure 71).

An Easy Way to Understand Slipping and Skidding in an Airplane

Airplane Slipping:
Nose pointed
outside the turn.

Airplane Flying Coordinated:
Nose pointed
in direction
of turn.

Airplane Skidding:
Nose pointed
inside the turn.

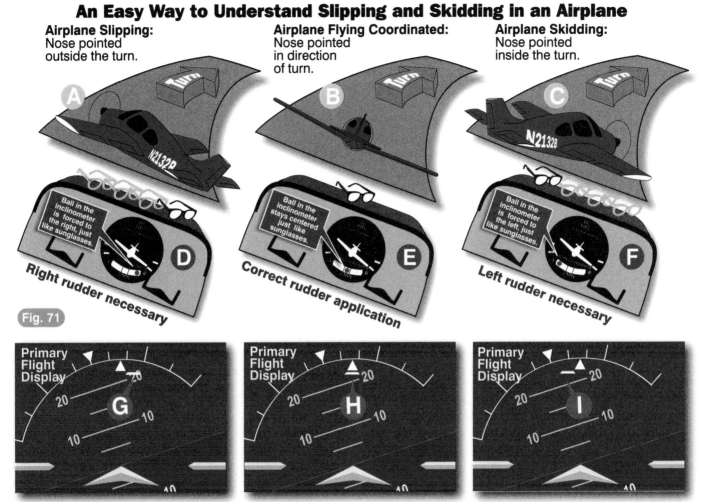

The primary flight display above shows how the moveable slip-skid (trapezoid) bar indicates a slipping turn (position G), a coordinated turn (position H) and a skidding turn (position I). These three indications correspond with the indications in the inclinometers (D, E and F) above.

its centered position. This deflects the ball in much the same way sunglasses scoot across your car's dash when rounding a sharp corner. Proper airmanship when flying IFR has it that you'll make coordinated turns, thus keeping the ball centered by using the rudder. In the case of a PFD, the sliding trapezoid bar (Figure 70, position C) slides to the right or left of the triangle to indicated the turn's coordination.

Figure 71 shows an airplane in a turn. Airplane A's nose is pointed outside the turn (probably because insufficient right rudder or too much right aileron is applied). The ball in the inclinometer (position D) and/or the PFD's trapezoid bar (position G) slip to the right, toward the inside of the turn, much like airplane A appears to be doing. In other words, you need to point the nose slightly to the right for a precisely aligned turn. By adding enough right rudder to align the airplane in the direction it's turning (airplane B), the ball (or coordination bar if you're using a PFD) returns to the center, as shown by inclinometer E and/or the PFD coordination bar (position H).

Airplane C's nose points toward the inside of the turn (probably because too much right rudder is applied or insufficient right aileron is used.) The ball in inclinometer F and/or the PFDs trapezoid bar (position I) skid to the left, toward the outside of the turn, much like airplane C

appears to be doing. Adding a little left rudder keeps the nose pointed in the direction the airplane's turning and centers the ball or trapezoid bar.

Stated simply, step on the ball (or the PDF's deflected trapezoid bar). If the ball is deflected to the right or left of center, add enough right or left rudder to center the ball. Flying IFR doesn't mean you shouldn't fly coordinated. Yes, you may be in clouds and no one can see you, but your passengers can feel it. Your gyros can feel it too. Flying coordinated means you'll never need to worry about passengers asking you to turn off the airplane's turn signal because the clicking noise is bothering them. If someone said this, you'd have to fess up and tell them that airplanes don't have blinkers. Then you'd be forced to tell them that it's just the inclinometer's ball banging back and forth against its stops because coordinated flying isn't one of your specialities. Ouch!

Now let's move on to the turn coordinator's turn needle. This is the small symbolic airplane in the center of the instrument capable of rotating right or left.

Unlike the spinning gyros in the attitude indicator and heading indicator, the turn coordinator's gyro is usually spun by electricity and that fact is normally noted on the face of the instrument. This is what causes the whining sound you hear when the airplane's master switch is first turned on during preflight (if you hear the whining sound and the master isn't on, then it's probably coming from the motor in your instructor's propeller hat, or from a passenger who just wants to go to lunch).

The turn coordinator's gyro is electrically powered to keep at least one gyro instrument operating in the event of a failure of the airplane's vacuum pump. As an instrument pilot, you should consider this a blessing. If the vacuum pump fails, the airplane's bank is controllable in IMC by reference to the turn coordinator alone.

Figure 72A and B show the internal workings of the turn coordinator. The turn coordinator's gyro is free to move in only one dimension, instead of three like the attitude indicator. During any *rolling*, *turning*, or *yawing* movement, the instrument's gyro feels a force applied to its side. This causes the gyro to precess in a predictable manner.

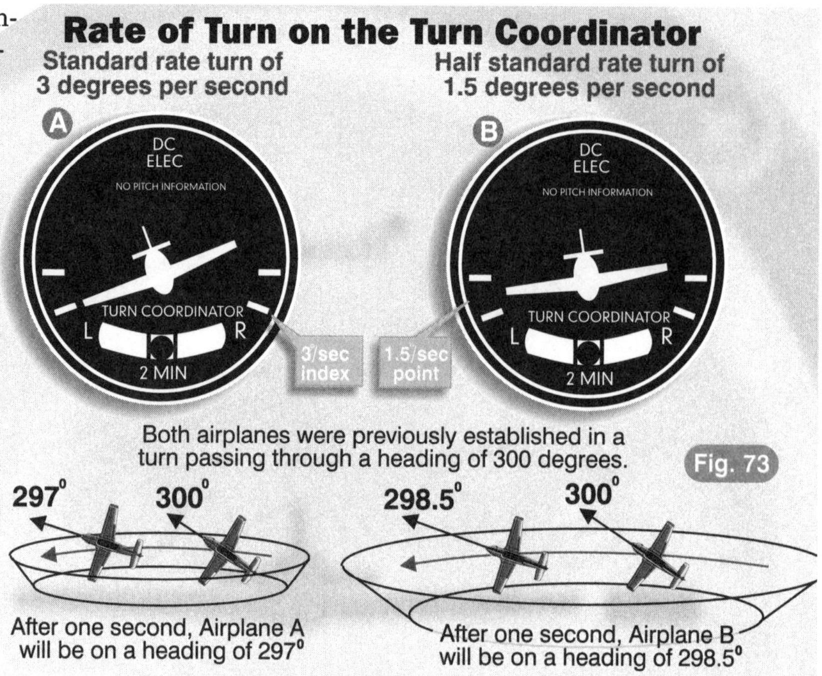

To present turn information, the turn coordinator relies on *gyroscopic precession*. I assume that you've read the sidebar on gyroscopic precession presented on page 2–35. Don't worry if you don't understand the fundamental physical principle behind gyroscopic precession. After all, trying to understand the physics of precession may actually cause your brain to rotate 90 degrees in its socket. Oh what a feeling! Just make sure you know that precession causes a force applied to a spinning body (the gyro) to be felt 90° in the direction of rotation. The turn coordinator doesn't show bank angle even though it may appear to do so. So don't be fooled by this. Only *direction* of roll or yaw and *rate of turn* are derivable from the turn coor-

Rate of Turn on the Turn Coordinator

Standard rate turn of 3 degrees per second **Half standard rate turn of 1.5 degrees per second**

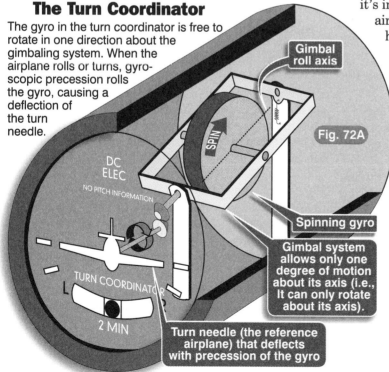

Both airplanes were previously established in a turn passing through a heading of 300 degrees.

After one second, Airplane A will be on a heading of 297°

After one second, Airplane B will be on a heading of 298.5°

Fig. 73

dinator. Refer to the attitude indicator for bank angle. The deflection of the turn needle represents the airplane's rate of turn.

Figure 73 shows two turn coordinators, each with a different amount of wing deflection of the symbolic airplane. Airplane A's wing is deflected to the white index mark, indicating the airplane's heading is changing at 3° per second. In aviation parlance this is called a *standard rate turn*. Since there are 360 degrees in a full circle, it takes 120 seconds or two minutes to make a complete turn (360°/3° per second). This is why the instrument is labeled *2 min*. This is not an instruction for an over easy turn indicator.

Despite sounding like we're cooking eggs in the cockpit, it's important to know these things. Look at miniature airplane B's wings in Figure 73. They are deflected halfway between the zero and three degree per second turn marks. The rate of turn is 1.5° per second. At this slower rate, the airplane takes twice as long to make a complete 360° turn.

Why would you want to know the rate at which your airplane changes headings?

The Turn Coordinator

The gyro in the turn coordinator is free to rotate in one direction about the gimbaling system. When the airplane rolls or turns, gyroscopic precession rolls the gyro, causing a deflection of the turn needle.

Gimbal roll axis

Fig. 72A

Spinning gyro

Gimbal system allows only one degree of motion about its axis (i.e., It can only rotate about its axis).

Turn needle (the reference airplane) that deflects with precession of the gyro

The Inside of a Turn Coordinator

Gyro

Courtesy Bob Crystal

Fig. 72B

The Turn Coordinator (Rolling Right/Left)

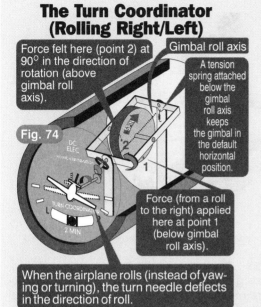

Force felt here (point 2) at 90° in the direction of rotation (above gimbal roll axis).

Gimbal roll axis

A tension spring attached below the gimbal roll axis keeps the gimbal in the default horizontal position.

Fig. 74

Force (from a roll to the right) applied here at point 1 (below gimbal roll axis).

When the airplane rolls (instead of yawing or turning), the turn needle deflects in the direction of roll.

The Turn Coordinator (Yawing or Turning)

When the airplane yaws or turns to the right, force is applied to the gyro at point 1 (above the gimbal's roll axis). Gyroscopic precession causes this force to be felt 90° in the direction of rotation, or at the top of the gyro at point 2. This rolls the gyro counterclockwise, resulting in a turn needle deflected to the right.

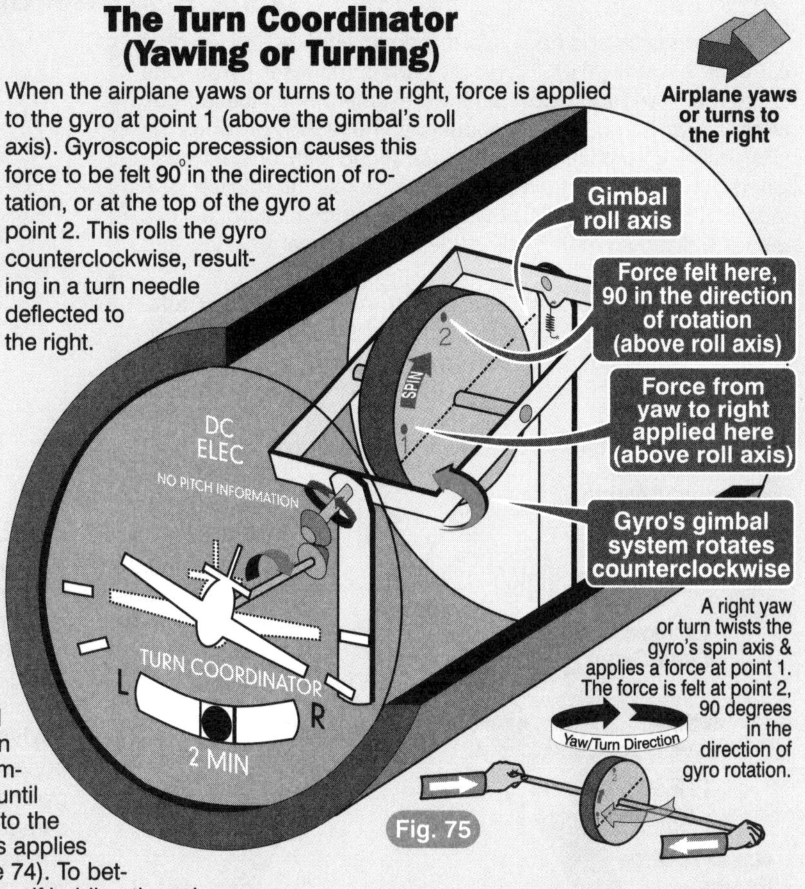

Airplane yaws or turns to the right

Gimbal roll axis

Force felt here, 90 in the direction of rotation (above roll axis)

Force from yaw to right applied here (above roll axis)

Gyro's gimbal system rotates counterclockwise

A right yaw or turn twists the gyro's spin axis & applies a force at point 1. The force is felt at point 2, 90 degrees in the direction of gyro rotation.

Yaw/Turn Direction

Fig. 75

The turn coordinator's gyro in Figure 72A spins on its axis while held on a gimbal (the gimbal is connected to its base at a rearward up-sloping angle and is free to rotate only in one direction about its own axis). A small spring applies a slight tension on the gimbal which normally holds it in the horizontal position until the airplane *rolls, yaws* or *turns*. As the airplane rolls to the right, the gyro's spin axis is also forced to rotate. This applies a force to the bottom of the gyro at position 1 (Figure 74). To better understand how this force is applied, visualize yourself holding the axis of a spinning gyro (one hand on each side of the gyro) parallel to the floor. Twist the axis so that your right hand moves toward the ground and the left hand moves toward the ceiling. This simulates an airplane rolling to the right and results in a force applied to the gyro at position 1. Gyroscopic precession causes this force to be felt 90 degrees in the direction of gyro rotation at position 2. Since position 2 is above the gimbal's roll axis in Figure 74 (remember, the gimbal slopes at a rearward angle), the gimbal rotates counterclockwise. Mechanical gearing results in the *turn needle* (symbolic reference airplane) deflecting to the right, thus indicating a roll to the right.

In addition to the direction of roll, the turn coordinator also shows the direction of *yaw* and the *rate* at which the airplane changes *headings* (Figure 75). Yawing to the right applies a force to the gyro above the gimbal's roll axis at position 1. (See the small insert at the bottom right of Figure 75 to understand how the *yaw* or *turning* force is felt by the gyro.) Gyroscopic precession results in this force being felt 90 degrees in the direction of gyro rotation at position 2. This causes the gimbal system to rotate counterclockwise and, because of mechanical gearing, deflects the turn needle to the right. Once *established* in a right turn, this force is continually applied to position 1, resulting in a needle deflection which represents the airplane's rate of turn (how fast the nose moves across the horizon). The turn needle doesn't represent the angle of bank. It only shows direction of roll, yaw and the rate of turn. In fact, it's possible to bank the airplane to the right (or left) while adding opposite rudder to keep the nose from moving (heading is constant) and the turn needle shouldn't deflect. Try it with your instructor.

Standard Rate Turn Calculations

A standard rate turn simply means that the nose of the airplane changes direction at three degrees per second. The easiest way to figure out what bank is required for a standard rate turn is to drop the last number off the airspeed and add these two numbers to the number five. If the airspeed is 125 knots, then the bank required for standard rate is 12 + 5 or 17 degrees. If the airspeed is 90 knots then the standard rate bank is 9 + 5 or 14 degrees. If the airspeed is 600 knots then the bank required is 65 degrees. This would be real interesting for the passengers! There is a good chance some of the older passengers will experience a dislodging of their uppers. The general rule is to never exceed 30 degrees of bank under IFR conditions, no matter what is required for a standard rate turn.

Keep in mind that the rate of turn will decrease (i.e. the miniature airplane in the turn coordinator will show less of a deflection) if the bank is held constant and the airspeed is increased. Why? At a constant bank angle, a higher airspeed means the airplane covers a great distance, thus the airplane takes a longer time to turn to a new heading (or change headings) since it is covering a greater distance in the turn. Conversely, if the bank is held constant and the airspeed decreased, the rate of turn will increase. This is one reason that airplanes flying at faster speeds would normally have to bank at steeper angles if they wanted to make a standard rate turn. This is why it's recommended that pilots not exceed 30 degrees of bank under IFR conditions.

Three Ring Laser Gyro

To provide pitch and bank information an attitude and heading reference system (AHRS) typically uses three laser gyros, one for each airplane axis. Computer assessment of all these three gyros (along with other components of the AHRS) provides the basic heading and attitude reference along with present position, groundspeed, drift angle and attitude rate information. The onboard computer begins assessing this information once it has been initialized by determining the initial vertical position and heading.

The ring laser gyro uses laser light to measure angular rotation. Each gyro (one for each airplane axis) is a triangular-shaped, helium-neon laser that produces two light beams, one traveling in the clockwise direction and one in the counterclock-

Courtesy of JAXA

Inside The 3-Ring Laser Gyro

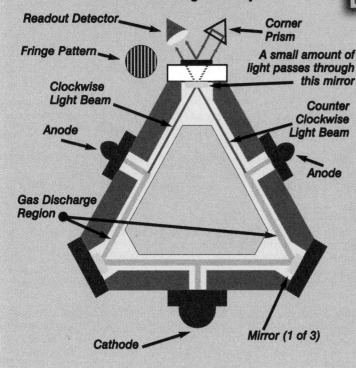

Readout Detector

Corner Prism

Fringe Pattern

A small amount of light passes through this mirror

Clockwise Light Beam

Counter Clockwise Light Beam

Anode

Anode

Gas Discharge Region

Cathode

Mirror (1 of 3)

wise direction. Production of the light beams, or lasing, occurs in the gas discharge region by ionizing a low pressure mixture of helium-neon gas with high voltage to produce a glow discharge. Light produced from the lasing is reflected around the triangle by mirrors at each corner of the triangle to produce the clockwise and counterclockwise light beams.

When the laser gyro is at rest, the frequencies of the two opposite traveling laser beams are equal. When the laser gyro is rotated about an axis perpendicular to the gyro unit, a frequency difference between the two laser beams results. The frequency difference is created because the speed of light is constant. One laser beam will thus have a greater apparent distance to travel than the other laser beam in completing one pass around the cavity.

As a small amount of laser light from the two lasers passes through the mirror at the top of the diagram. Both light beams are now combined. If movement of the gyro has changed the frequency of the laser light, then the combined beams will produce a fringe or interference pattern. This is a pattern of alternate dark and light stripes. The onboard computer's analysis of this fringe pattern provides pitch and bank information to the airplane's instrument systems.

Assume your heading indicator failed and you had to make turns using only the compass (this topic is coming up next). Since the compass has its own special errors, it can be difficult to read while turning. Making standard rate turns helps you project when you'll be on the desired heading without having to be a master at compass error interpretation.

For instance, suppose you're on a heading of 300 degrees and need to turn to 360 degrees. That's a 60 degree difference in heading. At 3° of turn per second (a standard rate turn is assumed) you'll need to turn for 20 seconds. Start the turn, time it and roll out after 20 seconds. You'll be on a heading of north and won't need to look at the compass to know when to roll out. Which, by the way, is a good thing since the compass' turning error is quite noticeable on this heading. The turn coordinator is a welcome ally in the event of gyro failure in IMC.

As a preflight check, make sure the needle on either the turn coordinator deflects when a heading change is made. The ball should also move to the outside of the turn when taxiing (no, you're not expected to keep the ball centered when taxiing; no one is that coordinated). Most turn coordinators have small red warning flags that show when power to the instrument is lost. You'll want to occasionally include this in your scan of ancillary items when flying IFR. Also, because the turn coordinator is normally electrically powered, any intentional shutdown of the electrical system in flight (perhaps due to an electrical fire) renders this instrument inoperative.

As a final note, if you ever had to make the steepest turn possible using only the turn coordinator for bank information, do it this way. Begin a coordinated turn and let the turn needle rotate until it hits its stop limit. Now back off on the bank just enough to make the needle move away from its stop limit. Vary the bank to keep the needle tapping against its stopping limit. Of course, I'm hoping that you never need to make a steep turn under IMC in partial panel conditions. No one deserves to have their heart valves flap this much.

The Magnetic Compass

The magical mystery tour is almost over, but the last is far from the least as we turn our attention to one of aviation's oldest, simplest, and most low-tech instruments—the magnetic compass.

In a world of ever fancier (and more expensive) gadgets, the mag compass holds its own. It requires little to keep it going, and while it has its quirks, in the final analysis it always points the way.

The story goes like this. The gruff older captain of an ocean-going ship was never one to back down from any challenge. One stormy night he spotted what appeared to be the lights of another ship heading in his direction. He ordered the signalman to send the following message: "Change your course now." He received the following reply: "No, you change your course now." Angered by the response, the captain replied, "Hey pal, you change your course. I'm the captain of a big ship." The reply, not long in coming, was, "Hey pal, I'm a lighthouse." Now that's what we call affecting an action at a distance.

The magnetic compass (Figure 76) is similarly affected by something a long distance away. It responds to the natural phenomenon of the earth's magnetic pole, otherwise known as its *magnetic field*. This field is constantly pulling one end of the compass' needle, keeping it pointing north (Figure 77). Despite some peculiar errors in the compass, it is one of the oldest and most reliable navigational instruments known to man (next to moss, which grows on the north side of trees. Of course, this doesn't explain why all four corners of my shower point north). Let's take a look at how the compass works and examine a few of its inherent errors.

Looking inside the magnetic compass (Figure 78) you'll see a small magnetic needle connected to a circular compass card. Both the card and the needle are free to rotate on a central pivot (Figure 79). One side of the needle is called the *north-seeking end* (the dark-colored side in all my drawings) and it always points toward the earth's magnetic north pole. Thus, like a gyro fixed in space, the needle

Magnetic Compass

Fig. 76

The Magnetic Compass Needle

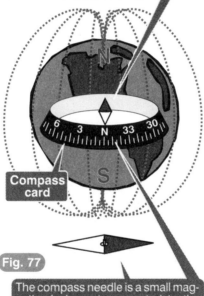

The north-seeking end of the compass needle always points toward the magnetic north pole.

Compass card

Fig. 77

The compass needle is a small magnetized element connected to the compass card and resting on a pivot allowing it to rotate within the compass housing.

Vertical Magnetic Compass

The vertical magnetic compass is a totally new concept. Unlike the wet compass shown in Figure 76, this one is a dry compass. It has no internal liquids and contains only gimbals, gears and a magnet.

Inside the vertical compass you'll find a square magnet with a gear attached to it. The entire piece is suspended on a gimbal. A second gear is connected to the first and is attached to a shaft that turns the vertical compass card.

Unlike the wet compass, the vertical compass has the advantage of not being affected by the typical lead and lag errors associated with use of the wet compass. Nor does it have the problem of springing a leak at inopportune times (which is every time when flying IFR or VFR).

This compass also has the advantage of looking like a directional gyro. It is much easier to use for navigation than the standard horizontally-fixed wet compass.

Like the wet compass, the vertical compass requires no power (except for internal lighting).

The Insides of a Magnetic Compass

Fig. 78

Compass Needle

Courtesy Bob Crystal

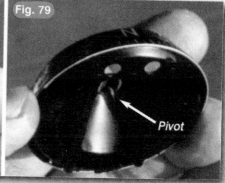

Fig. 79

Pivot

attempts to remain stationary. As the airplane changes direction, it rotates around the needle and its attached card, resulting in new headings appearing in the compass' window, as shown in Figure 80 (and all this time you've been thinking that the compass card actually does the rotating. That's OK. A lot of people still think that the Iron Age was a time when people wore neatly pressed clothing). The airplane's actual heading is read under a reference line (the *lubber line*) running down the center of the window.

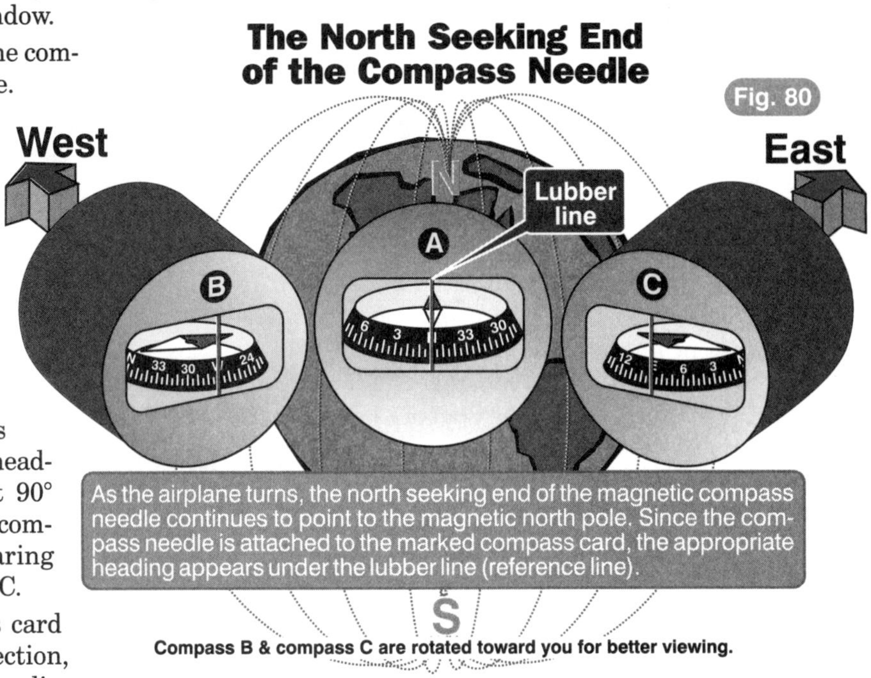

The North Seeking End of the Compass Needle

West   **East**

Fig. 80

Lubber line

As the airplane turns, the north seeking end of the magnetic compass needle continues to point to the magnetic north pole. Since the compass needle is attached to the marked compass card, the appropriate heading appears under the lubber line (reference line).

Compass B & compass C are rotated toward you for better viewing.

Take notice that the numbers printed on the compass card appear to be in the wrong place. Don't worry, they've had this figured out now for several centuries. In Figure 80, Compass A is heading north, yet westerly headings are shown on the right side of its card (i.e., 320°, 300° and W or 270° which is not visible yet). Easterly headings are shown on the left side of its card (i.e., 030°, 060° and E or 090° which is also not yet visible). This makes sense when you consider that as the airplane turns left, toward the west, it pivots about the compass card as shown by Compass B. Eventually, westerly headings appear under the lubber line. A right 90° turn causes the airplane to pivot about the compass card, with easterly headings appearing under the lubber line as shown by Compass C.

Flying a desired heading on the compass card requires you to turn in the opposite direction, which centers the heading under the lubber line. For instance, if the heading you seek to fly is visible to the right of the lubber line, turn to the left to center its value (now you know why the heading indicator is so useful when flying IFR!). An easy way to remember this is to think of using the sides of the compass to scoop or pull the desired heading toward the lubber line. If I'm flying heading 270 degrees (compass B) and want to turn to 300 degrees, I'll see the 300 value to the left of the 270 value. Therefore, I'll make a right turn as I think of using the left side of the compass to pull the 300 heading value to the lubber line.

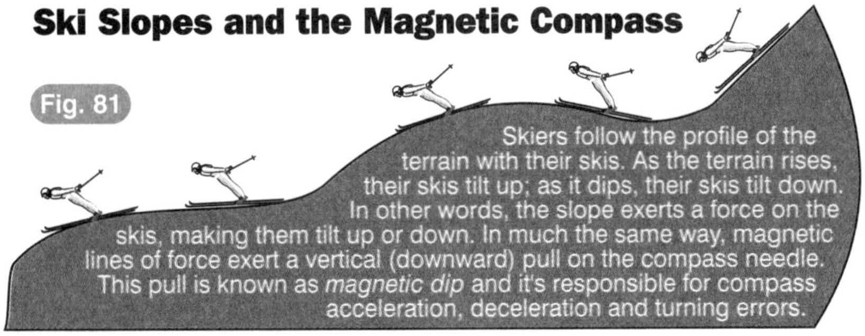

Ski Slopes and the Magnetic Compass

Fig. 81

Skiers follow the profile of the terrain with their skis. As the terrain rises, their skis tilt up; as it dips, their skis tilt down. In other words, the slope exerts a force on the skis, making them tilt up or down. In much the same way, magnetic lines of force exert a vertical (downward) pull on the compass needle. This pull is known as *magnetic dip* and it's responsible for compass acceleration, deceleration and turning errors.

Understanding how the compass works is easier when we think of comparing a compass needle with skis. Skis are similar to compass needles in how they respond to

changing terrain. In Figure 81, notice that as the terrain dips, so do the skis. If the terrain slopes upward, the skis slope upward. If the terrain dips downward, the skis dip downward. The magnetic compass needle is like a ski and the earth's magnetic field is like the snowy terrain. The compass needle will always try to dip to follow the direction of the magnetic field.

The earth's magnetic field is shown in Figure 82. Notice that the field dips downward at nearly a 90° angle at the poles, while there is very little dip in the equatorial regions. For most of the United States, the downward dip angle is around 70°. Just like skis following dipping terrain, the magnetic compass needle wants to tilt downward with the magnetic field. This is called *magnetic dip,* and is the only kind of dip pilots serve at parties.

It's also a serious problem for the magnetic compass. Unrestrained, this dip could render the compass unusable as a navigational device, since the card could get hung up on its pivot or in its container.

Magnetic Dip

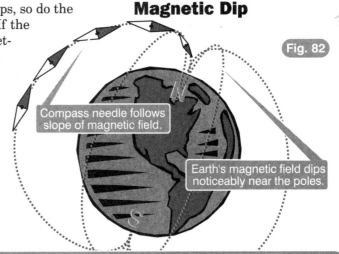

Fig. 82

Compass needle follows slope of magnetic field.

Earth's magnetic field dips noticeably near the poles.

The magnetic compass needle, like skis, follows the slope of the Earth's magnetic field. Where the slope dips downward (near the poles), the compass needle also dips. This phenomena is known as magnetic dip.

The Remote Indicating Compass (RIC)

Some ideas should never be put into practical use. For instance, we now have an automobile car alarm that beeps you when your car is being burgled? Yep. Not only will you lose your car, you might also get beat up by the thugs doing the stealing. Brilliant, eh? There is one idea, however, that was too good not to put into practical use. That's called the *remote indicating compass* (*RIC*).

The remote indicating compass is essentially a heading indicator that automatically aligns itself to the proper magnetic direction without the pilot getting involved in the process. The RIC consists of two panel mounted components and two remotely located components (thus the genesis of the word remote in RIC). One of the common panel mounted components is the horizontal situation indicator or HSI (or other PNI-*pictorial navigation indicator*) as shown in Figure 83. The other component is a slaving meter/compensator unit (Figure 84).

Fig. 83

One of the two remotely located components is the magnetic flux detector (flux valve) which is located somewhere on the airframe (usually a wing tip) away from sources of magnetic interference (Figure 85). The other component is an electrically powered directional gyro unit remotely located on the airframe, too. Here's how the device works.

Fig. 84

SLAVE IN

First, a flux valve senses magnetic direction by detecting the earth's lines of magnetic force in its spokes as shown in Figure 86. Changing headings results in a change in the concentration of these lines of force throughout the individual spokes, which provides the means of sensing direction.

Electrical signals from the flux valve are then sent to a small electric motor in the remotely located directional gyro, which alters the position of (precesses) that gyro (no, there's no gyro in the HSIs found in most airplanes). As a result, the remotely located directional gyro is kept aligned to the airplane's current magnetic heading. The information from the remotely located directional gyro and flux valve is then sent to the HSI. Small motors in the HSI unit turn its vertical compass card to provide the airplane's correct magnetic heading. This process is called *slaving*, and it's what's being referred to when someone speaks of a *slaved gyro* (and no, you don't need to try and free all the world's slaved gyros, either).

Fig. 85

Magnetic Flux Detector

The slaving meter tells you when there's a difference between the airplane's actual magnetic heading and the heading displayed on the heading indicator. When the heading indicator in the RIC is in slaved mode, (i.e., the *slave in* button is pushed), the slaving needle should be centered, indicating that no error is present. When turning, however, the needle will usually deflect right or left as this system's gyro automatically slaves in attempting to catch up with the airplane's actual heading.

In the *slave in* mode, it's possible to have an error between the airplane's actual heading and the heading displayed on the HSI. If so, the slaving needle will deflect to the side of the heading pointer where the correct heading exists. A right needle deflection (a deflection to the + side) indicates that the correct heading is to the right of the indicated heading. A left needle deflection (a deflection to the - side) indicates that the correct heading is to the left of the indicated heading. To correct this error, you should push the *slave in* button and enter what is known as the *free gyro* mode. Now you should use the right or left compensator button as appropriate to center the slaving needle. At this point you should check the heading indication against the airplane's magnetic compass as a confirmation of the correct heading. You can now fly using the HSI's heading indicator in free gyro mode, but you should treat it just like a regular directional gyro and cross check its reading against the magnetic compass every 15 minutes or so and use the compensator buttons to correct for any heading drift. When you land you should have the RIC system checked for proper operation.

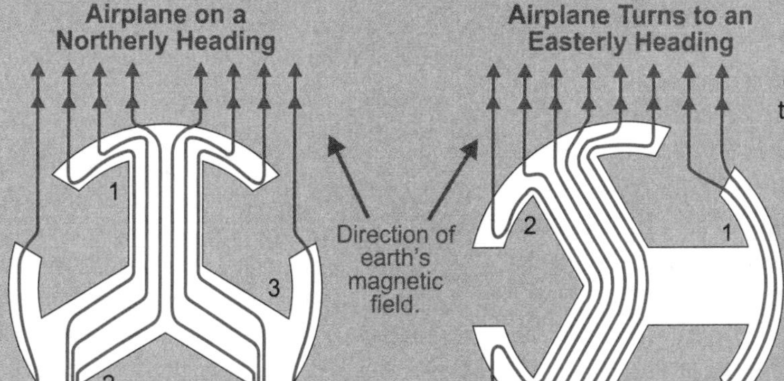

For example, suppose your heading indicator shows 200 degrees but the slaving meter needle shows a right deflection (a "+" side deflection). This means that the airplane's actual heading is somewhere to the right of 200 degrees (perhaps it's 210 degrees). To correct this problem, push the *slave in* and enter the *free gyro* mode. Now push the right compensator button until the slaving meter needle centers. Then check the heading in the HSI against the airplane's actual magnetic heading as shown on the magnetic compass.

If the slaving meter needle shows a *left* deflection (a "–" side deflection), enter the free gyro mode then depress the left compensator button until the slaving meter needle centers. The HSI's compass card will rotate to the right and indicate the airplane's actual magnetic heading. For example, the indicated heading may change from 310 degrees to 300 degrees (if the HSI's compass card rotates to the right or clockwise, then the indicated headings become smaller, don't they?).

Fig. 86

The RMI's Flux Valve

Airplane on a Northerly Heading

Airplane Turns to an Easterly Heading

Direction of earth's magnetic field.

Arm 1 - Largest voltage
Arm 2 - Voltage = to arm 3
Arm 3 - Voltage = to arm 2

Arm 1 - Smallest voltage
Arm 2 - Voltage = to arm 3
Arm 3 - Voltage = to arm 2

Magnetic Dip Correction

Instead of the simplified compass-needle drawing shown above, the compass actually has two needles, side-by-side with their north-seeking ends aligned. These needles are located on the bottom portion of the compass card and the entire card is suspended by a pivot. This gives the card a pendulous-type mounting (diagram below is also highly simplified for easy understanding).

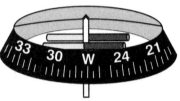

The earth's magnetic field tries to pull or "dip" the compass needles and the card downward as shown below. This would render the compass useless if it remained this way.

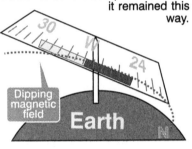

If the compass card is tilted as shown above, the card naturally tends to return to a near level position because of the "pendulum" effect. With the mass of the needles and additional items, the card remains nearly level despite magnetic dip as shown below.

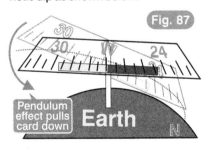

Fig. 87

Wait a minute! If the compass was originally called the *whisky compass* then it may still contain whisky. How will I know if I don't taste it. Wait another minute. I'm only 16 and can legally buy a compass, so it can't contain whisky. Hmmm.

Acceleration and Deceleration Errors
(on easterly & westerly headings)

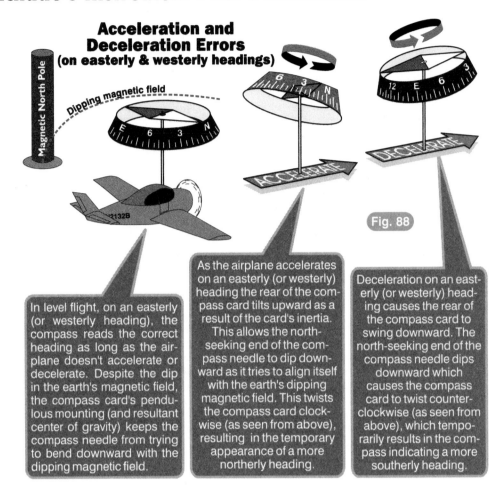

Fig. 88

In level flight, on an easterly (or westerly heading), the compass reads the correct heading as long as the airplane doesn't accelerate or decelerate. Despite the dip in the earth's magnetic field, the compass card's pendulous mounting (and resultant center of gravity) keeps the compass needle from trying to bend downward with the dipping magnetic field.

As the airplane accelerates on an easterly (or westerly) heading the rear of the compass card tilts upward as a result of the card's inertia. This allows the north-seeking end of the compass needle to dip downward as it tries to align itself with the earth's dipping magnetic field. This twists the compass card clockwise (as seen from above), resulting in the temporary appearance of a more northerly heading.

Deceleration on an easterly (or westerly) heading causes the rear of the compass card to swing downward. The north-seeking end of the compass needle dips downward which causes the compass card to twist counterclockwise (as seen from above), which temporarily results in the compass indicating a more southerly heading.

Fortunately, the compass has been cleverly designed in such a way that the compass card's pendulous mounting acts to counter this dip (Figure 87). As long as the compass card is allowed to hang parallel to the earth, it's not restricted by the dipping magnetic field. Therein lies the problem.

When the airplane accelerates or decelerates the free-swinging compass card's inertia resists the speed change. This causes the compass card to tilt within its case. What results is something known as the *acceleration-deceleration errors* which are experienced when flying easterly and westerly headings.

Whenever you make a turn, the compass card no longer hangs parallel to the earth's surface. Ordinarily, a turn won't affect the compass' reading unless the airplane is heading in a northerly or southerly direction at the time. If it is, the compass card will temporarily lead or lag behind the airplane's actual heading. These are called the *northerly turning errors (even in a southerly direction)*. Let's examine the acceleration and deceleration errors first.

Acceleration and Deceleration Error

Accelerating or decelerating on an easterly or westerly heading causes the compass to temporarily read in error. Accelerating causes the compass to give a more northerly heading than the one being flown. Decelerating causes the compass to read a more southerly heading than is actually being flown. An easy way to remember these errors is with the acronym, ANDS. This stands for: **A**ccelerate **N**orth, **D**ecelerate **S**outh.

Acceleration-deceleration errors occur because a speed change forces the compass card to tilt within its case (Figure 88). As the card is forced to tilt, its pendulous properties are no longer as effective in correcting for the earth's dipping magnetic field. The compass needle's north-seeking end points downward in the direction of the dipped magnetic field. This results in a temporary heading error while the speed change is in progress.

Turning Errors

Turning errors are experienced only on northerly or southerly headings. These errors are caused by a tilting compass card when the airplane banks in a turn. Now the pendulous properties of the card can't prevent the compass needle's north-seeking end from pointing downward in the direction of the dipped magnetic field. This results in the appearance of a temporary heading error.

As the airplane turns, for instance, from or through a northerly heading, the compass reading lags the airplane's heading (Figure 89). Airplane B is in a left turn and its heading is approximately 360°. Yet its compass shows a heading of 030°—lagging behind its actual direction. Airplane C is in a right turn and its heading is also nearly 360°. Its compass shows a heading of 330°, which is lagging behind its actual direction. As the airplane turns away from a northerly heading, these turning errors disappear and the airplane's correct heading appears under the lubber line. Airplane A has no turning error because it's not in a turn. Its compass reads correctly.

The turning error experienced on a southerly heading is shown in Figure 90. Heading directly south (Airplane A) with the wings level (the North Pole is on the bottom of this figure) produces the correct reading in the compass window. As the airplane turns from or through a southerly heading, the compass reading leads the airplane's actual heading. As Airplane C turns from or through a southerly heading, its compass reading also leads the airplane's actual heading. As a heading of east or west is approached, the turning errors disappear.

Northerly Turning Error

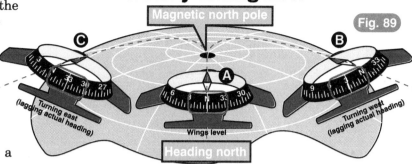

Fig. 89

As the airplane turns through or from a northerly heading, the compass needle (lying within the banked card) aligns itself with the earth's dipping magnetic field. This causes the card to twist, resulting in a heading that temporarily lags the airplane's actual heading.

Southerly Turning Error

While on a southerly heading, the magnetic field rises upward from below the airplane. When the airplane turns from or through this southerly heading, the compass needle twists to align itself with the earth's dipping magnetic field. Thus, the compass card shows a heading that temporarily leads the airplane's actual heading.

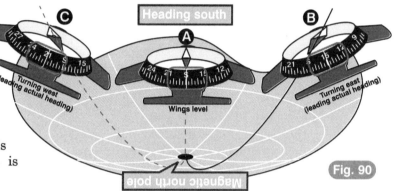

Fig. 90

Turning Errors as Seen in the Cockpit

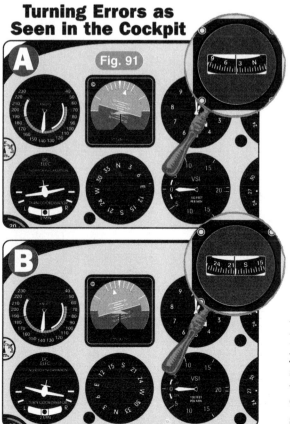

Fig. 91

A good memory aid to help you compensate for these turning errors is *OSUN* or *overshoot south, undershoot north*. When turning toward a heading of north from the east or west, you want to overshoot the northerly heading you want to roll out on by the approximate degrees of latitude in your present location. You'll also want to factor in the number of degrees you normally lead the turn for rollout.

For instance, suppose you're making a left turn to a heading of north with a 16 degree bank at a latitude of 30 degrees. On what heading should you begin your rollout to end up on a compass heading of north? Since this is a compass turn to a heading of north, you'll want to undershoot your rollout, meaning that you should start your rollout before the compass indicates a heading of north. If the latitude is 30 degrees and you're using 16 degrees of bank, you'll want to roll out when the compass indicates 030 + 8 degrees, or 38 degrees (Figure 91A). Remember, you want to undershoot north which means you add the bank-lag factor to the degrees of latitude.

Now, suppose you're making a right turn to the south at the same bank. On what heading should you begin your rollout to end up on a compass heading of south? Since this is a compass turn to a heading of south you'll want to overshoot your rollout, meaning that you should start your rollout after the compass passes a heading of south. In this instance, the latitude is 30 degrees and you'll subtract the 8 degrees of bank to give you a rollout lead of 22 degrees (Figure 91B). In this example you want to fly past the heading of south (overshoot) to a heading of 202 degrees before beginning the rollout.

As a final note, despite there being no turn errors on a heading of east or west, you may still experience them when you're not precisely on a specific heading of 090 or 270 degrees. So if you're turning to an easterly or westerly heading from a northerly direction, begin your rollout approximately 10–12 degrees before reaching the east or west heading. This compensates for a common 16 degree bank used in many turns as well as the slight compass lag factor. When turning to an easterly or westerly heading from a southerly direction, begin your rollout approximately 5 degrees before this east or west heading is reached. This is only an approximation, but it helps get you better established on the proper headings in these instances.

It's important to remember that compass errors are ultimately caused by the dip of the earth's magnetic field. If it weren't for this phenomenon, troublesome compass errors wouldn't exist. With all these errors, why do we have a compass in the airplane in the first place? Because it works. Basically, the compass has only one moving part (liquid not included), making it one of the most reliable pieces of equipment in the airplane next to the ashtray. It doesn't depend on electricity, gyroscopes, vacuum pumps, or anything else to work. Unless someone has sucked the liquid out of the unit, the magnetic compass will provide the most accurate heading information during straight and level, unaccelerated flight. If that's not convincing, just remember, it doesn't need batteries!

Regarding the heading indicator, you don't need to worry about turning errors or acceleration/deceleration errors. The heading indicator is gyro-stabilized and its accuracy isn't affected by turning or a change in speed. There is, however, one thing you need to be aware of. When initially setting the heading indicator to the value in the magnetic compass, make sure the airplane is in wings-level, unaccelerated flight (this is the only time you can be sure the compass value is reliable). This prevents flying an incorrect heading because the indicator was set incorrectly.

Of course, there's one additional thing called *compass deviation* that you should consider before setting your heading indicator to the magnetic compass before an IFR flight. The compass, while simple in its operation, can sometimes be a devious device, especially when electrical equipment is in use in the airplane. Here's why.

Some items in the airplane have a strong magnetic field that causes the compass needle to turn or deviate slightly, resulting in an error. If you think about it, the airplane has quite a few little things that can generate deviant magnetic fields, including radios, alternators and generators, motors, lights, tools, magnetized metal parts, and flight instructors with very large fillings (OK, just kidding).

To correct for these problems, mechanics place the airplane in the center of an airport's *compass rose* (a painting on the ground with verified, accurate directions) and point the nose in precise magnetic directions shown around the circle. The airplane's equipment is turned on to obtain the maximum amount of (and normally encoun-

tered) magnetic interference. The actual magnetic direction is measured against the compass' indications. This process is known as *swinging the compass*. To the extent possible, adjustments are made to the compass to eliminate the discrepancies. Any remaining deviation between the actual magnetic heading and the compass' heading is noted on a *compass deviation card* (Figure 92) mounted near the magnetic compass.

When setting the heading indicator, read the compass then check the compass deviation card for deviation on or near that heading. Apply the correction, then set the heading indicator to this value. For instance, suppose you're in the runup area and the compass shows a heading of east. According to the compass deviation card in Figure 93, the deviation is -4 degrees on this heading. So set your heading indicator to 86 degrees instead of 90 degrees.

And remember to check the compass during taxi to make sure it swings freely and appears to indicate the correct heading as well as ensuring that it's adequately filled with fluid. Learn to use the compass properly and you'll always have one backup instrument to keep you flying straight when the chips (like those from a just-disintegrated vacuum pump) are down.

That concludes our back-of-the-panel tour. You now know more about the instruments than the vast majority of instrument pilots, so it's time to move on and find out how to scan these instruments and control the airplane under IMC.

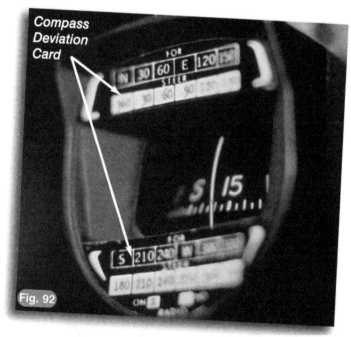

Fig. 92

Typical Compass Deviation Card

FOR (MAGNETIC)	N	30	60	E	120	150
STEER (COMPASS)	O	28	57	86	117	148
FOR (MAGNETIC)	S	210	240	W	300	330
STEER (COMPASS)	180	212	243	274	303	332

Fig. 93

Chapter 3
A Plan for the Scan

Like a teenage couple who can't wait to sneak a kiss, instrument pilots in training are often far too eager to get to what they think is the fun part—the instrument approach. Having rushed through learning the scan, these immature instrument lovers make something that should have been easy a lot more difficult than it is. Instant message—if your scan isn't solid, if you don't have confident and full control of the airplane, you are going to have a very hard time flying good approaches, holding an altitude, or doing any of the myriad other complex tasks involved in an instrument flight. What's worse is, you always *will* have difficulty until you correct the underlying problem. So don't let it be a problem to start with.

What you'll discover when beginning instrument training is that reading about the instrument scan is a far different experience than actually doing it. Doing it is much easier. But there *is* a method to the madness, and having at least some understanding of that method gives you a mental roadmap that will make the journey easier and more fun. That's why we're here.

Most of you won't get vertigo and topple off your chair while reading this section, but more than a few could experience various kinds of disorientation—physical and mental—while learning to scan the instruments. This is a case where, without a doubt, practice *does* make perfect. You must practice your scan frequently, relentlessly, and aggressively. Accept no substitutes for practice, because there aren't any. No, not even this book. Like a good book on yoga, the contents describe something very pleasurable, but if you want to feel the fun you have to go out and do it.

Here are a few tips that can help.

First, your instructor should spend time showing you that the airplane is flown the same way (uses the same control techniques) on instruments as it is in visual flight. This may seem unremarkable and obvious, but many students think they're learning how to fly all over again when they start instrument training. You are only learning a different way of getting the information that enables you to do *exactly* what you did before in terms of basic airplane control. After all, the cockpit instruments do nothing more than simulate what you can't see outside (Figure 1). A climb is still a climb, a turn is still a turn. You will, of course, be adding some new tricks, such as flying instrument approaches, but nothing has changed in terms of how you turn and bank, fly straight and level, or climb and descend.

Second, a little more time invested up front learning the basics of attitude instrument flying and a solid instrument scan will save you a *lot* of time, grief, and frustration later.

Training Frequency

DATE 19___	AIRCRAFT TYPE	AIRCRAFT IDENT	ROUTE OF FLIGHT		NR INST APP	REMARKS AND ENDORSEMENTS	NR LD
			FROM	TO			
2-13	BE-36	N2132B	KSNA	KSNA	1	Basic Instrument Scan Intro	
2-14	BE-36	N2132B	KSNA	KSNA	1	Bank Control Basics	
2-17	BE-36	N2132B	KSNA	KSNA	1	Pitch-Power Control Basics	
2-20	BE-36	N2132B	KSNA	KSNA	1	Charlie Pattern-Scan Basics	
2-21	BE-36	N2132B	KSNA	KSNA	1	Cnst. Rate/AS Climbs and Descents	
2-24	BE-36	N2132B	KSNA	KSNA	1	Partial Panel Flying Basics	

Fig. 2

It's not at all unusual for the first six instrument training lessons to be dedicated entirely to learning the basics of pitch, bank and power control.

When instrument training is done properly, it's not unusual to spend six flight hours of flight time (plus the necessary ground school time), learning nothing but pitch, bank, and power control (Figure 2). Sometimes it takes this amount of time to learn the basics of cross-checking and interpreting your instruments. That's fine. Think of it as an investment that will pay rich rewards for years to come.

Over the years, several innovative methods have been created to help instrument students develop their instrument scan. These mostly reflected the rise (and fall) of technology. One method, for example, involved placing a remote-controlled light over each instrument, mounted by way of a suction cup. The instructor would selectively push buttons on his or her remote box, illuminating a light and drawing the student's attention to the instrument he or she should have been paying attention to at that instant. It was an

Fig. 1

innovative idea that often sent students into near epileptic seizures as they tried following the flashing display. It also took the fun out of one major holiday in December for many of these unfortunate students. Though rarely seen in an airplane these days, the technique has been widely adopted by cell phone manufacturers, so at least some good came of it.

Another method involved the use of a device that was often the weapon of choice in science fiction movies—the laser (Figure 3). At some unfortunate moment in time, laser pointers became small and relatively inexpensive. Even college professors could afford them, not to mention flight instructors. Instructors would selectively illuminate an instrument with the evil eye of the red-beamed laser pointer, presumably focusing the students' undivided attention on that instrument.

Many students wound up seeing red, in part because the glass covering the instruments would often reflect the laser beam onto an innocent object, such as the ashtray. The untethered student brain dutifully added the butt bin to his or her scan. This never helped anyone fly the airplane better, even on Ash Wednesday. Fortunately, the lasers weren't powerful enough to burn a hole in a jacket or we'd have been creating smoking jackets to go with the ashtrays.

Surely there must be a more practical way to learn how to scan your flight instruments. Fortunately, there is.

It's a method of scanning that involves both of your eyeballs (unless you're a private "pirate" and wear a patch over one eye), operating under your sole control. No lights or ray guns are involved in the process, and it doesn't require batteries. I've used this method to teach instrument students for many years, with great success, and I'm pleased to offer it for your use.

Here's what we need to cover before you get the goodies on the scan. First we'll look at the three fundamental skills of attitude instrument flying (another name for flying by reference to your instruments). Then, we'll examine the *primary/supporting* concept of instrument scan. Once you have a grasp of these fundamentals I'll show you a nifty three-step method of using the primary/supporting concept of instrument scan. Master this three-step process and you'll definitely find the whole of instrument training a more enjoyable experience.

The Three Fundamental Skills of Attitude Instrument Flying

As you've probably guessed from the title above, there are three fundamentals to attitude instrument flying as shown in Figure 4. They are: *instrument cross-check*, *instrument interpretation* and *aircraft control*.

Let's discuss each of these in detail but keep the following point in mind. Even if you're training in an airplane with a PFD instead of the older mechanical-type flight instruments, the flight instruments are still flight instruments. They provide you with the same information despite being dressed up to look a little different. So while we talk about scanning mechanical gauges you should always keep in mind that this information applies to more advanced instrument displays, too.

High Tech Methods to Learn Scanning

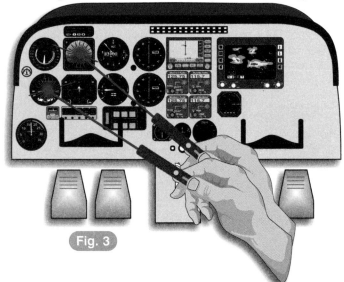

An Alert Controller's Alert

Glide slope information was in this B737 flight crew's backup plan, but not in their scan.

"We informed the controller that we should be able to fly a visual if we could get a turn toward the field. The controller gave a descent to 2,000 feet and a turn inbound to intercept the localizer. I immediately began to configure the aircraft while in a descending right turn to final. The Captain called the field in sight. I slightly overshot the localizer while looking for the field and the controller gave us a right turn to re-intercept. I saw a reddish-white light ahead which I thought was the visual approach slope indicator (VASI) for Runway 12L, but I could not see the runway lights. The controller asked us again if we had the field in sight and then advised that he was getting a low altitude warning on our flight path.... I quickly leveled off. We were at 1,000 feet, four miles from the airport. I then saw the runway lights and continued for an uneventful landing.

Lessons learned: Don't attempt to fly a visual approach unless the field is in sight.... Maintain the glideslope.

I was so fixated on configuring the aircraft, looking for the field, and maintaining the localizer course that I dropped the glideslope out of my cross-check...."

NASA Callback Report

1. Instrument Cross-Check

Contrary to popular belief, cross-checking is not something priests do before the Sunday sermon. Instrument cross-checking (also known as *scanning*) is officially defined as *the continuous and logical observation of instruments for attitude and performance information*. Sounds impressive, huh? It means that to fly an airplane on instruments, you must look at the appropriate instrument at the appropriate time. OK, all together now. DUH. Cross-check any other way and you'll double cross yourself.

Here's an important concept, so fasten your mental seatbelt. We cross-check instruments because no one instrument in the airplane has all the information we need. There, I've said

The Instrument Cross Check

I'll take one of these, two of those and four of the other. Thank you very much.

Fig. 5

it, and I feel better. Cross-checking reflects the messy reality that there is no magic instrument you can look at that tells all. These are mechanical instruments, not Hollywood gossip reporters. And even if there *were* such

an instrument, I wouldn't want you to be foolish enough to entrust your safety entirely to any one thing that can fail. You are always going to need the information from multiple instruments to know about and control what's going on with your airplane at any instant (Figure 5).

You're probably thinking, Can't I just check up on it once in a while? Sure. As long as the while is a few seconds. Airplanes are like puppy dogs. Be unvigilant for even an instant and Biscuit wanders away to wreak havoc. Even when properly trimmed, airplanes can wander from an established attitude. And not just toward fire hydrants, either. Little things like atmospheric turbulence and instrument error can make it difficult to keep an airplane in a constant attitude. Maybe cosmic rays and phases of the moon, too. Sometimes it seems the plane has a mind of its own and one that doesn't want to mind your mind.

Because information must come from multiple sources, and because that information must be refreshed constantly, gaining skill at cross-checking the instruments is central to early instrument training. It is your equivalent of learning to control the Force. As the immortal philosopher Yoda said, "Try not. Do, or do not. There is no try." And so it is with instrument flying. Cross-check. Do, or do not. There is no try.

Since there's no single instrument in your basic training airplane that gives you the information of all the instruments, you must learn to absorb and *interpret* information from each instrument. In the early

stages of your training, however, you'll have to overcome several natural tendencies that keep you from cross-checking properly. One of these is a tendency to fixate on an instrument.

An Early Warning Sign of Fixation

Fig. 6

This is known as the lookey-loo problem. Driving past the scene of an accident, you are intrigued by the chaos and destruction, not to mention the flashing lights and the fire engines that look just like the model you put together when you were eight years old. You stare, you ogle, and before you know it, you rear-end the car ahead of you. This is known as an unlucky lookey.

In instrument flying, fixation occurs when you stare at a particular instrument to the exclusion of other instruments (Figure 6). You won't typically do this because one instrument is prettier than the others. You'll probably do it out of a misplaced attempt to make the instrument obey your mighty and powerful will. In this case, the Force isn't with you but you sure would like it to be. For example, if your altitude is off by a few hundred feet, you might focus on the altimeter to the exclusion the other instruments. The result? Your airplane wanders away from the desired attitude and performance condition. With one exception we'll chat about later, *Fixation* and *scan* are polar (and sometimes tropical) opposites. If you are doing one, you can't be doing the other at the same time. Try not. Do, or do not. Fixate or scan.

Another kind of fixation happens when you scan an instrument that doesn't need scanning. For instance, suppose you want to make a 180 degree turn, and you initiate it by rolling into a standard rate turn to the right. It will take approximately one minute to make this turn (at 3 degrees/second, it takes 60 seconds to make a 180 degree turn). If you included the heading indicator in your scan for the first 50 seconds of your turn, this would be considered a form of fixation. After all, why look at it after you've begun the turn when it doesn't provide you with any information that's useful or actionable? If you answered, "Because it's pretty," consider art lessons instead of flying lessons.

Another problem you might have during the instrument cross-check is instrument *omission* (Figure 7). This does not mean you left the altimeter on the runway, either. Suppose you roll out of a 180 degree turn using your attitude indicator. If you don't know that there could be a slight precession error present, you would be likely to omit either the heading indicator or the altimeter from your scan. Doing so could allow the airplane to wander away (possibly toward a fire hydrant like that puppy).

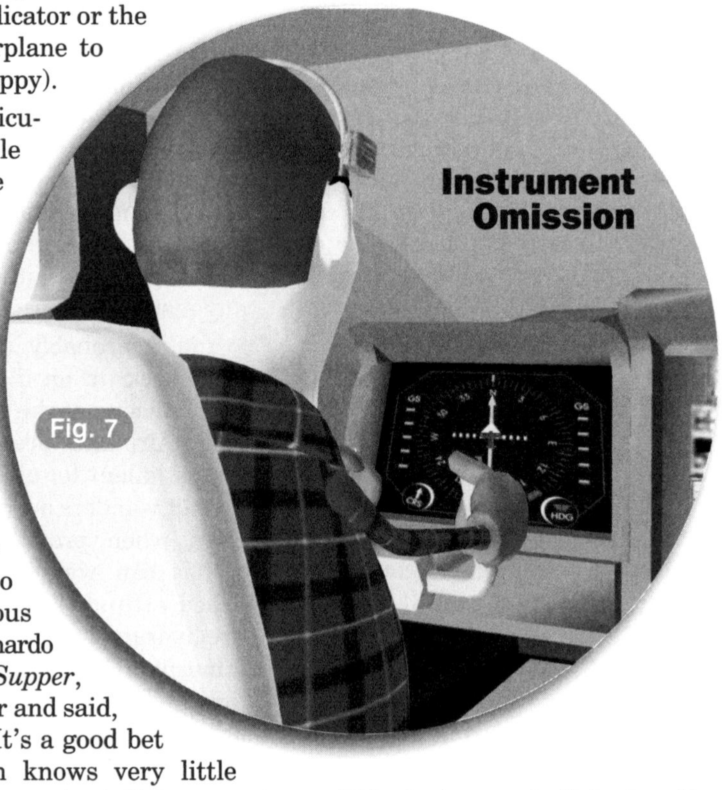

It's also possible to place too much emphasis on a particular instrument during your instrument cross-check. While you can hold a heading for quite a while just by using the attitude indicator, you should still include the heading indicator in your scan. While the attitude indicator allows you to keep the wings level, it doesn't give you precise heading information.

2. Instrument Interpretation

So far, we're talking about how to acquire raw information. It's all just naked numbers until processed by your brain into something that (we hope) makes sense. Learning to interpret your instruments is the second fundamental skill of attitude instrument flying.

Instrument Omission

Fig. 7

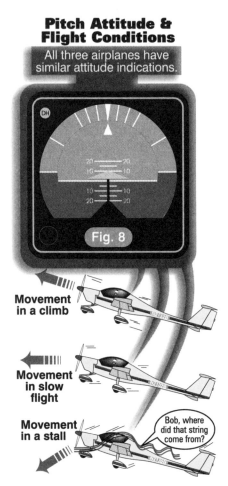

Pitch Attitude & Flight Conditions

All three airplanes have similar attitude indications.

Fig. 8

Movement in a climb

Movement in slow flight

Movement in a stall

Bob, where did that string come from?

Have you ever met someone who looked at a famous painting, like Leonardo da Vinci's *Last Supper*, pointed his finger and said, "Dat bootiful"? It's a good bet that this person knows very little about how to interpret art. It happens to would-be instrument pilots, too. For some, the pretty numbers never quite add up to anything meaningful. Instrument flying is about thinking. You must constantly analyze the incoming information, make sense of nonsense and know how to interpret the data using every resource at your command.

Ask some pilots what it means if you look at the attitude indicator and see a ten-degree nose-up pitch, and they'll immediately and confidently tell you the airplane is climbing. Maybe. Maybe not (Figure 8). It could also be operating on the back side of the power curve and descending! Interpretation requires that all the appropriate instruments be considered when evaluating airplane performance. You'd need to consider information from the airspeed indicator, the altimeter, the vertical speed indicator, and the power instruments (RPM or manifold pressure) to really know what this pitch attitude means. Information always requires interpretation in instrument flying.

Instrument interpretation is similar to art interpretation in that you get better at it with practice (you don't, however, get to say things like, *ooh, wow, I like it, dat purdy* and *golly*, unless you really want to, of course). After your first few hours of instrument training, you'll start to see attitude and performance relationships emerge. You'll learn what performance to expect from different combinations of instrument indications. These patterns will become an indispensable part of your IFR education.

The Primary Flight Display (PFD) and the Instrument Scan

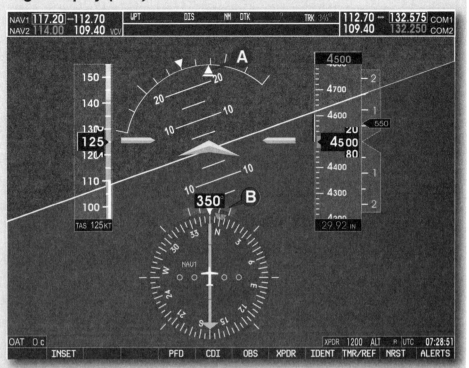

One of the big questions asked by pilots flying airplanes with primary flight displays concerns the difference between scanning this instrument and scanning a panel with the traditional round-dial instruments. While PFD instruments provide the same information found on round-dial panels, there is one small difference to be noted.

Considering the three fundamental skills of attitude flying, the first and third skills (*instrument cross check* and *airplane control*) are exactly the same when using a PFD. The second skill, *instrument interpretation*, is slightly different. That's because instead of using an analog-type instrument with a pivoting pointer(s) on the airspeed indicator and altimeter, the PFD uses a digital tape display. Reading a digital display of airspeed and altitude is similar to the difference between a watch with moving hands and one with a digital readout. Number values and their positions relative to the center of the instrument display are part of the interpretation process in determining your airspeed and altitude.

Courtesy Garmin

Trend lines (shown as magenta lines next to the airspeed and altimeter tape) help you in anticipating or maintaining your airspeed and altitude in much the same way the rate of mechanical hand movement once did on round-dial flight instruments.

The only other significant difference between primary flight displays and round-dial instruments is the lack of a traditional turn coordinator on a PFD. Traditional turn coordinators include both an inclinometer and rate indicator. Most PFDs don't have a single instrument display that shows both rate of turn and turn coordination. Instead, turn coordination is shown just below the attitude indicator's sky pointer (position A). Your rate of turn in degrees per second is directly above the heading indicator as a magenta rate line in the instrument above (position B). Two white lines provide a reference for a half-standard rate turn and a full standard rate turn.

Making a standard rate turn is done by rolling into a 20 degree bank on the attitude indicator (a bank that approximately produces a standard rate turn at common cruise speeds), then adjusting that bank until the magenta rate line reaches the standard rate index. Therefore, if any portion of a scan requires you to look specifically at the turn coordinator, you'd look at the magenta rate line (position B) for this information then glance at the inclinometer below the sky pointer (position A) as necessary.

Of course, if you're asked to scan your engine instruments, you'll most likely have to look at the multi-function display to find them (position C).

Other than the difference in how turn coordination and rate is presented, there is no other significant difference in terms of instrument scan between a PFD and round-dial instruments. You simply cross check the necessary instrument, interpret it then use that information to control the airplane. In this chapter I'll discuss instrument scan using round-dial instruments since the pictures of specific instruments makes it easier to convey the basic principles of instrument flight.

Finally, keep in mind that PFDs can provide much more information on their display than a typical round-dial panel. In particular, identifying instrument failures is much easier on a PFD because the warning flags are impossible to miss (position D).

Courtesy Garmin

3. Aircraft (Airplane) Control

Aircraft control is the third fundamental of attitude instrument flying. You can have the best cross-check on the planet and superior knowledge of instrument interpretation, but you've got nada if you can't use these skills to control the airplane. Aircraft control is why you are acquiring and interpreting information.

Controlling an airplane is a matter of selecting a specific attitude and power condition for the performance you desire at any given moment. Since an airplane's attitude consists of both pitch and bank, all major changes of attitude involve pitch, bank, and power control (Figure 9).

Pitch control is achieved by manipulating the elevators to rotate the airplane about its lateral axis. The following are the pitch instruments you're likely to use (I've left out the ashtray, in case your instructor doesn't use a laser):

Attitude indicator (AI)

Altimeter (ALT)

Airspeed indicator (ASI)

Vertical speed indicator (VSI)

The attitude indicator is a pitch instrument because it shows the angle the airplane's nose makes with the horizon. When the airplane pitches up or down, this usually results in a change in indication on the altimeter, airspeed indicator and vertical speed indicator. Interpreted correctly, changes on any or all of these instruments provide you with a good understanding of the airplane's present pitch attitude as well as how that attitude might be changing.

Bank control is achieved by changing the angle the wing makes with the horizon by use of the ailerons (accompanied by rudder to remain in coordinated flight). The following are the bank instruments you're likely to use:

Attitude indicator (AI)

Heading indicator (HI)

Turn coordinator (TC)

Magnetic compass

The attitude indicator is also a bank instrument because it shows the angle the wings make with the horizon. It might be less obvious that the heading indicator is also a bank instrument. Why? Because banking an airplane usually results in a change of heading (coordinated turns assumed here, of course). A change of heading provides you with an indirect indication that the airplane is banking. The same can be said for the magnetic compass. The turn coordinator can also provide an indirect indication that the airplane is rolling into a bank or changing headings as a result of a bank.

Power control is accomplished by using one or more of the following instruments:

Tachometer (RPM)

Manifold pressure (MP)

Airspeed indicator (ASI)

Sure, it seems obvious that the RPM (tachometer) or MP gauge is a power instrument. There are times, however, when the airspeed indicator will be the best instrument to use as an indication of engine power. Straight and level flight is a good example of this. If you want to fly straight and level at a specific airspeed, you don't care what the tachometer or MP gauge reads (as long as they aren't redline). You care only that the throttle is moved until the airspeed indicator displays the right value. In this instance, you focus on the airspeed indicator to know how much power to apply, not the tachometer (RPM). There are a few other conditions where the airspeed indicator becomes a power instrument, and I'll cover these later.

The Way of the Scan

Now that you have a basic understanding of attitude instrument flying's fundamentals, let's take a look at some concepts of how to scan your flight instruments.

Fig. 9

Much ink and some blood has been spilled arguing over Over time, instructors have settled on a couple of general approaches that differ slightly in their emphasis, with one generally being more applicable for general aviation pilots and the other for those flying bigger airplanes. These approaches differ in the emphasis each places on particular instruments in various phases of flight.

Let's first examine *the control and performance concept* of instrument scan. It's very important that you have an idea why high performance airplane pilots, those heavy metal captains, often find this method of instrument scan quite valuable. Then we'll focus on one of the most useful and practical approaches to scanning instruments known as *the primary/supporting method*.

Control and Performance Concept

The control and performance concept of instrument scanning is often used by pilots flying high performance airplanes (although it's perfectly OK to use in smaller airplanes, too). This method involves thinking of airplane control as the result of *attitude and power equaling performance*. The method places a great deal of emphasis on the attitude indicator in selecting an appropriate attitude to achieve a given performance. The reason this method is more suited to higher performance airplanes is that these aircraft typically have more sophisticated attitude indicators that permit finer, more precise pitch and bank adjustments. (Given the PFDs in today's sophisticated TAAs or technically advanced "GA" aircraft, you'll easily find the same level of instrument sophistication.)

The control and performance concept places all the flight instruments into three categories: *control* instruments, *performance* instruments and *navigation* instruments.

Before I discuss these categories, take a look at the scan sequence below. This gives you the big picture sequence for how a pilot would scan his or her instruments whenever he wanted to make a major attitude change (go from one flight condition to another, such as a climb to a descent, a turn to a climb, straight and level to a climbing turn, and so on).

Using the control and performance concept to make a major attitude change, a pilot would follow these steps:

Establish the attitude and power for a desired condition on the control instruments

Trim for hands-off flight (no, this isn't a form of showing off as in, "Look ma, no hands" flight).

Cross-check the performance instruments to ensure Step 1 is providing the desired performance, and

Adjust the attitude or power on the control instruments if necessary.

Keep in mind, the above sequence is used every time a pilot makes a major attitude change. Of course, you need to know what the control and performance instruments are, right? Figure 10 shows how these instruments are categorized.

Notice that there are only two control instruments, the power gauge(s) and the attitude indicator. You control the airplane by making a pitch or bank change solely by reference to the attitude indicator (can you see how important this instrument is?) The throttle is also moved as necessary and the power gauge (the tachometer [RPM] or manifold pressure [MP]) is observed.

Once the attitude and power conditions are selected, the airplane is trimmed to remove any flight control pressure (remember, we're building skills not muscles here).

Then the performance instruments are observed.

Of course, if your airplane has a highly accurate and finely calibrated attitude indicator, the performance instruments should indicate the values you'd expect for the chosen flight condition. In other words, if you selected a climb attitude straight ahead with climb power, the airspeed, altitude (or rate of climb in this case) and heading should be what you'd expect them to be. If they aren't, then detect any change on the appropriate

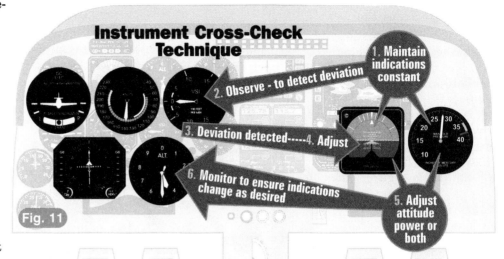

Fig. 11

performance instruments, return to the control instruments, make a slight adjustment in attitude and/or power, then monitor the performance instruments to see if this gives you the correct performance values. The process of scanning back and forth between control and performance instruments is repeated until everything is where it should be.

Realistically, 99% of the time when looking at the control instruments, you'll be watching the attitude indicator. It's not really necessary to spend much time at all looking at the RPM/MP gauge. So, when using the control and performance concept your scan should look something like that shown in Figure 11. Yes, the geometry of this scan method makes it appears that the attitude indicator is the center hub of a bicycle wheel, with the performance instruments making up its spokes.

The Primary/Supporting Method

The primary/supporting method of instrument scanning is widely used to teach instrument students in general aviation airplanes. Unlike the control and performance method, which derives its name from the fact that airplane performance is determined by attitude and power conditions, the primary/supporting method has you determining airplane performance in relation to *pitch*, *bank*, *power*, and *trim* control. The flight instruments are grouped by how they relate to these control functions and airplane performance. For purposes of this method, flight instruments are divided into two groups, primary instruments and supporting instruments (why do I think you could have guessed that?).

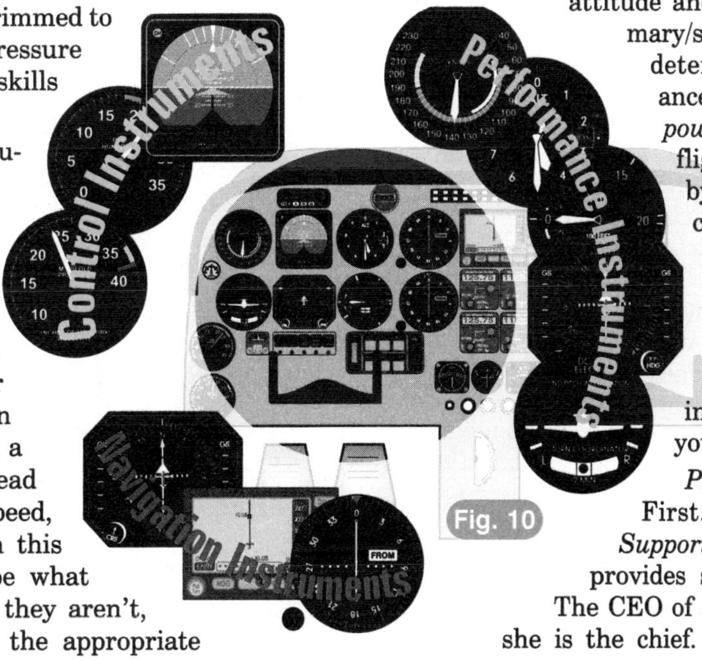

Primary means, well, primary. First. Primo. Most important. *Supporting* means everything that provides support for what's primary. The CEO of a company is primary. He or she is the chief. Others support (to varying

Fig. 10

degrees). The pilot-in-command is primary; the co-pilot and others are supporting.

In our previous discussion, you learned that controlling the airplane requires manipulating the plane's pitch, bank and power. Figure 12 identifies four pitch instruments, four bank instruments and three power instruments. In each category (pitch, bank, and power), *for any given condition of flight* there will be one and only one instrument that's primary. Easy, huh? All you have to do is figure out which one it is at any particular moment. Those that don't serve as primary instruments in a given situation become supporting instruments, by default (as a technical note, there are some instruments that don't provide any useful information in certain flight conditions. These instruments aren't considered supporting at that instant, and no, this does not include the flight instructor). The big question is, how can we tell which instruments are primary?

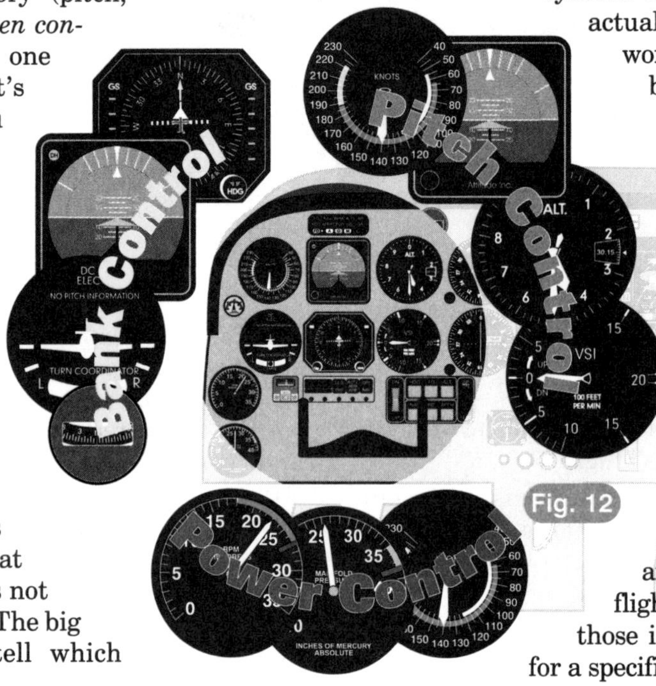

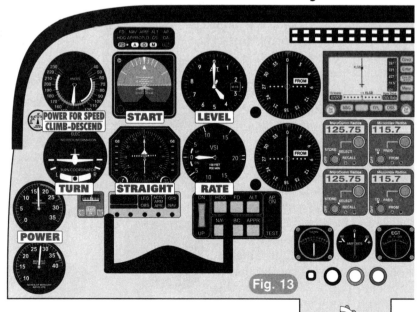

Fig. 12

Here's a little something that I devised a long time ago called the E-Z-2-USE Scan System to help students answer this question. Figure 13 is an instrument panel with flight instruments already labeled for you. It would be very wise to memorize this labeling scheme. It will be quite useful when you begin instrument training.

Consider this technique the McDonald's-menu method of instrument identification. At one time, a McDonald's employee ordered your food by looking for a button imprinted with a picture of the item you want. No muss, no fuss and no special skills—like reading—required, either. Of course, after you receive your meal you might say to the clerk, "Nice day," and he would look at his panel then reply, "Sorry, I don't see that button." No biggie. You were being nice and you still get your burger. Pilots, too, can get what they want (i.e., finding out which instruments are primary) by looking for the words that represent the various flight configurations. The instrument above each word is the primary instrument for that condition of flight. It shouldn't be too much of a jump for you to determine if an instrument is primary for pitch, bank or power.

Let's see how this works in practice.

If you want to maintain **straight-and-level flight**, look for the words STRAIGHT and LEVEL on the panel. In this flight condition, the altimeter (above the word LEVEL) is

primary for pitch and the heading indicator (above the word STRAIGHT) is primary for bank (I use the word *straight* as a synonym for *bank* since both terms refer to preventing the airplane from turning). The airspeed indicator (above the word POWER-FOR-SPEED) is primary for power. Yes, you read that correctly and no, your eyeballs don't need recapping. There are actually two instruments with the word POWER below them. That's because the airspeed indicator is primary for power when we want to maintain a constant airspeed (thus the name POWER-FOR-SPEED below it). The FAA assumes that, in level flight, you're always holding a specific airspeed. Otherwise, the RPM/MP gauge is primary for power (we'll discuss the power/airspeed relationship in greater detail later on).

What are the supporting instruments for pitch, bank, and power in straight-and-level flight? By referring to Figure 14 those instruments that aren't primary for a specific condition of flight become supporting instruments.

For our first example, the attitude indicator and vertical speed indicator are supporting *pitch* instruments; the attitude indicator and the turn coordinator are the supporting *bank* instruments and the RPM/MP gauge is the supporting *power* instrument. Figure 15 depicts the primary/supporting instruments for an airplane established in straight-and-level flight.

The E-Z-2-Use Scan System

Fig. 13

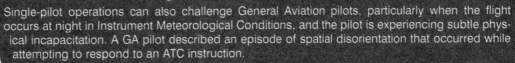

A Tight 360

Courtesy Microsoft

Single-pilot operations can also challenge General Aviation pilots, particularly when the flight occurs at night in Instrument Meteorological Conditions, and the pilot is experiencing subtle physical incapacitation. A GA pilot described an episode of spatial disorientation that occurred while attempting to respond to an ATC instruction.

[During] ILS approach at night in IMC, allowed the aircraft to reach a 60-degree bank before recovery in attempt to comply with ATC request for a "tight 360." Did not complete the 360° turn. After recovery from unusual attitude, rejoined localizer to airport, switched to local advisory service...all without properly canceling IFR clearance after entering VFR conditions.

The pilot listed contributing factors in the continuation to his report:

Pilot was fatigued after 6 hours of flight and attack of shingles (i.e., spinal/cranial nerve inflammation). Pilot should have refused ATC request for a "tight 360." (I question the wisdom of 360° turns at night during an ILS approach at any time.)

"Recovery was delayed by not being on critical instruments while attempting to get flight director to make the 360 and not lose positional awareness relative to ILS course."

"Recent experience not adequate for 360's at night in IMC."

The reporter had flown only a few hours in the last 90 days before the incident occurred. In hindsight, a safer response would have been to inform ATC, "Unable 360."

NASA Callback Report

Supporting Instruments for Straight and Level Flight

Fig. 14

Primary Instruments for Straight and Level Flight

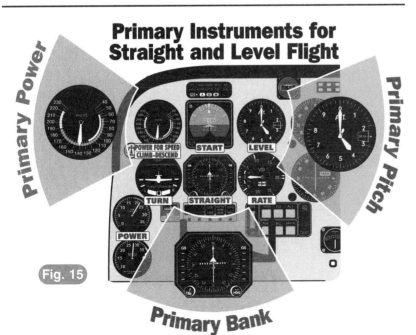

Fig. 15

Pilot Picassos

My friend and fellow flight instructor Tim Peterson shared a little secret with me about how he helps his students understand the airplane's panel. He has them draw it.

Yep, he sits them down in the pilot's seat, gives them a pencil and large pad and sets them to work replicating what they see.

Does this work? You bet it does, and here's why.

Have you ever had to walk through a portion of town that you've only driven through? If so, I'm sure you immediately realized how much you'd failed to notice. Anything we do that slows us down forces us to pay more attention to detail. Walking versus driving is a good example. Drawing what we see instead of just looking at something is another example.

When you try this with your students, they, too, will be amazed at what they didn't see. They may, for instance, notice the two diagonal white lines on the face of the attitude indicator. These are the 20 degree and 45 degree bank lines. They may also notice that most mixture control knobs have little spikes (thorns) on them. This is to remind you (by feel only) that the knob you're touching isn't the throttle nor does it control the carburetor heat.

Students may even discover that the airplane has an alternate static system (which isn't used to provide additional static to the radios, either). Oil pressure levels, cylinder head temperatures, maximum RPM limits and instrument locations are just a few of the many additional items that students will discover when they take the time to draw the entire panel.

The next time you have a student and an airplane sitting idle, give him or her a chance to learn something interesting about the airplane's instruments. You might even try this yourself. While your student's work may not end up in the Guggenheim Museum, it will certainly familiarize him or her with the intimate details of the airplane's panel.

Primary/Supporting Instruments

Fig. 16	Pitch	Bank	Power
Straight and Level Primary ⟶ Supporting	ALT ───── AI, VSI	HI ───── AI, TC	ASI ───── MP/RPM
Airspeed change in straight and level: Primary ⟶ Supporting	ALT ───── AI, VSI	HI ───── AI, TC	**MP** Primary to initiate airspeed change, supporting when established. **ASI** Initially supporting then primary once airspeed is established.
Entering a level turn (standard rate): Primary ⟶ Supporting	ALT ───── AI, VSI	AI ───── TC	ASI ───── MP/RPM
Stabilized in a turn (standard rate): Primary ⟶ Supporting	ALT ───── AI, VSI	TC ───── AI	ASI ───── MP/RPM
Airspeed change in a level turn: Primary ⟶ Supporting	ALT ───── AI, VSI	TC ───── AI	**MP** Primary to initiate airspeed change, supporting when established. **ASI** Initially supporting then primary once airspeed is established.
Transition from S&L to constant A/S climb: Primary ⟶ Supporting	AI ───── ASI, VSI	HI ───── AI, TC	MP ───── –
Straight constant airspeed climb: Primary ⟶ Supporting	ASI ───── AI, VSI	HI ───── AI, TC	MP ───── –
Entering a straight constant-rate climb: Primary ⟶ Supporting	AI ───── ASI, VSI	HI ───── AI, TC	MP ───── –
Straight, constant-rate stabilized climb/descent: Primary ⟶ Supporting	VSI ───── AI	HI ───── AI, TC	ASI ───── MP/RPM
Constant airspeed descending/climbing turn: Primary ⟶ Supporting	AS ───── AI, VSI	TC ───── AI, HI	MP ───── –

At this point I'm not interested in how you'd scan these instruments. I'm only interested in helping you determine which instruments are primary and supporting for a particular condition of flight. It's important to know which is which because the next phase of your training involves a three-step scan procedure whose second step involves identifying these primary instruments. To make things easier for you in this department, you can always refer to Figure 16, to help you understand the primary and supporting instruments for each condition of flight.

More Primary and Supporting Lessons

What are the primary and supporting instruments for maintaining a **level turn** (keep in mind that *level* as used in aviation means holding altitude)? Referring to Figure 17, look for the words LEVEL and TURN on the panel. The altimeter (above the word LEVEL) is primary for pitch, and the turn coordinator (above the word TURN) is primary for bank). The airspeed indicator (above the words POWER-FOR-SPEED) is primary for power since we're assuming that a constant airspeed is always maintained in level flight.

What are the supporting instruments for pitch, bank, and power in a level turn? Once again, those that aren't primary are supporting. The attitude indicator and vertical speed indicator are supporting pitch instruments; the attitude indicator is also a supporting bank instrument, and the RPM/MP gauge is a supporting power instrument if a specific airspeed is being maintained. These instruments are shown in Figure 17.

Primary/Supporting Instruments for a Level Turn

Fig. 17

This is getting easier, right? I hope so.

What are the primary and supporting instruments for a **straight climb**? Since the heading indicator is above the word STRAIGHT, it's primary for bank. The airspeed indicator is above the word CLIMB, so it's primary for pitch, and the RPM/MP gauge is primary for power in this instance (the airspeed indicator can't be primary for both pitch and power at the same time). The attitude and vertical speed indicators are supporting pitch instruments while the attitude indicator is also a supporting bank instrument. There is no supporting power instrument in this instance. These instruments are shown in Figure 18.

Primary/Supporting Instruments for a Straight Climb

Fig. 18

What are the primary and supporting instruments for a stabilized **constant rate descent**? This is the type of descent you're likely to use when flying a precision approach (one that has a glidepath). These approaches require a specific rate of descent for a particular groundspeed, as shown in Figure 19. In other words, to remain on a three degree glidepath, flown at a groundspeed of 120 knots, a descent rate of 637 feet per minute is required. Therefore, the vertical speed indicator is above the word RATE so it becomes the primary pitch instrument for a constant rate descent (and a constant rate climb, too). Since precision approaches are normally flown on a constant heading, the heading indicator is primary for bank. Precision approaches are also done at a constant airspeed (to ensure that a constant groundspeed is maintained), thus the airspeed indicator is primary for power. The attitude indicator is a supporting pitch instrument. Notice that the altimeter doesn't fit a supporting role as a pitch instrument in this type of descent. Why? Because it offers no information whatsoever that could help you maintain a specific rate of descent or climb (a subtle distinction, but worthy of notice). The attitude indicator and turn coordinator are supporting bank instruments, and the RPM/MP is a supporting power instrument.

Primary/Supporting Instruments for a Constant Rate Descent

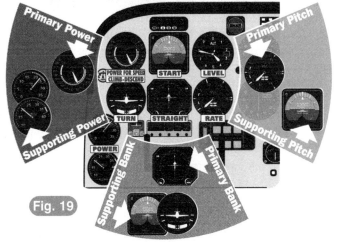

Fig. 19

Now it's time to nudge your noodle a bit. Suppose we wanted to **change airspeed** while we were in level flight or in a turn. Which instruments are primary and supporting in these two conditions?

The primary and supporting pitch and bank instruments don't change for either of these conditions, but the power instruments do (Figure 20). When changing airspeed, the RPM/MP gauge becomes temporarily significant, thus it becomes primary, with the airspeed indicator a supporting instrument. After all, we may look at the RPM/MP gauge as we set the power value (Figure 20, position A) used to give us the target airspeed (approach airspeed, for instance). Once the desired airspeed is reached, the airspeed indicator becomes primary for power and the RPM/MP gauge becomes a supporting power instrument (Figure 20, position B). As a general rule, any time the throttle is being moved to a specific setting, the RPM/MP gauge becomes the primary power instrument.

Primary/Supporting Power Instruments for Airspeed Change in Level Flight

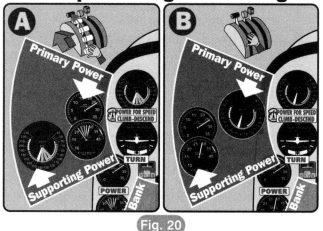

Fig. 20

What we haven't talked about yet is **transitioning between different attitudes**. This is where the attitude indicator plays a very big part in attitude instrument flying. As a general rule, whenever you're transitioning between attitudes (i.e., making a major attitude change), the attitude indicator becomes primary for either pitch and/or bank during the transition. This is why the word START is found under the attitude indicator. All major attitude changes should start with a look at this instrument. Major attitude changes include rolling into or out of a turn, pitching up or down to climb or descend, or any combination of these. All these attitude changes are initially made by focusing on the attitude indicator until the transition is complete. This is a very important point for you to understand.

For instance, if you're transitioning from straight and level flight to a constant-airspeed climb, the attitude indicator is the primary pitch instrument during the transition. The airspeed indicator and vertical speed indicator become the supporting pitch instruments as shown in Figure 21. Once you're *established* in the correct attitude, the airspeed indicator becomes primary for pitch and the

attitude indicator and vertical speed indicator become the supporting pitch instruments (as we've previously shown in Figure 18).

Here's another example. Suppose you're transitioning from straight and level flight into a level, standard rate turn at a specific airspeed. You'll enter the turn using the attitude indicator, so you'll start your scan there. During the transition, as you're rolling into the turn, the attitude indicator is primary for bank, the altimeter is primary for pitch, and the airspeed indicator is primary for power as shown in Figure 22. The turn coordinator is supporting for bank, the attitude indicator and vertical speed indicator are supporting for pitch, and the RPM/MP is supporting for power. Once the turn is established, the primary and supporting instruments are the same as those previously shown in Figure 17.

Of course, there are many subtleties that we'll cover regarding what to do in correcting for small altitude and heading variations. These aren't too important right now. I'm more interested in putting your knowledge of primary and supporting instruments to work in that three-step scan procedure I talked about earlier. We've put in a lot of effort figuring out how to decide which instruments are primary and secondary. Besides the fact that it's on the FAA knowledge exam, why do you care? Because this information is going to determine how you scan the instruments at any moment, and scanning the instruments if the core skill of instrument flying.

Instrument Scanning: Doing the Three-Step

All knowledge begins with definition. No, I didn't make that up. It sounds too good. Besides, it's true. Before I can show you how to scan instruments, I want to be sure you understand what I mean by the term *instrument scan*.

When I speak of instrument scan, I'm talking about how you will check the primary and supporting instruments, interpret them, then use them to ensure that the airplane is being controlled properly. All of this can be packaged into a three-step scan procedure that you'll use every time you make a **major attitude change**. These three-steps will now be officially called our *instrument scan procedure*.

Primary/Supporting Instruments Entering a Climb from S&L Flight

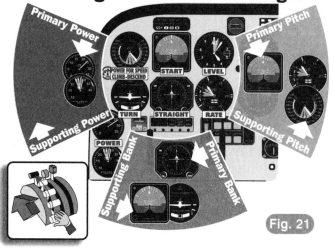

Fig. 21

Primary/Supporting Instruments Entering a Level Turn from S&L

Fig. 22

The Scan Starts with The AI

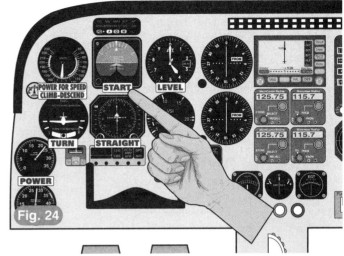

Fig. 24

Think about it this way. If you want to enter a climb, a descent, a turn, or any other maneuver that instrument pilots make, you'll simply run through the three steps that I'll give you. You *don't* need to memorize a specific scan pattern for each maneuver you want to accomplish. Imagine having to say to yourself, "OK, I'm going to enter a climb so what's the specific scan pattern required to do this?" or "I'm returning to straight and level flight from a climbing turn so what's the scan pattern for this maneuver?" This would be cruel, like using turtles for speed bumps. I wouldn't want to punish that three pound brain of yours with an exercise that requires as many scan patterns as there are basic flight maneuvers (and there are quite a few, too).

Instead, you only need to remember three steps along with the instrument labeling system I showed you in Figure 13. You'll do the three steps in order every time you

want to make a major attitude change (i.e., climb, descend, turn, enter a climb from a turn, enter straight and level flight from a climb and so on). All three steps together should take approximately 10 to 15 seconds to complete. Figure 23 shows the three steps and the order in which to do them.

I'll speak only of primary instruments in the three-step instrument scan procedure. Any pitch, bank or power instrument that isn't primary becomes a supporting pitch, bank, and power instrument by default.

Here's the big picture of the three steps in action:

Begin any major attitude change by placing the airplane in the new attitude, adjust the power and trim if necessary, all the while checking that no instrument has failed or is reading erroneously.

Radial cross-check the primary instruments, making small corrections on the attitude indicator if necessary.

Make a final trim adjustment, and then monitor all six flight instruments to maintain the new attitude.

The specific details and reasons for each of the three steps follow.

Step 1 of the Three-Step Scan

The first step in the three-step scan is to select the *attitude, power,* and *trim* conditions for the new flight attitude and confirm the correct operation of the attitude indicator. This first step is executed by focusing *solely* on the attitude indicator. That's why it's labeled START as shown in Figure 24 (hopefully, someone won't try and start the engine by tapping on this instrument). Select the attitude that your experience says will provide the flight conditions you're after. You don't have to be perfect, just reasonably close.

The big question here is whether it's reasonable to focus your attention on only the attitude indicator when changing attitudes. After all, the attitude indicator could fail and lead you astray (like scanning

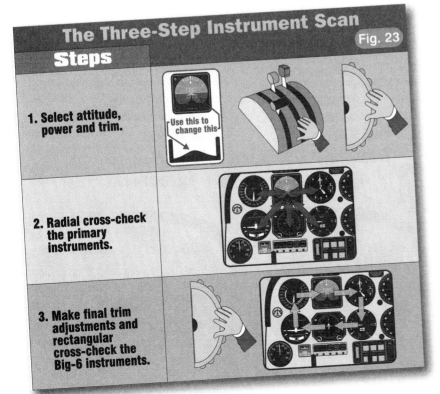

The Three-Step Instrument Scan Fig. 23
Steps

1. Select attitude, power and trim. | Use this to change this

2. Radial cross-check the primary instruments.

3. Make final trim adjustments and rectangular cross-check the Big-6 instruments.

that ashtray). Knowing how to identify and correct for this failure is the defensive countermeasure that balances the emphasis you'll place on this instrument.

In Step 1 of our scan, you *compare* and *validate* the results of control input to the response of the attitude indicator (Figure 25). If you detect or suspect any discrepancy between control input and attitude response, you

Control Deflection and Appropriate Instrument Response

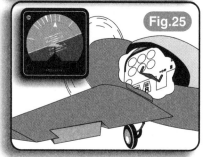

Fig.25

should immediately glance at the *inverted V* flight instruments (Figure 26) and do the inverted V cross-check. These instruments consist of the attitude indicator, the turn coordinator, and the vertical speed indicator. All three of these instruments operate on separate and independent power sources. They also provide you with separate sources of pitch and bank

The Inverted "V" Instruments

Fig. 26

Triangles of Agreement

Triangle of agreement is a fancy term for the common sense concept of cross-checking multiple, independently powered instruments that provide redundant information in order to quickly detect when something isn't working correctly. It's not to be confused with the Bermuda triangle, which is where instrument and even entire airplanes stop working correctly (and even disappear, so they say). In the aviation instance, the *turn* triangle of agreement (see picture below) consists of the attitude indicator, turn coordinator and magnetic compass. All three of these instruments respond to a turn. During a turn, all three of these instruments should reflect similar rates and directions of turn. If they don't, you will quickly and cleverly realize that your Titanic is in search of an iceberg. In other words, something's wrong with a flight instrument and you need to find out which one it is before you're sunk (or up to your neckline in trouble).

Letting common sense continue to rule, if two out of three instruments agree, the third is the leading failure candidate. If you suspect a failure of the attitude indicator, consult the other two instruments of the triangle, starting with the turn coordinator. If the turn coordinator does not reflect the attitude indicator's expected direction and rate of turn, the magnetic compass gets the deciding vote. Check it for movement. The instrument in disagreement with the other two is *it*.

On most modern day general aviation airplanes, the turn coordinator is electrically operated, the attitude indicator is vacuum powered, and the magnetic compass is Mother Nature powered. This is the aviation version of the Declaration of Independence. Each instrument is powered independently. That makes it highly unlikely any two (or all three) would fail at once due to a failure of the power source (if they did, you would want to stay away from Las Vegas, since it would be a sure sign you were running a tad low on luck). This independence is why these three instruments are nominated for membership in the turn triangle of agreement. Why isn't the heading indicator part of this triangle? The heading indicator, on many airplanes is vacuum powered. Since it operates on the same power system as the attitude indicator, a failure of the vacuum system would render both these instruments inoperative.

The pitch triangle of agreement (see picture below) consists of the attitude indicator, altimeter and alternate static system. The attitude indicator and the altimeter operate on separate power sources—vacuum and static pressure. Neither the airspeed indicator nor the vertical speed indicator should be used as the third instrument in the triangle, because both these instruments operate on the same static source as the altimeter.

If a pitch discrepancy exists between the attitude indicator and the altimeter, it is possible the static source is blocked. If it is, the VSI and airspeed indicator will also be in error. The appropriate action is to eliminate the altimeter as source of error. Simply activate the alternate static source and note any change in altimeter indication. If the altimeter 's indication doesn't change with the selection of the alternate static source, then the attitude indicator is in error. If the altimeter's indicator changes, then leave the alternate static source open. If the alternate static source is inside the cockpit there will be an initial but slight jump of the needle due to lower pressure.

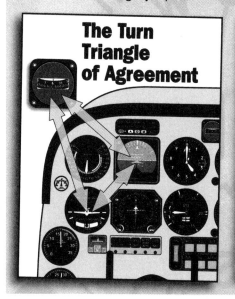

The Turn Triangle of Agreement

The Pitch Triangle of Agreement

information. If the turn coordinator and the attitude indicator show conflicting bank information, or the VSI and attitude indicator present conflicting pitch information, you know that the attitude indicator or one of these other two instruments is providing false information. Which one is it? To solve the problem you refer to something known as the *pitch triangle of agreement* if it's a pitch discrepancy, or the *turn triangle of agreement* if it's a turn discrepancy. Make sure you read the *Triangles of Agreement* sidebar to become familiar with these concepts.

When the initial attitude is selected (or is being selected), the power is adjusted for the flight condition you're seeking. For instance, when initiating a climb, the power is added *as* the nose is raised (or *after* the nose is established in the proper nose-up attitude; either way is acceptable). This sequence reflects the adage, *pitch plus power equals performance*. It's good form to select climb power *after* the nose begins coming up. This procedure virtually eliminates the chance of engine overspeed, which could occur if power is applied while the airplane is still in level flight.

When initiating a descent at cruise speed, power is *simultaneously* adjusted along with the attitude for the descent. The more closely simultaneous these two actions are, the less airspeed variance you will experience. If you selected a nose-down attitude and then reduced the power, you could acquire excess airspeed or overspeed the engine. This produces a whining sound, which comes from your instructor as he begs you to reduce the power more quickly the next time. You also run the risk of suddenly having a liquid cooled airplane if you have passengers aboard.

Since we've discussed why the attitude indicator is a primary instrument during major attitude changes, note that the same applies to the brief interval when power is being adjusted. As the power lever is moved, the RPM/MP gauge is primary. Once the power setting or the intended results of that power setting approach the desired value, the RPM/MP gauge becomes supporting for power.

Once an attitude is selected and power is adjusted, trim should be applied to keep the selected attitude constant. This initial *gross* application of trim should be just enough

to keep the airplane's attitude from wandering (I don't mean gross in the sense that someone contorts himself and wiggles all around when using the trim wheel, either). The final and more accurate application of trim is accomplished in Step 3. Give the trim wheel a couple of good turns as experience indicates, then go to Step 2.

Step 2 of the Scan

Step 2 directs you to radial cross-check the primary instruments. To radial cross-check means to start the scan at the attitude indicator, marked START, move to an instrument (a primary instrument in this step—remember that the primary instruments have been labeled for easy identification), extract information from it, return to the attitude indicator and make any correction in attitude, if necessary. This is called the radial cross-check because the visual scanning track is from the attitude indicator out to the primary instrument, then back to the attitude indicator, repeating this process as often as necessary to make the primary instrument read as it should. Radial cross-checking the panel instruments creates what appear to be spokes radiating from the attitude indicator to the other instruments, as shown in Figure 27. After we examine Step 3 of this scan, we'll take a closer look at examples

The Radial Cross-Check

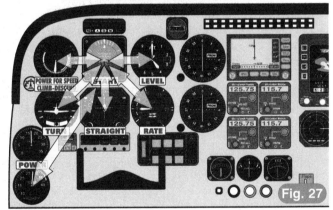

Fig. 27

of how to apply Step 2 in some of the most common attitude changes you'll make during instrument flying.

RADIAL CROSS-CHECKING: Pitch Then Bank, or Bank Then Pitch?

In Step 2 of the three-step scan, should you radial cross-check the primary pitch or the primary bank instrument first? My preference is to radial cross-check the primary pitch instruments first. Here's why. Most of the smaller airplanes we fly have good lateral stability. In other words, when they bank, they don't normally flip over and fall out of the sky. In fact, turns done at standard rate typically fall within the shallow bank limit. Within this limit, the airplane wants to return to level flight, not steepen its bank. Therefore, I'm not as worried about my airplane deviating from its heading nor increasing its bank if the bank instruments aren't scanned first.

I am concerned, however, that I may exceed my assigned altitude by 300 feet or more—the limit beyond which ATC squawks louder than your transponder. That's why the pitch instruments in my examples are radial cross-checked first, the bank instruments second, and the power instruments last. In other words, I scan the primary instruments from the top of the panel downward. Being 30 degrees off an assigned heading for a *very short* period of time doesn't normally ring bells and whistles in the radar center. Being off an assigned altitude by 300 feet or more gets you one of those calls you don't want, along the lines of "Cessna 9999K, exactly what *are* you doing?" That's ATC's way of saying everything is not OK. Power changes are the least critical and take the least time of all to correct.

Step 3 of the Scan

The last step in the three-step scan process is to make the final trim adjustments using the VSI and monitor the new aircraft attitude on the *BIG-6* instruments (Figure 28). Step 3 is accomplished after all the primary instruments have been radial cross-checked and are indicating the proper values.

The Big-6 Instruments.

Fig. 28

Elevator trim should be used first, followed by rudder trim (if available), followed by aileron trim (if available) last. For most small general aviation airplanes, elevator trim will usually be all that's available. To properly trim the airplane for pitch, I find it best to use the VSI. This instrument is very sensitive for *small* pitch changes and will indicate almost immediately the direction of movement. The VSI also has a large, noticeable needle swing that is visually easy to identify. When leveling off, or when established in a climb or descent, trim for a constant VSI indication.

A *gradual* easing of control pressure will reveal whether or not the airplane is properly trimmed. There is never any reason to completely let go of the controls when trimming, to see what the airplane will do. This will cause you more heartaches than it's worth, and if you have passengers it may cause heart attacks as well if you yell, "Look, no hands."

If the airplane is in fact far out of trim, just letting go of the controls leads to an immediate and substantial excur-sion from your assigned altitude. This is not one of those excursions that comes with a tour guide and a map, either. Not only do you run the risk of ATC yelling at you, but you've just doubled your workload, because now you have to return to the previous flight condition before you can even begin retrimming.

Let's make it easy by taking it easy. Ease up just a bit on the control pressure, take a quick peek at the VSI needle, and make any needed change in the trim. Repeat as needed. Very small adjustments in trim are easily made without having to recapture a runaway airplane. Another valid reason to hold on while trimming is turbulence. In turbulent air, you can still apply aileron control while trimming for pitch.

Once the airplane is properly trimmed, use the rudders to control the direction of the aircraft if your hands are needed elsewhere (not to strap on your parachute, either). Yep! In this situation, you don't need to worry about the ball in the inclinometer. As they say in Las Vegas, let it roll.

Simply apply enough rudder pressure to keep the airplane on the heading you've chosen, and use those hands to sort charts, tune radios, and complete important cockpit chores such as eating your salami and pickle sandwich. This is usually referred to as *walking* the plane, sort of like walking the dog except you don't need anything with the word *scooper* in it to do it. The airplane may wander up and down a bit, but it won't stray a great deal from the configured flight condition. This is consistent with what you already know. You walked the airplane down a runway for takeoff and you walked a heading with your feet to land.

Minor heading changes are easily walked enroute, too. As an aside, if your hands are occupied with charts and the airplane begins to climb a bit, slight pressure on one rudder pedal then the other will result in a tiny loss of lift and increase in drag. This often causes the airplane to stop an errant climb while your hands are occupied. Finish the sandwich and get back to business.

After the final trim adjustments are made, the *BIG-6*—the six main panel instruments—are rectangular cross-checked. The rectangular cross-check is exactly what the name suggests. It's simply a way of monitoring the six

Tattle Tale Turn Indicator

There is a little-used instrument that is actually easier to employ than the magnetic compass for detecting turns—the ADF. It's my opinion that instrument pilots should always have the ADF equipment tuned to an NDB station with a strong signal (assuming there is an ADF on board, of course). In the event the turn triangle of agreement needs to be consulted, ADF needle movement would be a pretty sure indication that the aircraft is turning, and an equally good indication of the direction in which the turn is being made. In the event all the flight instruments fail, the ADF could provide enough information to keep the heading constant.

Don't have an ADF? What about a GPS? You can accomplish the same thing with a GPS operating in the ground track mode. For instance, the GPS in the picture to the right is set to the HSI ground track mode. Any change in heading is revealed by a change in ground track on the moving map's graphic display. With a little practice, you'll be able to maintain a wings-level attitude just by using the GPS's HSI display (or any other comparable display showing ground track change). Of course, this assumes that the GPS has a sufficiently quick screen refresh rate so the heading change can be seen without delay. I've used the ground track display on several handheld GPS units to keep the airplane going straight in a simulated failure of all my airplane's bank instruments.

main panel instruments while looking for deviations. It's usually done in a sideways fashion, going clockwise from the top row to the bottom row of instruments in a circular fashion as shown in Figure 29. It's perfectly appropriate for you to select any scanning pattern that's comfortable. If you can make your eyeballs independently roll in opposite directions, maybe you can invent a scan that qualifies for the next Olympics. As long as you transfer the information from panel to brain, mission accomplished.

Rectangular Cross Checking the Big-6 Instruments.

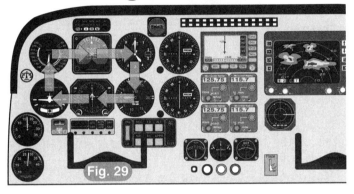

Fig. 29

The objective is to monitor deviations from the established attitude. When you detect small deviations, small adjustments should be made on the attitude indicator to maintain the conditions you want. Rectangular cross-checking the BIG-6 instruments is the condition in which you'll spend most of your time. It is the normal condition between major attitude changes.

Each of the first two steps of the three-step scan process should take about five seconds. There are instances where you must return to Step 2 of the scan. In turbulence, or on an instrument approach, you may find yourself obliged to rapidly radial cross-check the primary instruments to maintain precise control of the airplane. Radial cross-checking is a lot of work visually, intellectually, and emotionally. It is possible to radial cross-check all the instruments on the panel, but this is usually unnecessary and becomes very tiresome. Radial cross-check only those instruments needed to control the airplane in any given flight configuration.

There you have the basic three-step scan procedure to be used any time you make a major attitude change. With practice you'll easily glide between all three steps. Yes, it does take practice, which is something you can do on your computer-based flight simulator. I encourage you to use these steps, and use them consistently, every time you make a major attitude change. A good part of instrument training is teaching your brain reliable, fail-safe patterns through frequent and consistent repetition.

Now that you understand these three steps, let's examine four scenarios in which

Step 2 is used to radial cross-check the proper instruments after making a major attitude change. Keep in mind, the airplane in the following scenarios has just been established in its new attitude as a result of Step 1 of the scan. Now it's time to look at the details of how Step 2 is applied.

Radial Cross-Checking for Straight and Level Flight

Let's assume that you've just made a major attitude change from some other attitude and have just established yourself in straight and level flight. Here's how you would radial cross-check the primary instruments as required in Step 2.

First, radial cross-check the altimeter (primary for pitch), the directional gyro (primary for bank) and the airspeed indicator (primary for power) as shown in Figure 30. Radial cross-check all these instruments at least once, quickly, before spending additional time radial cross-checking any particular instrument.

For instance, when beginning the radial cross-check of the altimeter, look for needle movement, and then return to the attitude indicator. If the altimeter needle was moving, make a small pitch change on the attitude indicator to neutralize this movement. It's important to stop a straying parameter first, and then make finer corrections later. Next, radial cross-check the heading indicator. Observe it, and then return to the attitude indicator. If the heading indicator's compass rose is turning (or is not turning in the direction you commanded), make a small and appropriate bank correction on the attitude indicator. Use five degrees of bank to stop deviations that are off by not more than 20 degrees. Finally, radial cross-check the airspeed indicator

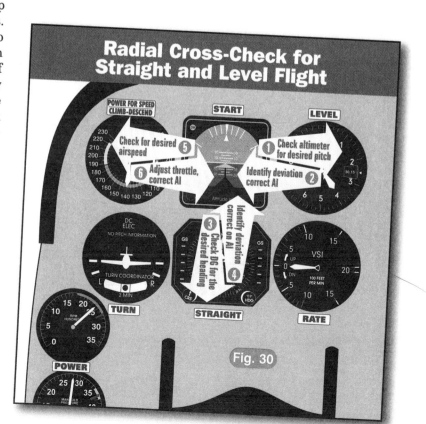

Fig. 30

The Flight Director Bars

The Flight Director System

What is the airplane's flight director (FD)? It's a wonderful device that helps "direct" you to fly a desired/selected attitude. It does this by providing a visual cue on your attitude indicator (AI) in the form of yellow V-bars, which are similar to the crosshairs of a gunsight. The yellow command V-bars, shown on the figure to the left, move up and down and rotate left and right. By changing the airplane's attitude (pitch and bank) to keep the AI's miniature airplane (i.e., the orange triangle) nested in the V-bar's groove, you are able to maintain a specific attitude. I'm speaking of an attitude that you have chosen on the autopilot system's Mode Controller (MC). If your plane has any other kind of attitude, you need more than a flight director.

When the FD is activated, you can select any of several functions from the Mode Controller, as shown in the bottom right hand figure. The FD V-bars will then move to keep you flying the mode selected. For instance, if you select NAV and are on an intercept heading to a course previously set in your HSI, the V-bars will begin moving to indicate when you need to turn to intercept the course. Once you're established on the course, the V-bars will move to indicate any attitude change needed to compensate for wind.

Of course, this is all done with the autopilot in the OFF mode. When the autopilot is turned on, the airplane will pitch and bank automatically to keep the AI's miniature airplane nested in the V-bars, flying the mode you've set into the Mode Controller. Take no offense, but you're just an observer in this scenario. A very interesting observer, I hope.

The Mode Controller

DN HDG FD ALT AP ON
NAV BC APPR
UP TEST

---

to check that the power selected is appropriate. If it isn't, change the power setting to achieve the target airspeed (we'll always assume that a specific airspeed will be flown during straight and level flight, thus requiring the airspeed indicator to be the primary power instrument in this condition).

After initially radial cross-checking all three primary instruments, you should alternately radial cross-check the altimeter and heading indicator again, making small corrections on the attitude indicator to fine-tune the attitude, stabilizing these instruments to make their indications read correctly. It's not necessary to radial cross-check the

primary power instrument (the airspeed indicator) as often as the other primary instruments, since airspeed isn't as critical as pitch and bank values.

Radial Cross-Checking for a Level Turn

Let's assume that you've just established yourself in a level turn. Here's how you would radial cross-check the primary instruments as required in Step 2.

Radial cross-check the altimeter (primary for pitch), the turn coordinator (primary for bank), and the airspeed indicator (primary for power) as shown in Figure 31. Radial cross-check all these instruments at least once, quickly, before spending additional time radial cross-checking any particular instrument.

Radial cross-check the altimeter first and look for needle movement. Return to the attitude indicator and make a small pitch change to neutralize any movement of the altimeter's needle. Then, radial cross-check the turn coordinator and ensure that it's indicating a standard rate turn in the appropriate direction. Return to the attitude indicator and make any change in bank necessary to keep the airplane in a standard rate turn. Finally, radial cross-check the airspeed indicator and change the power as required to achieve the desired airspeed (once again, we'll always assume that a specific airspeed will be flown during a turn, thus requiring the airspeed indicator to be the primary power instrument in this condition).

After initially radial cross-checking all three primary instruments, alternately radial cross-check the altimeter and turn coordinator again, making small corrections on the attitude indicator to fine-tune the attitude, stabilizing these instruments to make them read correctly. Once again, it's not necessary to radial cross-check the primary power instrument (the airspeed indicator) as often as the other primary instruments since airspeed isn't as critical as pitch and bank values.

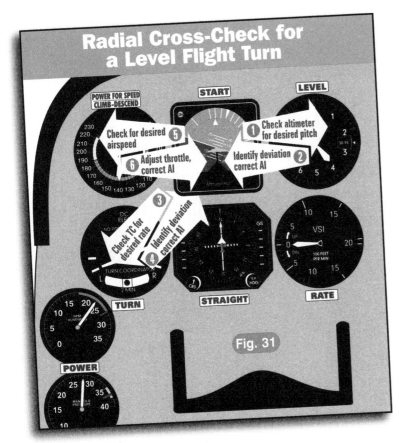

Radial Cross-Check for a Level Flight Turn

Fig. 31

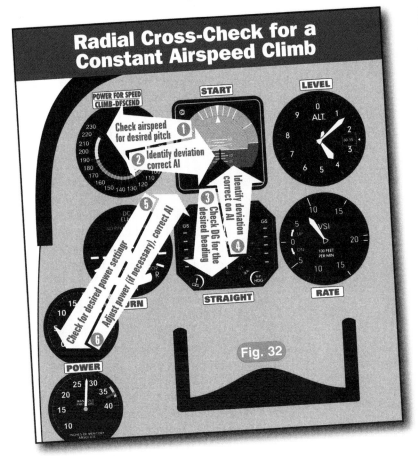

Radial Cross-Check for a Constant Airspeed Climb

Fig. 32

the airspeed needle). Wait to see what happens. Next, radial cross-check the heading indicator. Make a small bank correction to achieve the correct heading. Then radial cross-check the tachometer/manifold pressure gauge once, quickly, to be sure you've got the power setting you want.

After initially radial cross-checking all three primary instruments, alternately radial cross-check the airspeed indicator and heading indicator again, making small corrections on the attitude indicator to fine-tune the attitude, stabilizing these instruments to make them read properly. From this point on, I'll assume that you know to radial cross-check all three primary instruments first before returning to radial cross-check them again as a fine-tuning measure. I'll also assume that you'll know not to radial cross-check the primary power instrument (the tachometer/manifold pressure gauge) as often as the other primary instruments since climb power is usually achieved more by feel than continued visual observation.

Radial Cross-Checking for a Constant Airspeed, Climbing or Descending Turn

Let's assume that you've just made a major attitude change and have established yourself in a constant airspeed climbing or descending turn. Here's how you would radial cross-check the primary instruments, in keeping with Step 2.

Radial Cross-Checking for a Straight, Constant Airspeed Climb or Constant Airspeed Descent

Let's assume that you've just established yourself in a straight, constant airspeed climb (Figure 32) or a constant airspeed descent (Figure 33). Here's how you would radial cross-check the primary instruments as required in Step 2.

Radial cross-check the airspeed indicator (primary for pitch in a climb or descent), the heading indicator (primary for bank), and the tachometer/manifold pressure gauge (primary for power in a constant airspeed climb or descent). Radial cross-check all these instruments at least once, quickly, before spending additional time radial cross-checking any instrument in particular.

Once again, radial cross-check the primary pitch instrument (the airspeed indicator) first. Make small pitch changes on the attitude indicator to achieve the target airspeed. It's important to understand that there is no appreciable lag in the airspeed indicator's reading itself. The apparent lag comes from the airplane's inertia. It takes a little time for the airplane to speed up or slow down. Be careful not to chase the airspeed indication. Change pitch and be patient (or become a mental patient as you go crazy trying to catch

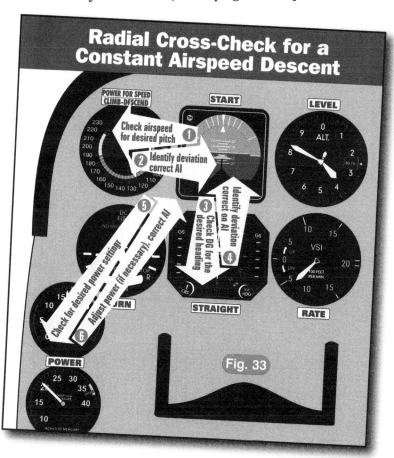

Radial Cross-Check for a Constant Airspeed Descent

Fig. 33

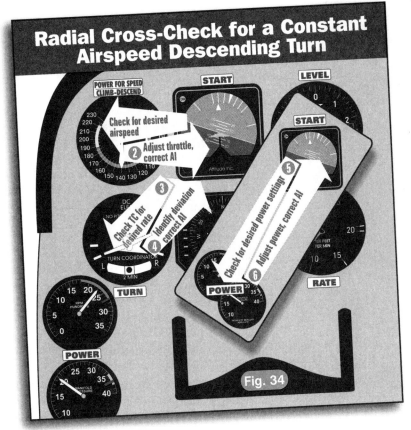

Radial Cross-Check for a Constant Airspeed Descending Turn

Fig. 34

Radial cross-check the airspeed indicator (primary for pitch in a climb or descent), the turn coordinator (primary for bank) and the tachometer (primary for power in a constant airspeed climb or descent) as shown in Figure 34. Radial cross-check all these instruments at least once, quickly, before spending additional time radial cross-checking any particular instrument.

Radial cross-check the airspeed indicator first. Make small pitch changes on the attitude indicator to achieve the correct airspeed. Once again, the airspeed indicator's apparent lag comes from the airplane's inertia. Don't chase the needle. Change pitch and wait to see what happens. Next, radial cross-check the turn coordinator. Make a small bank correction on the attitude indicator if needed to achieve the targeted turn rate.

Partial Panel Flying

Partial panel flying is not a flight made on a day when you didn't finish paneling the den. It's what happens when one (or on a really bad day, more) of the six main flight instruments on your panel fails (Figure 35). Perhaps this explains why they call it partial panel. After all, you don't realize how partial you are to these things until one or more are missing.

Like hairstyles, instrument failures come in several varieties (although few are colored pink and purple). While any one of the six main flight instruments can fail, some failures are more of a concern than others. If your static system becomes clogged, you'll lose your altimeter and vertical speed indicator. Yes, that's a problem, but if you have altitude encoding equipment ATC can provide you with the missing altitude information. Hopefully you

won't lose your radio and static system at the same time, which could also cause you to lose your cool. You can also break the glass in the vertical speed indicator to obtain an alternate static source (yes this works, but don't do it on a PFD), assuming that your airplane isn't equipped with a less fractious alternate static source.

Losing the airspeed indicator because of a plugged pitot tube isn't a serious problem, either (assuming the pitot drain hole remains open, which is often the case). Of course, this doesn't mean your blood pressure won't rise. It probably will. While the airspeed indicator is a valuable instrument, you can fly the airplane without it working as long as you know the attitude and power settings that you use for climb, cruise and descent.

That's one of many reasons it's important to pay attention and get a feel for these things when all is well. Then, if the airspeed indicator goes south while you're flying north, just fly the airplane as you normally would while making sure that the readings on the vertical speed indicator stay within the typical range of past performance. If your airplane typically climbs at less than 600 feet per minute, then you wouldn't expect to suddenly show a 1,000 feet per minute climb rate just because your airspeed indicator failed. If the rate is a 1,000 feet per minute, it's Nature's way of telling you you've got a bad attitude, or certainly one that's too steep. It also may explain the presence of a wailing stall horn. If you know your airplane's performance for the altitude you're at, the vertical speed indicator can be substituted as the primary pitch instrument in the climb.

What happens if the turn coordinator fails? Since it is usually an electrically powered instrument, its operation is dependent on the airplane's electrical system. While you might miss the rate of turn information, you certainly

Partial Panel Flying

Fig. 35

Small Deviations from Altitude and Airspeed

Fig. 36

Use Half the Altitude Deviation to Return to the Desired Altitude

Fig. 38

A Little Bit Off—Correcting Small Altitude and Heading Deviations

In our discussion so far, I've only mentioned attitude changes that are considered major. This leaves out sergeants, lieutenants, and colonels, not to mention what happens if your airspeed, altitude or heading assignment is off by only a small amount. You wouldn't go through the three steps of the scan procedure just to correct for an altitude deviation of only 100 feet, would you? I doubt it. That would be like renting a Learjet to fly five miles. Fun, but not economical. In the real world, pilots are pretty good about fudging and fiddling to get done what needs to get done. Here's how to do it when you're "just a little" off. Suppose you're in straight and level flight and notice that your airspeed is a little low and the airplane is climbing slightly (Figure 36, position A). Since altitude and airspeed are interchangeable in this instance, you can simply apply a little forward pressure on the elevator to correct the problem. Excuse me, it's not a problem, it's just a temporary energy control discrepancy. It's not your fault. Well, it is but we won't admit it. If airspeed is high and the airplane is descending slightly (Figure 36, position B), simply apply a little back pressure on the elevator to return to the correct flight condition. If airspeed and altitude are *both* high or low, then a change in both pitch and power will be necessary to return to the correct altitude and airspeed.

What about small altitude and heading deviations? As a rule of thumb, if you notice an altitude deviation of 100 feet or less, use a half-bar-width correction on the attitude indicator to slow, then stop, the altimeter needle (Figure 37). When the altimeter needle stops, the airplane is in level flight. Make an additional adjustment on the attitude indicator (perhaps another half bar width) to return to the assigned altitude. If the altitude deviation is more than 100 feet, use a full bar width to slow then stop the altimeter needle. An important general concept to get here is that in instrument flying, we make control changes that are proportional to the amount of change we seek. If you're only looking for a tweak, don't make major changes to get there or you'll spend the day chasing your tail, and make a rudder failure of everything.

Half-Bar Attitude Change on Different Attitude Indicators

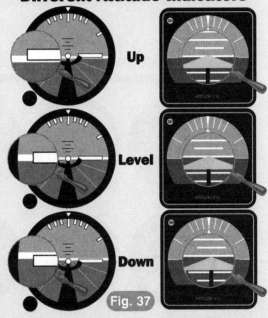

Up

Level

Down

Fig. 37

If you try to stop and return the altimeter needle to the correct reading all in one step, you risk overcontrolling the airplane. *Return to the appropriate altitude at a rate approximately double the error in altitude* as shown in Figure 38 (but no more than 200 feet per minute, since this would be considered overcontrolling the airplane, in bad form, and cause other pilots to stop talking *to* you and start talking *about* you). For an altitude deviation of 75 feet, you would return to the original altitude at a rate of 150 feet per minute on the VSI. For an altitude deviation of 150 feet, you'd return to the original altitude at a rate of 200 feet per minute (not 300 feet per minute, since this might be considered overcontrolling in some circles? not crop circles, either).

The VSI gives you an indirect indication of pitch attitude, thus making it a trend as well as rate instrument. It's a trend instrument because it shows immediate vertical movement, which in non-turbulent conditions is an excellent indication of pitch change. When you observe a slight altitude deviation, apply light pressure on the elevator to return the VSI's needle to zero. Then relax the corrective pressure. In most instances, the altimeter will show little or no altitude deviation.

What about small heading deviations? As a general rule, use an angle of bank no greater than the number of degrees to be turned, but not in excess of the bank required for a standard rate turn. The big question is, "At what altitude or heading deviation is it necessary to return to the original altitude with a major attitude change in lieu of using only a small correction on the attitude indicator?" My personal limits are 200 feet and 15 degrees of turn. Your mileage may vary. Anything less than these values and I'll apply the Fudge Factor Method and return to normalcy by making small corrections on the attitude indicator instead of going through all three steps of the instrument scan procedure.

Steep Turns

Steep turns weren't designed to see if your Foggles would slip down over your eyes during high G forces. They actually help increase your proficiency at basic instrument flying. Because of the high load factors associated with the major attitude change of turning steeply, your radial cross-checking skills will quickly be honed to a sharp edge.

In Step 1, enter the steep turn by selecting the attitude, power and trim conditions that you think will yield the correct result. Roll the airplane so that the bank pointer rests half way between the 30 and the sixty degree bank mark (Figure 39). This represents a ban of 45 degrees. Some airplanes have diagonal marks for the 15 and 45 degree bank positions (Figure 40). These marks make it a bit easier to hold these specific bank angles since there's no bank pointer reference for these positions. Because of the greatly reduced vertical component of lift, you'll have to apply a large amount of back pressure to increase the angle of attack during the roll-in. Simultaneously, add sufficient power (a setting you should learn from experience) to maintain the desired airspeed.

45 Degree Bank Steep Turn

Fig. 39

Steep Turn Using an AI's Diagonal Bank Lines

Fig. 40

Suppose you let the bank accidentally increase beyond 45 degrees but don't compensate with an increase in elevator back pressure alone. Doing this will cause the airplane to pitch down due to the decrease in vertical lift component, resulting in an increase in airspeed. Attempting to raise the nose with the elevator alone will cause the bank to increase, increasing the tendency of the nose to dip further. If this scenario sounds like trouble, permit me to introduce you to a *diving spiral*. Increasing the elevator back pressure without shallowing the bank will only tighten the spiral. The right way out is to decrease the bank slightly with the coordinated use of aileron and rudder and elevator back pressure. If the airspeed increase is rapid, then reduce power. Be prepared to release a little of the elevator back pressure as the airplane pitches up.

The best way to become skillful at steep turns is to practice them by gradually increasing the bank until you're at a maximum of 45 degrees. I've always found the VSI to be a valuable aid in helping maintain altitude in these turns. In fact, I tend to radial cross-check the VSI almost twice as often as I do the altimeter in a steep turn.

As soon as the airplane is established in the bank, begin radial cross-checking the altimeter (primary for pitch), the attitude indicator (primary for bank), and the airspeed indicator (primary for power) as shown in Figure 41. I also recommend that you scan the vertical speed indicator. The size and sensitivity of the VSI's needle makes it easy to detect altitude deviations and apply an immediate correction. radial cross-check the altimeter, then the VSI, repeating this tradeoff during the turn. Every once in a while, radial cross-check the inclinometer (check for coordination) and the heading indicator (check for the the approach of the correct rollout heading).

One of the challenges of steep turns is to compensate for the airplane's natural overbanking tendency. This usually occurs with banks in excess of 30 degrees. At 45 degrees of bank, you can bet that the airplane will want to increase its bank. It's usually necessary to hold aileron *opposite* the direction of turn, to prevent overbanking, as well as adding the necessary and appropriate rudder pressure to keep the airplane in coordinated flight. Most of the time, you'll only need small elevator corrections to maintain altitude while the bank in held constant with ailerons.

Primary Instruments for a 45 degree Bank Steep Turn

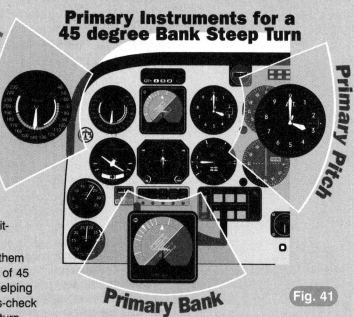

Fig. 41

don't need it to fly on instruments. Make your turns at 15 to 20 degrees of bank and be happy. At the typical speeds flown by general aviation airplanes, this bank range will keep you close to the bank necessary for standard rate turns. Keep in mind that you can still obtain turn-quality information from the ball in the turn coordinator. The ball is powered by gravity and gravity doesn't seem to fail all that often.

Vacuum Pump Failures

Now we come to the more serious matter of a failed vacuum pump (Figure 42), an ironic situation that leaves you in a vacuum but doesn't produce one. Recall from Chapter 2 that the vacuum system powers the attitude indicator as well as the heading indicator (assuming you don't have an electrically slaved gyro such as with a horizontal situation indicator or HSI). Therefore, a vacuum system failure results in the double whammy of losing both the attitude and heading indicator (of course, it's likely that you still have use of the VSI, altimeter, airspeed indicator, and turn coordinator).

Before we talk about how to fly on partial panel, let's ask how you would know that that a vacuum pump has failed. An obvious clue is that that the needle of the suction gauge (Figure 43) indicates little or no vacuum pressure. This assumes, of course, that this gauge is part of your instrument scan. Unfortunately, many instrument pilots fail to scan the vacuum gauge in the same way they fail to scan the ammeter. It's always a good practice to look at the vacuum gauge (ammeter, too) every few minutes as part of your regular scan.

The moment you suspect a pitch or bank discrepancy on the attitude or heading indicator, confirm that an instrument problem exists by performing the inverted V cross-check.

The response of the vacuum instruments provides you with another clue to vacuum pump failure. Under instrument conditions, airplanes spend most of their time in straight and level flight, which makes it more likely that a vacuum pump failure will occur in this condition. Most pilots I've spoken with say that as the gyro of the attitude indicator loses its spin, the instrument begins indicating a slight bank. According to these same pilots, the heading indicator isn't as likely to show as much movement as its gyros spin down. Of course, if either of these instruments fail in a turn, it's more likely that they will fail to respond at the proper rate or in the proper direction to control inputs.

The moment you suspect a pitch or bank discrepancy on the attitude or heading indicator, confirm that an instrument problem exists by performing the inverted V cross-check. Then use the pitch or turn triangle of agreement to determine which instrument has actually failed. Covering up the failed instrument keeps it from distracting you. If you don't have an official no-peekie instrument cover, then use a piece of paper or a dollar bill (to represent what the instrument is now worth to you in your given situation).

Flying Instruments on a Partial Panel

With the attitude indicator and heading indicator inoperative (no electrically slaved heading gyro assumed here), you're left to control the airplane by what has become classically known as the *needle, ball, and airspeed method* of instrument flying (Figure 43). In terms of the control/performance concept, you've lost your main control instrument—the attitude indicator. Now you must make pitch and bank inputs using only your performance instruments as

Partial Panel Flying on Needle, Ball and Airspeed

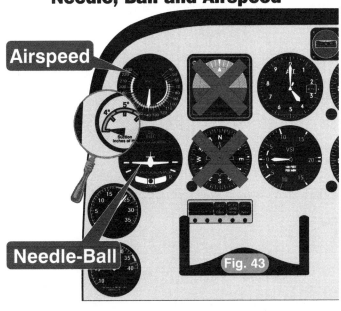

Fig. 43

Partial Panel Instrument Loss

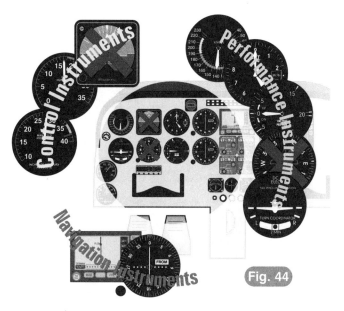

Fig. 44

Partial Panel Instrument Category

Fig. 45

shown in Figure 44. In terms of the primary/supporting method, you won't have the attitude indicator to use as a primary pitch and bank instrument for transitioning between major attitudes. You also won't have use of the heading indicator as a primary bank instrument for all those maneuvers involving straight flight (straight and level, a straight climb or descent, etc.). In this situation, the turn coordinator becomes the primary bank instrument. Figure 45 shows how the pitch, bank and power categories of the flight instruments.

Either way, partial panel flying shouldn't present a big problem for you. Why? Because when flying on needle, ball, and airspeed, you'll learn to visualize the pitch or bank attitude necessary to fly the airplane. Figure 46 shows the basic three-step scan technique when operating partial panel flying.

To enter a partial panel climb from cruise flight, use the same three-step scan technique we've already discussed. Begin by selecting the attitude by *gently* raising the nose. Without the attitude indicator to give you an indication of the proper pitch attitude, you must rely on your past experience to determine the appropriate amount of elevator back pressure appropriate for the entry. Obviously, you aren't going to pull so hard as to point the spinner towards Jupiter, are you? I hope not. As the nose pitches up and the airspeed begins decreasing, you'll be able to *imagine* the airplane's attitude. Make small adjustments in elevator pressure

or position to give you the correct climb speed. Power and trim are applied as if the attitude indicator was working properly. Remember, because of airplane inertia, the value shown on the airspeed indicator will appear to lag the airplane's actual airspeed. Don't chase the airspeed needle. It's a game of catch you can't win.

If you want to begin the climb or descent at a speed slower than what you are flying at the time, slow the airplane down in level flight first, making sure to retrim in

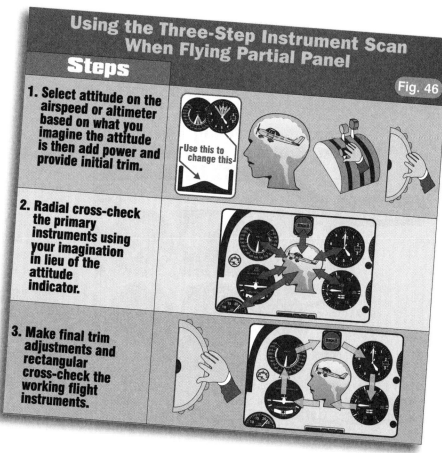

Using the Three-Step Instrument Scan When Flying Partial Panel

Fig. 46

Steps

1. **Select attitude on the airspeed or altimeter based on what you imagine the attitude is then add power and provide initial trim.** *Use this to change this*

2. **Radial cross-check the primary instruments using your imagination in lieu of the attitude indicator.**

3. **Make final trim adjustments and rectangular cross-check the working flight instruments.**

the process. Once the target speed is reached, commence the climb or descent as previously described.

Partial panel turns are a bit more challenging. The turn coordinator now becomes your primary means of turning the airplane. Remember, the turn coordinator doesn't provide any direct information on your bank, only your direction of roll as well as the direction and the rate of turn. Unless you keep all turns coordinated, you can't be sure that you're maintaining the proper bank for a standard rate turn.

When rolling into a turn, the turn needle will initially deflect in the direction of roll but it will not precisely reflect the airplane's present rate of turn. Once the turn is established, you may need to apply more rudder and/or aileron pressure to achieve a precise standard rate turn. This problem is more likely to occur when rolling out of a turn or rolling into a turn in the opposite direction. As the rollout begins, it may appear that the airplane is already turning opposite to its original direction. The secret to handling this peculiarity of the turn coordinator is to avoid overcontrol of the aileron and rudder.

Partial panel turns are made much easier by using the clock instead of relying solely on the magnetic compass. Remember, the compass experiences turning errors on headings of north and south (as we'll cover shortly). Instead of trying to correct for these errors under instrument conditions, it's much easier to estimate the time required to turn to a heading and use the airplane's clock to count off the time.

For instance, turning from 270 degrees to a heading of 360 degrees is a 90-degree heading change. At three degrees of turn per second (a standard rate turn), you'll need to turn for 30 seconds to arrive on the new heading. Thirty degrees of heading change requires 10 seconds of turn; 60 degrees, 20 seconds of turn and 180 degrees, one minute of turn.

For shorter turns of 15 degrees or less, you might use half-standard rate. Simply keep the needle between the "zero turn" and "standard rate" index marks. This provides you with a 1.5 degree/second turn rate. A 15 degree turn at half-standard rate will take 10 seconds.

The secret to making accurate timed turns is to compensate for needle over- and under-deflections. If the turn needle was deflected a little beyond the standard rate index for a few seconds, then compensate by deflecting it the same amount for the same elapsed time on the opposite side of the index. Of course, it's much better to keep the turn needle on the index to begin with.

Finally, if you must make a steep turn under partial panel conditions, there's only one way to do it. Bank the airplane until the turn needle hits the stops of the instrument case, then decrease the bank just enough so that the needle keeps tapping its stops. This provides you with the steepest bank possible under these conditions.

General Jimmy Doolittle - Blind Flight

The first blind flight was achieved on September 24, 1929 when U.S. Army Lt. James Doolittle, working with the Guggenheim Foundation, took off from Mitchell Field, Long Island, N.Y., flew a 15-mile course, and landed safely without ever seeing the ground.

In the front cockpit was Lt. Benjamin Kelsey, serving as safety pilot should some kind of emergency develop, but during the complete flight he held his hands outside the cockpit where they could be seen at all times....

Courtesy NASA Library

Magnetic Compass

Altimeter

Artificial Horizon

Rate of Climb Indicator

The instrument panel used by Doolittle on the first blind flight

In Doolittle's own words:

"As far as I am concerned, the most useful contribution that I made to aviation was in 1928, and in 1929, when under the auspices of the Guggenheim Foundation I conducted a series of experiments in blind flying and participated in the development of the instruments necessary to do the job. Among the instruments were the artificial horizon, directional gyroscope, and of course we worked with sensitive altimeters although I had no hand in the development of those....

On a day late in the fall of 1929, I took off, flew a set course, and landed, being up about fifteen minutes, without having seen the ground. I was covered with a canopy. In the front seat I carried Second Lieutenant, now Brigadier General, Kelsey, who was a safety pilot, to make sure that I didn't run into anybody else while up there, but he didn't touch the controls. This was the first time that a flight had been made —take-off, flight and landing—completely on instruments. I think that flight and the assisting in the development of the instrumentation necessary to do the flight was my greatest contribution to aviation. I had worked on it over a year. I started in 1928, got the airplanes, the equipment, assisted in the development of the equipment. I made dozens and dozens, literally hundreds, of practice flights, before making this final flight."

Unusual Attitudes and Their Recoveries

The most basic goal of instrument flying is to always know which end is up. Seems easy, until you try it, especially if a flight instrument goes bad or you become distracted and let the airplane do bad things.

An airplane that has seriously departed from what you want it to be doing at any given moment is in an unusual attitude. At that juncture, you aren't exactly the pilot in control. The airplane may be banking too steeply, overspeeding in a descent, be nose-high to the extent that a stall is imminent, or nose-low and headed for a graveyard spiral. Whatever the situation, you need to know how to regain control. We call this *unusual attitude recognition and recovery,* and every instrument pilot should be familiar with its principles.

And you thought it was just flight instructors who had unusual attitudes, didn't you?

The first step in unusual attitude recoveries is recognizing when you're in an unusual attitude. One clue is a vague feeling that everything isn't quite right. The rule here is simple. If your attitude or airspeed seems unusual, you're there. In other words, if the instruments indicate that the airplane is pitching, banking or speeding beyond what you want, you

Fig. 48

need to do something to stop the progression and return the plane to the proper conditions.

Some attitudes aren't all *that* unusual and don't require the dramatic responses we associate with a great episode of *ER.* For instance, if the airplane is slightly nose high, you can tell by looking at the altimeter, vertical speed indicator, airspeed indicator, and the attitude indicator, in that order (Figure 47). Nose-low attitudes are identified by the same instruments but with some needles moving in the opposite direction (Figure 48).

If the unusual attitude is moderate or worse, then you do not have time to finish *War and Peace* before responding appropriately. The fact that you are reading *War and Peace* while flying instruments may be part of the problem, of course. In this situation, your instinct may be to go for the attitude indicator as an indicator of what's up (or down, as the case may be). That's fine, unless the attitude indicator is the source of the problem. It might have failed, resulting in an unusual attitude, or it might have tumbled as a result of the unusual attitude you're in. Yes, some attitude indicators have pitch and bank limits that, when exceeded, cause the instrument to tumble and read unreliably. Besides, in extreme unusual

attitudes, an attitude indicator can be difficult to read even if it hasn't tumbled (Figure 49). In these situations, it's best to rely on the airspeed indicator, altimeter, vertical speed indicator, and turn coordinator to effect a safe and prompt recovery.

Nose-High Unusual Attitude Recovery

Suppose you are distracted by something in the cockpit. Looking back at the instruments, you notice that the airspeed is decreasing rapidly (Figure 50A). You're probably in a nose-high attitude. Your first response should be to:

1. Increase your power in proportion to the rate at which speed is decreasing (Figure 50B).

2. Apply forward elevator pressure to prevent the airplane from stalling (Figure 50C).

3. Level the wings by reference to the turn coordinator (Figure 50D).

4. Center the ball to keep the airplane coordinated (Figure 50E).

These actions are taken as close to simultaneously as possible.

Next best thing is to do them in the order presented. A banked condition is not as severe during a climb as it is during a descent. After all, if the bank is increasing in a nose-high attitude, the nose will naturally lower itself as

Fig. 47

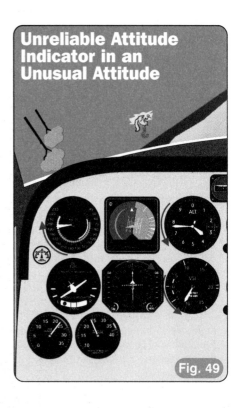

Fig. 49

a result of the diminishing vertical component of lift.

You can assume that the airplane is in straight flight when the turn coordinator's needle shows no deflection and the ball is centered. When the airspeed and altimeter needles reverse and stabilize their direction, you're in a level pitch attitude (Figure 49F).

Nose-Low Unusual Attitude Recovery

Suppose you are distracted in the cockpit (you really need to not be so distracted so often). Returning to the instruments, you notice the airspeed increasing at a breathtaking rate, just as in one of those old movies where the hero is about to do a free furrowing of someone's farm (Figure 51A). Since you don't dig it, your course of action is to:

1. Reduce power, thus preventing excessive airspeed and altitude loss (Figure 51B).

2. Immediately correct for any banked condition by looking at the turn coordinator to level the wings and center the ball (Figure 51C). Use coordinated aileron and rudder pressure. (If you tried to raise the nose while the airplane was still in a bank you'd most likely tighten the spiral and increase the bank, which would result in a further tendency of the nose to pitch down. This is precisely the opposite of what you want to happen. It also results in something known as a graveyard spiral. If that doesn't sound good, it's because it *isn't* good.)

3. Now raise the nose by a smooth application of elevator back pressure (Figure 51D). You want to be careful to avoid overcontrolling during this recovery.

4. When the airspeed and altimeter needles stop and reverse direction (Figure 51E) you can assume that you're in a level flight attitude. Of course, you should look at the rate at which these needles are changing speed and direction to better determine when you're nearing level flight attitude. You don't want to overcontrol during the recovery and go from frying pan to fire by raising the nose too high and having another unusual attitude to deal with.

Once the airspeed, altimeter and turn coordinator needles are stabilized (Figure 51F), you can incorporate the attitude indicator back into your scan. On the other hand, if the attitude indicator is unreliable in this instance (because it has exceeded its limits) you can determine the proper attitude to fly by using the airspeed indicator and altimeter. The vertical speed indicator is useful here too, but it's not as reliable in

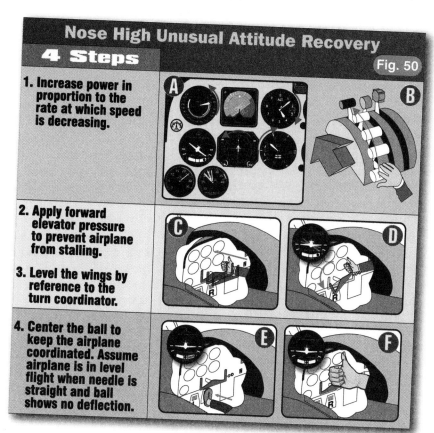

Nose High Unusual Attitude Recovery

4 Steps

Fig. 50

1. Increase power in proportion to the rate at which speed is decreasing.

2. Apply forward elevator pressure to prevent airplane from stalling.

3. Level the wings by reference to the turn coordinator.

4. Center the ball to keep the airplane coordinated. Assume airplane is in level flight when needle is straight and ball shows no deflection.

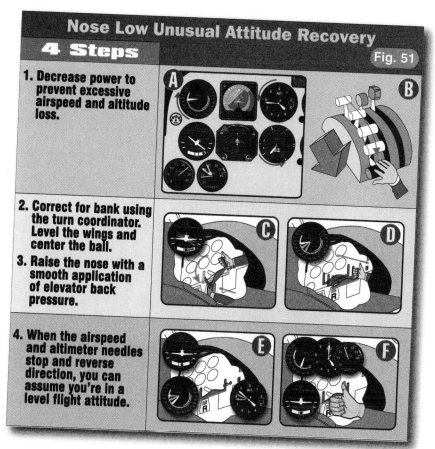

Nose Low Unusual Attitude Recovery

4 Steps

Fig. 51

1. Decrease power to prevent excessive airspeed and altitude loss.

2. Correct for bank using the turn coordinator. Level the wings and center the ball.

3. Raise the nose with a smooth application of elevator back pressure.

4. When the airspeed and altimeter needles stop and reverse direction, you can assume you're in a level flight attitude.

turbulent air. If you were on a heading issued by ATC when the unusual attitude occurred, you should return to that heading but only after you've stabilized the airplane in straight and level flight. Remember, you want to get your bearings and composure first (aviate) before doing what ATC wants (navigate) or responding to an ATC query (communicate).

There is one more type of unusual attitude recovery from a nose-low attitude that requires a very different control response. Suppose you're being vectored for an instrument approach with the gear down and the airplane trimmed for a slower speed (a lot of nose-up trim is common in these conditions). Let's assume that you became distracted and the airplane enters a bank, then pitches nose down.

As the speed increases, the large amount of nose-up trim helps tighten the spiral (like the graveyard spiral discussed previously). As you identify the unusual attitude in these instances, you'll quickly reduce power and roll to a wings-level attitude. As you do, you'll experience a very large nose up pitching attitude caused by the higher airspeed and nose-up trim. Imagine that. You roll out, and instead of having to pull back on the elevator to return to level flight you'll actually have to push forward to prevent passing through level flight. When operating at slower speeds associated with the terminal environment, be aware of this type of elevator response in an unusual attitude recovery.

Failing to keep the airplane properly trimmed increases the likelihood of ending up in an unusual attitude. A disorganized cockpit is another hazard, since it leads to distractions that in turn contribute to odd attitudes. So is reading *War and Peace* while enroute.

During your instrument scan, if you notice an instrument discrepancy, immediately perform the inverted V cross-check. If there is a discrepancy between pitch and bank indications, isolate the suspect instrument group (i.e., pitch or bank instruments) and use the appropriate triangle of agreement to determine which instrument is reading incorrectly. Don't delay this process when you first suspect a problem with an instrument, and don't stare at the suspect instrument, either. Both can lead to an unusual attitude. The last thing you want is to end up in an unusual attitude with a failed instrument, not knowing which one has failed.

Finally

Finally, if I could give you only one bit of advice on learning to fly instruments, I'd say don't be in too much of a rush to fly instrument approaches. Learn to scan your instruments properly. Build a solid instrument scan foundation, and everything that rests on it will be better. You'll have less frustration learning, and be a better instrument pilot in the end.

Mechanics of the Human Mind

A general aviation pilot rushed to make a VIFNO (Void If Not Off by) departure time for an IFR flight at night. Once in the clouds, he suffered a gyro failure and subsequent disorientation. He reported to ASRS that his prior instrument and simulator training were unequal to the "mechanics of the human mind" experienced during the incident:

I filed an IFR flight plan. I filed and received a void clearance to depart less than 10 minutes from the time it was issued. I quickly preflighted the aircraft, started the engine, taxied to the runway and performed a fast prop and mag check. I departed and called Approach on climbout and heading 220 degrees. While I made radio contact with Approach, I noticed the attitude indicator showing a bank in excess of 50 degrees, while the heading indicator appeared to be spinning. I tried to roll wings level with the turn coordinator, but found myself losing altitude quickly. I was able to recover below the cloud deck and asked Approach for heading and distance to departure airport. I remained VFR and landed.

I feel several factors led to this:

1. My accepting a clearance which left me little time to prepare the aircraft and myself for a flight in night IMC.

2. The aircraft was probably running for 5 minutes or so after sitting outside for 2 days in 40° damp weather. This didn't allow enough time for the gyros to completely spin up. The attitude and heading gyros are older units with many years and hours of service. These will be overhauled.

3. Partial panel procedures. All my initial and recurrent partial panel training has been accomplished using suction cup style covers over the attitude and heading indicators. In this actual event, I found it difficult to ignore the erroneous information presented by these instruments. **(Rod Says, "Try covering the failed instrument with a dollar bill.")** *I found myself overcorrecting and my instrument scan diminished and was more fixation than scan. I wish there were an acceptable method of reducing vacuum to create a realistic partial panel training environment. This [would] help pilots to modify their instrument scan and 'tune out' the failed gyros.*

4. I found [that] my thought processes and instrument scan declined with the seriousness of the situation. When faced with unusual attitudes [at] 2,000 feet or less AGL, decision making ability suffers and thought processes narrow and become focused on one aspect of the situation instead of analyzing and evaluating the whole situation. Practicing unusual attitudes under a hood with an instructor cannot create the fear and alarm needed to enlighten the pilot on the mechanics of the human mind."

While our reporter searches for improved training aids for partial panel operations, he plans to work with an instructor on gyro failure and other emergencies.

Postflight Briefing #3-1

Higher Learning

Attitude and Airspeed Transitions

Step 1 of the three step instrument scan allows us to transition from one major attitude to another. While this step is pretty simple to accomplish, there are a few details I want you to know to make your transitions go a bit smoother. As you have already learned, during major attitude transitions, the attitude indicator often becomes both the primary pitch and bank instrument. Master these details and you'll be one flight level up on the average instrument pilot.

Transitioning From a Turn to Straight and Level Flight

During the transition from a turn to straight and level attitude, the attitude indicator becomes primary for pitch and bank (Figure 52). The secret to rolling out of a turn on a specific heading, however, is to know how to lead the rollout. When making a standard rate turn, it's best to lead the rollout by using half the bank angle. For instance, if your bank angle is 16 degrees (common for the airspeeds most small airplanes fly at), then you'll want to lead the turn by eight degrees.

AI is Primary for Pitch and Bank When Transitioning From a Level Turn to Straight and Level Flight

Fig. 52

Since you don't normally make trim adjustments during a standard rate turn, Step 1 simply consists of rolling to straight and level flight attitude on the attitude indicator. When the rollout is complete you radial cross-check the primary instruments for straight and level flight—the altimeter for pitch, the heading indicator for bank, and the airspeed indficator for power (constant airspeed assumed here).

Transitioning From Straight and Level to a Straight Climb

Figure 53 shows the proper scan when transitioning from straight and level flight to a straight climb. During the transition to climb attitude in Step 1, the attitude indicator is primary for pitch and the heading indicator is primary for bank.

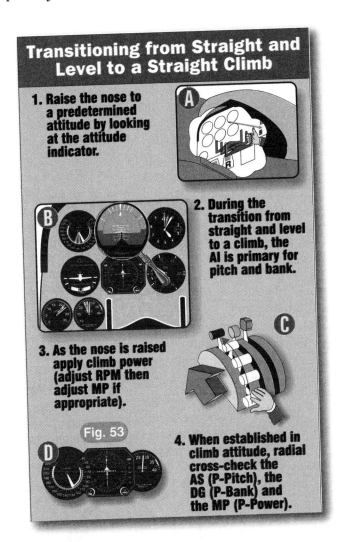

Transitioning from Straight and Level to a Straight Climb

1. Raise the nose to a predetermined attitude by looking at the attitude indicator.

2. During the transition from straight and level to a climb, the AI is primary for pitch and bank.

3. As the nose is raised apply climb power (adjust RPM then adjust MP if appropriate).

Fig. 53

4. When established in climb attitude, radial cross-check the AS (P-Pitch), the DG (P-Bank) and the MP (P-Power).

Begin by raising raise the nose to a predetermined attitude by looking at the attitude indicator. Apply climb power as the nose is raised (the power gauge is the primary power instrument in this transition). You can also apply power after becoming established in the new attitude. (Keep in mind that if you're flying an airplane with a controllable propeller, you'll probably want to increase the RPM to its climb setting first, and then apply power. I'll just assume that you are aware of throttle/propeller etiquette and will manipulate these controls properly from now on.) The objective is to prevent engine overspeed, which can happen in some airplanes if climb power is applied while the airplane is still in level flight. Complete the remaining parts of Step 1 (attitude, power, and trim), then make an initial application of trim to reduce control pressures. Once again, any time the throttle is in its climb or descent power position or is being moved to a specific setting, the power gauge (RPM or MP) becomes the primary power instrument.

Once you're established in a climb attitude, radial cross-check the airspeed indicator (now primary for pitch since we normally climb airplanes at a constant airspeed, thus the name, *constant airspeed* climb.), heading indicator (primary for bank), and the power gauge (primary for power).

For most small airplanes somewhere around 5 to 10 degrees of nose-up pitch is used for a climb attitude. It's important to note that the amount of nose-up pitch required for your airplane varies based on the airspeed you're seeking, the air density, the airplane's weight, etc. Under normal circumstances it's not necessary to slow the airplane down to climb speed before beginning a climb. If you're cruising above the targeted climb speed, simply raise the nose and assist the climb by converting excess forward energy into climb energy.

Transitioning From Straight and Level to a Straight Descent (Constant Airspeed)

Figure 54 shows the proper scan when transitioning from straight and level flight to a straight descent. During the transition, you'll first slow the airplane down to the desired descent speed (Figure 55 will show you how to do this), then you'll select the desired descent attitude shown in Figure 54, Step 2. During this nose down transition, the attitude indicator is primary for pitch and the heading indicator is primary for bank.

Simultaneously reduce power when lowering the nose (the power gauge is the primary power instrument in this

Transitioning from Straight and Level to a Straight Descent at a Constant Airspeed

1. **Reduce speed in level flight (see Figure 55).**
2. **Simultaneously reduce power and lower the nose.**

Fig. 54

3. **During the transition from straight and level to a descent, the AI is primary for pitch and bank.**

4. **When established in descent attitude, radial cross-check the AS (P-Pitch), the DG (P-Bank) and the MP (P-Power).**

transition). Complete the remaining parts of Step 2 by making an initial application of trim to reduce control pressures.

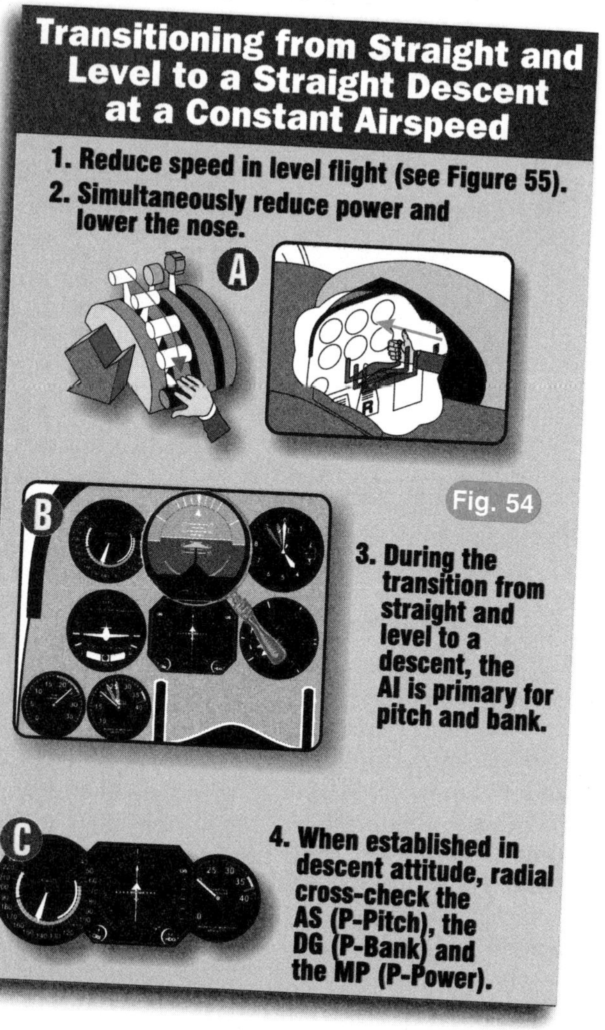

Once you're established in a descending attitude, radial cross-check the airspeed indicator (now primary for pitch), the heading indicator (primary for bank), and the power gauge (primary for power).

Increasing or Decreasing Airspeed While in Straight and Level Flight

Suppose you want to change airspeed while in level flight. You might want to do this before beginning a descent, a climb, to accommodate an ATC request, or for other incredibly good reasons (such as when your flight instructor asks you to).

Figure 55 shows the proper scan when transitioning to a slower airspeed in straight and level flight. Since changing airspeed in this condition isn't a major attitude change, you'll use a combination of Step 1 and Step 2 of the instrument scan. During this maneuver, it's important to coordinate pitch, bank, and power while maintaining straight and level flight as the airspeed changes. Here's a recommended sequence for decreasing the airspeed.

Begin by reducing power to below the setting needed for the new airspeed. In other words, exaggerate (underpower) the initial power change so that the airspeed will change at a reasonable rate. As power is reduced, simultaneously apply back elevator pressure to hold altitude, apply the appropriate amount of rudder pressure to keep the airplane coordinated and apply a slight amount of nose-up trim to reduce control pressures. To maintain straight and level flight, you'll need to radial cross-check the altimeter (primary for pitch), the heading indicator (primary for bank), and the power gauge (initially this is primary for power; as the correct airspeed is approached, the airspeed indicator becomes primary for power). Once the airspeed you're after is reached and stabilized, apply any additional trim that's needed, then begin Step 3 (rectangular cross-checking the instruments).

When transitioning to a higher airspeed in straight and level flight, the same principles shown in Figure 55 apply. The main difference is that the elevator and the throttle are being moved forward, not rearward. Begin by increasing power to greater than what is needed to sustain the new airspeed (make sure you move the propeller control knob first if it's necessary to keep RPM values higher than MP values). In other words, overpower the initial power change so that the airspeed will change at a reasonable rate. As power is increased, simultaneously apply forward elevator pressure to hold altitude, apply the appropriate amount of rudder pressure to keep the airplane coordinated, and apply a slight amount of nose-down trim to reduce control pressures. To maintain straight and level flight during this transition, radial cross-check the altimeter (primary for pitch), the heading indicator (primary for bank), and the power gauge (once again, this gauge is initially primary for power; as you approach the target airspeed, the airspeed indicator becomes primary for power). Once the targeted airspeed is reached and stabilized, apply any additional trim that's needed, then begin Step 3 again.

It's interesting to note that the attitude indicator isn't considered a primary pitch or bank instrument when transitioning between airspeeds in straight and level flight. Why? Because you want to remain in straight and level flight as the airspeed changes and the attitude indicator doesn't give you the necessary information to remain in this condition, as we've already learned.

Transitioning From Straight and Level Flight to a Descending Turn

Figure 56 shows the proper scan when transitioning from straight and level flight to a descending turn. First, slow the airplane down to the desired airspeed while in level flight. During the transition to a nose-down, banked attitude shown in Step 2, the attitude

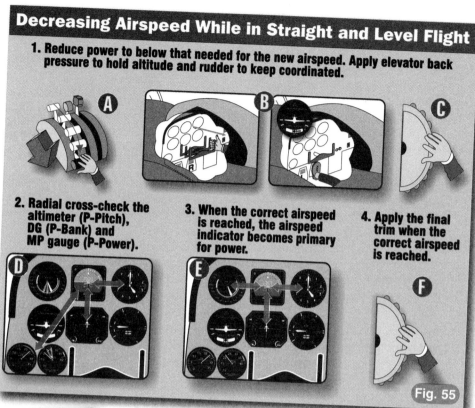

Decreasing Airspeed While in Straight and Level Flight

1. Reduce power to below that needed for the new airspeed. Apply elevator back pressure to hold altitude and rudder to keep coordinated.

2. Radial cross-check the altimeter (P-Pitch), DG (P-Bank) and MP gauge (P-Power).

3. When the correct airspeed is reached, the airspeed indicator becomes primary for power.

4. Apply the final trim when the correct airspeed is reached.

Fig. 55

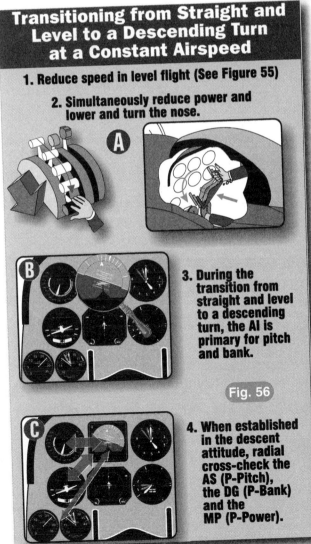

Transitioning from Straight and Level to a Descending Turn at a Constant Airspeed

1. Reduce speed in level flight (See Figure 55)

2. Simultaneously reduce power and lower and turn the nose.

3. During the transition from straight and level to a descending turn, the AI is primary for pitch and bank.

Fig. 56

4. When established in the descent attitude, radial cross-check the AS (P-Pitch), the DG (P-Bank) and the MP (P-Power).

indicator is primary for both pitch and bank. Lower the nose and bank the airplane to a predetermined attitude by looking at the attitude indicator.

Simultaneously reduce power while lowering the nose (the power gauge is the primary instrument in this transition). Complete the remaining parts of Step 2 by confirming the correct operation of the attitude indicator and make an initial application of trim to reduce control pressures.

Once you're established in a descending-turn attitude, radial cross-check the airspeed indicator (now primary for pitch), the turn coordinator (primary for bank), and the power gauge (primary for power).

Leveling Off from a Climb or a Descent

Figure 57 shows the proper technique when transitioning from a straight descent to straight and level flight. The procedure in Figure 57 can also be used to level off from a climb, too. During the transition from a climb or a descent to straight and level flight, the attitude indicator in Step 1 is primary for pitch, and the heading indicator is primary for bank. Begin by raising or lowering the nose to a level flight attitude by looking at the attitude indicator.

If you're transitioning from a climb to level flight, allow the airplane to accelerate to the target airspeed before reducing power (the power gauge is primary for power during the acceleration). It is necessary to coordinate the needed forward elevator and rudder pressures as the airplane accelerates.

If you're transitioning from a descent and want to maintain your airspeed, reduce power to a setting that maintains that speed (the power gauge is primary for power during the transition). Complete the remaining parts of Step 1 by confirming the correct operation of the attitude indicator, and trim to reduce control pressures.

Once you're established in the straight and level flight attitude, radial cross-check the altimeter (now primary for pitch), the heading indicator (primary for bank), and the airspeed indicator (now primary for power). Keep in mind that any time the throttle is in its climb or descent power position or is being moved to a specific setting, the power gauge (RPM or MP) becomes the primary power instrument.

During the level-off from a climb, it's best to begin the transition to level flight before reaching the target altitude. How much before? Try leading the altitude by 10% of the rate shown on the VSI. When transitioning from a climb or descent, the airplane will continue to climb or descend at a decreasing rate. Since the FAA specifies that all climbs and descents should be made at no more than 500 fpm during the last 1,000 feet of altitude change, you'll generally use 50 feet as your lead.

Leveling off from a descent is also accomplished by starting above the target altitude by about 10% of the rate of change on the VSI. If you want to level off at a higher cruise speed than you had during the descent, begin adding power at 100 to 150 feet above the level-off altitude. The airplane will accelerate and be closer to the appropriate airspeed when leveling off. How much power should you add? Take your best guess (your guess will get better with experience).

Radial Cross-Checking for a Constant Rate Descent

Figure 58 shows the primary instruments and the proper radial cross-check when making a constant rate descent. This is a descent conducted at a specific airspeed and specific rate of descent. When established in the descent, the VSI becomes primary for pitch, the heading indicator becomes primary for bank, and the airspeed indicator becomes primary for power (the throttle position determines the airspeed flown, thus the airspeed indicator is primary for power).

The constant rate descent is normally begun by reducing power and letting the airspeed decrease to a target value, at which time you further reduce power, then lower the nose to a predetermined attitude that you expect will provide the correct descent rate. An initial application of trim is made to stabilize the airplane, and the proper operation of the attitude indicator is confirmed, completing Step 1 of the scan.

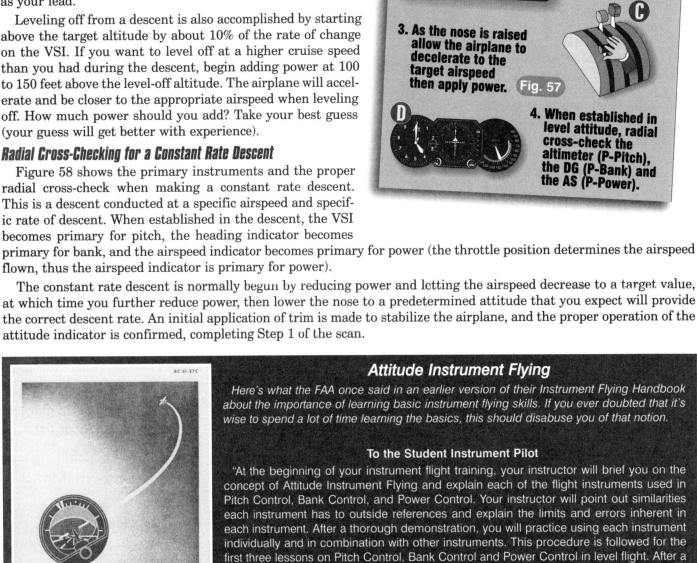

Leveling off From a Climb or Descent

1. Raise the nose to level flight attitude by looking at the attitude indicator.

2. During the transition from a descent to straight and level, the AI is primary for pitch and the DG is primary for bank.

3. As the nose is raised allow the airplane to decelerate to the target airspeed then apply power. Fig. 57

4. When established in level attitude, radial cross-check the altimeter (P-Pitch), the DG (P-Bank) and the AS (P-Power).

Attitude Instrument Flying

Here's what the FAA once said in an earlier version of their Instrument Flying Handbook about the importance of learning basic instrument flying skills. If you ever doubted that it's wise to spend a lot of time learning the basics, this should disabuse you of that notion.

To the Student Instrument Pilot

"At the beginning of your instrument flight training, your instructor will brief you on the concept of Attitude Instrument Flying and explain each of the flight instruments used in Pitch Control, Bank Control, and Power Control. Your instructor will point out similarities each instrument has to outside references and explain the limits and errors inherent in each instrument. After a thorough demonstration, you will practice using each instrument individually and in combination with other instruments. This procedure is followed for the first three lessons on Pitch Control, Bank Control and Power Control in level flight. After a short time, you will be making a logical cross-check and not merely scanning the instruments. *Approximately 6 hours of flight time plus the necessary ground school is usually required to cover the first three basic lessons.* Your instructor will monitor your progress closely during this early training to guide you in dividing your attention properly. The importance of this "division of attention" or "cross-check" cannot be emphasized too much...."

AC 61-27C

INSTRUMENT FLYING HANDBOOK

U.S. DEPARTMENT OF TRANSPORTATION
FEDERAL AVIATION ADMINISTRATION

Radial Cross-Checking for a Constant Rate Descent

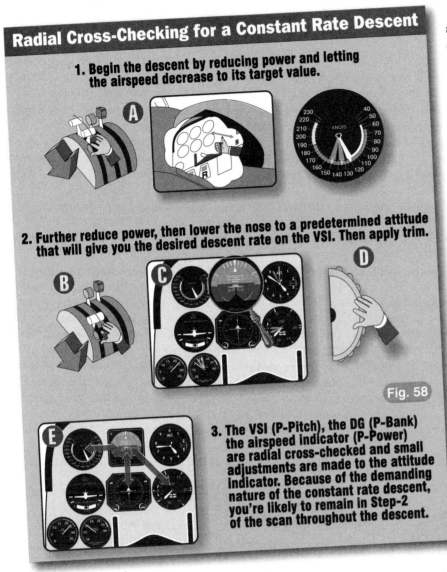

1. Begin the descent by reducing power and letting the airspeed decrease to its target value.

2. Further reduce power, then lower the nose to a predetermined attitude that will give you the desired descent rate on the VSI. Then apply trim.

Fig. 58

3. The VSI (P-Pitch), the DG (P-Bank) the airspeed indicator (P-Power) are radial cross-checked and small adjustments are made to the attitude indicator. Because of the demanding nature of the constant rate descent, you're likely to remain in Step-2 of the scan throughout the descent.

Next, the VSI, heading indicator, and airspeed indicator are radial cross-checked and small adjustments made to the attitude indicator, yielding the correct values of the primary pitch, bank and power instruments respectively. Because of the demanding nature of the constant rate descent, you'll never quite reach Step 3 of the scan. In fact, you'll most likely remain in Step 2, radial cross-checking the primary instruments throughout the descent.

It just so happens that the constant rate descent is the type of descent you'll use when flying the glideslope of an instrument landing system (ILS) approach. In addition to the primary pitch, bank, and power instruments, you'll have to add the primary navigation instrument to your scan, too. I'm speaking of the ILS indicator, in this instance. At a given groundspeed, a specific descent rate is required to maintain the correct position on the glideslope. We'll discuss this in greater detail later.

With all the emphasis on how the airplane instruments work, what about the person flying it? That means you. We should definitely know something about how you work in the airplane (or don't work properly as is sometimes the case). In the next chapter we'll take a look at the psychological and physiological factors that play an important part in safe flying.

Postflight Briefing #3-2

Stop and Return Localizer Needle Technique

Here's a simple but effective way to stop a moving localizer needle and return it to center. Let's assume that you've intercepted the localizer whose inbound direction is 360 degrees (Steps 1 and 2). You notice the needle moving to the right (Step 3). The very first thing to do is roll to the 10 degree bank mark on your attitude indicator (Step 4) then "immediately" roll back to level flight (Step 5). *Don't hold the bank here.* As a general rule, you don't want to go changing headings more than just 2 or 3 degrees if the needle isn't moving quickly. In this instance, you rolled 10 degrees "in" then immediately rolled "out" changing headings by just a few degrees. Now you've probably stopped the needle's movement (Step 6). To return the needle toward its center position, roll into a 5 degree bank (Step 7), then "immediately" roll back to level flight (Step 9). *Don't hold the bank here.* You're just rolling in and rolling out. That's all. You should see

the needle move toward the center position (Step 8) and, depending on the winds, hopefully keep the needle centered on the current heading (Step 10).

Fig. 59

ILS Flying Tips and Techniques

During your ILS approaches, do the needles bounce around like the bamboo sticks of two Samurai warriors in training? If so, maybe I can help. Let's start with a basic review of the attitude flying techniques involved with the ILS.

First, the descent rate on an ILS approach is dependent on the airplane's groundspeed. While the glideslope is inclined at a specific angle, your groundspeed determines how fast you must descend to remain at that specific angle. Increase your groundspeed and you must descend faster to remain on glideslope. Decrease your groundspeed and you must descend slower to remain on glideslope. The question is, how do you manipulate the flight controls to remain on the glideslope when your groundspeed changes (such as when you encounter windshear)? Here's the FAA's recommended technique.

If you encounter a headwind-to-tailwind type of windshear, then your airspeed will initially drop (Figure 59). The nose tends to pitch down and your rate of descent will increase. The airplane, in this instance, tends to go below the glideslope. Your initial reaction should be to add power to counteract the decreased airspeed and to resume your previous approach airspeed.

This is your initial reaction. Once the airplane stabilizes, however, you'll have a higher groundspeed as a result of the tailwind. Therefore, you'll need to *reduce* power in order to decrease your airspeed, thus maintaining the glideslope at your previous rate of descent (the assumption here is that you want to maintain the glideslope at the previous rate of descent. You might want to increase power to maintain the previous approach airspeed and just increase your rate of descent. Why? Because you may one of those people who likes to start the time at the FAF even on an ILS, just in case it's necessary to convert the approach into a non-precision localizer approach).

If you encounter a tailwind-to-headwind type of windshear, your airspeed will initially increase (Figure 60). The nose tends to pitch up and your rate of descent will decrease. The airplane, in this instance, tends to go above the glideslope. Your initial reaction should be to reduce power to counteract the increased airspeed and to resume your previous approach airspeed. This is your initial reaction. Once the airplane stabilizes, you'll have a lower groundspeed as a result of the headwind. You'll need to *increase* power to increase your airspeed and maintain your previous rate of descent on the glideslope.

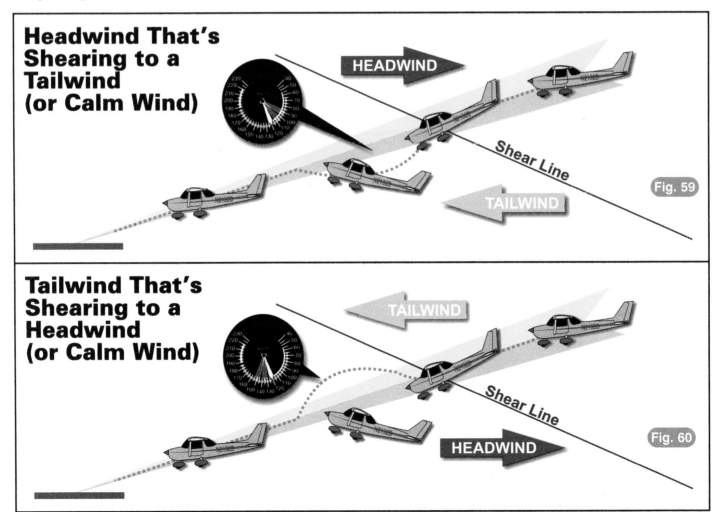

Headwind That's Shearing to a Tailwind (or Calm Wind)

HEADWIND

Shear Line

TAILWIND

Fig. 59

Tailwind That's Shearing to a Headwind (or Calm Wind)

TAILWIND

Shear Line

HEADWIND

Fig. 60

Chapter 4
Humans: The Plane Brain

Billy Bob and Bubba went duck hunting. Bubba said, "Hey Billy Bob, how come we're not catching any ducks?" Billy Bob replied, "I don't know, maybe we're not throwing the dog high enough."

I think it's safe to say that neither of these folks would be good at problem solving. Fortunately, the NTSB has a crack team of investigators, gifted with enormous frontal lobes, who *are* good at solving problems. That's why we can say with some certainty that around 75% of all accidents involve some degree of pilot error. In other words, it's not the airplane—the actual machine—that presents the biggest obstacle to aviation safety today. It's the person doing the flying who holds the key to increasing safety aloft. We have met the enemy, and it is us.

For many years aviation's movers and shakers worked to make aviation safer by improving the aircraft. That was a good choice at the time, given that in the early days a lot of flights ended both early and unexpectedly due to mechanical failures. That left a lot of people who should have been up in the air down on the ground. Today, it's rare for an airplane to fail catastrophically, or even have to land because of a mechanical issue. Airplanes have become remarkably reliable. Modern aviation is a world where some of our newest airplanes have ballistic recovery systems (otherwise known as a built-in parachute), which can lower a suddenly non-flying assembly to earth safely.

That leaves us with the plane brain—the pilot. While airplanes have evolved a lot in the last 50 years, pilots have not. They remain largely furless and often fearless primates who can go to great lengths to spoil a perfectly fine flight. Most have superbly crafted cerebral cortexes (thinking parts), yet they somehow overlook this crucial piece of equipment when deciding what to do.

The brave new frontier of aviation safety deals with making the *pilot* behave more safely and sanely. Some say that evolution would eventually work by eliminating the unthinking from the gene pool, but it's a slow and tragic mechanism. Evolve or dissolve, in a manner of speaking. Such harsh methods are hard on everyone.

That's why many aviation educators and safety specialists want you to learn about how human factors influence aviation safety. They hope you'll think rather than plink in the drink. The goal here is sort of instant evolution, in which you skip over the part where the genes are trimmed from the pool and proceed directly to enlightenment, wisdom, and good behavior.

I'm going to divide the effort into two parts—mind and body, also known as psychology and physiology, or mentation and machine. There are several good reasons for doing this, and then there's the reason I'm doing it, which is that people like things that come in twos. They think the second one is their free bonus.

PSYCHOLOGICAL FACTORS

I hope you don't mind, but let's start by talking about your mind (Figure 1).

I want to start there because it's about all that separates you from other mammals that are *not* allowed to apply for a pilot's license, let alone an instrument rating. It is also the organ most responsible for aviation accidents.

While everyone's fear scenario is an incapacitating heart attack or stroke enroute, the fact is we lose far more pilots every year to bad judgment than to bad arteries. Take a look at any summary of accident reports and you will find that the great preponderance of problems relates to failures of the mind, not the body.

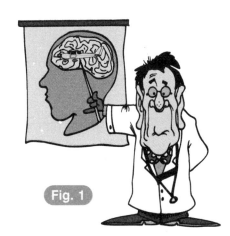

Fig. 1

Pilots aren't stupid. It takes considerable mental material to earn a pilot's license. But the very personality traits and talents that make us pilots can turn on us, leading to the bad decisions that show up repetitively on the accident blotter. Running out of fuel, flying into forecast icing, buzzing a girlfriend's house, continuing under VFR into IFR conditions, losing control, failing to obtain a weather briefing—the list is a litany of things done by people who knew better than to do those things.

Judgment isn't like physiology. It's hard to see, and it's harder still to measure. The mind is infinitely more complex and considerably less accessible than the rest of the body. We can do a coronary bypass, but not a bad decisionmaking bypass. We can do LASIK to improve a pilot's vision, but we devote a lot less attention to sharpening his or her thinking. Time for a change.

When pilots run out of fuel or fly into weather that they can't handle, it's rarely lack of knowledge that got them in trouble. It's failure to use the knowledge they had to achieve the best possible result. It would be impossible to get your pilot's license without knowing how to calculate the fuel needed to get from Point A to Point B, given certain wind conditions. But knowing how to get pilots to make that calculation and check it and not cut corners and not fudge in order to stuff in more baggage for their ski trip—that's the challenge of aviation psychology.

You know all you need to know. You know what you *should* do. Now you need to understand why sometimes people just like you don't do it. That's the subject of this section, which I hope you will read as if your life depended on it.

Because it does.

Good Pilots and Bad Decisions

Every so often you'll read about a pilot who fails to perform a thorough preflight and taxis to the runup area dragging a concrete block from his rear tiedown hook. Had he even bothered to look back there, or had he done a proper preflight walk around, he'd have remembered to untie the tiedown rope. Now he never needs to worry about finding a tiedown spot at any airport. He's even got his own inexpensive radar altimeter (in the form of a plumb bob) hooked to his tail. As soon as he hears concrete contacting asphalt, it's time to flare. His landings are now cast in concrete.

Does such a pilot have good judgment? I don't think so. The sad fact is that even good pilots make bad decisions sometimes, and some pilots make bad decisions quite regularly.

Fortunately, exercising good judgment is something we can do on the ground or in the air. With a few simple tools, you can keep yourself from being the victim of an embarrassing, perhaps even deadly, error in judgment.

The exercise of good judgment *can* be taught, despite a once popular belief to the contrary. We now know that good judgment does not only come with years of experience. No matter what your experience level, you can learn to identify and control several of the variables leading to poor decisions. For instance, it's possible to identify attitudes that are hazardous to safe flight as well as learn how to modify our personal behavior. These are just a few of the useful techniques that help you make better decisions as an instrument pilot.

I want to emphasize that there isn't a dichotomy of "good" and "bad" pilot personalities and judgment behaviors. There is a whole continuum, and on any given day any of us can land anywhere on that spectrum of behavior. You'd best not live in a glass cockpit if you're going to cast

the first spinner. Given the right (or wrong) combination of circumstances, even "good" pilots can fall into one or more of the dangerous behavior traps.

Let's look closely at a few of the most important essentials of aviation decision-making.

Two Types of Decisions

Decisions fall broadly into two categories: those tied to time constraints and those not tied to time constraints. A time-constrained decision requires an immediate solution. For example, if you have an engine fire, pronto is not soon enough for me. If, on the other hand, your number two communications radio (your backup) failed in IMC (instrument meteorological conditions), you wouldn't necessarily rush to solve this problem. You can often take your time and collect information before deciding on a course of action.

Time-constrained decisions are best handled by training. If an engine quits in IMC and you only had one to begin with, then it's your training that determines how safe you'll be. Had you practiced circling down above an airport using the moving map display on your GPS, then you would have increased the chances of making the best of a very bad situation. If you start picking up ice despite the lack of icing in the forecast, you need to start thinking how to handle that problem *tout suite* or the outcome won't be too sweet. Can you get above the clouds? What about a descent to above-freezing temperatures, if such temps exist below you? Perhaps a 180 degree turn or a landing at the nearest suitable airport is best. You must decide, and do so soon.

Most of the aviation decisions you make don't require immediate action. Preflight is a good example. It's rare to hear of someone having an emergency when preflighting the airplane. After all, if the engine quit during preflight, how in the world would you know? It's not even running. You get the point, right? You have the time to carefully consider all the available information. You can make (or fail to make) many important decisions during the preflight phase of your flight. And this is what makes the results of a NASA study all the more interesting. The research revealed that 80% of the poor decisions leading to an in-flight incident occurred during the preflight phase, when pilots had all the time in the world to get it right.

Fuel exhaustion is a good example of this type of error. Have you ever thought about the fact that people run out of fuel mostly because they didn't take enough? In this case, *enough* means figuring out what you need to get from hither to yon taking into consideration winds and other factors, then making a reasonable allowance for contingencies and reaching alternates in case of problems. This calculation is not only legally required of instrument pilots, but it's also prudent if you are contemplating flight

Thanks for the Memories

Most folks want a better memory, at least when they can remember that they want it. Memory is an important part of the instrument flying process. An instrument pilot has to remember a lot of small things as well a lot of big things, not to mention many in-between things. Here are a few concepts to consider about how your memory works and how to make it work better for you.

Memory works in a multistage process involving three systems: *the sensory register*, *working* or *short term memory* and *long term memory*. Each functions in a slightly different way.

The sensory register receives input from the environment through your senses based on what you think is important, and discards what's perceived as extraneous. This is why a mother responds immediately to the sound of her crying baby at night, while other family members might not notice it (or pretend not to notice if getting out of bed is involved).

This is also why you will usually respond to certain environmental stimuli such as a panel warning light, regardless of the flying chores you may be involved at the time. The moment you notice the warning light, important information passes into working or short term memory. Here, the information may stay or fade rapidly, depending on your priorities. For instance, when ATC calls your "N" number, this activates the sensory register and places the controller's call in your short term memory queue. Trained pilot that you are, you know that you'll soon have to respond or the controller will call again (requiring you to dredge up some good excuses from long term memory). If ATC calls and gives you a new transponder code, and this information makes it to your short-term memory (you register it), it won't remain there for long. That's why it's called *short term* memory!

Normally, information only has about a 20 second lifespan in short term memory, varying slightly depending on the nature of your priorities. You can help information stay longer by repeating it out loud. This is one good reason to always read back your clearances. Rehearsing, repetition, sorting, rhyming, associations, mnemonics or categorizing the material into systematic chunks is called *coding*, and it's another way to help information stay in short term memory and move it into long-term memory if you want. Most commercial memory courses just teach various coding techniques.

For instance, if ATC clears you to fly via Victor 11 and climb to 11,000 feet, you may notice the similarities between the first two numerical values to help remember the information until you can write it down. Saying to yourself, "Fly eleven to eleven," should keep the information present until you grab your pencil (or spray can, chunk of charcoal or whatever you copy clearances with). If you want to remember to place your GPS in OBS mode versus Leg mode before crossing FISHY intersection, you could visualize a big FISH (for FISHY intersection), swallowing a BUS (for OBS) out of which runs a lone LEG (for Leg mode). Depending on the amount of information given and your skill, it can take several seconds to properly code information (to make the chunks, rhymes, verbal repetitions, etc.). Interrupt the process and all the short-term information is likely to be lost within 20 seconds from short-term memory.

Short term memory has a capacity limit, in addition to its time limit. It's usually capable of handling about seven bits or chunks of information at a time. A seven digit telephone number is a good example. If your friend has too many digits for a phone number, you might want to get some friends in your area code (or get used to playing with the cat on Saturday night). This is why you shouldn't count on keeping a long clearance in short term memory. Of course, if you're good at coding, you can overcome this problem, keeping the material in short-term memory for a much longer period of time.

Actual learning doesn't take place until the information moves into long term memory, where it's stored for future use. By use of the coding concepts listed above as well as by rote memorization, it's possible for information to move from short term to long term memory, where it can remain stored for a lifetime. I'm not speaking of remembering all the transponder codes and clearances you've ever received, either. You're only a man who flies in the rain, you're not Rainman. I'm speaking of the information that will have value to you in the long term, like flying skills, foreign languages or, heaven forbid, foreign flying skills. The more extensive the coding process, the easier it is to recall information in the long term.

Keep in mind, however, that it takes effort to move information beyond short term memory. Good students are hip to this point and go out of their way to acquire some basic skill at mnemonics to help them learn more efficiently. A mnemonic is a word whose letters (or the word itself) help trigger your memory. I'M SAFE, for *illness, medication, stress, alcohol, fatigue,* and *eating,* is an example of a mnemonic.

Make a quick trip to the bookstore and ask the book specialist where the self-help section is. If this person says, "If I do that, then you won't be helping yourself," suggest that you're also looking for a book on how to do karate chops. I'm sure the specialist will immediately offer to help you find a book on memory techniques.

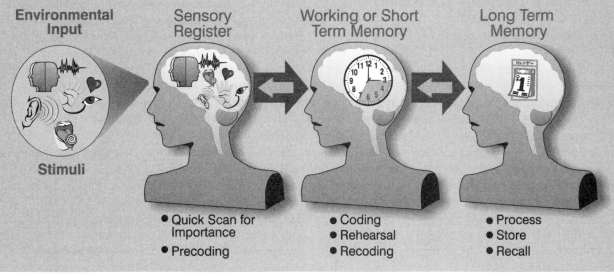

Environmental Input	Sensory Register	Working or Short Term Memory	Long Term Memory

Stimuli

- Quick Scan for Importance
- Precoding

- Coding
- Rehearsal
- Recoding

- Process
- Store
- Recall

Hitting the Spot

Distractions are a common factor in flying. Usually they are overcome by concentrating on the task at hand or through the use of checklists. But, as this pilot and his instructor learned, when fixation and fatigue team up with a distraction, costly mistakes can result.

"The instructor told me to execute a spot landing on the second stripe of the runway centerline. Abeam the numbers I reached forward to the place where the landing gear switch is found [on my type aircraft], but where the cowl flaps control is located on this type aircraft. I closed the cowl flaps, but before I reached for the landing gear switch, the instructor startled me by switching the radio back to Approach Control. He informed Approach that we were remaining in the pattern. I switched back to CTAF and announced our position. I proceeded to "complete" the [landing] check, turned final, and adjusted power to ensure that we would touch down on the designated spot. I fixated on the spot landing target and failed to make my customary recheck of "three green." Evidently, the instructor distracted himself as well when he made the radio call because he did not catch my failure

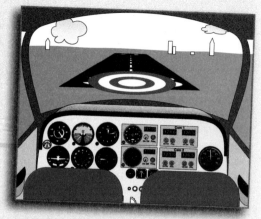

to lower the gear abeam the numbers. He also must have fixated on the spot-landing target. The airplane's gear up warning horn was inoperative and did not sound. The prop struck the runway as the belly settled onto the second stripe of the centerline. The sound of metal striking concrete was horrible, but the actual landing was surprisingly soft."

Distraction, fixation, and motor memory confusion all played a roll in this unfortunate incident, but the underlying cause was fatigue. My sleep-deprived mind focused reasonably well on one thing at a time, but was thrown off by a relatively minor distraction. The assumption that I could safely fly dual when I was too tired to fly solo was my basic mistake. If one is too tired to fly solo, one shouldn't take the controls of an airplane period.   ***NASA Callback Report***

into unfavorable weather, where a sudden change in conditions can mean your primary airport is no longer in the plan. Instrument pilots *must* have a Plan B, and the fuel to get there.

It's not too difficult to figure what's needed, yet one study found that 70% of fuel exhaustion accidents occurred within 10 miles of the destination airport. Close, so close, and yet so far. Unlike darts and horseshoes, almost does not count in aviation.

Of course, pilots could handle this problem by planning a flight, then switching the destination to an airport that's 10 miles closer. You're right, that seems ridiculous, doesn't it? I think it's much simpler to do some proper preflight planning to begin with. Thoughtful preparation, having sufficient fuel reserves and careful planning are the ways to prevent accidents.

The most important decisions you'll make in an airplane have already been made. Before you ever leave the ground, know how to handle the most common in-flight emergencies, know how to overcome your temptation to please other folks (passengers, other pilots in the cockpit, the FBO manager, etc.) that might adversely influence your flight safety, and know that you should never try and save an airplane at the risk of human injury.

As an extreme example, suppose you're flying an airplane with a ballistic parachute system and find yourself critically low on fuel in IMC over mountainous terrain. Wouldn't it be better to deploy the chute and descend to earth in a gentle manner rather than ride a gliding airplane through the clouds into what might be a granite wall? While it's necessary to carefully examine all the information before making such a decision, your willingness to sacrifice your airplane to save yourself and your passengers is a decision that should be made long before you enter that airplane.

Of course, any decision you make in an airplane, time critical or not, requires that you have sufficient knowledge and skill to reach a reasonable conclusion.

Factors That Influence Our Decisions

Knowledge

Several factors influence our ability to make good aviation decisions.

First, to successfully cope with any aviation situation you need knowledge. This is typically acquired during flight training, where you learn things such as how to anticipate, detect and avoid icing conditions aloft; selecting an alternate if the flight can't be completed as planned; and so forth. These are a just a few of the many practical topics you'll be exposed to during the course of your instrument training (I said practical topics, so don't expect to learn something like how to look good in sunglasses).

Sufficient information is available to you as an instrument pilot to handle nearly any problem you might encounter aloft. Your job to seek it out, understand it and apply it as you see appropriate. How do you get this information? There are only two ways. Ask a lot of questions and read a lot of books. Sorry, no knowledge implants, brain transplants or injections will do the trick. Sleeping on a book doesn't work (Sorry Edgar Cayce). All that does is give you knowledge of neck cramps. Hard work is involved. It's called *studying*.

As I see it, you have an obligation to yourself and all your future passengers to ask a question of every competent instrument pilot you meet. For instance, the next time you encounter a skilled instrument pilot, ask him or her how to determine clouds are free from thunderstorms. You might also ask what degree of convective activity the person considers dangerous enough to be avoided. What about asking how someone might handle icing on the air-

frame? The list is endless. Of course, you'll have to measure the value of each statement based on the credibility of the person offering the advice.

There are also a lot of good books on the market, as well as many good instructors and seminars to help make you the educated pilot you'd like to be. In the appendix of this book I suggest an assortment of books that would be useful additions to your library. If you're not reading one or two aviation books a month as well as subscribing to and reading a few of the top aviation magazines, your education is probably deficient in some respects. The good news is that you can do something about it. So read!

Skill

In addition to knowledge, you must develop skill in applying that knowledge. That's why the FAA requires a minimum of 40 hours of actual or simulated instrument flight time for the instrument rating. This also explains why you can't obtain an instrument rating via a home correspondence course using Microsoft Flight Simulator.

Realistically, most folks take well over 40 hours of instrument flight time to obtain the skill necessary to fly instruments. Does this mean that these skills can't be acquired in less time? Not at all. The secret to doing so lies in having a good instructor, a good flight training syllabus, time to train, and a PC simulator at home on which to practice.

That's right. You can make tremendous improvements in your instrument skills by practicing with simulation software on your personal computer. At this stage of the game you don't necessarily need rudder pedals with your simulation software, either. A good joystick and capable programs will do it.

After you've learned the basics of attitude instrument flying, you will focus on the perceptual and cognitive aspects of training. Instrument scanning while handling distractions is a good example of how a PC simulator can help you. You can increase the demands placed on you by

setting the software to fail instruments randomly (as they might actually do in a poorly maintained airplane), or you can fly some of the larger and faster airplane models that are available. For instance, if I want to challenge myself I'll fly the Boeing 737 offered by my PC simulation software. This exercise helps inch up my instrument flying performance and gives me a good reason to practice speaking with my deep and oh-so-fake airline captain voice.

While knowledge, skill, and a basic understanding of how decisions are made is important, there's another aspect of decision making to consider. It involves the traps that instrument pilots set for themselves, and which too often lead to dangerous or deadly situations.

Self Awareness and Hazardous Thinking
Common Behavioral Pilot Traps

If there is such a thing as an enemy to a pilot, then it's the pilot himself. It's often our inability to deal with some very common behavioral traps that gets us into trouble.

You don't want to stumble into these traps. I'm specifically referring to traps like always trying to complete the flight the way you planned it, trying to please your passengers, trying to meet schedules, and trying to demonstrate that you have the right stuffing. Well, at hundreds of miles per hour, the fabled right stuffing can turn you and your airplane into bent stuff.

Below I list 12 common traps. Anyone can fall into any one of them at any time. You aren't immune because you're a nice person, a captain of industry, or a 10,000 hour pilot. Most experienced pilots have fallen into one or more of these somewhere along the way. If they were lucky, they escaped unscathed and learned from the experience. I want you to learn from *their* experience. So here's your chance. Avoiding these traps requires recognizing the behaviors or tendencies associated with them, and then learning to short circuit the cycle before you fall into the trap.

Peer Pressure. No, this doesn't have anything to do with flying near the beach. It's simply poor decision making based on emotional response to peers rather than evaluating a situation objectively. You're at the airport with two pilot friends, and they want to make a flight under conditions you're not confident flying in. The pressure is on. The trap is baited. Are you taking the bait?

Mindset. This trap results from a pilot's inability to recognize and cope with situations that differ from those anticipated or planned. Just because the briefer said it would be sunny with no wind at the destination does not mean it will be sunny with no wind at the destination. Things change. If you keep flying as though there were no wind in the face of 30-gusting-to-40, you're headed for this trap.

Get-There-Itis. This condition is common among pilots, and it's one of the leading causes of accidents. It clouds the vision and impairs judgment. The typical scenario is that you've invited some family, friends, or business colleagues to go away for the weekend. Reservations are made, deposits are deposited, and everyone is eager to go. You take off, and along the way the weather worsens. You know how much everyone is looking forward to The La La Spa & Grill for the weekend. The trap is set. Will you divert and land at an alternate airport or plow ahead?

Get-There-Itis is suspected to be the root cause of another malady that I just made up called Break-and-Crumple-Your-Airplane-Itis. It is sometimes combined with the Peer Pressure trap. And on a really bad day, you can get those two *plus* the Mindset trap. The outcome is often not pretty.

Duck-Under Syndrome. This is a tendency instrument-rated pilots have to sneak a peek by descending below minimum altitudes during an instrument approach. "Just a few more feet and I just know I'll be able to see the runway." This trap is based on a belief that there is always a built-in fudge factor that can be used whenever you need it, or from an unwillingness to admit defeat and shoot a missed approach. Pilots from China might call this the Peaking-Duck-Under-Glass-Syndrome. It's often combined with the Get-There-Itis trap, creating a dynamic duo that's a real killer.

Scud Running. This is dangerous! Scud running involves flying beneath ragged clouds or other obscuring layers at very low altitudes, pushing the capabilities of the pilot and the aircraft to (and beyond) the limits.

Bob was so far behind the airplane that there was no way he was getting hurt if there was an accident.

Scud running involves trying to maintain visual contact with the terrain while avoiding physical contact with it. You are getting an IFR rating so you don't have to do this sort of thing. Don't get trapped into doing it.

Continuing Visual Flight Rules (VFR) into Instrument Conditions. This scenario often leads to spatial disorientation or collision with the ground and/or obstacles. Oddly enough, instrument pilots often fall prey to this mistake, particularly when they are rated but not current. The temptation is to say to oneself, "Self, technically you aren't current, but you *are* an instrument rated pilot, so you can certainly handle a simple IFR flight like this." Sounds like a trap to me. In the accident report, they will note that you were rated but not current, if that's any consolation.

Getting Behind the Aircraft. The only time it's good to get behind the aircraft is when you untie the tail before departure. Unfortunately, some pilots allow events or the situation to control their actions, rather than the other way around. This condition is characterized by a constant state of surprise at what happens next. Pilots in this condition often look like they drew their eyebrows in at too great an angle during makeup time. Always keep in mind that you are called the Pilot in Command for a reason. Act like it.

Get-Home Itis

A general aviation pilot, on the last leg of a two-day cross-country trip, succumbed to some self-imposed holiday pressure. The reporter admitted to being "mentally and physically fatigued, and with a severe case of 'get-home-itis' due to the holiday." When the weather did not cooperate with the pilot's holiday plans, all the pre-flight planning—and the fuel reserves—went down the drain.

"My weather briefing had forecast quartering tailwinds, which unfortunately were not the case. The winds had shifted to a direct headwind, blowing strong. The fuel tanks were reading a quarter-full. According to the flight time and the fuel gauges, I believed I had plenty of fuel to reach my destination.

I was about 10-12 miles from home, and 2 miles past Airport A. As I experienced more turbulence, I noticed my fuel gauges were reading lower than moments before, and my engine began to run rough. I turned toward Airport A, then suddenly my engine stopped. The restart attempt was a failure, so I called Airport A and declared an emergency. A normal approach to landing was performed, coasting to the side of the runway to wait to be assisted off by a tug."

To prevent this type of situation, always allow more time, be prepared to make an extra fuel stop, keep a current weather update, and never allow "get-home-itis" to push you and your airplane into a situation you may regret.

ASRS receives many reports on this subject, but get-home-itis during the holidays may be more pronounced than at other times of the year. The added factor of unexpected winds and weather increases the potential for incidents or accidents.

NASA Callback Report

Loss of Positional or Situational Awareness. This condition is another case of getting behind the aircraft, which results in not knowing where you are, failing to recognize deteriorating circumstances, and/or misjudging how fast your situation is worsening. A good IFR pilot is always aware of where he or she is. Losing awareness can, for example, lead to accepting an incorrect or dangerous ATC instruction. Don't fall into the trap of letting someone else (ATC) fly the plane for you. Know where you are at all times. Be aware of what's around you. And know what your total situation is, including any changes from what was expected.

Operating Without Adequate Fuel Reserves. Ignoring minimum fuel reserve requirements, either while operating VFR or IFR, is usually the result of overconfidence, lack flight planning, or contempt for the regulations. Sometimes all three are involved. In other words, you can fuel some of the people some of the time but you can't fuel everyone all the time (especially when they need to be fueled). There is no law against carrying more than the minimum reserves, by the way. Since aerial refueling is not an option for non-military planes, having enough go-juice on board is essential. Don't fall into the trap of assuming everything (weather, wind, lack of delays) will be optimal, and thus cutting your reserves in order to avoid a fuel stop or carry more baggage.

Descent Below the Minimum Enroute Altitude. Here, the Duck-Under trap manifests itself during the enroute portion of an IFR flight. The trap is set when you think

checklists, etc. It can mean failing to have current charts on board, failing to keep maintenance current, or failure to do the calculations on the assumption that because you've flown the route before, you'll have enough fuel under today's conditions. This is a problem associated with a pilot's unjustified reliance on his or her short and long term memory, regular flying skills, repetitive and familiar routes, etc. Sometimes familiarity breeds *content*, a trap for which you should have contempt.

These are the 12 biggies that could stop you as fast as a tiny insect trying a short field landing on flypaper. All of these involve choices made by the pilot to do something that wasn't wise. Now it's time to look at the reasons why pilots make one of these poor choices in the first place. A good place to start is with the hazardous thought patterns that all pilots have, have had, or might have at some time when flying an airplane.

Hazardous Thought Patterns & Their Antidotes

An important factor affecting the quality and safety of flight is a pilot's attitude. Unlike personality, most psychologists agree that you can change an attitude. Your attitude is a state of mind, a feeling, a disposition. Not all attitudes, unfortunately, are conducive to safe flying. The following are five attitudes that aviation psychologists believe to be particularly hazardous to safe flight (Figure 2). The antidotes for these poisonous attitudes are shown to the right in Figure 2.

Hazardous Attitude Antidotes	Fig. 2
Attitude	**Antidote**
Anti-authority: Don't tell me.	Follow the rules. They are usually right.
Impulsivity: Do something quickly.	Not so fast. Think first.
Invulnerability: It won't happen to me.	It could happen to me.
Macho: I can do it.	Taking chances is foolish.
Resignation: What's the use?	I'm not helpless. I can make a difference.

it's just a little under, and just for a little while, so what's the big deal. None, if you don't hit anything. Just keep in mind that there *is* a reason it is the *minimum* enroute altitude.

Flying Outside the Envelope. This occurs from a pilot's unjustified reliance on the (usually mistaken) belief that the aircraft's high performance capability meets the demands imposed by the pilot's (usually overestimated) flying skills. It also can result from believing there's such a great margin of safety built in that you can do almost anything without the airplane coming apart. And sadly, it sometimes results from pilots not even knowing the limits.

Neglect of Flight Planning. This trap includes all elements of preflight planning and preparing, inspections,

Anti-authority—You've met this person. He or she inevitably says, "Nobody tells *me* what to do." Folks like this often rebel against the rules and regulations on which safe flying (and most other societal commitments) are built. This hazardous attitude causes some pilots to deliberately break rules intended for the safety of themselves and others. These are the pilots who buzz houses, bust curfews, ignore ATC directions and requests, and tend to get abusive with instructors, FAA examiners, and other authority figures.

I knew of a pilot who removed the right seat from his airplane so there would be no place for an instructor to sit and tell him what to do. It's a good bet that he had the North American distributorship on anti-authority attitudes.

Impulsivity—Some people often feel the need to do something and do it immediately, often long before determining if it's the *right* thing to do. This sort of person will do the first thing that comes to mind, without thinking about what the best alternative might be. This is why I always get a little nervous when a pilot I'm flying with suddenly says, "Hey, watch this." It's likely that he's about to engage in some strange behavior that he probably hasn't thought about very carefully. Having a front row seat at Aviation Impulsive Theater is not my idea of having a good time.

Invulnerability—It's not uncommon for people to feel that accidents happen to others, not to them. These folks know that accidents can happen, and they know that anyone can be affected, but they never really feel or believe they will be personally involved. It's kind of like being a teenager. A pilot with this attitude is more likely to take chances and increase risk. Pilots like this often think they are Supermen. But Superman doesn't really need an airplane, does he?

Macho—Usually thought of as the exclusive preserve of male pilots, I've seen more than a few females who are every bit as macho as the next guy. The macho pilot is always trying to prove that he or she is without fear, concern, or hesitation of any sort. This is sometimes a residue of having seen too many John Wayne movies as a youngster. Most pilots are susceptible to this hazardous attitude, which can lead to taking risks to impress others. This is why it's best not to fly with any pilot who says something like, "Float like a butterfly, swoop like a bee, that's why all the other pilots want to fly like me." Yikes!

Resignation—Pilots who think, "What's the use?" are people who don't feel in control of the events in their lives or their airplanes. They often blame bad luck and fate for whatever happens. They tend to not seek information and not make positive decisions. Instead, they drift along, hoping that good things happen while doing little or nothing to ensure that they do. It's as if they fold their hands, sit back and do nothing, like a little pilot-passivist. While that behavior may generate empathy and attract swarms of TV and newspaper reporters, it's not likely to make you any safer in the air. I once again remind you that you are the *Pilot in Command*.

Psychologist Martin Seligman opened a vast window with his experiments in the 1970s and 80s into what became known as *learned helplessness*. It was Seligman who helped define and refine the concept of animals (and people) who, feeling themselves helpless, acted helpless whether or not they could have done something useful themselves in a given situation.

In the popular vernacular, such people (pilots are not) are thought of as *wimps* or *wusses*. They are people who, to varying degrees, feel they are powerless and ineffective in the world, and thus just give themselves over to whatever hand fate deals them. This is *not* a healthy attitude for an instrument pilot, who must constantly be in confident command of the airplane and ready to take whatever measures are needed to assure the safety of the flight.

These attitudes contribute to poor judgment. They can drive you to decisions that involve excessive risk. Once you've recognized and acknowledged one or more of these attitudes in yourself, you've taken the first step to neutralizing their dangerous effect on your decision making process.

Remember, most people have these attitudes to some degree. To be frank about it, all of us, at one time or another, have probably acted macho, impulsive, or invulnerable. Avoiding problems with judgment means that you should be aware of how these attitudes can impair your ability to fly safely.

The next step is to counteract these attitudes with the appropriate antidote. This means redirecting the hazardous attitude so that correct action can be taken.

Hazardous Attitude Antidotes

Recognition of hazardous thoughts is the first step toward neutralizing them. After recognizing a thought as hazardous, the pilot should label it as hazardous, and then state the corresponding antidote. Antidotes should

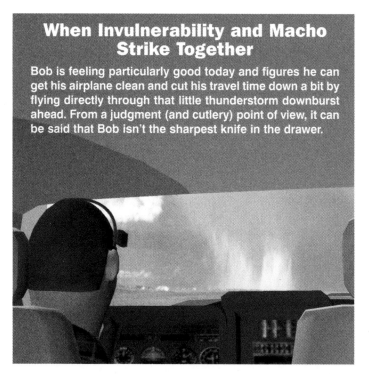

When Invulnerability and Macho Strike Together

Bob is feeling particularly good today and figures he can get his airplane clean and cut his travel time down a bit by flying directly through that little thunderstorm downburst ahead. From a judgment (and cutlery) point of view, it can be said that Bob isn't the sharpest knife in the drawer.

be memorized for each of the hazardous attitudes so they automatically come to mind when needed (Figure 2).

At this point, however, any intelligent person is bound to ask, "If I am acting in a hazardous manner, how is it possible that I'd be self-reflective enough to identify it, much less apply an antidote to stop it?" Great question!

The fact is that hazardous attitudes are *temporary* dispositions, not *permanent* ones. Like the temporary feeling of fear or anxiety, hazardous attitudes stand out from the background of your personality sufficiently enough for you to recognize them, but only if you know they exist in the first place. This is why we're discussing them hear. Now that you know they exist, you're in a better position to do something about them. Do what? How about talking to yourself.

Perhaps, at one time or another, you've found yourself anxious, rushed, or panicky and told yourself to, "Calm down, relax, take your time." The amazing thing is that self-talk actually works in modifying your behavior, especially in high anxiety conditions. That's why it also works well in controlling behavior associated with any of the five hazardous attitudes. The next time you recognize that you're demonstrating any of the five hazardous attitudes, apply the accompanying self-talk antidote.

Anti-authority: Don't tell me.
Antidote: Follow the rules. They are usually right.

Impulsivity: Do something quickly.
Antidote: Not so fast. Think first.

Invulnerability: It won't happen to me.
Antidote: It could happen to me.

Macho: I can do it.
Antidote: Taking chances is foolish.

Resignation: What's the use?
Antidote: I'm not helpless. I can make a difference.

Do antidotes actually work? You bet they do, and I'm not just saying that so that you'll keep reading this book, either. They work, and they can save your life for one very important reason: You can be the best stick and rudder pilot on the planet (or other planets, too) but this means nothing in terms of safety if you let a bad attitude influence your behavior. That's a fact. So be proactive, tune your personal antenna to recognize and identify these attitudes and, if you catch yourself exhibiting one or more, don't be surprised. It happens to the best of us. The difference is that good pilots use the antidote to prevent bad behavior

Concluding Thoughts on These Thoughts

Always be aware that the very qualities that make instrument pilots good are the ones that can injure them. The line is thin between positive personality traits for aviators and an extension of those same traits that leads to hazardous thinking. As a good IFR pilot, you need to be confident (but not macho). You need to be in command (but not anti-authority). You need to be decisive (but not impulsive). You need to feel assured (but not invulnerable). And you need to be capable (not resigned). Striking the right balance is an ongoing challenge.

You may be sitting there thinking, "Only wackos do dumb things in an airplane. I'm a safe pilot and wouldn't dream of doing such nonsense." Yet the macho attitude is nothing more than an extension of this same thought process. I don't know where the dividing line is between the two for you, but I think you do. At least you have the best chance of figuring out where that line is.

Finally, be aware that almost all aviation accidents are caused by human error. Pilots can do a lot to prevent accidents. We are not subject to the vicissitudes of luck or fate. Safe flying is within the control of every pilot. Fate is not the hunter, and we're neither sitting ducks nor turkeys.

Advanced IFR Decision Making Concepts

Now that you've developed an understanding of the psychological factors in decision making, let's advance our knowledge by learning how to use good judgment in the airplane. Of course, not everyone on this planet exercises good judgment, either in or out of the cockpit. For instance, every so often you'll read that someone in a black wetsuit, floating on a surfboard and dangling four limbs over the side, was attacked by a great white shark. Isn't that amazing? What was this person thinking? Doesn't dressing up this way make you look like the shark's favorite food—the seal? Is it the shark's fault he was served breakfast on board, poolside? You could say the surfer sealed his fate in opting to dress as he did.

As an instrument pilot, using good judgment is something you can do on the ground or in the air. I'd suggest both places. With a few simple tools, you can keep yourself from being eaten by some of aviation's well known predators.

The exercise of good judgment can be taught, contrary to the once-popular belief that good judgment only came with years of experience. We now know that you can learn to identify and control several of the variables leading to poor decisions. Let's examine a few of the essentials about what it takes to be an effective decision maker in the cockpit, as well as the resources needed to make those decisions. For the sake of advanced study, I'll assume that you'll go on to become a commercial pilot and fly professionally, even if that means flying pipeline patrol, flight instructing, flying for a business or just flying alone in a professional way.

Professional Operations

As an aspiring commercial/instrument pilot, it's important to consider how your actions affect not only your safety, but also the safety of your passengers. Flying passengers for hire is another way of saying, "It's not all about you." Instead, it's also about your charges, and the responsibility you have for their health and well being. Remember, when you transport passengers, these people look to you for their safety. It's a mighty responsibility and one that demands that you be on your best behavior. Do I sound a little like your dad? Good. (But don't worry. You don't have to mow the lawn.) We all need to be reminded just how important our responsibility is in taking care of our passengers.

Being a professional pilot means doing a *lot* more than just flying the airplane. You are also responsible for how the paying guests feel about their flight and your company. Many pilots (or the cabin crew, speaking on their behalf) get on the PA and say, "We know you have choices. Thank you for choosing Upstart Airlines today." You know why they say that? Because it's true. Every flight is an opportunity to win—or lose—future business. And guess what, Captain? *Your* livelihood is tied to how many of those people choose Upstart again. First you have to make them safe. Then you have to make them happy.

Like it or not, you are in the public relations business. Unfortunately, the only communications capability for which we train and test pilots is plane-to-ATC. Too bad. There should probably be a "social skills" item on the FAA checkride, though if there was, I'm afraid a lot of folks would still be waiting for their licenses. Attention in the cockpit: Being able to copy and read a clearance is *not* the only form of communications skill you need to develop. "Roger" is not a conversation.

That's why I recommend that any aspiring commercial pilot read Dale Carnegie's book, *How to Win Friends and Influence People*. Dale Carnegie understood the essentials of "interactive" long before PlayStation and the Internet. This is, without a doubt, the best book ever written on the basics of getting along with people. Some people didn't have mommies and daddies who taught them how to play nice and speak well with others. Believe me when I say that you won't last long as a commercial pilot if you don't know how to get along with people. You won't! Reputation is everything, and once the word is out that your mere presence in any social situation causes it to end, your professional flying days are over. So get with this book and read it, then reread it every year as a matter of personal maintenance.

Professional pilots care for hundreds of passengers...

...or they care for just a few at a time.

The Three C's Forgotten

Our next reporter was intent on building his multi-engine time. He cut a good deal (or so he thought) with an entrepreneurial "old-timer"— but ended a cross-country flight lucky to be in one piece, and a lot wiser.

In an effort to build multi-engine time, I agreed to fly with an operator who had business all across the country. I agreed to pay for all fuel plus a high hourly rate. It is nearly impossible to rent a multi-engine [aircraft] with low time. As we flew across the country, the list of mechanical problems grew at an exponential rate. The owner of the aircraft was an old timer who was afraid of airspace and considered the FARs an infringement of his freedom. He referred to Class B and restricted areas as "the little blue lines." He preferred to go GPS direct and not talk to anyone if he didn't have to. At one point, I had him fly because the weather was low, and the flight terminated by flying tree-top level in rain and low ceilings. When I began to fly again, he was in such a hurry he pressured me to fly VFR into what appeared to be a thunderstorm. That's when I started down through a hole and ended the flight.

I landed at the primary airport in Class C [airspace]. Because of my lack of familiarity and a badly precessing directional gyro, I nearly landed on the wrong runway without clearance. I'd had enough and didn't feel safe in this airplane, so I got out 1,500 miles from home. I felt good about this decision. It's better to be on the ground wishing you were in the air, than in the air wishing you were on the ground.

This incident brings to mind three other C's that were sadly lacking throughout this flight: good CRM, clear aircraft command, and common sense. We're glad our reporter decided to ground himself and subsequently communicate with ASRS.

NASA Callback Report

There's another way to learn how to get along with others, and that's to associate and study those who are already skilled at this behavior. That's why working with an experienced pilot, such as in a copilot situation, can be such a valuable experience. Watch and learn. That's the key. Ask yourself just what is it that makes this individual so professional and capable at dealing with people as well as planes. If he *isn't* professional and capable, ask yourself the same question—why?

One of the best ways to know how to treat your passengers is to ask them. That's right. In the appropriate setting, it's perfectly acceptable to ask your passengers how you can best serve them. For instance, before a flight you might ask your passengers if they have any questions about the flight or the airplane. Perhaps some are concerned about turbulence or about flying at night, or whether the wings will come off if you hit a bump while taxiing. This is your opportunity to put them at ease with a few carefully placed thoughts regarding aviation safety. It's also your chance to be gracious, understanding, and a good listener as well as great gabber. Of course, if you're flying a plane with 150 passengers, person-to-person comm might be a bit difficult to accomplish. With three or four passengers, though, you should have no trouble handling a few questions from the crowd.

There's another essential concept you need to consider when flying professionally. You are "on" from the moment you get near the airport to the time you leave it. Even when you think that no one is watching you, behave as if everyone is, because they just might be. When you're at the airport you need to act professionally at all times, regardless of whether you're in the pilot's lounge or the parking lot. You absolutely cannot afford any lapses in behavior. Even if you don't usually say "please" and "thank you," or wash your hands after using the bathroom, you'd better be doing it once you hit the airport. There are passengers, and potential passengers, every-

where. Your behavior is constantly being scrutinized, and anything you say and do *can* be used against you.

Any passenger who sees you fly into a rage because someone took the parking spot you thought was yours will not be happy to later find you are the captain of his or her flight. And just imagine how uncomfortable both of you will feel if that passenger is the one who took your spot.

A big part of flying is the part that's not about flying. People who succeed at this as a career have the whole package. If you know there are some bells and whistles missing from *your* pilot package, get to work. People skills can be learned, just as aviation skills can.

Being Pilot In Command

What would you think if I told you that even if you fly a Cessna 172, you have the same authority as the captain of a Boeing 777? It's true, though you have no say-so over his or her 777. There is only one regulation authorizing PIC authority, and that's FAR 91.3, which applies to anyone who flies anything (Area 51 UFO vehicles are an exception). This means that even if you're operating under FAR Part 121 or 135, this regulation is the one that applies to the PIC. The problem here is that most pilots aren't taught how to be pilot in command. They sort of accept the authority without acknowledging or really understanding the responsibility.

The way the FAA looks at it, as PIC you have the final authority and the final say as to the operation of your aircraft. FAR 91.3 is one of the clearest, most succinct and least ambiguous regulations ever written, and for good reason, too. The

No Matter How You Square It
P +IC = PIC

FAA wants to make sure you know, unambiguously, that you're the one in command and you're the one responsible for making the proper decisions on an airplane. And also that you're the one on whom they'll pin the tail if anything goes wrong.

Years ago I met a fellow who ran a medevac helicopter operation. He said that when he hired someone to fly his medical helicopters, he hired them on the basis that these people would tell him "no" when it was appropriate to do so. In other words, he wanted his pilots to have the leadership and strength of character to say that they shouldn't go flying when the risks were too great.

The reality is that many folks are just plain scared to say "no" when it's not safe to fly. That's not the type of person this man wanted piloting his machines. Just imagine how difficult a decision it must be to say "no" to a medevac flight to retrieve someone injured on a freeway somewhere when the weather makes it unsafe to fly. Do you have the mental sinew to make this call, based on your level of experience? If not, then you need to reconsider your priorities because this is precisely what the pilot in command is expected to do.

Sure, you say that telling the boss "no" might mean you get fired. OK, that's possible. You might also say that this is just unfair, even though it's the right thing to do. Yes, that's true. My reply would be that life doesn't have to be fair (check your contract), but it's not as if death gives you some sort of advantage. Being PIC means that you have to be willing to take charge, be in charge and make the necessary decisions willingly, without concern for your personal needs when the needs of others are more important. That's hard language, but it's the way the world works.

A friend who once did the hiring for Flying Tiger airlines told me that they never hired pilots. Instead, they hired captains, even though this person would sit in the flight engineer's seat for many years. Flying Tigers wanted pilots who were captain material, not just pilot material. There *is* a difference.

Sometimes you'll have to make decisions that are unpopular and might upset or disappoint your passengers. The weather might require delaying or even canceling a flight. Sure, the passengers won't like it, but if that's the appropriate thing to do then it must be done. Do you have the character to behave in the right way? Hopefully you do, since this is part of what being PIC is all about. Of course, there's much more to being PIC of an airplane, too. So let's see what else is involved.

> *Sure, you say that telling the boss "no" might mean you get fired. OK, that's possible. You might also say that this is just unfair, even though it's the right thing to do. Yes, that's true. My reply would be that life doesn't have to be fair (check your contract), but it's not as if death gives you some sort of advantage.*

Crew/Cockpit Resource Management

Crew/cockpit resource management (CRM) is all about using the resources that are available to you during your duty as PIC. These resources might be the human resources you have in a copilot, the hardware you have in the cockpit, or the information available to you via that hardware or from ATC. It's a major misconception that only pilots of multi-pilot crews can use CRM or CRM philosophy. Single-pilot operators also need to know how to make better use of all the resources available to them, perhaps even more so than those who've got triple redundancy and a six-planet GPS.

Human Resources

Those resources include all the people with whom you routinely work in preparing and executing a flight—weather briefers, line personnel, mechanics, crewmembers, pilots and air traffic controllers. The real issue here

CRM in Action and At Its Best

CAPTAIN AL HAYNES

Editor's note. On July 19, 1989, United Airlines Flight 232 departed Denver at about 2:09 p.m. and climbed uneventfully to a cruise altitude of 37,000 feet. At approximately 3:16 p.m. the crew notified ATC the #2 engine had failed and that the aircraft was only marginally stable. What followed was one of the most compelling dramas in aviation history as the crew fought to control and eventually land the huge jet, which was effectively without flight controls due to loss of its entire hydraulic system.

Although 112 people died in the landing, the wonder is that 184 survived. Many of the lessons learned that day continue to be taught to successive generations of pilots and emergency personnel.

The captain of Flight 232, Al Haynes, was one of the survivors. He continues to present the story of Flight 232 and its lessons so that others can continue to learn from the experience. The following is excerpted and edited from one of his presentations, made at NASA's Ames Research Center, Edwards, California.

ATC: 232 heavy, say souls on board and fuel remaining.

UAL 232: We have 396, [unreadable].

ATC: United 232 heavy, Sioux City.

UAL 232: Confirm we have no hydraulic fluid, which means we have no elevator control, almost none, and very little aileron control. I have serious doubts about making the airport. Have you got someplace near there that we might be able to ditch? Unless we get control of this airplane, we're going to put it down wherever it happens to be.

ATC: United 232 heavy, say again? 232 heavy, think you'll be able to hold about a 240 heading?

UAL 232: We're going to turn into it about right now.

ATC: When you turn to that 240 heading, sir, the airport will be about oh, 12 o'clock and 38 miles.

UAL 232: Okay, we're trying to control it just by power alone. We have no hydraulics at all, sir. We're doing our best here.

[portion omitted]

UAL 232: United 232. We're starting a left turn back to the airport. Since we have no hydraulics, braking is going to really be a problem. I would suggest the equipment be [placed] toward the far end of the runway. And I think under the circumstances, regardless of the condition of the airplane when we stop, we're going to evacuate, so you might notify the ground crew that we're going to do that.

ATC: United 232 heavy, wilco, sir, and if you can continue that left turn to about a 220 heading, sir, that'll take you right to the airport.

United 232 heavy, you're going to have to widen out just slightly to your left sir, to make the turn to final, and also to take you away from the city.

UAL 232: Whatever you do, keep us away from the city.

ATC did keep us away from the city, and we did land the airplane, though I feel that "land" is a rather loose term for what actually happened. In the final analysis, though, we were successful in preserving the lives of 184 people.

Captain Haynes says, "I think there were five factors that contributed to the degree of success that we had at Sioux City: luck, communications, preparation, execution and cooperation." Rod Machado says, "This is an example of leadership and cockpit management at its best." **Excerpted from *Speaking of Flying* with permission**

is whether or not you're making good use of these resources. Let's examine how you'd use a copilot if you were lucky enough to have one on your flight.

Let's say you're flying for a Part 135 charter operation and the flight requires a copilot. Obviously this flight won't be in a Cessna 152 or there wouldn't be much room for the passengers, would there? What does a copilot do for you? The answer is, anything you want. Within reason, of course. They don't do windows or ironing.

Copilots are wonderful resources if you know how to use them properly. Tuning radios, finding charts, making calls to ATC or the automated flight service station, monitoring your performance and gaining experience are all part of what copilots do. My friend, retired TWA Captain Dave Gwinn, once told me that when he was a copilot he looked at his job as one where he always tried to make the captain look good. In other words, he'd remind the captain of the assigned altitude as they approached it, he'd call out localizer or airway intercepts, he'd tune radios and make ATC calls and so on.

The real problem with copilots is pilots. Most pilots are independent people and like to do things themselves. That may be OK as long as the situation isn't demanding. But in some situations it's easy to be overwhelmed by the workload. Even then, some pilots will try doing it all themselves while their copilots sit nearby, actively idle. Improper (or no) use of a copilot is one of the main reasons pilots fail checkrides on airplanes where there's a two pilot crew.

I'll take this a step further and say that even on airplanes where only one pilot is necessary but a passenger occupies the right seat, this person should be informed that he or she might be asked to do a bit of work. I don't mean fly, but perhaps hold or fold a chart. Of course, the more aviation experience a person has, the more they can do for you.

IFR Currency: It's Almost Summertime

With an experienced copilot sitting in the right seat, you have a wonderful resource to tap. You can bounce ideas and questions off this person. But don't bounce paper balls off his forehead (copilots hate that). Remember, two heads are better than one, unless you don't know where you're heading or you're paying for everyone's haircuts.

Using your copilot (and other human resources) properly means that you know something about communications, teamwork, task allocation, and decision making. You must be able to communicate your thoughts, needs, and desires properly to these resources. So how do you know if you're communicating properly? The best way to tell is to ask if you're getting the help you requested. It's simply a matter of feedback. If you ask your copilot for assistance in finding a chart and he's busy wadding up a paper ball to throw at the flight attendant, then you're not communicating properly, are you?

Looked at in a more academic way, the communications aspect of CRM becomes a matter of inquiry, advocacy, and assertion. As PIC, you may have to ask a lot of questions to get the information you need. Once you have these information tidbits, you may need to press ATC, your copilot, and your company to do what you think is safe at the time. For instance, if your copilot is suggesting that you fly to the destination despite one of your two engines running rough, you might need to explain and justify your position to the copilot. This assumes, of course, that you have the time to do this.

Which brings us back to the fact that when all is said and done and communicated, *you* are the pilot in command and the final decision is entirely yours. That's true whether the flight vessel is a 172 or a 757. Your job is to make the best possible use of all resources to gather the information needed to make a wise decision, but making that decision is your job. That's why you are called the *pilot in command*. When it comes to the cockpit, it's one man or woman, one vote.

One of the initial problems with CRM was the failure of crew members to recognize the difference between experience and inexperience. If a copilot said, "Captain, I'm not comfortable with what you're going to do," and the captain replied, "Well, I'm going to do it," then this certainly wasn't what the spirit of CRM intended.

Instead, the captain should reply with something like, "Well, here's why we need to do it this way," followed by an explanation. The intent here is for the captain to educate the copilot based on his or her years of experience. After all, the first officer will eventually replace the captain someday and he or she would certainly benefit from the captain's experience. In this sense, CRM implies that captains be educators as well as professional pilots. This shouldn't be too demanding since most folks fill an educational role in one way or another, especially if they have children. Of course I'm not suggesting that a captain treat a copilot like a child. After all, he can't restrict a copilot's allowance since the airlines the copilot's working for has probably already done this based on the typical new-hire pay rate.

Hardware

No, I don't mean things like wrenches and screw drivers. I mean things like the advanced, automated equipment found on many of today's modern airplanes. CRM means knowing how to use this equipment and when to use it (or stop using it, as the case might be).

Take, for instance, the newest GPS equipment on the market, Garmin's G1000 (I know, you'd *like* to take it, too). This is an amazing piece of equipment. It can provide you with instrumentation when used as the primary flight display (PFD), or location when used as a multi-function display (MFD). It can provide you with checklist information and engine instrumentation readings and help you with situational awareness, among many other things. There are rumors it will provide dinner recipes and advice for the lovelorn if you know certain secret codes.

The versatility comes at the cost of complexity. Some instructors say that it can take as much as 20 hours of flight and ground training to become sufficiently familiar with the G1000 to allow safe IFR flight. Twenty hours? Yep. What about those who use this equipment but don't use it often enough to remain proficient in its use? You can bet that more than one pilot has scared himself by hopping in an airplane with advanced avionics equipment for an IFR flight only to find out that he can't remember how to set the GPS unit up for the approach. If the display flashes "Dear Abby," or has a recipe for Salisbury Steak, you are in over your head, especially if you're a vegetarian. You don't want to go there.

That's why the use of an autopilot is nearly mandatory on airplanes with advanced equipment. The autopilot is the ultimate CRM tool. It's like a copilot except that it doesn't wad up paper balls and throw them back at you (at least the older versions don't).

Many years ago, a NASA study of single-pilot IFR operations suggested that single-pilot IFR drivers were best served by a single axis (heading hold) autopilot, especially

Although summer is just around the corner, one winter-type woe often hangs around long after winter is officially past. Unforecast or unexpected IMC can turn an otherwise pleasant flight into a stressful one.

The flight was conducted in VMC. Turn to final approach course was a sharp descending turn from VMC into IMC. I immediately got disoriented and started hyperventilating. After a short period of time that felt like forever, I decided to abandon the approach and advised Tower Controller. I calmed myself down [subsequently]...and successfully completed an ILS approach and landing. Though I am legally current and have a significant amount of "real" instrument time given my level of experience, I plan to grab an instructor and go get some more training, particularly with the VMC-to-IMC transition.

Our reporter has the right idea. A springtime "tune-up" is a good plan for pilots, and for aircraft, too.

NASA
Callback
Report

The Workload-Performance Graph

The amount of effort exerted by a pilot for a given period of time varies based on the demands of the task. As the accompanying graph clearly shows, preflight requires very little extended effort compared to approaching and landing an airplane.

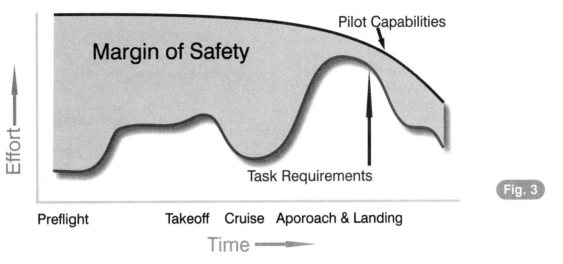

Fig. 3

if it was named Otto. Multi axis autopilots tended to take the single pilot IFR driver out of the performance loop. The pilot ended up flying the autopilot and not the airplane. That led to the pilot often getting so far behind the airplane that if there were a crash, he wouldn't arrive at the scene for an additional 30 minutes. Of course, then he could blame it all on Otto.

Things have changed. Now, if you're doing anything other than flying on the PFD or looking at the moving map (i.e., pushing buttons, checking menus, etc.), the autopilot should be flying the airplane. To do otherwise is to invite an ATC heading, altitude or clearance violation.

Information Workload

IFR pilots, especially those in single-pilot operations, can only do so many things at one time. That's usually one less than the number of things that need doing. Sure, there are some among us who can multitask in the sense that we can fly and talk on the radio at the same time. Copying a clearance while flying, navigating, and working advanced avionics often overloads even the most capable pilot, especially if he's fiddling with the CD changer at the same time. That's why the very best pilots know the secret word that helps reduce cockpit workload to a workable minimum. Would you like to know what it is? Standby. That's the word to say, not my request that you stop reading.

When you're busy and ATC calls, you don't have to take that call. You can simply say, "Standby." ATC understands that, don't they? After all, isn't this exactly what they tell you when you call and *they're* busy? And guess what? They'll respect you in the morning (or afternoon, or whenever you get back to them). Some pilots, in an attempt to maintain their burnished on-the-air image, never turn down an ATC call, even when they've got a one-track mind and four channels of input happening. The result is mistakes, repeats, and other things that compromise the safety of flight. As soon as you're really ready, call ATC and communicate. That's how pro pilots fly IFR.

Sometimes things get busy in the cockpit. That's why the two most important things in aviation are the next

two things. By that I mean you should always be asking yourself what the next two things are that you need to accomplish to get the IFR flying job done. Doing your IFR chores ahead of time (like obtaining the ATIS, setting the radios up for the approach, etc.) is essential to minimizing your cockpit workload. This is especially important during the critical phases of flight.

In fact, you could become so overwhelmed when preparing to fly an approach that the only reasonable behavior is to abandon the approach and come around again for another try. That is why it's important to do as much as possible as early as possible in the flight. You never know what will happen later. You can be sitting there eating your salami sandwich and thinking, "I'll get the ATIS in a few minutes," when suddenly you get a routing change, and the heading indicator goes belly up. Now who's got time to get the ATIS? The following graph (Figure 3) gives you a good idea of just where the workload increases and pushes the limits of our performance when flying single-pilot IFR.

Aeronautical Decision Making [ADM]

How good are your aviation decisions to date? How did you learn ADM?

Very few pilots have had formal training in ADM, yet many are effective decision makers. Why? They developed some strategy that lets them to make the right decision at the right time. Perhaps they learned it by watching their instructor, or they acquired the common base of knowledge possessed by most people. Maybe the tooth fairy gave it to them as a bonus. It doesn't matter. They've got it. But even if they and you do have it, there's nothing that says you can't become a better aviation decision maker by using some of the newly developed ADM tools now at your disposal.

ADM is a systematic approach to understanding and modifying the mental process used by pilots to determine the best course of action in any given circumstance. This is a process that builds on the traditional concepts of decision making as shown in Figure 4, but is modified slightly in consideration of the fact that the person making the decision is probably moving in a metal tube at several hundred miles per hour. Thus, ADM helps minimize the probability of pilot error by providing the means to analyze changes that occur in flight and evaluate how these changes could affect the outcome of that flight.

For instance, in the traditional decision making model (Figure 4), the need to make a decision occurs when the pilot notices that something has changed or hasn't changed when it was expected to (Figure 4, position 1). Ice may be detected on the wings (change) or the throttle is moved forward in cruise flight and the power doesn't increase (no change). The pilot must recognize this change or the lack of it for good decision making to occur (Figure 4, position 2). Failure to notice the change can lead to a mishap. Change indicates an appropriate response is necessary to favorably modify the situation (Figure 4, position 3). Now the pilot must evaluate all the possible responses using skills, procedures, techniques or book know how to solve the problem (Figure 4, position 4). Lack of ability in either of these areas can lead to a mishap (Figure 4, position 5).

Traditionally, ADM addresses all aspects of decision making in the cockpit and identifies the steps involved in good decision making. We've already discussed many of these steps, but here they are for your consideration once again:

1. Identifying personal attitudes hazardous to safe flight.
2. Learning behavior modification techniques.
3. Learning how to recognize and cope with stress.
4. Developing risk assessment skills.
5. Using all resources.
6. Evaluating the effectiveness of one's ADM skills.

Let's look at what we've already learned, and examine in some detail the factors we haven't discussed so far.

We've already learned to identify personal attitudes hazardous to safe flight along with the behavior modification techniques that work as antidotes to counter these attitudes. We've learned a bit about how to cope with stress and use CRM. Now it's time to develop some useful risk assessment skills. One of the most useful tools from ADM is the risk assessment model in the form of the acronym DECIDE—Detect, Estimate, Choose, Identify, Do, Evaluate.

This is a six-step process that provides you with a logical way to approach decision making. The model represents a continuous loop process of decision making that is useful when a pilot is faced with a change in a situation where somebody had better decide something pretty soon. This model focuses on the intellectual component of the decision process but it can also influence the motivational component of judgment as well.

The secret here is to practice using the DECIDE model in all your decision making. Then, when it's needed aloft,

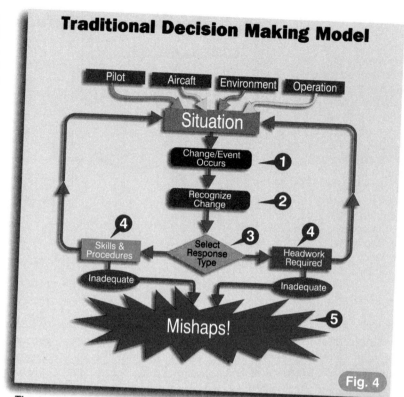

Traditional Decision Making Model

Fig. 4

The traditional decision model doesn't incorporate attitude awareness, stress management and CRM as does the non-traditional ADM model (Figure 5).

the process will be more natural and more likely to positively affect the outcome of important decisions in the air.

I don't want you to think that in the event of an inflight problem, you'll simply pull out a piece of paper, review the DECIDE checklist, and excellent answers will appear (brought by that same tooth fairy, no doubt). It doesn't work that way. This model works best when it is internalized to the point of being intuitive. When you need it most is when you'll have the least time to think about each step.

Detect. The decision maker detects the fact that change has occurred.

Estimate. The decision maker estimates the need to counter or react to the change.

Choose. The decision maker chooses a desirable outcome (in terms of success) for the flight.

Identify. The decision maker identifies actions that could successfully control the change.

Do. The decision maker takes the necessary action.

Evaluate. The decision maker evaluates the effect(s) of his action countering the change.

Let's see this is applied to a critical in-flight situation by assuming you're at cruise altitude and have started picking up ice. We'll follow the ADM model here (Figure 5).

The first step is to *detect* the ice on the wings (Figure 5, position A). This is easy during the day, when ice begins clouding your windshield. It's a bit more difficult at night, when you can't see anything ahead of you because you're flying night IFR. That's why using a flashlight at night to look at the wings and windshield is useful in detecting ice.

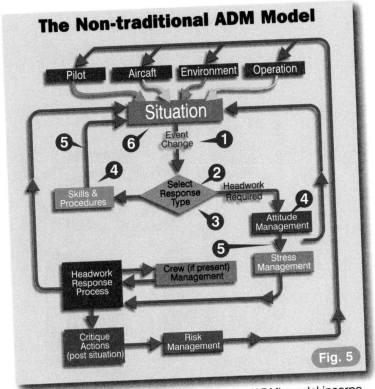

The Non-traditional ADM Model

Fig. 5

The non-traditional aviation decision making (ADM) model incorporate attitude awareness, stress management and CRM. This provides a pilot with a better chance of making a good decision.

theory, try getting to where the air is so cold that ice won't form, but it's likely to be a cold day in the underworld before you get there in a small, underperforming, single-engine airplane. Given your situation, and through the use or your skills and knowledge, you determine that the cloud tops are 1,000 feet above you based on a recent pilot report, so climbing seems like a wise idea. If, at any time, you identify that you're feeling like you have no control over the situation, you might engage in a little attitude management and invoke the resignation hazardous thought antidote and say to yourself, "I'm not helpless. I can make a difference." Step five requires you to *do* the action you selected in step four (Figure 5, position 5). So you request a climb from ATC.

Step six requires you to *evaluate* the effect of this decision (Figure 5, position 6). Has the formation of ice stopped? It has. Sure, you still have a bit of ice on the plane, but that's OK for now. You're flying and doing so safely. Now you can run through the DECIDE model again, asking yourself what you need to do now given that you may have to reenter the clouds at below-freezing temperatures. In other words, start again with step one and ask yourself what it is that you've just detected. The answer is, "I'm now flying on top of the clouds in below freezing temperatures and the cloud tops are rising ahead of me." That's a potential problem that requires full use of the DECIDE model. It's possible that in running through the model again, you'll decide that it's best to land at an alternate airport, perhaps one in a direction of lowering cloud tops (but increasing cloud bases, if possible).

There's a bit more to good decision making, however, than just having a useful model in the ADM process. Sometimes you need additional skills that fall outside the normal parameters of academic psychology. And these are the skills you'll learn as you fly IFR. So start slow, then try new things, visit new places and fly new airplanes. Each action will contribute to your continuing education.

If you're in conditions conducive to icing, you need to be proactive and check for it occasionally. So you say to the co-pilot, "Icy up here" and he says, "I see, too." Detection in action.

Step two requires you to *estimate* the need to counter or react to this change (Figure 5, position 2). Without experience in handling ice, you have very little basis on which to make a choice. You do know (because you've read *Rod Machado's Instrument Pilot's Survival Manual* as well as this book) that even a small bit of ice can be detrimental to airplane performance. You estimate that there is an urgent need to act.

Step three requires you to *choose* a desirable outcome for this situation (Figure 5, position 3). Living through it is a good one, and so is getting rid of the ice on the wings or at least stopping it from accumulating. So just how are you going to do that?

Step four wants you to *identify* the actions needed to accomplish step three (Figure 5, position 4). This is often a decision about which of your skills and procedures to use, plus attitude management, stress management, and CRM necessary to solve the problem.

In this situation, the very best thing you can do is get the airplane to a place where the air is above freezing or, if that's not possible, get out of the clouds. These are often your only two choices when it comes to icing. You could, in

Decision Making: Final Thoughts

Learning how to make good decisions in the cockpit is both an art and science. Sure, you can learn a lot from a book like this one. Ultimately, however, you need to fly in order to learn good decision-making skills. There's simply no alternative here. Making mistakes is part of the process. The good news is that based on what you've read so far, you're less likely to make the mistakes that can put you and your passengers in a neck brace.

The second piece of good news is FAR 91.3. You *are* the pilot-in-command, Captain. The decision to fly safely and well, the decision to put the safety of you and your passengers ahead of all other considerations, is entirely yours.

Bob, you just landed gear up, what happened?

Ahh, I rushed through my traditional decision model, skipped steps 2 and 3 and accidentally went right to step 5.

Crunch!

PHYSIOLOGICAL FACTORS

I remember hearing an Indian guru trying to convince a skeptical audience about his mystic beliefs. He said, "OK, I want you to know that life is an illusion. It's just an illusion." At this point most folks in the audience looked at him and raised an eyebrow.

Feeling the discomfort, the guru immediately said, "Oh, don't get me wrong. It's a very *good* illusion. I grant you that!"

I'll leave it up to you to decide whether or not life on Planet Earth is an illusion. What I can tell you for sure is that in the cockpit, under instrument conditions, you are subject to many illusions that stem from your body's physiology. Your job as an instrument pilot is to know what these illusions are and how to compensate for them.

Spatial Disorientation

That's *spatial*, not *special*, disorientation, although the event is pretty special the first time it happens to you under instrument conditions. Let's assume you are an intelligent person (flattery should get me somewhere). You think you always know which end is up, right? You will come to find out differently. Welcome to the wonderful world of instrument flying, where things are not always as they seem to be (that's an allusion to an illusion).

We take a *lot* for granted as ground-based organisms. The earth is always beneath our feet, up is up, down is down, and rarely do the twain (Mark or otherwise) meet. We forget (or don't think about the fact) that it's our sense of sight during visual flight that helps us determine the relationship between aircraft attitude and the earth's surface.

Ask most people what they see with and they'll answer, "My eyes." The eyes may have it when it comes to data acquisition, but they are only the first stop in an incredibly quick and remarkably complex journey that winds up with the brain taking a series of electrochemical impulses and turning them into something of which it can make sense. Usually.

The Inside of the Human Ear

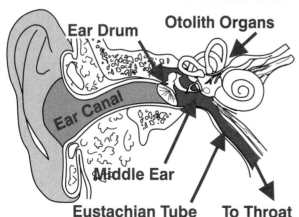

Fig. 6

The Inner Ear

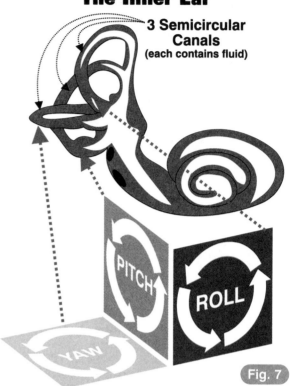

3 Semicircular Canals
(each contains fluid)

Fig. 7

The three semicircular canals are positioned at right angles to each other to allow the brain to sense motion in three planes: yaw, pitch and roll. Fluid within these canals moves relative to the canal walls. This bends the small hair filaments aligning the inside of the canal walls activating nerves which alert the brain to movement.

Absent the normal visual input, the brain is left to its own devices. This can be scary for both the brain and its owner. When flying in the clouds, we control the airplane solely by reference to the instruments. *Look ma, there's no there out there.* Deprived of the normal visual cues, the body can send some very unusual messages to the brain, creating a profound conflict between what the "seat of your pants" is telling you and what the instruments say. This conflict is known as s*patial disorientation* or *vertigo*. Elvis, before he left the building for the last time, had it right. You're all shook up.

Your first taste of vertigo is one of instrument training's rites of passage. Suddenly, your mind (also known as the "seat of your pants," geography aside) tells you that you're turning. The instruments are showing straight and level flight. Who (or what) is right? Which do you believe? It's an updated version of the old TV show "To Tell the Truth."

You've now arrived at a defining moment. The whole process of instrument training consists of teaching a pilot to always, always, always believe the instruments. Check them, cross-check them, be constantly alert to the possibility of failure, but when push comes to turn, what the instruments say is what you do. It's matter over mind.

Regardless of how much experience you have, or how great a gymnast you were in high school, or your ability to do skateboard wheelies on a railroad tie, vertigo *can* affect you.

There are tax exemptions and jury duty exemptions. There are no vertigo exemptions. Your instructor will probably go to great lengths to induce vertigo early in your training. This is not considered student abuse. In fact, it's good. Knowing what vertigo feels like and how it affects you is an important experience to have. That way, if and when you experience it on your own, you'll handle it calmly, like an Indian guru lying on a bed of nails (who thinks of the experience as a free acupuncture treatment, not a body piercing event).

Vertigo is caused by problems associated with our three sensory systems: vestibular, kinesthetic, and visual.

The visual system is exactly what is sounds like—information sent to the brain by the eyes. The kinesthetic system is the sensory information sent to the brain by sensors in our skin and from areas deeper within our body. This is the much-mentioned seat-of-the-pants sensation. You don't have to be a rocket scientist to understand how both of these systems work. The vestibular system, however, rocks. Literally. It's sort of a liquid-and-bone-based internal gyroscope. Let's take a closer look.

The vestibular system consists of the semicircular canals, located in the inner ear (Figure 6). These canals include three circular tubes, each containing a fluid whose movement causes the bending of small hair filaments (known as *otolith organs*) located at the base of each canal Figure 7. Movement of the fluid within the tubes, caused by acceleration (a change in direction or velocity), causes the hairs to move in relation to the stones, alerting the brain that the body is in motion (Figure 8). These were the *original* rolling stones!

Notice that the tubes in Figure 7 lie in three separate planes (geometric planes, not airplanes), corresponding somewhat to the three axes of the airplane. This alignment allows you to sense angular acceleration in any one of these planes. In other words, you can sense yaw, roll, and pitch, giving you in two ears the capabilities of a panel full of airplane instruments. And as long as all the instruments (internal and external) agree, everything's fine. It's when there's a disagreement that trouble arrives for a visit.

When you move your head or accelerate the airplane (change speed or direction), fluid within the semicircular canals moves, as shown in Figure 8, position B. Since the fluid within the canals has a small amount of inertia (a tendency to resist change of motion), it tends to remain stationary for a short period of time before moving. Thus, the canals can be said to rotate around the fluid within them. Eventually the fluid catches up to the movement of the canal and the feeling of turning stops (position C). Even though you're still turning, you don't feel it. However, when you stop turning, the fluid continues its motion for a short period of time because of its inertia (position D). This signals your mind that you've entered a turn in the opposite direction.

The semicircular canal system evolved as a ground-based system. On the ground, gravity always pulls the body in only

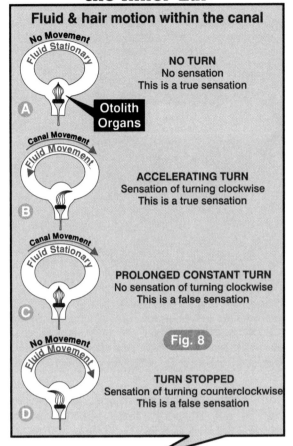

Acceleration and the Inner Ear

Fluid & hair motion within the canal

A — No Movement / Fluid Stationary
Otolith Organs

NO TURN
No sensation
This is a true sensation

B — Canal Movement / Fluid Movement

ACCELERATING TURN
Sensation of turning clockwise
This is a true sensation

C — Canal Movement / Fluid Stationary

PROLONGED CONSTANT TURN
No sensation of turning clockwise
This is a false sensation

Fig. 8

D — No Movement / Fluid Movement

TURN STOPPED
Sensation of turning counterclockwise
This is a false sensation

When the head is rotated (accelerated) in any direction, the fluid within one or more of the canals bends small hairs (known as otolith organs) at the base of the canals as shown in position B. Because of inertia, the fluid lags behind the rotation of the canal which bends the fine hairs. This stimulates nerve endings alerting the brain that the body is turning. After acceleration, the fluid eventually catches up with the canal's movement and stimulation stops (position C). This signals the brain that you are no longer turning even though you're still in a turn. When you stop the turn, the fluid moves in the opposite direction. This gives you a sensation of turning in the opposite direction (position D).

3 Semicircular Canals
(each contain fluid)

Ground Instruction Gone Bad

Now listen up. Your ears have canals in them and they also contain fluid. Got that?

"I am in the clouds and need help."

A case of "get-home-itis" and an inadequate contingency plan for avoiding flight into IMC combined to put this pilot into a desperate situation. Once again, an air traffic controller's assistance helped to prevent an accident.

"Conditions were getting worse by the minute. There were scattered thunderstorms throughout the area. This prompted me to hurry my preflight and departure. I was also trying to get to a meeting scheduled for later that afternoon. I thought that if I could get about one mile from the end of the runway, I could make the determination of whether or not I would be able to make the flight home. If conditions were not favorable to continue, I would do a 90/270 degree turn back and land. Immediately after takeoff (1/2 mile and 300 feet), I was in the clouds. This was not what I had planned and fear and panic set in. Next came spatial disorientation.

Unknowingly, I put the plane in a hard bank to the left and a very steep climb. Nothing was making sense to me and the next thing I remember was seeing the VSI pegged off scale (greater than 2000 foot per minute descent). I broke through the clouds long enough to see the ground coming up, which is a view I had never seen before and hope never to see again. I thought of how stupid I was to get into this mess. I pulled up hard. I remember doing this several times in the next few minutes of trying to stabilize the aircraft. The oscillations became less severe as I regained control of the aircraft.

My mind was not able to digest the tremendous amount of data it was receiving and I was trying to hang on by a thread. My first [radio] transmission was, '[Approach] this is XXX and I am in trouble. I am in the clouds and need help. I need a vector to get out.'

Approach responded by giving me a squawk code and then a heading and altitude. I was able to climb, but my heading was all over the place. Approach then said that I should be out of the clouds in about three or four miles. About 20 seconds later, I saw an opening to go down through the clouds and I took it.

As I look back, it was incredible how fast things went bad. Why did I ever take off with conditions as bad as they were and getting worse? Why didn't I listen to any of the people I had talked with prior to takeoff that recommended not going? I truly believe in safety first, yet everything I did showed just the opposite. I have learned a great deal from this event and I hope that those who choose to listen might learn from my story.

NASA Callback Report

one direction—straight downward. In flight, however, gravity is not the only force pulling on the body. Centrifugal force as well as gravity tugs on the seat of the pilot's pants, as shown in Figure 9.

This explains why your eyes may tell you one thing when looking at the instruments, while your brain and your body tell you something entirely different. Now you know why you want to be like a musician—trust your instruments. The flight instruments, that is. Don't go tooting your own horn and claim that makes you an instrument pilot.

Of course, you only want to rely on your instruments if you're not experiencing an instrument failure and being lead astray by one gone bad (instrument, not musician). That's why the inverted-V scan and the triangles of agreement (discussed in Chapter 3) are your friends. They help you quickly identify a failed instrument.

Let's take a look at some of the most common illusions that spring forth from the inner ear and can lead to spatial disorientation. All of these are variations on a theme in which the sensory mechanism is fooled into giving false indications because of abrupt acceleration or deceleration in one direction or another.

I don't want you to live in mortal fear of changing direction. In reality, most of these effects are rare, and the majority of instrument pilots fly for a lifetime and never experience them except in training, where they're deliberately provoked. Then again, if it happens to you, understanding *what* is happening and why could be worth its weight in parachutes.

Figure 10 shows some of the major performers in the semicircular canal dance. All are variations on one theme—fluid in motion stimulated the otolith organs, creating a situation in which you are directionally challenged for varying amounts of time.

What You See Isn't What You Get (Necessarily)

In addition problems originating in the inner ear, there are two other illusions affecting the visual system that can disorient you during instrument flight. One of these is known as the *false horizon* and the other is *autokinesis*.

The false horizon illusion often results when a cloud or light source creates a perceived horizon that's not the real horizon. The aurora borealis, certain patterns of ground

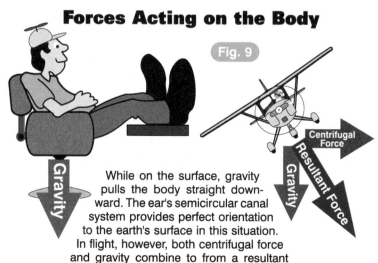

Forces Acting on the Body

Fig. 9

While on the surface, gravity pulls the body straight downward. The ear's semicircular canal system provides perfect orientation to the earth's surface in this situation. In flight, however, both centrifugal force and gravity combine to from a resultant force which makes the seat-of-the-pants sense completely unreliable as a source of attitude information. This false sense is called *vertigo*.

Major In-flight Illusions and the Results They Produce

Name	Maneuver	Semicirculars	You Feel
The Leans	Enter bank at very slow rate	Fluid in roll-detecting tubes isn't set in motion	Bank in opposite direction as fluid moves when roll stops.
Coriolis Effect	While in a prolonged turn, move your head in another geometric plane	Fluid, already in motion, senses direction in which you moved your head	Plane turning or accelerating in a different axis from where it really is
Graveyard Spiral	Roll into level flight after a turn	Fluid keeps going	A turn in the direction opposite that of the original turn. You respond by re-initiating the original turn, which drops the nose. You respond with back elevator, which tightens the turn and increases the rate of descent.
Somatogravic Illusion	Rapid forward acceleration	Fluid is pressed backward in the semicircular canals	Plane is nose-up and compensate by lowering the nose, perhaps even diving.
Inversion Illusion	Sudden downward acceleration Abrupt transition from climb to straight-and-level	Fluid moves upward in the semicircular canals	Plane is inverted or tumbling backward
Elevator Illusion	Sudden upward acceleration, such as an updraft	Fluid forced downward in the semicircular canals	Plane is climbing

Fig. 10

light, and stars can all create a false horizon. One of the most common forms of false horizon occurs when you climb or descend through an overcast cloud layer whose tops or bottoms aren't parallel with the real horizon (Figure 11). In these instances it's both tempting and easy to bank the airplane and align it with the sloping clouds. This illusion is especially strong when the real horizon is obscured by haze or fog. Your brain makes sense of what it's seeing by comparing it to prior knowledge, and as far as it knows, horizons should be straight and level. You will be surprised at how difficult it can be to fly at an angle to the only visible semblance of a horizon line. My advice in such a circumstance is that you don't look! If your brain doesn't like what it's seeing, fly the instruments.

Contrary to what you might think, autokinesis isn't something experienced in an automobile. It's a visual illusion that occurs when you stare at a stationary light in a dark background for several seconds. The light appears to move because of small, frequent, involuntary movement of the eye, especially when there's nothing interesting to look at. As a result, there's a tendency to try and align your airplane with the light's false movement, resulting in an unusual attitude. Heading toward the light may be good for newly departed souls and moths, but it's bad for pilots. To prevent being one of the newly departed souls, don't stare at stationary light sources. Believe me when I say that more than one pilot flying IFR on top of the clouds has yanked and banked in response to staring at the planet Venus.

False Horizons

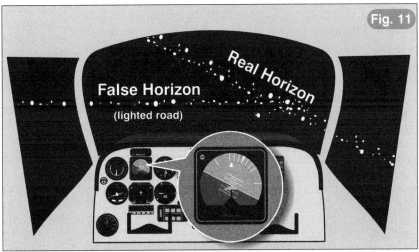

Fig. 11

In the example above, a lighted road can be misinterpreted as the actual horizon at night. Such an event is very disconcerting to a pilot.

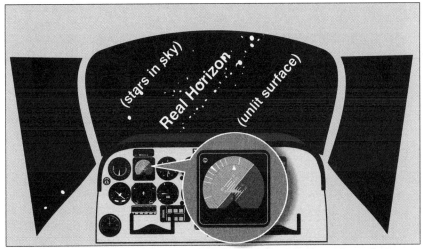

When the foreground is unlit and the background contains stars, it's relatively easy for a pilot to think he or she has gone inverted.

Will large glass cockpit displays help prevent a pilot's susceptibility to spatial disorientation?

VS

There is some speculation that use of large PFDs (primary flight displays) might reduce a pilot's susceptibility to spatial disorientation. At the minimum, it helps a pilot overcome the disturbing feelings produced by vertigo. According to some pilots, as the simulated horizon approaches the real horizon in dimension, there is less and less of a tendency for a pilot to think of the display as an instrument, instead thinking of it as a picture of the actual horizon. Of course, seeing the actual horizon all but eliminates the disturbing effects of vertigo.

Experiencing Spatial Disorientation for Fun

I'm a big fan of spatial disorientation, but only when it's experienced while wearing a view limiting device and having a top notch instructor in the right seat. I'm a fan because everyone should experience it during their training, under controlled conditions, before they experience it in real life, in an airplane, in the clouds.

To help you better understand this concept, we'll look at several maneuvers that are known to induce vertigo in suspecting and unsuspecting pilots. Hopefully, your instructor will demonstrate these maneuvers so you can feel what's so special about spatial disorientation.

The information that follows should:

● Help you understand the conditions under which you might get vertigo.

● Help you understand how susceptible every pilot is to vertigo.

● Show you how difficult it is to believe your instruments when bodily sensations differ from instrument indications.

● Reduce the chance of being dangerously disoriented.

● Show you how quickly vertigo can be induced by certain head movements and give you confidence in overcoming the effects of vertigo.

How Centrifugal Force Forces Its Hand

The culprits here that can fool your body under instrument conditions are acceleration forces (i.e., centrifugal force) and gravitational forces. Centrifugal force from uncoordinated turns, climbing turns and turbulence often overpowers the gravitational sense that keeps us oriented to earth (Figure 12). It can induce a feeling that the airplane is doing something it's not doing, or it can keep you from having any sensation. The latter is just as dangerous, since the absence of sensation can lead you to believe that the airplane isn't doing something when it actually is.

Diving or Rolling Beyond the Vertical Plane

Here's a maneuver that can produce extreme disorientation. Begin by sitting normally while in straight-and-level flight, with your eyes closed (or with your gaze lowered to the floor). Your instructor starts a positive, coordinated roll toward a 30 or 40 degree angle of bank. During the roll, tilt your head forward, look to the right or left, then immediately return your head to an upright position. Your instructor will time the maneuver so the roll is stopped just as you return your head to the upright position. The result is usually an intense disorientation. You should experience the sensation of falling downward into the direction of the roll. Please, whatever you do here,

How Centrifugal Force Affects You

Sensation	Induced By:	Fig. 12
Climbing	**Fly at approach speed. Close your eyes. Accelerate, still in straight and level flight.**	
Climbing	**Close eyes while flying straight-and-level. Instructor does slow, coordinated 1.5G turn through 90 degrees.**	
Diving	**Same as above, but keep eyes shut until plane is about halfway recovered from turn.**	
Tilting right	**Eyes closed. Straight and level flight. Instructor flies a slight to moderate left skid.**	
Motion in reverse direction of the turn	**Eyes closed, instructor positively rolls to 45 degree turn maintaining heading and pitch attitude.**	

don't yell, "Enterprise, emergency beam out," or your instructor will know for sure that the Star Trek uniform you've worn for the last five lessons is how you actually dress, despite your protestations that your real clothes are still at the cleaners.

Remember, the instructor is doing the flying during these demonstrations, although it's perfectly fine for you to do the flying with your eyes closed where it's applicable. This just makes for a more powerful demonstration in some instances. All the instructor has to do is tell you what control inputs to make and how to make them. You've still got your eyes shut and head tilted as appropriate. Then, when your instructor says you've completed the maneuver, try to return the airplane to straight-and-level flight.

This is where the games really begin. Now you're reacting to what your senses are telling you, not what the instruments are saying (because you can't see the instruments with your eyes closed, right?). When you're really good and disoriented, your instructor should say something to get you to open your eyes (not your checkbook). Hopefully he won't yell, "Check!" If he does, toss your checkbook out the window. Once you've opened your eyes, take note of the airplane's attitude. And yours! So much for the notion that you always know what's up.

How to Cope With Spatial Disorientation

The very first step in coping with this problem in knowing what causes it, and how and when it can happen. This knowledge allows you to remain on the alert for the illusions that cause vertigo. It's also important to get a good weather briefing so you can anticipate weather conditions that might set the scene for a higher-than-normal likelihood of having vertigo-inducing illusions.

You're particularly interested in sloping cloud conditions revealed in pilot reports, and any adverse weather where you plan on arriving during dusk or darkness (such conditions can prevent you from identifying the real horizon). It's also important to avoid rapid head movements, particularly when you're close to the ground, such as during takeoffs and approaches. Instrument proficiency is your best ally in avoiding the hazards of spatial disorientation.

Structure of the Human Eye

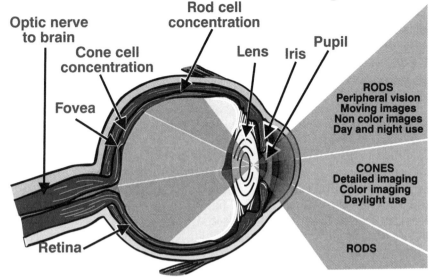

The human eye has separate structures for aiding both night vision and day vision. Cone cells, located within the fovea, are very effective during the day for detailed imagery and color imagery. Rod cells, located outside the fovea, are best used for detection of moving images and noncolor images. They are effective during day and nighttime hours.

Fig. 13

Flight Vision

Make no mistake about it, vision is your most important sense. There is no such thing as a medical wavier for instrument pilots without vision in both eyes. *The Braille Instrument Flying System* isn't likely to appear at a pilot shop near you anytime in the future. Your vision is important for many reasons. First, you obviously need it to fly the airplane. You also need it to read charts, look for traffic, and scan instruments. Let's learn a little about how the eye functions. Then we'll talk about the many optical illusions that can affect you during instrument flight.

Your Eye – Figure 13 shows a side view of the human eye. Light passes through the pupil and lens, and then falls on the retina at the back of the eye. Light sensitive cells of the retina are made up of individual cells known as rods and cones.

Cone Cells – Cone cells are concentrated in a small section in the center of the retina known as the fovea. These cells decrease in number with distance from this center point. While the eye can observe approximately 200 degrees of arc at a glance, only the light falling on the fovea has the ability to send the brain a sharp, clearly-focused image. All light falling outside the fovea is of less

A Peak Experience

After clearing a desert peak, this B737 Captain was able to offer some sage advice on visual approaches.

"It was a clear night, and we were on vectors to intercept the localizer for a visual approach to Runway 11L. Level at 6,000 feet, approximately 18 miles out, the enhanced ground proximity warning system (EGPWS) gave a "Terrain, terrain" warning due to a 4,682 foot peak just south of the localizer at 15 miles. The First Officer had begun a normal descent for landing prior to intercepting the localizer. Mistake #1: As we were anticipating a visual, the ILS approach was not thoroughly briefed. If it had been, the high terrain would have been noted. Mistake #2: Due to a long day, some fatigue, complacency, and a clear night with unlimited visibility, we accepted a visual too far out and began a visual descent too soon. The good news: technology saved the day.

NASA Callback Report

detail (Figure 14). For example, an airplane at a distance of 7 miles which appears in sharp focus within the foveal center of vision would have to be as close as 7/10 of a mile in order to be recognized if it were outside the foveal field of vision.

Cone cells let you perceive color. When you look directly at an object, most of the image is focused on the fovea. Unfortunately, the cones don't work well when it's dark. This explains why it's difficult to perceive color at night.

Rod Cells – No, they didn't name them after me. Rod cells, concentrated on the outside of the fovea, are dim-light receptors. Since these rods are located outside the fovea, they are responsible for our peripheral vision, as shown in Figure 15. Moving images are more easily detected by rod cells than by cone cells. Catching an object out of the corner of your eye is an example of rod cells at work.

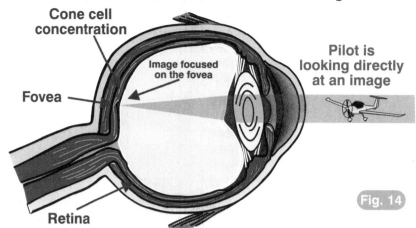

Cone Cells of the Human Eye

Looking directly at an object focuses the image on the fovea. The image falls on the cone cells that are effective at distinguishing color and image detail. Unfortunately, cone cells are less effective when it's dark. This is why it's difficult to distinguish color and detail at night.

As I've already mentioned, cone cells don't work well in the dark, which explains why it's difficult to see an object at night even though you're looking directly at it. This is why we have a night blind spot in the center of our vision where the light from a dimly lit object falls directly on the fovea (Figure 15).

If you want the best view of a dimly lit object, you need to expose the rods to the light. You can do this by using your peripheral vision for off-center viewing. Simply look 5 to 10 degrees to the side from the center of the object you want to view. This allows some of the object's reflected light to fall on the rods. You can demonstrate this process at night by looking directly at an airplane's strobe light head on and offset a few degrees. A direct view dims the object, while an indirect view increases its brightness. Think of looking at a dim object at night as you might think about looking at a carnival worker. In other words, try not to look directly at their tattoos for fear of finding misspelled words.

Night Vision

How well you see at night is determined by the amount of light passing through the pupil. Pupils close to prevent the eyes from receiving too much light and open when light intensity diminishes. The problem is that it can take 30 minutes or more for your eyes to completely adapt to the dark, a process that is both mechanical and chemical. You can, however, achieve a moderate degree of dark adaptation within 20 minutes under dim red cockpit lighting. This is one reason you want to avoid very bright lights for at least 30 minutes before takeoff if you're planning on flying at night. If you must use a bright white light in the cockpit at night, try closing one eye while the light is in use. This keeps the closed eye night adapt-

The Parallax Effect

The "parallax effect" describes a type of visual illusion in which the position of an object in 3-dimensional space appears to change, due to a shift in the position of the observer. The parallax effect can make distant fixed objects, such as a planet or star, appear to be close and in motion. The twinkling planet Venus is a well-known example in aviation. Tower controllers have often cleared Venus to land, while pilots have mistaken the planet for nearby aircraft position lights.

The parallax effect is especially apt to occur during night operations when there may be few, or no, visible references to the horizon as an aircraft moves through space. Several ASRS reports illustrate, beginning with a first officer's account of a nighttime evasive maneuver that startled crew and passengers:

"I observed what I believed to be an imminent traffic conflict. I manually overrode the autopilot and started an immediate left turn. The perceived conflict was a result of slight parallax of green and red wingtip lights of another aircraft. A bright white star also appeared as one of the running lights on the perceived conflict. The maneuver was a gut reaction on my part, as I perceived the aircraft to be within a few thousand feet from us. Passengers and flight attendants who were not seated with their belts fastened were upended in the cabin. One passenger received an abrasion to a knee and one complained of a neck injury. After landing there were no passengers requiring medical attention. The aircraft was inspected for overstress and no discrepancies were found."

A conservative approach, followed by the first officer in this instance, is to avoid the perceived hazard first, and verify the nature of the hazard afterwards. Although this report didn't mention crew fatigue as a factor, fatigue is known to be associated with susceptibility to the parallax illusion. U.S. Air Force research has shown that a few minutes of breathing 100% oxygen will help to refocus a pilot's thinking and eyesight.

NASA Callback Report

ed (Be cautious! This looks like a wink and one of the passengers may think you're trying to put the make on him or her).

Using sunglasses for protection from bright light and glare during the daytime is most helpful in preventing night vision deterioration, as well as preventing eye strain and eye damage. This is especially important when flying above an overcast that may reflect a great deal of sunlight. Find sunglasses that absorb at least 85% of the visible light (15% transmittance) and have minimal color distortion. Usually, a green or neutral gray is a satisfactory color. Polarized lenses should always be avoided, especially if you're using a moving map display or fly a glass cockpit. These lenses may show strain patterns in laminated windshields and create optical distortion when reading certain flight instruments (they may even prevent you from reading the symbols on instruments incorporating anti-glare filters). I'd also recommend that you stay away from sunglass frames like Elton John wears (especially the flaming pink flamingo glasses, which don't help anyone fly better). I make it a point to ensure all my sunglasses have a high degree of impact resistance. Why? They are excellent eye protectors in the event that something penetrates the windshield.

Rod Cells of the Human Eye

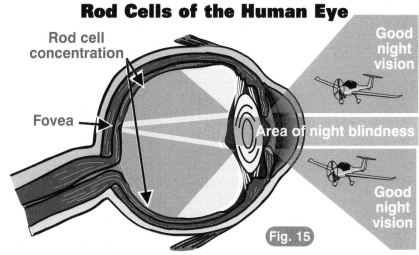

Fig. 15

Looking directly at an object at night makes it difficult to see. At night it's best to look 5 to 10 degrees offset from center for better vision. This allows the light from dimly lit objects to fall on the rod cells (surrounding the foveal region) which are better for night vision.

Aging and Night Vision

We'd all like to think we're forever young, but there are undeniable effects of aging and one of the most noticeable is a decline in night visual ability.

This happens for number of reasons. First and foremost, significantly less light hits the retina as we age, due mostly to a reduction in pupil size. By age 60, even in the daytime, the retina receives only one-third the amount of light it did at age 20. At night, the retina of an 80-year-old receives one-sixteenth the light that falls on the retina of a 20 year old.

As if this weren't bad enough news, other aspects of night vision are also adversely affected with age. The time it takes to achieve dark adaptation lengthens with the shadow of the years. Remember those rods I mentioned before (the ones not named after me)? They contain a chemical called rhodopsin. At night, the light photons fall on this chemical, causing it to split into two components (retinal and opsin) that signal the brain that light has been received. The two chemicals eventually recombine. The length of time it takes for this recombination increases as we get older, meaning that on average there isn't as much active rhodopsin around to absorb photons and thus detect light.

This explains why it takes us longer to achieve dark accommodation as we age. In bright light, all the rhodopsin is split into its component parts. Turn down the lights and you initially have no un-split rhodopsin in the rods to detect photons. If you're young, the reunion of retinal and opsin happens quickly, so you can see well in the dark pretty quickly. If you're less young, you have to wait longer for the reunion and thus for your night vision to come up to speed (whatever speed that might be).

Color vision and contrast sensitivity also decline with increasing age, making it more and more difficult to discern that anything is out there, let alone what the anything might be. Some colors (primarily blues and blue-greens) are more affected and thus less detected than others.

Finally, the ability of the lens bend and focus an image sharply on the retina starts to wane, which is why most of us wind up wearing glasses by age 40 or so. The

The Parallax Effect - Part Dieux

When to Their Wondering Eyes Should Appear

The parallax effect also can be experienced by several observers at the same time, as reported by a general aviation pilot who described a night flight with companions:

There were 3 of us in the cockpit, including 1 non-pilot. We were heading northbound over the peninsula. All 3 of us looked off to the 9 o'clock position and saw 2 landing lights which appeared to be a single large aircraft approaching at a very rapid rate. We banked to the right and pulled the throttle to idle in an attempt to avoid what appeared to be an imminent collision course. We then returned to level flight to see that the perceived aircraft was still approaching from the same direction and was now much closer. After another brief moment, we realized that what we were looking at was the landing lights of two separate aircraft approaching from the west and that we were experiencing a visual illusion. It was not until the aircraft finally got close enough to see the position lights that we were able to distinguish one aircraft from the other.

NASA Callback Report

lens, supple in youth, becomes less flexible and can't be bent over as great a range to focus images from both near and far.

Haze and Collision Avoidance

Keep in mind that all objects (traffic included) appear to be farther away in hazy conditions. The mind equates difficulty in seeing an object with increased distance. As a result, under hazy conditions you might (intentionally or unintentionally) allow another airplane to get closer to you than you otherwise would before taking corrective action.

Wearing yellow lens sunglasses is often recommended for hazy, smoggy conditions. Yellow lenses allow for greater definition and contrast of objects. I keep a pair in my flight case for hazy days (I also have a pink-rimmed pair in case I meet Elton John at the airport). Yellow lens sunglasses put a little more strain on my eyes if I wear them for a long time, but the payoff is in easier identification of traffic in smoggy and hazy conditions.

Scanning for Traffic During the Day

Avoiding midairs is predicated upon one important premise—you must look outside the cockpit. Ah, did you think that once you became a big instrument pilot you no longer had to see-and-avoid? Wrong. When you are in VMC (even while on an IFR flight plan), you are every bit as responsible for seeing and avoiding as when you are flying VFR.

Far too often, pilots spend their time staring at instruments instead of honoring the see and avoid concept in VMC. How much time should be spent looking outside and inside the cockpit? Many years ago a military study indicated that on a 17-second cycle, approximately 3 seconds should be spent inside the cockpit with 14 seconds spent looking outside. That's approximately a one-second-inside to five-seconds-outside ratio. These are good numbers to follow.

Looking outside the cockpit is one thing, knowing how to look is another. Scanning for traffic requires that you understand another peculiarity about the eye—objects are difficult to detect when the eye is in motion. Effective scanning requires holding the eyes still for a very short time to detect objects. Perhaps the best way to scan is to move your eyes in a series of short, regularly spaced movements that bring successive areas of the sky into the central visual field. The FAA suggests that each movement should not exceed 10 degrees with each area being observed for at least 1 second to enable detection, as shown in Figure 16.

The Sector Scanning Method

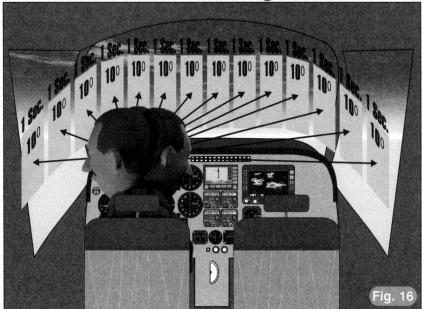

Fig. 16

One method of scanning is using the Sector Scanning method. You simply scan one area 10 degrees in width for one second before moving onto the next sector. By moving your head in a series of short movements, the eye is stationary long enough to focus on an object. This includes scanning the area behing you, too.

Scanning Through 360 Degrees

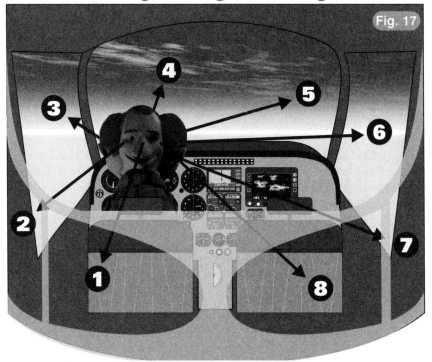

Fig. 17

Effective scanning assumes that you'll scan 360 degrees for traffic. Starting at the rearmost window, scan in a clockwise direction until reaching the right rearmost window. Sometimes it may be physically difficult to turn your head in a rearward direction. If so, make right or left turns to effectively scan the rear of the airplane.

The brain of anyone reading this book (in English) is already trained to process sight information presented from left to right (it probably works differently for those whose native languages are read right-to-left). You will probably find it easier to start your scan from over your left shoulder, proceeding to the right across the windshield, as shown in Figure 17.

Whatever you do, don't forget to scan the area behind you. Many years ago an Aircraft Owner's and Pilot's Association study found that the majority of midairs occur when one aircraft overtakes another (one study showed that 82% of the accidents happen this way). Obviously this is a faster aircraft overtaking a slower one. This becomes a greater concern when you're operating in an area where fast and slow aircraft mix.

Scanning the rear quadrants may take some neck bending or turning of the aircraft, depending on the aircraft configuration. Unless you've seen the movie *The Exorcist,* you might not realize that such neck twisting is possible. But even if your head can't spin on its axis, make gentle turns in the airplane to take a peek at what's behind you (Figure 18). Making gentle turns is also a good idea when climbing or descending on an airway to check for traffic.

Rearward Clearing Turns

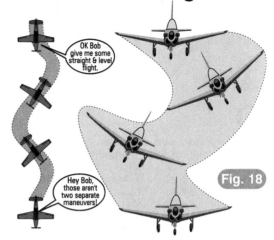

In some airplanes, the only way to see what's behind you is to make clearing turns while looking rearward. Don't be reluctant to make turns as often as is necessary to watch for faster traffic approaching from behind.

Another consideration when scanning is to avoid being a victim of *empty-field myopia.* This condition usually occurs when you're flying above a cloud or haze layer with nothing specific to focus on outside the airplane. In such conditions the eyes to relax and seek a comfortable focal distance ranging anywhere from 10 to 30 feet. This means you can be looking outside the airplane without seeing traffic. To overcome this problem, try to fix your eyes momentarily on a ground object off in the distance (if possible) before resuming your scan.

If you spot a target and it has no apparent motion, it's either coming directly at you, moving directly away from you, or it's a big bug that ended its life on your windshield. A target moving directly toward you can close the distance in a very short time. The rate of closure is *your* speed PLUS its speed. Figure 19 demonstrates how quickly aircraft can converge. Little or no relative movement also happens when aircraft are converging, as shown in Figure 18. If you detect

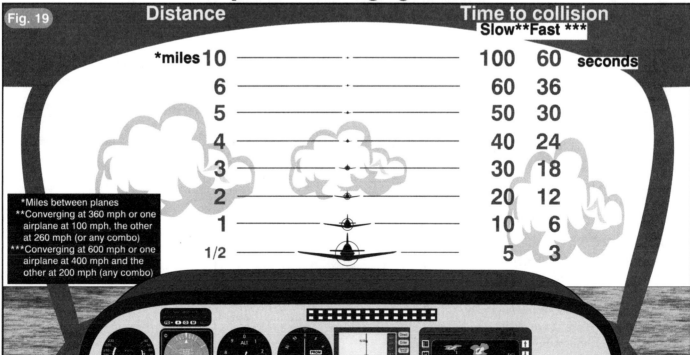

Airplanes converging head-on cover distances quickly. Additionally, there is little or no relative movement between targets making it more difficult to identify a collision threat. For instance, a slower airplane and a faster airplane converging at a rate of 360 mph (or any combination of speeds equaling 360 mph as shown by the "slow" speed column) have 20 seconds before impact when two miles apart. A 500 mph airliner and a 100 mph airplane (600 mph converging speed as shown by the "fast" speed column) have 12 seconds before colliding at a distance of 2 miles.

Determining Direction of Airplane Travel by Use of Its Position Lights

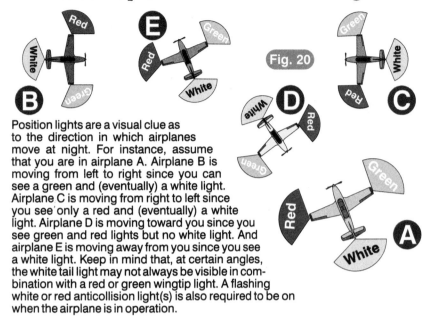

Fig. 20

Position lights are a visual clue as to the direction in which airplanes move at night. For instance, assume that you are in airplane A. Airplane B is moving from left to right since you can see a green and (eventually) a white light. Airplane C is moving from right to left since you see only a red and (eventually) a white light. Airplane D is moving toward you since you see green and red lights but no white light. And airplane E is moving away from you since you see a white light. Keep in mind that, at certain angles, the white tail light may not always be visible in combination with a red or green wingtip light. A flashing white or red anticollision light(s) is also required to be on when the airplane is in operation.

a target with little or no relative motion in your windshield, it's best to take evasive action immediately. Don't just wait for the target to grow larger—make a turn. Make the target move.

Night Scanning For Traffic

While it's easier to spot aircraft lights at night, this doesn't necessarily mean it's easier to identify the aircraft's direction of movement, much less its size and shape. That's why airplanes are required to have their position lights on from sunset to sunrise (anticollision lights are to be on when the airplane is in operation). You can determine the direction of airplane travel by noting the position of the airplane's red navigation light (on the left wing), the green navigation light (on the right wing) and the steady white light (on the tail). The red or white anticollision light is often visible from many directions (see Figure 20).

And don't neglect the issue of autokinesis, discussed earlier. Avoid it by using the proper scan technique.

Airplane Blind Spots

All airplanes have blind spots, where traffic is difficult to see. High wing aircraft make seeing above difficult, while low wing aircraft make seeing below difficult (biplane pilots have both problems). Figure 21 shows how these blind spots look on different aircraft. This doesn't mean these areas should remain invisible. You can see them by turning the airplane or lifting a wing, to compensate for the areas blocked by aircraft structure.

Scan the *entire area* for collision avoidance prior to starting any maneuver. *Entire* means everywhere—above and below, in front and behind. Pilots of high wing airplanes should lift their wing slightly and look up before starting a turn (tell the passengers that you're looking for traffic if you're worried that they may think you don't know which way to turn). This prevents turning into an airplane that is descending from your direction of turn. Pilots of low wing airplanes need to be especially alert to clear the areas below them during descents. If you're flying a low wing airplane, be sure to make clearing turns during descents to check for otherwise-invisible traffic below you. If you're flying a low wing airplane, don't forget to also look in the direction *opposite* the turn. Why? The outside wing often prevents you from seeing converging traffic. In short, do what your mom told you to do. Look both ways, and then look up, down, behind and ahead. Remember to keep your head outside the cockpit (no, that will mess up your hair; I mean keep your eyes outside the cockpit).

Whatever you do, don't be shy about turning that airplane and looking around when operating in areas of high traffic density. It's possible for a low wing and a high wing airplane to remain within each other's blind spots, as shown in Figure 21 (which is like the blind flying lead with the blind, but only worse in this instance).

Blind Areas Common to High and Low Wing Airplanes

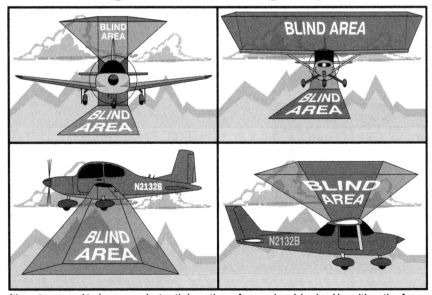

It's not unusual to have a substantial portion of your view blocked by either the fuselage or the wings. Compensating for those areas of blocked view requires that you make turns and gentle pitch changes. Fig. 21

When you're within five miles of an airport below 3,000 feet AGL, it's time to heighten your vigilance. One study of midair collisions found that 77% of all midairs occurred in this area. The same study reported that 49% occurred within five miles and 500 feet AGL of the airport. This translates into a need to be careful when you're approaching an airport to land. Never assume you're the only one out there. In fact, assume the opposite. Always fly as if there were planes nearby. Look for them. Sometimes you'll surprise yourself and see them.

Don't let the presence of a tower controller, radar advisories or on-board traffic detection systems decrease your caution. Too many people die or are injured by complacency. Many a midair has occurred within view of a tower controlled field. Remember, in Class D airspace, controllers separate traffic on the ground, but not in the air. Therefore, you are are *always* responsible for you own see-and-avoid traffic separation, even when the tower is in operation or when you are receiving radar advisories.

With this refresher on the visual system in mind, let's see how your eyes and the environment in which you'll fly can trick you into seeing things differently than they really are.

Optical Illusions

Unless you're Batman, it's unlikely that using echolocation will do you much good when flying instruments. Besides, your constant pinging is sure to irritate both passengers and controllers. That leaves vision as the most important (human) sense for safe (human) flight.

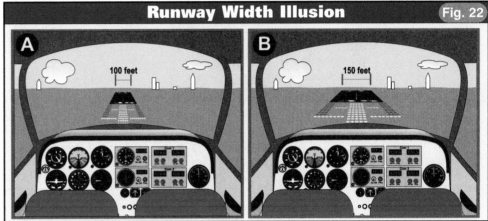

A narrow runway creates the illusion that you are higher than you actually are (position A). A wide runway (position B) creates just the opposite illusion, often making you feel you are lower than you actually are.

There's an old saying that "Seeing is believing," and perhaps it is for mere mortals. For pilots, however, that's not always true. Certain terrain features and atmospheric conditions create optical illusions and mess with your ability to see what's really out there. These illusions are primarily associated with landing. Since, at the end of an instrument approach, you must transition from reliance on instruments to visual cues outside the cockpit for landing, it's important to be aware of and ready to react to these illusions and the problems they cause.

To borrow and slightly alter a popular expression, "Illusions happen." They happen because the eyes' interpreter—the brain—makes certain assumptions about size relationships and what they say about distance. Some of these are lifelong mental impressions based on the world as viewed from the ground; others are things learned from flying. These visual impressions work when the underlying assumptions are correct, but they can mislead when conditions vary from "normal."

Here are several major illusions that can lead to landing errors.

Runway Width Illusion
Approaching a runway that's narrower than usual creates the illusion that your airplane is higher than it actually is (Figure 22A). If you don't recognize this illusion, you'll fly a lower than normal approach, which increases the risk of striking objects along the approach path or even landing short of the runway (which is what can happen if you strike a particularly large object along the approach path). A wider-than-usual runway has the opposite effect (Figure 22B). It creates the illusion that you're too low on approach, increasing the risk that you'll level out too high and land hard or overshoot the runway.

Runway Slope Illusion
When approaching an uplsoping runway and/or up-sloping terrain, you might experience the illusion of being higher that you actually are (Figure 23). If you don't recognize this illusion, it's possible to fly a much lower approach than normal. Approaching a downsloping runway and/or downsloping terrain can produce the opposite effect, resulting in a feeling that you're lower than you should be. This results in flying a higher-than-normal approach.

An upsloping runway creates the illusion that you are higher than you actually are (position A). A downsloping runway (position B) creates the illusion of being too low.

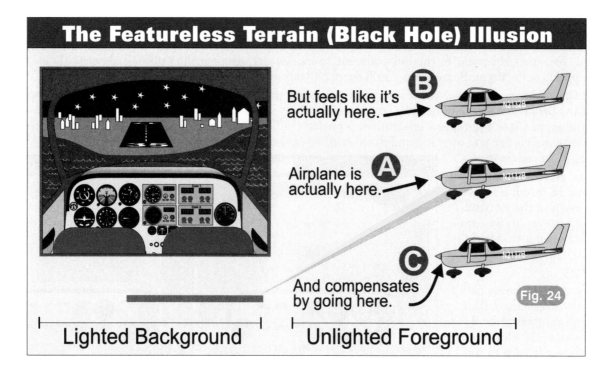

The Featureless Terrain (Black Hole) Illusion

But feels like it's actually here. **B**

Airplane is actually here. **A**

And compensates by going here. **C**

Fig. 24

Lighted Background   Unlighted Foreground

Featureless Terrain Illusion

The absence of ground features, such as when flying an approach over water, dark areas, or snow-covered areas, creates the illusion that the airplane is at a higher altitude than it actually is. This illusion is often referred to as the "black hole" illusion or the "black hole" approach," and it can cause you to feel that you're much higher (sometimes twice as high) as you actually are (Figure 24). The net result is that you compensate by flying much lower than you want to be or than is safe.

Water Refraction

If rain isn't distracting enough, rain on the windscreen can create the illusion you're higher than you are, because the horizon appears lower than it is (due to refraction). This can result in flying too low for safety.

Haze

Haze in the atmosphere can create the illusion of being farther from the runway than you actually are. As a result, you might fly a higher-than-normal approach, since higher altitudes are associated with greater distances from the runway.

Conversely, if the air is extremely clear, you might feel like you're closer to the runway than you actually are. The result is that you'll fly a lower approach since lower altitudes are associated with being closer to the runway in preparation to land. Also, be alert for how water can diffuse light and adversely affect your depth perception. The lights and terrain features you normally use to gauge height during landing become less reliable in such conditions.

Fog

If you're on an approach and penetrate a fog layer, you might experience the illusion of pitching up. If you don't recognize this, you might try to compensate by steepening the approach and turn your airplane into a lawn dart.

Ground Lighting Illusions

During an approach, it's possible to mistake lighting along a single path such as a road, and even lights on a moving train, for runway and approach lights (you'd think the train's horn and the crossing gate lights would provide a clue, but some people remain clueless). This is why you want to review the airport diagram of every approach to check for the type of approach lighting that's available for that runway (Figure 25). At least you'll know what shape of lighting is available (if any) when you approach minimums. While we'll learn about approach lighting systems later, take note of the small picture of the approach lighting system that exists before the threshold of Runway 30 on the Long Beach airport diagram. This gives you a rough idea what that approach lighting system will look like on the approach.

Airport Lighting

The airport sketch found on IFR approach charts provides you with a very good idea of the type of lighting (approach, runway, etc.) that's available at the airport. While you'll learn more about this lighting in Chapter 5, be aware that advanced knowledge of the location and type of lighting can help prevent mistaking a lighted road for a runway.

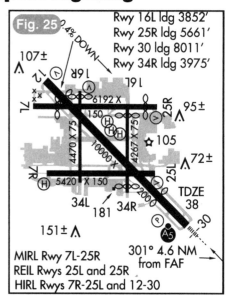

Fig. 25

Rwy 16L ldg 3852'
Rwy 25R ldg 5661'
Rwy 30 ldg 8011'
Rwy 34R ldg 3975'

MIRL Rwy 7L-25R
REIL Rwys 25L and 25R
HIRL Rwys 7R-25L and 12-30

301° 4.6 NM from FAF

TDZE 38

Many years ago at my home airport, a Twin Otter (that's an airplane, not an aquatic animal from a big family) mistook a busy, well-lighted road for the runway and crashed when the airplane ran into several light poles. It's also important to keep in mind that bright runway and approach lighting systems, especially where few lights illuminate the surrounding terrain, can create the illusion of less distance to the runway. Not recognizing this illusion can result in an excessively high approach and excessively low feelings about the outcome.

Preventing Landing Errors Due to Visual Illusions

There are several ways to control how visual illusions affect you during instrument approaches. In addition to studying your approach chart's airport sketch for additional lighting, you should also look for possible illusion-type distraction in your *Airport/Facility Directory* (Figure 26). You're looking for roads that may contain straight lighting, such as the two roads that intersect just prior to the threshold of Runway 28L at Hayward Executive (Figure 26, position A). It's conceivable that you might be holding a 15 degree right wind correction angle on this approach and have the nose nearly aligned with the road to the right of the runway when the runway is actually to your left. This is one reason you must anticipate how holding a wind correction angle during approach might affect your view. You should also look for information on runway slope (shown as *.4% up E* in this diagram) and terrain information (Figure 26, position B). Pay attention to minimum altitudes during all approaches. Make sure you use any glidepath aid available at the airport (VASI, PAPI, etc.) and use the VDP (Visual Descent Point) for non-precision approaches if one is available on your approach chart.

Finally, maintain your instrument flying proficiency if you're planning on doing low visibility approaches in bad weather. Proficiency becomes especially important when you consider that the chances of being involved in an approach accident increase when an emergency or other activity distracts you from flying your airplane.

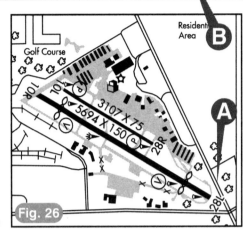

HAYWARD EXECUTIVE (HWD) 2 W UTC−8(−7DT) N37°39.54′ W122
52 B S4 **FUEL** 100LL, JET A OX 1, 3 TPA—See Remarks
RWY 10R−28L: H5694X150 (ASPH) S−30, D−75 MIRL 0.4% up E
RWY 10R: REIL. VASI(V4R)—GA 3.0° TCH 25′. Thld dsplcd 816′.
Tree. Rgt tfc.

You can tell a lot about the environment of the approach end of the runway by looking at the airport sketch in the Airport/Facility Directory. The roads that cross in front of Runway 28L at Hayward Executive (position A) could be misinterpreted for the runway in low visibility conditions, especially if the roads are lit and a crosswind is involved.

Vision Under Dim and Bright Illumination

In case you haven't noticed by now, when the light is dim you can't see your charts or instruments very well. In fact, they may be unreadable, which frightened some folks into thinking they were illiterate when, in reality, their cockpit lights weren't on. So keep those cockpit lights up when necessary. Which lights? Let's see.

As explained earlier, in darkness, vision becomes more sensitive to light, a process called *dark adaptation*. Using red cockpit lighting makes you look like a traveling house of ill repute, but it also helps preserve your dark adaptation. Unfortunately, red light distorts colors, especially on aeronautical charts, and makes it very difficult for your eyes to focus on objects inside the airplane. So use it only where optimum outside night vision capability is necessary. On the other hand, make sure you have white cockpit lighting available when it's needed for reading maps and instruments, especially under IMC conditions.

Dark adaptation is impaired by exposure to cabin pressure altitudes above 5,000 feet (you'll find out why shortly),

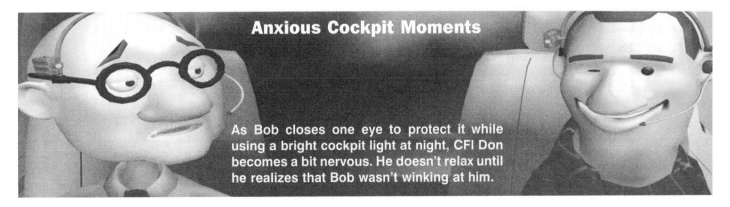

Anxious Cockpit Moments

As Bob closes one eye to protect it while using a bright cockpit light at night, CFI Don becomes a bit nervous. He doesn't relax until he realizes that Bob wasn't winking at him.

carbon monoxide inhaled through smoking or from exhaust fumes, deficiency of Vitamin A in the diet, and by prolonged exposure to bright sunlight. Since any degree of dark adaptation is lost within a few seconds of viewing a bright light, you should close one eye when using a light, to preserve some degree of night vision (but tell others what you're doing so they don't mistake this as your letting them in on a secret that you haven't yet told them). During night flights in the vicinity of lightning, turn up the cockpit lights to help prevent loss of night vision due to the bright flashes.

Understanding how our vestibular and visual systems work is fundamental to safe instrument flying. None of this knowledge, however, does you much good if improper respiration or an inadequate supply of oxygen keeps your brain from getting the molecular nourishment it needs to function. Nor will you or your passengers even feel like flying instruments if you don't know how to handle the discomfort of a plugged eustachian tube. Let's make sure you have a strategy for dealing with these problems.

Hypoxia: Low O, Too

Hypoxia is a state of oxygen deficiency in the body sufficient to impair functioning of the brain and other organs. While the percentage of oxygen in the atmosphere doesn't change with an increase in altitude (it stays about 21%), the amount of pressure that forces oxygen into our body decreases, causing hypoxia. Because of this lower pressure, pilots flying at high altitudes (50,000 feet and above) often wear pressure suits. (That's pressure suit, not power suit—i.e., double breasted black suit with red tie—which would look pretty dumb at 50,000 feet anyway.)

The effects of hypoxia occur at altitudes as low as 5,000 feet, beginning with a deterioration of night vision. The eyes require a great deal of oxygen to function properly. They are one of the first organs to experience the effects of reduced oxygen within the body. Other significant effects of hypoxia often don't occur in the normal, healthy pilot below 10,000 feet. If you smoke, then all bets are off. Smoking reduces the altitude at which the effects of

hypoxia are experienced (it also increases the chance of your power suit catching on fire!).

Above 10,000 feet MSL, most individuals begin to experience some decrease in their judgment, memory, alertness and coordination. The ability to calculate also becomes impaired for most individuals as the effects of hypoxia increase.

Time of Useful Consciousness	
Altitude	**Before Snooze**
45,000 feet MSL	9 to 15 seconds
40,000 feet MSL	15 to 20 seconds
35,000 feet MSL	30 to 60 seconds
30,000 feet MSL	1 to 2 minutes
28,000 feet MSL	2.5 to 3 minutes
25,000 feet MSL	3 to 5 minutes Fig. 27
22,000 feet MSL	5 to 10 minutes
20,000 feet MSL	30 minutes or more

Without supplemental oxygen, the time at which you'll remain "usefully" conscious varies dramatically with different altitudes (and individuals, too) as shown in the chart above.

Hypoxia is such a serious and insidious problem because its effects develop gradually and are usually difficult to recognize. Headache, drowsiness, dizziness, and either a sense of well-being (otherwise known as euphoria) or belligerence can occur. (You sometimes get a similar feeling when studying the Federal Aviation Regulations—especially the headache and dizziness part.)

Hypoxia

Both pilots and controllers are educated to recognize the effects of oxygen deprivation and hypoxia. This training can be vital in safely resolving oxygen-related pilot incapacitation. Several ASRS reports illustrate:

"While at FL250 on an IFR flight plan, my oxygen line became disconnected from the regulator. I could hear the oxygen escaping and thought the regulator had not sealed on the portable tank behind the passenger seat. As I had changed tanks within the past 15 minutes, I attempted to tighten the regulator, but to no avail. I recognized hypoxia coming on, pulled power back, disconnected the autopilot, and lost consciousness. I became conscious at 17,000 feet. The plane was descending and in a bank. I leveled the plane and declared an emergency and told the controller I had lost my oxygen supply and had lost consciousness. I landed at the nearest airport. Upon landing, I saw the line to the regulator had come off....

I have since found that if the oxygen line is kinked the line will pop off the barbed fitting on the regulator, so in the future I will secure a clamp at this attachment."

Portable oxygen tanks and lines should be inspected and secured during preflight to prevent potentially lethal "kinks" in the oxygen supply.

NASA Callback Report

The Air Up There Is Rare

"During a test flight, I received a clearance to climb and maintain FL250. I was using supplemental oxygen. After about 20 minutes, I began to experience hypoxia, but I had no awareness of it at the time. This resulted in loss of altitude control by as much as 2,000 feet. Center asked me to report my current altitude, which I was unable to do due to mental confusion and inability to read my altimeter. I was given a clearance back to my home base. I wrote it down, but was unable to read it. With difficulty, and assistance from Center, I managed to descend to a lower altitude. I violated clearance limits more than once on the way down. Center was not happy. I neither felt the need for, nor requested, any assistance from Center. I now realize I was in serious trouble with acute hypoxia."

The reporter believes that the oxygen flow rate may have been inadequate for the altitude flown. A full-size face oxygen mask might have provided more reliable delivery of correct amounts of oxygen. This reporter and other pilots of unpressurized aircraft that fly at high altitudes might consider high-altitude pressure chamber training, offered by the Air Force and the FAA. Hypoxia recognition is a beneficial by-product of this training. Information and application forms for this training may be obtained from local FAA Flight Standard District Offices. Courses are offered for small fees at appropriately equipped Air Force bases.

NASA Callback Report

The higher the altitude, the less time it takes for hypoxia to start robbing you of your flying faculties (no, this is *not* a university aloft). In fact, it's not unusual for pilot performance to deteriorate seriously within 15 minutes at 15,000 feet, and at higher altitudes you become unconscious in mere moments. Figure 27 identifies the time of useful consciousness (TOC) at various altitudes without the use of supplemental oxygen. TOC is how long you are at least minimally brain functional and useful as a pilot. After that time, the airplane is on its own.

Preventing hypoxia means avoiding higher altitudes unless you have and use supplemental oxygen. You should avoid flying at more than 10,000 feet during the day or more than 5,000 feet at night without the use of oxygen. These levels are lower than the limits set by FAR 91.211. Nevertheless, it's best to follow the conservative path, both to account for variations in individual physiology and also to provide a reasonable margin of safety.

Pilots using supplemental oxygen need to avoid using greasy or oily rags around oxygen systems. Petroleum-based products and oxygen don't mix. Actually, they *do* mix—all too well. They are a very dangerous combination that can cause a fire, explosion, and definitely serious injury. In fact, the military recommends that their pilots not use lip balm (ChapStick and similar products) when they plan on using oxygen. Why? Because lip balm is petroleum based. Perhaps that's why military pilots call it LIP-BOMB. Just think, you could have lips heavily coated with lip balm, go on oxygen, hear a boom, and then spend the rest of the flight looking around the cockpit for your lips. Can you imagine how difficult it would be to call the tower on the radio without your lips?

Hyperventilation

I once asked a student starts shallow, quick breathing or panting. This fellow replied, "It means he's been eating Milk-Bone dog biscuits." Either that or the pilot is in labor.

Hyperventilation is abnormally quick, shallow breathing. It can happen when a person is scared, tense, or otherwise stressed. Rapid breathing has the effect of changing blood chemistry by expelling too much carbon dioxide. The level of carbon dioxide is one of the signals the body uses to regulate breathing. The symptoms of hyperventilation include lightheadedness, suffocation, drowsiness, tingling in the extremities, and coolness. Incapacitation in the form of a lack of coordination, disorientation, and painful muscle spasms can result, followed by unconsciousness.

You can reduce or eliminate the symptoms of hyperventilation by bringing the rate and depth of your breathing under control. By purposefully slowing your breathing rate, you allow the carbon dioxide to rebuild within the body, eventually reaching the level where it signals "all's well" to the system. The symptoms disappear within a few minutes.

Talking loud is one way to overcome the effects of hyperventilation. This forces you to wait longer between breaths, and builds up the body's carbon dioxide level (it also causes other people to stare and point at you, but when you're hyperventilating, you don't really care). Some people recommend breathing into a paper bag to help build up the carbon dioxide (this is also said to cure hiccups, so if you are hyperventilating *and* have the hiccups, this works great). Simply hold the bag over your nose and mouth and breath normally until the symptoms subside. Bag the idea of putting the entire bag over your

Hyperventilation Tip #1

In counteracting hyperventilation, it's best to hold the bag as you breathe into it instead of taping it to your head.

Hyperventilation Tip #2

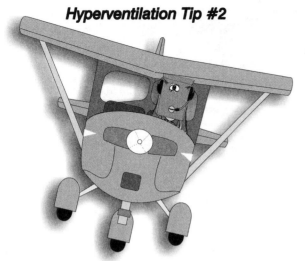

In counteracting hyperventilation, it's best not to put the bag over your head and poke out eye and mouth holes.

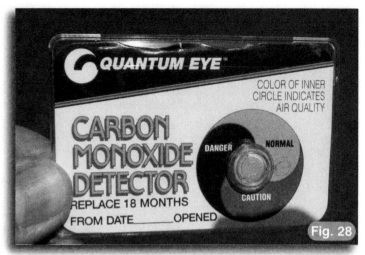

Fig. 28

A stick-on carbon monoxide detector is insurance for a problem that can take your breath away (OK, prevent oxygen transport).

head even if you poke holes out for the eyes. This is no time to get a little instrument work in. Besides, it scares the passengers!

The early symptoms of hyperventilation and hypoxia are similar. They can even occur at simultaneously (if so, you'd definitely be having a bad flying day and M&M's would probably melt in your hand). If you find yourself using an oxygen system because of hypoxia or hyperventilation, set the oxygen regulator to give you maximum oxygen flow. This recommendation may appear contradictory to you. After all, if you are hyperventilating, you need carbon dioxide, not oxygen. The problem is that you may not be sure which it is—hypoxia or hyperventilation. It's best to attack the problem as hypoxia first by going on oxygen. Next, check to see if the regulator (the oxygen regulator, not the voltage regulator) is functioning properly. Then you should give attention to consciously slowing your breathing rate.

CO Oh No

Carbon monoxide (CO) is a colorless, odorless, tasteless gas. It has a much stronger affinity than oxygen for *hemoglobin,* the substance in your blood that normally transports oxygen. If a hemoglobin molecule is occupied with a CO molecule, oxygen can't get aboard and be transported. Good night, Irene.

CO poisoning is cumulative and dangerous. It can incapacitate quickly, and it is rapidly fatal. Because of the

already-reduced oxygen supply at higher altitudes, you're even more vulnerable to the effects of CO poisoning as you head upward.

Carbon monoxide is a byproduct of combustion. Every winter, many people across the country lose their lives when they burn charcoal or other substances indoors for heat without adequate ventilation. And you've probably read stories of people who ended their lives by running tubing from the car's exhaust to the closed interior of their auto, then started the engine.

For pilots, the greatest CO danger arises from exhaust gases leaking into the cockpit. This occurs because of a leak in the exhaust system or because there is a leak in the heater, which uses exhaust gases to warm air that is sent to the cockpit. Heaters normally work by passing outside air over the heater's manifold, then directing the air into the cabin. If a leak occurs, raw exhaust can be imported directly into the cabin.

Because CO gives no direct evidence of its presence, you need help to know it's there. There are many commercially available CO monitors that can be put in the cockpit to warn of the presence of this silent killer (Figure 28). They vary in cost and sophistication, and none, to my knowledge, utilize a canary in a cage, either.

If you notice the odor of exhaust or experience symptoms of headache, drowsiness, dizziness, or loss of muscular power when the aircraft heater is in use, immediately

CO Oh No

A General Aviation pilot, thwarted by closed airport restaurants, initially thought that his nausea and dizziness during flight were due to skipping breakfast.

"I remember not being able to find my approach plates, even though they were on the floor beside me. I tried three times to set my destination into the GPS. I was confused as to what to do and panic began to set in. Fortunately, I was able to acquire the airport and complete the approach visually. Upon landing, I discovered that my carbon monoxide detector was jet black! I now suspect my disorientation was a result of carbon monoxide exposure."

Aviation supply shops have no "missing breakfast detector" available at any price. However, small, lightweight carbon monoxide detectors are available for less than $10, and change colors to inform aircraft occupants of the presence of this odorless gas. **NASA Callback Report**

CO Oh No-Aircraft Check-Ups

Having the aircraft in top shape is equally important for a safe flight, as this government pilot learned.
"I was on an IFR flight plan at FL190. I became nauseous, had tingling in my arms and hands, and my eyes were burning and watering. I got on oxygen, which seemed to help for a while, but then the symptoms returned. [At my destination], I asked for a special VFR clearance and radar vectors to final. I declared an emergency to receive priority handling. After an uneventful landing, I was met by an ambulance and transported to the hospital. Tests were inconclusive."

A hole was found in an air duct in the aircraft, and it is possible that exhaust fumes were piped into the cabin. The hole has been repaired, and the aircraft now has a carbon monoxide detector in it.

NASA Callback Report

turn off the heater and open the air vents. Consider opening the windows if that can be done in flight in your aircraft (consult the Pilot's Operating Handbook). The smell of exhaust gas should be considered the prelude to an emergency. You must act immediately.

If your physical symptoms are severe or continue after landing, seek medical treatment.

The U Station

The bane of many pilots is a tiny, flaccid tube called the *eustachian tube* (pronounced U-STAY-SHUN) as shown in Figure 29. The middle ear is like the inside of a drum, a closed, air-filled chamber sealed on one side by the appropriately named eardrum. The eustachian tube, barely more than an inch long, connects the middle ear to the back of the nose. It's a two-way conduit into the otherwise-sealed middle ear, made up of bone for about one-third its length and cartilaginous tissue for the rest. The tube permits the middle ear to add or release air to keep the middle ear at the same pressure as its surroundings.

The eustachian tube is normally closed. This keeps minor fluctuations in pressure and loud sounds from affecting the middle ear. In an ascent, when air pressure outside the middle ear is decreasing, the tube opens for a second or two, permitting higher pressure air from the middle ear to flow out, equalizing the pressure inside the ear with that of the cabin. This process, often accompanied by a slight crackling sound, is rarely a problem.

On the way down, however, it gets a lot harder to go with the flow, or rather to get the flow to go. Now there is high pressure on the outside, and low pressure trapped in the middle ear. The collapsed eustachian tube is like a soft hose with a crimp in it. It doesn't open as readily as it did when you were upward bound. You're now in the position of trying to force water back into the hose.

Nasal congestion makes the problem a lot worse, since it puts additional pressure on the collapsed tube. Now it's like a hose with a crimp in it *and* someone standing on the crimp. If you can't get the tube open, you have what's known as an *ear block*. Contrary to the

belief of some pilots, this is not a hit in the head from an NFL lineman, though if you ever get an ear block, you may well feel like you've got an entire football in your ear.

If you can't equalize the pressure, the result is somewhere between excruciating and devastating. Recall that the middle ear is a sealed chamber. Air expands or contracts with changes in pressure, in keeping with the laws of physics. Something has to give. As the pressure differential builds on descent, your eardrum bows inward, pressing on sensitive nerves. If the pressure differential becomes too great, the eardrum ruptures. As I hear it, this is not generally considered to be fun.

The first line of defense against ear block is to stop descending, and sometimes to climb back to a higher altitude. The lower you go, the greater the pressure differential, and the less likely you are to succeed at springing the trapdoor open.

The second thing to do is to swallow, yawn, or tense the muscles in your throat. Jutting out your lower jaw as far as it will go can do the trick, too. What you're trying to do is straighten the eustachian tube and give it the best chance of opening and equalizing the pressure. When this happens, it's generally accompanied by a loud popping sound and an enormous sense of relief.

> *Though almost nobody has heard of it, the Toynbee maneuver is a far preferable method of opening the eustachian tube...instead of blowing against the closed nostrils, you simply swallow.*

The Inside of the Human Ear

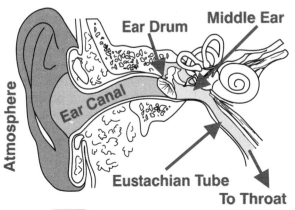

Ear Drum · Middle Ear · Atmosphere · Ear Canal · Eustachian Tube · To Throat

Fig. 29

No go? OK, time for the heavy artillery. Virtually every pilot and flight instructor will tell you to perform the *Valsalva maneuver,* in which you close your mouth, pinch your nose, and breathe out in short puffs against the closed nostrils. *I don't recommend that you do this.* The Valsalva maneuver is potentially damaging, and it's unfortunate that it has been so blithely handed down as the way to clear a closed eustachian tube. Even airline flight attendants tell passengers to perform the Valsalva maneuver.

What's the right answer? Though almost nobody has heard of it, the Toynbee maneuver is a far preferable method of opening the eustachian tube. The Toynbee maneuver is a variation of the Valsalva maneuver. Both start by closing off the nostrils (pinch them closed). However, in the Toynbee maneuver, instead of blowing against the closed nostrils, you just swallow.

Swallowing with your nostrils closed off has the effect of decreasing the size of the oropharyngeal (mouth and throat) space, much as if you had stepped on one end of an inflated balloon. This increases the pressure of the air in that space, forcing air back up the nose, and with any luck at all the U-tube pops right open. If not, keep swallowing slowly, but do not blow. You can damage your inner ear. Even when the Valsalva maneuver is successful, it can force unwanted, bacteria-laden material into the middle ear. Remember, one end of the U-tube is planted in your upper nose. So take a tip and Toynbee.

Knowing what you now know about where the eustachian tube is, perhaps you understand why you should NOT fly with a cold, other upper respiratory infection, or allergies. Not even a little bit of a cold. Not even slight allergies. The bad news is that I know you will eventually ignore this advice. The good news is that I know you will probably only ignore it once, because the resulting ear block will be a very memorable experience.

An upper respiratory infection is like standing on the garden hose. The water just doesn't have much chance of getting through. When it comes to your ears, there is no such thing as a "minor" cold. The least bit of fluid and gunk in your head compresses the eustachian tube and makes equalizing the pressure on descent almost impossible.

Share what you've learned about the U-tube with your passengers. Don't subject them to the pain and possible injury of an ear block by taking them aloft if they have nasal congestion.

And be aware that in very young children, especially infants, the eustachian tube is particularly difficult to open. There are several reasons for this, including the fact that the tube is only about half as long, the bony portion is proportionally longer, and the tube lies at a somewhat different angle than it does in an adult. These differences explain why you so often hear screaming infants on descent in commercial aircraft. I may start a support group called Tots for Toynbee.

If you do land with an ear block and it doesn't clear shortly after landing, give your doctor a call. On several occasions—one involving just me, another involving a passenger—I had to climb back to altitude to reduce the pain of ear block. The doctor and my wife both thought I was just looking for another excuse to go flying. A very gradual descent eventually helped relieve the pain.

The Ultimate Human Performance Checklist

No pilot worth his or her weight in GPS database cards would operate an airplane without using some type of checklist. Why then should you operate yourself—your mind and body, that is—without doing the same, especially when conducting an instrument flight where there is little margin for error? A checklist gives you the opportunity, before taking off, to take inventory of your psychological and physiological readiness to fly the airplane. Can you think of a better time to make this review? I suggest that before every flight you use the mnemonic "I'M SAFE" (*Illness, medication, Stress, Alcohol, Fatigue, Eating*) to run your human factors checklist. Let's examine each item and see how it relates to your performance in the cockpit.

Unscheduled Rest Periods

The effects of fatigue on pilot performance have been much studied in multi-crew air transport operations, but fatigue is also problematic in single-pilot operations. A single-pilot cargo flight, for example, may involve long periods of silence, restricted pilot movement, reduced cockpit ventilation, vibration, and other conditions known to invite drowsiness.

The result? In a few cases reported to the ASRS, pilots flying alone have fallen asleep while airborne. A few recent examples reported by air taxi pilots.

"I was on an IFR flight plan from ABC to XYZ, and about halfway to XYZ I fell asleep. The autopilot was on, and the heading indicator was set on a due west heading, and the altitude was set at 8,000 feet. I didn't wake up for 30 to 45 minutes. When I woke up I was about 90 nm south of the VOR. I couldn't get ABC or XYZ air traffic control on the radio, so I tried ZZZ, and it took 2 or 3 frequencies to finally make contact. I turned due North to point the airplane in the right direction, and climbed to 10,000 feet for right altitude for direction of flight, and for better radio/nav reception and better fuel consumption. I didn't think I had enough fuel for XYZ, so I chose to land at ZZZ. I landed at ZZZ with about an hour of fuel."

Later I was supposed to call XYZ Tower about the incident, and they said it was a "pilot deviation" event. I asked what that was, and [they] told me that I went beyond the IFR clearance limit. I filed and was cleared to XYZ, but didn't land at XYZ, then passed XYZ. Problem: lack of sleep. To correct the situation: Get 6 to 8 hours sleep, keep oneself busy in the cockpit [with] altitude changes, drink water, and open air vents/air conditioning. **NASA Callback Report**

Illness. Do I have any symptoms?

Be cautious if you're thinking about flying when ill. Many day-to-day illnesses degrade your performance to unsafe levels. Judgment can be impaired, along with memory, the ability to calculate, and alertness. Beyond difficulty in filling out the Hobbs meter sheet, these problems are serious and could impair your ability to safely fly an airplane. You owe it to yourself and your passengers to be as fit as possible when you park yourself in the pilot's seat of any airplane, and that goes double any time you are flying IFR.

Medication. Have I been taking prescription or over-the-counter drugs?

If you don't think your performance can be degraded by over-the-counter medication, then you've probably never taken any nor have you read the labels. Look on the back of a box of an antihistamine. Notice the nice warning that says, "When using this product, marked drowsiness might occur, be careful when driving a motor vehicle or operating machinery."

Does that mean you shouldn't take the family bulldozer to the market for some milk? Implied in this statement is a warning of performance degradation. Certainly this applies to airplanes as well as to cars (and bulldozers, too). For instance, some antihistamines can make a pilot more susceptible to hypoxia (oxygen deficiency), and many of them (including the "non-drowsy" ones) make people sleepy. You're likely to feel the effects of oxygen deficiency at lower altitudes.

While antihistamines are an obvious no-no, many drugs have less-obvious effects that can cause a decrement in pilot performance. If you're taking any medication, call your family physician to determine its side effects. Better yet, call your Aviation Medical Examiner. AME's are often familiar with the ways in which medications affect the skills needed by a pilot. What's not a "side effect" for an automobile driver can pose a major problem for a pilot.

Stress. Am I under psychological pressure from work or home situations? Do I have money, health, or family problems?

Stressed out? Kind of sounds like your body or mind has been pulled taut, almost to its breaking point, doesn't it? The analogy is apt in the sense that stress is the body's response to the demands, either pleasant or unpleasant, placed on it. Tension, fatigue, decreased performance, immobilization and even panic are sometimes the result of excess stress. The fact is that stress is inevitable; how we handle it differs from person to person, and from time to time for any one person. Given that the effects of stress can be cumulative, it's best to examine how it affects us and how to better manage it.

Be glad you have a small amount of stress. The only practical way to avoid it is being dead, which is a big price to pay for living stress free. But with too much stress your piloting performance plummets faster than an Internet stock after the bubble burst.

FAA Policy for Medication Usage

The Federal Aviation Regulations include no specific references to medication usage. FAR 61.53 prohibits acting as pilot-in-command or in any other capacity as a required pilot flight crewmember, while that person:

1. Knows or has reason to know of any medical condition that would make the person unable to meet the requirement for the medical certificate necessary for the pilot operation, or:

2. Is taking medication or receiving other treatment for a medical condition that results in the person being unable to meet the requirements for the medical certificate necessary for the pilot operation.

Further, FAR 91.17 prohibits the use of "any drug that affects the persons faculties in any way contrary to safety."

The FAA generally disallows certain types of drugs that are continuously used for treatment. These include, but aren't limited to, anticoagulants, antiviral agents, anxiolytics (anti-anxiety), barbiturates, chemotherapeutic agents, experimental, hypoglycemic, investigational, mood altering, motion sickness, narcotic, sedating, antihistaminic, steroids, or tranquilizers.

However, there is no official FAA "list" of drugs that is available to the public.

Unscheduled Rest Periods - Part Dieux

In another incident, a pilot on a night flight did not feel fatigued, but was unable to communicate with ATC after "closing his eyes":

"While at cruise at 4,000 feet indicated (MSL), while flying on autopilot for nearly 2 hours, I closed my eyes to rest prior to making a landing. I entered a dreamlike state wherein I could hear radio communications in my headset, but I lacked the situational awareness to respond to them. I had impairment of my perception of the passage of time for an estimated 45 nm or about 15 minutes. When I regained my situational awareness, I was 10-15 nm northwest of destination. I called the Center to reestablish communications and was given a radar vector back to the airport.

[Contributing factors]: A longer than normal flight due strong headwinds; extremely clear flight conditions with numerous shooting stars; extremely cold air temperatures with dry cabin heated air; later than normal flight departure time; very little radio communications traffic; long periods of silence except for engine drone. Pilot did not have a sense of fatigue when the incident occurred, but eyes were hot, dry and tired from this two hour flight."

Because individuals may vary widely in sleep requirements, pilots need to know their own sleep needs and be aware that reduced rest for more than a few days is a "red flag" for flight safety.

NASA Callback Report

The onset of stress initially improves performance, but only up to a point, as shown in Figure 30. That's why some folks do better on checkrides than in the last hours of training before the test. Performance deteriorates as your ability to cope diminishes. Don't worry, you're not alone here. All human beings have their stress limits. Superman doesn't count, because he's not really human. Besides, anyone in tights has probably learned to live with being up tight most of the time.

How do you know if you're subject to excess stress? There are usually three types of symptoms: emotional, physical, and behavioral. Now, if you're an individual who focuses his or her aggressive feelings inward, you might experience physical symptoms such as depression, preoccupation, sadness, and withdrawal (just like we all feel when we're forced to visit the Department of Motor Vehicles every few years).

Those folks who take frustrations out on other people or other objects (doors, walls, raw drywall, and more doors) exhibit few physical symptoms. Giving an airport line worker a black eye because you're stressed out is nature's way of moving the physical symptom from your fist to his eye socket. And since such people are often in jail, the decision of whether or not to fly is often moot. They'll tell you they're not in the moot to fly.

Behavioral and emotional symptoms of stress can also surface as decreased performance, panic, immobilization, or over-compensation, denial, suspicion, paranoia, agitation, restlessness, defensiveness, excess sensitivity to criticism, a tendency to be argumentative, arrogance, and hostility (hopefully no one would have all these symptoms at once, because no one would speak to such a person). If you are experiencing any of these symptoms, then you're experiencing excess stress. So what do you do to deal with the problem?

Obviously, if you can remove yourself from the condition responsible for causing the stress, this is a good start. On the other hand, knowing how to avoid situations that cause excess stress in the first place is

the best idea. At least avoid these circumstances until you've better prepared yourself to handle the expected stress.

For instance, if you haven't flown instruments in serious weather in a long while, don't make your first flight a five-hour epic into the teeth of a raging storm. You're likely to experience a lot of stress. Take a more experienced pilot along with you to regain your confidence. Or make

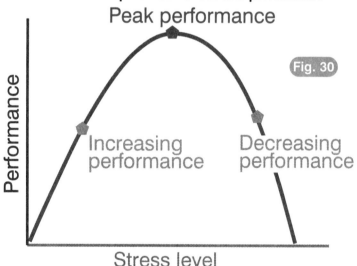

A - Relationship between stress and performance

Fig. 30

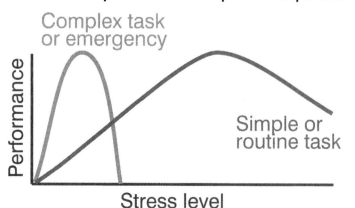

B - Stress and performance in complex and simple tasks

the trip in sections, flying shorter legs where you can land, refuel your airplane and you, and obtain an update on the latest weather. Perhaps the best idea is to make the trip another time, when the weather isn't as challenging or when you have flown hard IFR more recently. After all, you're not a scheduled airline (I'm assuming), so you have the flexibility to choose your departure date and time.

There are many other techniques to help you reduce stress, and a few involve Tibetan humming, incense and robes (if these are just the things you need to relax in an airplane, please send photos.) You've got to find what works for you. Stress reduction begins with stress recognition. You now know most of the symptoms. Conditioning yourself to relax and think clearly when stressed is your challenge and the challenge of everyone who flies. Here are a few additional tips that will help you accomplish this objective.

First, avoid situations that could distract you from flying the airplane. If ATC offers you a new clearance while aloft, tell them to stand by until you're ready to copy it. Don't just say, "Bring it on," if you're not prepared to copy, evaluate and confirm/deny the new route.

If your airplane has an autopilot, use it when the workload becomes excessive. Airline pilots have copilots, so why shouldn't you use your autopilot as a copilot? It works about the same, you don't have to feed it, and it doesn't talk back. Does life get any better? I submit that it does not.

If an emergency occurs, talk to yourself. Be your own best buddy. The mind reacts to your voice much the same way it reacts to someone else speaking to you. Imagine having Neil Armstrong in the cockpit with you saying, "OK, let's relax and take it step-by-step. Fly the vehicle first, watch your airspeed, look out for that crater." (OK, forget that one.) You'd respond in a calm manner, right? Science says that the same thing happens when you talk to yourself.

OK, is it no smoking within 50 feet or no drinking within 50 feet of the airplane?

Know your airplane before you go. There's no excuse for not knowing all the emergency procedures and safety systems associated with your airplane. Those procedures and systems are there to help you. What good do they do if you don't use them or even know they exist?

The Chinese takeout general, Sum Chew (or was that Sun TZU?) once suggested that if you know your enemy and know yourself, you will not be in peril in a thousand battles. Knowing yourself, your personal limits, what you can and can't do, is an important step in keeping stress at a manageable level.

Don't allow small mistakes to become big ones. Eastern Airlines Flight 401 provided a now-legendary example when it descended into the Florida Everglades because the autopilot kicked off as all three crewmembers focused on

a failed landing gear light. If you have a non-critical problem in flight and you want to review it, do so on the ground, not in the air, lest you run aground and have more problems to review.

Finally, if you're too stressed, park your plane. Better yet, don't even depart. I have much more respect for pilots who avoid flying because they're stressed and never have to demonstrate their stress-coping skills than those who fly stressed and can barely cope despite their skills.

Alcohol. Have I been drinking within 8 hours? Within 24 hours?

An old mariner who had spent many years on boats decided to take flying lessons. He showed up drunk for a flight, walked over to the airplane, untied all the ropes, threw them in the air and yelled, "Cast off!" You might say he didn't know the ropes but he would have probably hanged himself if he'd actually flown that day.

Don't even think about mixing flying and alcohol. Your performance is easily impaired by alcohol consumption, and impairment happens from the first sip, not just when you're looking or acting "drunk." As little as one ounce of liquor, one bottle of beer or four ounces of wine impairs flying skills.

Keep in mind that legally you may not operate an aircraft within eight hours of having consumed *any* alcohol. Also be aware that the effects of alcohol can linger long after eight hours. Judgment, coordination, and other items you really want to have available as an instrument pilot can be impaired even when you don't have an obvious hangover. It's usually best to wait at least 12 to 24 hours between the bottle and the throttle, depending on the amount of alcohol consumed.

Fatigue. Am I tired and not adequately rested?

Who isn't tired of hearing about fatigue? Well, I'm not. It's a serious issue and one that often isn't apparent to a pilot until he or she makes a serious mistake. Fatigue can be either acute (short-term) or chronic (long-term). A normal occurrence of everyday living, *acute fatigue* is the tiredness felt after long periods of physical and mental strain, including strenuous muscular effort, immobility, heavy mental workload, strong emotional pressure, monotony, and lack of sleep. Acute fatigue is prevented by adequate rest, regular exercise, and proper nutrition.

Chronic fatigue occurs when there is not enough time for a full recovery from repeated episodes of acute fatigue. Recovery from chronic fatigue requires a prolonged period of rest. You've got to sleep, baby. No way around it. If you're reading this in bed, maybe it's time to close the book and get to sleep. No matter which kind of fatigue you're suffering from, unless adequate precautions are taken, personal performance can be impaired and adversely affect pilot judgment and decision making.

Eating. Have I eaten enough of the proper foods to keep adequately nourished during the entire flight?

Pilots are notorious for living on the flotsam and jetsam from airport vending machines, which contain too much caffeine and sugar, and too little real nutritional value. While some people think eating junk food is part of maintaining the pilot image, the reality is that your brain needs a steady and substantial flow of energy to provide peak performance.

With the ample supply of protein food bars and healthy snacks that's now available, it's almost unimaginable that a pilot would fly without food on board the airplane (unimaginable, that is, unless the pilot is wearing a sign that says, "I will fly for food"). And don't forget water,

either. Most folks walk around in a nearly dehydrated state. The problem becomes much worse at altitude, where the air is drier. And if you fly in an air conditioned airplane (wow, are you lucky!), then you need to drink even more water to keep hydrated.

There you have it, from illness to eating and everything in between. Pilots using the I'M SAFE checklist are less likely to suffer an impairment that far too often leads or at least contributes to an accident. Statistics show that impairment contributes to many more accidents than mechanical problems. Please commit this checklist to memory and use it before every flight.

Now that you've navigated your way through some very important concepts on human factors, it's time to find your way to the chapter on electronic navigation. Let's look at the different forms of navigation used by instrument pilots and learn how each system is used during instrument flying.

Your Stress Index

What is the worst kind of stress?

The most harmful form of stress is not just the result of a major life crisis, death of a spouse, divorce, loss of a job or critical incidents like those of 9/11/01. While the stress associated with these events is often severe, it is also short-lived and therefore has little time to cause damage to our bodies if it's dealt with appropriately. Such stress can, however, cause an already full load of stress to become overwhelming.

Far worse, scientists now theorize, is the chronic, uncontrolled low-level tension caused by our responses to the pressures and irritations of everyday life, such as difficulties at work or at home, anger, rejection, interruptions, being late for work, financial anxieties, arguing with a loved one, and deadlines. Each little frustration that occurs throughout the day speeds the heart rate, dilates the pupils and floods the bloodstream with powerful hormones. Over the long haul, this uncontrolled low-level tension forces the body to go into overdrive, sapping our energy and damaging our physical and emotional health.

So, how stressed do you think you are right now? Not sure? Take the following stress index test to get a clue. Here's what I want you to do. Circle the number that comes closest to representing how relevant the statement is for you right now. Then score yourself, using the key at the bottom of the page.

The scale is 1 (not pertinent to me) to 5 (very pertinent to me).

1 2 3 4 5   A close family member died in the past 12 months.
1 2 3 4 5   I moved to a new town in the past 12 months.
1 2 3 4 5   I changed jobs in the past 12 months.
1 2 3 4 5   My son/daughter left home in the past 12 months.
1 2 3 4 5   A close friend/family member who is ill depends on you for care.
1 2 3 4 5   I've had a major health problem in the past 12 months.
1 2 3 4 5   A close relationship ended in the past 12 months.
1 2 3 4 5   I lost my job or retired in the past 12 months.
1 2 3 4 5   I got married in the past 12 months.
1 2 3 4 5   I took on a lot of debt in the past 12 months.
1 2 3 4 5   I got divorced or separated in the past 12 months.
1 2 3 4 5   I lost a lot of money in the past 12 months.
1 2 3 4 5   I have ongoing marital problems.
1 2 3 4 5   I have ongoing sexual problems.
1 2 3 4 5   I have ongoing financial problems.
1 2 3 4 5   I have ongoing trouble with friends or relatives.
1 2 3 4 5   I have ongoing problems meeting family demands.
1 2 3 4 5   I have ongoing pressure at work or school.
1 2 3 4 5   I have ongoing pressure with emotional problems.
1 2 3 4 5   I am constantly facing do-or-die deadlines.
_____   TOTAL SCORE (add up all numbers)

SCORING KEY

20 - 35 Virtually stress free (a good level for flying safety)

36 - 50 Somewhat stressful (think carefully about how stress might affect your ability to fly safely).

51 - 75 Stressed— watch out (not a good time to go flying unless you're flying Microsoft Flight Simulator).

76 - 100 Super stressed— reduce all pressures in your life or someone will be calling 911 (I wouldn't recommend getting near an airplane).

Chapter 5
Electronic Navigation

It's hard to believe that there was actually a time in aviation history when pilots flew IFR with little more than an ADF and a compass. Yes, it's true. And holy crosses, lit candles, and nativity scenes weren't involved, either.

We're fortunate to have all the cockpit goodies available in today's modern airplanes, especially given that these goodies are so reliable (assuming that you didn't obtain these toys from some guy in a van, of course). VOR, GPS, PFDs (primary flight displays), and MFDs (multifunction displays) are just a few of the cockpit tools to feel good about. Let's learn how to use some of these navigation devices by starting at the beginning with the *radio wave* (no, that's not how folks in avionics shops say "hi" to each other).

Electronics 101

During my first day in high school electronics class, the instructor asked if I knew how to make a radio work. I replied, "Yes sir. There's a small knob on the left. Just switch it on." Short circuit. I spent a long time after that translating colored resistor bands into their numerical values. I hope this introduction will be a bit more pleasant.

As you probably know, gamma rays, X-rays, light, radio waves, and heat all make up what's known as the electromagnetic spectrum (no, X-ray glasses are not part of that

spectrum and they don't work, either). Radio waves are just a small part of this electromagnetic spectrum, but for pilots they are a very important part because they're used for navigation and communication.

Radio waves come in frequencies (as opposed to, say, jackpots in Las Vegas, which come infrequently). The lower the frequency of a radio wave, the longer the wavelength (Figure 1). The longer the wavelength, the more likely the wave is to stay near the earth's surface and avoid flying off into space. That's why the automatic direction finding (ADF) equipment in your airplane is capable of receiving nondirectional beacons (NDBs) that are far away and often beyond your line of sight. NDBs operate in the 190 to 535 kHz (kilohertz) range. That's low, as frequencies go. Low frequency waves with long wavelengths are able to crawl around obstructions and hug the earth's surface, making reception beyond the horizon more likely for NDB stations (Figure 2). High frequency transmissions tend to keep going in a straight line, which would be just great if the earth had proved to be flat. As most pilots know, it isn't.

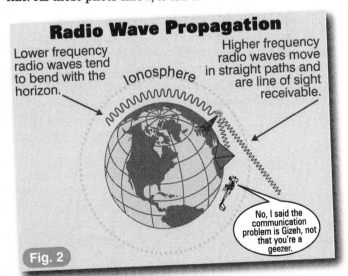

Radio Wave Propagation

Lower frequency radio waves tend to bend with the horizon.

Higher frequency radio waves move in straight paths and are line of sight receivable.

No, I said the communication problem is Gizeh, not that you're a geezer.

Fig. 2

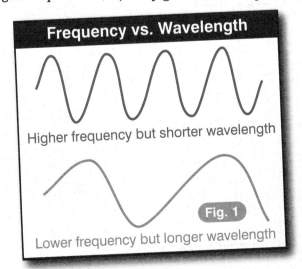

Frequency vs. Wavelength

Higher frequency but shorter wavelength

Lower frequency but longer wavelength

Fig. 1

Now you know one of the many reasons there were (until recently and with the advent of GPS), so many NDB stations used for navigation in Alaska. With that state's large assortment of mountains, ADF was a more reliable means than VOR of getting from one place to another without having to worry about knocking the antlers of some unsuspecting moose.

The downside of low-frequency transmission is that it's more affected by atmospheric phenomena such as lightning and St. Elmo's fire. It's no mystery that Paul Ryan's

Who Hertz?

Hertz (abbreviated Hz) is the official international unit of frequency measurement. One hertz is one of anything per second; in the case of electromagnetic radiation, it equals one cycle per second, but it would be equally correct to say that your heart normally beats at about 70 hertz.

Once upon a time, we just said "cycles per second," and a thousand of those were a kilocycle; a million, a megacycle. Many people still use these terms in referring to radio frequencies. The figure below shows the radio frequency spectrum and includes the term *GHz* representing gigahertz or one billion hertz.

Hertz as a unit of measure is named for a German physicist, Heinrich Hertz, who made many significant contributions to our understanding of electromagnetic radiation. Hertz built the first apparatus that produced radio waves. So the next time you call the tower, you can thank your Hertz. And no, he's not the Hertz who will rent you a car when you land.

Radio Frequency Spectrum

10 kHz to 30 kHz	Very Low Frequency (VLF)
30 kHz to 300 kHz	Low Frequency (LF)
300 kHz to 3 MHz	Medium Frequency (MF)
3 MHz to 30 MHz	High Frequency (HF)
30 MHz to 328.6 MHz	Very High Frequency (VHF)
328.6 MHz to 2.9 GHz	Ultra High Frequency (UHF)
2.9 GHz to 30 GHz	Super High Frequency (SHF)
30 GHz and above	Extremely High Frequency (EHF)

original Stormscope (an onboard device used to detect lightning) was really a low frequency radio receiver at its core. By detecting the low frequency emanations from a lightning strike and depicting the strike on a display, A Stormscope could help pilots avoid thunderstorms. Hallelujah, and pass the static.

Very high frequencies (VHF, 30-328 megahertz) require line of sight for reception. This is a classic case of "What you see is what you get." Radio stations hidden by obstructions or lurking beyond the horizon are less likely to be received, and the problem increases with the frequency. This is why your distance measuring equipment or DME (operating on higher frequencies between 962-1213 MHz) is usually the first thing to lose its grip when tracking a VOR (*very high frequency omni directional radio range)* station (which operates on frequencies between 108.0-117.95 MHz).

One of the benefits associated with higher frequency radio waves is that they are less affected by atmospheric phenomena, such as lightning and static electricity. That's why your communication and navigation radios work even during thunderstorm conditions, though if you're out there flying

around in thunderstorms I suspect that at least a half dozen of the nearest ATC facilities will probably hear you screaming without benefit of a radio.

That concludes your short course in electronics. You may want to sit back for a while and chant "Ohm." With the necessary knowledge now wired into your cranium, let's examine how the VOR works.

VOR Navigation

IFR navigation began when pilots flew low enough in poor weather to follow telegraph and telephone poles from one city to another. The IFR approach lighting system might even claim as its origins the bonfires set by airport operators to help pilots flying in bad weather home in on the airport. Perhaps this explains the origin of the phrase, "He landed hot." That was simply a pilot who didn't use his brakes and ran into the fire. These fireworks eventually led to light beacons and four course radio ranges (Figure 3), which were used into the middle 1950s. The early 1950s brought widespread implementation of the VOR airway system, which is still in use today and makes up the Federal Airway system, also known as our highways in the sky.

As you probably recall from your private pilot training, VOR navigation allows you to track to and/or from a VOR station on any one of 360 radials corresponding to one degree on the compass. We'll cover the process of navigation shortly, but you should know just a tiny bit about the electromagnetic magic that makes this happen.

First, the VOR station transmitter uses a single signal with two components (Figure 4A). One component is a constant-phase signal; the other is a rotating signal that's out of phase with the first signal in every position around

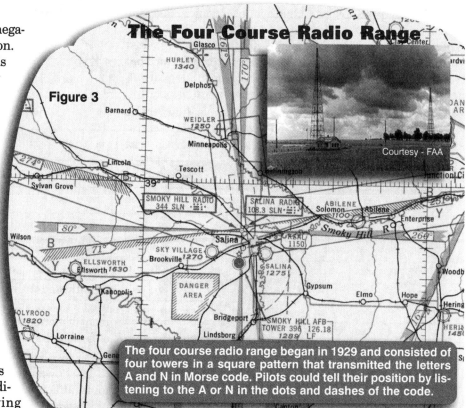

The Four Course Radio Range

Figure 3

Courtesy - FAA

The four course radio range began in 1929 and consisted of four towers in a square pattern that transmitted the letters A and N in Morse code. Pilots could tell their position by listening to the A or N in the dots and dashes of the code.

the VOR except at magnetic north. Your VOR receiver (Figure 4B) measures the phase difference between these two signals to determine which radial you're on in relation to that station. Voice transmission can ride along on this transmitted signal, too (though not all VORs have voice transmission capability).

You've undoubtedly seen VOR stations from the air (Figure 5A). They have the appearance of a small taco stand, and are often sited in the middle of nowhere, which is probably where you found yourself the first time your flight instructor asks you to find the VOR during your private pilot training.

When flying IFR, it's extremely important to identify the VOR station before using it. There are two reasons for this. First, to make sure you have the correct station. And second, to make sure the station is functioning correctly. The way to do this is to tune in the station, turn up the nav radio volume, and listen to the VOR's identification, which is either a three-letter Morse code identification every five seconds, or a combination of code and voice ID with the voice heard every 15 seconds (Figure 5B). Voice identification always includes the word "VOR" as in "Woodside VOR," usually intoned by someone who sounds recently exhumed from an ancient burial site. If the station is undergoing routine maintenance (not to repair a taco-making machine) the facility may radiate a T-E-S-T code (- • ••• -) or the code may be removed. VOR stations have an automatic monitoring system that shuts down the station if there is an equipment problem. It then alerts the authorities. Stations also have a standby transmitter that's activated automatically when signal problems occur (such as when someone bangs too hard on the station's door because they want tacos).

Because VORs transmit at the high end of the frequency spectrum, their operation is generally limited to line of sight. Now, there are only so many VOR frequencies to go around. Because of worries like frequency overlap (and other reasons, too), the FAA places limits on the altitude and distance over which VORs can be used for navigation. The important thing to remember is that VORs are useful for navigation for the distances and directions shown on your IFR charts (unless Notices to Airmen indicate otherwise). In general, it's also reasonable to say that they're useful for distances of at least 40 miles at the normal minimum IFR altitudes.

Now that you know the basic electronics associated with VOR, let's talk about how to use it.

VOR Signal Generation

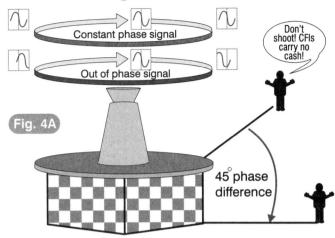

Fig. 4A

A Typical VOR OMNI Display

Fig. 4B

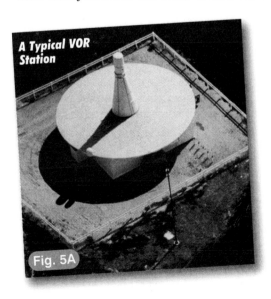

A Typical VOR Station

Fig. 5A

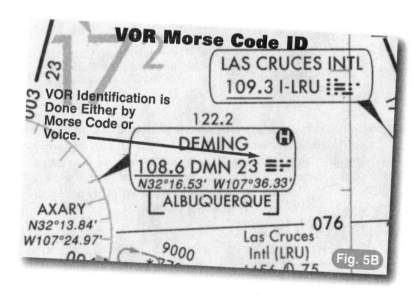

VOR Morse Code ID

VOR Identification is Done Either by Morse Code or Voice.

LAS CRUCES INTL
109.3 I-LRU

122.2

DEMING

108.6 DMN 23
N32°16.53' W107°36.33'

ALBUQUERQUE

AXARY
N32°13.84'
W107°24.97'

076

Las Cruces
Intl (LRU)

9000

Fig. 5B

VOR Scalloping

There's something fishy about VOR scalloping, which is the untimely and seemingly inexplicable swings the VOR sometimes makes. I'm here to explain the inexplicable. There are reasons, and for once it has little to do with your piloting technique. Certain propeller RPMs can cause the VOR needle to fluctuate as much as plus or minus six degrees. If you see such needle behavior, try changing the RPM slightly and see if this smoothes out the roughness. Terrain can also interfere with VHF reception and cause scalloping. It's always a good idea to consider these problems prior to carping about a VOR station or the aircraft equipment not working properly. While most pilots like scallops, no one likes scalloping. So feed your shellfish desires to fly well and be prepared to adjust the RPM slightly to prevent VOR needle scalloping.

Your VOR Equipment

Most IFR-equipped airplanes have two VOR receivers on board (Figure 5C). Usually this is a combination of a navigation receiver and a communications transmitter-receiver in one package, which is referred to as the *navcomm*.

Your VOR receiver is connected to the VOR indicator, shown in Figure 6. The display consists of:

•A vertical needle (also known as a *course deviation indicator*, or *CDI*) that swings/moves right or left;

•A *signal flag* (also known as an ambiguity indicator) with three possible indications: TO, FROM, or OFF (although it could say NAV or just be red to indicate a warning), and

•An *omni bearing selector (OBS)* or *COURSE SELECTOR* knob.

Fig. 5C — Typical VOR Receivers

The VOR Indicator

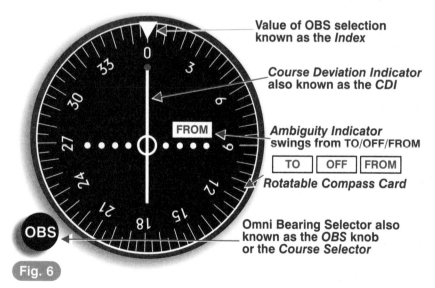

Value of OBS selection known as the *Index*

Course Deviation Indicator also known as the *CDI*

Ambiguity Indicator swings from TO/OFF/FROM

| TO | OFF | FROM |

Rotatable Compass Card

Omni Bearing Selector also known as the *OBS* knob or the *Course Selector*

Fig. 6

Surrounding the needle is a circular, moveable compass rose controlled by the COURSE SELECTOR. Rotating the COURSE SELECTOR moves a specific compass value under the inverted white triangle or index at the top of the instrument. Today, you may use use a horizontal situa-

VOR Radials

Think of the VOR as a transmitter that radiates 360 individual radials from its center. These radials are oriented to the magnetic north pole. You may navigate to or from the station on any of these radials via your airborne VOR equipment.

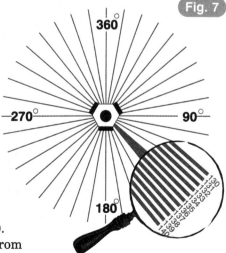

Fig. 7

tion indicator (HSI) during your instrument training, even if you fly a basic single-engine trainer like a Cessna 172. Since you already know something about the VOR display, let's confine our discussions about VOR navigation to the HSI. Take some time to read the HSI sidebar before continuing. You'll get better acquainted with this instrument when we use it in the following navigational examples.

VORs and Highways in the Sky

As you know from your private pilot training, VOR navigation allows you to track to or from a station on any one of the 360 degree flyable courses (Figure 7). I suspect you probably still remember your confusion about tracking to and from

The Horizontal Situation Indicator

THE HORIZONTAL SITUATION INDICATOR - HSI

Heading Bug Aircraft Heading Course Selection Arrow

Course Deviation Indicator

Slaved Compass

Course Deviation Indicator

TO/FROM Indicator (triangle)

Glide Slope Information

Symbolic Airplane

Course Selector

Reciprocal Course Pointer Heading Bug Select Knob

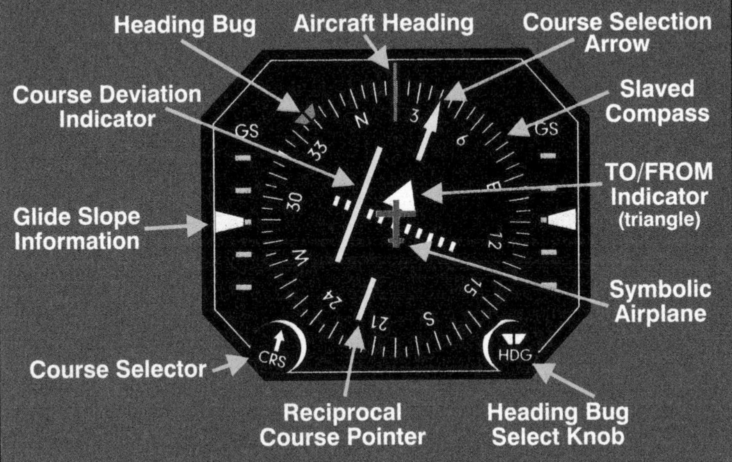

HSI & VOR SIMILARITIES

The Horizontal Situation Indicator (HSI) is VOR unit combined with a heading indicator (electrically slaved to a compass). Instead of a needle that swings, its course deviation indicator (CDI) slides sideways, away from the course selection arrow, to indicate the direction and amount of course deviation. The TO/FROM indicator is a single white triangle that automatically flips toward the head or tail of the course selection arrow, depending on whether the selected course takes you to or from the station. The heading bug is simply a heading reminder that can be set on any heading value. The small symbolic airplane always points straight ahead, in the direction the airplane is headed. Course interception is made easy by turning until the symbolic airplane is pointed toward the horizontally displaced CDI. Thus, the HSI provides a picture of your airplane, relative to the selected course.

When Airplane B intercepts the course, the CDI aligns itself with the course selection arrow. The airplane now heads in the direction of the selected course (068°) and flies to the station. Upon station passage the TO/FROM triangle will automatically flip & point toward the bottom of the course selection arrow.

Airplane C flies over the VOR and turns to a heading of 150° to intercept the 110° radial from the station. The pilot rotates the course selection arrow to 110° (the desired outbound radial). The TO/FROM triangle automatically flips & points toward the bottom of the course arrow, indicating that the course selected is from the station. The symbolic airplane is pointed toward the displaced CDI indicating that, under a no wind condition, the airplane will intercept the 110° radial.

DUPREE
122.1R
116.8 Ch115 DPR
HURON

CHEYENNE EAGLE AIRPORT

FAITH AIRPORT

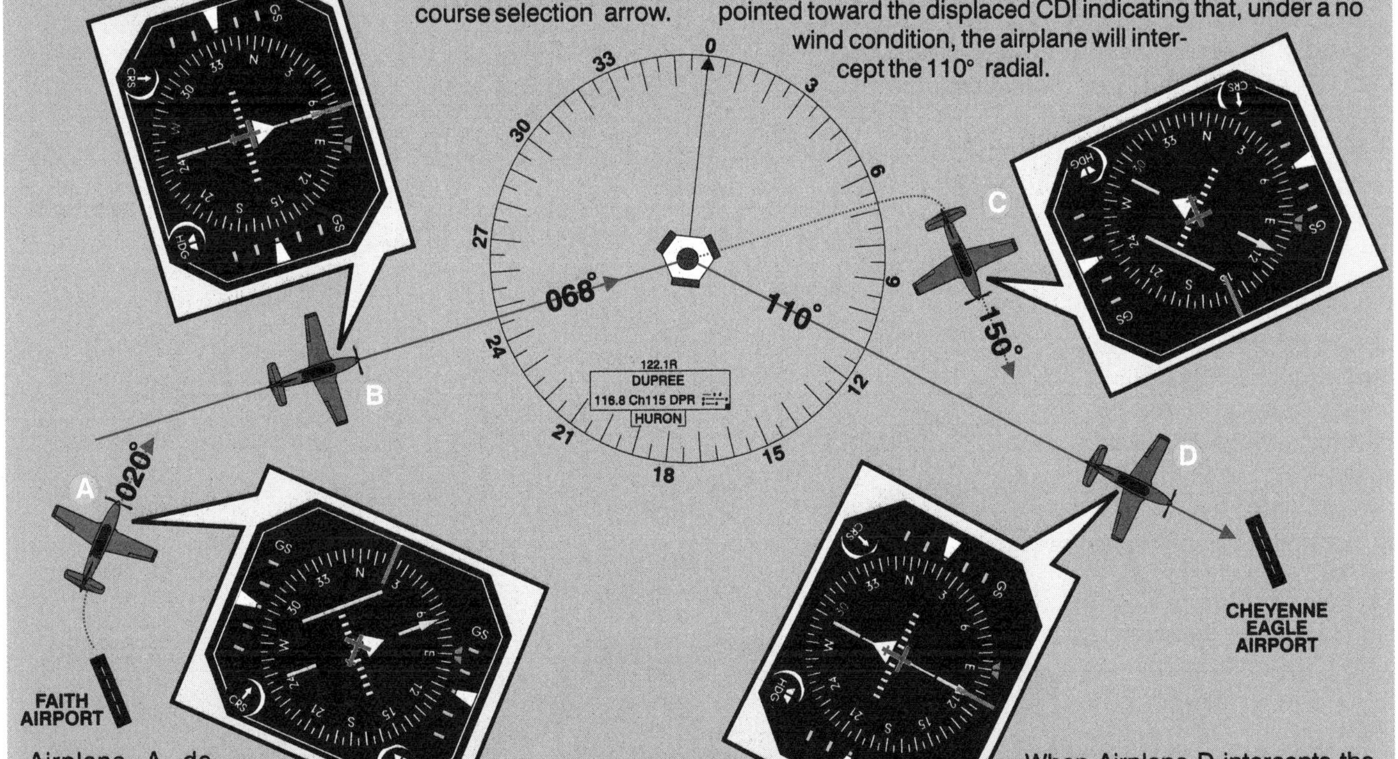

Airplane A departs Faith airport on a heading of 020° with its HSI set to intercept the 068° course to the VOR. The course selection arrow is set to 068 degrees and the TO/FROM indicator shows that, upon course interception, Airplane A would be headed to the station. The symbolic airplane points in the direction of the displaced CDI indicating that the airplane is on an intercept course.

When Airplane D intercepts the 110° radial, the CDI centers and the pilot flies a heading of 110° on the slaved compass. With a FROM indication (triangle pointed toward the bottom of the course selection arrow), Airplane D is tracking outbound from the station on the 110° radial.

a VOR station on a radial. How do you track to a place on something that radiates from it? As you discovered, you do it the same way you drive into town on a highway that leaves it. If you're approaching from the south, you can track to a VOR on the 180 degree radial (Figure 8). This is the same thing as saying you're tracking to the VOR on the 360 degree course. On a heading of 360 degrees, when you cross the VOR, you're tracking outbound on the 360 degree radial or the 360 degree course. Same thing, just different position in relation to the station.

If you don't feel comfortable with these concepts yet, a quick review of the VOR section in Chapter 11 of my *Private Pilot Handbook* is in order before you read on. For the purposes of this advanced book, I'll continue the convention started in the *Private Pilot Handbook* by using the term *courses* and *radials* interchangeably for clarity.

How to Navigate with VOR

When flying by VOR, the first thing to do is to tune and identify the VOR station you want to use for navigation. After placing the frequency in the appropriate nav receiver, check for either the voice or Morse code identification, then dial in the desired course. Some people have a difficult time figuring out how to listen to ATC and the VOR identification at the same time. Often, the easiest way is to just to turn up the VOR identification to a slightly lower volume than that set for ATC and listen for the Morse code in the background. If that doesn't work, tell ATC that you'd like to leave the frequency for 30 to 60 seconds. You'd be surprised how often they grant this request. Just remember to say 30 seconds, not 30 minutes as one pilot did in a moment of confusion. The controller came back with, "Am I really that bad to talk to, 2132 Bravo?"

By rotating the HSI's course selection arrow with the course selection knob (also known as the Course Selector or Omni Bearing Selector or OBS for short) you can select any one of the VOR's 360 flyable courses. Let's suppose you selected 360 degrees (or 0 degrees—same thing) with the OBS, as shown in Figure 9, position A. Your airborne HSI equipment now automatically orients itself to tell you where the 360 degree course is located, as shown in Figure 9A. As you can see, the 360 degree course runs completely through the VOR in a direction of 360 degrees. If you had selected the 270 degree course, your VOR equipment would orient itself to the 270 degree course as shown in Figure 9B. Selecting 030 degrees with the course selector orients you to the course shown in Figure 9C. And selecting 240 degrees orients you to the course shown in Figure 9D.

VOR Radials and Courses

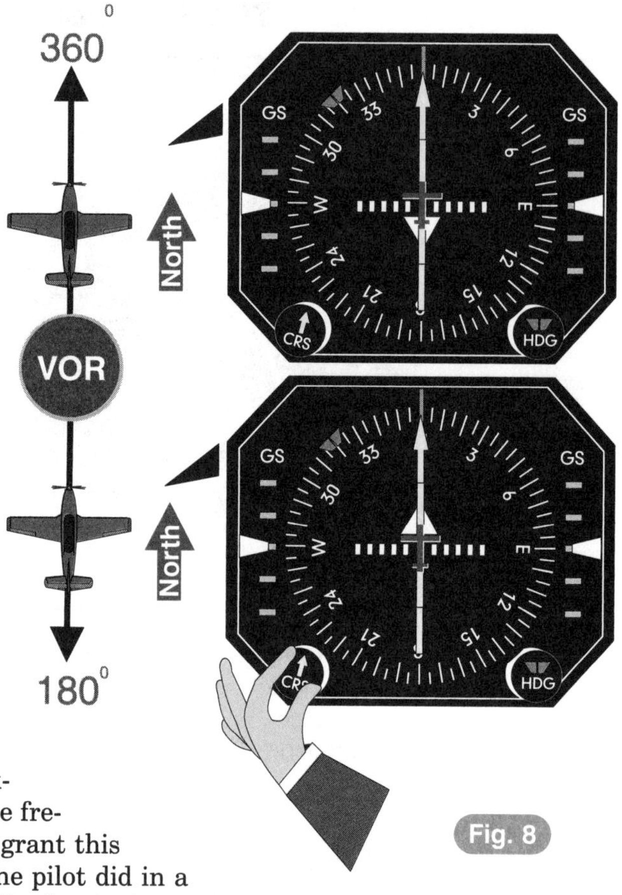

Fig. 8

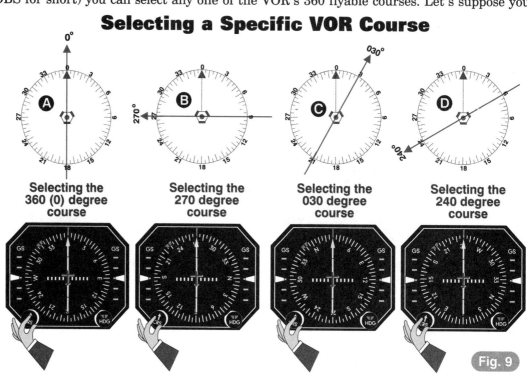

Selecting a Specific VOR Course

A Selecting the 360 (0) degree course

B Selecting the 270 degree course

C Selecting the 030 degree course

D Selecting the 240 degree course

Fig. 9

Rotating the OBS to a specific course number, orients your airborne VOR equipment to tell you where you are in relation to that course. You may chose any one of 360 different courses using the OBS.

VOR Radials Widths and Deflections

If you treat VOR needles like hypodermic needles and dislike both, it may be because of a common misunderstanding regarding the VOR display. Have you ever wondered whether the five dots (or four dots plus the center circle or donut as pilots sometimes call it) on the face of the VOR are important? Well, they are. When navigating by VOR, each dot deflection represents a two-degree course deviation. In other words, VOR needle deflection represents your angular divergence from the course centerline, not a mileage distance from it. For instance, if you're supposed to be tracking outbound on the 360 degree radial and have a five dot right needle deflection as shown in Figure 10, then you're actually on the 350 degree radial from the station (five dots represents 10 degrees of course deviation and a right needle represents being left of course. Therefore, you're on the 350 degree radial from the station).

Have you ever wondered why, when approaching a VOR station with only a small needle deflection (say one dot or two degrees)

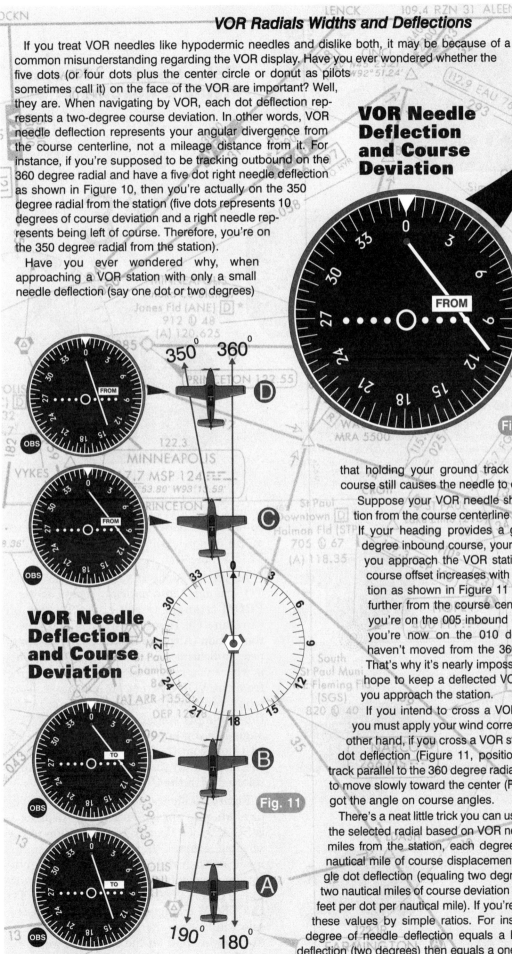

VOR Needle Deflection and Course Deviation

Fig. 10

VOR Needle Deflection and Course Deviation

Fig. 11

that holding your ground track perfectly parallel to the chosen course still causes the needle to deflect? Here's why.

Suppose your VOR needle shows a two-and-a-half dot deflection from the course centerline as shown in Figure 11, position A. If your heading provides a ground track parallel to the 360 degree inbound course, your needle will continue to deflect as you approach the VOR station. That's because your angular course offset increases with decreasing distance from the station as shown in Figure 11 position B, despite never moving further from the course centerline. In position A of Figure B, you're on the 005 inbound course to the VOR. In position B, you're now on the 010 degree inbound course and you haven't moved from the 360 degree course centerline a bit. That's why it's nearly impossible to maintain your heading and hope to keep a deflected VOR needle from moving further as you approach the station.

If you intend to cross a VOR station with a centered needle, you must apply your wind correction to a centered needle. On the other hand, if you cross a VOR station and the needle shows a five dot deflection (Figure 11, position C) and you're flying a ground track parallel to the 360 degree radial, then your VOR needle will begin to move slowly toward the center (Figure 11, position D). Now you've got the angle on course angles.

There's a neat little trick you can use to determine your distance from the selected radial based on VOR needle displacement. At 60 nautical miles from the station, each degree of needle deflection equals one nautical mile of course displacement. Thus, at 60 nautical miles a single dot deflection (equaling two degrees of course deviation) results in two nautical miles of course deviation (this approximately equates to 200 feet per dot per nautical mile). If you're good at division, you can reduce these values by simple ratios. For instance, at 30 nautical miles each degree of needle deflection equals a half-mile off course. A single dot deflection (two degrees) then equals a one nautical mile course deviation.

In Figure 12, we've selected the 360 degree course with the course selector. To fly this course, you should head your airplane in a magnetic direction of 360 degrees on the heading indicator (position A). Assuming you've done this, and your airplane is in position A, the HSI shows a course deviation indicator or CDI (the split needle) with a TO triangle indication. Keep in mind that if the triangle is pointed toward the course selection arrow tip, then your course is oriented to the VOR station. If it's pointed to the tail of the course selection arrow, your course is oriented from the station. Get the point? Because you paid attention in your high school geometry class, you understand triangles, and now you know whether you are

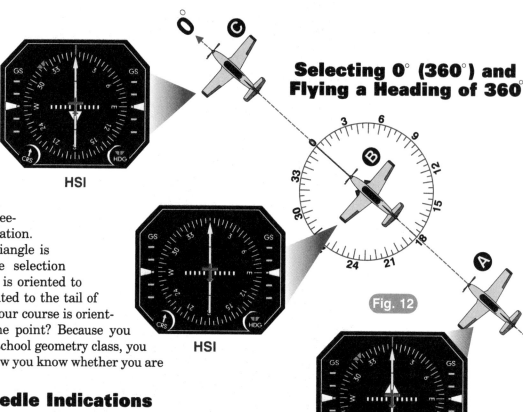

Selecting 0° (360°) and Flying a Heading of 360°

Fig. 12

HSI Needle Indications

All airplanes are heading 360 degrees. Airplane (A), (C) and (E) have a right needle indication, implying the 360 degree course is to their right. They would turn right to get on the selected course. Airplane (B), (D) and (F) have left needles indicating the 360 degree course is to their left. They would turn left to get on the selected course. Airplanes (C) and (D) have no traingle showing, indicating that the airplane is abeam the station in a zone of ambiguity.

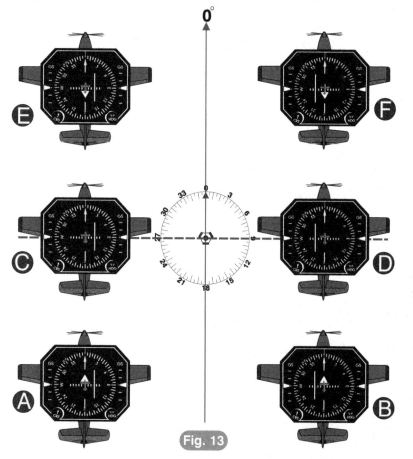

Fig. 13

coming or going in an airplane. Hey, math rules! From here on in we'll just reference an up or down pointed triangle as a TO or FROM indication.

As you fly along the selected course, the TO triangle automatically changes to a FROM triangle as you cross the station (Airplane C). However, when directly over the station (Airplane B), the triangles disappear, indicating a position of ambiguity. This is where you're neither going to nor coming from the VOR (it's not an indication about what your brain might be doing at the time). Simply stated, the TO or FROM triangle lets you know whether you'll be headed to or from the VOR station if you turn the airplane in the direction of the course selected with the CDI centered.

Figure 13 shows several HSI indications in relation to airplane positions. Airplane A is heading 360 degrees (the direction of the selected course). Its airborne HSI equipment shows a right needle with a TO indication (remember, I'll assume you know that TO and FROM indications mean TO and FROM triangles). This means that the selected course is to the right and, if Airplane A were on the course, it would be headed to the station. Airplane A must turn to the right to intercept the selected course. So must Airplanes C and E. Airplanes B, D and F must turn left to intercept. Notice that when you are abeam (90 degrees to the side of) the station, the ambiguity indicator doesn't show any triangle. This means that you are in the zone of ambiguity and are neither going to nor coming from the station.

Let's say Airplane A in Figure 14 turns right to a heading of 045 degrees to intercept the 360 degree course to the VOR. As it approaches the course, the needle begins to center as shown in positions B and C. (I'll say "needle" instead of "CDI" from now on and if the mere mention of the word "needle" frightens you, I'll say, "So sorry," right now.) Once the needle is centered, the airplane should be heading 360 degrees if you want to fly the selected course to the station (airplane D). Airplanes E, F, G and H show a similar sequence of intercept with a FROM indication. Airplanes F and G intercept the 360 route at a 45 degree angle (an intercept heading of 315 degrees is 45 degrees to the left of 360 degrees).

As you already know, a right or left needle deflection on a typical VOR display doesn't tell you where the airplane is relative to the selected course *unless* you physically turn the airplane to the direction set in the course selector or if you imagine yourself turned and pointed in that direction. HSI's are unlike VOR displays because the display typically rotates with a slaved compass (the *slaved* compass is electronically connected to a magnetic flux detector and a gyro. See page 2-47 for details). This means that the fixed airplane symbol in the center of the HSI's display, the one that is always pointed to the airplane's present heading, provides a clear visual picture of how to turn to intercept the selected course.

Note: It takes 15 seconds at standard rate to turn 45 degrees. So start turning when you feel you are within 15 seconds of intercept.

Intercepting a VOR Course

After turning to intercept a selected VOR course, watch the movement of the CDI (needle). When the needle is centered, you should be flying the heading of the course selected by the OBS (360°or 0° in our case with no wind assumed).

Fig. 14

Note: It takes 15 seconds at standard rate to turn 45 degrees. So start turning when you feel you are within 15 seconds of intercept.

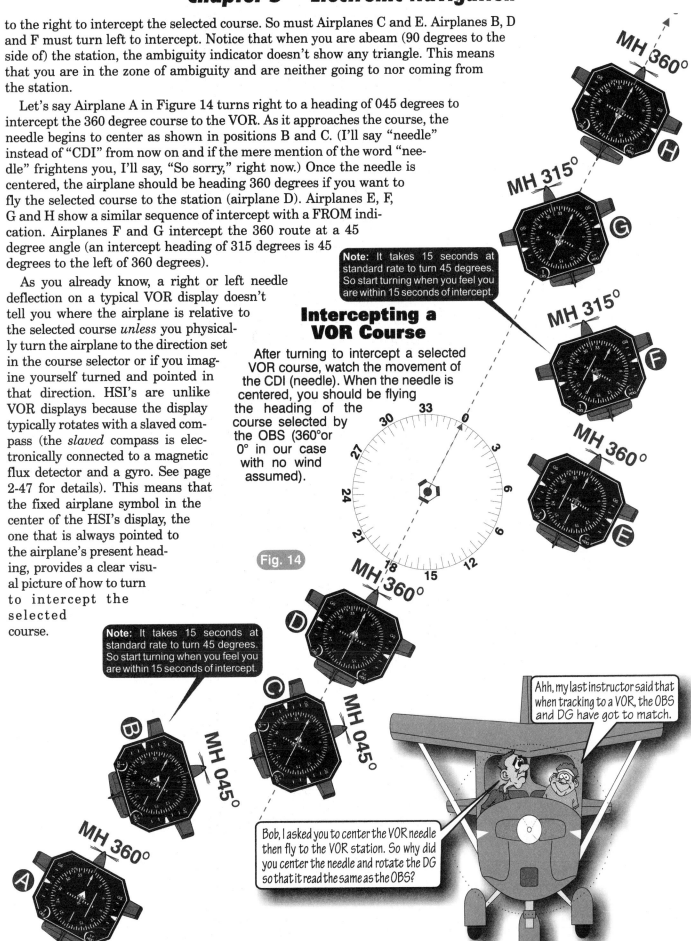

Ahh, my last instructor said that when tracking to a VOR, the OBS and DG have got to match.

Bob, I asked you to center the VOR needle then fly to the VOR station. So why did you center the needle and rotate the DG so that it read the same as the OBS?

HSI Indications and Their Direct Representation of Course Location

The red symbolic airplane situated in the center of the HSI's display provides you with a precise visual indication of the direction to turn to intercept the selected course. You simply turn the airplane in the direction of the CDI to approach the selected course. The white triangle either points toward or away from the course selection arrow indicating that the selected course will take you to or from the station, respectively.

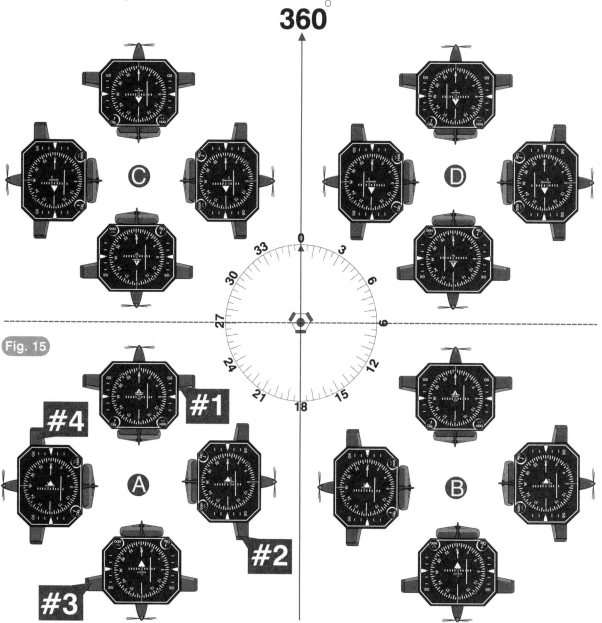

For instance, with the course selector set to 360 degrees, the HSI indication on the airplanes in Figure 15 (quadrant A) all show a split needle deflected to the right of the selected (360 degree) course with a TO indication. If you want to intercept the selected course you must turn toward the split needle. Airplane A1 shows that the 360 degree course is to the right and the small symbolic airplane in the center of the HSI shows you are paralleling the course. Airplane A2 shows that the small symbolic airplane is pointed directly at the selected course and that you'll eventually intercept the course on the present 090 degree heading.

Airplane A3, on a heading of 180 degrees, shows that the selected course is to the left of the small symbolic airplane, meaning that you must turn left to intercept the

course. Airplane A4, on a 270 degree heading, shows the small symbolic airplane heading directly away from the selected course. A 180 degree turn is necessary to intercept this course. Once the course is intercepted, all airplanes in quadrant A would need to turn to an initial heading of 360 degrees to track this course to the station, as is indicated by the white triangle pointing toward the tip of the course selection arrow.

On the other hand, if all the airplanes in quadrant D turned toward the split needle, intercepted the course, and then flew an initial heading of 360 degrees, they would track from the station on the 360 degree course. This situation is indicated by the white triangle pointing toward the tail of the course selection arrow.

Flying a Selected Course to, Then From a VOR Station

In position A, ATC instructs you to intercept and proceed inbound to the VOR on the 210 degree radial. Let's say you want to intercept the radial at a 30 degree angle. With your OBS set to 030° your turn to a heading of 360° to intercept the selected course (Airplane B). The HSI clearly shows the course to your left and that you will intercept it on your present heading. When intercepting the 030 degree course to the station you fly a heading of 030° (Airplane C) then fly to and from the station (Airplane D & E) to Ozoo airport.

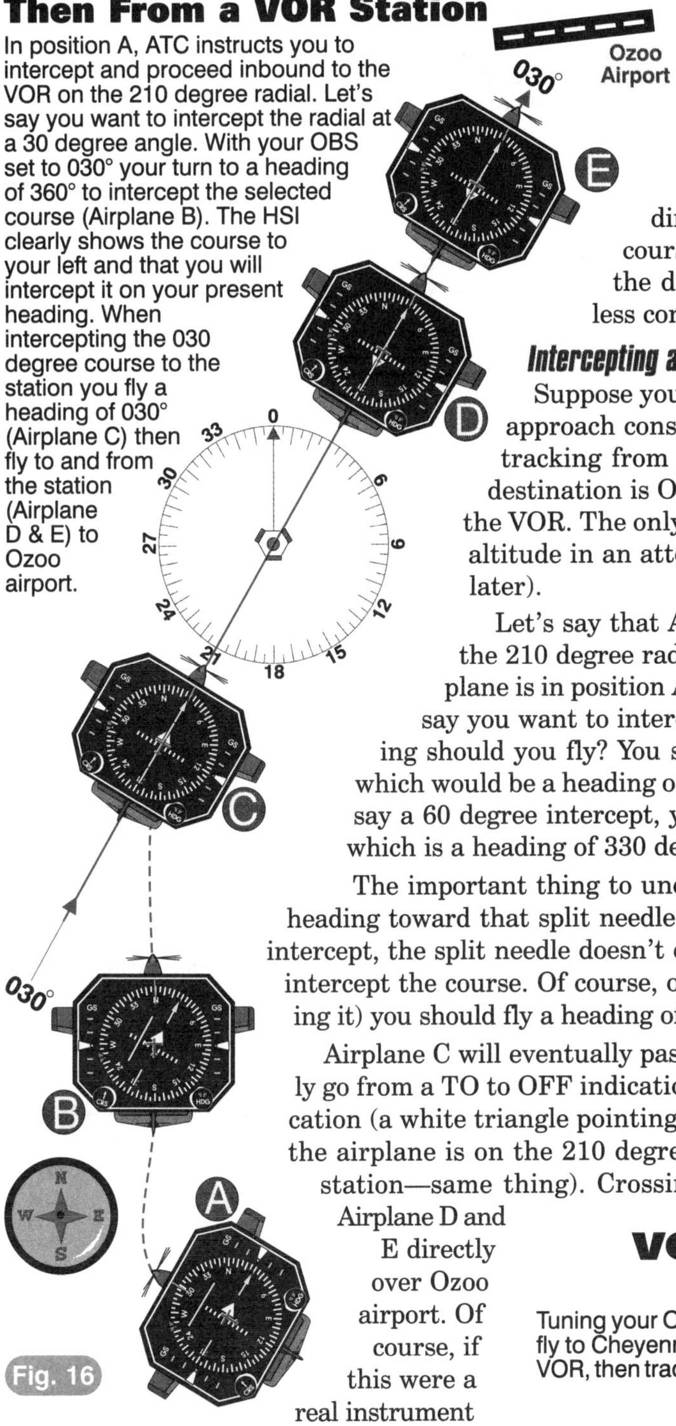

Ozoo Airport

030°

The important thing to understand about the HSI here is that its pictorial presentation allows you to fly toward the needle to intercept the course. This is certainly the opposite of what you learned when using an ordinary VOR display, isn't it? Without the benefit of a VOR display that rotates on a slaved gyro (usually electrically operated), you could only make sense of where the selected course was if you first imagined yourself flying the same direction as the selected course then asking yourself if the course (thus, the needle) was to your right or left. HSIs remove the difficulty of course interpretation and make IFR flying a lot less confusing.

Intercepting a VOR Course

Suppose you want to fly an instrument approach into Ozoo airport. The approach consists of intercepting the 030 degree course to the VOR, then tracking from the VOR on the same course as shown in Figure 16. Your destination is Ozoo airport, which is directly on the 030 degree course from the VOR. The only thing we won't do here is to descend to a minimum descent altitude in an attempt to land at this airport (we'll talk about how to do this later).

Let's say that ATC tells you to intercept and track inbound to the VOR on the 210 degree radial (which is the 030 degree course to the station). Your airplane is in position A and you set your HSI's course selector to 030 degrees. Let's say you want to intercept the 030 degree course at a 30 degree angle. What heading should you fly? You should turn 30 degrees to the left of the 030 degree course, which would be a heading of 360 degrees (position B). If you wanted to take a larger bite, say a 60 degree intercept, you would turn 60 degrees to the left of the selected course, which is a heading of 330 degrees.

The important thing to understand here is that to intercept a course, you've got to be heading toward that split needle when using the HSI. The picture doesn't lie. If, during the intercept, the split needle doesn't eventually move toward the center, then you're not going to intercept the course. Of course, once you're on the selected course (OK, a little before reaching it) you should fly a heading of 030 degrees and track to the station (position C).

Airplane C will eventually pass over the VOR and its TO/FROM triangle will automatically go from a TO to OFF indication (no triangle showing), and then to a FROM triangle indication (a white triangle pointing to the bottom of the course selection needle). In position C the airplane is on the 210 degree radial from the station (or the 030 degree course to the station—same thing). Crossing the VOR with the needle centered will eventually put Airplane D and E directly over Ozoo airport. Of course, if this were a real instrument approach you'd have to time your arrival over Ozoo or use GPS or DME to help identify its location. More on this subject later.

Fig. 16

030°

Flying from the VOR on a Selected Course

Here's another, more common example of how to fly a VOR approach to an airport using your HSI. Suppose after departing Faith airport, as shown in Figure 17, your IFR clearance instructs you to intercept the 248 degree radial to Dupree VOR then, when crossing the VOR, the approach chart requires you to fly

VOR Navigation From Faith to Cheyenne Eagle

Tuning your OBS to 068° takes you direct to the Dupree VOR from Faith airport. To fly to Cheyenne Eagle airport, select the 096° course on your OBS when over the VOR, then track outbound to Cheyenne Eagle.

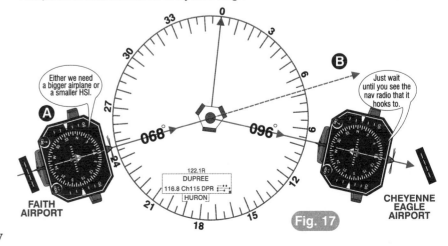

Either we need a bigger airplane or a smaller HSI.

Just wait until you see the nav radio that it hooks to.

068°

096°

122.1R
DUPREE
116.8 Ch115 DPR
HURON

FAITH AIRPORT

CHEYENNE EAGLE AIRPORT

Fig. 17

How to Flip a Recip

Finding the reciprocal (the 180 degree opposite) of a heading ties pilot minds in knots rather than knots. It doesn't have to be that way. You can quickly and easily calculate any reciprocal. Want to see how? Watch. Start with the heading you want to find the reciprocal of. Let's try something tough, like 247. Subtract 200 and add 20 to get the correct answer of 067. How hard was that? You could do it because you're adding and subtracting even numbers, which is easy to do mentally.

If the heading you start with is 180 or less, you can ADD 200 and then SUBTRACT 20. So, to convert the 067 heading to its reciprocal, add 200 (267) then subtract 20 and voila, we're back to 247!

outbound on the 096 degree radial to Eagle airport. How would you accomplish this?

You'd begin by setting your HSI to intercept and track to Dupree VOR on the 248 degree radial. This involves finding the reciprocal (see the How to Flip a Recip sidebar), which is 068 degrees. This is the setting for our HSI's course selection to track inbound to the VOR on the 248 degree radial.

As soon as you depart, you'll intercept the radial at some reasonable angle, as previously discussed. Once you're over the VOR, you'll turn to a heading of 096 degrees and rotate the course selector to 096. Now you'll make any course corrections to center the CDI and track to Eagle airport. As discussed before, if this were a real instrument approach, you'd either measure your time from Dupree VOR to the airport or use some other means

of identifying your arrival over Dupree (perhaps a DME reading), and begin your descent to the minimum descent altitude for this approach. Some instrument approaches allow you to use a VOR cross radial to identify when you're at the destination airport (also known as the missed approach point). Let's see how this is done.

Dual VORs for Position Fixing

Fixing your position (not that anything is actually broken) with dual VORs is rather common in IFR flying. Figure 17 shows a simulated instrument approach to Ozoo airport. The inbound approach course consists of the 080 degree radial from Birdtalk VOR and the missed approach point is identified by the 025 degree radial from Rocket VOR. Your No. 1 nav radio is tuned to BRD VOR and the omni display—the HSI—has its course selector set to 080 degrees and shows a FROM indication. To identify the missed

VOR Service Volumes

Just because there are hundreds of VORs scattered across the country doesn't mean you can tune in any particular one and expect to navigate with it from sea to shining sea. The VOR transmitter only has so much power and has limits on the distance, both vertically and horizontally, over which it can be used by a pilot. This limit is known as its *standard service volume*. There are only so many VOR frequencies to go around, so the FAA ensures that VORs operating on similar frequencies don't interfere with one another. Service volumes are important if you'd like to fly IFR directly between different VOR stations not connected by an airway. If so, then you'd want to flight plan for VORs and flight altitudes that allow you to remain with these standard service volumes (SSV) as shown in Figure 18. The following are the SSVs for the T (terminal), L (low altitude) and H (high altitude) class of VOR stations.

VOR/DME/TACAN Standard Service Volumes- SSV Class Designator
Altitude and Range Boundaries

T (Terminal)
From 1,000 feet above ground level (AGL) up to and including 12,000 feet AGL at radial distances out to 25 nm.

L (Low Altitude)
From 1,000 feet AGL up to and including 18,000 feet AGL at radial distances out to 40 nm.

H (High Altitude)
From 1,000 feet AGL up to and including 14,500 feet AGL at radial distances out to 40 nm.

From 14,500 AGL up to and including 60,000 feet at radial distances out to 100 nm.

From 18,000 feet AGL up to and including 45,000 feet AGL at radial distances out to 130 nm.

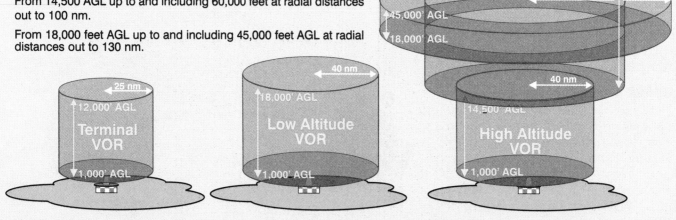

Fig. 18

Using Your No.2 VOR (or HSI) for Position Identification

Airplanes A, B & C are tracking outbound from Birdtalk (BRD) VOR on the 080° radial as shown by their No.1 HSI. The No.2 HSI is set to receive the 025° course from Rocket (RKT) VOR. When Airplane (C) is on the 025° course "FROM" the station, the No. 2 HSI needle should center indicating a position directly over Ozoo airport. This form of VOR cross-referencing is an excellent way to help identify your position. It's customary to use a course from a VOR to identify your position rather than a course to a VOR.

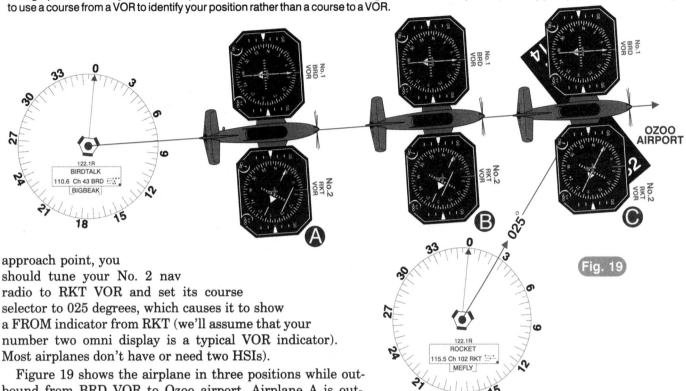

Fig. 19

approach point, you should tune your No. 2 nav radio to RKT VOR and set its course selector to 025 degrees, which causes it to show a FROM indicator from RKT (we'll assume that your number two omni display is a typical VOR indicator). Most airplanes don't have or need two HSIs).

Figure 19 shows the airplane in three positions while outbound from BRD VOR to Ozoo airport. Airplane A is outbound from BRD VOR to Ozoo airport. Its No. 2 VOR shows a right needle with a FROM indication. Once again, as you learned in private pilot school, to make sense of the needle and flag of a typical VOR display, imagine Airplane A facing in a direction of 025 degrees (i.e., parallel to the 025 degree course from RKT). You can clearly see that the 025 degree course is to airplane A's right side. If Airplane A were on the 025 degree course, it would be going FROM the RKT VOR. Therefore, the No. 2 VOR for Airplane A shows a right needle with a FROM indication. As we approach Ozoo airport, the needle in VOR No. 2 moves toward the center of the instrument, as shown by airplane B's VOR indication. When the No. 2 VOR needle centers, we know we're over Ozoo airport, as shown by Airplane C.

Reverse Sensing

One of the interesting things about using the HSI is that you can often avoid being confused by the dreaded demon known as *reverse sensing*. No, this doesn't mean that your sense of touch, sight or smell is inside out. It means that you are attempting to travel to a VOR with a FROM indication or from a VOR with a TO indication. This results in the VOR display showing a needle displaced in the opposite direction from your actual position in relation to the desired course, as shown in Figure 20. This problem occurs because you failed to dial in the correct course with the course selector.

Reverse Sensing of the VOR Needle

If you are attempting to go to the VOR with a FROM flag indication, the needle will indicate the course in the opposite or reverse direction as is shown by Airplanes Y and Z. If you mentally rotate Airplanes Y & Z in the direction of their OBS setting (or 140°), you'll see that their needles are correctly sensing course direction. For proper sensing, you must rotate the OBS of Airplanes X, Y & Z to 320°, since this is the direction of the inbound course to the VOR.

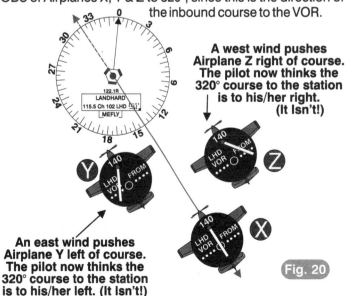

A west wind pushes Airplane Z right of course. The pilot now thinks the 320° course to the station is to his/her right. (It Isn't!)

An east wind pushes Airplane Y left of course. The pilot now thinks the 320° course to the station is to his/her left. (It Isn't!)

Fig. 20

Time-Distance to a VOR Station

Here's a little trick that can help determine your time or distance to a VOR station if you don't have DME capability. When inbound to a VOR station, turn 90 degrees and measure the amount of bearing change per given amount of time. Once you have this, then use the following formula:

Minutes to a station = (60 x minutes between bearing)/degrees of bearing change.

Distance to a station = (TAS x minutes between bearing change)/degrees of bearing change.

For instance, suppose ATC has instructed you to track inbound to the Landhard VOR on the 140 degree radial as shown in position X of Figure 20. In the heat of the moment (this mistake is common even if the heater isn't on) you forget to set your course selector to 320 degrees (the inbound course) as you turn to a heading of 360 degrees. As the airplane moves toward the station and drifts to the right of course (position Z), the needle in your VOR deflects to the right instead of the left. Naturally (even if you're not a naturalist) you'll turn to the right, which will further displace the needle to the right. Something similar will happen when you turn to the left to intercept the course as shown in position Y. As you remember from your private pilot training, if you turned the airplane around to a heading of 180 degrees and tracked outbound from the station, the needle would display your position to the course accurately.

Using an HSI display for VOR navigation has several benefits, one of which is that you aren't as likely to experience problems with reverse sensing as shown in Figure 21. That's because the HSI provides a picture of the airplane's position relative to the desired course. It can do so because VOR information is displayed on a slaved compass display. The depicted course always turns with the airplane. In other words, if the split CDI needle is to your left while heading 320 degrees, then the course will be to your left (position E) even with the course selector set to the reciprocal of the inbound heading. The depicted course will be to your right if you're in position D, even with the reciprocal value set in the course selector. This means if you are navigating to a station on the 320 degree inbound course, you can turn 180 degrees and navigate from the station on the 140 degree radial without moving the course selector to a value of 140. Of course, there's no practical reason to do this and that's why you shouldn't do it. You should always set in the correct course value regardless of the HSI's forgiving nature. On the other hand, not setting the correct course value can cause a reverse-sensing problem when flying a localizer back course approach. More on this later.

HSI and Reverse Sensing - Not!

Because the HSI displays course deviation information over a slaved gyro, the CDI (the selected course) always rotates to show its actual position in relation to the airplane's present heading. That's why reverse sensing is no longer the problem it once was. Even when you select the reciprocal of the proper course, CDI displacement, the CDI will show the correct orientation of the selected course. But make sure to set in the correct course, nevertheless.

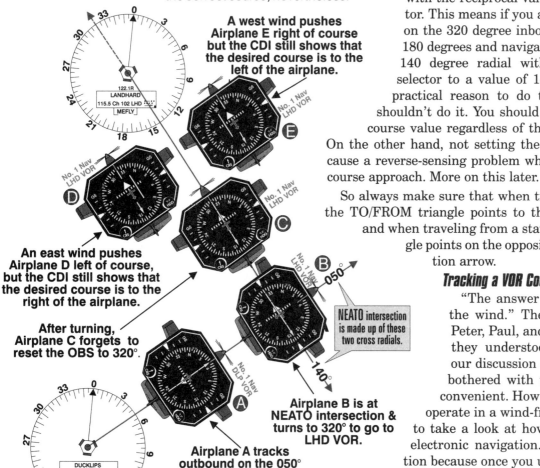

A west wind pushes Airplane E right of course but the CDI still shows that the desired course is to the left of the airplane.

An east wind pushes Airplane D left of course, but the CDI still shows that the desired course is to the right of the airplane.

After turning, Airplane C forgets to reset the OBS to 320°.

NEATO intersection is made up of these two cross radials.

Airplane B is at NEATO intersection & turns to 320° to go to LHD VOR.

Airplane A tracks outbound on the 050° radial from DLP.

Fig. 21

So always make sure that when traveling to a VOR station the TO/FROM triangle points to the course selection arrow and when traveling from a station, the TO/FROM triangle points on the opposite side of the course selection arrow.

Tracking a VOR Course - A Wind-Wind Situation

"The answer my friend, is blowing in the wind." The popular 60s folk group Peter, Paul, and Mary weren't pilots, but they understood our dilemma. So far, our discussion of VOR navigation hasn't bothered with the effects of wind. How convenient. How unlikely. Since we seldom operate in a wind-free environment, we need to take a look at how to correct for it during electronic navigation. I say electronic navigation because once you understand the concept of wind correction you can apply this knowledge to any form of electronic navigation (i.e., ADF, GPS, Loran, etc.).

Wind Correction While Tracking a VOR Course Inbound

Airplane (A) has just intercepted the 030° course to the station and is flying a parallel heading of 030°. Wind from the west blows Airplane (B) right of course. Airplane (C) turns left to reintercept the original course at a 20° angle on a heading of 010°. When established back on course, Airplane (D) uses a wind correction angle of 10° to the left of the selected course. A magnetic heading of 020° carries Airplanes (D & E) to the VOR station.

MH = Magnetic Heading of airplane

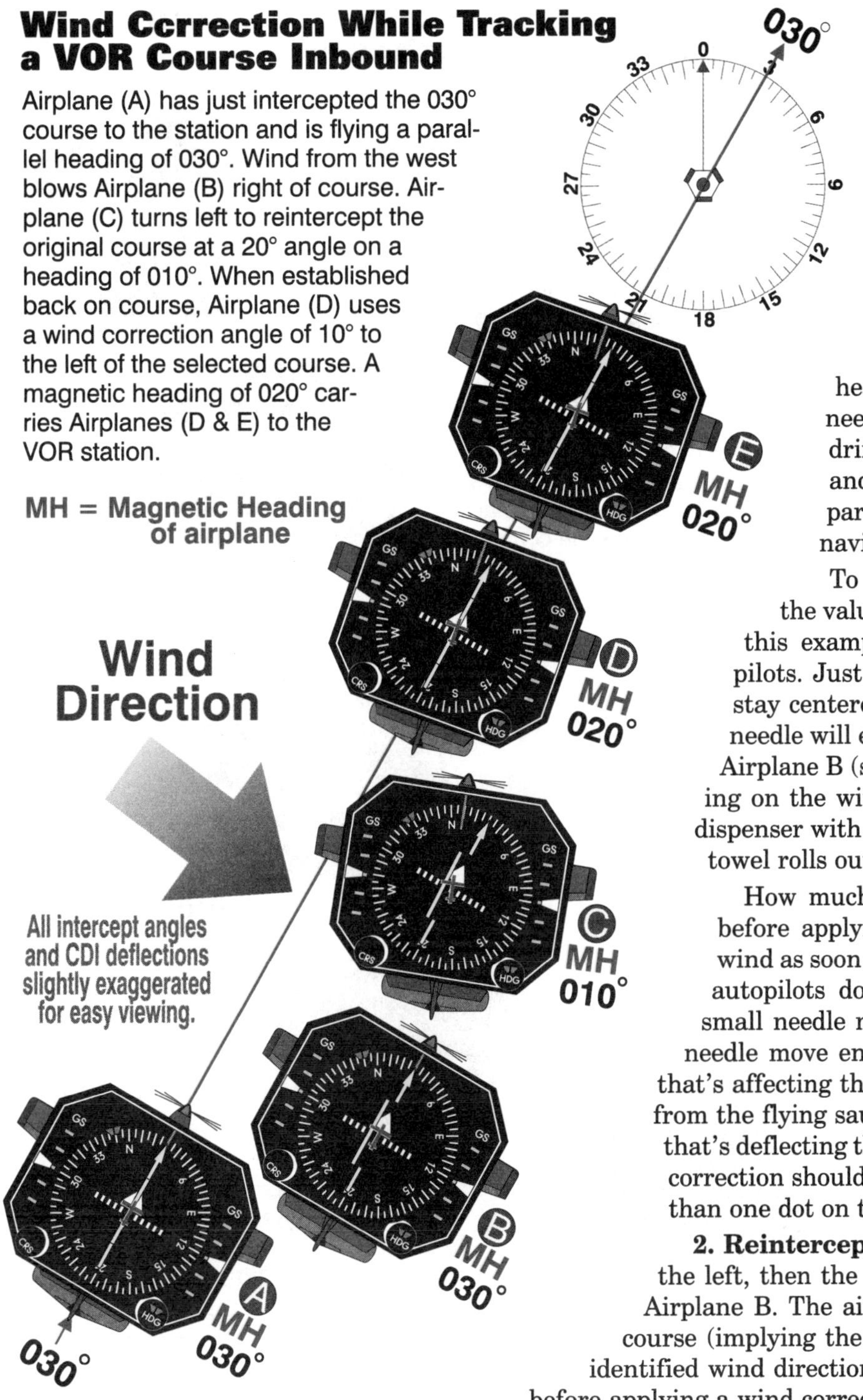

Wind Direction

All intercept angles and CDI deflections slightly exaggerated for easy viewing.

Fig. 22

MH 020° (E)

MH 020° (D)

MH 010° (C)

MH 030° (B)

MH 030° (A) 030°

The answer *is* blowing in the wind. Our job is to find it. Wind correction is broken down into four components: Identifying the effect of wind on the airplane, reintercepting the course, applying a wind correction, and adjusting the correction. Here's how it works.

1. Identifying the Effect of Wind – Figure 22 depicts Airplane A as having just intercepted the 030 degree course to the VOR. In a no-wind condition, Airplane A could hold a 030 degree heading and fly to the VOR with a centered needle. But with wind, Airplane A is going to drift off course. Determining wind direction and making the proper correction is thus paramount (not Fox or MGM) to successful navigation.

To determine wind effect on the airplane, fly the value set by the course selector (030 degrees in this example). Now comes the hard part for most pilots. Just wait. If there is no wind, the needle will stay centered (or nearly so). If a crosswind exists, the needle will eventually show a deflection, as depicted by Airplane B (sure, sometimes this takes a while, depending on the wind. It's like using a bathroom hand towel dispenser with a gear ratio of 10,000 to 1. By the time the towel rolls out, your hands are already dry).

How much of a needle deflection should you allow before applying a correction? Realistically, correct for wind as soon as you notice any needle movement, just as autopilots do. Unfortunately, it's very difficult to see small needle movements. That's why it's best to let the needle move enough to determine that it's actually wind that's affecting the airplane and not some errant signal (say from the flying saucer that's been following you for an hour) that's deflecting the needle. It's reasonable to say that a wind correction should be applied before the needle deflects more than one dot on the HSI's face.

2. Reintercepting the Course – If the needle moves to the left, then the selected course is to the left, as shown by Airplane B. The airplane has been blown to the right of the course (implying the crosswind is from your left). Once you've identified wind direction, the second step is to get back on course before applying a wind correction. Of course, you could turn 90 degrees and reintercept the course, but this would cause ATC to ask all sorts of playful and silly things such as, "What in tarnation are you doing?," and, "Are you out of your mind?" and "Just where do you think you're going?" Aren't those controllers so playful sometimes? Well, if you want to play, this may not be the best way to do it. I suggest that you intercept the course at an angle of around 20, 30 or even 40 degrees (if the wind is strong), and fly toward it as shown by Airplane C. Remember, ATC expects you to track the centerline of an airway, so do what you have to do to get back on centerline.

3. Applying a Wind Correction – Once reestablished on course, the third step in tracking is to apply a wind correction. As we previously discussed, the airplane must be angled by some amount into the wind. How much? That depends on the wind speed and wind angle as well as your airspeed. But none of that really matters, because you are going to use the empirical method, also known as "fly it and try it." Just use one-half of your intercept angle—10 degrees, in this case. Try it and see if it works. Once you're on course, turn the airplane 10 degrees to the right (for a heading of 020 degrees) as shown by Airplane D and wait to see what happens.

Airplane D has a wind correction angle of 10 degrees while heading 020 degrees. Airplanes D and E are tracking directly *to* the VOR station on the 030 degree course. The needle hasn't moved. My congratulations to you if you're able to find the proper wind correction angle on the very first try (make sure you brag about it to everyone in the cockpit and do a lot of gloating, because you probably won't be as lucky next time). Even experienced pilots can't always do this. Realistically, you're probably going to make a *minimum* of two attempts at determining a wind correction angle before you find the right one. And then it might not stay right, because the wind feels no obligation to remain a nice, steady force in order to ease our calculations.

4. Adjusting the Wind Correction – Figure 23 depicts a situation similar to Figure 22. The difference is that you're now tracking *from* a station using the previous 10 degree wind correction angle, as shown by Airplane A. Soon the airplane begins to drift, as shown by Airplane B. It's now obvious your wind correction angle must be changed. Return to 010 degrees, the original intercept angle, and reintercept the course as depicted by Airplane C. Since a heading of 020 degrees (10 degree wind correction to the left) didn't keep you on course, increase the wind correction angle by 5 degrees.

Flying 015 degrees as shown by Airplane D might be a satisfactory correction. If, however, the needle moved to the right, indicating the airplane was flying across the 030 degree course to the left, then our wind correction angle was too large. As least now you know the wind correction angle is between 10 and 15 degrees.

Sometimes, if the wind varies, the entire flight consists of constantly changing the wind correction angle. This is especially true if you're changing altitudes or flying near mountainous terrain, where wind is often highly variable. As you become more skilled at tracking, you'll find that you can apply small corrections to stop the needle from moving before it ever gets away from the center. With that kind of skill, the wind can shift every minute and it won't faze you.

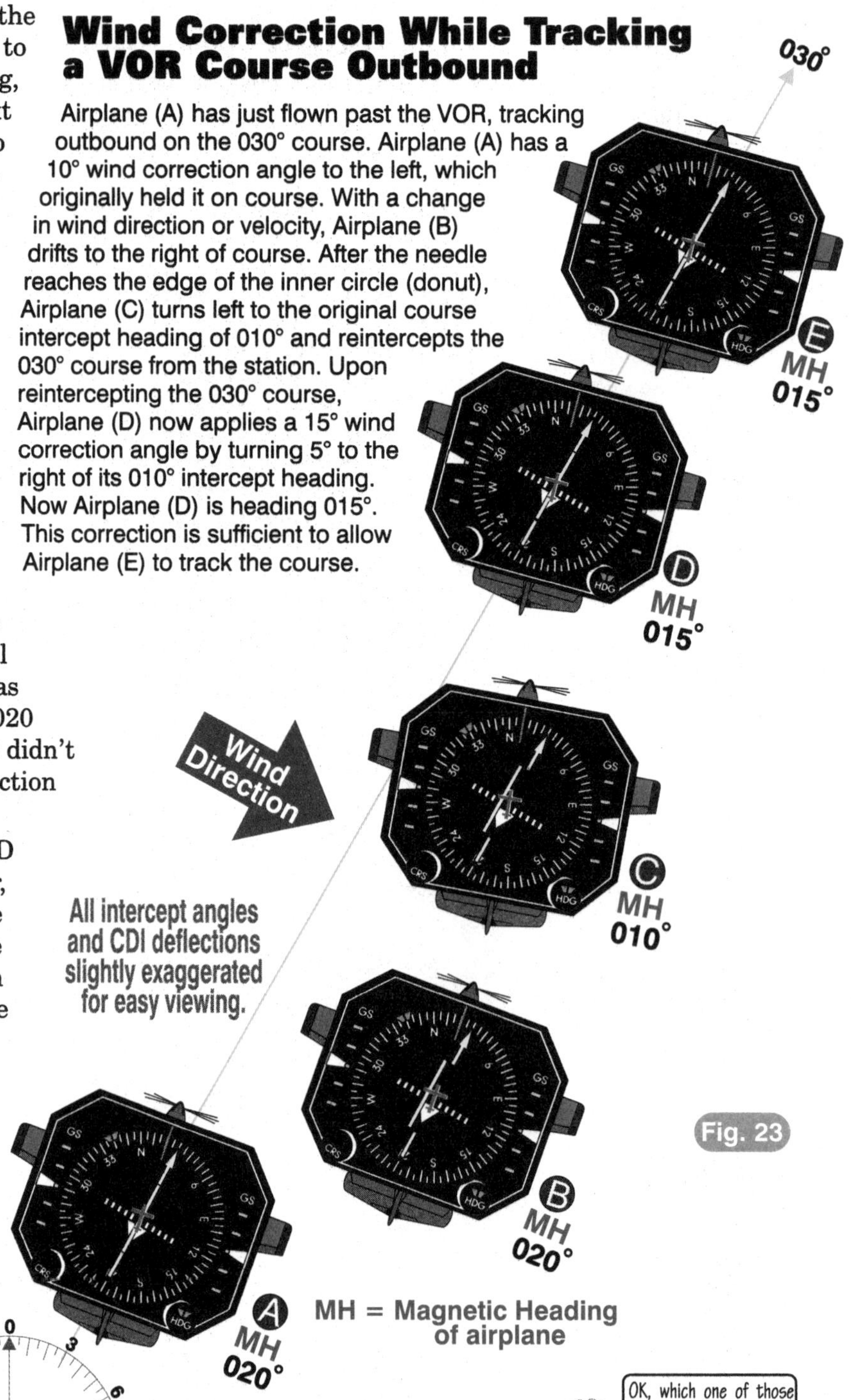

Chasing the Needle

One of the big problems IFR pilots have is that they wind up chasing the VOR needle during enroute and approach navigation. Staying on course centerline is important, especially when you're in the clouds and can't see the terrain. But this sometimes leads pilots to rack their planes back and forth in a desperate (and usually futile) attempt to catch the needle because they fail to remember the basics of tracking. VOR needles become quite sensitive when closing in on VOR ground

Wind Correction While Tracking a VOR Course Outbound

Airplane (A) has just flown past the VOR, tracking outbound on the 030° course. Airplane (A) has a 10° wind correction angle to the left, which originally held it on course. With a change in wind direction or velocity, Airplane (B) drifts to the right of course. After the needle reaches the edge of the inner circle (donut), Airplane (C) turns left to the original course intercept heading of 010° and reintercepts the 030° course from the station. Upon reintercepting the 030° course, Airplane (D) now applies a 15° wind correction angle by turning 5° to the right of its 010° intercept heading. Now Airplane (D) is heading 015°. This correction is sufficient to allow Airplane (E) to track the course.

All intercept angles and CDI deflections slightly exaggerated for easy viewing.

MH = Magnetic Heading of airplane

Fig. 23

stations. That's why it's important to keep the omni display in your scan and detect needle movement as early as possible. Since many instrument approaches involve flying directly over VOR stations, you'll want to make sure you establish a wind correction angle early to keep the needle centered as long as possible. So, when you get close to the station, make small adjustments to keep the needle centered.

VOT - VOR Test Signals

Since VOR navigation is such an integral part of IFR navigation, the FAA requires you (per FAR 91.171) to ensure that your VOR equipment is operating properly before using it under instrument flight rules. There are five basic means of testing your VOR for accuracy: using a VOT, using a certified airborne checkpoint, a certified checkpoint on the surface, cross checking one VOR receiver against another in the same airplane, or creating your own airborne checkpoint. Let's examine each.

VOT or a "VOR Test" signal is a signal transmitted from a nearby VOT test facility. Figure 24 shows an *Airport/Facility Directory* (A/FD) excerpt indicating the VOT frequency (see top of this figure) for Phoenix Sky Harbor international airport and Prescott's Love field. Essentially, this facility transmits a single signal (the 360 radial/course) in all directions. By tuning the VOT frequency into your navigation radio, you should hear a series of dots or a continuous tone as a means of identifying the test signal. Next, by rotating the course selector to 180 degrees, the CDI should center with a TO indication (Figure 25A). If it doesn't, then center the needle and note the bearing under the course selector.

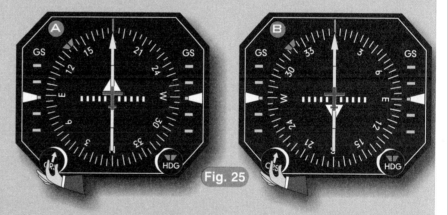

VOR TEST FACILITIES (VOT)

Facility Name (Airport Name)	Freq.	Type, VOT Facility
Phoenix Sky Harbor Intl.	109.0	G
Prescott (Ernest A. Love Fld)	110.0	G

You'll find the VOR receiver checkpoints in the rear of the *Airport/Facility Directory*.

VOR RECEIVER CHECK POINTS

Fig. 24

Facility Name (Airport Name)	Freq/Ident	Type Check Pt. Gnd. AB/ALT	Azimuth from Fac. Mag.	Dist. from Fac. N.M.	Check Point Description
Arcata (Arcata)	110.2/ACV	G	148	0.7	On runup area apch end Rwy 32.
Chico (Chico Muni)	109.8/CIC	G	302	1.1	On north runup area.
Clovis (Fresno Yosemite Intl)	112.9/CZQ	A/1400	130	7.2	Over apch end Rwy 11L.
Compton Woodley	113.6/LAX	A/1000	091	10.0	Over apch end Rwy 28L.

Rotating the course selector to 0 degrees should center the needle with a FROM indication (Figure 25B). If it doesn't, then center the needle and note the bearing under the course selector. The allowable error here is +/- 4 degrees. In other words, if the needle centers with course selections between 176-184 degrees or 356-004 degrees, your VOR equipment is acceptable for use in the IFR system (Figure 26). When using the VOT on RMI equipment, the head of the RMI's needle should read 180 degrees with any course selection. The +/- 4 degree error applies with the RMI here, too. A good way to remember the "180 and TO" indication is to think of doing this test in a Cessna 182. By default, setting the course selector to 360 should result in a FROM indication.

Believe it or not, VOT checks can be done on the ground or in the air but only where specifically approved by the *Airport/Facility Directory* (A/FD). The VOT check should be conducted on the ground (as indicated by the G under "type-facility") for the two airports shown on the bottom of Figure 24. In addition to VOT, there are other types of airborne and ground VOR receiver checkpoints established for determining VOR accuracy. You can read about these on the following page.

To be legal when flying IFR, your VOR equipment must have had a *logged* accuracy check

Fig. 25

within the preceding 30 days. The regulations say that you must log your signature, place of the VOR test, the error shown by the test, and the date. Think SPED for signature, place, error and date. This logging can be done on any record sufficient to prove that the equipment was legal for use. It should not be accomplished after an incident, while the FAA accident investigator is interviewing you.

VOT Check in Action

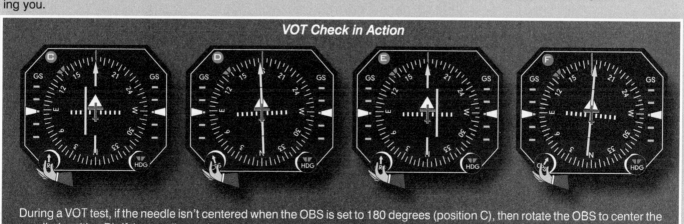

During a VOT test, if the needle isn't centered when the OBS is set to 180 degrees (position C), then rotate the OBS to center the needle (position D). If the needle can be centered by rotating the OBS no more than 4 degree either side of 180 degrees (as also shown in position E and F), then the VOR equipment is considered accurate enough for IFR flight. The same +/- 4 degree variance also applies when the OBS is set to 360 degrees and a FROM indication is shown.

Fig. 26

VOR Ground and Airborne Test Signals

Let's assume you're at Chico airport and want to do a typical ground VOR check (see Figure 27). The frequency to use is 109.8 MHz and the radial to which to set the OBS is 302. You should be in the north runup area when doing this check. The allowable error for a VOR ground check is +/- 4 degrees. In other words, you should be able to center the CDI by rotating the course selector 4 degrees either side of the depicted radial (302 degrees in this case) defining that checkpoint.

The *A/FD* also defines airborne checkpoints as indicated by the letter "A" and an altitude and location at which to conduct the check as shown in Figure 27. Suppose you were flying over Clovis airport, flying at 1,400 feet over the approach end of

Fig. 27	VOR RECEIVER CHECK POINTS				You'll find the VOR receiver check-points in the rear of the *A/FD*
Facility Name (Airport Name)	Freq/Ident	Type Check Pt. Gnd. AB/ALT	Azimuth from Fac. Mag.	Dist. from Fac. N.M.	Check Point Description
Arcata (Arcata)	110.2/ACV	G	148	0.7	On runup area apch end Rwy 32.
Chico (Chico Muni)	109.8/CIC	G	302	1.1	On north runup area.
Clovis (Fresno Yosemite Intl)	112.9/CZQ	A/1400	130	7.2	Over apch end Rwy 11L.
Compton Woodley	113.6/LAX	A/1000	091	10.0	Over apch end Rwy 28L.

Runway 11L with your VOR tuned to the CZQ VOR and the OBS set to 130 degrees. When flying over this location the CDI should center within +/- 6 degrees of the 130 degree radial for the VOR to be considered legal for IFR flight.

Fig. 28

When cross-checking two VOR receivers against one another, you should tune the two nav radios to the same frequency and center their respective needles. The maximum allowable error between the course selections is 4 degrees with the needle centered.

You can also make your own airborne checkpoint by selecting a VOR radial lying along the centerline of an established airway. Select a prominent ground point along that radial that's more that 20 nautical miles from the station and maneuver over that point at a reasonably low altitude (obviously you won't be doing this while flying on an IFR flight plan or in IMC conditions). Finally, note the VOR bearing indicated by the receiver. That bearing should be within +/- 6 degrees of the published airway radial.

You can also check one VOR against another in the same airplane as shown in Figure 28. This assumes you have two navigation radios on board. If you do, then tune both to the same VOR station, identify that station, center the CDI and note the course selection bearing. The maximum permissible difference between these two bearings is 4 degrees (not +/- 4 degrees, either). In other words, if one VOR indicated 140 and the other indicated 144, both of these units would be acceptable for IFR flight. The theory here is that if two VOR units in the same airplane have nearly the same degree of error (4 degrees or less), then neither has an error so large as to make IFR flying dangerous.

As with the VOT check, to be legal when flying IFR, your VOR equipment must have had a *logged* accuracy check within the preceding 30 days. The regulations say that you must log your signature, place of the VOR test, the error shown by the test, and the date. Think SPED for signature, place, error and date. This logging can be done on any record sufficient to prove that the equipment was legal for use. It generally cannot be accomplished after an incident, while the FAA accident investigator is interviewing you.

Finally, if you have an acceptable error in your VOR equipment, don't try compensating for it by adding or subtracting a few degrees off your course selection. In some cases pilots have done the math wrong and compounded the navigational error without realizing it. Just accept the error and be happy. After all, the FAA is happy with it, so you should be, too. If the error is greater than allowed by the regulations or outside your comfort zone, then have a qualified avionics technician check the equipment.

Having Fun at Your Instructor's Expense

I think I'd like to fly the VOT approach. It so easy to keep the needle centered on that approach, especially when the VOR has no errors. OK, just kidding on that one.

Bobette. What type of IFR approach would you like to fly to impress the FAA designee?

Distance Measuring Equipment [DME]

DME, shown in Figure 29, provides you with nautical mile distances from many VOR stations. This equipment usually displays groundspeed as well. It's a wonderful device, making cross-country flying and position fixing considerably easier. Let's examine how it works.

A Typical DME Receiver

Fig. 29

DME is one of those great devices that is nearly the exact opposite of your average teenager in that it does so much and demands so little. The DME equipment in the airplane operates by sending out paired pulses with a specific time spacing. These pulses are received at the ground station, which then transmits paired pulses back to the aircraft at the same pulse spacing but on a different frequency. The round trip time for the signal exchange is measured in the airborne DME unit and translated into distance from the aircraft to the ground station.

DME provides you with the distance (in nautical miles) to whatever VOR station you've selected. It can also be associated with other navigational facilities such as an instrument landing system (ILS/DME) or a localizer (LOC/DME). DME operates in the ultrahigh frequency (UHF) spectrum at frequencies between 962 MHz and 1213 MHz.

Not every VOR has a DME station associated with it. How can you tell which ones do? I'm glad I asked. Figure 30, position A depicts a VORTAC. While VORTAC sounds like the name of someone from Germany or the Klingon homeworld, it's actually the combination of a civilian VOR station and a military navigation station called a TACAN (Tactical Air Navigation station). TACAN stations operate on higher frequencies, but what's important to you is that they include DME capability, as indicated by the presence of a UHF Channel number (e.g., Ch 77 at Salt Flat VOR). The

aviation authorities have happily worked out an arrangement whereby the UHF DME frequency is paired with a specific VFH VOR frequency. When you tune your DME equipment to Salt Flat (113.0) you're actually tuning it to read Channel 77, too. Be happy. Your tax dollars are at work here.

Figure 30, position B represents a combination VOR and DME station at Pinon VOR. Once again, the presence of the UHF DME channel (Ch 41) is the give away that DME exists at this location.

No DME is available at Guadalupe VOR (Figure 46, position C) since there is no UHF Channel frequency in Guadalupe's information box. Figure 30, position D represents a pure TACAN station. To use DME at this location you'd have to know the UHF-VHF frequency pairing schedule for Vandenberg TACAN.

Most aircraft have a combination VOR and DME receiving units which provide for automatic DME reception (Figure 31). Sometimes DME is separate from the VOR unit, and the frequency for its use must be tuned separately from the VOR as shown in Figure 29.

Collin's VOR and DME Receiver

Fig. 31

Since DME can be co-located with a VOR or a localizer (LOC), how do you know if it's still operational? After all, the DME transmitter could fail while the VOR portion kept working. You can tell if DME is operational when you

Identifying Sites Transmitting DME Information

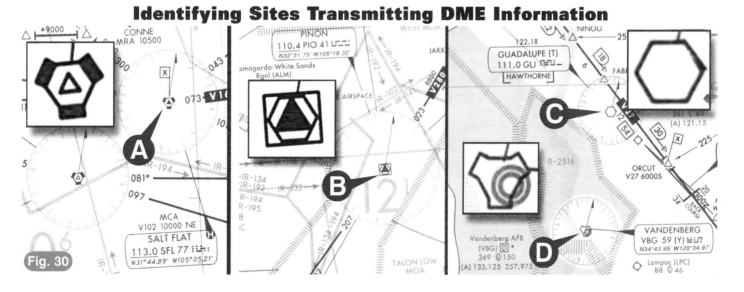

Fig. 30

DME Slant Range Mileage

DME measures slant range mileage. At 6,000' AGL directly over the station, Airplane (B's) DME reads 1 mile (1 nm = appx. 6,000'). The greatest DME error occurs directly over the station. At greater distances from the station this slant range error diminishes. Airplane (A's) DME readout is Appx. 10 nm.

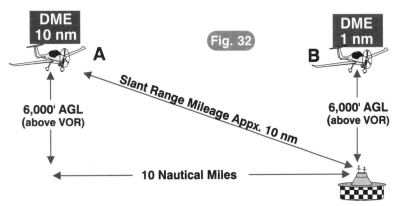

Fig. 32

GPS Horizontal Mileage

GPS mileage between waypoints is actual horizontal distance, not slant range distance as experienced with DME receivers. The measurement error can be as little as just a few meters when the GPS isn't experiencing integrity errors (you'll learn about these soon).

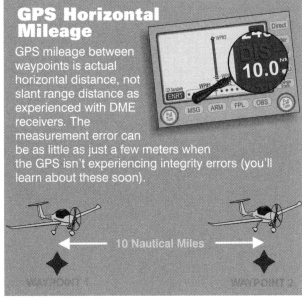

hear a Morse code identifier with a tone that's somewhat higher than the tone associated with a VOR or LOC identification. In fact, that higher pitched tone will be heard once for every three or four times that the VOR or LOC tone is heard. If, however, you hear only one higher pitched identifier every 30 seconds, then the DME portion of the station is working but the VOR or LOC is not. Of course, instead of a higher pitched tone, the FAA could have just mentioned the term "DME" somewhere during the transmission. That would let all of us with hearing less sensitive than a bat's actually detect it. Then again, it's good to be a bat.

What DME Really Tells You – If you stretched a piece of string (a very long piece of string) between the airplane and the VOR, then measured it, you'd have the distance shown on the DME. This is the *slant range distance,* as shown in Figure 32. This is not your precise horizontal distance from the station. You can ignore the slant range error if your airplane is one nautical mile or more from the ground station for each 1,000 feet of your altitude. In these instances, consider your slant range distance equal to the airplane's horizontal distance from the station. However, if you're directly over the station, then DME errors can be rather large. Airplane B's DME reads one nautical mile (approximately 6,000 feet) yet it is directly over the station. This makes sense, when you think about it. The airplane *is* one mile from the DME. One mile up, that is.

Position Fixing With DME – Do you have to be tracking a VOR radial to obtain DME information? Absolutely not. The DME equipment doesn't know where you're going or coming from, and unlike your flight instructor, it doesn't care. Simply select the VOR frequency in the DME receiver and read the DME display.

DME offers several possibilities for identifying your position. Figure 33 shows some examples. Figure 33A shows an airplane on the 130 degree radial at 10 miles from the station. That's a very precise position fix. Figure 33B shows the airplane on the LCB 200 degree radial at seven miles from the BAD VOR. Figure 33C shows the airplane at the intersection of two DME arcs from separate VOR stations. Use whatever combination of navaids you like to fix your position.

DME Arcs

Many instrument approaches incorporate something known as *DME arc transitions,* sometimes known to pilots as Noah's Arc because they noah wanta fly them (by now, you should see these coming and duck). Take a look at the Elko Regional VOR/DME approach (Figure 34). Instead of flying a straight-line navigational route onto the primary approach structure, the DME arc provides you

3 Different Ways of Determining Position With DME Equipment

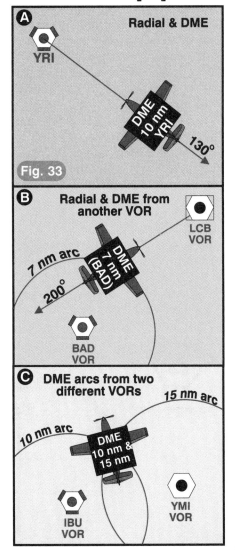

with a curved path (arc) to fly that aligns you with the approach. These arcs are circular routes with a specified DME distance from the VOR station. In Figure 34, a 10 nm arc transition about the Bullion VOR takes you from OLGAA intersection and onto the approach structure (the 324 degree course inbound to Bullion VOR). Let's see how we'd go about flying the DME arc, assuming we're inbound on the 241 degree radial to Bullion VOR.

Since flying a DME arc requires that you stay on the arc as much as possible, you need a strategy to do this. Unlike using a GPS moving map display, you can't see the DME arc using your VOR equipment. Instead you have to visualize it by selecting radials and flying perpendicular to them. While there are several ways to do this, it's pretty easy to do with an HSI. Here's an extremely easy way to fly an arc. It requires minimal work and keeps the chance of confusion to a minimum.

When tracking inbound to BQU on the 241 degree radial, check your DME readout. When you're .5 nm from the arc (a 10.5 DME reading in this instance or a DME reading of 9.5 miles when approaching from the opposite direction) you'll want to turn right 90 degrees (or left if it's a left circling arc) and begin flying the arc (Figure 35A). A .5 nm lead is just fine for groundspeeds of 150 knots or less. Use a larger lead for higher ground speeds. What initial heading should you turn to as you approach the arc? Look for the heading on your slaved

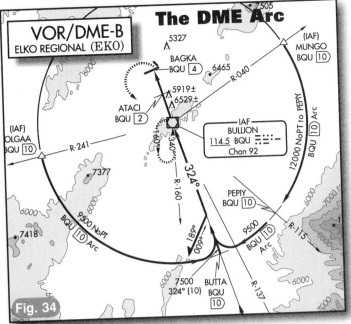

gyro that's 90 degrees to the right of your pre-intercept heading. In Figure 35A, this heading is approximately 150 degrees (pick the nearest whole 10 degree reference).

In Figure 35B it appears you're now flying perpendicular to the original inbound course and the CDI is moving toward the bottom of the instrument. So rotate

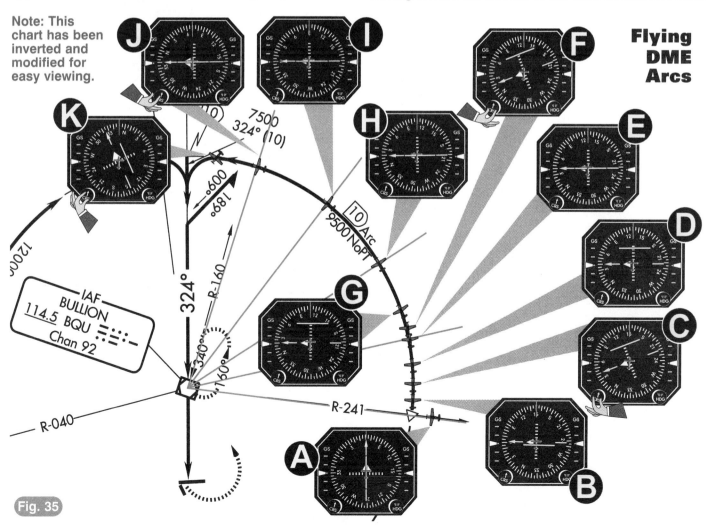

Note: This chart has been inverted and modified for easy viewing.

Fig. 35

Note: This chart has been inverted and modified for easy viewing.

Flying DME Arcs

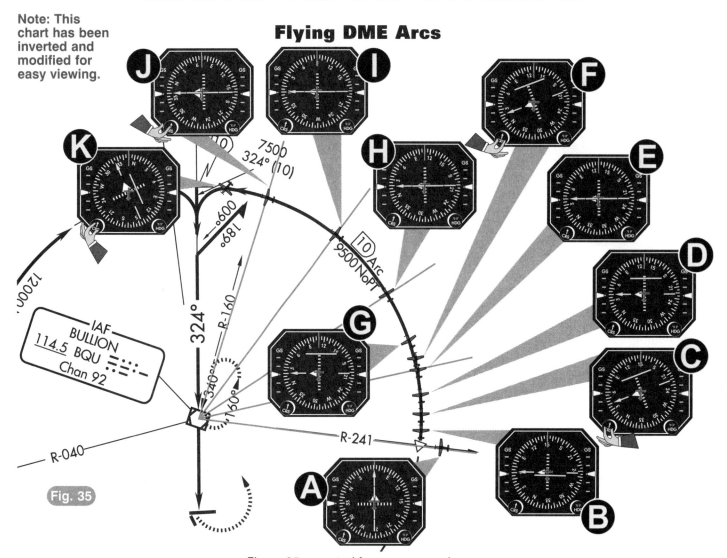

Figure 35 repeated for your convenience.

the OBS to the nearest whole 20 degree increment (or 040 degrees), which always means you'll move the CDI head so that it drops below the inside wing (the left wing in this instance) as shown in Figure 35C.

Now the easy part begins. Turn your airplane so that the miniature airplane in the HSI window shows you're flying directly towards the selected course (flying perpendicular to the CDI) as shown in Figure 35D. This means you're now on a 90 degree intercept to the next closest 20 degree inbound course (the 040 degree inbound course in this instance). At this point, look at the DME reading and, if it doesn't indicate the DME arc distance of 10 miles, then turn 10 degrees (right or left as appropriate) if you're one mile outside the arc; 20 degrees if you're 2 miles outside the arc and 30 degrees if you're three miles outside the arc. If you're inside the arc, maintain your heading until reaching the arc.

When the CDI centers (Figure 35E), rotate the OBS and point the course selector to the next 20 degree increment below the wing as shown in Figure 35F. Turn left to fly perpendicular to the selected course (Figure 35G) and be ready to modify your heading 5 to 10 degrees (or more if you have to due to excessive wind drift) to maintain a DME reading of +/- 1 mile of the arc radius.

When the CDI centers as shown in Figure 52H, repeat the same process until you come within 20 degrees (or so) of the inbound course as shown in Figure 52J.

When you are at or when you pass the DME arc's lead radial (the 160 radial [R-160] or 340 degree inbound course) set the course selector to the inbound course of 324 degrees as shown in Figure 52K and as the CDI centers, turn inbound to intercept the course.

That's it. Not too tough, right? This does, however, take a bit of practice before you begin to feel comfortable flying the arc. Keep in mind that, when flying DME arcs, your course selector should always be set to reference course to the VOR station, thus your VOR equipment should always show a "TO" indication to the station. When making 20 degree changes with the course selector, you'll always rotate the OBS so the course selector's head moves behind the wing, not ahead of it. Why? It's simple geometry. Since you'll always turn into the arc and since the course selector is moved behind the wing, this means any turn will move you first toward a perpendicular path toward the next 20 arc increment.

Now, there are certainly more precise ways to fly a DME arc but they do take a lot of work. It makes sense to work smarter (and easier) by using the pictorial presentation of the HSI to fly the arc and minimize the amount of head-work you need to do. Doing so means you free up your mental muscle to help you keep a good mental picture of where you are in relation to the inbound approach course. This is especially important considering that the wind drift angle is constantly changing throughout the arc. Your objective should be to keep within one mile of the arc at all times. It's also easier to maintain the arc if you keep slightly inside of it, because if you want to return to the center of the arc you just hold your heading until the DME indicates you're on the arc.

Of course, flying a DME arc is a lot easier if you are equipped with an RMI. Using an RMI in a no-wind condition theoretically means you'd only need to keep the RMI needle pointed to a wing (Figure 36).

Here's one way to fly a DME arc with an RMI:

1. With your RMI bearing pointer pointed to a wingtip reference and the aircraft at the designated DME range, maintain a constant heading (Figure 36A) and allow the bearing pointer to move 5 to 10 degrees behind the wingtip (Figure 36B). This will cause the DME distance to increase slightly (Figure 36B).

Using the RMI to fly DME Arcs

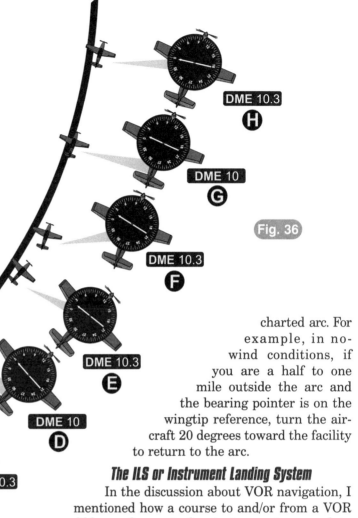

Fig. 36

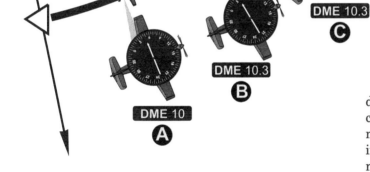

charted arc. For example, in no-wind conditions, if you are a half to one mile outside the arc and the bearing pointer is on the wingtip reference, turn the aircraft 20 degrees toward the facility to return to the arc.

The ILS or Instrument Landing System

In the discussion about VOR navigation, I mentioned how a course to and/or from a VOR could be used as part of an instrument approach to an airport by providing a pilot with lateral (horizontal) guidance to an airport. Along this course a pilot can descend to the minimum altitudes shown on an approach chart, and, hopefully after arriving at the lowest minimum altitude at or before the missed approach point, be in a position from which a safe descent and landing can be made.

I'll discuss how to fly instrument approaches in more detail later. Meanwhile, there is another variety of instrument approach that involves not only lateral guidance (like a VOR approach) but vertical guidance, too. Vertical guidance is provided by a glideslope to help guide the pilot down on a sloping electronic signal. Any type of approach that utilizes a glideslope is called a *precision* approach.

2. Turn toward the VOR station to place the bearing pointer 5-10 degrees ahead of the wingtip reference (Figure 36C), then maintain heading until the bearing pointer is again behind the wingtip. Continue this procedure to maintain the approximate arc (Figure 36D through 36H).

3. If a crosswind is drifting you away from the facility, turn the aircraft until the bearing pointer is ahead of the wingtip reference. If a crosswind is drifting you toward the facility, turn until the bearing is behind the wingtip. This will allow you to return to the arc, at which point you can continue using the tracking procedure previously described.

4. As a guide in making range corrections, change the RB 10-20 degrees for each half-mile deviation from the

Procedures without glideslopes, such an ordinary VOR approach, are called *non-precision* approaches (it's not called non-precision because of the way some pilots fly it, either). Precision approaches typically offer you a better chance of landing under reduced visibility conditions because they guide you to a lower altitude and place you in a better position from which a landing is more likely. The most common type of precision approach is called the *instrument landing system (ILS) approach* (Figure 37).

The ILS consists of four components (Figure 38):

1. A localizer that provides lateral (horizontal) guidance.
2. A glideslope that provides vertical guidance, usually down a three degree glideslope.
3. Marker beacons to help mark or identify your position/range along the approach path.
4. Approach lights to help you transition from instrument flying to visual flying when landing.

Let's discuss each component in detail.

The Localizer

The localizer (LOC) is a single electronic course aligned with the runway centerline (Figure 38). You track the localizer just as you would a VOR course. The only difference is that the localizer offers much more accurate lateral guidance. This means that the folks who design instrument approaches can allow you to descend to lower altitudes, since they can keep you confined to a tighter horizontal flight path (more "local," thus "localized") where there are fewer obstructions to protect you from.

That's why the localizer, whose transmitter is typically located at the far end of the runway (Figure 38), is only 3 to 6 degrees wide instead of being 20 degrees wide like a VOR course, as shown in Figure 39. (See: *SIDEBAR: VOR Localizer Width and Details on page 5-26*.) Since runways vary in length, the localizer width varies between 3 and 6 degrees so that it can be adjusted to provide a width of

The ILS Approach Chart

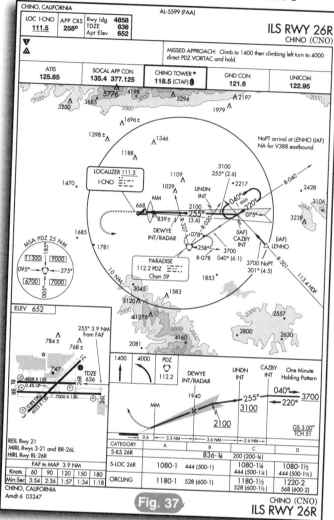

Fig. 37

The Instrument Landing System

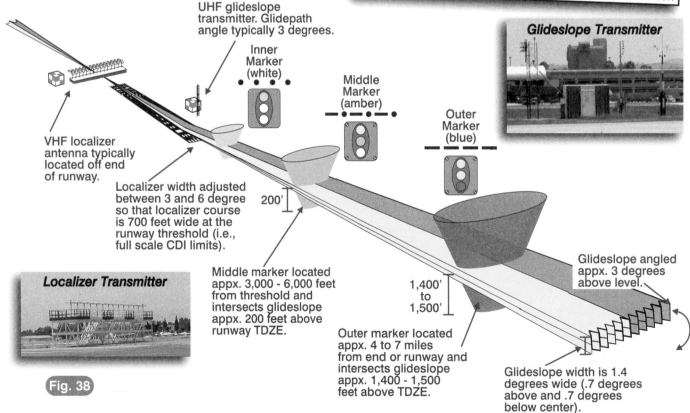

Fig. 38

UHF glideslope transmitter. Glidepath angle typically 3 degrees.

Inner Marker (white)

Middle Marker (amber)

Outer Marker (blue)

Glideslope Transmitter

VHF localizer antenna typically located off end of runway.

Localizer width adjusted between 3 and 6 degree so that localizer course is 700 feet wide at the runway threshold (i.e., full scale CDI limits).

200'

Middle marker located appx. 3,000 - 6,000 feet from threshold and intersects glideslope appx. 200 feet above runway TDZE.

Localizer Transmitter

1,400' to 1,500'

Outer marker located appx. 4 to 7 miles from end or runway and intersects glideslope appx. 1,400 - 1,500 feet above TDZE.

Glideslope angled appx. 3 degrees above level.

Glideslope width is 1.4 degrees wide (.7 degrees above and .7 degrees below center).

approximately 700 feet at the landing threshold (Figure 39). Figure 40 show how the localizer width might vary to reach a 700 foot span on both long and short runways. This arrangement provides pilots with similar course sensitivity when flying a localizer at the most important part of their approach, which is when they're near the runway threshold. Each dot of localizer deflection represents approximately 300 feet of horizontal displacement at the outer marker, and 100 feet of horizontal displacement at the middle marker. Now that's sensitive.

Localizer sensitivity is just one of the reasons to establish the proper drift correction before reaching the outer marker when flying an ILS approach. If you keep your heading corrections small, perhaps just two degrees or so, you'll be less likely to end up with a full-scale localizer needle deflection on an ILS approach.

Comparing Localizer and VOR Course Widths

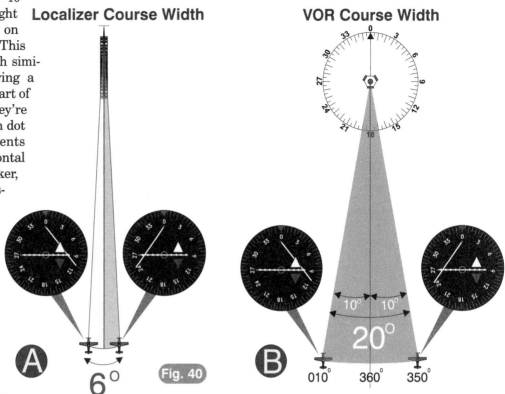

Localizer Course Width

VOR Course Width

Localizers broadcast on frequencies between 108.1 and 111.95 MHz, in odd tenths only. When identifying the localizer frequency, you'll hear a three-letter Morse code identification preceded by the letter "I" (two dots). For example, the Chino ILS 26R approach is identified by the Morse code for letters ICNO. It's also possible to listen to voice transmissions on the localizer. This would come in handy if you lost reception on your communication radios. You could still receive ATC instructions when flying an ILS (in all lost communication events, you want to keep your nav radio volume turned up in case ATC is trying to chat with you over nav frequencies). The localizer's electronic beam has limits of coverage shown in Figure 41.

Localizer Width Variation With Runway Length

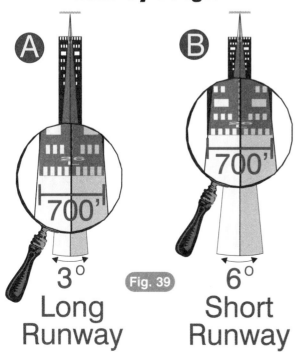

3° Long Runway

Fig. 39

6° Short Runway

Localizer Area Coverage

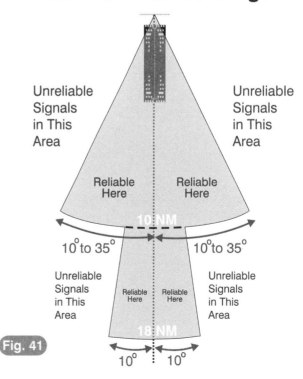

Fig. 41

Localizer Width and Details

It's important to remember that the localizer width varies between airports. If a particular localizer's width is five degrees, then a full-scale deflection (that's five dots of deflection and not a fully deflected needled banging against the instrument's casing) represents 2.5 degrees to the side of the runway centerline.

Practically speaking, the number of degrees of needle deflection is rather meaningless to you, since you don't know the precise width of the localizer. Unless you're flying with a copilot named Euclid, it's not likely that anyone will ever ask you the question, "Hey, I've got to know how wide this localizer is. Tell me. I can't live without this information." If, however, your name is Euclid, then just assume that the localizer is *approximately* five degrees in width and has the dot-distance deflection relationship shown in Figure 42. Roughly speaking, with a localizer five degrees in width, each dot deflection at the middle marker represents 100 feet of lateral distance from the course centerline. Each dot deflection at the outer marker represents 300 feet lateral distance from the course centerline.

Let's go back to the question of a five-dot versus a fully-deflected needle indication. What's the difference? It could be the difference between landing safely and never landing at all. Some instructors will say you should execute a missed approach if you drift too far off the localizer (for whatever reason this might happen). The question is, How far is too far? Since there's no official answer to this question, here's a common sense response. If the needle is deflected five dots or less (this is not considered a full scale deflection), then you might still consider yourself on the localizer, although not *precisely* on it by any means. In other words, you aren't exactly where you want to be, but you know where you are (Figure 43 A,B,C).

On the other hand, if the needle is fully deflected (hitting against the stops), then you really *don't* know where you are (Figure 43D). You *could* be just a little noogie past five dots and thus a few hundred feet off course, or you could be miles off and in totally unprotected and unknown territory. "Low and don't know" is not generally considered a good instrument flying strategy.

Keep in mind that there is often a difference between what you'll do on the IFR checkride and what you'll do in real life. The instrument rating *Practical Test Standards*, for instance, requires an applicant to execute a missed approach when the CDI shows more than 3/4 scale deflection.

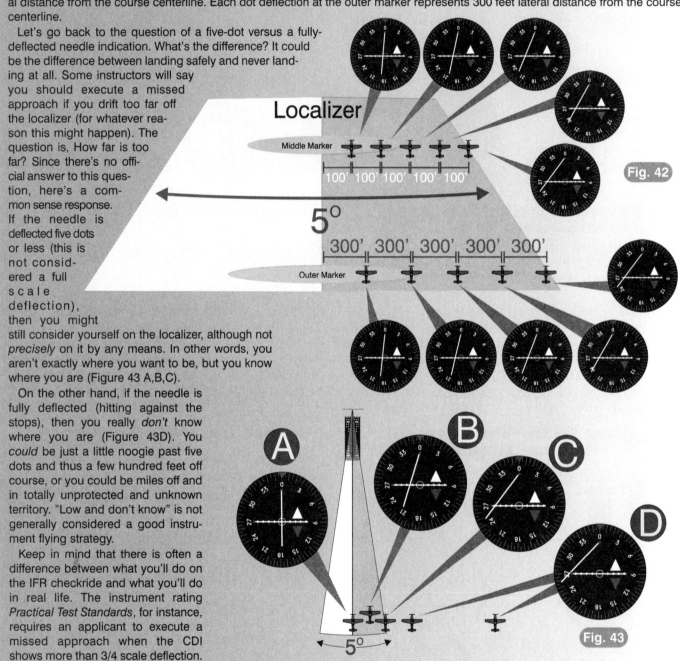

Fig. 42

Fig. 43

When you tune a localizer course, the CDI indicates if the airplane's position is right or left of the selected course. Just as with interpreting the needle on a VOR, you have to mentally orient yourself in the direction of the selected course for the terms *right* or *left* to have meaning. Rotating the OBS has no effect on the CDI. Go ahead, try it. Spin that bad boy. Unlike a VOR, which can provide idle-time entertainment for pilots who like to teach their needles to dance, a localizer is not an entertainment center. You are tuning in a specific course aligned with the runway. It's a good practice to rotate the OBS and set the inbound localizer course under the course index, as a heading reference. Since the localizer antenna is located at the end of the approach runway, CDI sensitivity increases as you approach the antenna. When making a missed approach at an airport, you will often overfly the antenna and continue outbound on the localizer. In this instance, there is no reverse sensing. A right or left deflected needle still means the course is right or left, as shown in Figure 44.

Localizer Course Orientation

Fig. 44

Localizer Transmitter

6°

Flying the Localizer Backcourse (Reverse Sensing)

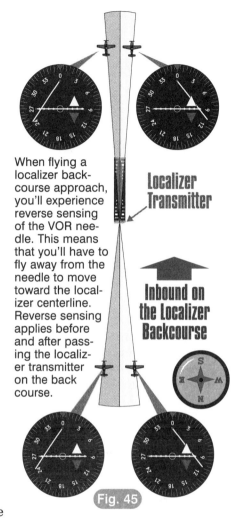

When flying a localizer back-course approach, you'll experience reverse sensing of the VOR needle. This means that you'll have to fly away from the needle to move toward the localizer centerline. Reverse sensing applies before and after passing the localizer transmitter on the back course.

Localizer Transmitter

Inbound on the Localizer Backcourse

Fig. 45

When flying a normal localizer approach, you fly *toward* the needle to get on course. However, if you are flying a localizer *back-course* (BC) approach, you've just gone down the rabbit hole with Alice, and everything is backwards. You now have *reverse sensing*. This does not mean the ability to detect if the airplane is backing up. As shown in Figure 45, you'd have to fly *away from* the needle to remain on centerline.

The easiest way to navigate with reverse sensing is to think of the side of the omni display's case as being used to pull the needle back to the center position. In other words, if I had a right needle, I'd make a left turn and pull the needle back to the center of the display. Of course, some airplanes have a back course switch (often labeled *BC*) that compensates for the reverse sensing, allowing you to fly as though you were using normal sensing.

Reversed sensing when flying a back course approach isn't a problem when using an HSI display, since this instrument depicts the airplane's position (the tiny airplane in the center of the display) in relation to the course, as shown in Figure 46. You set the HSI's course selector to the inbound (front course)

Comparing Localizer VOR Needle Sensing on Front and Back Courses

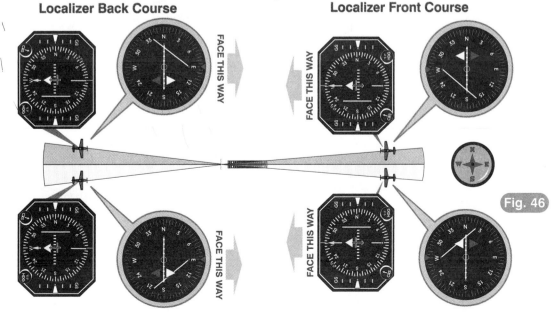

Localizer Back Course

Localizer Front Course

With the course selector on the HSI set to 270 degrees (the direction of the inbound localizer course), the HSI's CDI correctly displays the position of the localizer relative to your heading, whether or not you're flying the front or back course of the localizer. The VOR omni display, however, shows how the sensing is reversed when flying inbound on the localizer back course.

FACE THIS WAY

FACE THIS WAY

FACE THIS WAY

FACE THIS WAY

Fig. 46

The Back Course Switch

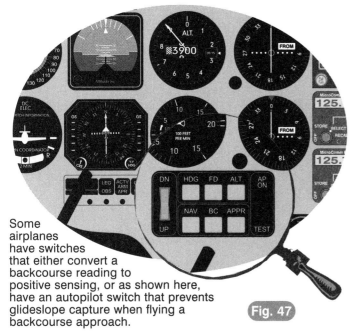

Some airplanes have switches that either convert a backcourse reading to positive sensing, or as shown here, have an autopilot switch that prevents glideslope capture when flying a backcourse approach.

Fig. 47

localizer direction and fly toward the needle. When inbound on the localizer back course with the course needle set to the front course, the tail of the HSI's course selector is at the top of the instrument and you have normal sensing. If, however, you set the HSI's course selector to the back-course direction you have reverse sensing. This is one good reason to always keep the HSI's course needle set to the direction for the inbound, front course.

Keep in mind that the autopilots on some airplanes have a BC switch (Figure 47) that allows the autopilot to track inbound on the back-course localizer and lock out the glideslope. Back course approaches don't use the

HSI/Omni Glideslope Indicators

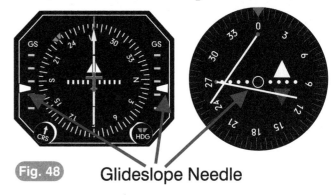

Fig. 48   Glideslope Needle

glideslope, and any glideslope indication you might see is invalid and must be ignored.

The Glideslope

The next component of the ILS is the glideslope. This is essentially an electronic beam angled upward at an angle from 2.5 to 4 degrees, with an average angle of 3 degrees. To fly a full ILS approach (both localizer and glideslope), you need either an HSI or ILS omni display (Figure 48) that provides two needles: one for the localizer and one for the glideslope. The glideslope needle is the horizontal needle that moves up and down and indicates where the angled beam is in relation to your airplane. As you approach the glideslope from below (while holding a constant altitude), the glideslope needle moves downward in the omni display (Figure 49A). This indicates that you're flying into the glideslope's descending path.

When the needle centers (Figure 49B), you're on the glideslope and should begin a descent at a rate that keeps the needle centered (*See sidebar: Descent Rates and the Glideslope on page 5-30*). If you're above the glideslope

Glideslope Display Indications

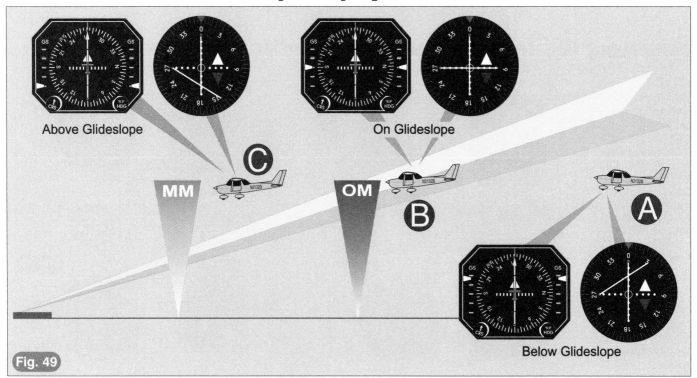

Above Glideslope   On Glideslope

Below Glideslope

Fig. 49

Glideslope Transmitter Location

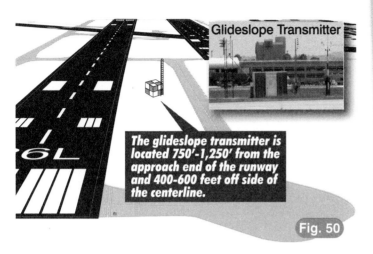

The glideslope transmitter is located 750'-1,250' from the approach end of the runway and 400-600 feet off side of the centerline.

Fig. 50

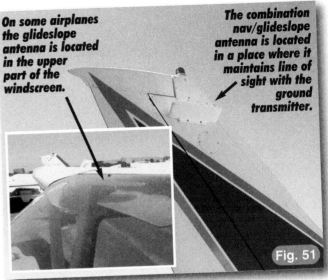

On some airplanes the glideslope antenna is located in the upper part of the windscreen.

The combination nav/glideslope antenna is located in a place where it maintains line of sight with the ground transmitter.

Fig. 51

(Figure 49C), you have to increase your rate of descent to recapture it. The secret to keeping the glideslope needle centered is to use your VSI as your primary pitch instrument, as discussed in Chapter 3 on instrument scan. Of course, you could center the needle by turning the instrument off, but this wouldn't be sporting, would it? Besides, like VORs, both the localizer and glideslope operational status is indicated by the appearance of warning flags/symbols.

Of course, you're probably wondering how engineers get that beam angled upward at a precise angle. Think about it this way. They took something similar to a localizer antenna and turned it sideways and tilted it upward. Since most pilots aren't named Marconi, I'll leave it at that. You should know that the antenna generating the glideslope signal is located 750–1,250 feet from the approach end of the runway and 400–600 feet off to one side of centerline (Figure 50). It's not placed there to keep pilots from knocking it over with their wing tip, though that is one additional benefit. This is where the folks who design these things (all curiously named Marconi) decided it would work best.

The ground based glideslope transmitter transmits its signal on an ultra high frequency or UHF (so bats can use, too). Look near the top of your airplane's windshield or tail and you're likely to find the glideslope receiving antenna (Figure 51), when it remains in the line-of-sight of the transmitter. Figure 51 shows a combination navigation radio and glideslope antenna as a single unit.

If you thought the localizer was sensitive, you'll be amazed to know the glideslope's beam is approximately 1.4 degrees wide. Pilots normally fly the glideslope down to approximately 200 feet height above touchdown (HAT), which is the height of the runway's TDZE or touchdown zone elevation (the TDZE represents the highest portion of the runway during the first 3,000 feet of its length as shown in Figure 52). Of course, the glideslope is angled to keep you free of obstructions during your descent. Larger obstructions along the localizer require a steeper glideslope (perhaps one as steep as 4 degrees). Fewer obstructions along the approach path may permit a glideslope angled as low as 2.5 degrees.

Perhaps you've heard of the fellow who etched his name on his dentures with an electronic engraving tool. Clearly a form of false identification. Another form of false identification is when you try to receive a glideslope at vertical angles higher than that for which it was approved. This is the proverbial slippery slope. At higher angles, it's possible to receive a signal but it is not an *accurate* glideslope indication.

The Touchdown Zone

Touchdown Zone Elevation (TDZE) is the highest portion of the runway's first 3000 feet of length.

Fig. 52

Descent Rates and the Glideslope

The following chart provides your rate of descent for a given ground speed and glidepath angle. This chart helps you determine your approximate descent rate when flying the glideslope on an ILS approach. For instance, if you expect your groundspeed to be 90 knots while flying a 3 degree glideslope, then you can initially plan on a descent rate of 478 feet per minute. By pegging the VSI needle on this number after intercepting the glideslope you probably won't need to make many additional pitch and power adjustments to maintain your glideslope track.

GS Angle	Feet /NM	Groundspeed (Knots)								
		30	45	60	75	90	105	120	135	150
2.0	210	105	160	210	265	320	370	425	475	530
2.5	265	130	200	265	330	395	465	530	595	665
2.7	287	143	215	287	358	430	501	573	645	716
2.8	297	149	223	297	371	446	520	594	669	743
2.9	308	154	231	308	385	462	539	616	693	769
3.0	318	159	239	318	398	478	557	637	716	796
3.1	329	165	247	329	411	494	576	658	740	823
3.2	340	170	255	340	425	510	594	679	764	849
3.3	350	175	263	350	438	526	613	701	788	876
3.4	361	180	271	361	451	541	632	722	812	902
3.5	370	185	280	370	465	555	650	740	835	925
4.0	425	210	315	425	530	635	740	845	955	1060

ILS RWY 26R CHINO (CNO)

Chino's glideslope angle is three degrees. At 90 knots ground speed, it takes a descent rate of 478 feet per minute to remain on the glideslope. At 478 feet per minute you're descending at 318 feet per nautical mile.

Pilots find this out when their descent rates become extremely high during the approach (as if they're riding in a manhole cover instead of an airplane). Angles between 9-12 degrees (instead of 2.5-4 degrees) tend to be where false glideslope signals are received. Perhaps your instructor will fly you along the localizer at several thousand feet above the airport one day so you can see the false glideslope signals that occasionally present themselves. This is why ATC tries to set pilots up to intercept the glideslope from below during radar vectors. At a point approximately 3,500 feet from the threshold, a normal glideslope will be at a vertical distance of approximately 200 feet; at 4 to 7 miles it will be at approximately 1,500 feet. Now, let's connect the localizer and glideslope with the marker beacons.

The Marker Beacons

Marker beacons are ground stations that transmit a VHF signal vertically to marker beacon receivers in the cockpit (Figure 53). A pilot must fly over (or nearly so) the marker beacons to receive their signals. Marker beacon receiver sensitivity is selectable as *high* or *low* on many units. The low-sensitivity position gives the sharpest indication of position and should be used during an approach. The high-sensitivity position provides an earlier warning that the aircraft is approaching the marker beacon site.

There are three types of marker beacons that can be associated with an ILS: the *outer* marker, the *middle* marker and the *inner* marker.

What's the purpose of these beacons? They provide you with an aural and visual alert of your position along the localizer. Think of these as the aviation version of a hotel's wakeup call. As you recall, a normal glideslope has an approximate vertical elevation of 200 feet at a point 3,500 feet from the runway threshold. When you are flying an

ILS approach, you are normally allowed to descend to an altitude of 200 feet above the runway's touchdown zone elevation. (Figure 54). At this height you make a decision as to whether or not you have the required minimum visibility to land (this value is shown on the approach chart). Without this visibility and without the runway environment in sight, you must execute a missed approach.

Marker Beacon Receiver

The three marker beacon lights are usually found above the radio stack. The marker beacon audio selector switch is found on the audio panel.

Fig. 53

The decision altitude (DA) is a critical height for instrument pilots. That's why the FAA places something known as a *middle marker* (MM) transmitter approximately 3,500 feet from the threshold (the actual distance typically varies between .4 and .7 nautical miles or 2,400 feet to 4,200 feet). While on the glideslope, at decision height (DH) you should see a flashing amber light somewhere on your panel and hear a series of Morse code dots. This is how the middle marker is identified. If you don't hear the dots, the beacon is having an identity crisis and is unreliable. Of course, this assumes that you have the marker beacon equipment turned on and that it's operating properly. The purpose of the MM is to alert you that you're at or near DA.

That's the way it should work in a perfect world. But sometimes it's difficult for the folks who install ILS hardware to place the marker beacon transmitter at the precise location it should reside along the approach course. That could be, for instance, because someone is living at the precise point where the FAA would like to install its marker beacon. There's nothing worse than having an enormous and powerful transmitter sitting in your bedroom, even if you have a magnetic personality (or want one). It makes some people feel like a marked man. Nevertheless, it's reasonable to assume that the middle marker will be pretty close to 3500 feet from the threshold.

Decision Altitude on an ILS Approach

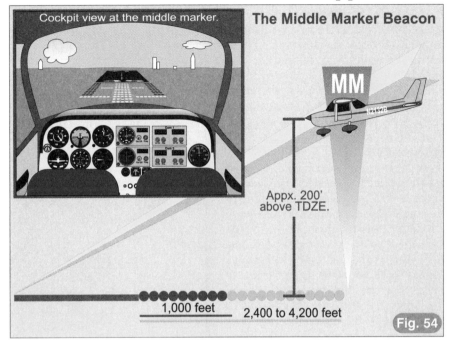

Fig. 54

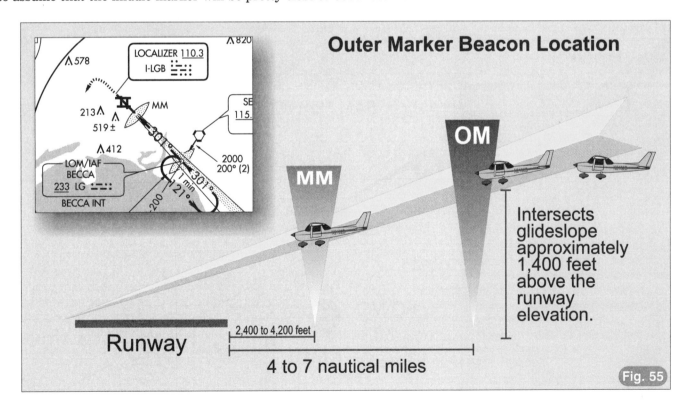

Fig. 55

An outer marker (OM) is often installed at a point four to seven miles from the runway threshold (Figure 55). The intent here is to alert you by placing the marker beacon approximately where you intercept the glideslope and begin your descent to the runway. The place where you often (but not always) begin this descent is called the FAF or *final approach fix*. The outer marker is identified by a blue flashing light in your cockpit and a series of Morse code dashes. If you get the blue flashing light *without* the Morse code, you are flying too low over a Kmart.

On occasion, an NDB beacon is associated with a marker beacon. Such a combination is called a *compass locator* or (Figure 56A). These are wonderful combinations, since you can use your ADF to identify the position of the marker beacon as well as using the airplane's marker beacon receiver. Perhaps the most important reason for compass locators is that they provide you with the ability to fly an NDB approach, too. After all, marker beacons aren't directional (they project vertically), so they can't be used for ADF navigation (besides, the marker beacon is VHF, not LF). It's helpful to note that NDBs have three-letter Morse code identifiers (Figure 56B). NDBs established as outer compass locators (co-located with the OM, sometimes referred to as an LOM or *locator outer marker*) use the first two letters of the three-letter localizer ID (Figure 56C). NDBs established as middle compass locators (co-located with the MM, sometimes referred to as an LMM or *locator middle marker*) use the last two letters of the three-letter localizer ID.

The Compass Locator

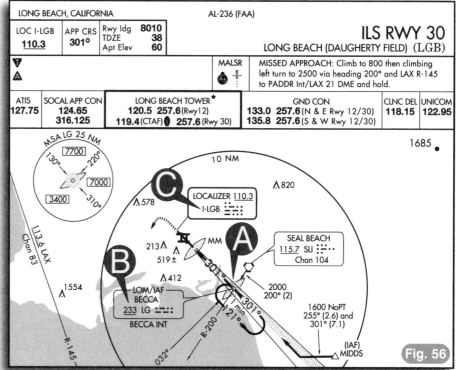

Fig. 56

To learn something about the inner marker (IM), take a look at the *Inside the Inner Marker* sidebar.

Inside the Inner Marker

You won't hear much about inner markers, because to most general aviation pilots they are irrelevant. The inner marker (IM), where installed, is located on the front course between the MM and the landing threshold (Position A). It marks the point at which an aircraft is at decision height on the glidepath during a Category II ILS approach (Position B). There aren't a lot of Cessna 172s equipped to fly a CAT II approach (pronounced "cat two" but officially spoken as a "category two" approach), which is why most pilots go a lifetime without ever needing to know about an inner marker. Therefore, if someone tells you that you need to get in touch with your inner marker, they're talking about what goes on inside your brain, not at an airport somewhere.

Each marker beacon has its own song to help you identify it. You're not expected to sing along, but you do need to know who's calling the tune.

The OM is identified by a low-pitched tone, continuous dashes at the rate of two per second, and a purple/blue marker beacon light.

The MM is identified by an intermediate tone, alternate dots and dashes at the rate of 95 dot/dash combinations per minute, and an amber marker beacon light.

The IM, where installed, is identified by a high-pitched tone, continuous dots at the rate of six per second, and a white marker beacon light.

The back-course marker (BCM), where installed, is identified by a high-pitched tone with two dots at a rate of 72 to 75 two-dot combinations per minute, and a white marker beacon light.

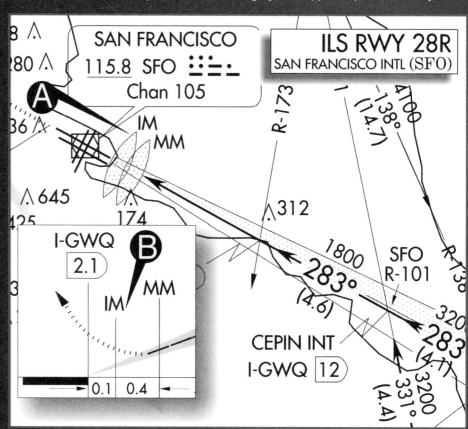

Light Up My Life: The Approach Lighting System (ALS)

Finally, we arrive at the last part of the ILS, the *approach lighting system* (ALS). Sherlock Holmes apprentice that you are, you've probably noticed that the ILS brings you to within approximately 3,500 feet of the runway threshold at a vertical height of 200 feet (Figure 57). That's an awfully thrilling place to leave a pilot hanging, especially when most of the ILS approaches we fly (known as Category I ILSs) require only a half mile visibility and no minimum ceiling height for landing. This is precisely why the approach lighting system was developed. Keep in mind that when all the fancy electronic stuff is done, you still have to make the last bit of the approach visually. From DA (Decision Altitude, sometimes referred to as DH or Decision Height), it's "no see, no go." The ALS is there to help pilots flying on instruments transition to visual flight for landing.

The folks who developed the ALS should be named Einstein for their sheer brilliance in designing such a system of lights. Relatively speaking, of course. When you are at or near DA on an ILS, you don't have a lot of time to identify the ALS. That's why there are two basic light systems: precision and nonprecision instrument runway approach lighting (Figure 58). (See page 17-1 for a definition of *precision instrument runway*.)

Two common precision instrument runway ALSs are named ALSF-1 and ALSF-2. The ALSF l and ll systems are often 2,400 to 3,000 feet in length and

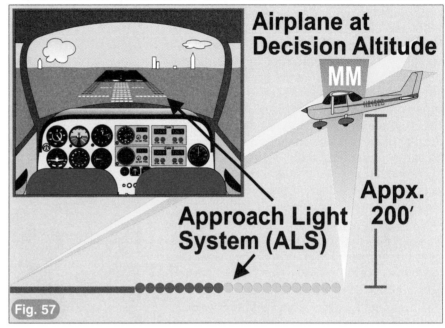

Decision Altitude and the Middle Marker

Airplane at Decision Altitude

MM

Approach Light System (ALS)

Appx. 200'

Fig. 57

Common Varieties of Approach Lighting

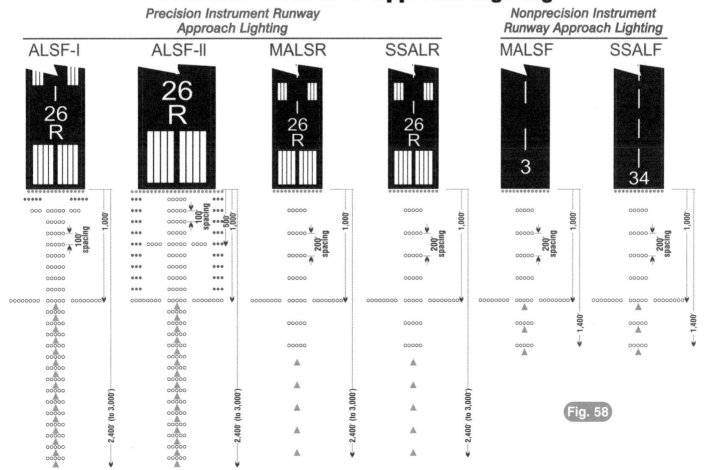

Precision Instrument Runway Approach Lighting

Nonprecision Instrument Runway Approach Lighting

ALSF-I   ALSF-II   MALSR   SSALR   MALSF   SSALF

Fig. 58

stop at the runway threshold. The "F" in the ALSF designation stands for sequenced flashing lights (brilliant white bursts of light appearing as a ball of light moving toward the runway). Where possible, sequenced flashing lights are built into the approach lighting system and stop at the approach light's decision bar, which is located 1,000 feet from the runway threshold (Figure 59). Because they appear to run quickly as they flash in sequence, the sequenced flashing lights are sometimes called "the rabbit." So don't call the animal protection squad if you hear a pilot ask the controller to "Kill the rabbit". They're not cooking up a hasenpfeffer dinner date. It's simply a request to turn off the sequenced flasher, which some pilots find so intense it makes them tense (and makes it difficult for them to make the instrument to visual transition for landing, too). As a general rule, any ALS system that's 2,400 to 3,000 feet in length is usually associated with a precision instrument runway as shown in Figure 60 B and D.

Nonprecision instrument runway ALSs are typically (but not always) 1,400 feet in length as shown in Figure 60, A, C and E. Here are examples of the five additional categories of approach light systems:

1. Figure 60A shows a typical MALS or *medium intensity approach light system*, consisting of seven white light bars separated by 200 feet in length for a total length of 1,400 feet.

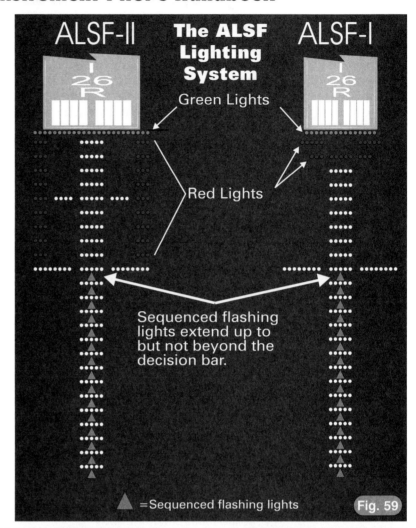

Fig. 59

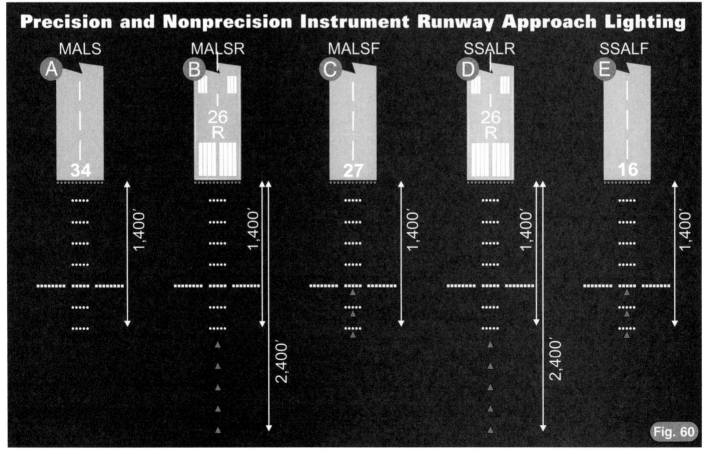

Fig. 60

2. Figure 60B is a medium intensity approach light system with runway alignment indicator lights (RAIL), called MALSR for short. RAIL is a series of five or more sequenced flashing (SF) lights that are separate from the 1,400 foot ALS system. MALSR systems are typically 2,400 feet in length.

3. Figure 60C is a medium intensity approach lighting system with sequenced flashers (MALSF for short) and it's typically 1,400 feet in length. The MALSF has sequenced flashing lights embedded in the outer three white light bars. When the SF are embedded this way it often tells you that there is extensive ambient and background lighting nearby (such as that from a city or road lighting) and it's necessary to have the flashers closer to the runway to help you accurately identify the landing area.

4. Figure 60D shows a simplified short approach lighting system with RAIL (SSALR for short). A simplified short approach lighting system can be upgraded to 2,400 to 3,000 foot in length. The sequenced flashers (SF)

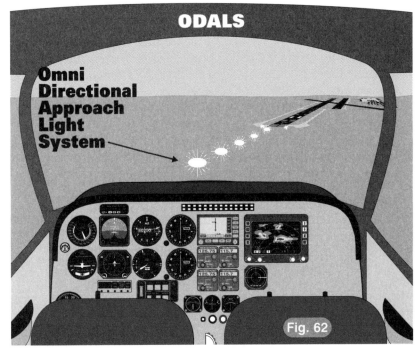

The ODALS (short way of saying omni directional light system) help guide airplanes to the runway threshold under low visibility conditions.

in this system have a separate on-off switch but do not have a separate intensity control. Instead, the SF match the intensity settings of the steady burning runway lights and runway edge lights.

5. Figure 60E shows a simplified short approach lighting system with sequenced flashing lights (or SSALF for short). This system is similar to the SSALR except that its SF are embedded in the outer three white light bars.

A few other types of approach lighting are available at some airports. One type is the REIL or *runway end identification lights* (Figure 61). These are two synchronized flashing white lights placed on each side of the runway threshold to help pilots identify the end of the runway. Another type is called ODALS or *omnidirectional approach light system* (Figure 62). This system usually consists of seven omnidirectional flashing lights extending up to 1,500 feet from the runway threshold. The ODALS helps guide airplanes, under reasonable visibility conditions, to the runway threshold. The first five of these lights are aligned with the runway centerline while the other two are located on either side of the runway threshold.

The REIL (pronounced like "REEL") lights, helps pilots find the runway threshold under low visibility conditions.

Years ago a friend took an emergency survival course where he was sent into the forest with a live chicken. He acted quick and made a quiche, but he couldn't get the little guy to eat it. He survived. I guess you'll survive too, even if you don't know that there are a few other types of electronic approach courses that you might encounter as an instrument pilot. But you should know something about them. They are the simplified directional facility (SDF), the localizer type directional aid (LDA), and the microwave landing system (MLS), though it's highly unlikely you'll encounter this last one. The closest I've ever come to a microwave system in an airplane was when United Airlines reheated my in-flight meal enroute to Albuquerque one time. Let's take a closer look at these aids.

Simplified Directional Facility (SDF)

The simplified directional facility (SDF) wasn't designed for instrument pilots who need their instrument flying simplified. An

SDF is sort of a localizer that's somewhat out of spec, and it is usually an accommodation to local obstructions that make a normal ILS or localizer installation impossible. An SDF course may or may not be aligned with the runway. The course may also be wider than that of a localizer (it's either 6 or 12 degrees in width), which results in less lateral precision along the approach course (Figure 63). The reason for the wider angle is to provide better course guidance and flyability based on obstructions present along the approach.

Don't look for the SDF antenna at the end of the runway, either. It may be offset from the runway centerline to provide the minimum number of obstructions along the approach, which is why the course might not be aligned with the runway. The angle of convergence between the final approach course and the runway bearing should be determined by reference to the instrument approach chart. This angle of offset is usually not more than 3 degrees. You should note this angle, since the approach course originates at the antenna site, and an approach continued beyond the runway threshold would lead the aircraft to the SDF offset position rather than along the runway centerline.

Usable off-course indications are limited to 35 degrees either side of the course centerline. Instrument indications in the area between 35 and 90 degrees from the course centerline are not controlled and should be disregarded.

A three-letter identifier is transmitted in code on the SDF frequency. There is no letter "I" (two dots) transmitted before the station identifier, as

The LDA or Localizer Directional Aid Approach

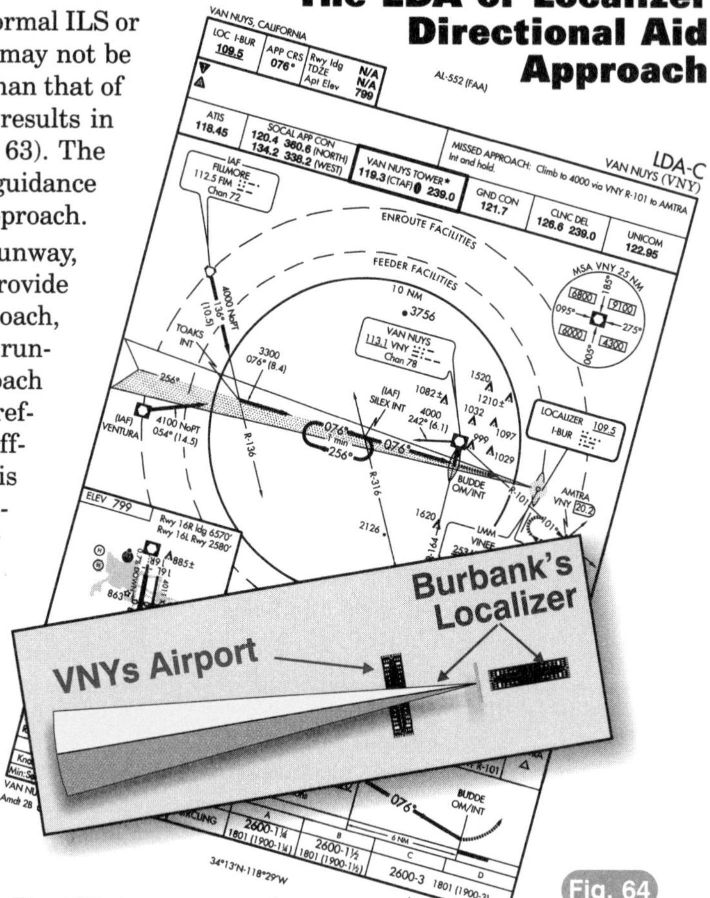

Fig. 64

The LDA is an approach to an airport that makes use of another airport's localizer.

An SDF Approach

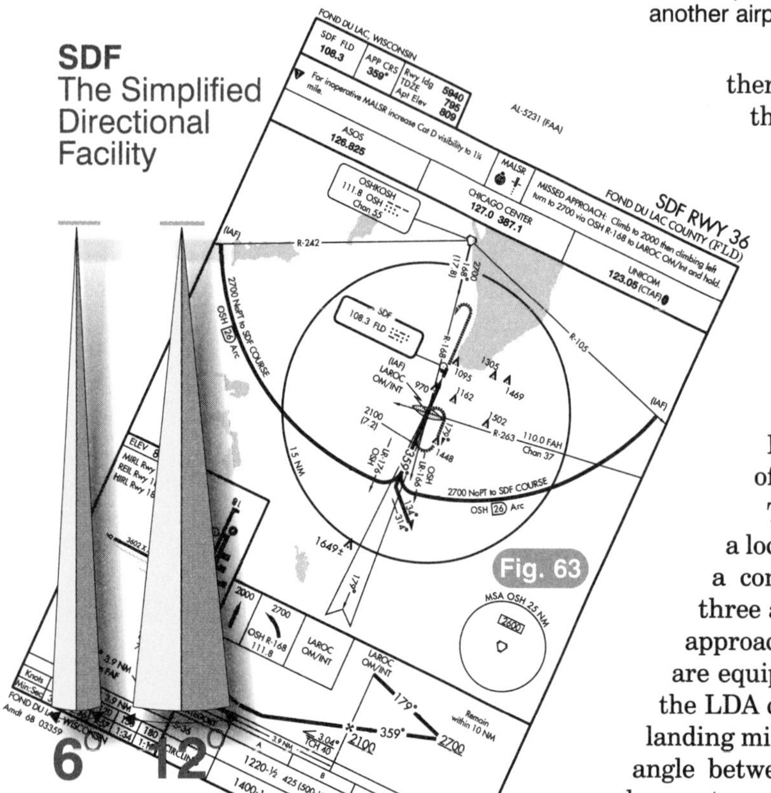

SDF
The Simplified Directional Facility

Fig. 63

The SDF approach is similar to a localizer approach except that it's easier (both in expense and logistics) to install at an airport.

there is with the LOC. For example, the identifier for the Fond du Lac SDF is FLG (Figure 63).

Localizer Type Directional Aid (LDA)

This one's pretty simple. The LDA is a secondhand localizer signal. Sometimes, the localizer for one airport happens to pass over or near the vicinity of another airport. Since the FAA's big on sharing, it will often let the second airport tag along and use the same localizer. Figure 64 is the Van Nuys, California LDA chart, which uses the localizer at Burbank for its approach. It's the aviation version of a hand-me-down, but it's a little more palatable.

The LDA is comparable in utility and accuracy to a localizer (since it's still a localizer), but is not part of a complete ILS. The LDA course width is between three and six degrees, and thus provides a more precise approach course than an SDF installation. Some LDAs are equipped with a glideslope but, as in the case of VNY, the LDA course is not aligned with the runway. Straight-in landing minimums may nevertheless be published where the angle between the runway centerline and the LDA course does not exceed 30 degrees. If this angle exceeds 30 degrees, only circling minimums are published (more on straight-in and circling minimums later). The identifier is three letters preceded by "I" transmitted in code on the LDA frequency. For example, the identifier for Van Nuys, California, LDA is I-BUR.

Area Navigation–RNAV

Have you ever heard someone use one term that can mean a lot of different things? For instance, if you say someone is cool, that can mean they are nice, they wear sunglasses, they know poetry or they had an accident in a cyrogenics lab. The same goes the term RNAV (pronounced *R-nav*), otherwise known as *area navigation*.

RNAV is a navigational process allowing point-to-point navigation without requiring that you overfly any navigational aids. Simply stated, if you have RNAV equipment on board you can fly direct from one point to another without having to follow traditional navigational routes, i.e., airways.

RNAV is primarily accomplished using one of three radionavigational systems: VOR/DME-RNAV, Loran, and global positioning system (GPS, or satellite). In our modern day IFR system, when someone uses the term RNAV, they're usually referring to area navigation by GPS. Sure, Loran and VOR/DME-based RNAV are still

RNAV (Area Navigation) Based on VOR

A Waypoint (artificial VOR) is created by tuning the VOR frequency, a specific radial and specific distance from Sinbad VOR. Your airborne VOR equipment now thinks that this waypoint is the actual VOR. You now track to this waypoint using the same methods used to track a VOR.

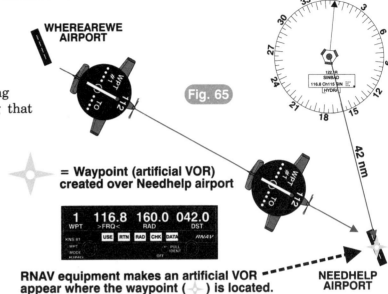

Fig. 65

= Waypoint (artificial VOR) created over Needhelp airport

RNAV equipment makes an artificial VOR appear where the waypoint ( ) is located.

in use, and they'll probably be around for a while, but GPS is the dominant technology and the one the FAA is committed to. So let's see how each type of RNAV does what it does.

RNAV Based on VOR/DME

An early type of RNAV equipment used VOR and DME to create moveable, artificial navigational stations known as *waypoints* (Figure 65). A waypoint is nothing more than a point you pick in space (well, not in outer space. I mean Planet Earth) and use as a spot that you navigate to or from. In this instance, it's sort of a virtual VOR, a beacon without a house. Most waypoints are defined in terms of their latitude and longitude coordinates. Since any spot on earth can defined by such coordinates, it's possible to create a waypoint for every spot on earth (including a lot you wouldn't want to fly to). There aren't, however, enough pizzas in the world to keep you fed given the amount of time required to do this, so pilots just create the waypoints necessary to define legs for cross-country flight or intersections for use when flying instrument approaches. We'll talk more about these types of waypoints shortly. For now, just realize that you can use any VOR radial and distance value to define a waypoint. This is known as *rho-theta* waypoint definition, which is all Greek to me. This may be as close to a fraternity or sorority as many of us will ever get.

Another Way of Thinking About How Rnav Works

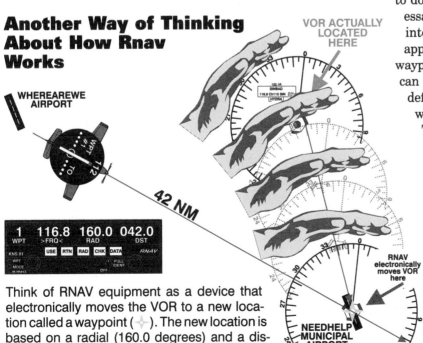

Think of RNAV equipment as a device that electronically moves the VOR to a new location called a waypoint ( ). The new location is based on a radial (160.0 degrees) and a distance (042.0 nautical miles) from the original VOR (116.8 MHz).

Fig. 66

Using typical RNAV equipment, shown in Figure 66, you could create an artificial VOR (the waypoint I mentioned) by selecting a radial and DME distance from a real VOR station. For example, suppose you wanted to fly direct from Wherearewe airport to Needhelp airport. To do so you would create a waypoint using the Sinbad VORTAC. Ideally, you would locate this waypoint (artificial VOR) directly over Needhelp airport. This waypoint would be identified by the 160 degree radial and the 42 nautical mile distance from the Sinbad VORTAC.

To do this, set your RNAV equipment to the Sinbad VOR and select your first waypoint to lie at 160 degrees and 42 miles. Now you've programmed the RNAV equipment to pretend there is a VOR at this radial and distance point. Your RNAV equipment electronically creates an artificial VOR at this position. As far as your onboard VOR equipment that's connected to the onboard VOR/DME-RNAV unit is concerned, there is a real VOR at this waypoint. It can't distinguish the difference. Your VOR equipment provides you with the appropriate needle and flag movement in reference to waypoint No. 1. With many RNAV units, you can create several waypoints at a time—waypoint 2, waypoint 3, etc.—although one is plenty for this flight.

Before you depart, make sure your RNAV equipment is in the proper mode

Multiple Waypoints for Area Navigation (RNAV)

Multiple waypoints may be necessary for navigation when traveling cross country. Each waypoint is defined by a radial and distance from the VOR nearest the desired route. The number of waypoints you choose is limited by the number your RNAV equipment can handle.

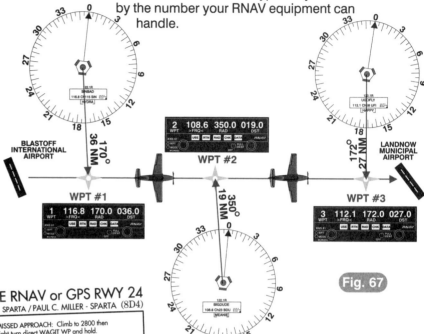

Fig. 67

so that its navigational information is sent to the VOR's cockpit display (check your equipment manual to determine how to do this. If your instructor is named Manuel, then check with him since the name is close enough). In other words, your VOR omni display may be set to read your number one navigation radio. To set it to display signals from the false VOR you've just created (the waypoint in this instance), you may have to throw a panel switch that sets the VOR face to read from the VOR/DME-RNAV unit. Now you just rotate the OBS, center the needle with a TO indication and track directly to waypoint number 1, located on Needhelp airport. Your VOR display and DME readout will work as if a mobile VOR/DME station on a flatbed truck was driven onto the field at Needhelp airport.

On longer flights, you may want to include additional waypoints. Figure 67 shows a flight with three waypoints used to define the route. You would fly to waypoint No. 1. Then, when over it, fly outbound from it until midway to waypoint No. 2. Then you would select Waypoint No. 2 in your RNAV equipment and fly to it, repeating the same process.

Flying an instrument approach using VOR/DME RNAV is done in a similar manner. For instance, Figure 68 shows the

---

SPARTA, MICHIGAN

VORTAC MKG	APP CRS	Rwy ldg	2925
115.2	**239°**	TDZE	761
Chan **99**		Apt Elev	761

AL-6186 (FAA)

VOR/DME RNAV or GPS RWY 24
SPARTA / PAUL C. MILLER - SPARTA (8D4)

▼ Use Grand Rapids altimeter setting.
⚠ NA

MISSED APPROACH: Climb to 2800 then right turn direct WAGIT WP and hold.

GRAND RAPIDS APP CON *	UNICOM
124.6 257.6	**122.8** (CTAF)

1	115.2	083.8	024.7
WPT	>FRQ<	RAD	DST

USE RTN RAD CHK DATA   *RNAV*

KNS 81
WPT
MODE   PULL
KING   OFF   IDENT

2800
225° (6.3)
TRUFA

4 NM
059°
239°

IAF
WAGIT
N43°13.18'-W85°28.82'
115.2 MKG 083.8°-24.7
660

2500
239°
(5)

(FAF)
(DADFY)
5 NM from MAP WP
N43°10.50'-W85°34.60'

920±

MAP
DIPOL
N43°07.83'-W85°40.37'
115.2 MKG 099.1°-16.3
660

930±

Λ1319

This approach is defined by a waypoint created off the MKG VOR at 083.8 degrees at 24.7 nm.

Fig. 68

ELEV 761

239° to
MAP WP

0.6% UP
TDZE
761
2925 X 50

2800		WAGIT

| | 059° → | 2800 |
| WAGIT WP | ← 239° | |

4 NM
Holding Pattern

(DADFY)
5 NM from
MAP WP

DIPOL
MAP WP

239°
2500

5 NM | 5 NM

	A	B	C	D
CATEGORY				
S-24	1320-1	559 (600-1)	NA	
CIRCLING	1360-1	1380-1	NA	
	599 (600-1)	619 (700-1)		

REIL Rwy 24
LIRL Rwy 6-24

SPARTA, MICHIGAN
Amdt 2 03247

43°08'N - 85°41'W   SPARTA / PAUL C. MILLER - SPARTA (8D4)
VOR/DME RNAV or GPS RWY 24

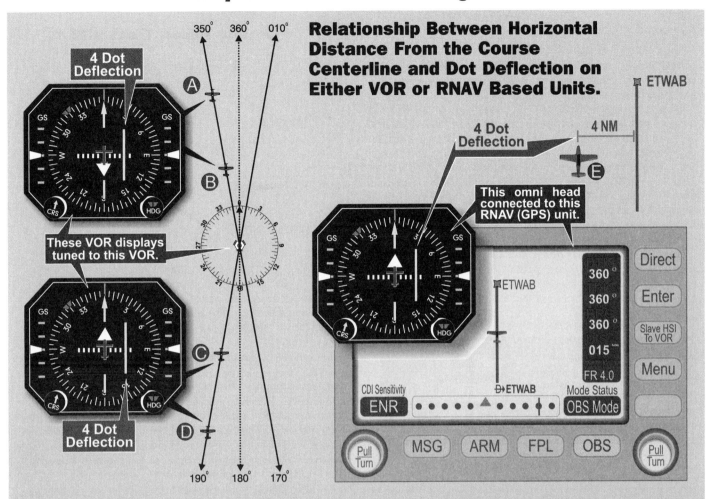

Relationship Between Horizontal Distance From the Course Centerline and Dot Deflection on Either VOR or RNAV Based Units.

One thing that is distinctly different when using RNAV for navigation—either VOR/DME RNAV or GPS (as shown above)—is the meaning of CDI deflection. Unlike direct VOR usages, each dot deflection of the CDI on an omni display connected to an RNAV unit represents one nautical mile of course deviation (four dots equals four nautical miles as shown in position E). There's no angular course relationship in regard to the dot-distance relationship, as there is with VOR where each dot represents two degrees of course deviation (positions A through D). With GPS or VOR/DME-RNAV, the value of deviation stays the same regardless of your relationship to the waypoint. If you're using GPS or VOR/DME RNAV to navigate along an airway, then four dots of deflection means that you're probably operating on the edge (or near the edge) of that airway.

VOR/DME RNAV Rwy 24 approach to Sparta airport (this approach can also be flown with a GPS which we'll talk about shortly). A single reference waypoint (WAGIT) based on the 83.3 degree radial from the MKG VOR at a distance of 24.7 miles makes this approach possible. This reference waypoint now becomes the pseudo VOR that your VOR equipment in the airplane now references. WAGIT as well as the other fixes along the approach path are identified by latitude and longitude as well as by direction and distance from MKG VOR. Some RNAV units (such as LORAN and GPS) can use latitude and longitude coordinates to help identify a waypoint or an intersection.

Of course, to fly this approach on your VOR/DME-RNAV unit, it must be approved for IFR flight. The only way to confirm this is to check the airplane flight manual supplements to be sure (this same bit of advice applies to all other RNAV units such as Loran, GPS, etc.). Don't just assume that every RNAV unit is approved for IFR flight just because it's bolted to your instrument panel.

Keep in mind that for VOR/DME-RNAV approaches to be developed and approved for use by the FAA, there must be a VOR/DME facility nearby to allow the creation of waypoints. Many airports across the country still use VOR/DME RNAV approaches.

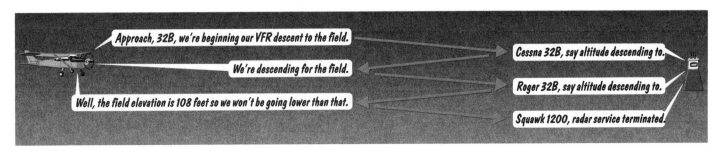

Loran

Loran is another form of area navigation. The term Loran stands for **lo**ng **ran**ge navigation and it consists of a worldwide system of very low frequency signals, at one time used primarily for maritime purposes. Since Loran was originally used by boaters, some pilots think they can't use it unless they're flying a seaplane. Not true, Seabiscuit. Figure 69 shows a typical Loran unit. Loran is an example of the tremendous impact the electronics revolution has had on aviation. Originally, Loran units were too bulky and slow for aviation use, but they worked just fine in boats. As microprocessors became faster, cheaper, and more capable, the cost of Loran units plummeted, much like a ship's anchor when thrown overboard. Loran units eventually decreased in size and weight, making them more feasible for small aircraft. Several years ago it was possible to find a Loran unit in even a basic trainer airplane, much like GPS Today.

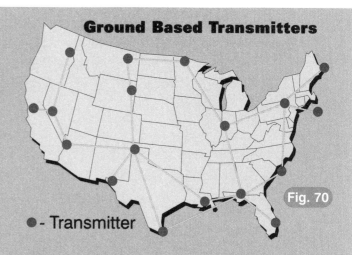

Ground Based Transmitters

● - Transmitter

Fig. 70

Loran works by using ground-based transmitters arranged into chains (Figure 70). These transmitters operate at frequency pulses of 100 kHz, and as we have previously learned, the low frequency, the signals travel great distances unobstructed by terrain. Your Loran receiver monitors all the stations within selected chains (consisted of four to six individual transmitters) then measures the arrival time difference (TD) between signals from different stations. This allows the unit to create a line of position (LOP), which enables your unit to tell you where you are in terms of latitude and longitude (unless converted via a database into airports, intersections, etc.).

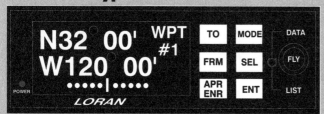

A Typical Loran Unit

Fig. 69

For instance, Figure 71A shows a signal exchange between stations M and W. With two stations exchanging signals, the given constant time difference between the signals from these two stations can be represented as a hyperbolic curve of a known location. Since we know the locations of these two stations, we can immediately determine that the airplane in position A is located somewhere along that hyperbolic curve (you don't, as yet, know precisely where). To determine our precise location the Loran unit needs to reference the signals from another set of stations. Figure 71B shows the signal exchange between stations M and X. By referencing the intersection of to hyperbolic curves (Figure 71C) our LORAN unit can determine out geographic location.

Along with our position, the Loran can also provide us with ground track, groundspeed, distance to destination, ETA and crosstrack error (to be discussed shortly).

Once again, if you plan on using your Loran for IFR flying it must be an IFR-approved unit. Don't just assume that because you have a Loran in your airplane that it's legal for IFR flying. It must be approved, which among other things means it has to have a current database (the portion that contains information on intersections, approaches, airports, etc.), be installed properly, etc.

Loran can provide you with the same features you'll find in a VOR/DME-RNAV unit and more. IFR-approved units have the ability to store flight plans (in this instance, flight plans means a sequences of waypoints that make up flyable routes), the emergency location of the nearest airport and vertical navigation capabilities (to be discussed later).

Like all navigation units, Loran is subject to errors (especially if you've had to bang on it with your shoe over the years to keep it working). Static discharges, precipitation static (remember, low frequencies are in use here) and electrical noise from your airplane's electrical equipment (or an electric eel, if you're in a seaplane) can all affect its operation. Many of these problems are dealt with right at the beginning, when these units are installed for IFR use. As an aside, Loran is most accurate when its signals travel over seawater during the day, and least accurate when the signal comes from over land and large bodies of fresh water or ice at night (it's also inaccurate if it was once used as a boat anchor). Accuracy also decreases with an increase in distance from the station.

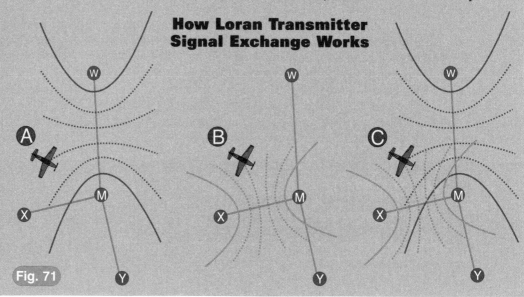

How Loran Transmitter Signal Exchange Works

Fig. 71

The Global Positioning System – GPS

GPS: Details, Details

The global positioning system or GPS consists of 24 satellites revolving around the earth in six orbital planes (orbital planes, not airplanes) as shown in Figure 72. Handheld or panel mounted GPS receivers allow you to determine your location in terms of latitude and longitude anywhere on earth with a degree of accuracy that would make a surgeon wielding a scalpel look like a caffeine-crazed badminton player.

GPS is the most sophisticated form of area navigation. It allows you to travel from one waypoint, as defined by the coordinates of latitude and longitude, to another. By telling your GPS that you want to go from your present position (the GPS always knows its current lat and long after you turn its power on) to a distant waypoint, it electronically knows where to point your airplane's nose in order to get there. GPS units typically tell you where to go by showing the bearing to that waypoint, or by providing a course deviation indicator on a display similar to that of a common VOR (or the GPS may be slaved to the omni display—VOR or HSI—in your airplane).

Now, if you had to look up the latitude and longitude of the destination waypoint for every trip, you'd go wacko and probably never go anywhere. Fortunately, GPS units have databases with the lat/long information for nearly all important airports, aerial intersections, navigation aids and other significant places. You need only select the name or letter/number identifier of any airport, intersection, or navaid in the GPS, push a few buttons/knobs, and bingo (that magic word you learned in church), you're on your way to that place (Figure 73).

Going Direct With GPS

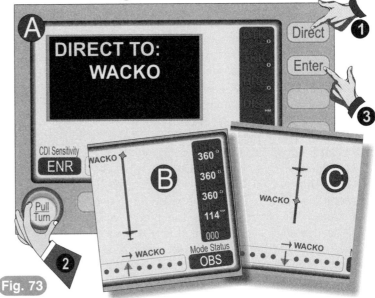

Fig. 73

Going direct to an intersection is a fairly simple process with many GPS units, often involving no more than just a few steps.

Let's say, for instance, that you wanted to go to WACKO intersection as shown in Figure 73A. Select the letters WACKO in the GPS's window, and push the appropriate buttons. Now you legitimately have the means to go WACKO. If your GPS has a moving map display, you can see your track to WACKO along with other information such as groundspeed, track, crosstrack error (more on this in a bit) and so on (Figures 73B and C).

GPS is only one form of area navigation. For instance, airliners have LNAV (Lateral Navigation) equipment. Airliners also have flight management systems (FMS), VLF/Omega, and the others we've already discussed. GPS is most common form in use by general aviation IFR pilots. So it's the one we'll spent a lot of time discussing. From now on, if you see the term RNAV (GPS), it means area navigation based strictly on GPS.

Global Positioning System (GPS)

The Satellite

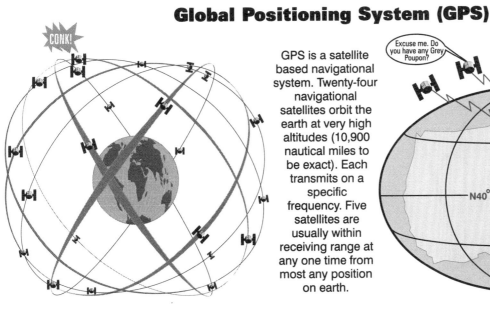

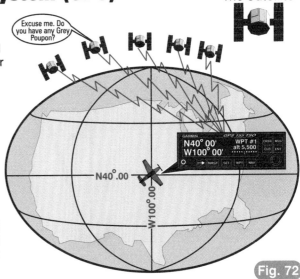

GPS is a satellite based navigational system. Twenty-four navigational satellites orbit the earth at very high altitudes (10,900 nautical miles to be exact). Each transmits on a specific frequency. Five satellites are usually within receiving range at any one time from most any position on earth.

Fig. 72

Terms You Need to Know: The Basics

Discussing RNAV (GPS) approaches requires us to come to terms with a few terms. Vocabulary is important here if you're going to get the concepts etched in your cranium. Figure 74 identifies some of the basic GPS navigation terms.

Let's assume that you've programmed your GPS to take you to a destination airport, which we'll call Waypoint 2. Because the GPS knows the lat/long of the starting point (even if you're in cruise flight somewhere), it always assumes that this is the departure waypoint. We'll call this point Waypoint 1. The line between these two points is called the *desired track* (no doubt your instructor desires that you to be on this track, too). Under a no-wind condition, with perfect navigational skills, you'd fly the desired track (DTK) heading and eventually arrive at your destination.

As you know, our universe is very good at amusing itself. One way it does this is by allowing your airplane to be blown around by the wind. The universe really gets a kick out of this, as your empennage gets a kick out of the wind. The airplane's *actual track* (TK) has now diverged from the DTK.

The universe just can't contain itself with all the fun it's having at your expense. GPS units show your actual track (TK). If this

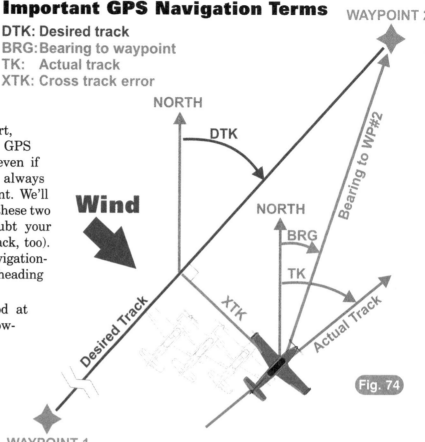

Important GPS Navigation Terms

DTK: Desired track
BRG: Bearing to waypoint
TK: Actual track
XTK: Cross track error

Fig. 74

value is different from the desired track (DTK), then the universe has just scored big time. How far are you off course? The GPS will tell you by expressing the discrepancy in terms of something known as the *cross track error* (XTK).

Figure 74 shows that the airplane is to the right of the desired track. For example, if the GPS says Fly Left 2.7 miles (different GPS units have different ways of displaying this), it means that you are offset to the right from your original course, the desired track (DTK), by 2.7 miles. Therefore, you should obviously turn left to get back on course.

The XTK is very important to you for several reasons. Obstacle-protected airspace is the primary one. If an airway's MEA provides protection for four nautical miles on each side of centerline, then an XTK of five nautical miles should raise your blood pressure to a little above that found in a fire hose. That's one reason XTK messages are written in terms such as *Fly left 5 miles*. And I would have no problem if they read, *Fly left 5 miles, you're about to hit a guy on a mountain bike*. XTKs are also valuable when flying RNAV (GPS) instrument approaches, where there is less tolerance for deviation from obstacle-protected airspace as you approach the airport.

Important GPS Navigational Terms

DTK: Desired track
BRG: Bearing to waypoint
TK: Actual track
XTK: Cross track error

Fig. 75

If your airplane were off course to the right, as shown in Figure 74, then you'd have the option of going directly from your current spot to Waypoint 2, in lieu of re-intercepting the original desired track (DTK). Pilots often do this by pushing the GPS's Direct button (the one that's really worn down) and establishing a new desired track (DTK) to Waypoint 2. Of course, a pilot who keeps establishing new desired tracks (DTK) every few minutes, is homing to the station, not tracking to it. It's best not to keep homing unless, even if you're homely. Instead,

How GPS Works Inside

The Mask Angle

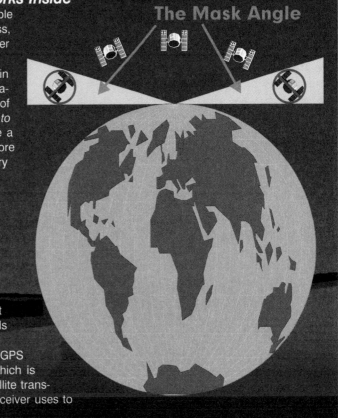

The little GPS receiver in your panel (or hand) is a rather remarkable device. It's doing all the things you wished you'd done in math class, such as getting the right answer, and it's doing them a *lot* quicker than you and I ever did.

Ranging and calculation of position from a group of satellites in space, which act as precise reference points, is the basis of operation for GPS operation. GPS receivers use data from a minimum of four satellites above something known as the *mask angle as shown to the right* (the lowest angle above the horizon at which it can use a satellite). The GPS unit takes complex information from four or more satellites and in a virtual instant calculates where it and you are. Try doing *that* in your head, whiz kid.

GPS receivers measure what we might best call a "working distance" from a satellite using the travel time of a radio signal (even though no actual radio may be involved). Because the clock in the airborne receiver is not nearly as accurate as the atomic clock carried on each satellite, the elapsed time for the signal to reach the receiver is not known with perfect accuracy. However, the answer is equally incorrect for each satellite being observed, which is what enables the receiver to eventually calculate the correct answer.

Multiplying the approximated elapsed time by the speed of light (the rate at which the signal traveled from satellite to receiver) yields the working distance also known as the *pseudorange*.

In addition to knowing the pseudorange to a satellite, your little GPS receiver needs to know the satellite's exact position in space, which is known as its *ephemeris*. Sounds temporary, doesn't it? Each satellite transmits information about its exact orbital location, which the GPS receiver uses to precisely establish the position of the satellite.

Using the calculated pseudorange and position information supplied by the satellite, the GPS receiver/processor mathematically determines its position by calculating the one precise spot (accurate to within about 60 feet) at which a mathematically-constructed sphere (actually, a hyperboloid, for those who really liked math class) around each of the satellites intersects. This sphere has a radius equal to the time delay between the satellite and the receiver multiplied by the speed of light, and you need a minimum of four hyperboloids to mathematically arrive at one unique point in space. Yes, really. And frequently, too. While doing that calculation once would probably take you all day (or the rest of your life) with pencil and paper, your GPS unit repeats it many times every minute and it never gets tired or wants to go to recess.

While it's at it, and to keep from getting bored while onboard, the GPS receiver computes navigational values (e.g., distance and bearing to a waypoint, groundspeed, crosstrack error, dinner time, etc.) by using the aircraft's known latitude/longitude and referencing these to a database built into the receiver.

you should use the GPS's bearing (BRG) information to help you identify and correct for wind.

The BRG is the heading you must fly to get to your next waypoint in a no wind condition. Suppose the pilot of the airplane in Figure 75 flies the bearing (BRG) to the station on his heading indicator. Under a no wind condition, the bearing (BRG) and the actual track (TK) should be the same. If these two values begin to differ, then wind is blowing the airplane off course. So, do something about it. Apply a wind correction. You'll know the wind correction is sufficient when the bearing to the station (BRG) remains the same as the airplane's actual track (TK). Now you're on your way directly to Waypoint 2, rather than using the ancient Greek philosophy of aerial navigation which was written by some guy name Homer for his skills as homing (OK, I made this one up).

Your GPS in Action

Let's take a look at how to use GPS for basic navigation. We'll do so by seeing how a generic GPS unit is operated to go to a place and to fly a flight planned route. The intent here is not to teach you how all GPS units work.

Instead, it's to show you what's common to most IFR-certified, panel-mounted GPS units. Wayward to a waypoint. Keep in mind that for an installed GPS to be used for IFR enroute and approaches, your flight manual supplement must indicate that this unit is approved for IFR flight. Handheld GPS units are not legal for IFR enroute and approaches, although you can certainly use one for situational awareness.

Your GPS receiver (I'll just say GPS from now on) can take you to any point on the globe. Doing so requires it to figure out where it is at the moment, and know the latitude and longitude coordinates of the point to which you want to go. That's why we use aviation databases that include the names and letter/number identifiers for all the important spots on the globe (except for your house). We need only dial the letter/number identification for the airport, navaid, intersection, or user-defined waypoint into our GPS, push a button or two, and we're off (no, not off course, but off as in ready). Let's see how to find the airport identifier for our destination, so we don't get off course, off key, or off color.

Figure 76 shows an *Airport-Facility Directory* excerpt for Carlsbad's McClellan-Palomar airport. Next to the airport's name is its identifier (CRQ) in parentheses. If your GPS requires that you manually enter the airport letter

The Airport Identifier

CARLSBAD
McCLELLAN–PALOMAR   (CRQ)   3 SE   UTC–8(–7DT)   N33°07.70' W117°16.81'
331   B   S4   FUEL   100LL, JET A   OX 3, 4   TPA—See Remarks   ARFF Index A   **Fig. 76**   LOS ANGELES
RWY 06–24: H4897X150 (ASPH–PFC)   S–60, D–80, DT–110   HIRL   L–3C
IAP, AD

by letter (instead of spinning through a list of alphabetized airport identifiers) then you add a "K" in front so that it looks like KCRQ (Figure 77). If the airport's identifier contains numbers (e.g., L66, Q49, S52), place these identifiers directly into the GPS without the special K prefix. Keep in mind that the letter "K" identifies an airport in the continental United States while the

means we're going TO the active waypoint. The active waypoint (the one to which you're presently navigating) is shown above the CDI and right of the horizontal arrow. Enroute (ENR) is shown as the current flight mode; the CDI is operating with *enroute sensitivity*. This means that each dot on the built-in CDI scale represents one nautical mile off course (enroute sensitivity is the default sensitivity for most GPS units).

The First Step in Going GPS Direct

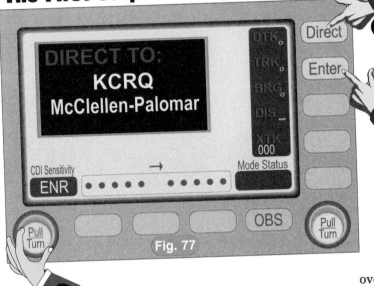

Fig. 77

Notice what happens to the CDI's up/down triangle when you fly beyond KCRQ (Figure 79). The triangle flips downward, behaving just like the TO/FROM flag in an ordinary VOR, indicating that you've flown beyond the chosen waypoint. This is called *to/from* navigation, and it's one of two course status modes common to GPS units. This is known as the "OBS Mode."

The other tracking mode is called *to/to* navigation (referred to as "Leg Mode"). This is not something done only by a ballerina. In this case, you're flying from one waypoint to another in a sequence, just as if you were following a flight plan consisting of several segments, or flying an instrument approach made of up several waypoints. With to/to navigation, the GPS arrow references only the waypoint ahead of you, not the one you've just flown over. It's as if the GPS took Bob Dylan's advice to don't look back. In to/to navigation you're always looking ahead. What's left behind is left behind for good. This is a very happy navigation mode, because you'll only see up arrows.

letter "P" identifies airports in Alaska (with a few exceptions) and "C" identifies airports in Canada. If you're inserting a three-letter navaid identifier (as opposed to a four letter airport identifier) into the GPS, don't worry about the GPS confusing it with any three-number-letter airport identifiers. Navaid identifiers don't use numbers. Remember, there are many ways to look up airport and intersection identifiers. The A/FD is only one of many resources.

Putting the GPS to use, let's go direct from our present position to KCRQ. With the GPS warmed up and a current database that's ready for use, we push the Direct button to activate a direct-to menu, as shown in Figure 77. The pull-turn knobs allow us to select KCRQ in the menu. Now we press Enter to make the airport the active waypoint. On some GPS units you must press Enter twice to confirm your selection as the active waypoint (not because the GPS was purchased at a discount shop and had a suspicious tire track over the box it came in).

Our DTK, TRK, and BRG to KCRQ are 360 degrees at a distance of 114 nautical miles, as shown in Figure 78. The CDI built into the GPS shows an up arrow with a centered needle. This

Your GPS not only takes you direct to any waypoint, it also lets you select any course you want to that waypoint.

Going GPS Direct to KCRQ

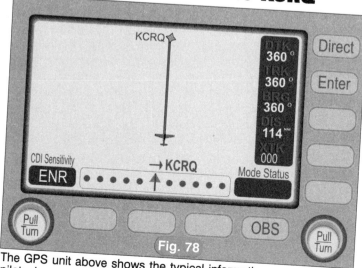

Fig. 78

The GPS unit above shows the typical information available to the pilot when going direct to a waypoint. Heading, distance, ground-speed, and CDI info are available.

For instance, Figure 80 shows that I've pushed the OBS button. Now the selection of a particular course to the active waypoint that's shown on the moving map is dependent on what I select with the HSI's OBS. In other words, the GPS unit is now allowing you to track to KCRQ as if this waypoint were a VOR station. With the OBS knob, you can select any of 360 individual courses to or from this waypoint. Are you impressed or what?

To/From Navigation

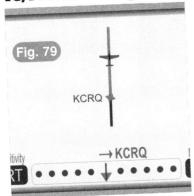

In OBS Mode you're using to/from navigation. Your GPS now acts similar to a VOR with the typical To/From indications in the form of a flipping triangle on the CDI.

Let say you want to intercept and track the 330 degree course to this waypoint instead of flying direct to KCRQ, as you were doing in Figure 78. Perhaps you're opting for this specific course to avoid restricted airspace that's directly ahead of you, or because it's a lucky number you got in a fortune cookie when you had lunch at the Juan Flew Lo Mexican-Chinese restaurant. Reason is irrelevant here. First, you'll need to push the OBS button and rotate the HSI's OBS to 330 degrees (Figure 80). From the look of the HSI, it appears that you're a little less than five miles to the left of the course, based on a fly-right cross-track error of 4.9 miles (remember, a five dot deflection on the CDI represents five nautical miles deviation to the side of the selected course). On many GPS units with a moving map capable of color, the map will show a difference in color between the course to the active waypoint and the one beyond this waypoint. In this case, we'll show the course to the active waypoint in a lighter color than other courses shown on this map.

When you intercept the 330 course, the needle in the HSI will, once again, center with a TO (up triangle) indication, as shown in Figure 81. This GPS is set to read track-up on its display. Some can be set to read north up, which can make you throw up if you don't know how to select the desired option. Once you intercept and are tracking the course, that course is shown vertically on the map.

As you fly beyond the waypoint, as shown in Figure 82, the HSI shows a FROM (down triangle) indication. I'm showing you this here because I want to remind you that when the GPS's OBS function is selected, the active waypoint acts somewhat like a VOR station. This allows you to pick and choose any course you want, and track either to or from it just as you would when tracking to or from a VOR station.

With this basic understanding of GPS in hand (and in mind), let's take a look at flying from waypoint to waypoint as you'll typically do on

To/From Navigation with GPS

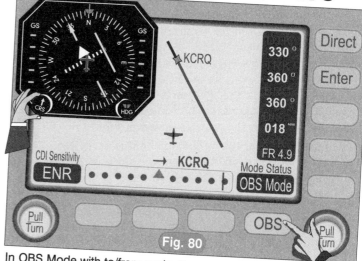

In OBS Mode with to/from navigation, you can select a specific course on which you can fly to or from a desired waypoint.

To/From Navigation with GPS

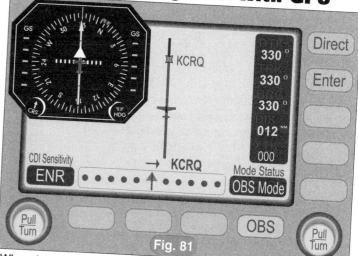

When intercepting the desired bearing, you'd turn inbound and track it as you would a VOR course.

GPS in OBS Mode

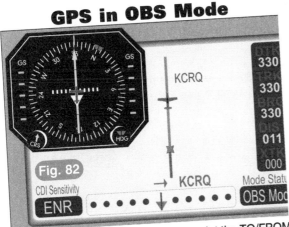

When flying beyond the active waypoint the TO/FROM triangle flips to a FROM indication.

a flight plan or a GPS instrument approach consisting of several legs. Once you learn how to do this, you'll be able to get a leg up on everyone who navigates without benefit of GPS.

Flight Plans Made of Several Waypoints

Most GPS units allow you to enter a flight plan by pressing the FPL button. I'm not speaking of an FAA flight plan here. Instead, I'm referring to a series of waypoints that make up a longer route of your choosing (or that have been chosen for you on a GPS approach chart). From here, you enter waypoint after waypoint, using the method offered by the personality of your particular GPS (Figure 83).

Let's say you were over John Wayne airport and wanted to fly to Long Beach airport, and then on to Santa Barbara airport, with San Francisco airport as your final destination (we'll assume that you're high enough to avoid the Class B airspace at Los Angeles). In most GPS units, you can activate the flight plan with the push of a few buttons/knobs. (Note: the active flight plan window shows you the route you're currently flying. On most GPS units, you can have several other flight planned routes stored for future use. Using them simply means bringing these routes to the active flight plan window by pushing a button or two or three or four. If you have a copilot, you can get him to do this for you as long as you don't push his or her buttons). After you enter the waypoints or activate a stored flight plan, you can begin the trip, as shown in Figure 84.

In our GPS unit, the waypoint identifiers KSNA and KLGB, found above the internal CDI, show the leg you're flying. The active flight plan window shows the same leg with the arrow indicating that the current leg of the flight is from KSNA to KLGB. Of course, the active flight plan window may not be continuously visible in your GPS. You may have to manually select it when you want to view all the legs in your planned flight. It's also possible to view the route data (DTK, TRK, BRG, DIS, XTK, etc.) for the active leg of your planned flight. I show these values as already selected and active on our virtual GPS unit.

Figure 84 shows something that is very different and very important. The Mode status indicator depicts something new, called Leg Mode. This is not something you can only see at a beauty contest or a marathon. Recall that when we push the OBS button, the Mode status indicator reads OBS Mode. This means that we can manually choose the specific route we want to fly to any specific waypoint. In other words, if the direct route shown from KLGB to KSBA took me near restricted airspace, I could push the OBS button and select a route around it, as shown in Figure 86.

If you didn't manually push the OBS button to enter OBS Mode, what would the Mode status indicator read? The default mode for most GPS units is often known as the Leg Mode. Leg Mode is the mode you'll normally be in when you activate and fly a stored flight plan, as shown in Figure 86. It's called Leg Mode because the GPS automatically creates direct legs between the individual waypoints in your planned flight. After you overfly a waypoint in Leg Mode, the GPS automatically sequences to the next waypoint in your flight.

Creating a GPS Flight Plan

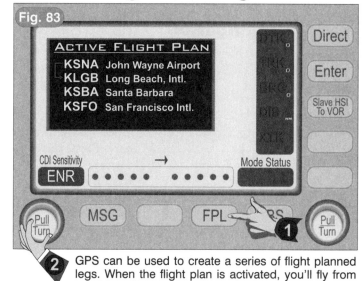

GPS can be used to create a series of flight planned legs. When the flight plan is activated, you'll fly from one leg to the next in to/to navigation in Leg Mode.

Activating a GPS Flight Plan

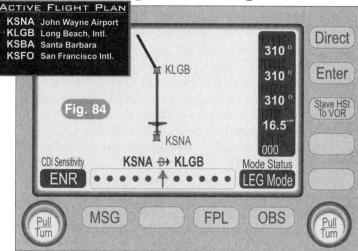

Once the GPS flight plan is activated (meaning that you push the appropriate buttons in the GPS window), you'll see the active leg in one color while the next leg to be flown will usually be identified by another color.

Switching to OBS Mode

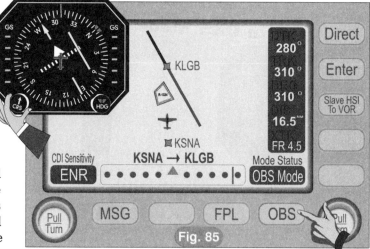

Sometimes it's necessary to leave Leg Mode for OBS Mode to accomplish a specific navigational task.

In Leg Mode, the GPS uses to/to navigation. The moving map always shows your relationship to the waypoint ahead of you, not from the waypoint behind you. That's why the arrow in the CDI points up (a TO indication) and continues to point up as the GPS references the next waypoint in the route. Figure 86 shows this process in action as KLGB is crossed. This is why the continued referencing to the next waypoint in the flight plan is sometimes called auto-sequencing. After you cross over a waypoint in your flight plan, the GPS literally puts that behind you and automatically sequences to the next waypoint in the flight plan. The auto-sequencing concept is very important when it comes to flying GPS approaches, which you'll learn about very soon.

You can suspend Leg Mode at any time by pushing the OBS button. Doing this suspends the GPS's auto-sequencing between waypoints in your active flight plan. Why would you want to suspend the Leg Mode? ATC might, for example, want you to hold at one of your route waypoints or hold in a direction different than that at which you approach the fix. This is an important point, so let's examine it a little more.

Assume you've been asked to hold east of the active waypoint (KSBA) in a direction of 250 degrees inbound,

Flying the Flight Plan in Leg Mode

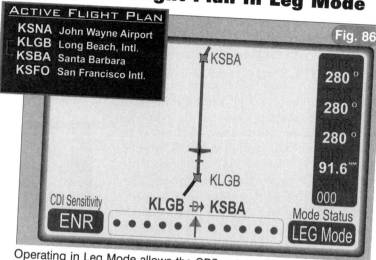

Operating in Leg Mode allows the GPS unit to automatically display the next waypoint and leg of flight (thus, the name Leg Mode).

Entering OBS Mode to Hold

Fig. 87

When holding is required while in Leg Mode, it may be necessary to enter OBS Mode to prevent the auto-sequencing of flight legs.

as shown in Figure 87. If you left the GPS in Leg Mode, it would automatically sequence to the next waypoint in your flight plan (to KSFO) as you crossed KSBA. That would mean the GPS showed your position with respect to KSFO, not KSBA. Well, that's not going to help you if you're supposed to hold at KSBA, is it? That's why you need to keep the GPS from auto-sequencing to the next waypoint in the active flight plan, which can be accomplished by pushing the OBS button.

With auto-sequencing suspended, you can select the route to the active waypoint, which remains KSBA. When

crossing KSBA, you would rotate the OBS to 250 degrees, as shown in Figure 87. After crossing KSBA, you'd turn outbound to 070 degrees for a direct entry and fly the holding pattern. Remember, since you're in OBS mode, the GPS won't auto-sequence to KSFO, so you can cross KSBA as many times as you (or ATC) like during holding and KSBA will remain the active waypoint. Once you're done holding, pushing the OBS button returns the GPS to Leg Mode and continues your flight planned route to San Francisco. This time, when you cross KSBA auto-sequencing resumes and KSFO, the next waypoint in your flight plan, becomes the active waypoint.

Now that you understand flight plans, you're ready to fly any of the flight planned routes stored in your GPS's database. These flight-planned routes can be instrument approaches, STARs and DPs, or those you've created for personal use. Remember, not all GPS units are alike. They do, however, have many similarities and most of what I'm describing is true for most units. I can't overemphasize how important it is for you to study the GPS owner's manual and learn all the details peculiar to the unit you're flying with. It's also very helpful to download the GPS PC simulator that many manufacturers make available for their products. We'll spend more time on GPS when we get to the chapter on flying RNAV (GPS) approaches.

It's time to hold on, as we now turn the page and our attention to holding patterns.

Center, this is 2132B, I'm a Cessna 150. Do you have a groundspeed readout on me?

Ahh, just barely! Can you lean forward a bit? That may help.

Postflight Briefing #5-1

The Radio Magnetic Indicator (RMI)

The *radio magnetic indicator (RMI)* is essentially a rotating needle mounted over a slaved compass, as shown in Figure 88 (and no, there's no music to be heard over the device, despite the word *radio* in the name). The rotating needle is slaved to the compass card so that it always indicates the course to the VOR station with the head of the needle. The tail of the needle points to the course or radial from the station. The slaved compass card rotates as a heading indicator does. The airplane's heading can be found under the index at the top of the RMI. (The RMI needle information is correct only if the slaved compass is correct. Check it against the wet compass occasionally.)

The easiest way to learn how to use the RMI is to observe how the instrument's display orients you to a VOR station. Airplane A in Figure 89 is on a heading of 060 degrees, as indicated by the RMI's slaved compass. The RMI needle is pointing directly to the VOR station. Notice that Airplane A is physically located on the 360 degree course to the station (or the 180 degree radial from the station). Also notice the RMI needle points to 360 degrees on the slaved compass and the tail points to 180 degrees.

OK, can you feel those neurons firing and synapses welding to form new ideas? This is really easy. The RMI needle always points to the course TO the VOR station. The tail of the RMI needle always points to the radial you're on FROM this station. What course is Airplane C on to the station? Yes, it's on the 180 degree course (needle's head) to the station and the 360 degree radial (needle's tail) from the station. Of course, Airplane C is flying a heading of 300 degrees and will fly right across the 360 degree radial from the station.

Airplane B, on the other hand, is headed directly toward the station on a heading of 270 degrees. Its RMI needle is pointing dead ahead at 270 degrees. Airplane B is headed to the station on the 270 degree course or inbound on the 090 degree radial (same thing). Airplane D is headed toward the station on the 090 degree course or inbound on the 270 degree radial (same thing).

How The RMI Indicates Courses and Radials

The head of the RMI indicates your course to the VOR station. Simply turn to center the RMI needle at the top of the instrument and you'll be headed directly to the station. The tail of the RMI needle always tells you what radial you're on from the station.

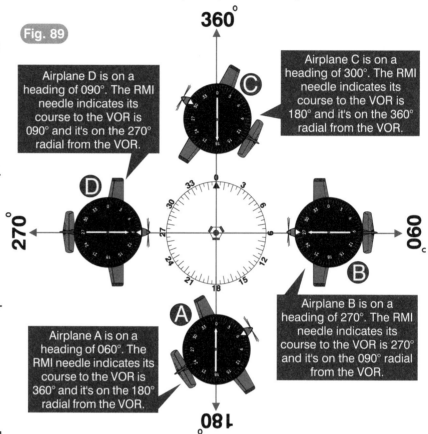

Fig. 89

Airplane D is on a heading of 090°. The RMI needle indicates its course to the VOR is 090° and it's on the 270° radial from the VOR.

Airplane C is on a heading of 300°. The RMI needle indicates its course to the VOR is 180° and it's on the 360° radial from the VOR.

Airplane A is on a heading of 060°. The RMI needle indicates its course to the VOR is 360° and it's on the 180° radial from the VOR.

Airplane B is on a heading of 270°. The RMI needle indicates its course to the VOR is 270° and it's on the 090° radial from the VOR.

Double Needle RMI

The double-needle RMI can have either needle set to point to an NDB (non directional bearing) or a VOR station. Two selectors, each marked to represent a specific needle, are located at the bottom of the instrument.

The Radio Magnetic Indicator

The RMI (Radio Magnetic Indicator) is essentially a heading indicator with a rotating needle on its face. The top of the needle points to the VOR station. The number the needle points to is the bearing or course to the VOR. The number the tail of the needle points to is the radial the airplane is on from the VOR.

Airplane heading

Head →

← Tail

Radial from the VOR station

Course to the VOR station

Fig. 88

ADF   VOR   VOR   ADF

Fig. 90

Orientation with the RMI is really simple (even if you're not from the Orient). If you want to know what your course is to the station, just look at the number to which the RMI needle points (this is easy, especially if you're good at recognizing numbers by their shape). If you want to know what radial you're on from the station, look at the tail of the RMI needle. One last thing. Sometimes RMIs have two needles instead of one. To keep them from being confused with one another, the second needle is different, as shown in Figure 91. Each needle can be designated to represent VOR or ADF information. This is accomplished by the selecting switches at the bottom of the instrument. We'll learn more about RMI usage when we cover ADF navigation, in the next section. Wait, wait, don't run off like I know you want to. ADF navigation should stand for "Always Dumbfounded". I guarantee that if you can navigate using ADF, all other forms of navigation will be a breeze. So stay put amigo, and read the next section. It's worth it.

ADF: Bearing Down on Homing In (or, How to Be a Homeboy)

Why should you learn something about automatic direction finding (ADF) navigation as an instrument pilot? After all, you're no longer required to fly a nondirectional beacon (NDB) approach on your instrument checkride (you can, for instance, substitute a GPS approach for it). The fact is that ADF navigation principles are still covered on the instrument pilot knowledge exam. But that's not the most important reason for having an understanding of ADF navigation. If you understand ADF navigation, you're a rare breed of person. I've never known anyone who'd mastered ADF and was poor at navigating with any other type of equipment (assuming they knew how to use that equipment—GPS, for instance). The principles here are worth learning even if you don't have an ADF in your airplane. So, if you'd like to be in the top 1% of pilots with regard to navigation skills, then take the time to learn the following lessons well.

Look at the numbers on the compass card of the ADF display in Figure 91. They're fixed, down and welded about as tightly as the gear on a 172. The card doesn't automatically rotate as does the compass card of an RMI. You can manually rotate the card, which we'll discuss later. For now, however, forget those numbers! Yes, that's right, forget them! As far as you're concerned right now, those numbers only identify 30 degree incremental positions to the left and right of the nose. Don't attach any significance to them. Treat each of these numbers like most people treat the Surgeon General's warnings on a cigarette package—know that it's there, but don't look at it.

The Automatic Direction Finder (ADF)

Fig. 91

The numbers found around the ADF compass card must be manually rotated by turning the "HDG" knob. They are not part of a slaved (electric) gyro and do not reflect the airplane's heading. We normally leave the compass card set with a "0" under the index for basic ADF work. The "0" represents the actual airplane's nose.

Homing With the ADF

The ADF indicator's needle points directly to the NDB. For Airplane A to go to the NDB it must turn right to center the needle on the ADF's nose (the "0" under the index). Keeping it there, the airplane travels to the NDB as shown by Airplane B. When over the station, the needle reverses direction pointing to the ADF's tail as shown by Airplane C.

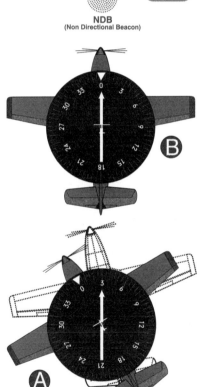

Fig. 92

NDB
(Non Directional Beacon)

OK, here is one of the most powerful and simple rules you'll ever see for navigation with the ADF. To go to any NDB station, simply tune in that station's frequency, identify it (usually by Morse code) and turn the airplane so the ADF needle points to the nose of the symbolic airplane on the ADF display as shown in Figure 92, Airplanes A and B. The symbolic airplane represents the real airplane's orientation. It's always pointed toward the white triangle at the top of the ADF indicator, which represents the airplane's nose. Simply turn toward the tip of the needle to go to the station.

ADF Orientation

Airplanes A, B and C are flying directly to the FLYNICE NDB. Airplane E is flying directly away from the NDB. Airplane D must make a left turn and Airplane F must make a right turn to travel to the NDB.

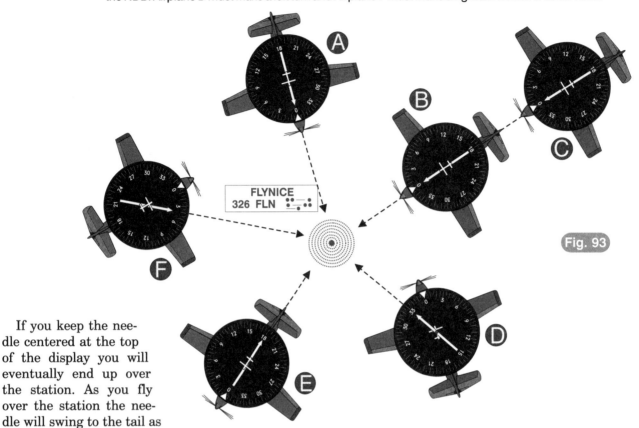

Fig. 93

If you keep the needle centered at the top of the display you will eventually end up over the station. As you fly over the station the needle will swing to the tail as shown by Airplane C in Figure 92. This type of tracking is known as *homing*. It involves no wind correction, but it works every single time. Don't forget it. Figure 93 shows airplanes A, B and C homing directly to the Flynice NDB. Airplane E is flying directly away from the station by keeping the needle on the tail of the ADF display.

Airplane D's ADF needle points to the left of the nose. Making a left turn centers the needle at the top of the display. Airplane F's ADF needle shows the NDB station to the right of the airplane's nose. Turning right centers the needle at the top of the display.

NDB vs. VOR Routes

Traveling along a VOR route is relatively easy. You simply select the appropriate course from A to B (the OBS is set to 090°) and keep the needle centered. Traveling along a similar route to and from an NDB isn't as simple as with VOR navigation. NDB navigation requires that you understand the concept of bearings to and from the station.

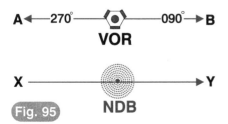

Fig. 95

Frankly, if I had my way, we'd stop here and consider ourselves done with the ADF discussion. All you really need to understand about ADF navigation is how to home with it. The instrument pilot knowledge exam, however, demands a slightly more sophisticated knowledge of ADF navigation. Study the following and find some solace in knowing that this information will help you become an overall better navigator (not a navigator who wears overalls).

Tracking a Magnetic Bearing – Homing is the easiest method of ADF navigation (perhaps it's called homing because pilots can always find their way home using this technique). There is another method, however, that allows

NDB and VOR Signal Directions

The NDB signal is nondirectional in that it radiates its energy outward, in all directions, from its center.

NDB
Non Directional Beacon

VORs, on the other hand, are designed to radiate electromagnetic radiation by a reference and a variable phase signal so that 360 specific "directional" radials are identifiable.

Fig. 94

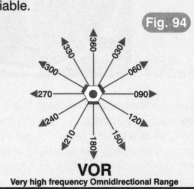

VOR
Very high frequency Omnidirectional Range

you to intercept and track magnetic bearings directly to and from an NDB. This is done in much the same way as the RMI is used. Let's start from the beginning.

Figure 94 shows an NDB and a VOR station. NDBs are unlike VORs in that their signal is nondirectional. Hey, they don't call them *nondirectional beacons* for nothing, you know. This means the NDB's signal radiates outward and equally indistinguishably in all directions, while VORs have 360 specific radials on which we can navigate. We can, however, imagine 360 bearings running through an NDB in much the same way courses run through a VOR. First, we need to define what a bearing is.

Examine the diagram in Figure 95. If you were instructed to fly from position A directly to position B, you could do so with great precision by using the VOR. You would track inbound on the 270 degree radial and outbound on the 090 degree radial. You would know your exact position with respect to these radials by looking at the VOR needle. Suppose you were asked to fly from position X directly to position Y using your ADF. How would you know your airplane is tracking directly along the specified course?

You need to know two things before answering this question. First, the airplane must be heading in a direction of 90 degrees (we'll assume no wind for these examples). Heading 90 degrees will certainly point you in the direction of location Y, as shown in Figure 96A. However, heading 90 degrees will also allow you to fly a parallel course offset from the originally desired path, as shown in Figure 96B. We need one additional bit of information. If the ADF needle points to the nose of the display airplane while it is heading 090 degrees, then it is precisely on the course from X to Y, as shown in Figure 96C.

After crossing the NDB station in Figure 96C, the airplane will be flying the desired course to Y if its heading is 090 degrees and the ADF needle points directly to the tail. Airplanes flying a parallel route between X and Y in Figure 96D don't meet both requirements to be on the specific course.

In Figure 96D, both airplanes flying from X to Y are heading 090 degrees, but the ADF needle points somewhere other than to the nose or the tail. A very important principle has just been uncovered. Even though NDBs are nondirectional in their signals, we can still fly specific directional routes using the ADF and our heading indicator. These routes are called magnetic bearings, and they can be flown to or from an NDB.

Tracking to an NDB With ADF

We want to discover how to fly a specific track from X to Y, to and from the NDB, using our ADF equipment (position A). Flying a heading of 090° allows you to fly parallel to the desired track (we'll assume no wind in this example). But how do you know if this parallel route is directly over the desired track from X to Y?

After all, your airplane may be a little north or south of the desired route from X to Y despite flying parallel to it as shown below.

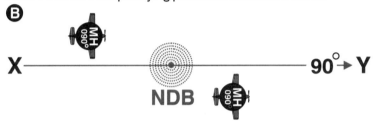

If, while flying a heading of 090°, the ADF needle points directly to the nose (#1) or the tail (#2), then you can be sure that you're tracking directly from X to Y.

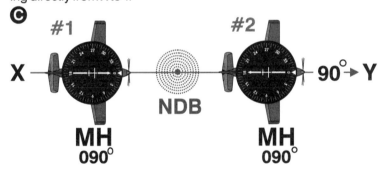

If the ADF needle of airplane #3 or #4 isn't pointed directly toward the nose or tail of the ADF, then, despite a heading of 090° the airplane is parallel to, rather than on, the desired course from X to Y.

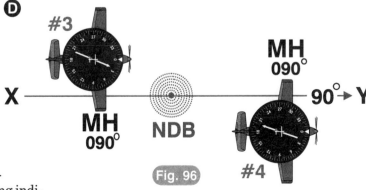

Fig. 96

Bearings "TO" and "FROM" an NDB

Airplane A is on the 270° bearing to the station.
Airplane B is on the 045° bearing from the station.
Airplane C is on the 135° bearing to the station.
Airplane D is on the 225° bearing from the station.
Airplane E is on the 180° bearing from the station.

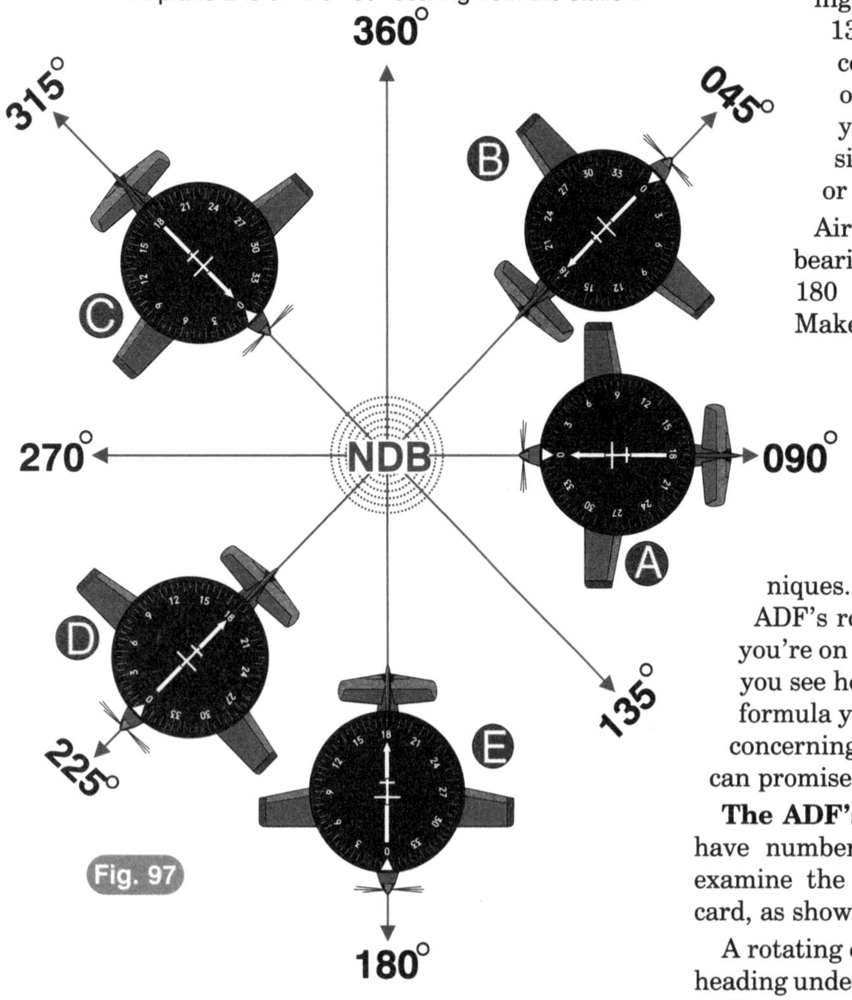

Fig. 97

Figure 97 shows several airplanes, all of which are on specific magnetic bearings to and from a station. Airplane A is heading 270 degrees with the ADF needle pointed to its nose. It's on the 270 degree magnetic bearing to the station. Airplane B is on the 045 degree magnetic bearing from the station and Airplane C is on the 135 degree magnetic bearing to the station. Of course, we don't have TO/FROM/OFF flags on an ADF. It should be obvious whether you're going toward or away from any station, since the needle is pointed either to the nose or the tail of the ADF's compass card.

Airplane D is flying the 225 degree magnetic bearing from the NDB and Airplane E is on the 180 degree magnetic bearing from the NDB. Make sure you understand this important principle: When the needle is pointed directly to the nose or the tail of the ADF, the direction the airplane is heading is also its magnetic bearing to or from the NDB (we're still assuming a no-wind condition).

Now you're ready for two nifty techniques. First, I'm going to show you how to use the ADF's rotating compass card to identify the bearing you're on to or from an NDB. You'll do a backflip when you see how easy this is. Second, I'll show you an easy formula you can use to solve any written test question concerning ADF navigation (and there will be some, I can promise you that).

The ADF's Moveable Compass Card – Most ADFs have numbered compass face cards that rotate. Let's examine the utility of this manually rotating compass card, as shown in Figure 98.

A rotating compass card allows you to set the airplane's heading under the heading index (white triangle at the top of the instrument). Unlike the RMI, which has a slaved

The ADF's Moveable Card

Fig. 98

Turing this knob rotates this card

HDG

By rotating the HDG knob and setting your airplane's heading under the index, the tip of the ADF needle points to the bearing you're on to the station and the tail points to the bearing you're on from the station.

Using the Moveable ADF Compass Card to Intercept a Bearing "TO" the NDB

Airplane A has a moveable compass card set to the airplane's present heading of 090°. The head of the ADF needle now points to the bearing the airplane is on to the NDB and the tail points to the bearing the airplane is on from the NDB. Airplane A is on the 060°/240° bearing to and from the NDB respectively. Airplane B has intercepted the 360° bearing to the NDB. Airplane C is on the 300°/120° bearing to and from the NDB respectively.

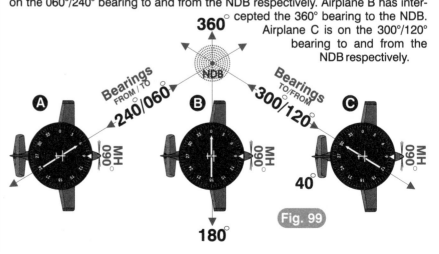

Fig. 99

gyro compass, the moveable ADF card must be manually rotated to the airplane's current heading. But you're a big, strong pilot so you can do it, and doing so has a practical purpose. Rotating the ADF compass card to the airplane's heading results in the needle pointing to the bearing the airplane is on to or from the NDB. The ADF's needle is then interpreted in exactly the same way as the RMI's needle.

If you manually rotate the ADF card to the airplane's magnetic heading of 090 degrees, the ADF needle always points to a number that's the magnetic bearing *to* the NDB (that's right, now and only now is it OK to pay attention to the numbers on the face of the ADF card). Airplane A in Figure 99 is on the 060 magnetic bearing to the NDB. Airplane B is on the 360 degree (0 degree) bearing to the NDB and Airplane C is on the 300 degree bearing to the NDB.

Pretty easy to use, isn't it? If you were instructed to identify crossing the 360 degree bearing to the NDB you would wait until the ADF needle pointed to 360 degrees or 0 degrees. If you were in Airplane A, you would know you hadn't crossed the 360 degree magnetic bearing to the station since the needle doesn't point to 360 degrees. You know you will eventually cross the bearing if your heading is held constant. Why? Because the ADF needle always moves toward the tail if your heading is constant (any NDB station in front of you will always end up behind you if you hold a constant heading). Airplane C has flown beyond the 360 degree bearing to the NDB because the head (point) of the ADF needle has fallen past the 360 value on the ADF's card. That needle will not move back up as long as the airplane's heading is maintained unless there is a profound and sudden reversal of the fundamental magnetic properties of the earth, in which case you will most certainly have other issues besides finding the NDB.

Using the Moveable Compass Card to Intercept a Bearing "FROM" the NDB

Airplane A is on a heading of 320° to intercept the 020° bearing from the NDB. The tail of Airplane A's needle indicates it is on the 070° bearing from the NDB. If the head of the needle always falls when a constant heading is maintained then the tail must always rise. Airplane A continues on its heading until reaching position B where the rising tail points to the 020° bearing from the NDB. If Airplane B continues on its present heading, the ADF tail will continue to rise and eventually indicate a position on the 355° bearing from the NDB as shown by Airplane C.

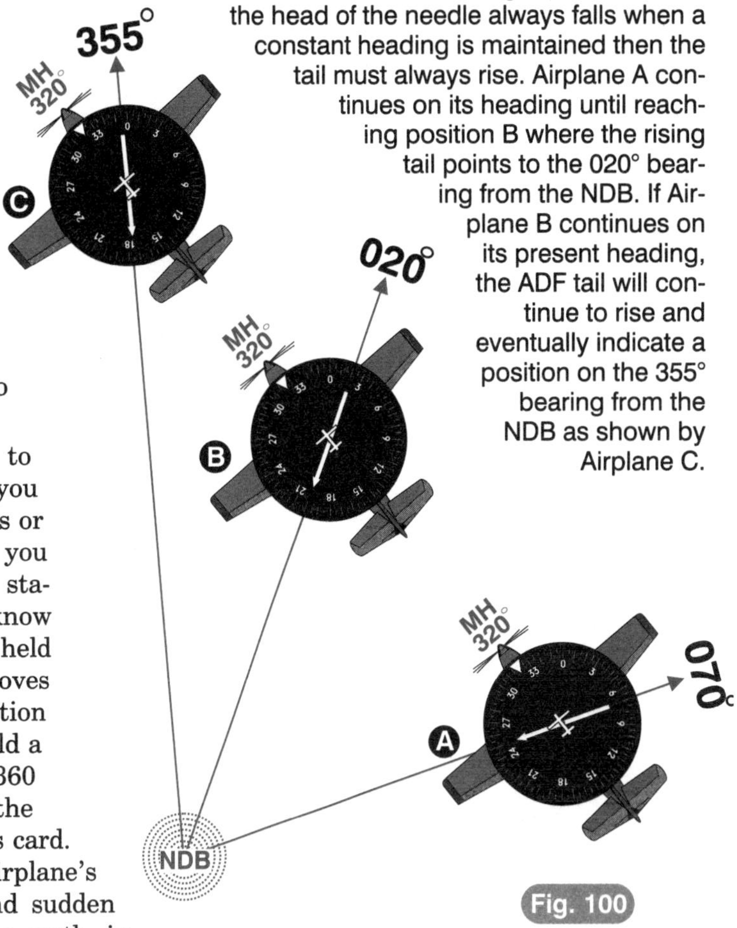

Fig. 100

These same procedures apply when intercepting a magnetic bearing from the NDB with a moveable ADF card. In Figure 100, Airplanes A, B, and C are on a magnetic heading of 320 degrees. Suppose you are asked to report crossing the 020 degree magnetic bearing from the station. The moveable compass card has been rotated so that your heading of 320 degrees is set to the top of the compass card. How will you know when you're crossing the desired bearing? You'll know when the tail of the ADF needle points to 020 degrees as is shown by Airplane B. In this instance, the tail of the ADF's needle points to the magnetic bearing from the NDB. Of course, Airplane C has flown beyond the 020 degree bearing. How do you know? If the head of the ADF needle always moves aft under a constant heading, the tail can only rise. There's no room for argument here: head falls, tail rises.

The tail of airplane C's ADF needle has risen above 020 and it certainly won't move back down. Knowing the ADF tail will rise allows you to determine what magnetic bearing you'll intercept from any NDB station. The only problem with using a moveable compass card is that you must constantly keep twisting it as your heading changes.

Hey, you can't believe everything you hear. A friend of mine told me about a radio station for folks who are hard of hearing. Its identification letters are KWAT. You can, however, believe ADF navigation is made very simple when you use the rotating compass card to help determine your magnetic bearing to and from the station.

The ADF's Fixed Compass Card – At the very beginning of our discussion I said to think about the numbers on the ADF's fixed card as index marks. I didn't want you to think they represented anything useful at that stage of this presentation. However, the numbers on the fixed card (the card with "0" set at the top) do have value, especially when solving knowledge exam questions. The following information is for doing just that—answering written test questions *only*. Don't attempt to navigate this way in an airplane. It's just not practical. If you do try it in the air, I guarantee your mind will come to a stop quicker than a lawnmower cruising over a tree stump. Unlike bachelors who paint every six months instead of cleaning their apartments, we only do practical things in airplanes. Math just doesn't add up at any altitude.

First, let's define a few terms. The *relative bearing* is the actual number the needle points to on the face of the ADF's fixed compass card. It's called *relative* because it's measured clockwise from 0 degree to 360 degree to the right of the nose, not because your mother-in-law got her nose bent to the right in a recent WWF tag team match. In other words, if the needle were pointed 10 degrees left of the top of the compass card as depicted in Figure 101, we could say its relative bearing is 350 degrees. ADF card B shows a relative bearing of 70 degrees; Card C shows a relative bearing of 270 degrees and Card D shows a relative bearing of 330 degrees. Remember, relative bearings are "relative" or counted to the right of the top (nose) of the ADF compass card.

During a written test, there is a nifty way to find your bearing to the NDB station using the relative bearing and the airplane's magnetic heading. By adding the relative bearing, shown on the face of the ADF compass card, to the airplane's magnetic heading, found on the heading indicator, you can find your magnetic bearing to the NDB. In other words:

Measuring Relative Bearings

The Relative Bearing is simply the number the ADF needle points to. It's measured on a fixed ADF card to the right, relative to the nose or the "0" on the card.

Fig. 101

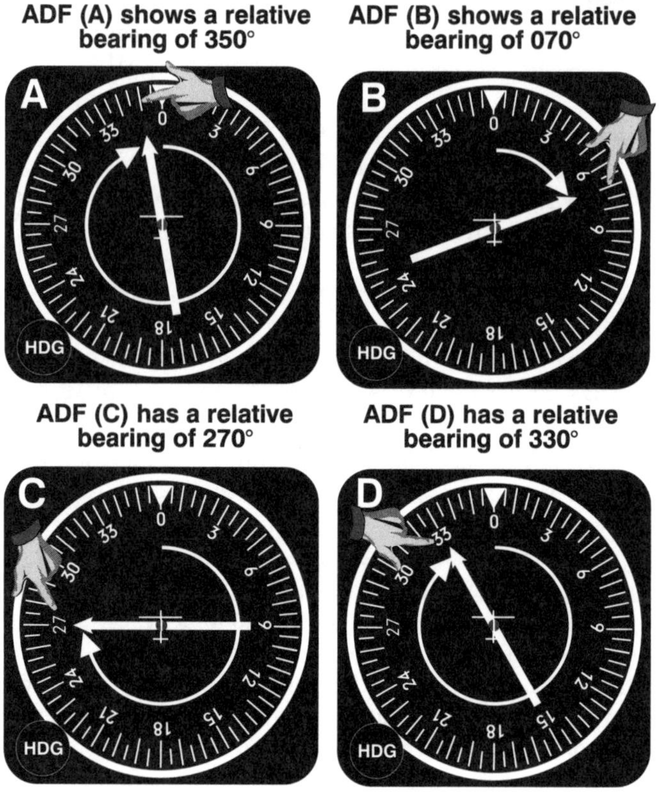

ADF (A) shows a relative bearing of 350°

ADF (B) shows a relative bearing of 070°

ADF (C) has a relative bearing of 270°

ADF (D) has a relative bearing of 330°

RB + MH=MBTS

Relative bearing+Magnetic heading= Magnetic bearing to the station

To understand how to use this formula, examine Figure 102. Airplane A has a relative bearing of 080 degrees shown on the face of its ADF compass card. Its heading is 310 degrees. Use the formula to find its magnetic bearing to the station. First we add, RB + MH = MBTS or (080 degrees)+(310 degrees)=390 degrees—the magnetic bearing to the station. As we've previously learned, any magnetic bearing greater than 360 degrees means a complete circle has already been made and the heading count should begin anew.

In our example, we'll subtract 360 degrees from 390 degrees, leaving us with a 30 degree magnetic bearing to the station, as depicted in Figure 102. Suppose we wanted to know our magnetic bearing *from* the station. Simply add or subtract 180 degrees from the bearing *to* the station to get its reciprocal. If we are on the 030 degree magnetic bearing *to* the station, the magnetic bearing *from* the station is (30 degree + 180 degrees)=210 degrees.

What is the magnetic bearing to the station of Airplane B in Figure 102? Adding the relative bearing of 300 degrees to a magnetic heading of 270 degrees gives us a magnetic bearing to the station of 210 degrees (570-360; your answer always has to be 360 or less). What is airplane B's magnetic bearing from the station? Simply subtract 180 degrees from 210 degrees to get 030 degrees, as shown in Figure 102.

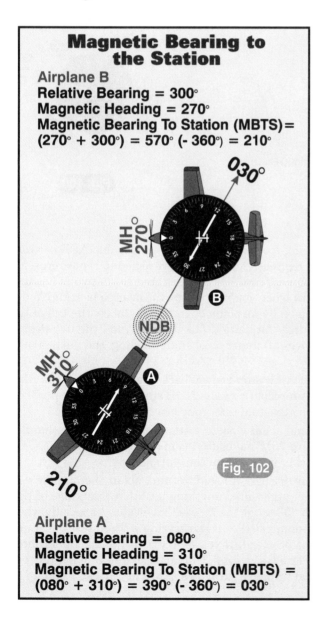

Magnetic Bearing to the Station

Airplane B
Relative Bearing = 300°
Magnetic Heading = 270°
Magnetic Bearing To Station (MBTS)=
(270° + 300°) = 570° (- 360°) = 210°

Fig. 102

Airplane A
Relative Bearing = 080°
Magnetic Heading = 310°
Magnetic Bearing To Station (MBTS) =
(080° + 310°) = 390° (- 360°) = 030°

Advanced ADF Navigation

Now that we understand determination of when an airplane is on a specific NDB magnetic bearing, let's examine what happens when the airplane's heading changes. Airplanes A, B, C and D in Figure 103 are all situated on the 360 degree magnetic bearing to the NDB. Conversely, we can say that all four airplanes are also on the 180 degree magnetic bearing from the station. For this discussion, let's talk about magnetic bearings *to* the station. Of course, because these airplanes are not flying 360 degrees, they will eventually move away from this magnetic bearing. Let's assume they remain stationary, as shown in Figure 103.

Airplane A's ADF needle points to the left wing or 90 degrees to the left of the nose. How many degrees would Airplane A have to turn to the left to get its ADF needle on the nose? Yes, the answer is 90 degrees. As Airplane A turns left, the ADF needle will continue pointing to the NDB. If Airplane A's heading is east or 90 degrees, at the completion of a 90 degree left turn its new heading will be 360 degrees and the needle will be on the ADF's nose.

Airplane B is heading 270 degrees and the ADF needle is pointing directly off the right wing. If Airplane B turns 90 degrees to the right, the ADF needle will end up pointing to the nose and the airplane's heading will be 360 degrees. Sound familiar? This means that both Airplane A and B, if they immediately turned to a heading of 360 degrees, would be flying to the NDB station on the 360 degree magnetic bearing.

These same principles apply on a magnetic bearing *from* the station. The ADF needle on Airplane E is 30 degrees to the left of the tail. If Airplane E is turned 30 degrees to the right, where would the ADF needle be? Yes, right on the tail. Remember, the needle will remain pointing directly to the NDB and the airplane (our ADF compass card) appears to rotate around the needle. To clearly understand this point, look at all the airplanes in Figure 103. The ADF needle points to the NDB despite all the variations in airplane headings. Which way and how many degrees would Airplane F need to turn to establish itself outbound on the 360 degree magnetic bearing? The answer is 30 degrees to the left.

Now you understand how the airplane can be established on a magnetic bearing while the ADF needle points to the right or left of the nose or tail. This becomes important when making corrections for wind while remaining on the specified magnetic bearing.

NDB Bearings

The 360° and 180° bearings to and from the NDB station are shown below.

360°

MH 030°

F

MH 330°

E

NDB

MH 330°

D

MH 030°

C

MH 270°

B

MH 060°

A

180°

Fig. 103

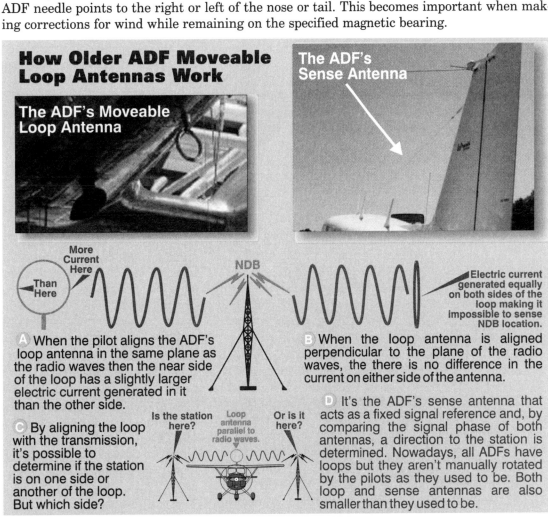

How Older ADF Moveable Loop Antennas Work

The ADF's Moveable Loop Antenna

The ADF's Sense Antenna

More Current Here

Than Here

NDB

Electric current generated equally on both sides of the loop making it impossible to sense NDB location.

A When the pilot aligns the ADF's loop antenna in the same plane as the radio waves then the near side of the loop has a slightly larger electric current generated in it than the other side.

B When the loop antenna is aligned perpendicular to the plane of the radio waves, the there is no difference in the current on either side of the antenna.

Is the station here?   Loop antenna parallel to radio waves.   Or is it here?

C By aligning the loop with the transmission, it's possible to determine if the station is on one side or another of the loop. But which side?

D It's the ADF's sense antenna that acts as a fixed signal reference and, by comparing the signal phase of both antennas, a direction to the station is determined. Nowadays, all ADFs have loops but they aren't manually rotated by the pilots as they used to be. Both loop and sense antennas are also smaller than they used to be.

Another Way of Determining Your Magnetic Bearing To or From an NDB – Figure 104 shows ADF indications on several different airplanes. Each airplane is obviously on one of the marked magnetic bearings to or from the station. Yet each airplane is headed in a direction different from that magnetic bearing. Here's the question: Is it possible to determine your magnetic bearing to or from the station by examining the airplane's heading and the angle the needle is deflected to the right or left of the nose or tail? Yes, it is. To find your magnetic bearing to or from any NDB station, simply ask yourself the following two questions:

1. How many degrees must you turn the airplane to the right or left to center the ADF needle on the nose (if you want a magnetic bearing to the NDB) or the tail (if you want a magnetic bearing from the NDB)?

2. What is the airplane's new heading after turning by this number of degrees?

The answer to question two is your magnetic bearing to or from that specific NDB. Let's see how this works. Using the method above, what magnetic bearing is Airplane H on from the NDB? Since we're dealing with a magnetic bearing *from,* we'll concern ourselves with the angle between the needle and the tail. The ADF needle in Airplane H is 75 degrees to the left of the tail. A right turn of 75 degrees puts the needle on the tail (this answers question 1). Since Airplane H is heading 330 degrees, a right turn of 75 degrees puts the airplane on a new heading of 405 degrees. Remembering that directional answers must always be 360 degrees or less, you subtract 360 from 405. This gives you a value of 45 degrees, which answers question 2.

What is Airplane D's magnetic bearing to the NDB? Airplane D must turn 45 degrees to the left to center the ADF needle on the nose (this answers question 1). Starting on a heading of 090 degrees, a 45 degree turn to the left puts the airplane on a new heading of 045 degrees with the needle centered on the nose (this answers question 2). Airplane D's magnetic bearing to the NDB is 045 degrees.

Use these two questions to determine the other airplanes' magnetic bearing to and from the NDB. Remember, if you obtain a value greater than 360 degrees,

BEARINGS TO AND FROM AN NDB

Each of the airplanes below are on a specific bearing to and from the NDB. To determine which bearing the airplane is on to or from the NDB, you must ask two questions. First, how many degrees must the airplane turn (either right or left) to center the ADF needle on the nose of tail of the ADF display (for either a bearing to or from the NDB, respectively)? Second, what is the airplane's new heading after turning by this number of degrees? This heading represents the airplane's bearing to or from the NDB.

MH = Magentic Heading

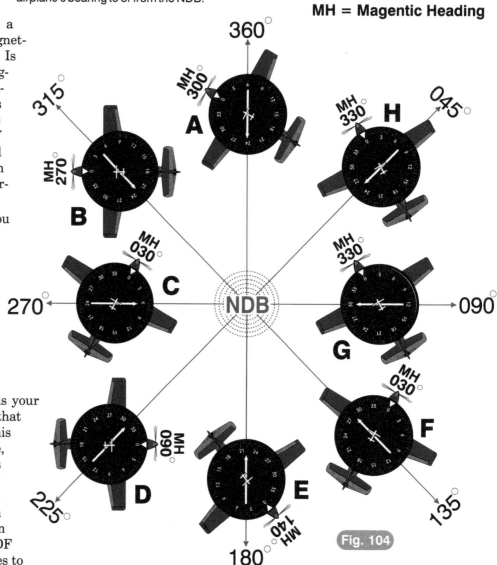

Fig. 104

subtract 360 from the number. There's no such thing as a heading of 400 degrees. If a controller ever asks you to turn left or right to 400 degrees, be very suspicious. This is like trying to mail an avocado with food stamps. If an instructor asks you to do this, tell him or her to get their stabilizer checked because they're acting pretty unstable.

Correcting for Wind – Is it possible to do everything in aviation and never make a mistake? No way. It's not possible in aviation or in life. That's why your first few attempts at navigating with ADF will make you feel bit uncomfortable, much like wearing exploding underwear— otherwise known as *Fruit of the Boom.* This is especially true if you're attempting to track NDB bearings in strong winds. Fortunately, we can apply some of the same philosophy that worked for making VOR wind corrections to ADF navigation.

Figure 105 shows several airplanes tracking to and from the NDB on the 360 degree magnetic bearing. The wind conditions vary for all four airplanes. Notice that Airplane A has a wind from the left (west) and is angled 15 degrees into the wind. Even though the airplane is flying a heading of 345 degrees, the airplane remains on the 360 degree magnetic bearing to the station. Since the NDB station is to the right of Airplane A's nose, the ADF needle remains deflected 15 degrees to the right. A general rule about ADF wind correction is that if your wind correction angle is sufficient, the angle between the ADF needle and the nose or tail remains equal to that wind correction angle. In other words, if your wind correction angle is 15 degrees, the ADF needle deflects 15 degrees on the appropriate side of the nose or tail.

Airplane B has a wind from the right (east). Crabbing into the wind on a heading of 015 degrees, Airplane B tracks directly to the NDB. Consequently, the ADF needle deflects 15 degrees to the side the station is on. In this instance, the station is to the left of Airplane B's nose and the needle deflects 15 degrees to the left of the ADF's nose.

Airplane C is experiencing a wind from the left (west) as the pilot attempts to track outbound on the 360 degree magnetic bearing from the NDB. The pilot applies a 15 degree wind correction angle to the left by turning to a heading of 345 degrees. The ADF needle deflects 15 degrees left of the tail—the side of the tail where the NDB is located. If this wind correction angle is sufficient, Airplane C will remain on the 360 degree magnetic bearing while on a heading of 345 degrees.

Airplane D experiences a wind from the right (east) as the pilot attempts to track outbound on the same magnetic bearing from the NDB. A 15 degree wind correction angle is applied to the right. Even though the airplane is heading 015 degrees, it remains on the 360 degree magnetic bearing from the station. The ADF needle shows this wind correction angle by deflecting 15 degrees to the right of the tail—the side of the tail where the NDB is located.

Figure 106 shows a smaller and more common wind correction angle experienced under light wind conditions. Airplanes A and B need to angle only 5 degrees into the wind to remain on track to and from the NDB.

ADF Wind Correction

A wind correction angle of 15° is applied under different wind conditions on bearings to and from the NDB.

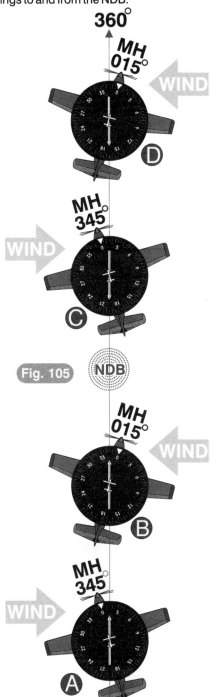

Fig. 105

ADF Wind Correction Angle

Wind Correction Outbound

When tracking outbound from the NDB station, a 5° wind correction angle (to the left) is used to maintain a track along the 360° outbound bearing. The NDB is now 5° to the left of the airplane's tail. Consequently, the ADF needle points 5° to the left of the ADF's tail.

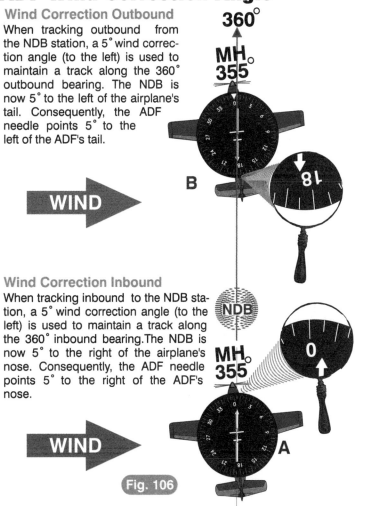

Wind Correction Inbound

When tracking inbound to the NDB station, a 5° wind correction angle (to the left) is used to maintain a track along the 360° inbound bearing. The NDB is now 5° to the right of the airplane's nose. Consequently, the ADF needle points 5° to the right of the ADF's nose.

Fig. 106

Here's the most important thing I want you to understand about wind correction with the ADF. When a wind exists, the airplane can track a specific magnetic bearing to and from an NDB while pointing in a direction different from that of the bearing. This is the basic premise for wind correction regardless of whether you're using the VOR, ADF or any other means of navigation.

While modern, fancier, and seemingly easier navigational methods are rapidly pushing ADF into the background, a working knowledge of this stalwart system could prove to literally be a beacon in the night for you when other methods fail. The ADF is a simple, reliable, low-tech, highly stable system that might just prove to be there for you when all else literally fails. Being a good instrument pilot means knowing how to use everything at your disposal to navigate. ADF remains one of those tools.

Postflight Briefing #5-2

Antenna's Galore

As an instrument pilot, you need to know two basic principles about antennas. Their size is related to their function and they have to be properly placed on the airplane if they are to work correctly.

An antenna's size is related to the wavelength and frequency of the equipment it supports. Higher frequencies mean shorter wavelengths and that means shorter antennas for better reception. Transponders operate in the higher frequency range of 1,030-1,090 MHz. This means they need short antennas (about 3 inches long) as shown in Figure 107.

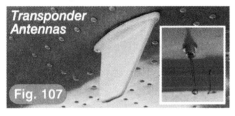
Transponder Antennas
Fig. 107

DME equipment also operates on higher frequencies in the range of 960 to 1,215 MHz. Thus, DME antennas are similar in size to transponder antennas (about 3 inches in length) to better receive these shorter wavelength signals (Figure 108). Both transponder and DME antennas are typically found on the bottom of the airplane for better line-of-sight reception with the transmitting/receiving ground station.

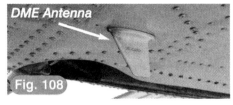
DME Antenna
Fig. 108

Communication antennas receive signals in the frequency range between 118.0-136.975 MHz. Their relatively lower frequency means slightly longer wavelengths, thus requiring antennas larger than that used with your transponder and DME (Figure 109). These antennas are often found on the top of the airplane's fuselage. Since VHF requires line-of-sight with the receiving station, this antenna location prevents shielding the VHF signals.

Comm Antenna
Fig. 109

VOR navigation antennas operate in the 108.0-117.95 MHz frequency range. These antennas are similar in size to the comm radio antennas and are often located at the top of the airplane's vertical stabilizer (Figure 110). These antennas can either look like two thick wires, a looping tube or blades. It's common, however, for these VHF nav antennas to also provide reception for the airplane's glideslope. This is possible because many nav receivers have glideslope receivers built into them. Despite the higher frequency of the glideslope (in the 330 MHz range), signal reception isn't a problem since the glideslope signal is directional (toward the airplane that's on final approach) and the glideslope transmitting station is often close to the airplane when it's used (0 to 20 miles).

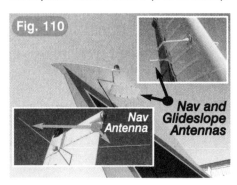
Fig. 110
Nav and Glideslope Antennas
Nav Antenna

The airplane's marker beacon equipment operates on a frequency of 75 MHz. Since airplanes fly over the marker beacon transmitter (not under it), the marker beacon antenna is located on the bottom of the airplane (Figure 111). Of course, you might assume that the lower frequency would make this antenna longer than the VHF antennas. Since airplanes fly at 200 to 3,000 feet above the marker beacon transmitter, this antenna can be made small because of its proximity to the transmitting station.

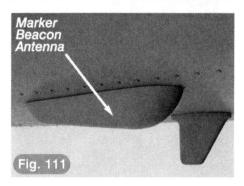
Marker Beacon Antenna
Fig. 111

The ADF antenna is a combination of both a loop and sense antenna as shown in Figure 112A (not long ago the sense antenna was separate from the loop antenna). The Stormscope antenna is nothing more than a loop antenna (Figure 112B). Both ADF and Stormscope use low frequencies for reception, thus the similar appearance of each antenna.

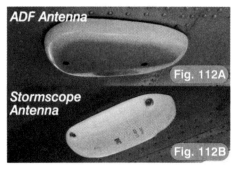
ADF Antenna
Fig. 112A
Stormscope Antenna
Fig. 112B

Your airplane's GPS antenna is normally located on top of the airplane's fuselage giving it an excellent view of the horizon and space (Figure 113). It's also one of the shortest antennas on the airplane since its operating frequency is so high. Combined GPS/comm antennas are now available, too.

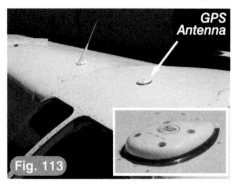
GPS Antenna
Fig. 113

Chapter 6
Holding Patterns

You've got to know when to hold 'em,
Know when to fold 'em,
Know when to walk away,
Know when to run.

Kenny Rogers
The Gambler

"Hold 'em or fold 'em" is a card player's decision, but when ATC tells a pilot to hold, the controller holds all the cards. Holding is a non-negotiable invitation to chase your own tail for a bit while the controller makes the flow go.

Contrary to popular belief, controllers do not issue holding instructions just to hear pilots stammer and sweat, though that's often a secondary result. ATC's primary job is to keep airplanes under IFR control separated. Just like the college prank of stuffing students into a phone booth, there are only so many airplanes that will fit into a controller's not-so-tiny-but-still-crowded block of airspace while maintaining the required separation. When things get a little too jammed, the controller has to give somebody a timeout.

Holding patterns are aviation's means of allowing pilots to stop in midair so the controller can buy a bit of time. Airplanes are

unique (you knew that) in the sense that you can't just tell them to stop. Instead, we have them fly a racetrack pattern around a point defined by one or more navigational aids. We don't want to fold 'em, we just want to hold 'em so everyone can walk away at the right time.

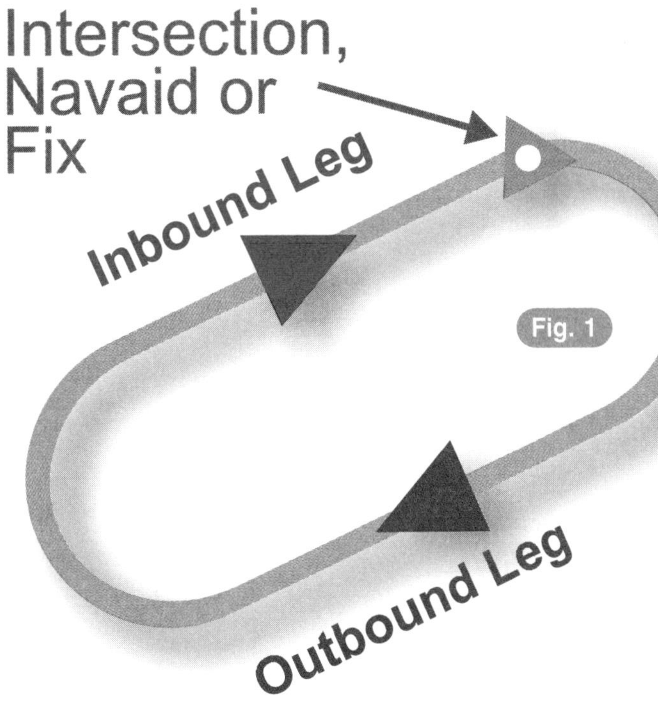

Besides overcrowding, another important reason to hold is if radio communication is lost. Many times an initial IFR clearance will clear you to a point short of the destination, and you will be told to expect further clearance (EFC) by a specific time. If you arrive at the intersection without operable communications radios, the rules say you're to hold until your EFC time and then proceed along the flight planned/filed route. ATC will know to make way for you even though you're incommunicado.

As an instrument pilot, you'll need to know how to define a holding pattern, as well as how to enter one. Sometimes this can be a challenge for instrument students, because it's often the first time they're called upon to simultaneously fly the plane and learn to think ahead of it. That's why the mere mention of holding patterns often sends instrument students running like chickens with the Colonel in close pursuit. Well, don't chicken out. In this chapter I'll tell you all about your rights (and lefts), the commonsense principle that underlies all holding pattern entries, and a 10 cent solution to finding the right way into any holding pattern. So hold on. Here we go.

A Day at the Racetrack

There's only one basic form for a holding pattern. It's racetrack shaped, as shown in Figure 1. Unlike airport traffic patterns, when it comes to holding patterns *right* turns are standard. Left-hand traffic patterns are useful to

Intersection, Navaid or Fix

Inbound Leg

Outbound Leg

Fig. 1

The holding pattern has one basic form, as shown above. There's always a place and direction to hold, an inbound and outbound leg and whether the turns will be to the right or left.

VFR pilots because the PIC usually sits on the left side of the airplane. This makes it easier to see the runway environment when landing. For instrument pilots, it doesn't really matter which seat is occupied when it comes to holding patterns, because looking out the window is irrelevant when flying inside a cloud.

If you're going to hold, you need a place at which to hold. This is the focal point of the holding pattern and it can be an intersection, navaid, DME fix, or even a waypoint. There's always a bearing, radial, course or airway leading inbound to this fix, which is why this is called the *inbound* leg of the holding pattern (Figure 2).

The Holding Pattern Inbound Leg

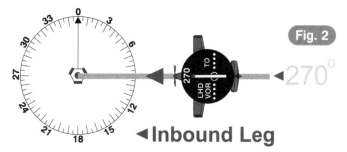

Fig. 2

◄**Inbound Leg**

There will always be a point (navaid, fix, waypoint) at which you'll hold and you'll always head directly inbound to this point on what is referred to as the *inbound leg* of the holding pattern.

The *outbound leg* begins after you've crossed over the holding fix and made a 180 degree turn. At the completion of the 180 degree turn you will be abeam the fix (approximately) as shown in Figure 3. From there, you'll start your time and fly the direction of the outbound leg for one

The Holding Pattern Outbound Leg

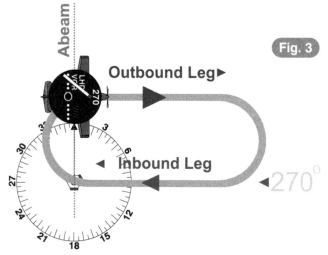

Fig. 3

The *outbound leg* of the holding pattern is flown in the opposite direction of the inbound leg.

minute (Figure 4). (Technically speaking, you'll only be able to precisely determine when you're abeam the fix if you have ADF or a moving map display. If you don't have either of these, then just start your outbound leg timing when you roll out of the turn.) At the completion of one minute (in a no-wind condition) you'll turn 180 degrees to intercept the inbound leg. If there is no wind, you'll find

Timing the Outbound Leg

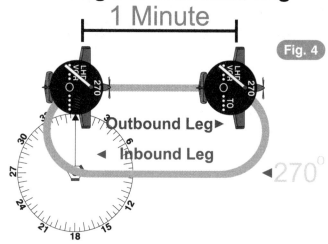

Fig. 4

You'll initially fly the outbound leg for one minute then turn to intercept the inbound leg.

that it will take one minute to fly the inbound leg (Figure 5). This sequence repeats itself until ATC or the regulations allow you to leave holding and proceed on course.

Before we proceed further, consider that when ATC gives you instructions to hold, you can expect the following information to be stated in the clearance:

The direction the holding pattern lies in, defined from the holding fix (N, NE, E, SE, S, etc.).

A place to hold: an intersection, navaid, DME fix or waypoint.

A radial, course, bearing, airway or route on which to hold.

Leg length in miles (or minutes) if you're using DME or area navigation.

A direction of turn, either standard or non-standard when holding.

Time to expect further clearance (EFC), if appropriate.

We'll talk more about these individual items in a bit as well as discuss how to enter a holding pattern as well as exit one. For now, keep in mind that when you're asked to hold, this means you are essentially keeping your airplane within the limits of the airspace, both vertical and horizontal,

Timing the Inbound Leg

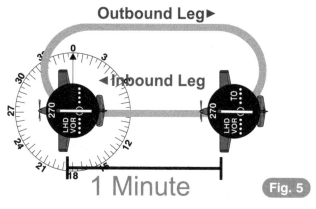

Fig. 5

In a no-wind condition, flying the outbound leg for one minute should result in a one minute inbound leg.

Timed Approaches From a Holding Fix

One time a doctor asked me what I thought of collagen. I said that I thought everyone should get an education. He seemed flustered and changed the subject by asking me what I thought about the problems with Beirut. I said I thought he was a great ball player. Now that was a communication problem that caused confusion, much like the confusion many instrument students experience when they first read about timed approaches from a holding fix.

Timed approaches from a holding fix are often made when ATC has many airplanes arriving for an approach at the same time (they are often done in non-radar environments). To deal with the problem, the controller might stack one airplane on top of another in a holding pattern at 1,000 foot vertical intervals (this often takes place at some fix that's part of the instrument approach structure, like the final approach fix or outer marker) as shown in the figure to the right. Then, when appropriate, the controller will request

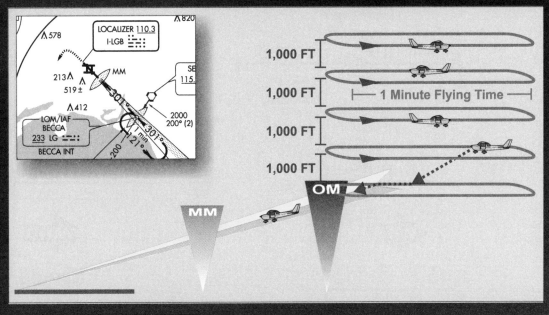

Courtesy Microsoft Flight Simulator

that an airplane (usually the lowest one in the stack, of course) leave the holding fix at a specific time and fly the approach. Now you know why you must be good at modifying your holding pattern legs to arrive over the holding fix and departing it inbound for the approach.

Timed approaches may be conducted when the following conditions are met:

1. A control tower is in operation at the airport where the approaches are conducted.

2. Direct communications are maintained between the pilot and the Center or Approach controller until the pilot is instructed to contact the tower.

3. If more than one missed approach procedure is available, none require a course reversal.

4. If only one missed approach procedure is available, the following conditions are met:

(a) Course reversal is not required; and,

(b) Reported ceiling and visibility are equal to or greater than the highest prescribed circling minimums for the approach chart.

5. When cleared for the approach, pilots shall not execute a procedure turn (14 CFR Section 91.175).

Holding Above 14,000' MSL

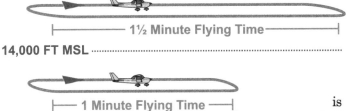

Fig. 6

that the controller has provided for you. Stay within these limits and you don't have to worry about invoking the CDW or *collision damage waiver* in your airplane rental agreement (sorry, only cars have CDWs, because only cars have bumpers).

The objective when flying a holding pattern is to have a one-minute inbound leg (unless you're holding above 14,000 feet MSL, in which case you'll want a 1 ½ minute inbound leg) as shown in Figure 6. Flying a one-minute inbound leg is a snap in a no-wind condition. Fly outbound for a minute, turn inbound, and it should take one minute from the time you fully reverse course to reach the holding fix (Figure 7). Blow a little wind on this mixture, however, and things change. Now you must modify the time you fly your outbound leg to allow you to end up with an inbound leg that's one minute in length.

No Wind Holding

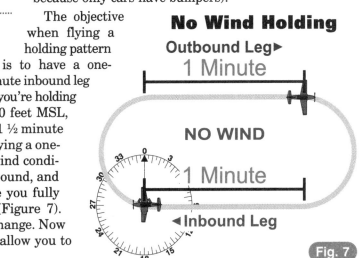

Fig. 7

Adjusting the Outbound Leg to Give You a One Minute Inbound Leg

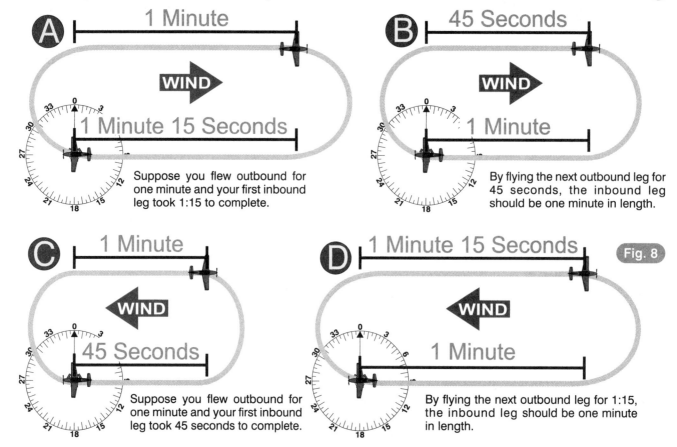

A 1 Minute / 1 Minute 15 Seconds — Suppose you flew outbound for one minute and your first inbound leg took 1:15 to complete.

B 45 Seconds / 1 Minute — By flying the next outbound leg for 45 seconds, the inbound leg should be one minute in length.

C 1 Minute / 45 Seconds — Suppose you flew outbound for one minute and your first inbound leg took 45 seconds to complete.

D 1 Minute 15 Seconds / 1 Minute — By flying the next outbound leg for 1:15, the inbound leg should be one minute in length.

Fig. 8

That's why when you enter a holding pattern and cross the holding fix, you fly a one minute outbound leg then turn to intercept the inbound leg. You time the inbound leg and hope it's one minute long. If it is, then you should immediately run to Las Vegas and bet big time, because it's your lucky day. If there's wind aloft, it's likely that your inbound leg will be longer or shorter than a minute. No problem. Just take the difference and add it (if the inbound leg was too quick) or subtract it (if the inbound leg took too long) to your next outbound leg (Figure 8).

For instance, suppose your first inbound leg is one minute and 15 seconds. It's likely that you have a tailwind on the outbound leg (or a headwind on the inbound leg) as shown in Figure 8A. To compensate, take the difference in time between the inbound and outbound legs and add or subtract this from the time on your next outbound leg (you should intuitively know whether to add or subtract this time). Once again, if your first inbound leg was one minute and 15 seconds you have a tailwind on the outbound leg. So, fly the next outbound leg for 45 seconds as shown in Figure 8B. This should give you the desired one minute inbound leg times on all further holding pattern circuits. If, on the first pattern circuit, your inbound leg was only 45 seconds long (Figure 8C), then fly your next outbound leg for one minute and 15 seconds (Figure 8D). This is a fairly accurate way of modifying the outbound leg to provide you with an inbound leg one minute in length.

So what's the big deal about flying a holding pattern that has a one minute inbound leg? The basic reason is

to have a holding pattern that takes a known period of time to complete and knowing this means you can modify (cut short) your outbound leg if ATC were to ask you to leave the fix at which you are holding (the holding fix) at a specific time. When might ATC do this? One common instance is where you're doing what is known as *timed approaches from a holding fix* (see sidebar previous page).

When doing timed approaches from a holding fix, ATC might ask you to leave a holding fix inbound at a specific time. I'm talking about leaving that point at a specific minute here, so you must be Johnny on the "Mickey

Timing the Holding Pattern

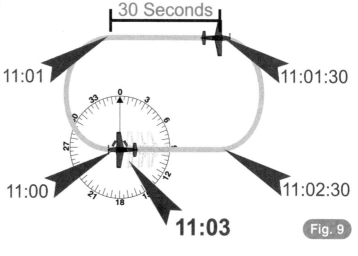

30 Seconds

11:01   11:01:30

11:00   11:02:30

11:03

Fig. 9

Mouse watch" spot with time management. If it takes you four minutes to fly a complete holding pattern (two minutes for two 180 degree turns and two one-minute legs) then you should know how to modify your pattern to cross the holding fix at the specified time. For instance, suppose the time is 11:00 and you've just reaching the holding fix (Figure 9). Suddenly, ATC asks you to report the fix inbound at 11:03. You've got to go out, turn around, and get back in three minutes instead of the usual four. How long do you fly the outbound leg? Try flying the outbound for 30 seconds before turning inbound (a no-wind condition is assumed here).

Maximum Holding Speeds

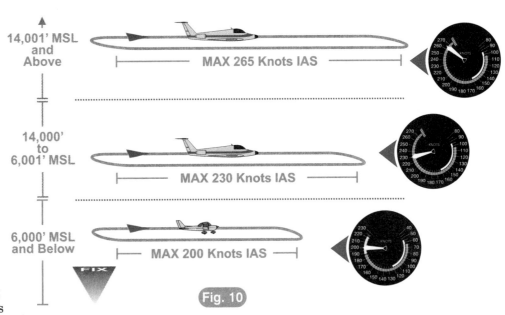

14,001' MSL and Above — MAX 265 Knots IAS

14,000' to 6,001' MSL — MAX 230 Knots IAS

6,000' MSL and Below — MAX 200 Knots IAS

Fig. 10

In case you're thinking about purchasing a used SST on e-Bay and doing your instrument training in it, here's a note of caution. You can't fly the holding pattern at the speed of sound, because you'll hear about it an hour after you land. Why can't you fly a holding pattern at any airspeed you want? Well, because the FAA says so, but they say it for a good reason. Part of the holding pattern concept is that you'll remain within a well-defined chunk of airspace. Protecting you from other airplanes, protruding mountains, and other immovable objects depends on ATC

having some idea of how big the holding pattern will be, and ten miles a minute is not part of the plan. If you're holding anywhere at or below 6,000 feet MSL, the maximum holding speed is 200 KIAS; from 6,001 to 14,000 feet MSL, the maximum holding speed is 230 knots; from 14,001 feet MSL and above, the maximum holding speed is 265 knots (Figure 10). Keep in mind that when cleared to a fix at which you'll hold, you should start your speed reduction to at or below the holding speed when you are three minutes or less from the holding fix. This way you won't surprise ATC by slowing down 100 miles early.

Holding Via DME Mileage Legs

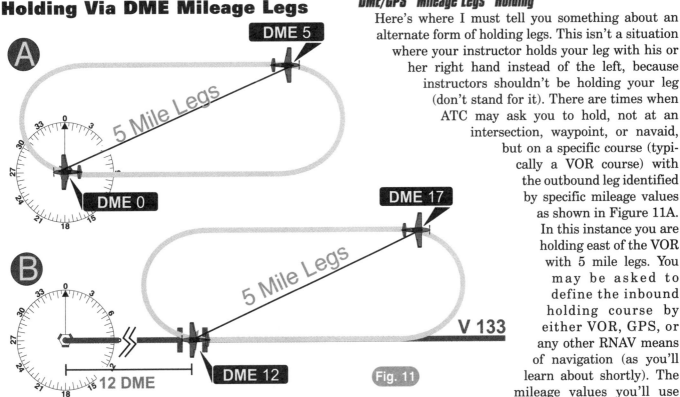

DME 5 — 5 Mile Legs — DME 0

DME 17 — 5 Mile Legs — V 133 — DME 12 — 12 DME

Fig. 11

DME/GPS "Mileage Legs" Holding

Here's where I must tell you something about an alternate form of holding legs. This isn't a situation where your instructor holds your leg with his or her right hand instead of the left, because instructors shouldn't be holding your leg (don't stand for it). There are times when ATC may ask you to hold, not at an intersection, waypoint, or navaid, but on a specific course (typically a VOR course) with the outbound leg identified by specific mileage values as shown in Figure 11A. In this instance you are holding east of the VOR with 5 mile legs. You may be asked to define the inbound holding course by either VOR, GPS, or any other RNAV means of navigation (as you'll learn about shortly). The mileage values you'll use

will always be in nautical miles, since all common forms of navigation equipment are calibrated in these values.

Suppose ATC said to hold east of the 12 DME fix on Victor 133, with 5 mile legs. The holding pattern would look like what you see in Figure 11B. When the DME read 12 miles, you turn outbound and fly until it read 17 miles. Then you turn inbound and repeat the process until ATC figures they've spun you enough and they finally have room for you.

When using GPS, instead of DME values, you use something known as ATD or *along track distance*. The ATD is simply the distance value shown on your GPS unit. If ATC asked you to hold on a specific course and fly 7 mile legs, then you'd do what was just described, using ATD values to determine when to turn inbound.

Holding Pattern Drift Correction

Before we look at how to draw a holding pattern on your chart and how to enter that pattern, we need to chat about something known as *drift correction*. Often, you'll have to apply a drift correction when holding. That's because the air moves (which is why we call such a thing, *wind*). Maybe it's not fair, but that's air. Not correcting for wind drift means your ground track will end up something like what's depicted in Figure 12A. If your patterns look like this, then you can honestly say that you want to fly badly (which has nothing to do with your desire to fly but has everything to do with the way you do it).

At this point in your flying experience, you should be able to identify the drift correction necessary to track the inbound leg of the pattern. If you can't, then Figure 12A indicates what will happen to you on the outbound holding leg. The racetrack shape of the pattern during two 180 degree turns makes it very difficult to remain close to the inbound leg. You could end up either undershooting or overshooting the inbound leg, depending on the wind direction. *No es tan bueno, amigo.*

Here's how to handle wind correction in the holding pattern. The most effective way to correct for wind on the outbound leg is to double the wind correction angle used on the inbound leg. For instance, if you used 10 degrees of drift correction inbound, use 20 degrees on the outbound leg. Doing so results in a slightly misshapen but correctly flown pattern, as shown in Figure 12B. The end result is that at the completion of your inbound turn you're positioned to roll out on the desired bearing or course.

Of course, if you want to get technical about it, it's legitimate to say that if your outbound leg is less than a minute, you'll need a slightly larger (than double) wind correction angle or you'll need a slightly smaller one if the outbound leg is longer than a minute, but that's really splitting "airs." In fact, in the AIM, the FAA recommends that the drift correction angle be tripled, not doubled, on the outbound leg. Realistically, tripling the drift

Holding Drift Correction

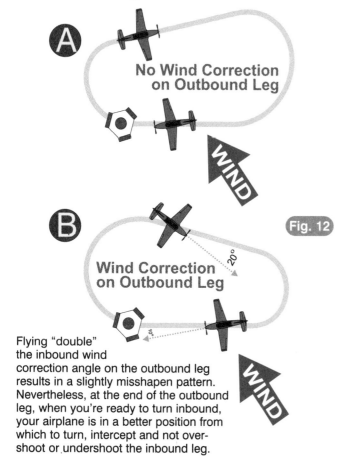

Flying "double" the inbound wind correction angle on the outbound leg results in a slightly misshapen pattern. Nevertheless, at the end of the outbound leg, when you're ready to turn inbound, your airplane is in a better position from which to turn, intercept and not over-shoot or undershoot the inbound leg.

Fig. 12

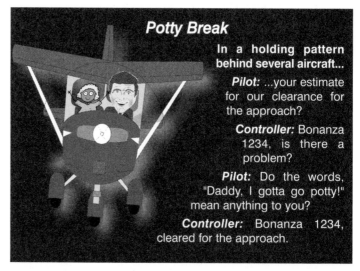

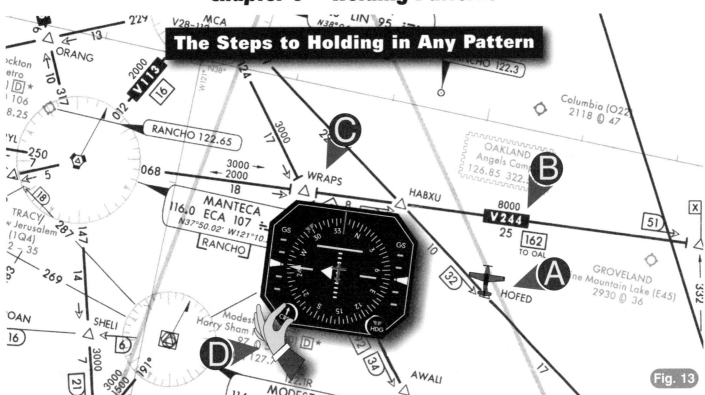

The Steps to Holding in Any Pattern

Fig. 13

correction works fine if you have a crosswind that's directly perpendicular to the holding course. We're rarely so lucky (or is it unlucky?). Doubling the angle works well most of the time, but don't flip your Euclid about getting four-decimal-point precision. This isn't rocket science because it's not going to take you to the moon. Make your best drift correction approximation (triple the wind correction on the outbound leg if you have to), then add or subtract from it on consecutive circuits around the pattern. I can pretty much guarantee that by the time you figure it out precisely, it will be time to move on.

Now that you have a grasp of the basics, let's examine the process by which you'll actually hold when ATC gives instructs you to.

One Step at a Time

A complex task can be made less complex by breaking it into smaller parts. Not doing so means that you may be the one doing the breaking down (emotionally, that is). That's why you'll want to use the following strategy when analyzing how to perform a holding pattern.

Heading Your Way: Step One

Step one in mastering a holding pattern is to acknowledge that a definite structure exists to the holding clearance. Here's an actual holding pattern clearance similar to the one you will receive from ATC:

Cessna 2132 Bravo, radar contact one mile north of HOFED intersection. Cleared to WRAPS intersection via heading three-four-zero degrees, intercept Victor 244 direct WRAPS. Hold east on Victor 244, left turns. Maintain 8,000 feet. Expect further clearance at zero-two-three-zero." Refer to Figure 13.

Don't panic (at least not until I tell you to do so). Your first priority is to determine how to get to the intersection

at which you'll be holding. This clearance says to fly a heading of 340 degrees, which is a radar vector to Victor 244. That wasn't so difficult, was it? So turn to a heading of 340 degrees as shown in Figure 13, position A.

Order: Step Two

This is a critical step, so no missteps, please. Immediately set the navigation radios to identify Victor 244 (Figure 13, position B) and prepare to track to WRAPS intersection (Figure 13, position C).

You may be tempted to begin drawing the holding pattern on your IFR chart right away, especially if your name is Michelangelo or your instructor was once a primary school art teacher. Be careful. If your instructor suddenly shouts, "Draw!" do *not* reach for your Smith & Wesson. And don't necessarily reach for your pencil, either. Start drawing the holding pattern on your chart too soon and before you know it you're not thinking about the route to the holding intersection. If you don't prioritize your chores, it will work against your successful mastery of instrument flying. *Aviate, navigate, communicate.* Remember these words, *and* their order. Size doesn't matter in IFR flying; order does. Aviate, navigate, communicate in that priority order and you'll be in control.

Once established on an intercept heading of 340 degrees, select the Manteca VOR frequency, increase the volume, listen to the station's Morse code identification, and rotate the OBS to 248 degrees, the reciprocal of 068 degrees, in that order (Figure 13, position D). You should identify the station when time permits. No, you don't have to do it immediately, but you certainly want to do it.

Chart Art: The Third Step

Once you know where you are going and how to get there, it's time to employ your copious free time to draw the holding pattern on paper (specifically, your IFR chart). Eventually you'll do this all in your head, but for openers it's best to do a doodle. Think of it as chart art.

Most pilots find it very helpful to draw the holding pattern on their IFR charts, which is why I recommend that you do so, too. Many students would rather draw this on their *instructor's* chart, thus leaving their own charts unsullied. Instructors are way too smart to let this happen. That's why I also recommend drawing the holding pattern in pencil and erasing it after the flight.

The Building Blocks of the Holding Clearance

Before you can draw the holding pattern on your chart, you have to know a little something about the holding clearance. Believe it or not (and some pilots don't), every holding clearance contains all the information you need to accurately depict the holding pattern on your chart. As we've already discussed, controllers will tell you the direction to hold from a particular fix, navaid, intersection, or waypoint; the radial, course, bearing, airway or route to hold on (the inbound leg); and, if the pattern is nonstandard, the controller will specify that left turns be made. If you don't receive *all* of these tidbits as part of your clearance, something is wrong. Speak up or forever hold your tongue depressor.

The Inbound Leg

As you can guess, the most important part of the holding pattern is the inbound leg. Without it, your pattern doesn't have a leg to stand on. The inbound leg is the course on which you navigate, for one minute, *to* the holding fix. The inbound leg of every holding pattern must be on some radial, bearing, airway or course—otherwise, how could you arrive back over the holding fix? The outbound leg of every holding pattern is always a heading that is

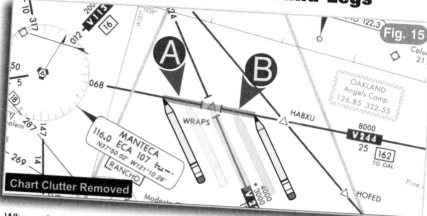

Two Choices for Inbound Legs

Fig. 15

Chart Clutter Removed

When a holding clearance instructs you to hold at an intersection (WRAPS in this instance) there are two possible choices for the inbound leg. The correct choice of inbound leg is dependent on the holding direction stated in the clearance.

simply the reciprocal of the inbound heading (plus or minus a wind correction) and that is normally also flown for a period of one minute.

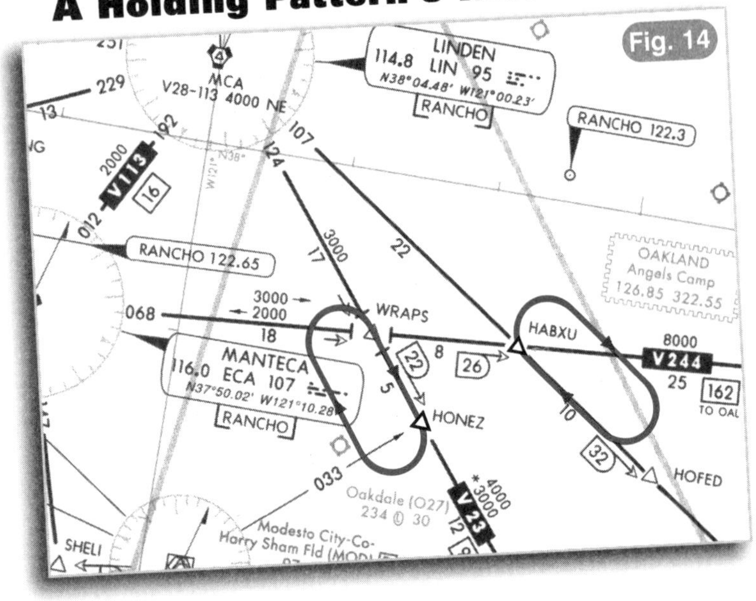

Figure 14 shows holding patterns at HONEZ and HABXU intersections. Like all holding patterns, these both have an inbound leg. The inbound leg to HABXU is on the 107 degree radial from Linden VOR, in a direction of 287 degrees (remember your basic VOR navigation here. To track the inbound leg to HABXU on the 107 degree radial, you will have to set the VOR's course selector to 287 degrees). The inbound leg to HONEZ, on the other hand, is on the Linden 124 degree radial, in a direction of 124 degrees.

Holding Pattern Strategy

To draw our holding pattern at WRAPS correctly, follow this step-by-step four-question sequence. It will be your guide to converting your clearance into a picture on your chart. Here are the four questions you'll want to ask yourself and the order in which you should ask them:

1. *What's the fix and the radial, bearing, airway or course on which I am to hold?*

2. *What are the two possible choices of inbound legs?*

3. *Which inbound leg is on the side of the intersection or fix specified in the holding direction?*

4. *Is it a right or left hand pattern?*

Question One

Asking, "What's the fix and the radial, bearing, airway or course to hold on?" identifies where you will hold and the navigable route you will fly inbound to the holding intersection. When ATC says to hold at a specific fix, you should immediately identify this spot on your chart. Hopefully you'll find it easily and won't mistake it for catsup spills, evidence of your last visit to a Bronto Burger stop, or blood, which would be evidence of your last lesson. Draw a line through this spot (the fix spot, not the blood spot) and along the radial, bearing, airway, or course on which you are to hold (Figure 15).

A Holding Pattern's Inbound Leg

Fig. 14

A Line to a Point, That's All It Is

Dan Hoefert

As an instrument student, I'm sharing my perspective on learning to hold. Initially, this highly understated task of "holding" seems like crosswind landings, geometry and trig all wrapped into one. Of course, it's not that bad, and once you get the hang of it, holding can be downright fun. Holding demands respect and involves a lot—notating ATC's instructions, reading back the instructions to ATC, understanding those instructions, sketching the hold, setting up the radios, establishing a course towards the hold, verifying frequencies, flying the entry, and (whew) finally flying the hold!

Here is my student-to-student tip for you. The inbound leg is just a *line to a point*—nothing more, nothing less.

This concept is very important. You already fly pattern legs with wind correction when you come in for a landing, right? On final, you actually perform a descending line-to-a-point, with wind correction. Well, I can tell you this much, flying an inbound holding leg is quite a bit easier than flying an inbound final leg to a landing.

First, understand and visualize that this line (inbound leg) extends from the point (fix or intersection) at which you will hold, with its tail end extending in the direction of the hold (N, NE, E, SE, S, SW, W, NW). You might even visualize this line as the shaft of an arrow extending from a bull's-eye, and note how the arrow's shaft extends in the same direction you were instructed to hold. If you can picture this much on your chart, then the pattern is all but laid out for you.

Second, always fly this inbound leg to the best of your ability. As with flying the final approach to a landing, flying a precise inbound leg (a line) to the holding fix is very important. Everything can get real complicated if your navigation is sloppy here. Work hard to establish and track the inbound leg while carefully noting your timing and wind correction. Fly the *line to a point*. Give this your best concentration. Flying a good holding pattern is a challenge, but a lot of fun, as well.

Hold on tight and best regards.

Dan Hoefert

Since you can be inbound to a point from either of two directions on a straight line, you can see how there might are two possible choices for the inbound leg. Of course, only one is correct. To find out which one, let's move onto the second question.

Question Two

Ask yourself, "In what direction, relative to the fix, are the two possible inbound legs?" The answer is always going to be two opposite directions (east-west, north-south, northwest-southeast), only one of which is your final, correct answer. Flying is wonderful, Alice, but this isn't Wonderland. Once you figure this out correctly, it won't be Wanderland, either.

Figure 15 shows that Victor 244 exists on both sides of WRAPS intersection. One possibility for an inbound leg is to the west of WRAPS on Victor 244 (position A); the other is to the east of WRAPS on Victor 244 (position B).

Figure 16 shows two possibilities for inbound legs when instructed to hold on Victor 244 at WRAPS intersection. There are only two choices of inbound legs at WRAPS on Victor 244. How are you going to pick the right one? The next question will allow you to determine which of the inbound legs is the correct choice.

Question Three

OK, you can just guess. Then you'll have a 50-50 chance of getting the right answer. Of course, this means that half the time the controller is going to be really, really upset with you. Why not make it a sure thing by asking yourself, "Which leg is on the side of the intersection or fix specified in

the holding direction?" You don't have to guess. The nice controller already told you the answer.

In this instance, the controller said, *"Hold east on Victor 244."*

This is the answer. And you didn't even have to travel to India and hire a guru to find this wisdom. The correct choice of inbound leg is the one that's east of WRAPS, as shown in Figure 16B. Now, don't get your wheel pants in bind over the fact that a direction of 68 degrees from WRAPS isn't exactly east, or 90 degrees. When dealing with holding patterns where there are only two possible choices for the inbound legs, the holding pattern direction can only fall into one of two categories (east or west, in this instance). *East-ish* is close enough here.

Question Four

The final question is, "Is this a right or left hand holding pattern?" Rest assured (but don't rest yet) that your

Two Choices for Inbound Legs

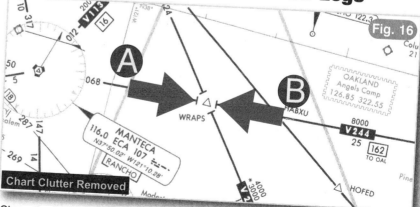

Since the holding pattern's inbound leg is "inbound" to the holding fix, the red arrows represent the two possible inbound legs when instructed to hold at WRAPS intersection on V244.

clearance always says whether you're to make right- or left hand-turns. Of course, usually it's said by not being said. Since standard holding patterns call for right turns, the controller won't mention anything about turns if the pattern is standard. If the controller wants you to make left turns, he or she will say so in the clearance. Think of it this way: unless told otherwise, you always get your *rights*. Since the controller in our example specified left turns, then you should fly the pattern as shown in Figure 17.

It should be clear to you that the holding pattern's lengthwise direction lies east of WRAPS intersection along Victor 244. I know you won't be misled by the holding pattern being offset to the bottom side of Victor 244. *Whether right or left turns are made has absolutely nothing to do with the holding pattern direction.* Thinking otherwise is as big a misconception as believing that propwash is something used to clean your airplane.

The Completed Holding Pattern

Fig. 17

If a controller doesn't mention anything about right or left hand turns, then you can assume that the pattern is "standard" right hand turns. In this instance, our clearance called for left hand turns, as shown above.

Holding East or West of WRAPS

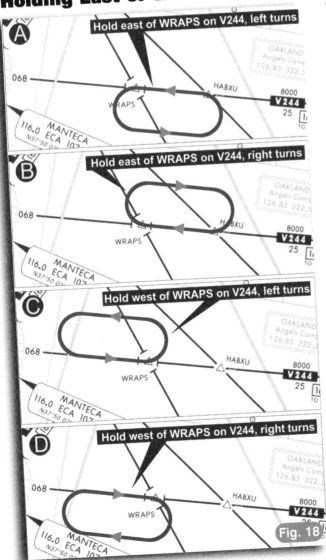

Ⓐ Hold east of WRAPS on V244, left turns

Ⓑ Hold east of WRAPS on V244, right turns

Ⓒ Hold west of WRAPS on V244, left turns

Ⓓ Hold west of WRAPS on V244, right turns

Fig. 18

Instrument students are often initially confused about this point, and that's certainly understandable. Right or left turns and the side of the inbound leg on which the racetrack is placed have nothing to do with the racetrack's direction (i.e., north, south, east, west, etc.) from the fix. Take a look at Figure 18, which shows four holding pattern variations at WRAPS along with their respective clearances. Hopefully you'll see that the holding patterns in Figures 18C and 18D are both located to the west of WRAPS intersection. Sure, 18C is located above V244 while 18D is located below, but this is just a function of one pattern being done with left turns and one with right turns, respectively. The elongated bodies of both patterns (thus their inbound legs) still lie west of WRAPS intersection.

Holding Pattern Entries

One of the most challenging things in instrument training is figuring out how to enter a holding pattern. Why is that? Because you may initially approach the hold from almost any angle. If you're lucky, you might be coming in lined up with the holding leg and just start flying loops. On the other hand, you might be coming from the opposite direction, requiring a full course reversal to get the airplane turned around and pointed in the right direction, and doing so without using up half the sky. Or you could be coming from anywhere in between these extremes.

Holding pattern entry generates much more angst than it deserves, but I feel your pain and it's not in vain. Before we launch into the details, I'll get you ahead of the game by explaining one simple, underlying principle of IFR holding patterns—*pattern entry is always based on doing what will keep you closest to the aerial racetrack while getting you onto the circuit.* That's the Secret of Pattern Entry. Now it's been told. Everything else is just a matter of how to do it.

There are three holding pattern entries recommended by the FAA. They are *direct*, *parallel*, and *teardrop*. Keep your mind's eye on the big picture. The overarching principle is to stay close to the pattern, and each of these entries yields the best solution over a certain range of angles at which you are initially approaching the hold. Unlike a Hollywood starlet, you want the entry that gives you the *least* exposure by keeping you closest to the allowable lateral limits of the holding pattern so you won't trim the tops off of trees and/or scare other pilots and migrating fowl by wandering into their airspace. This is the very best reason to enter the holding pattern as recommend by the FAA, though if you can think up something better and remain within bounds, it's certainly legal to do it.

Holding Pattern Entry Procedures

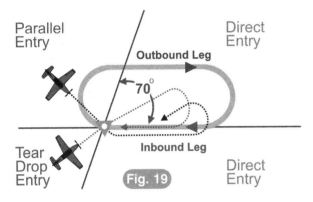

Fig. 19

Figure 19 shows the standard holding pattern entry procedure. Here's how to mentally construct this diagram. Imagine yourself standing on the holding fix and facing in a direction opposite that of the inbound leg (Figure 20). Now turn 70 degrees toward the holding side of the pattern (twist your body to the left in this instance). Draw a line in the direction you're presently facing and make sure it runs through the holding fix. Let's call this the 70 degree reference line (Figure 20).

If you're approaching from anywhere to the right of this line (Figure 21, sector A), make a *direct entry* into the pat-

The 70 Degree Pattern Entry Line

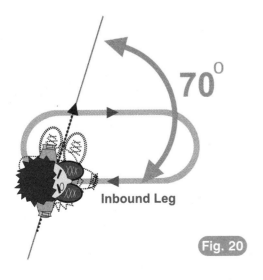

Fig. 20

tern. This means crossing the holding fix and turning to the direction of the pattern's outbound leg.

If you approach from anywhere to the left of the 70 degree reference line, but to the right of inbound leg direction (Figure 22, sector B), then make a *parallel entry*. This

The Direct Entry

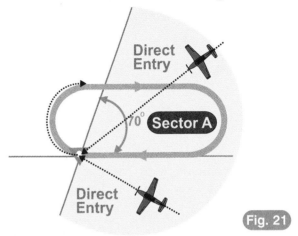

Fig. 21

means crossing the fix and flying opposite and parallel to the direction of the inbound leg for one minute. Then turn in the direction of the holding pattern through more than 180 degrees and intercept the holding course inbound (typically that would be a 210 degree turn).

The Parallel Entry

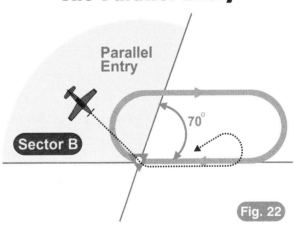

Fig. 22

If you're approaching from the only remaining sector (Figure 23, sector C), make a *teardrop entry* by flying to the holding fix, then turning outbound to a heading that's 30 degrees divergent from the direction of the outbound leg. Fly this heading for one minute, then turn to intercept the inbound course.

Now, a word here if I may about this imaginary 70-degree line we've just drawn in the sky. Students think there's something magic about this precise angle, and that if they're two degrees off they'll be doing the wrong thing and forced by ATC to fly forever in holding hell. Would you relax and feel better if I said, "Facing the fix, draw a line a bit more than two-thirds of the way to the holding side

The Teardrop Entry

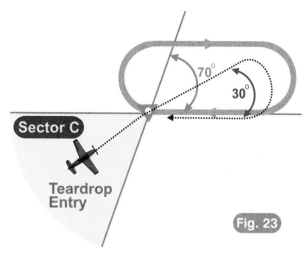

Fig. 23

The Holding Pattern Entry Decoder

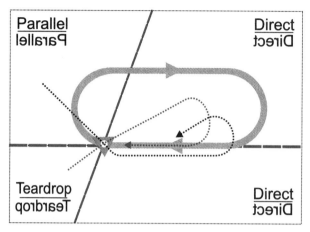

By photocopying this diagram on transparency material you can place it over any holding pattern (with right or left turns), and determine the proper type of entry.

Fig. 24

of the inbound course line. If you're more or less to the right of the line as you approach the fix, make a direct entry, if you're to the left of the line and right of the inbound leg, fly a parallel entry, and anywhere else, make a teardrop entry. To tell you the truth, that will work. Again, think about the underlying concept—the real question to ask as you approach the hold is, "What entry will keep me close and not require any maneuvers best left to a professional aerobatic pilot?"

When entering and flying a holding pattern, ATC expects you to make standard rate turns (three degrees per second) or a maximum of 30 degrees of bank or to use a bank angle provided by your flight director system (the flight director is not the instructor in the right seat, either). For most us, flying smaller airplanes, using standard rate turns does the job.

Now I have a little surprise for you. Here's an easy method to help you better evaluate the proper holding pat-

tern entry to use. It's a holding pattern orienter and I'd like you to create one then use it every time you're asked how to enter a holding pattern. I call it the *Plastic Overlay Method.*

The Plastic Overlay Method

The ultimate solution to deciphering holding pattern entries is shown in Figure 24. It's a little device I've nicknamed the *Rod Machado Holding Pattern Entry Decoder.* Cut the box out around the dotted lines, take it to Kinkos (which is a photocopy place, not a chiropractor's office which would be named, *No More Kinko's*) and have it photocopied on overhead transparency material.

This plastic overlay can now be used to decode any holding entry. After drawing the holding pattern on the chart,

The Holding Pattern Entry Decoder in Action

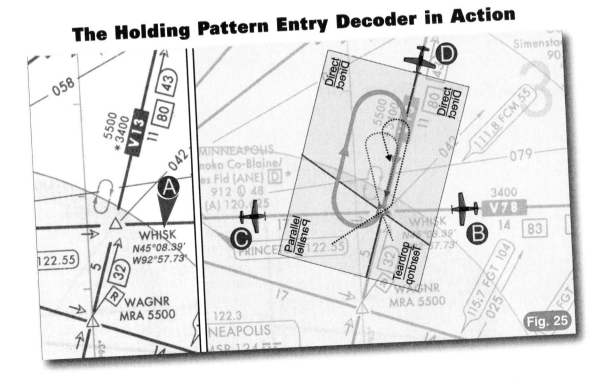

Fig. 25

The Holding Pattern Entry Decoder in Action

Fig. 26

lay the transparency over the drawn racetrack pattern. Determine from what direction you're approaching the holding pattern, then do what the plastic overlay says. Nonstandard (left-hand turn) patterns are easily handled by flipping the overlay over.

Let's try it. Assume you were instructed to hold at the published holding patterns shown at WHISK intersection as shown in Figure 25 position A (some charts show published holding patterns to make it easy for both you and ATC to communicate holding instructions). Lay the decoder over the pattern depicted at WHISK, overlap the decoder's intersection with WHISK and assure that the decoder's holding pattern matches the correct direction of the drawn pattern. If you were approaching WHISK from the east on Victor 78 (Figure 25, position B), the decoder says a *direct* entry would be the appropriate way to engage the pattern. Approaching from the west on Victor 78 calls for a *parallel* entry (Figure 25, position C). Approaching WHISK from the northeast, on Victor 13 (Figure 25, position D) calls for a *direct* entry.

Suppose you were instructed to hold in the published holding pattern at DELOW intersection shown in Figure 26, position A. Notice that this is a non-standard holding pattern. To use our holding pattern decoder we need to flip it over and place it on DELOW intersection as shown in Figure 26, making sure that we overlap the decoder's intersection with DELOW and that holding pattern matches the correct direction of the pattern on the chart. If you were approaching DELOW from the east on Victor 464 (Figure 26, position B), the decoder says a *parallel* entry would be appropriate. Approaching from the west on Victor 464 calls for a *direct* entry (Figure 26, position C). Approaching DELOW from the south (as if you're were using your GPS to go direct to the intersection) as shown in Figure 26 position D, calls for a *teardrop* entry.

Of course, when taking your FAA IFR knowledge exam you won't be allowed to bring this piece of plastic into the testing room with you. That's why I want you to memorize how this is drawn. When taking the test, draw it on a square piece of the note paper you're provided. Just remember how to draw the standard pattern, knowing that you can flip the paper over for non-standard entries. There's nothing wrong with placing this paper over the intersection at which you're holding on the IFR chart and eyeballing the correct entry.

As a final note on, during your IFR practical flight exam, you'll be expected to determine the correct holding entry within +/- 5 degrees. This is a good reason to use the pattern entry decoder on your checkride.

So now you've got a grip on holding. If you keep in mind the underlying ideas, holding is not difficult to understand or execute.

It's time to move on and take a closer look at how the IFR system operates.

Postflight Briefing #6-1

Hold Everything

Bruce Williams

I get lots of questions and comments from folks who argue about the recommended entries for holding patterns. Critics often say, correctly, that the standard entries are just recommendations (and a DPE I know recently pointed out that she can't fail an IFR candidate for not using one of the standard entries).

But here's a defense of using the recommended procedures. It's true that the "recommended" holding entry procedures described in the AIM aren't required and that controllers don't care how you enter a holding pattern (at least I've never talked to one who threw out the high and low scores and awarded points for artistic interpretation after issuing a holding clearance) if you are scrupulous about maintaining your assigned altitude. But the recommended procedures do offer several advantages.

First, they provide common operating practices that instructors can teach to the community of IFR students and aviators. Roll-your-own methods are fine and legal, but if you're juggling several students, picking up students mid-stream, or giving IPCs, using standard procedures certainly makes training more efficient and helps to avoid confusion. Pilots who move to other flight schools and instructors can count on the recommended methods being acceptable wherever they train and fly. Folks aspiring to airline and other professional careers will usually find that the "recommended" methods are the standards to which they'll be tested during interviews and trained and expected to fly if they're hired.

Next, IFR-approved GPS units and integrated systems like the Garmin G1000 typically provide messages that suggest one of the recommended procedures as you approach a charted hold. Now, the GPS isn't going to set off alarm bells if you look at the picture on the moving map, cross the fix, and then zig and zag your way back into the hold. But knowing how to apply the recommended procedures can still reduce your workload and provide an efficient path into the hold.

And not all entries are into holding patterns assigned as delaying tactics. Many instrument approach procedures, and even some SIDs and STARs, include charted holds that are used for course reversals (i.e., procedure turns) and as safe places to gain or lose altitude during the transition from the en route structure into the terminal environment and vice-versa. ATC doesn't usually drop such holds in your lap at the last minute, and by definition they're on a chart. Using the appropriate recommended procedure is an efficient and predictable way to fly those charted procedures, albeit not the only legally acceptable method. None of the foregoing is to suggest that creative folks can't come up with other methods that meet the basic safety/efficiency criteria. There are many ways to fly, for example, airport traffic patterns. But having standard procedures streamlines training, and, in theory at least, helps everyone in the system operate predictably and more safely.

Bruce Williams (bruceair.com)

Postflight Briefing #6-2

Practice, Practice, Practice...On Your Own

As an instrument student, you cannot legally file an IFR flight plan (either a paper flight plan or one arranged verbally with ATC). You must be instrument rated to do such a thing. This doesn't, however, preclude you from asking ATC for a practice instrument approach if you'd like to practice your instrument approaches, while wearing a view limiting device in VFR conditions with a safety pilot on board. This allows you to fly an instrument approach in VFR conditions with the safety pilot doing the things you can't do when you're unable to look outside the airplane.

After you've established communication with the appropriate ATC controller, ask for a *practice instrument approach*. These words tell the controller that you aren't filing an IFR flight plan and that you won't be operating in actual instrument conditions. Make sure you tell the controller how you'll terminate the approach (i.e., low approach, full stop landing, executing the published missed approach, etc.).

Of course, this assumes that you are sufficiently skilled to fly the approach you're shooting. In other words, if the controller asks, "2132 Bravo, I show you over the outer marker. Do you concur?" As you key the mic, he doesn't expect to hear the outer marker's beeping sound in the background while you say, "I don't know but I think someone's fries are done."

You must also ensure your instructor agrees that you're ready to practice your approaches with a safety pilot on board. You might also ask if he or she would approve your doing holding pattern practice, too. If it's not too busy, most controllers are more than happy to provide you with holding clearances.

For instance, when my instrument students are ready to practice holding without me on board, I have them call ATC and say something like the following, "SoCal approach, this is 2132 Bravo. I'm an instrument student and, workload permitting, would it be possible for you to give me a few holding pattern clearances at XXX intersection for practice?" But only do this when the controller is obviously not too busy. Although you can fly practice instrument approaches as well as holding patterns solo without wearing a view limiting device, it's always wise to have a competent and qualified safety pilot on board under these conditions.

Chapter 7
How the IFR System Works

Because You're Mine, I'll Fly the Line

Once upon a time, in aviation's early history, pilots flew in bad weather by using the telegraph, and it wasn't just to get a message. These pilots flew low enough to see and follow telegraph lines that stretched across the country. They also used railroad tracks because rails were easy to follow, especially if a train was using them at the time. Hence the belief of many that IFR *really* stands for "I follow railroads." Later, the first marker beacons were bonfires!

While some pilots were brave enough to fly like this, it left a lot to be desired from a safety standpoint. Survival, for example, was sort of a hit-or-miss proposition. Eventually, you couldn't miss hitting something. This was the original version of the old Groucho Marx TV show, "You Bet Your Life."

In these early days of flying the (telegraph) line, the risk of two pilots bumping into one another under low visibility conditions was probably the least of a pilot's problems. It was a pretty safe bet that at any given moment there'd only be one daredevil per thousand square miles or so. In the beginning, the biggest risk was running into tall objects, with "tall" being anything that was more than maybe 50 feet off the ground. Silos, small hills, big mountains, and the occasional smokestack were some of the risks these early pilots sometimes failed to conquer.

This situation changed with the invention of gyroscopic flight instruments and electronic radio and navigation systems. Suddenly, pilots could go without dread where angels feared to tread. It was now possible for pilots to have their airplanes, as well as their heads, in the clouds. Unfortunately, this increased the chances that two or more airplanes would find themselves using the same tiny bit of airspace at the same moment. Something had to be done to separate IFR pilots so they didn't have strange encounters of the unfortunate kind.

But let's back up for just a second and see how radio and the air traffic control system got started working together in the first place.

In the Beginning

It was a coincidence of convenience that the first powered airplane flight and the first long-distance radio transmission occurred in the same year—1903. The next time you talk to ATC, thank Elmo Pickerill. A one-time Associated Press telegrapher, he became enamored with the idea of putting radio in airplanes. In 1909, he approached Orville Wright and asked about renting an airplane and pilot to take him aloft for some tests. Wilbur knew his airplane's limits (and his own), and told Pickerill there was nothing available that would lift two men *and* all the equipment it would take to talk.

No problem for "Pick," a man of ample ambition and talent. He simply had the Wrights teach him to fly. Total training time: two months. This was long before the FAA got into the licensing business, of course. In August, 1910,

A Modern Air Traffic Control Facility

Courtesy FAA

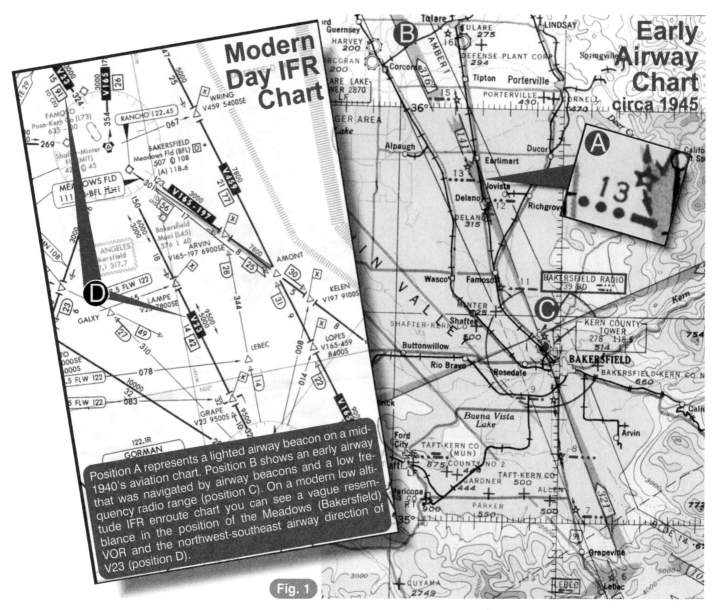

Position A represents a lighted airway beacon on a mid-1940's aviation chart. Position B shows an early airway that was navigated by airway beacons and a low frequency radio range (position C). On a modern low altitude IFR enroute chart you can see a vague resemblance in the position of the Meadows (Bakersfield) VOR and the northwest-southeast airway direction of V23 (position D).

Fig. 1

Pickerill made the first radio contact from an airplane. Now, consider this. Elmo Pickerill was the only person on board, and the technology of the time was a telegraph key, not a mic! Flying in an open cockpit, semi-controllable airplane, he made in-flight contact with three wireless stations aboard ships, two coastal stations, one temporary station in Manhattan Beach (NY) and one permanent station in New York City. This may be one of the most remarkable flying feats in history, and something to keep in mind next time you're thinking of complaining about pilot workload. Remember, this guy had no autopilot. In fact, he didn't even have a co-pilot.

The IFR system's origins are in the bag—the mail bag. It was the government's desire to create a practical means of moving the mail by plane that led to the initial navigational aids on which the navigational and communications system underpinnings of IFR flight were built. The first official air mail flight was a bit less than a full success. The pilot left Washington (amid much fanfare though no airfare), got lost, landed in Maryland, and sent the mail to its destination in New York by train. I guess his thought was, "Letter go."

To make the system work a bit better, Congress coughed up the bucks to build five of what were officially known as Air Mail Radio Stations between New York and Chicago. One was located in a chicken coop, which may explain why today's *Air Route Traffic Control Centers* (ARTCC) facilities often feel somewhat dark and closed in, and why the first instrument pilots were sometimes a bit chicken. Pilots went aloft equipped with homemade homing devices, some loops of wire as an antenna, and a lot of faith.

This system had its limits (clearly), one of which was daylight. There was no way airmail was going to be a practical and economical service if it couldn't move more mail more quickly, which meant a need to fly at night. Sound the bonfire music. On February 21, 1921, night cross-country instrument flight was invented. Two planes were launched in each direction from New York and San Francisco, their way marked by bonfires lit by volunteer civilians along the route.

If only Jim Morrison had been around to sing, "Come on baby, light my fire," the outcome might have been better. The two westbound flights were turned back by a snowstorm. One eastbound flight crashed in Nevada. Three

Fig. 2

In the early days of air traffic control (before radar), controllers would separate airplanes by identifying their position on large map boards with small strips of paper, often called shrimp boats, because they looked like tiny boats on a calm sea. When an airplane updated its position via radio, the shrimp boats were moved to match the target's updated position.

down. But the remaining plane actually completed its mission. One-for-four was apparently sufficient to prove the concept would in some sense work, though today's commercial air travelers expect a higher success ratio. Rotating beacons, better radio navigation devices, and all the other amenities we take for granted in flying IFR today followed.

The transcontinental airway system was actually under the aegis of the Post Office Department until 1926, when it was transferred to the Commerce Department. So the next time you launch an IFR flight, thank the mailman.

Enter ATC

On January 29, 1929 a beacon was turned on in the Nevada desert. When the switch was thrown, it completed a transcontinental system of lighted beacons that was the original federal airway. The light was a sight in the night. Bonfires out, beacons on, airplanes up. Figure 1 shows a mid-1940's aviation chart with lighted airway beacons (position A) and an early airway (position B) navigated by airway beacons and a Low frequency radio range (position C). Note, however, that a pilot still had to be able to *see* the beacons to get where he was going. This is why the initial decades of aviation were low and slow. The navigational aids were only an aid if you could see them. There was navigation, but not much communication.

About this time, the Airway Radio Stations became capable of voice transmissions. Yakkity yak, you could now talk back (and forth)! The system developed rapidly over the few years, expanding to 68 Airway Radio Stations blanketing the country by 1933. Commercial aviation became a reality as a result.

So did ATC, in a fashion. But it wasn't initially a government entity, and it wasn't called ATC. In 1935, four of the major air carriers (TWA, American, United, and Eastern) became concerned about keeping their airliners separated and they cooperated in creating the first aviation traffic

control facility at Newark, NJ. With more facilities under construction and on the drawing board, the government leaped into action. In June, 1936, the Bureau of Air Commerce assumed control of the three existing facilities and designated them Airway Traffic Control Stations. ATC was born. This was the beginning of the active control of instrument flights.

And it was an exciting time, too, because each facility made up its own system of markers ("shrimp boats"), progress strips, and other tracking paraphernalia. It wasn't until two years later that everyone got on the same page, or strip.

Shrimp Boats in Flight

In the early days of instrument flying, radar hadn't been developed as an effective tool for tracking things in the sky. So, air traffic controllers had to sit at a desk and move small markers (representing the airplanes) around on airway maps (Figure 2). These early paper markers were called shrimp boats because they looked like tiny boats on a calm

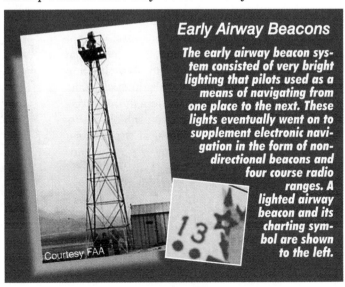

Early Airway Beacons

The early airway beacon system consisted of very bright lighting that pilots used as a means of navigating from one place to the next. These lights eventually went on to supplement electronic navigation in the form of non-directional beacons and four course radio ranges. A lighted airway beacon and its charting symbol are shown to the left.

Flight Data Progress Strips

Courtesy FAA

Fig. 3

Modern day air traffic control still uses paper strips (data progress strips) to keep track of each aircraft in the ARTCC system. In the event of radar loss, a controller can use these strips to maintain position awareness of the aircraft they represent.

them were popping up all over the country. One group of controllers would be responsible for the IFR traffic in their large geographical neighborhood, while other controllers across the country handled traffic in their local area. Eventually, controllers handling air route traffic were consolidated to form the Air Route Traffic Control Centers *(ARTCC)*. At present, there are 21 Centers in the United States, with some controlling more as much as 18 million square miles of airspace from the base of controlled airspace up to Flight Level (FL) 600, or 60,000 feet (Figure 5).

In Los Angeles, for instance, the Los Angeles Air Route Traffic Control Center (ARTCC) is located in Palmdale, California (Figure 6). It is responsible for about 178,000 square miles of

lake, and not because controllers were fishing for compliments or using origami to modify the paper pieces to resemble cute little decapod crustaceans. Shrimp boats were arranged on the map so IFR airplanes were adequately separated, based on the position reports received by ATC.

Pilots on an IFR flight plan regularly transmitted their positions to ATC at designated mandatory reporting points. These reports contained specific information, which pilots recalled by the letter sequence PTA-TEN: position, time, altitude, type of flight plan, estimate to the next compulsory reporting point, and name of the compulsory reporting point after that. Even in today's modern IFR system, controllers maintain paper strips for every airplane that they're controlling (Figure 3). If the radar system goes down because the mop manager knocks the computer's plug out of the wall, the controller can fall back on the strips if he or she has to (if he hasn't already fallen back on the floor in a coma).

Because sushi hadn't been invented yet, the shrimp boat method worked well back then, at least until someone sneezed and blew the map clean. Fortunately, this didn't happen that often, perhaps because controllers didn't catch colds back then. It was always a problem if the controllers lost track of who was at what intersection and when he was there. With the advent of civilian radar (RAdio Detection And Ranging) in the 1950s, the process of managing IFR traffic became much less cumbersome and much safer, too (Figure 4).

Eventually, aviation grew and there was an ever-increasing need for air traffic controllers. Soon, controllers and the places that house

airspace stretching from central California into Nevada and south to the Mexican border. And just because LA ARTCC is located in Palmdale, don't think there's any palmistry or soothsaying activities in modern air traffic management. There isn't! Instead, you'll find a sophisticated, high-tech approach to keeping IFR airplanes separated from one another.

Within each Center, there are smaller sections known as *sectors*. This is just good common sense. You want to give individual controllers responsibility for traffic in one or more sectors, so you give these sectors names so that everyone in the Center knows who's responsible for what airspace. Figure 7, position A is an excerpt from a low altitude IFR enroute chart

Air Traffic Control Today

Courtesy FAA

Fig. 4

The modern air traffic control system is now managed with the use of radar as well as an experimental system presently in development known as ADS-B (automatic dependent surveillance broadcasts).

ARTCC Coverage in the U.S.

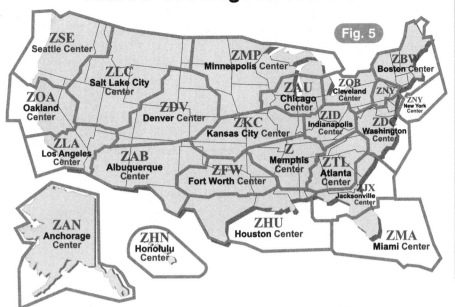

Fig. 5

showing the boundary between the Albuquerque and Fort Worth Centers. Within each Center frequency box is the name of the individual sector (i.e., Tucumcari and Plainview) in that location (Figure 7, positions B & C). Sectors can have names like the Bakersfield sector or the Hector sector for the poetically inclined. After all, there is something charming about getting a vector from the controller in the Hector sector.

Sectors are often named after geological and historical references located within their boundaries. Pilots no longer refer to individual controllers by their sector names as they once did. Now we just refer to all controllers by referencing the Center's name, such as LA Center or Albuquerque Center.

Oakland, CA ARTCC

Courtesy FAA

Fig. 6

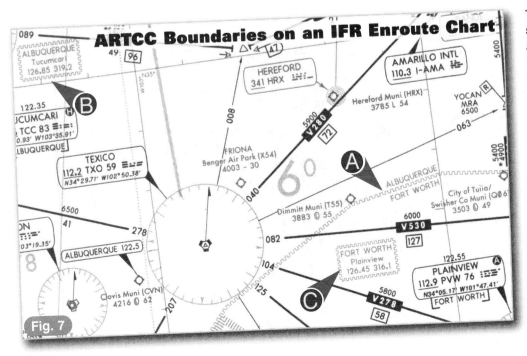

Fig. 7

The low altitude IFR enroute chart shows the boundary between the Albuquerque and Fort Worth Centers (position A) as a serrated blue line. Within each Center frequency box is the name of the individual sector (e.g., Tucumcari and Plainview) in that location (positions B and C). Sectors can have names like the Bakersfield or the Hector sector for the poetically inclined. When calling the Center controller in each sector, don't call him or her by the sector name. Instead use the name of the Center to address the controller. In other words, don't say, "Tucumcari sector, this is 2132B." Do this and the controller will know you never took your instrument checkride. Instead, say, "Albuquerque Center this is 2132 Bravo."

Within the 21 domestic ARTCCs across the country, controllers use radar to control traffic (Figure 8). There are still a few places in the country where radar coverage isn't available (and the local Baskin Robbins surprise flavor of the week is vanilla, too). This lack of coverage usually occurs at lower altitudes. No big deal here. For the most part, when you get high enough, you're identified on some controller's radar screen. It's the controller's job to keep IFR airplanes separated by five miles unless a smaller separation is permitted. For instance, if an airplane is within 40 miles of the controller's radar antenna, a controller can reduce the separation to three miles (Figure 9). Closer to the antenna means better target detection and target resolution.

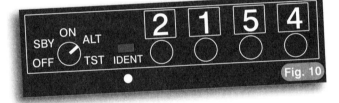
Courtesy FAA   Fig. 8

Radar Separation Standards

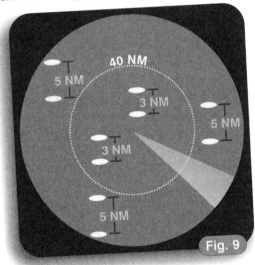

Fig. 9

Typical radar separation standards require that radar targets be separated by at least five miles unless they're within 40 nautical miles of the radar antenna where a three mile separation may apply.

You might, not unreasonably, be wondering why antenna distance is an issue since modern airplanes use transponders, which allow controllers to identify a target precisely (Figure 10). Well, identifying targets and separating airplanes in this manner only works if the

transponder and the ATC computer are both working properly. This isn't always the case, which means it's good to have sufficient separation between airplanes so controllers can revert to the older point-to-airplane-on-a-map method of keeping airplanes apart.

Transponder interrogation is known as the *secondary radar beacon system*. It's called *secondary* because the *pri-*

The Transponder

Fig. 10

mary method of radar identification consists of seeing your airplane as a little fuzzy white blip on the radar screen (Figure 11) in the absence of a transponder return and its accompanying datablock (Figure 12). If the controller loses the ability to use the secondary radar beacon

Required Reports to ATC

In addition to other required reports, the following reports should be made to ATC:

1. When vacating any previously assigned altitude or flight level (FL) for a newly assigned altitude or FL.

2. When an altitude change will be made, when operating on a VFR-on-top clearance.

3. When unable to climb/descend at a rate of a least 500 feet per minute.

4. When an approach has been missed (request clearance for specific action (e.g., to alternate airport, another approach, etc.).

5. Change in the average true airspeed (at cruising altitude) when it varies by 5 percent or 10 knots (whichever is greater) from that filed in the flight plan.

6. The time and altitude or flight level upon reaching a holding fix or point to which cleared

7. When leaving any assigned holding fix or point.

8. Any loss, in controlled airspace, of VOR, TACAN, ADF, low frequency navigation receiver capability, GPS anomalies while using installed IFR-certified GPS/GNSS receivers, complete or partial loss of ILS receiver capability or impairment of air/ground communications capability.

9. Any information relating to the safety of flight.

(The following reports are not required if in radar contact with ATC)

10. When leaving final approach fix inbound on final approach (nonprecision approach) or when leaving the outer marker or fix used in lieu of the outer marker inbound on final approach (precision approach).

11. A corrected estimate at anytime it becomes apparent that an estimate as previously submitted is in error in excess of three minutes.

Primary Radar Returns

Fig. 11

Primary radar returns are "raw" radar returns. This was the original means by which ATC identified targets when transponders weren't/aren't in use.

Secondary Radar Returns

The rectangle represents the digitized primary radar return.

AC speed 350 knots

1B

AAL 599
110   35

The slash represents the secondary radar return.

Dots are the AC flight path

AC altitude 11,000 feet

Fig. 12

Secondary radar returns are the means by which ATC identifies transponder equipped airplanes. Often called "data blocks," this computer generated data follows a target as it moves on the radar screen.

system, he loves the one he's with, which in this case means reverting to the primary radar.

The closer to the radar antenna, the better the resolution of a *primary* target. If the controller lets you and someone else have just three miles separation 150 miles out from the radar antenna, your little white fuzzball and the other airplane's little white fuzzball might appear to be one large fuzzball on the screen if the transponders aren't being processed for one reason or another. And if the controller can't figure out with some degree of precision where you are, you and the other airplane might indeed become "united" airlines.

Isn't it interesting that the modern IFR system still uses instrument procedures based on the possibility that the radar system will stop working, thus forcing the controller to revert to the shrimp-boat method of controlling IFR traffic? What's going on here? Isn't the modern ATC system reliable? Does is really stop working on occasion? Are there other reasons the IFR system makes this assumption? The answers are yes, yes, and yes again.

Redundancy is an important concept throughout the IFR system. Because the consequences of a failure are so great, every effort is made to provide backup for equipment and procedures. Look around your cockpit. Many of

Automatic Dependent Surveillance Broadcast

ADS-B or automatic dependent surveillance broadcast is a revolutionary new way of controlling air traffic. The concept is simple. ADS-B equipped aircraft broadcast their precise position via a digital datalink along with their airspeed, altitude, direction of movement (up, down, right, left). Air traffic control or other aircraft with ADS-B can identify targets in real time for air traffic control to avoid a traffic conflict.

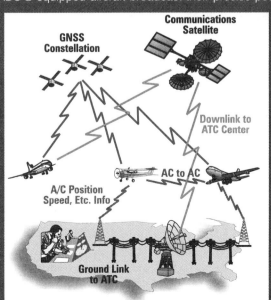

As a simplified example, consider an air-traffic control secondary radar. The radar measures the range and bearing of an aircraft. The bearing is measured by the position of the rotating radar antenna when it receives a reply to its interrogation from the aircraft, and the range by the time it takes for the radar to receive the reply. The beam of the antenna gets wider as the aircraft get farther from the antenna, thus making the measured position information less accurate. An ADS-B based system, on the other hand, would listen for position reports broadcast by the aircraft. These position reports are based on accurate navigation systems, such as satellite navigation systems (e.g. GPS). The accuracy of the system is now determined by the accuracy of the navigation system, not measurement errors. The accuracy is unaffected by the range to the aircraft. With the radar, detecting aircraft velocity changes requires tracking the received data. Changes can only be detected over a period of several position updates. With ADS-B, velocity changes are broadcast almost instantaneously.

The diagram to the left shows how ADS-B information is exchanged. A communications satellite helps provide voice capability between the aircraft and the ATC facility. The GPS satellite system provides position and altitude information and this information is relayed directly to the ATC facility via ground lines. Additionally, there is an airplane-to-airplane exchange of information.

An Air Traffic Control Clearance

Cleared (from Stockton Metro) direct Manteca VOR, V113 Linden VOR, V23 GALTS. Hold SE GALTS on V23, expect further clearance at 11:35

Fig. 13

IFR pilots are always given an ATC clearance. This provides a means of navigation to a destination and is ultimately most useful in the event communication is lost with a controller.

the instruments back each other up, so that a failure of one can be compensated for. Most people fly with two nav and two comm radios and an electrically driven gyro to back up the vacuum-driven one. Larger and more complex airplanes even require that there be two qualified pilots up front.

ATC does the same redundancy dance. There is a high level of duplication in its equipment, and extensive back-up plans in the event of partial or total failures of the computers, radios, screens, and other modern implements. The shrimp boats are part of that backup plan.

In fact, every step of an IFR flight is protected in this way. It's not that failures occur often. They don't. But assuring the safe conduct of a flight even when bad things happen is the goal of ATC.

It starts with your flight plan and clearance. To fly IFR in the IFR system, you need an instrument rating, an IFR-legal airplane, and you must be IFR current (more on these items in the regulations chapter). You also need to file an IFR flight plan and receive an IFR clearance. A clearance is a set of instructions on how to get from hither to yon, and it's issued on the underlying assumption that one of two

bad things could happen. Either your radio could cease working, or the controller's equipment could roll over and play dead. With an IFR clearance, you have a route, altitude and any pertinent restrictions to follow if and when you can't talk to anyone else or others can't talk to you. That's why you'll receive an IFR clearance on every IFR flight, without exception.

On the other hand, there's a pretty good chance you won't really fly precisely that clearance. Why? Because a controller may want you to fly radar vectors for at least part of the flight. What gives? Well, think of it this way. For lots of things, there's the formal way of doing it, and the real-world way. Your filed flight plan is the formality, the fallback position to be used if all else fails.

But with the ATC system straining to carry the load, controllers need to move as much metal as they can as quickly as possible, consistent with keeping everyone separated. It's sometimes more expeditious to move IFR airplanes via radar vectors in lieu of having them fly specific (and usually longer) routes from navaid to navaid.

As long as the controller is talking to you and can identify your airplane on radar, and as long as your radio is working, you'll simply do as the controller instructs. You'll mostly benefit as a result of these vectors. It saves you and everyone else a lot of time. If, however, you lose communication or the radar goes kaput, the controller expects you to fly the routes, altitudes and restrictions assigned in your IFR clearance (Figure 13). That's *your* shrimp boat, the backup that gives you a well-defined course of action if all else fails. The IFR clearance is simply a good backup plan, and a relatively failsafe one, too.

Basic VFR Weather Minimums

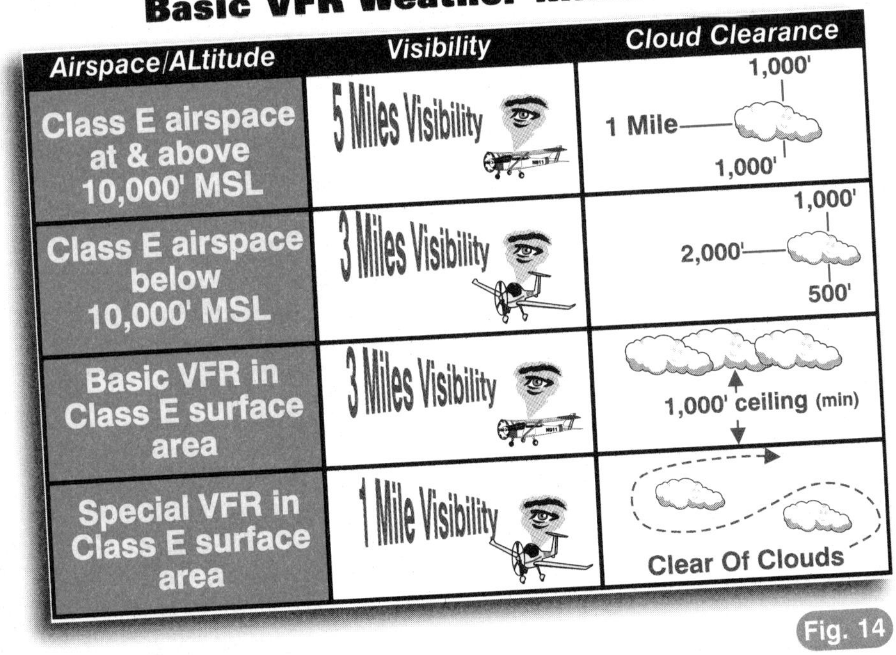

Airspace/ALtitude	Visibility	Cloud Clearance
Class E airspace at & above 10,000' MSL	5 Miles Visibility	1 Mile, 1,000', 1,000'
Class E airspace below 10,000' MSL	3 Miles Visibility	2,000', 1,000', 500'
Basic VFR in Class E surface area	3 Miles Visibility	1,000' ceiling (min)
Special VFR in Class E surface area	1 Mile Visibility	Clear Of Clouds

Fig. 14

Controlled and Uncontrolled Airspace

Years ago, when pilots began flying in the clouds under the direction of ATC, they were sequenced and separated from other known IFR traffic. The problem was, some folks liked flying in the clouds but they didn't like telling others (ATC, for instance) about it. You can imagine how this made those IFR pilots who were counting on ATC to keep them sequenced and separated from other airplanes feel. Something had to be done, and there weren't enough government men available to spank all those bad boys who'd do such a thing.

Enter controlled airspace (now called Class A, B, C, D, and E airspace).

Years ago, smart folks decided that if some airspace were controlled by requiring *stringent* cloud clearance and visibility restrictions, this might prevent pilots from trying to use the same cloud (the one that IFR qualified pilots wanted to use) at the same time. This thinking was the genesis of what is now known as our *basic VFR weather minimums* (FAR 91.155), as shown in Figure 14 and 15. It was the rule that required all pilots who weren't on an IFR flight plan to honor a minimum horizontal and vertical distance from clouds and specified flight visibility requirements.

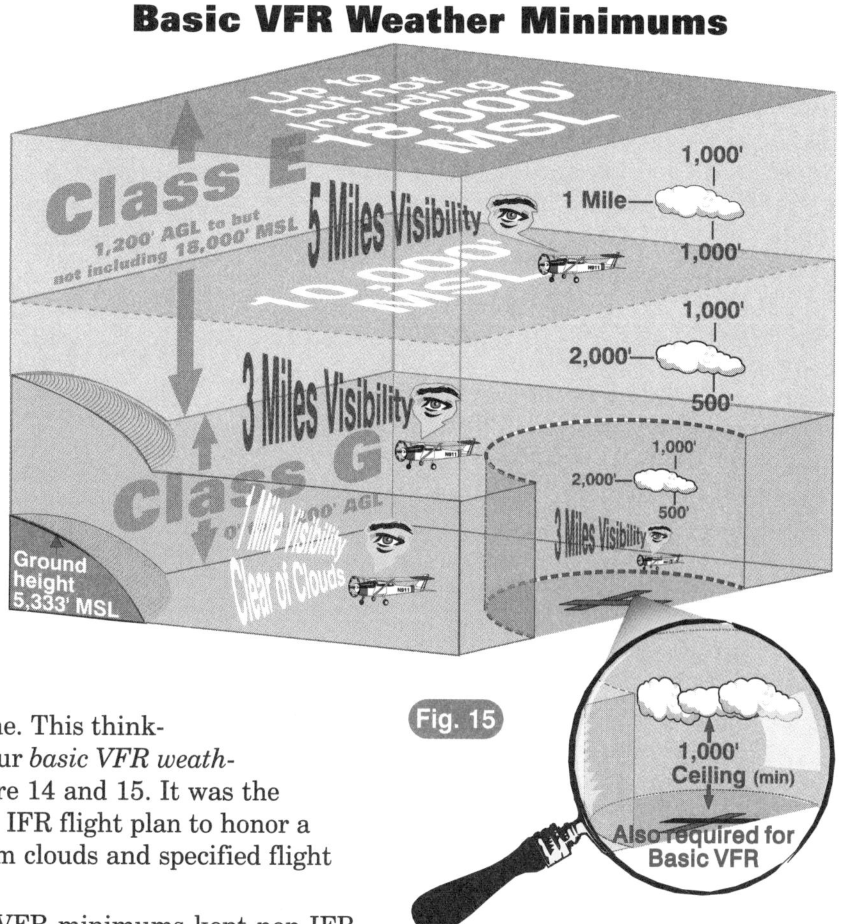

This made a lot of sense, given that these VFR minimums kept non-IFR qualified pilots away from a cloud. The result was to minimize the chance that an IFR pilot would exchange paint with someone flying too near the side of a cloud, flying between clouds, or flying with such lousy visibility that it would be impossible to see and avoid an IFR pilot who might pop out of the cloud at any minute. When it was decided to control airspace (really to control *pilots;* the airspace does what it wants) by imposing VFR weather minimums, a problem arose regarding what airspace should be made controlled and what should be left uncontrolled.

The answer everyone finally agreed on was that controlled airspace would include all that airspace that IFR pilots could use in a practical manner. The airspace between airports at less than 1,200 feet AGL is pretty useless for flying IFR enroute. Why? Because, when VORs were the main means of enroute navigation, it was difficult to receive a VOR reliably less than 1,000 feet AGL for more than 25 miles. Even today, there are no enroute airways having less than a 1,000 foot ground clearance (in a mountainous area, the minimum enroute altitude is 2,000 feet AGL). Terrain and obstructions were often the culprit here, in that they interfered with line-of-sight signal transmissions. That's why the controlled airspace across the vast majority of the country, known as Class E airspace, starts at 1,200 feet AGL (Figure 16).

Basic VFR Weather Minimums

Class E — Up to but not including 18,000' MSL

1,200' AGL to but not including 18,000' MSL

5 Miles Visibility — 1 Mile — 1,000' — 1,000' — 10,000' MSL

3 Miles Visibility — 1,000' — 2,000' — 500'

Class G — 1 Mile Visibility Clear of Clouds — 1,000' — 2,000' — 500'

3 Miles Visibility

Ground height 5,333' MSL

Fig. 15

1,000' Ceiling (min)

Also required for Basic VFR

Where Class E Airspace Begins

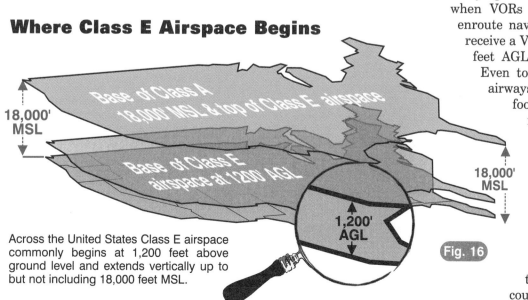

18,000' MSL

Base of Class A 18,000' MSL & top of Class E airspace

Base of Class E airspace at 1,200' AGL

18,000' MSL

1,200' AGL

Fig. 16

Across the United States Class E airspace commonly begins at 1,200 feet above ground level and extends vertically up to but not including 18,000 feet MSL.

Below this 1,200 foot AGL value, you'll mostly find uncontrolled (Class G) airspace, which has a less restricted cloud clearance and visibility requirement (Figure 17 and 18). The novelty here (whether this was intended or not) is that a VFR pilot can now fly 1,000 feet above 199-foot-tall buildings in a congested area (for an AGL altitude of 1,199 feet) and do so in uncontrolled airspace with only one mile visibility and remaining clear of all clouds (Figure 19). This means that a VFR pilot can get maximum utility out of his airplane (assuming he considers flying with this type of visibility as getting "maximum utility").

At 1,200 feet AGL and above, in controlled airspace, IFR pilots can mostly navigate by VOR-defined airways and ATC can usually provide sequencing and separation. Controlled airspace, then, consists of those areas where pilots can and are most likely to fly under instrument flight rules. That's why controlled airspace always encompasses an area four nautical miles to either side of an airway starting at 1,200 feet AGL (Figure 20, position A). This defines as the airspace of a Victor Airway. Within this area, the controlled airspace begins at 1,200 feet AGL as indicated by the faded blue lines (Figure 20, position B). The area outside the faded blue lines is uncontrolled airspace from the surface up to but not including 14,500 foot MSL (Figure 20 position C).

Class G (Uncontrolled) Airspace

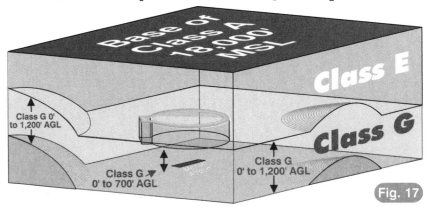

Class G (uncontrolled) airspace is commonly found below 1,200 feet above ground level. Because this is airspace that isn't commonly used by IFR and VFR aircraft during enroute travel, the VFR weather minimums are much less than they would be at higher altitudes where more and faster aircraft are found.

VFR Minimums in Class G Airspace

Airspace/Altitude		Visibility	Cloud Clearance
Class G airspace 1,200 feet or less AGL regardless of MSL altitude	Night	3 Miles Visibility	1,000' / 2,000' / 500'
	Day	1 Mile Visibility	Clear Of Clouds

Since the lowest VFR weather minimums are found in Class G airspace close to the surface, it's possible for a VFR pilot to obtain maximum utility out of his or her airplane when operating at low altitudes. On the other hand, it's important to keep in mind that one mile visibility is actually higher than the minimums found on some instrument approaches!   Fig. 18

Minimum Altitudes and Class G

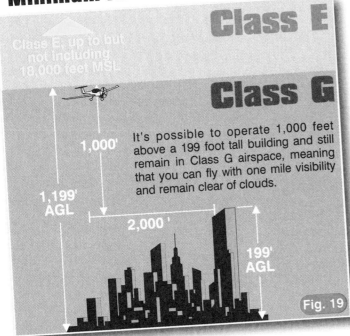

Class E, up to but not including 18,000 feet MSL

Class E

Class G

It's possible to operate 1,000 feet above a 199 foot tall building and still remain in Class G airspace, meaning that you can fly with one mile visibility and remain clear of clouds.

1,000'

1,199' AGL

2,000'

199' AGL

Fig. 19

Controlled airspace is often found in those areas around airports generally starting at 700 feet or 1,200 feet AGL where instrument approaches are conducted, even if there is no airway nearby, as shown in Figure 21, position A. Anywhere to the left of the blue faded line is controlled airspace beginning at 1,200 feet AGL (If these concepts seem unfamiliar to you then you might want to review *Rod Machado's Private Pilot Handbook, Chapter 9*.) At areas closer to airports having instrument approaches you'll see controlled airspace beginning even lower at 700 feet AGL as indicated by a magenta faded border (Figure 21, position B). This lowered base of controlled airspace helps airplanes on instrument approaches to remain within controlled airspace during their descent to the airport.

When an instrument approach allows a sufficiently low descent, it's possible that the controlled airspace might be lowered all the way to the surface, as shown at Visalia in Figure 21, position C. In this instance, the dashed magenta line around Visalia represents surfaced-based controlled airspace.

Controlled and Uncontrolled Airspace

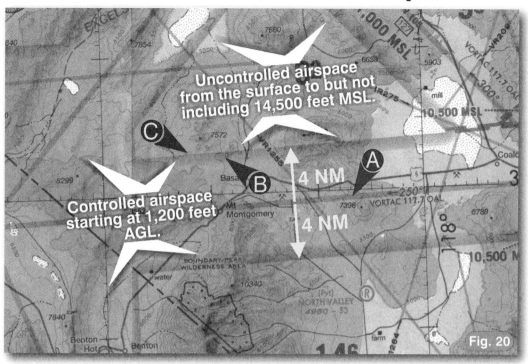

Fig. 20

But what about the airspace that doesn't have an airway running through it and is not located near any airport having an instrument approach procedure? It could be an area like that around Dixon airport, located in Wyoming (Figure 22, position A). Class G (uncontrolled) airspace exists above Dixon from the surface all the way to but not including 14,500 feet MSL. ATC doesn't typically work with IFR pilots in these areas because they are located in uncontrolled airspace.

Believe it or not, it's legal to fly IFR in Class G airspace below 14,500 feet MSL without filing an instrument flight plan or talking to ATC. To do so requires some explanation, and I'm not about to make it. That would be contributing to the delinquency of an adult. I won't discuss this idea anymore, given its terribly goofy nature. If you'd like to do something demonstrably safer, feed great white sharks by hanging a tuna from your mouth and leaning over a boat's railing. Naked. In rough seas.

Keep in mind that Class G (uncontrolled) airspace from the surface up to but not including 14,500 feet MSL is typically found near the high mountains of the West Coast and areas where there are no airways.

Where Controlled Airspace is Found

Fig. 21

Fig. 22

Most of the airspace below 1,200 feet AGL over the United States and outside of an airport's instrument approach environment is also uncontrolled (Class G) (refer back to Figure 16). This makes sense, since it's unlikely anyone can or would fly IFR at altitudes less than 1,200 feet AGL for any great length of time (enroute, for instance). This is why an IFR clearance applies only to controlled airspace. It's the type of airspace that pilots can safely use for navigation. Be aware, though, that this doesn't mean you won't climb through Class G (uncontrolled) airspace when you depart some airports on an IFR flight plan.

For instance, suppose you file an IFR flight plan for a departure from an airport where the controlled airspace (Class E) overlies the airport at 1,200 feet AGL (Figure 23, position A or B). In this instance, when departing IFR from Harris or New Coalinga, you'll have to fly through 1,200 feet of Class G (uncontrolled) airspace until reaching controlled airspace. If so, the IFR clearance you receive will read something like: *You're cleared to Divit airport, when entering controlled airspace, fly heading....* What you do in uncontrolled airspace (Class G) between liftoff and 1,200 feet AGL is your business, not ATC's (with one exception, which I will discuss when we cover IFR departures in Chapter 14). Hopefully you'll climb in a way that avoids any obstructions (yes, even if your airplane has an extremely big roll bar and you fly with two helmets instead of one).

Just to make myself clear here, you can depart any airport in the United States on an IFR *flight plan* even if that airport doesn't have a tower and even if it is in uncontrolled airspace. Your IFR *clearance* applies only when the airplane enters controlled airspace. The controller's obligation to you for sequencing and separation from other IFR airplanes starts where uncontrolled airspace stops. Now, controllers are great people, and if they know something is lurking out there, they'll tell you. But it's not their business to know what's in uncontrolled airspace, and in some cases they simply can't know because of radar

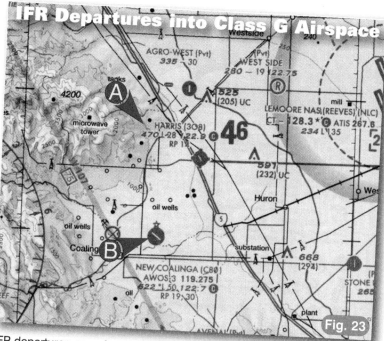

IFR departures are often made from airports lying in Class G airspace where the controlled (Class E) airspace begins at either 700 or 1,200 feet above ground level as is the case with New Coalinga and Harris, above.

or communications limitations. So if you're in G-space, the entire responsibility for separation is yours.

In reality, the only practical scenario where this would happen is if two airplanes were departing IFR from non-towered airports lying in uncontrolled airspace.

More on the ATC System

Air Route Traffic Control Centers normally control traffic starting at the IFR enroute altitude level. In many parts of the country, Center starts controlling traffic at approximately 6,000 feet MSL up to Flight Level 600 (60,000 feet), as shown in Figure 24. This is the top of the high altitude airspace structure. Above FL600 there is activity by the military and aliens who can't find a parking spot at Roswell or Area 51.

What about those folks who are departing or arriving at an airport? Don't they deserve radar coverage, too? They

Center, Tracon and Rapcons

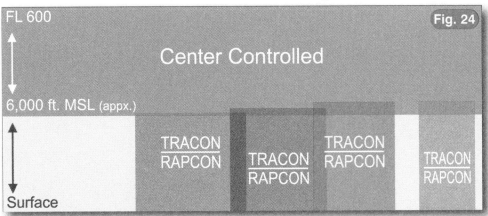

Free Flight

Sorry, but no freebies here. Free Flight is the FAA's move away from highly structured IFR routings and altitudes towards a more flexible system that allows pilots to choose their routes and altitudes, within limits, after notifying ATC of this change. The objective is to allow pilots to fly with greater route efficiency, with fewer deviations and without having to request route changes, such as when attempting to avoid severe weather. Free Flight is made possible given the point-to-point navigation capabilities of newer airplanes based on technology such as GPS and ADS-B.

Here's how it works. In Free Flight there are two spatial zones surrounding each aircraft, the *Protected Zone* and the *Alert Zone*. The smaller one is called the *protected zone* of an aircraft, and it must never be allowed to touch the protected zone of another aircraft. The larger *alert zone* extends well beyond the protected zone. If there is contact between two alert zones, then a signal is automatically sent to air traffic control and both pilots are warned that they may need to take evasive action. The size of these zones will vary based on the aircraft's speed, design, equipment, etc. How would a pilot know where other airplanes are, thus how to prevent overlapping zones? Along with a controller's suggestions, pilots will use cockpit traffic displays infused with new technology such as ADS-B, TCAs, etc.

sure do. That's why you'll often find an Approach and Departure Control using something known as ASR or *airport surveillance radar*. ASR is often found in busy terminal environments that handle IFR traffic operations below Center's airspace (sometimes Center does handle IFR traffic all the way to the ground). Approach Control handles all traffic approaching and departing local airports (call it Departure Control if you're departing an airport). Where Approach Control's jurisdiction ends either vertically or horizontally, Center usually takes over (Figure 24).

Approach Control is sometimes called a Terminal Radar Approach Control (TRACON) or a Radar Approach Control (RAPCON). A RAPCON is a radar facility that's often located in the same facility as the airport tower. Despite these monikers sounding like the names a Klingon would give its kids, the RAPCON may also be an Approach Control facility shared with a branch of the military, such as the U.S. Air Force. TRACONs are usually located in separate buildings, and provide radar service for many airports.

You might be surprised to know that there are instrument approaches consisting of nothing more than radar vectored guidance by controllers to a missed approach point. One of these approaches, which makes use of airport surveillance radar (ASR), is called a *surveillance approach,* and is only available at airports where civil radar instrument approach minimums have been published (more on this shortly). The only equipment required on the pilot's side for an ASR approach is an operable transmitter and receiver.

In a surveillance approach, the controller vectors you to the final approach and on final approach. These vectors take you to the missed approach point. The controller tells you when to start

your descent to the minimum descent altitude (MDA), which is posted in the Radar Instrument Approach Minimums (Section N1) of the government's approach chart booklet (Figure 25). When you're at the missed approach point on this approach, the controller tells you to execute the missed approach unless you have the required minimums for landing, as shown in Section N1. For instance, at Los Alamitos AAF, the minimum descent altitude for Category A, B, and C aircraft is 380 feet with a minimum flight visibility of ¾ mile (you'll learn about the details of MDA and aircraft categories in Chapter 11). If you request, the controller will provide you with recommended altitudes each mile along the approach path down to the last mile that is at or above the MDA. How's *that* for service? Needless to say, this is not how they routinely do it at LAX or JFK.

Another type of radar-guided approach is conducted using *precision approach radar* (PAR). Here, the controller provides highly accurate lateral and vertical guidance all the way down to a decision altitude, in much the

RADAR INSTRUMENT APPROACH MINIMUMS

RADAR MINS

LOS ALAMITOS AAF (KSLI), CA (Amdt 3A, 19 APR 01 USA)   Fig. 25

RADAR [12] - (E) 124.75 127.95 279.5 285.55 290.9 ▽   ELEV 35

	RWY	GS/TCH/RPI	CAT	NA DH/ MDA-VIS	HAT/ HAA	CEIL-VIS
PAR [3]	22L	4.0°/57/800	COPTER	185-¼	150	(200-¼)
	22L [5]	3.0°/43/800	AB	235-½	200	(200-½)
			CD	235-¾	200	(200-¾)
ASR	22L		ABC	380-¾	345	(400-¾)
			D	380-1	345	(400-1)
CIR [4]	22L		A	440-1	405	(500-1)
			B	500-1	465	(500-1)
			C	500-1½	465	(500-1½)
			D	600-2	565	(600-2)

Instrument approaches conducted via radar guidance (ASR or PAR) have their minimum altitudes and visibilities posted in Section N1 of the government's instrument approach chart booklet.

same way an ILS works. This PAR approach is accompanied by statements such as, "Slightly above glidepath," or, "Well below glidepath." It's sort of a talking ILS.

Given that the PAR glidepath descent angles used by the controller are published in Section 1, when the controller says you're on glidepath you should use the required glideslope descent rates we discussed in Chapter 5, page 5-30. For each mile along the approach, the controller will offer range information. Navigational guidance is provided until you reach decision altitude. Of course, if you don't have the required landing minimums at or past DA, you must execute the missed approach based on the instructions published or given to you by the controller.

FAA FLIGHT PLAN							
1. Type	**2. AIRCRAFT IDENT**	**3. AIRCRAFT TYPE/ SPECIAL EQUIPMENT**	**4. TRUE AIRSPEED**	**5. DEPARTURE POINT**	**6. DEPARTURE TIME**		**7. CRUISING ALTITUDE**
VFR					PROPOSED (Z)	ACTUAL (Z)	
X IFR	N2132B	BE36/G	174 KTS	KBFL	01:00Z		8000 feet
DVFR							

8. ROUTE OF FLIGHT
EHF V248 AVE V137 ROM V485 GILRO

9. DESTINATION (Name of airport and city)	10. EST. TIME ENROUTE		11. REMARKS		
	HOURS	MINUTES	NONE		
KSJC	01	09			Fig. 26

12. FUEL ON BOARD		13. ALTERNATE AIRPORTS	14. PILOT'S NAME, ADDRESS & TELEPHONE NUMBER & AIRCRAFT HOME BASE	15. NUMBER ABOARD
HOURS	MINUTES		Mr. Rod Machado PO Box 6030 San Clemente, CA 92674 999-555-1212	
04	13	KSAC	17. DESTINATION CONTACT/TELEPHONE (OPTIONAL) Mrs. Machado 999-555-1212	1
16. COLOR OF AIRCRAFT BLUE/WHITE				

In many cases, the only place you'll find published ASR or PAR approach minimums is at military airports. On the other hand, almost any Approach Control facility can offer you something known as a no-gyro approach. You'll find this service quite valuable if your directional gyro or compass becomes inoperative. You'd ask the controller for no-gyro approach or vectors. The controller will then tell you when to start and stop your turn. You're expected to use standard rate turns here. However, if you're making a surveillance or precision approach, ATC will advise you when you're on final and you're expected to use half-standard-rate turns until the approach is completed. Of course, this type of service doesn't work for other things. For instance, if you leave your thinking cap at home, you can't ask for a no-brainer approach. See what I mean?

Filing an IFR Flight Plan

You've probably heard your instructor talk about filing an IFR flight plan. If you're like me as an instrument student, you're probably wondering why you'd be doing woodwork when you're supposed to be learning to fly.

Well, there's no actual filing, as in using a rat tail file, going on here. Instead, filing an IFR flight plan means communicating with the AFSS (Automated Flight Service Station) either in person, over the phone, via radio or via the internet and providing them with a completed flight plan, as shown in (Figure 26). Keep in mind that a VFR flight plan is intended for search and rescue purposes should you fail to arrive at your destination. The route (and all the other data) you file in a VFR flight plan isn't

sent to ATC, but is kept on file by the FSS to be used in the event of a search. The route (along with your aircraft ID, equipment, destination, altitude) you file in an IFR flight plan goes to ATC for the obvious reasons that the controller needs to know the route you'll fly to your destination. (We'll cover how to flight plan a particular route in Chapter 16.)

The IFR flight plan you file provides the FSS specialist with information on your aircraft, destination, route, altitudes, fuel on board, and so on as shown on the flight plan form. The FSS specialist inputs this information and sends it to the ARTCC computer. The computer works on this information, checks for traffic conflicts, flow control, routing, and weather and finally issues an IFR clearance in the name of your airplane's tail number. It sits quietly in the Center computer until an FSS specialist or air traffic controller summons it up via his or her computer terminal at your request (or, depending on the particular ATC facility, it may automatically arrive at his or her desk a specific time before your proposed departure time).

Now, all this takes time, which is why you're asked to file an IFR flight plan at least 30 minutes in advance of the time you'd like to receive your clearance. Some pilots, having failed to think ahead, get snippy with the controllers when their clearance isn't available five minutes after they file. These people, who make pests of themselves, sometimes wait a really, really, really long time before their clearance is available. My words of wisdom— play nice with others, think ahead, and always be nice to the people who are trying to help get you off the ground.

When you're ready to pick up your IFR clearance (you'll do this on the ground, preferably after your airplane is preflighted and ready to go) you call the nearest AFSS via phone or radio, or call the ground controller via radio if you're departing from a tower-controlled airport (or the *clearance delivery* controller if this position exists at your departure airport). The controller will read you your IFR clearance and, good student that you are, you'll read it back to make sure you got it down correctly. Of course, your pencil tip may catch fire as you copy the clearance, because controllers often talk fast. So keep your fire extinguisher prepared, or ask for a watered down clearance. You may need foam on more than your latte. With IFR clearance in hand, you're ready to depart and enter the IFR system.

One of the very first things you'll notice as an instrument student is that the Center's computer often gives you a route that doesn't look anything like the one you asked for in your original flight plan. You might have spent hours picking the best IFR routing based on the shortest distance, the lowest altitudes, the fewest navaid frequency changes—and all for naught. When you receive your IFR clearance it looks like it was meant for someone else, someone who wasn't as committed, studious, and thoughtful as you. Well, it wasn't. This is what we call "life at the big city airport". Regardless of the route you file, the Center computer is going to give you the route that makes the ATC system work best. You can't yell at the computer, because computers don't have ears, and if they did, it wouldn't care. You can, however, negotiate with ATC if you get a route that really doesn't work for you.

Air Traffic Control Communication System

Air traffic control facilities must have a way of communicating immediately and efficiently with pilots and other ATC facilities. They do so using dedicated transmitters and landlines (a sophisticated telephone system) activated via the controller's push-button panel to the right.

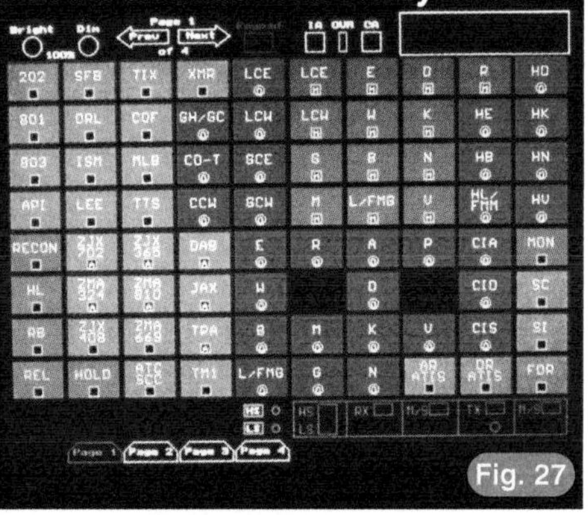

Fig. 27

That's right, you *can* negotiate. Suppose you're departing from a tower controlled airport. You call Clearance Delivery or Ground Control and say, "Divit Clearance, this is N2132 Bravo, request pre-filed IFR clearance to Lobrain airport, over."

The tower controller will often come back and tell you to standby, your clearance is *on request*. Of course, when I heard this as a student IFR pilot, I said, "OK, I'm requesting it...again."

In reality, the term *clearance on request* means that the tower controller is letting his fingers do the typing on his computer keyboard and requesting your clearance from the Center computer. When that clearance arrives, usual-ly within seconds, the controller will call you, ask if you're "ready to copy," and then read it to you. You're job is to copy it down. Then you'll read it back to make sure you or the controller didn't make a mistake in the communication process. Believe me, it happens. Look your clearance over carefully. Make sure all the essential elements are there, that the specified airways all exist, and that it gets you where you want to go. If it's not what you care to fly for some reason, the time to say something is while you're still on the ground, not in the air.

For instance, your IFR clearance might include routing over water and you didn't originally file for an overwater portion to your route. Perhaps you don't want to fly over water because you don't have a flotation device (which isn't your instructor, by the way. After all, he may be thinking you are his flotation device). Or maybe you can't swim. The best way to handle this problem is to call the controller and see if he or she can communicate with the Center or Departure controller and obtain a new clearance for you. Controllers have what is known as *landlines* (Figure 27), allowing them to easily communicate with one another in different ATC facilities. These lines are dedicated telephone connections directly to the nearest ATC facility (i.e., Center, Approach or Departure Control, FSS, etc.). Most often the tower controller can work a better route for you, though you may have to wait a while for the clearance and it may place you back in the queue for takeoff.

Sometimes you are offered only what you were given to start with, and must negotiate with the Center controller after you're airborne. At the airport café, this is known as "Tough taco," because that's the way life at the airport goes sometimes. ATC is balancing your request against its own operational realities, the needs of many other pilots, capacity limitations, equipment outages, and many other variables. Just remember what the Rolling Stones said: You can't always get what you want. The vast majority of the time, however, you and ATC will arrive at an agreement.

On some occasions, when departing a non-towered airport, you may receive a clearance from the FSS that doesn't fit your needs. In this instance, you should communicate with the FSS specialist (if you haven't already hung up the phone or signed off on the radio) and ask him or her to obtain a more acceptable routing for you. Either way, you often have a lot of options for getting what you want if you didn't get it the first time.

Non-Tower Airport Departures

If you're departing IFR from an airport that doesn't have a tower (or has one that's closed), your IFR clearance will normally be delivered to the FSS, Center or Approach facility nearest the point of departure. What I'm saying here is that the ATC computer is pretty smart. In fact, it's a whole lot smarter than the one with the Intel 256 MHz processor that's stashed in your attic. ATC's computer knows to send your IFR clearance to the ATC facility closest to your departure point, which is normally the Center or Approach control facility that you'll work with immediately upon takeoff. A quick look at your IFR approach and/or enroute chart will help you identify this facility.

IFR Operations Conducted Solely Within Approach/Departure Control Boundaries

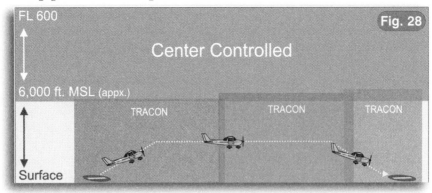

Tower enroute control (TEC) operations are IFR flights conducted solely within the boundaries of the approach and departure control areas with overlapping boundaries. These flights don't need to enter Center's airspace.

When filing a flight plan with the FSS, you should wait approximately 30 minutes after filing before calling ATC to retrieve your clearance. This is usually how long it takes the flight plan to be processed. Some pilots prefer to have the FSS specialists give them a call on their cell phone or local phone when the clearance is ready (good luck to you if you can get them to go along with this request. They are pretty busy, after all). This also serves to make you look important in front of your pilot buddies. After all, when the Flight Service specialist calls, you can tell your friends that the specialist was calling to get your advice on a complex weather problem involving a "trilateral bifurcated occluded frontal system." You can get halfway to your destination before your friends figure out that the only thing bifurcated and occluded is your brain.

When you depart an airport without a tower or Flight Service Station on the field, you are usually given a *departure window* as part of the IFR clearance. This is not something you open to catch a breeze before departure; it's a time period within which you *must* launch. The clearance might end with, "Clearance void if not off by 1315Z; if not off by 1315, advise Albuquerque not later than 1345 of intentions. Time now is 1305."

A clearance like this is like hearing the starting gun at the Olympics. You have a *maximum* of 10 minutes (in this case) to get airborne. If you're not airborne by 1315Z, *your IFR clearance is cancelled, kaput, void, inop and otherwise defunct and not usable.* Don't take off beyond the departure window time, because you're no longer guaranteed sole occupancy of the assigned airspace. There's no provision for the derision resulting from a collision. On the other hand, if your wheels lift off at or before the departure window time, even if you're not yet in contact with the controller listed in your clearance, you're still fine. If you think you won't make it by the assigned time, you can call back and ask for (and usually get) an extension. But you can't be late out the gate.

If you are a no-go for any reason, you are obligated to notify ATC within 30 minutes that you didn't make the departure window. This is a search and rescue provision. ATC has no way of knowing if you crashed after departure or just decided not to make the flight.

Taking a TEC [Tower Enroute Control]

Sometimes, filing an IFR flight plan is much easier than the process described above. This is especially true when

TEC Boundaries in Southern California

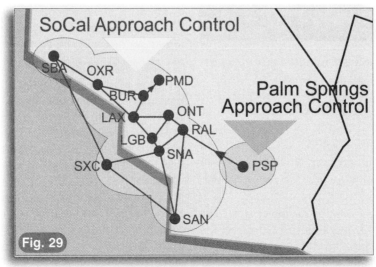

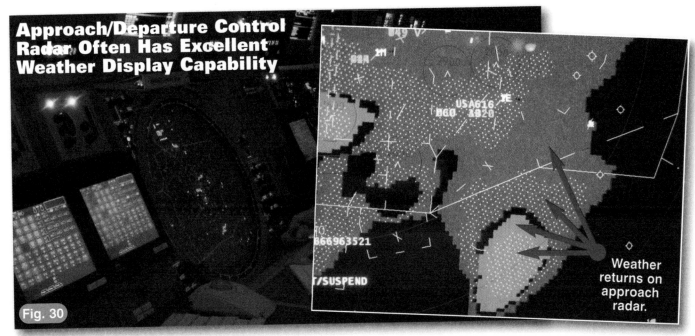

Approach/Departure Control Radar Often Has Excellent Weather Display Capability

Weather returns on approach radar.

Fig. 30

flying IFR in the *tower enroute control* (TEC) environment.

ARTCCs are often very busy handling enroute traffic. Someone eventually figured out that a lot of flights begin and end entirely within approach/departure control airspace. For instance, in Southern California airplanes regularly fly IFR from one airport to another and often don't need to go high enough to enter Center's airspace (Figure 28). Why get Center involved in things it doesn't need to be involved in? Thus was born something that came to be known as *Tower Enroute Control* or *TEC* for short.

TEC is for pilots who want to fly IFR within overlapping individual approach and departure control jurisdictions. In those areas not covered by these approach control facilities, Center assumes responsibility for controlling traffic. Tower Enroute clearances aren't available from Center. Under TEC, airplanes stay away from Center's airspace and generally operate below 10,000 feet MSL. They start out as and remain the responsibility of one or more contiguous (touching) approach control facilities.

The key word there is *contiguous*. TEC works as long as you can be passed from one approach or departure control facility to another. If there's a gap that's Center-controlled, your TEC ride is often over. For instance, in Southern California, you can fly from Santa Barbara (SBA) to San Diego (SAN), a distance of more than 160 nautical miles, and remain within SoCal Approach Control's airspace, as shown in Figure 29. You can even fly TEC from Palm Springs (PSP) to any airport covered by SoCal approach control since Palm Spring's approach control touches/overlaps SoCal's radar coverage. You can't, however, fly TEC north of Santa Barbara since there is no approach control coverage immediately north of this area. That means Los Angeles or Oakland Center will handle your IFR if you venture northbound of Santa Barbara.

In a few parts of the country (Los Angeles, California for instance) you can call the tower controller at your airport and ask for an IFR clearance to any other airport within the TEC area. Instead of having to file an IFR flight plan with the FSS 30 minutes prior to departure (via phone, the internet or radio), as you would if you planned on entering Center's airspace, you need only make a radio request to the tower and wait a couple of minutes. You just tell them you want a tower enroute clearance to X airport. You don't specify routing or altitudes, because the routes are already planned and published. Just pick up the mic, call the tower and request (in this example) Tower Enroute from Burbank airport to San Diego's Brown Field. Tower Enroute Control operations are easy to initiate, fast to get, and efficient for both pilots and ATC.

TEC clearances offer pilots a number of additional advantages. First, since TEC flights are usually operating closer to radar sites, these flights can be controlled with less horizontal separation. When IFR flights are conducted within 40 miles of Approach Control's radar antenna, a minimum of three miles horizontal separation is authorized. This means pilots can get into and out of airports faster when operating in the TEC system, because of the smaller required distance between aircraft.

Second, Approach Control's radar (Figure 30) is generally more sensitive in detecting weather (see Postflight Briefing #9-4, page 9-68, to learn more about Center and Approach radar weather information). With radar antennas closer to a pilot's position, weather radar returns are more defined and precise. This becomes valuable when you are trying to pinpoint specific areas of convective activity in IFR conditions. Since other airplanes on the same frequency are also in close proximity to the radar site, their pilot reports offer a fresher, more precise depiction of the weather. Approach Control's weather reporting capability is even better if the facility has ASR-9 radar equipment, which provides the controller with sophisticated weather identification capabilities.

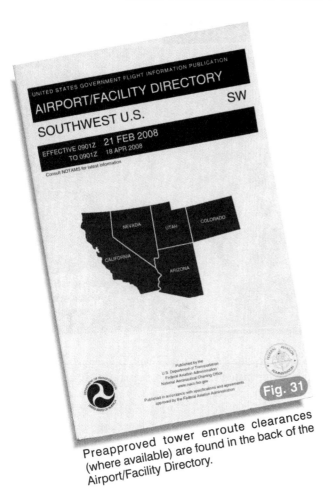

Preapproved tower enroute clearances (where available) are found in the back of the Airport/Facility Directory.

IFR request, though, you may be asked to file a flight plan with the nearest FSS.

Here's the way TEC works to get you into the IFR system. The tower controller requests an IFR clearance for you from the Center's computer. You are then assigned a pre-approved routing and altitude. These routings are available for you to review for planning purposes in the back of the *Airport/Facility Directory* for your region, as shown in Figure 31. The map or routes shown in this figure tell you where TEC is allowed. Let's take a closer look at these routes.

The FAA's TEC published routes are divided into four columns as shown in Figure 32. These are sometimes referred to as *preferential arrival and departure routings* (PDARs). The very top of the first column (Figure 32, position A) shows the area covered by these routes. In this case, it's the Burbank area. Below that you see three airports: BUR, VNY or WHP (Burbank, Van Nuys, or Whiteman). The routes listed in this section pertain if you are flying from any of these three airports to any of the airports listed below in column 1 (Figure 32, position B).

Let's say you want to fly IFR from Burbank to Long Beach (LGB). Column 2 identifies this route as BURL1 (Figure 32, position C). You could request "IFR to Long Beach via BURL1" from Clearance Delivery at Burbank and the controller immediately knows exactly what route you are requesting. You could also list BURL1 in the route box of the flight plan and the FSS specialist would know the precise route for which you were filing. You might, of course, be given a different TEC routing if traffic or other conditions require an alternate route.

Column 3 lists the precise routing that makes up BURL1 (Figure 32, position D). In this case, if you were

Third, TEC allows you easier access to the IFR system. If the tower controllers are too busy to accommodate your

TEC Clearances in the A/FD

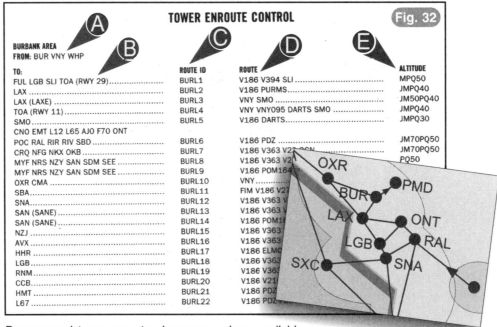

Preapproved tower enroute clearances, where available,
are found in the rear of the A/FD booklet. By filing the Route ID in the route
section of the flight plan, ATC's computer knows the route you want to fly on this flight.
It's the route you're most likely to be given when receiving your ATC IFR clearance.

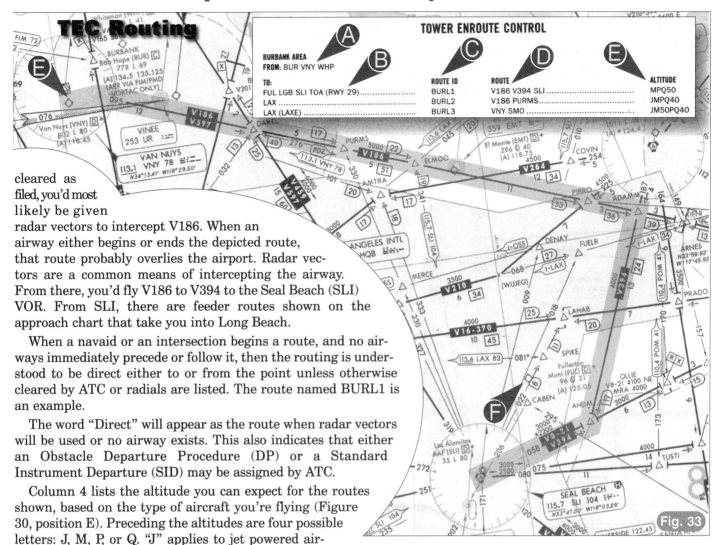

Fig. 33

cleared as filed, you'd most likely be given radar vectors to intercept V186. When an airway either begins or ends the depicted route, that route probably overlies the airport. Radar vectors are a common means of intercepting the airway. From there, you'd fly V186 to V394 to the Seal Beach (SLI) VOR. From SLI, there are feeder routes shown on the approach chart that take you into Long Beach.

When a navaid or an intersection begins a route, and no airways immediately precede or follow it, then the routing is understood to be direct either to or from the point unless otherwise cleared by ATC or radials are listed. The route named BURL1 is an example.

The word "Direct" will appear as the route when radar vectors will be used or no airway exists. This also indicates that either an Obstacle Departure Procedure (DP) or a Standard Instrument Departure (SID) may be assigned by ATC.

Column 4 lists the altitude you can expect for the routes shown, based on the type of aircraft you're flying (Figure 30, position E). Preceding the altitudes are four possible letters: J, M, P, or Q. "J" applies to jet powered airplanes. "M" applies to turboprop airplanes with a cruise speed of 190 knots or more. "P" applies to non-jet airplanes with a cruise speed of 190 knots or greater. "Q" applies to non-jet airplanes with a cruise at speed of 189 knots or less. If you're flying the route BURL6 from Burbank to Riverside (RIV), you can expect to fly at 7,000 feet if you're a jet powered airplane or a turboprop cruising at more than 190 knots (JM70). If you're in a Cessna 172, then you can expect to fly at 5,000 feet (PQ50).

Some routes may be slightly different based on the type of aircraft involved. Make certain you file the correct route for the type of aircraft you have on that day. Finally, even though it's not listed, you can plan an IFR flight to a satellite airport in close proximity to major airports via the same routing. Even though the intended airport doesn't have an instrument approach, you can cancel IFR at the appropriate time and descend to and land your intended destination in VFR conditions. Remember, you must be able to descend from your assigned altitude and land while the maintaining the appropriate VFR weather minimums.

When operating within a busy terminal area like Los Angeles, you will experience many PDARs. For an IFR flight from Van Nuys (Figure 33, position E) to Fullerton (position F), the shortest airway routing is via V186 to intercept V394, then to the SLI VOR. If you file for this route, even with the word *please* written in the remarks section of the flight plan, you are not going to get what appears to be the most direct and thus most logical route. This routing would take an aircraft directly across the LAX Class B airspace, where you'd be about as welcome as a fisherman with pole in hand at Seaworld. You'd probably scatter 777's like fish in an aquarium at their first sighting of tartar sauce.

The insert in the top right hand corner of Figure 33 shows the preferential departure and arrival route (PDAR) from Van Nuys to Long Beach. This route circumnavigates the LAX Class B airspace to the east.

Understand that TEC operations vary slightly across the country. You should check with the local Air Traffic Control facility for specific variations in these procedures. Count on slight variations in customs as well as procedures from state to state. No, no secret handshakes are involved as of this writing.

ATC's Favorite Route

As I mentioned previously, the Center computer issues routings that make the ATC system work best. These routings are sometimes called PRs or *preferred routes*. When a *preferred routing* has been established for your destination,

Low Altitude Preferred IFR Routes

LOW ALTITUDE

Terminals	Route	Effective Times (UTC)
SAN FRANCISCO/OAKLAND METRO AREA		
From SAN FRANCISCO Area: West Bay Airports		
Los Angeles Area	(70–90–110–130–150–170) V27 VTU V299 SADDE V107 LAX	1400–0800
From OAKLAND Area: East Bay Airports		
Los Angeles Area	(70–90–110–130–150–170) V109 PXN V113 V485 V299 SADDE V107 LAX	1400–0800

HIGH ALTITUDE

Terminals BURBANK	Route	Effective Times (UTC)
Chicago O'Hare	(all B747, B767, B727, DC10, DC87, L1011) DAG LAS BCE MTU OCS J94 ONL J148 MCW JVL–STAR	0000–2359
	or	
	(all other jets) DAG EED DRK J96 IRK BDF–STAR	0000–2359

Fig. 34

the computer will select this route automatically, regardless of the routing you requested, even if it doesn't appear logical to you (it is, however, logical to ATC). In this instance, the shortest distance between two points may be a curve, a zigzag, even a circle, under ATC's Law of Aviation Geometry.

The computer's program gives you a clearance based on predetermined routes in one of four categories: preferred IFR routes, preferential departure routings (PDR), preferential arrival routings (PAR) or preferential departure and arrival routings (PDAR). These preferential routes are based on flow control and traffic management considerations.

Preferred IFR routes can be found in the back of the *Airport/Facility Directory*, as shown in Figure 34. The directory specifies routing between busy terminal facilities. Preferred routes are not the same as the *preferential arrival and departure routings* or PDARs that we just discussed because they are not normally used for TEC clearances. Preferred routes are typically used for high-performance airplanes traveling from once Center to another. In Figure 34, if you were traveling from the Oakland area to the Los Angeles you'd probably be routed via V485 to V299 to SADDE intersection thence via V107 to LAX VOR. So you'd certainly want to file this route on your IFR flight plan when possible.

Now that you have a basic idea about how the IFR system works, it's time to take a look at the federal aviation regulations as they apply to an IFR pilot.

Postflight Briefing #7-1

Rick Crose

With GPS being used so frequently today, pilots have gotten lazy with their preflight planning. I see flight plans that indicate the point of departure with a destination airport listed that's hundreds of miles away. There is no route defining a pilot's intended direction of flight. Most pilots fail to take into consideration things like MOAs, restricted and prohibited airspace or anything that requires some level of flight planning awareness. Unfortunately, these same pilots often become upset when they receive an amended clearance to correct their lack of route flight planning. A pilot may get away with this in the heartland of America, but in the bustling metropolitan areas, it is not acceptable. It increases the workload on an already busy ATC system and causes frustration to both pilot and controller.

If you must file these simple flight plans, I recommend that you at least show one navaid that is initially 40 to 100 miles away from the point of departure to help controllers know what initial routing you are looking for. In busy metropolitan areas, the best way to get a clearance that is the same as what you filed is by picking out preferred IFR routes contained within the *Airport/Facility Directory*. These routes are near the back of the book and show the best ATC routings used to other airports.

Rick Crose, TRACON Controller

Chapter 8
The FARs Rule
Rules to Abide by When You Fly IFR

Flying an airplane in the clouds for long distances can be a bit risky, but it's a risk that's manageable. If this weren't true, only daredevils would fly IFR, and I'm not a daredevil, nor are all the fine folks who've obtained instrument ratings over the years. As an instrument pilot, you can easily manage risk by using the risk-avoidance knowledge complied by generations of instrument pilots. Where would you find this accumulated wisdom? In the book of Federal Aviation Regulations, that's where.

Think about it. The regulations are nothing more than compressed wisdom in the form of *do's* and *don'ts*, born largely from the mistakes of pilots who came before you. The genesis of most rules and regulations can be traced back to a set of events, probably accidents or potential accidents, which hurt or injured (seriously or otherwise) an aviator. What happened as a result? Bingo, a rule is born (along with a fun Catholic pastime). So, if you want to be a wise instrument pilot, don't think of the FARs as just things you can be busted for. Think of them as the literary form of wisdom that will keep you safe by following their script. This is the truth about the regulations.

Pilots tend to be an independent lot, sometimes with a chip in their dip that makes them inclined to say, "Rules are made to be broken." Before you think that way, consider what might have gone wrong to make someone write a rule.

In this chapter I present the specific FARs you need to know as an instrument pilot. I will tell you what you need to know to be competent and safe, and I won't bother you with all the unnecessary details. Keep in mind that all the FARs you learned while getting your license haven't evaporated into thin air. They're still there, and fully applicable. These are add-ons that govern how flights are conducted under instrument flight rules and how you can stay legal to do that type of flying.

FAR Part 61
FAR 61.3–Requirement for Certificates, Ratings, & Authorizations

To act as pilot in command (PIC) or as a required flight crewmember (copilot or flight engineer, for example) on an aircraft, you must have your pilot certificate, medical certificate (if required) and photo identification (a driver's license, for example) in your personal possession or readily accessible in the aircraft (Figure 1). Personal possession means it can't be in your house, unless you carry your house with you (which is possible only if you live in a travel trailer, preferably an Airstream).

Required Documents

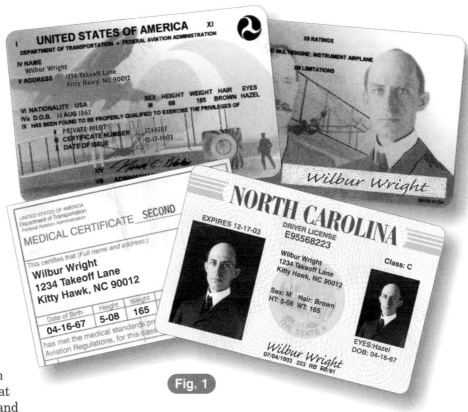

Fig. 1

As you know by now, a pilot certificate has no expiration date. But, as you'll soon see, it can be used only if you meet a few other requirements. For instance, to act as PIC you must have a current medical certificate with you. These documents need each other, and you need all of them to offer proof that you've acquired the skills needed to act as pilot in command (PIC) of an airplane, are healthy enough to do so, and that you are who you say you are.

You can be asked to present your pilot or medical certificate and photo ID for inspection by the Federal Aviation Administrator, a National Transportation Safety Board or Transportation Security Administration representative or any federal, state or local law enforcement officer (don't offer the lawman asking for your pilot certificate a box of nicely wrapped donuts, thinking you're supposed to give a present rather than present something. It doesn't work). The U.S. Customs service is also authorized to act on behalf of the FAA and request these documents. I can almost guarantee that doing steep turns around the White House will get your pilot and medical certificates inspected by some official looking person (and they'll probably want to inspect your home, and you know what a hassle it is to unpack that trailer).

Now, to act as pilot in command of an aircraft operating under instrument flight rules or in weather less than the minimums required for VFR (or special VFR), you must have an instrument rating. Have you ever wondered when an instrument rating is required for flight? Flying in less than basic VFR conditions is one of these times. For instance, if a particular type of airspace (Class E, for example) has basic VFR requirements of three miles visibility and minimum distances from clouds, then you must meet these requirements or, if you can't, you must then have an instrument rating, an instrument clearance, be instrument current, and in an airplane legal to fly on instruments. We'll discuss all of these in this chapter. Just to be clear about it, if the airspace in which you're flying requires 3 miles visibili-

The Airline Transport Pilot Rating

An airline transport pilot license automatically includes the commercial and instrument ratings.

ty and you only have 2.9 miles (seeing the sun through fog doesn't give you 93 million miles visibility, either), then you must meet all the requirements I just mentioned to fly IFR.

As an aside, whenever I'm asked if I have an instrument rating, I reply, "No, the FAA took it away from me." And it's true. They did. When I passed my airline transport pilot (ATP) checkride, I surrendered my commercial pilot certificate with an instrument airplane rating and obtained an airline transport pilot certificate, which supersedes an instrument rating (Figure 2). Consider this to be the FAA's version of supersizing your license. Any time the regulations require that the pilot in command have an instrument rating, an airline transport pilot certificate will suffice.

FAR 61.51—Pilot Logbooks

There is probably no subject more discussed and tangled over in pilot lounges and flight schools nationwide

Flying IFR on Your Instructor's Ticket

How is it that you can fly a Cessna 172 under actual instrument conditions on an IFR fight plan with your instructor on board? You certainly aren't the PIC here, right? That's correct. You're flying on your instructor's instrument rating, making the instructor the legal PIC for this flight. You're just a student and don't count. Well, you count, but not in a legal sense here.

On the other hand, the FAA says that if you're a private or commercial pilot and are the sole manipulator of the controls on an airplane for which you are rated, then you can log the time as pilot in command time. So, if you're rated to fly a Cessna 172, even if you are in actual IFR conditions, you can log that time in your logbook as PIC and as actual instrument time, too (see Figure to the right). Your instructor is obligated to sign your logbook since he gave your dual instruction. That means you'll probably have an equal amount of dual time logged as well.

On the other hand, any time your flight instructor gives you flight instruction, he or she can log that in *their* logbook as PIC time. It's sort of double time. Isn't it interesting that you can have two people logging PIC time in their logbooks while there's only one legal PIC on an airplane? The FAA allows you and your instructor to log PIC time as a reward for the experience you're obtaining (it beats getting cookies or candy from the feds as your reward, doesn't it?). But the FAA requires that only one person be the legal PIC of the airplane, and this is the person who'll have to do the explaining if something goes wrong with that airplane.

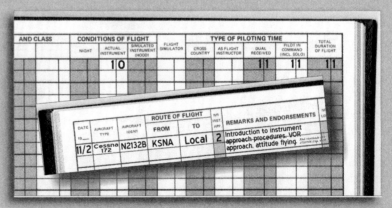

than pilot logbooks. I'm speaking about who can log what, when, and why. Many of these discussions revolve around what is considered instrument time and who is the PIC. As a legal matter, you're only required to log the time and experience necessary to meet the requirements for a certificate or rating, or to prove that you're current to act as PIC, to carry passengers or to file an IFR flight plan. Most of us log all the time that we fly, but there's no specific FAR requirement to do this. Of course, there's no requirement that any insurance company ever give you insurance, either. Insurance is another reason we log.

Instrument time (when you fly by reference to your instruments only) can only be logged when control of the aircraft is maintained solely by reference to instruments. Notice that no mention is made about the *ground* here. When logging flight time by reference to instruments, it doesn't matter whether or not you can see the ground (it only matters that you don't run into it).

Sometimes the slant of cloud layers makes it difficult to identify the actual horizon. Often the only way to fly in these situations is by continuous reference to your instruments.

It's possible to be flying in visual meteorological conditions (VMC) on an IFR flight plan above a solid undercast (that's where the clouds are beneath you—no, not beneath in the sense that they're not worthy to even be seen with you) with a good horizon and not see the ground. You can't log that as instrument time because you probably didn't need to fly by reference to your instruments.

On the other hand, I've been aloft above the clouds, in fantastic visibility, where the cloud deck slopes at an angle to the real horizon (Figure 3). This makes it nearly impossible to fly visually because it's impossible to determine where the horizon actually is (this is very disconcerting, too). In this instance, you'll have no choice but to fly by reference to your instruments. It's also possible that you can look straight down while in instrument meteorological conditions (IMC) and see a little patch of earth (hopefully you haven't slipped into a wormhole and changed planets) and still be controlling the aircraft solely by reference to instruments. You're still forced to fly by reference to your instrument in this instance.

The weather report or conditions don't necessarily dictate when you can or cannot log instrument time. Night

flight over a wide expanse of water while under an overcast or in conditions of low flight visibility might well be logged as instrument time if the only way you can control the aircraft is by reference to the instruments (Figure 4). Either way, if you're on an IFR flight plan and have no

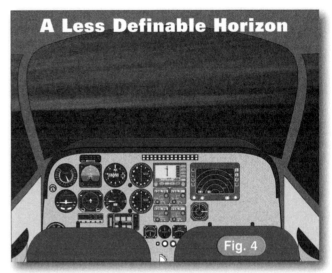

At night over the ocean or desert, it's sometimes difficult to identify the horizon. These are also times when it may be necessary to fly with continuous reference to your flight instruments.

choice but to fly your airplane solely by reference to your instruments, then it's entirely reasonable for you to log that time as actual instrument flight time. After all, if you can't (and "can't" is the key word here) fly by outside references, then your only choice is to fly by inside references.

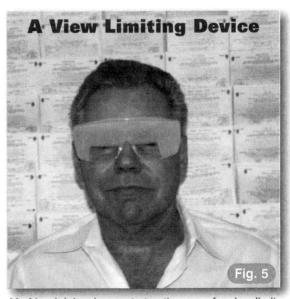

My friend John demonstrates the use of a view limiting device known as Foggles.

And when logging instrument time, you're either flying under simulated instrument conditions, meaning you're wearing a view limiting device such as a typical instrument hood or Foggles, as shown in Figure 5 (the airplane isn't considered a view limiting device, sorry), or in actual instrument conditions, meaning you're in the clouds.

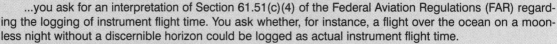

A Legal Interpretation: Logging Actual Instrument Conditions

Dear Mr. Carr:

...you ask for an interpretation of Section 61.51(c)(4) of the Federal Aviation Regulations (FAR) regarding the logging of instrument flight time. You ask whether, for instance, a flight over the ocean on a moonless night without a discernible horizon could be logged as actual instrument flight time.

..."Actual" instrument flight conditions occur when some outside conditions make it necessary for the pilot to use the aircraft instruments in order to maintain adequate control over the aircraft. Typically, these conditions involve adverse weather conditions.

To answer your...question, actual instrument conditions may occur in the case you described a moonless night over the ocean with no discernible horizon, if use of the instruments is necessary to maintain adequate control over the aircraft. The determination as to whether flight by reference to instruments is necessary is somewhat subjective and based in part on the sound judgment of the pilot. Note that, under Section 61.51(b)(3), the pilot must log the conditions of the flight. The log should include the reasons for determining that the flight was under actual instrument conditions in case the pilot later would be called on to prove that the actual instrument flight time logged was legitimate.

November 7, 1984

John H. Cassady-Assistant Chief counsel Regulations and Enforcement Division

If you're logging this instrument time to meet the recency of experience requirements of §61.57 (we'll discuss this rule next), you are required to record the location and type of any instrument approach you accomplished along with the name of your safety pilot, if a safety pilot is required (hopefully he or she won't be in the witness protection program and you can use their name).

If you're flying while using Foggles or the instrument hood, then you need to have a safety pilot along to help you look for traffic. That's a safety *pilot*, not a safety dog. One pilot tried to convince the FAA that he could safely use his dog—a pointer—as a safety pilot. He claimed that the dog always barked when it saw an airplane (it probably barked when it saw a cloud that looked like a biscuit, too). The FAA didn't buy that one, despite the dog being very smart for a pooch in its price range. Someday, if a dog can pass your medical eye test, this might be allowed. Then again, your medical would carry the limitation, "Pilot must wear dog on his head on all flights. No flights over Alpo factory allowed."

To act as a safety pilot, your right seat occupant must meet a few FAR requirements. He or she must have at least a private pilot license with category, class, and type rating (if necessary) for the aircraft used for the flight. He must have adequate vision forward and to each side to be able to scan for traffic. And no, he can't have a tail and eat dog biscuits, either. Your safety pilot does not have to have an instrument rating, but because the safety pilot is now considered a required crewmember, he or she does need to have at least a current third class medical.

The good news is that your safety pilot can log this time as PIC time if he or she agrees to (and is qualified to) act as the legal PIC for the flight. Now that's a good deal, isn't it? Two private pilots in one airplane, with both logging PIC time (essentially, the only instance where such a thing is possible).

FAR 61.57–Recency of Experience: Pilot in Command

If you thought that getting a flight review every 24 calendar months and doing three takeoffs and landings every 90 days just to carry passengers was the end of your currency requirements, think again. Once you obtain that instrument rating, you'll have to do a few things to keep current enough to use it.

What do you have to do to become and/or remain instrument current?

Simply stated, to act as pilot in command under instrument flight rules or to fly in weather conditions less than VFR minimums (we'll just say, "act as PIC under IFR conditions" from now on) you must, within the preceding six calendar months, have performed and logged six instrument approaches, hold-

Instrument Currency

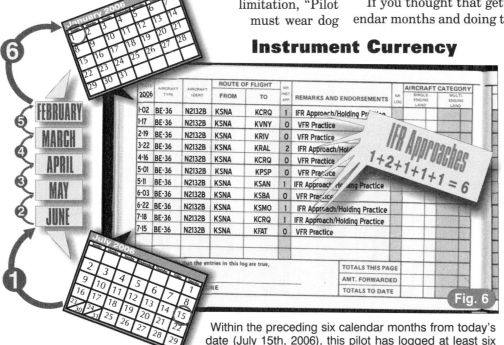

Within the preceding six calendar months from today's date (July 15th, 2006), this pilot has logged at least six instrument approaches and holding. Therefore, he or she meets the IFR recency of experience requirements.

ing procedures (meaning you entered or flew a holding pattern), and intercepting and tracking courses through the use of navigation systems (that doesn't mean celestial navigation systems, either. So don't let anyone named Kepler or Galileo sell you their sextant. You can't use it for currency). You're required to have completed these requirements in flight, in actual or simulated instrument conditions, in the same category of aircraft for which instrument privileges are sought, or in a simulator or flight training device (FTD) that is representative of the aircraft category you intend to fly.

Notice that there is no minimum flight hour requirement there. Just six approaches, a holding procedure and tracking courses is all that's necessary. The intercepting and tracking of courses using navigation systems seems redundant since it is difficult to imagine how you would execute an instrument approach without intercepting and tracking a course. But don't tell anyone I said that. It's between you and me, OK?

If today's date is July 15th, 2006, how do you know if you're current to act as PIC under IFR conditions? It's easy. July is the 7th month. Subtract 6, which puts you in Month 1 (aka January—if the start month is less than 7, add 12 then do the subtraction). Now scan backward in your logbook from today's date to January 1 (Figure 6). If you can count at least six approaches and holding work during this time, you're current to act as PIC under IFR conditions as of today, and through the end of the month.

Why through the end of the month? Because the count involves whatever happens in the preceding six calendar months as well as what's happening in the current month. Now, if you don't have six approaches and holding work within this time, then you must fly additional approaches and/or accomplish the holding requirements. Until you do, you can't act as PIC under IFR conditions.

Let's say that it's July 31st and the clock strikes midnight. It's now August, Cinderella. Eight minus six is two (or February). You're looking in your logbook early in the morning of August 1st and want to know if you're current to act as PIC under IFR conditions (Figure 7). You need to see if you've got the required six approaches and holding logged starting from the time beginning on February 1st, 2006 to the present day.

Let's suppose, however, that it's still July 31st and you don't have the six approaches and holding logged within the preceding six calendar months. You're not instrument current and cannot act as PIC of an airplane under IFR conditions. So, what can you do to get yourself current? One answer is to take a safety pilot with you and do a suf-

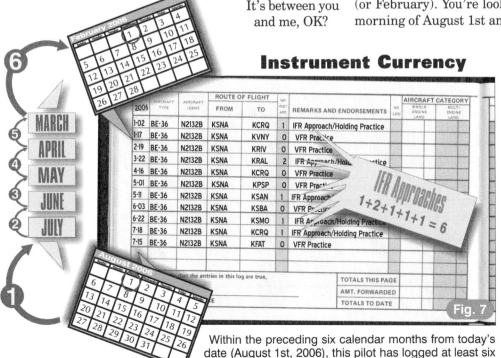

Within the preceding six calendar months from today's date (August 1st, 2006), this pilot has logged at least six instrument approaches and holding. Therefore, he or she meets the IFR recency of experience requirements.

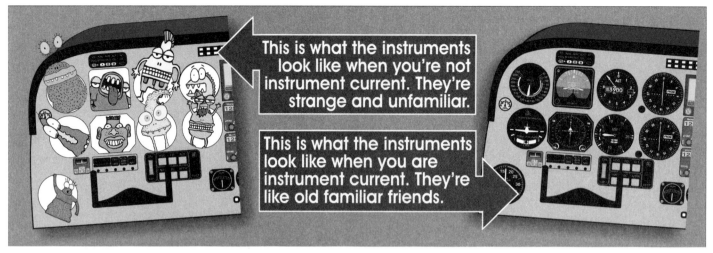

ficient number of approaches and holding under simulated IFR conditions (you wear the Foggles, the safety pilot doesn't—otherwise it wouldn't be too safe, would it?), then log this activity in your logbook. Obviously, you become current on the day you did all this work, but how long will you remain current if you didn't fly another approach? Seventh month (July) plus six is 13. For those of us operating on a conventional calendar, there is no Month 13. You've got too much of a good thing. Subtract 12. You're good to go through January, 2007, even if you never flew IFR during this period (Figure 8).

The regulations say that you now have six calendar months beyond July, 2006 (the month you were last current) in which to fly with a safety pilot and regain your instrument currency on your own by making those approaches and holding and logging them. This means you can get yourself current on your own all the way up to January 31st, 2007. If you don't do it by then, the only way you can get current is to take an instrument profi-

ciency check (IPC) with an authorized instructor. Use it or lose it is the FAA rule.

The IPC must be given in an aircraft of the same category as the one in which you wish to act as pilot in command, or in a flight simulator or flight training device representative of that category airplane. This check, consisting of a "representative number of tasks required by the instrument rating practical test standards" can be given by an instrument flight instructor or a designated pilot examiner authorized to give instrument rating practical tests.

Remember, your currency is only for the category of aircraft in which you completed the approaches and holding procedures. Rotorcraft currency doesn't count for airplane currency. And just in case you're wondering what special experience you'd need to have to be legal to do night, IFR, autogyro work involving an auto-tow from a mountainous airport, the answer is, skill at opening an parachute.

Instrument Currency

If you flew your wheel pants off and completed all six approaches and holding in one day (July 31st, 2006 in this instance), you're current to fly IFR through the end of January 31st, 2007.

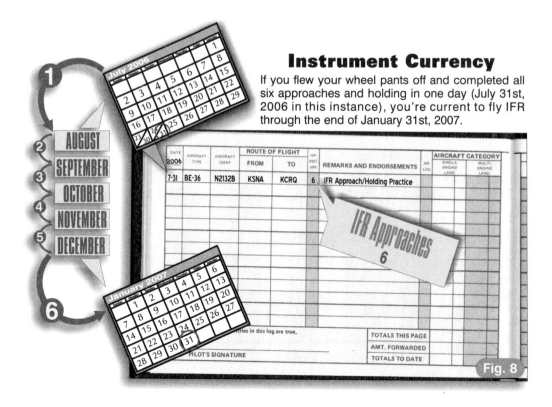

Instrument Currency in Practice

Let's see in detail what you'd have to do when checking your logbook to confirm IFR currency. Look at your logbook, in Figure 9 (we'll assume this is your logbook). Let's say the current date is September 9, 2006. How far back should you check to see if you are current today to act as pilot in command under IFR? Ninth month, so 9-6 is three. That would be March of 2006. Now let's see if there is enough experience logged to be current (remember, it doesn't matter if you flew it and didn't log it. If it's not on paper, it didn't happen as far as the FAA is concerned).

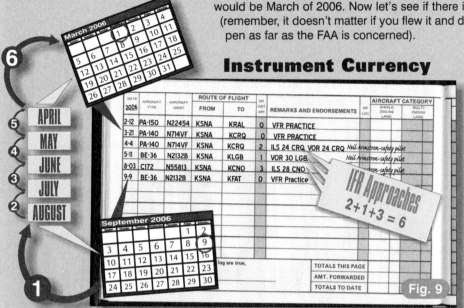

Instrument Currency

Fig. 9

There's a flight on April 4 in a Cherokee with an ILS at CRQ and a VOR approach to CRQ. There's another instrument flight on May 11 with a VOR approach to Runway 30 at LGB. Good. Now, in August there are three ILS approaches to Runway 28 at CNO. All of the approaches were done in simulated instrument conditions and the safety pilot's name is duly recorded (*duly* doesn't mean *dual* instruction, either). Looks like you're okay as far as six-month currency goes, doesn't it? Not quite.

There is no mention of holding procedures anywhere in this time period. So if you want to meet the IFR currency requirement, be sure and ask ATC for the full approach including the hold at the missed approach point (if there is a holding pattern at the missed approach point, that is). Controllers are often quite willing to work with you in terms of letting you fly the full approach and the holding pattern as long as traffic permits. On the other hand, you can just enter holding on your own, log it, and now you're good to go.

Let's look at another logbook page, in Figure 10. The current date is October 11, 2004. Are you current and if so, how long will you remain current? Ten minus six is four, so we go back to April. It appears that there are no approaches or holding patterns in April, May, or June. On July 17 there is an entry showing that you flew approaches to LAX, CNO, RAL and CRN and held at BOJAK and SBN (there's also a small hot sauce stain indicating someone had a taco, perhaps indicating a preference for fast airplanes and fast food). These approaches were flown in a FlightSafety International Citation simulator at Long Beach, CA.

In August, it appears that you became quite busy. There is an instrument proficiency check duly signed off by a CFII on August 5, 2004, which included an ILS Rwy 28R at MYF, an NDB Rwy 28R at MYF, a LOC-D at SEE, a VOR to SDM and a hold at the MZB VOR. Are you current for an IFR flight on October 11, 2004? You bet! However, this currency is based entirely on the IPC flight on August 4, 2004 administered by Roger Dodger, the local CFII, and that starts the clock all over again. Thus, you're legally current until February 28, 2005. This means that if you didn't fly at all beyond August 4, 2004 you'd be legally current for the next six months, and could get yourself current by flying the required IFR procedures with a safety pilot another six months. It would be 12 calendar months from the August date that you'd be required to have an IPC to fly IFR.

What about that flight in the FlightSafety simulator? FAR 61.51(g)(4) requires that if a simulator or flight training device is used to log instrument time, an authorized instructor must be present. Is it likely that you would be able to fly the simulator without a FlightSafety instructor present? Not really. Again, if it's not on paper, it didn't happen as far as the FAA is concerned. It's best to consult the FARs when making logbook entries that are somewhat out of the ordinary. It's a shame not to get credit for work you've done. The opera's not over until someone of enormous stature sings, and the flight isn't done until the paperwork is complete.

Want to know a good way to stay current? Just take that instrument proficiency check—your instrument rating checkride counts as an IPC, too—and then do, at minimum, one approach and one holding pattern every month. Your legal currency will never lapse and you'll be a better pilot for it.

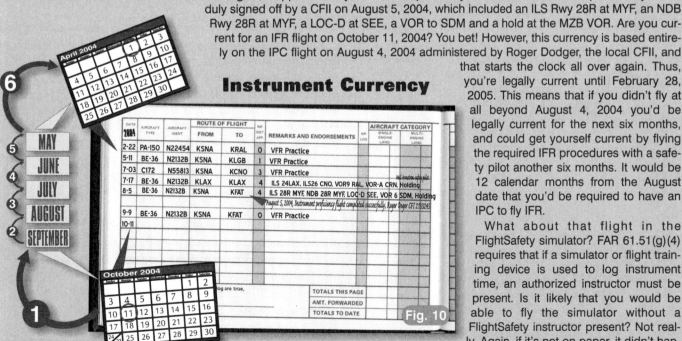

Instrument Currency

Fig. 10

FAR 61.133–Commercial Pilot Privileges and Limitations

If you hold a commercial pilot certificate and don't have an instrument rating (it's possible, if not practical), you will gain additional privileges by getting the instrument rating. Without an instrument rating, a commercial pilot will have a limitation placed on his certificate that states, "The carriage of passengers for hire in airplanes on cross-country flights in excess of 50 nautical miles or at night is prohibited." The instrument rating required to remove this limitation must be in the same category of aircraft. A ride in a single- or multi-engine airplane removes this restriction. In other words, an instrument rating in a rotorcraft isn't applicable to commercial pilot privileges in an airplane.

Just because you hold a commercial certificate and an instrument rating, you can't go out and set up your own little air taxi business, but you can fly for someone who does hold an air taxi certificate. Take a look at the sidebar, *What Can a Commercial Pilot Actually Do?* to determine what activities are legal for a commercial pilot who isn't operating under the commercial operating regulations like Part 121 and Part 135.

What Can a Commercial Pilot Actually Do?

Just what *does* a commercial pilot certificate allow you to do? You'll have to consult FAR 119.1 for the complete list but here is a partial list of the things that a commercial pilot, working outside the confines of a Part 121 or 135 operation, can do in an airplane.

(1) Nonstop sightseeing flights conducted with aircraft having a passenger-seat configuration of 30 or fewer, excluding each crewmember seat, and a payload capacity of 7,500 pounds or less, that begin and end at the same airport, and are conducted within a 25 statute mile radius of that airport in compliance with a letter of authorization as per FAR 91.147.
(2) Ferry or training flights;
(3) Aerial work operations, including:
  (i) Crop dusting, seeding, spraying, and bird chasing;
  (ii) Banner towing;
  (iii) Aerial photography or survey;
  (iv) Fire fighting;
  (v) Helicopter operations in construction or repair work (but it does apply to transportation to and from the site of operations); and
  (vi) Power line or pipeline patrol;
(4) Sightseeing flights conducted in hot air balloons;
(5) Nonstop flights conducted within a 25 statute mile radius of the airport of takeoff, carrying persons or objects for the purpose of conducting intentional parachute operations.
(6) Helicopter flights conducted within a 25 statute mile radius of the airport....

FAR Part 91- General

FAR 91.3–Responsibility and Authority of the Pilot in Command

Without a doubt, this is one of the most powerful regulations in the book. Essentially, it gives you, the pilot of a small airplane, the same authority as the captain of a Boeing 777, Airbus 380 or any commercial airliner (Figure 11). The regulation states that you, the pilot in command, are directly responsible for, and are the final authority as to the operation of the aircraft. It doesn't get much simpler than that.

The Pilot In Command

Fig. 11

The PIC is the boss, the one in charge, the captain, the person who makes the final decisions. All aircraft have a pilot in command. No exceptions.

Declaring an emergency is one of the most powerful and important powers conveyed by this rule. For instance, you might be experiencing icing problems and need ATC to make room for you in the approach queue for an immediate landing. Stating, "I'm declaring an emergency" puts all available resources at your beck and call, and gives you priority over *everything*. Yes, declare an emergency while Air Force One is on approach and the president suddenly becomes number two for landing. And I can pretty much guarantee you a personal interview with a real Secret Service agent, too.

If the emergency requires immediate action (are there any that don't?), this regulation allows you to deviate from any rule to the extent required to meet the emergency. In other words, if you're in deep wallow, do what you have to do and you can talk about it after you land.

Being pilot in command also means doing the other things that the pilot who is in command should do that don't involve manipulating the controls of an airplane. For instance, there are certain equipment requirements and maintenance checks required of aircraft that are used for IFR. We'll discuss these farther along in this chapter, but know this: You, as PIC, will always be held responsible for determining that all equipment is present and all required checks and maintenance have taken place before your flight.

This doesn't mean that you have to be Mr. or Ms. Goodwrench. In fact, most work on airplanes must be done by licensed mechanics (licensed as mechanics, that is, not air conditioning repair people). But it does mean you are the sole, whole, responsible person for seeing that what should be done has been done in terms of inspections, maintenance, and repair or tagging of equipment discrepancies (Figure 12). We'll walk through what those requirements are in a while. Just know for now that this is literally on your ticket.

Some pilots assume that because the pilot ahead of them thought the airplane was legal for his flight, that it's OK for their air adventure. Sounds right, but it's wrong. You may just be repeating someone else's mistake, and with your luck, *you'll* be the one who gets the FAA ramp check (and that is not a procedure where the FAA guy tests the concrete to see if it's solid).

"But," you say, "the aircraft and engine logs aren't readily available for inspection at the FBO where I fly. The person at the counter says that all checks are up to date." Really? And your check is in the mail? Since you worked hard to earn your license, maybe you'd better check on this check.

Think about it for a second. Moose, who uses industrial-strength mousse to spike his hair, is your counter person du jour. Moose is majoring in tattoo art, has flown only while using drugs that the FDA doesn't even know it should ban, and he thinks high maintenance is what his car and roommate require. Still want to take his word for it?

It if were your license at stake (and it is!), don't you think it would be best to insist on looking at the books, just to make sure (while avoiding being gored by the spikes in this fellow's hair helmet)?

You'll need to show the examiner on your instrument checkride that you know what equipment and checks the aircraft must have to be legal for flight under instrument flight rules. If you're concerned about Moose's reported

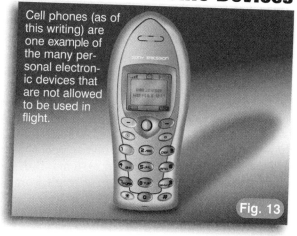

Portable Electronic Devices

Cell phones (as of this writing) are one example of the many personal electronic devices that are not allowed to be used in flight.

Fig. 13

homicidal tendencies when he's disturbed (which his psychiatrist says he is pretty much all the time), this is your saving grace. "Moose, my man," you say, "The Man is going to ask me to show I know, so help me out here by letting me practice. I need to be familiar with the aircraft and engine logs, so can I see them?"

FAR 91.21–Portable Electronic Devices

Can you hear me now? This is the FAR that's responsible for part of the cabin announcement you hear on every airline flight. The prohibition against operation of portable electronic devices (Figure 13) pertains to air carrier aircraft and any other aircraft being operated under IFR.

This prohibition does not apply to voice recorders, hearing aids, pacemakers, iPods, computers, electric shavers (meaning you can shave away that five o'clock shadow in first class despite the fact that you may have entered an earlier time zone) and any other devices the operator determines do not interfere with the navigation or com-

PED - Personal Electronic Devices

PED's designed to transmit are a special concern to pilots. These are devices, which by their nature and design, transmit intentionally. They include cellular telephones, citizens band radios, remote control devices, etc. (Figure 14). The Federal

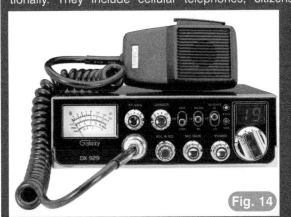

Fig. 14

Communications Commission (FCC) typically licenses these devices as land mobile devices. The FCC currently prohibits the use and operation of cellular telephones while airborne. Its primary concern is that a cellular telephone, while used airborne, would have a much greater transmitting range than a land mobile unit. This could result in serious interference to transmissions at other cell locations since the system uses the same frequency several times within a market. Since a cellular mobile telephone unit is capable of operating on all assignable cellular frequencies, serious interference may also occur to cellular systems in adjacent markets. The FAA supports this airborne restriction for reasons of potential interference to critical aircraft systems. Currently, the FAA does not prohibit use of cellular telephones in aircraft while on the ground if the operator has determined that they will not interfere with the navigation or communication system of the aircraft on which they are to be used. An example might be their use at the gate or during an extended wait on the ground, while awaiting a gate, when specifically authorized by the captain. A cellular telephone will not be authorized for use while the aircraft is being taxied for departure after leaving the gate. The unit will be turned off and properly stowed, otherwise it is possible that a signal from a ground cell could activate it. Whatever procedures an operator elects to adopt should be clearly spelled out in oral departure briefings and by written material provided to each passenger to avoid passenger confusion.

munication systems of the aircraft. So you don't have to worry about the flight attendant yanking out your pacemaker and giving it to someone who really needs it, like the senior flight attendant who almost always has a heart attack when she hears goofy questions such as, "Are we there yet?" (I mean from the captain, not the passengers.)

Interestingly enough, this FAR came into existence long before the widespread popularity of cellular telephones, and it is the FCC, not the FAA, that bans the use of cellular telephones when airborne. As of this writing, the FAA has not published any information or guidance for pilots regarding the effect, if any, that cellular telephones have on the communication or navigation systems. But given the almost certain thrashings that would result from people who were trapped in their seat next to someone yelling his way across the country, the ban is probably a lifesaver.

Flight Rules—General

FAR 91.103–Preflight Action

The FAA thinks you should think about your flight before you launch. That rule says that you, as pilot in command, will become familiar with ALL available information concerning that flight (it should also state that all passengers should visit the bathroom before each flight because that's a regulation we can use).

The regulation goes on to list some items that must be included in that information for flights under IFR or not in the vicinity of the airport ("vicinity" is defined as more than five miles from the airport according to a 1982 copy of *FAA General Aviation News*.) These mandatory checks are:

1. Weather reports and forecasts
2. Fuel requirements
3. Alternatives available if the planned flight cannot be completed
4. Any known traffic delays of which the pilot in command has been advised by ATC

For any flight, the PIC must know the runway lengths at the airports of intended use and the takeoff and landing data for the aircraft.

While not specifically called out, other types of information that you'd have a hard time explaining the absence of are:

1. NOTAMS for your route of flight
2. Configuration and boundaries of all Class B or C airspace along the route
3. Restricted and prohibited airspace and any weather reporting facilities and their frequencies
4. The ever unpopular and ever moving *temporary flight restrictions* (TFRs) as shown in Figure 15A

These are all things that any conscientious pilot would check before flight, but because it's a requirement, it helps to be able to prove you did it. That's why I recommend printing and carrying the weather for your route of flight. Besides, you'd be surprised how quickly you can forget the general weather patterns and specific reports when you suddenly have to alter your plan of action. Having those reports there to refresh your memory does more than just satisfy a rule. NOTAMs are a good thing to have printed out for later use, too.

Keep in mind that a valid aviation weather briefing (one that meets your legal requirement to receive a briefing before departing) can, as of this writing, come only from the FSS or DUATS. Watching the weather channel or talking to some fellow named *Bubba* with thick glasses, an umbrella and thermometer sitting on a porch somewhere in a remote part of America doesn't cut it. *Advisory Circular 00-62*, however, allows Web sites receiving the FAA stamp of approval to provide valid briefings. So you can expect to see many additional vendors providing access to weather information that will constitute a legal weather briefing.

Temporary Flight Restrictions Airspace

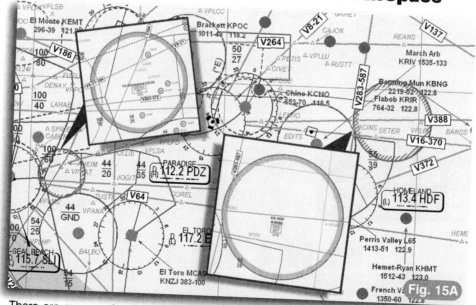

There are many web sites providing graphic depiction of TFRs. AOPA's flight planning software is another excellent source of graphic TFR information.

FAR 91.119—Minimum Safe Altitudes: General

It's worth a review of the minimum safe altitude rule prescribed in FAR Part 91 as it relates to you as a budding instrument pilot (even if your name isn't Bud). This rule designates certain minimum altitudes that you must maintain under specific circumstances. These altitudes are designed to protect people on the surface as well as the pilot and passengers on the aircraft. For some aircraft, the risk associated with flying too low is greater than for others. Airplanes, for instance, must be operated higher than helicopters because they require more distance to land. Just take a look at a helipad if you want proof (it's so small that they can only fit one letter of the alphabet in it).

None of the following minimum altitude rules pertain to takeoff or landing at an airport. Taking off or landing obviously requires climbs and descents at altitudes closer-than-normal to the surface. Here are the rules you need to understand:

Rule 1—No person may operate an aircraft below an altitude allowing an emergency landing to be made without undue hazard to persons or property on the surface in the event of an engine failure. This is another of the famous FAA catchall rules. For cars, there's always a "basic speed law" which says that no matter what the posted speed, you can't drive faster than the circumstances make prudent (that also means no passing a cop car, either).

In aviation, you can't fly any lower than what's safe. If something bad happens and you didn't have enough altitude to respond safely, then this proves you weren't high enough. You'll have a difficult time convincing an FAA inspector that flying 50 feet above a crowded beach on the Fourth of July is a safe practice (besides, you never want to give a 12 year old something to throw a sparkler at).

Common sense and good piloting practice dictate flying high enough so you can glide to an acceptable landing site. Professional pilots think this way and they never allow themselves to become trapped by circumstances and altitude.

Rule 2—When flying over any congested area of a city, town or settlement or over any open air assembly of persons, the aircraft must be operated at an altitude of 1,000 feet above the highest obstacle within a horizontal radius of 2,000 feet of the aircraft.

Figure 15B depicts a building, topping out at 750 feet MSL, in a congested area. An aircraft operating within 2,000 feet horizontally of that building needs to fly at a minimum altitude of 1,750 feet MSL for legal flight. The question pilots frequently ask is, "What is the definition of a congested area?" FAA officials have yet to officially define this concept. Frankly, it's often the NTSB (National Transportation Safety Board) that defines these concepts by legal precedent created when pilots are called into an NTSB hearing to explain their actions. By then, of course, it's too late for the pilot in question. One thing is clear though. You'll have a lot of explaining to do if you violate this regulation.

Minimum Safe Altitudes

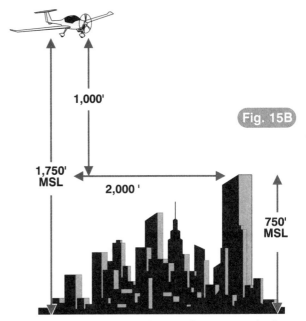

When flying over a congested area, pilots are required to operate 1,000 feet above the highest obstacle within a horizontal radius of 2,000 feet of the aircraft.

While a formal definition of "congested area" is lacking, we can pretty much see what the FAA considers a congested area by examining a few NTSB court decisions. On one occasion a pilot was cited for operating an airplane within a radius of 2,000 feet and less than 1,000 feet above a few isolated homes with smoke rising from their fireplaces. Smoke was a vital factor, since by its presence it implied the homes were occupied (or it was just one home occupied by the Marlboro man). From this we can conclude that an area can be "congested" without being population-dense.

On another occasion, a pilot wasn't cited for flying within a few hundred feet of an industrial warehouse. The reason? It was Sunday and no cars were in the parking lot. The implication here, again, is that the presence of people is the major factor in determining the congestion quotient of an area. You'll need to use your good judgment on this one because of the vague definitions involved. Be conservative. Don't fly too low where there are lots of people or when logic says there may be lots of people in the vicinity (such as a place with a sign outside that reads, "Free Food," because there are sure to be quite a few young, starving flight instructors on the scene).

One old timer summed it up very well when he said, "Never fly low enough so someone can get your aircraft tail number." Of course, that was the intelligent part of the statement. He went on to say, "If you want to fly low over people, do it over the entrance to an ophthalmology clinic."

Rule 3—When operating an aircraft over other than a congested area, no person may operate below an altitude of 500 feet above the surface, except over open water or sparsely populated areas. In those cases, the aircraft may not be operated closer than 500 feet to any person, vessel, vehicle or structure.

When over open water or a sparsely populated area you may take your plane right down on the deck if you wish (but you may not be operating with a full deck if you do it). But don't forget Rule 1. Go deck diving only if you can land safely in an emergency (see Rule 1) *or* can convince an inquiring FAA official that the reason you drew a crowd of scrap metal operators had nothing at all to do with the fact you were flying at 15 feet AGL. The moment you spot a person, boat, car (especially if the car has the letters "FAA" written on top it) or structure, you need to move away by a distance of at least 500 feet vertically or horizontally, as shown in Figure 16.

Minimum Altitudes

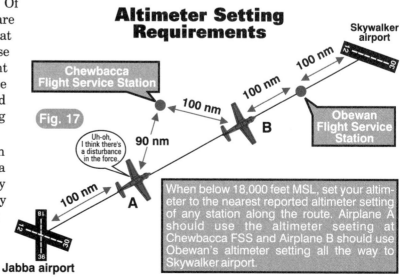

When operating over a sparsely populated area you are given more flexibility in choice of altitude. You must, however, remain at least 500 feet away from any person, vessel, vehicle or structure at all times.

So, how does this affect you as an instrument pilot? After all, you will be flying on prescribed routes with clearly defined minimum altitudes, won't you? Of course you will, most of the time, but there are times when you won't. There will be times that basic VFR minimums will exist (we'll review these in a bit) and you may wish to shoot an instrument approach at Bad Town airport and then, once clear of the clouds, proceed VFR to your FirstAid Town home base for a landing. Nothing wrong with that, is there?

That depends on what's between Bad Town and FirstAid Town. In the past, when there was a Meigs Field on the lake in Chicago, Illinois, many pilots would execute an approach to Midway Airport and then proceed VFR for a landing at Meigs. If the weather was basic VFR—1,000 overcast and three miles visibility—there was no way that operation could be conducted legally. Why? Chicago qualifies as a congested

area (as anyone who has attempted to make progress on the surface during rush hour can testify) and if the clouds were at 1,000 AGL there is no way to maintain the required cloud clearance AND maintain an altitude of 1,000 feet above all the houses, businesses and apartment buildings within a 2,000 foot horizontal distance. (Sources tell me it was possible *legally* to get to Meigs; however, it was by shooting an approach to Gary, Indiana and then proceeding up the lakeshore to Meigs Field.)

FAR 91.121–Altimeter Settings

Think of the altimeter setting as your own Project Mercury. As you can imagine, current and accurate altimeter settings are critical to safety—especially when flying solely by reference to your instruments. The altimeter is literally what's between you and running into something or someone. That why the FARs say that when you're below 18,000 feel MSL, you must have an altimeter setting from a station along your route and within 100 nautical miles of your aircraft (Figure 17).

When you're on an IFR flight plan, it's hard to avoid getting an altimeter setting. Controllers hand them out like a business card almost every time you cross air traffic control sector boundaries. I say, "almost" because controllers are human and can forget to provide this information. You'll want to be especially vigilant about obtaining an altimeter setting when you are in areas of rapidly changing weather. Remember the old adage of "high to low, look out below." If you cross from a high pressure area into one of lower pressure, you will be lower than what your altimeter indicates unless you've updated the altimeter setting.

The proper altimeter setting is vital not only in separating you from terrain and obstacles but also in separating you from other aircraft. The concept of separation sort of breaks down if everyone does their own altimeter thing, because then things aren't where they appear to be, and they appear where they ought not to be. If everybody in the area is working with the same altimeter setting, ATC will keep you separated from other traffic. That's certainly a desirable thing!

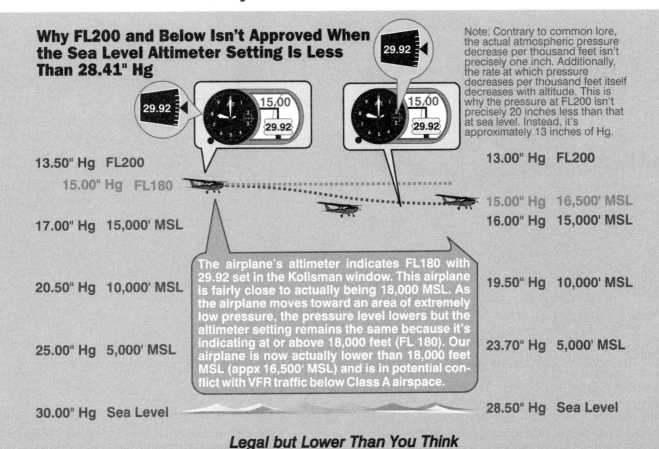

Why FL200 and Below Isn't Approved When the Sea Level Altimeter Setting Is Less Than 28.41" Hg

Note: Contrary to common lore, the actual atmospheric pressure decrease per thousand feet isn't precisely one inch. Additionally, the rate at which pressure decreases per thousand feet itself decreases with altitude. This is why the pressure at FL200 isn't precisely 20 inches less than that at sea level. Instead, it's approximately 13 inches of Hg.

13.50" Hg FL200
15.00" Hg FL180
17.00" Hg 15,000' MSL
20.50" Hg 10,000' MSL
25.00" Hg 5,000' MSL
30.00" Hg Sea Level

13.00" Hg FL200
15.00" Hg 16,500' MSL
16.00" Hg 15,000' MSL
19.50" Hg 10,000' MSL
23.70" Hg 5,000' MSL
28.50" Hg Sea Level

The airplane's altimeter indicates FL180 with 29.92 set in the Kollsman window. This airplane is fairly close to actually being 18,000 MSL. As the airplane moves toward an area of extremely low pressure, the pressure level lowers but the altimeter setting remains the same because it's indicating at or above 18,000 feet (FL 180). Our airplane is now actually lower than 18,000 feet MSL (appx 16,500' MSL) and is in potential conflict with VFR traffic below Class A airspace.

Legal but Lower Than You Think

If you are operating at and above 18,000 feet MSL (Class A airspace), all altimeters are required to be set to pressure altitude—29.92 inches Hg. It's possible that a strong enough area of low pressure could cause the 18,000 foot flight level to dip below Class A airspace (see Figure above). Recall from Chapter Two (on flight instruments) that pressure levels dip closer to the ground in areas of lower pressure. We keep our altimeter setting updated so we know our height above sea level. But IFR pilots flying at and above 18,000 feet set their altimeter's Kollsman window to 29.92 inches Hg and leave it set at that until cleared below 18,000 feet.

What this means is that in an area of exceptionally lower pressure, say 28.41 inches Hg at the surface, an IFR pilot with an altimeter set to 29.92 inches Hg might actually dip way down below 18,000 feet MSL. This is a problem because the pilot operating at or above 18,000 feet is supposed to keep his altimeter set to 29.92 inches   Hg and not to the local altimeter setting. In this instance, when the altimeter is set too high, it reads too high. The pilot is lower than he thinks. He could be operating a thousand or more feet below 18,000 foot MSL while his altimeter says he's 18,000 or higher. He might know this isn't his precise true height above sea level, but he thinks it's not too far off.

In reality, the VFR pilot flying below 18,000 foot MSL, say at 17,500 feet MSL in the vicinity who has his altimeter set to 28.41 inches Hg, might encounter the IFR pilot whose altimeter is reading 18,000 feet or higher. That's why, when the altimeter setting is as low as 28.41, the lowest flight level that the Class A airspace folks can use is FL 200. This is usually not a problem for people in the lower 48 states, but in Alaska they have mountains (Denali for one) that stick up into Class A airspace. If the pressure is too low in this area, FL180 might dip down too low, perhaps low enough to lead you into the side of Denali—and there's no "denaling" that this would be bad news for everyone on board. More commonly, when the local altimeter setting is below 29.92 inches, ATC can't assign pilots FL180.

When operating at or above 18,000 foot MSL, setting the altimeter gets really easy. You set it to 29.92 inches of Hg and leave it alone. In short, you're flying pressure altitudes when operating at or above 18,000 foot MSL. It's very important to remember that when you descend below FL180, the altimeter must be set to the current local altimeter setting.

FAR 91.123 – Compliance with ATC Clearance and Instructions

This regulation states that when an ATC clearance has been obtained, no pilot in command may deviate from that clearance unless an amended clearance is obtained, an emergency exists, or in response to a traffic alert and collision avoidance system resolution advisory. You have the same responsibilities here that you had as a student pilot, but since you will be getting many more ATC clearances now that you are going to be flying IFR, a bit of review is in order.

Essentially, when operating under an ATC clearance, you have to listen to and follow ATC, at least until you obtain an amended clearance (unless you have that emergency, or need to deviate in response to a traffic or a collision alert). Of course, if you receive a clearance and you're confused by it, you are required to request clarification. One of my friends was once given an amended clearance at midpoint enroute that took him back to the destination airport. He queried the controller about why he was being taken back along the same route to the departure airport. This was an obvious mistake, but the controller rose to the occasion and said something like, "Oh, well we didn't like

Operations in Class G Airspace

Class G (uncontrolled) airspace starts at the surface and ascends upward until reaching the base of Class E (controlled) airspace. Class G airspace may extend upward to 700 or 1,200 feet AGL or even higher. Generally, Class G airspace contains fewer big and fast airplanes (except in the vicinity of certain airports). Therefore, the visibility and cloud clearance requirement is usually not as great as in controlled airspace.

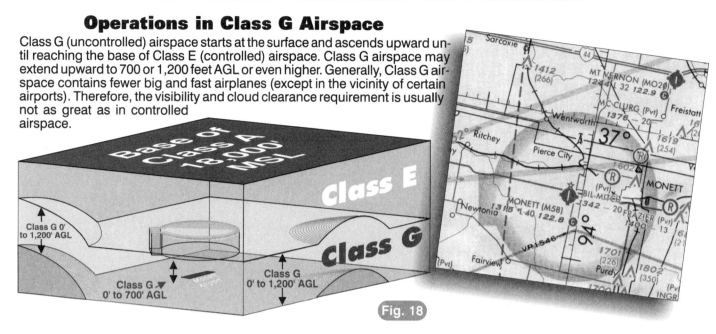

Fig. 18

the way things were going so we wanted you to start over and try everything again."

If you're in VFR weather conditions and can expect to remain that way (and you're not in Class A airspace, of course) and you get a clearance you don't like, you always have the option of canceling IFR and going on your own. Perhaps ATC is vectoring you out over water and you don't know how to swim, or you're being asked to fly at an altitude where even your astronaut merit badge doesn't make you comfortable. Canceling your IFR clearance is a perfectly reasonable option. It's done all the time. And no, you will not be hurting either the controller's feelings or her paycheck. She isn't doing piecework.

The IFR route you get will always get you where you're going, but not necessarily the quickest way. There are many considerations in concocting a route, and goodness only knows what the computer is thinking sometimes. But

traffic flow, weather, staffing, and other factors can all lead to odd clearances or weird midcourse corrections that seem a little, well, off course.

Canceling IFR isn't something ATC will ever offer. You have to initiate it, though I've occasionally heard controllers provide really strong hints to the really clueless. It's *your* IFR flight plan until you say you don't want it any longer. Good thing, too, because if controllers could dump pilots out of the system any time they felt crabby, we'd be walking to our destinations on occasion.

You can always exercise your emergency authority as pilot in command and deviate from any clearance or regulation to the extent necessary to resolve your emergency. If you deviate from your clearance due to an emergency (or to resolve a traffic alert and avoidance system advisory) you need to inform ATC of your deviation as soon as possible. Remember the basic rules of flying: aviate, navigate, communicate, in that order. So fly your airplane

Operations in Surface-Based Class E Airspace

Within the borders of the magenta (red) dashed line, Class E airspace descends all the way to the surface surrounding McComb-Pike airport. Since some instrument approaches bring pilots real close to the surface of an airport, this lower Class E surface area keeps them in controlled airspace during their descent.

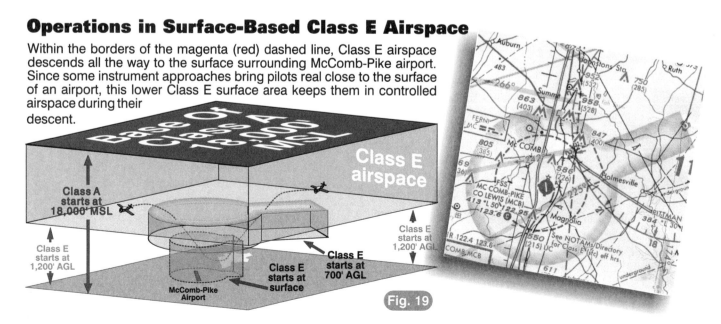

Fig. 19

first, point it in the safe/appropriate direction next, then tell ATC about what you're doing. Talking to a controller is the last part of your responsibilities, but it still *is* a part.

If you're given priority by ATC in an emergency, even if you haven't deviated from any rules or clearances, you may get to write a report. ATC can (but doesn't have to) ask that you submit a detailed report of the emergency to the manager of the facility that gave you priority within 48 hours. So be careful what you write, and not fiction, please.

Perhaps you've seen a sign in some establishments that says, "Your failure to plan ahead is *not* my emergency." Your need to get to a client meeting you didn't leave for early enough, to put the meatloaf in the oven in time for dinner, to pick up the kids after school, and similar sorts of things are *not* what ATC considers to be a valid emergency.

Keep your eye on the ball. Your job is to get you and your passengers back to earth safely, and if that requires that you declare an emergency, do so. The paperwork is a small price to pay compared to the payoff in assistance you'll get from ATC. Just make sure that if asked, the story you are prepared to tell sounds like an emergency to someone besides you.

You're not always going to appreciate some of the clearances you receive from ATC as an IFR pilot. This is especially true when it comes to weather deviation or avoidance. Remember, the person at the scope has the big picture view of who's in the system and what weather problems they're complaining about. His or her job is the safe and expeditious flow of traffic. You can always ask for an amended clearance to avoid a weather concern, but the controller may have to say *no* because he knows something you don't—like where the other IFR airplanes are.

It's also possible that the reason he can't grant your request is miles down the road. It's unlikely he's denying your request as a power play. If this were a power play, it would normally involve statements such as, "So you think you know what fear is, eh?" or "I think I need to hear the word, 'uncle' if I'm to sustain my good mood."

So what do you do if you're experiencing a distressful condition (or expect to experience one if you fly into an embedded thunderstorm) and need a deviation or a new or modified clearance and ATC isn't going along with your request? The first thing to do is to avoid getting into a heated (or even a cooled) discussion on the frequency (even if your heater is off). That's not going to do anything except raise blood pressure on both sides of the mic and block transmissions for other pilots. Instead, be specific, clear, and ask for what you need. If ATC isn't or can't cooperate, then you should exercise your emergency authority as PIC and declare an emergency.

FAR 91.126 Operating On or In the Vicinity of an Airport in Class G Airspace

With only a few exceptions, airports lying in Class G and Class E airspace don't have control towers (we won't discuss the exceptions because they are truly exceptions).

Since there are no operating control towers at these airports, pilots (IFR and VFR) must follow specific procedures to prevent bumping into each other.

When approaching to land at an airport without an operating control tower in Class G airspace (Figure 18), each pilot of an airplane must make all turns to the left. (The exception to this is when the airport displays approved light signals or visual marking indicating turns should be made to the right. In that case, the pilot must make right turns.)

If you're on an instrument approach into an uncontrolled airport and the weather is VFR and there is VFR traffic in the pattern, *you are in no way given priority over the other traffic in the pattern*. That's right. You still need to maneuver in such a way as to see and avoid other traffic. Sometimes this means leveling off above the minimum allowed altitude on the instrument approach (for example, the MDA or minimum descent altitude), overflying the airport, and entering the pattern like everyone else. Yes, I realize that this is a non-towered airport and that traffic patterns are recommendations and that straight-in approaches from an instrument approach aren't prohibited. Nevertheless, there are several court cases establishing a precedent that makes a pilot flying a non-standard pattern (and that includes pilots flying instrument approach under the above conditions) liable if an accident occurs.

Another part of this regulation requires that all helicopters approaching to land avoid the flow of fixed-wing aircraft. No, this isn't because the FAA doesn't want these two aircraft fraternizing and learning each other's secrets. It's because helicopters and airplanes have operating characteristics that are sufficiently different that mixing them can present problems. After all, helicopters can stop in mid air. Airplanes can stop in mid air too, but often only once.

FAR 91.127 Operations On or In the Vicinity of an Airport in Class E Airspace

For all practical purposes, this regulation is the same as FAR 91.126 for Class G airspace. As is the case with airports within Class G airspace, there are only a few airports lying within Class E (controlled) airspace that have control towers. We won't discuss these exceptions, either. The only significant difference between airports within Class E and Class G airspace is a FAR Part 93 departure requirement. FAR Part 93 contains noise abatement requirements. Wise pilot always try and follow noise abatement procedures at airports when possible.

Being good airport neighbors may sound like a cliché, but that doesn't make it a bad policy. A bad policy is where pilots put birdseed on the airport noise sensor, which makes all airplane engines sound like they chirp. "Well Mr. Machado, it seems your A36 Bonanza, the one that makes that pecking noise, exceeded the noise level for the airport. What do you have to say for yourself?"

"Well sir, if the noise was heard in the correct sequence, I'd say the pecking order at the airport hasn't changed."

FAR 91.129 Operations In Class D Airspace

Class D airspace generally extends upward from the surface to 2,500 feet above the airport elevation, as shown in Figure 20. Its radius around the primary airport varies, based on the instrument procedures for which the controlled airspace is established. I've seen the radius vary from a little less than three nautical miles to seven nautical miles, with the typical radius being a little less than five nautical miles. You'll be able to determine the specific size of an airport's Class D airspace by looking at the sectional chart. The Class D airspace, shown in Figure 20, looks somewhat like a can of tuna since it has a short, cylindrical shape. So, for the halibut, let's refer to Class D airspace as the tuna can.

this airspace. In other words, you must give the tower controller a call before entering the tuna can boundaries, have them acknowledge you, and once inside the can you must maintain communication at all times.

Pilots sometimes become confused about the precise definition of *establish communication*. Technically, you've established communication anytime ATC acknowledges your aircraft call sign (the airplane's N number, such as N2132B). For instance, on your initial call, while outside or above the physical dimensions of the tuna can, you give the tower your position, altitude, destination and any requests you have. They'll normally call you back using your aircraft call sign and give you directions for entering the traffic flow around the airport.

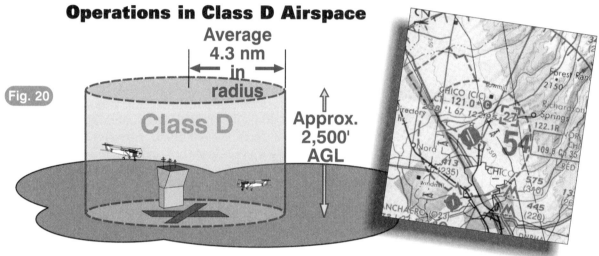

Operations in Class D Airspace
Average 4.3 nm in radius

Class D

Approx. 2,500' AGL

Fig. 20

Operating anywhere within the boundaries of Class D airspace requires that you establish and maintain communication with the Air Traffic Control tower prior to entering this airspace. While controllers don't provide separation between aircraft, they do provide sequencing as well as information about known air traffic.

The primary airport (the one for which the airspace is designated) has a control tower. There may be *other* airports that happen to lie within Class D airspace, and these may or may not have towers (see Figure 21). These secondary airports are referred to as *satellite* airports, and not because they always have objects orbiting in the pattern.

Equipment Required – The minimum equipment required to operate within Class D airspace is a two-way radio. A transponder isn't required. You can request permission from ATC to fly into or out of this airspace without a radio (you can't ask on the radio, since you don't have one). You might, for example, need to take your airplane to another airport to have the radio repaired. Calling ATC (the tower controllers) on the phone gets you instructions for departing and/or arriving at the airport without two-way radio communication.

Arrivals or Through Flight–If you want to fly through this airspace or land at the primary airport, you must establish two-way radio communication with the ATC facility that is responsible for that Class D airspace. Normally, this ATC facility is the control tower located at the primary airport. Once established, you must maintain communication with the air traffic control tower while in

If the controller says, "N2132B, stand by," you've technically established communication, and may continue into the tuna can toward the airport. If the controller says, "Aircraft calling Crumbling Tower, stand by" (that is, if you aren't called by your N-number name), then you have not established communications and should remain outside or above the tuna can. Of course, if the controller says, "N2132B, remain clear of Class D airspace" (they don't say, "...tuna can"), then you must follow their instructions even though two-way communication has been established.

These communication requirements are in force even if you are landing at one of the satellite airports within Class D airspace. In other words, if another airport lies within the boundaries of the tuna can, as shown in Figure 21 (typically an airport without an operating control tower), and you're interested in landing at that satellite airport, you must establish two-way radio communication with the air traffic control tower at the primary airport before entering this airspace. You must maintain this link during your flight to the airport.

Departures–If you're departing from the primary airport, you must establish and maintain two-way radio com-

A Satellite Airport Lying Within Another Airport's Class D Airspace

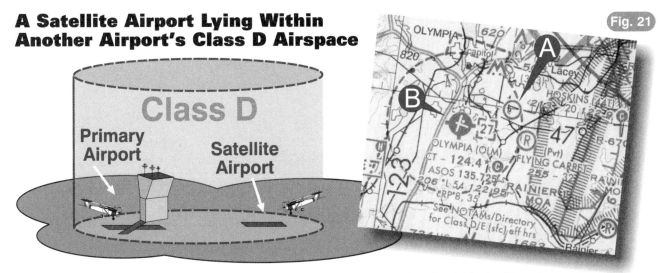

Fig. 21

Airports like Hoskins (position A) are called *satellite airports* because they lie within the Class D airspace of another *primary* airport like Olympia (position B). Communications are still required with the air traffic control tower at the primary airport when taking off or landing at Hoskins. When departing a satellite airport on an IFR flight plan, you should follow the communications procedures stated in your IFR clearance.

munication with ATC within Class D airspace. In other words, don't take off without calling the tower and listening to them while in the tuna can.

Suppose you're taking off from a non-tower satellite airport within Class D airspace, as shown in Figure 21. Do you still need to call the ATC facility for the primary airport? Yes. You must establish and maintain two-way radio communication as soon as practical after departing. In other words, take off and give the tower at the primary airport a call as soon as it's reasonable for you to do so. Let them know what you're doing, follow their directions, and keep listening to them while you're anywhere within the tuna can.

What if you're departing a satellite airport under IFR conditions? In that case you'll do exactly what your IFR clearance instructs you to do. This may mean contacting Departure Control or the Air Route Traffic Control Center in lieu of the local tower after departure. On the other hand, you may actually call the tower to receive your IFR clearance and it will be the tower controller that issues your departure instructions. Do what the clearance says and you will have met your communication obligation.

Communications Failure–It's possible, albeit not all that probable, that your radios could give up the ghost enroute. Does this mean you can't fly back into the Class D airspace you departed from? Not necessarily. A provision in this regulation allows you to enter Class D airspace under VFR conditions. In other words, you can get back into the tuna can as long as you have weather conditions at or above basic VFR minimums. How do you do it? Simply fly to the airport, enter the traffic pattern, watch the tower for light signals and land when you receive a steady green light from the tower (hopefully, you'll be looking at the tower and not a local traffic signal when you see the steady green light).

Minimum Altitudes–The important section here is the part saying that you must stay at or above the glideslope (until a lower altitude is necessary for landing) when approaching to land on a runway served by a visual approach slope indicator (VASI).

When You're Just Too Scared to Talk

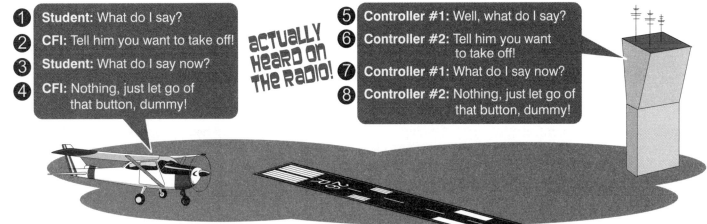

1. **Student:** What do I say?
2. **CFI:** Tell him you want to take off!
3. **Student:** What do I say now?
4. **CFI:** Nothing, just let go of that button, dummy!

ACTUALLY HEARD ON THE RADIO!

5. **Controller #1:** Well, what do I say?
6. **Controller #2:** Tell him you want to take off!
7. **Controller #1:** What do I say now?
8. **Controller #2:** Nothing, just let go of that button, dummy!

Dimensions of Class C Airspace

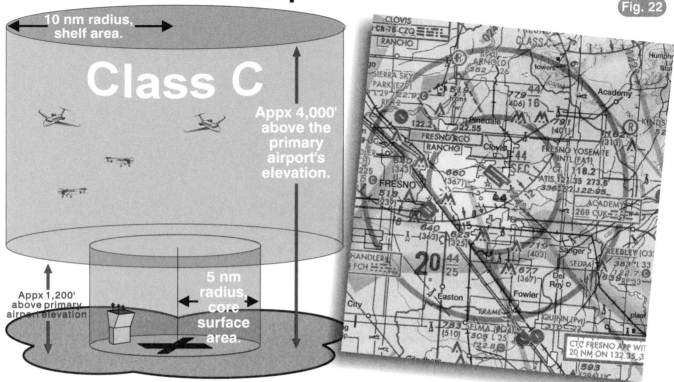

Operating anywhere within the boundaries of Class C airspace requires that you establish and maintain communication with the appropriate ATC facility (usually Approach Control) prior to entering this airspace. ATC provides *basic radar service, sequencing* and *separation* between VFR and IFR aircraft. It also provides this same service within a 20 nm radius of the primary airport (often defined as the *outer area,* an area that's not shown on the sectional chart). A mixture of faster and slower aircraft is common in Class C airspace.

Takeoff, Landing, Taxi Clearance–No person may, at an airport with an operating control tower, operate an aircraft on a runway or taxiway, or take off or land an aircraft, unless an appropriate clearance is received from ATC. A clearance to "taxi to" the takeoff runway assigned to an aircraft is not a clearance to cross that assigned runway or to taxi onto that runway at any point. It is, however, a clearance to cross other runways that intersect the taxi route to that assigned takeoff runway. Similarly, a clearance to "taxi to" any point other than an assigned takeoff runway is a clearance to cross all runways that intersect the taxi route unless specific hold short instructions have been given.

FAR 91.130—Operations In Class C Airspace

Figure 22 shows a typical chunk of Class C airspace. This type of airspace is larger than Class D airspace in that it has two cylindrical components instead of the single, tuna-can-shaped Class D airspace.

Class C is a double-decker tuna can. The physical dimensions of Class C airspace consist of a lower tuna can having a radius of five nautical miles and extending vertically from the ground to 4,000 feet above the airport elevation.

The upper, larger tuna can has a radius of 10 nautical miles. It usually starts at 1,200 feet and extends vertically to 4,000 feet above the airport elevation. For the sake of continuity, we'll refer to Class C airspace as the double

tuna can. (I do feel it's necessary to mention that this is a dolphin-free explanation of airspace. Just in case you thought there was something fishy going on).

Simply stated, Class C airspace goes with airports that handle larger, faster airplanes (generally this means significant quantities of commercial traffic and military bases). It's established to keep the small airplanes and bigger airplanes from bumping into one another. Since there are faster airplanes involved, it makes sense that the airspace must cover more area.

As with Class D airspace, there is a primary airport in the center of the double tuna can. This is the airport for which the Class C airspace was established. The double tuna can usually sits directly over this airport. As with Class D airspace, there may be satellite airports within the boundaries of Class C airspace. That means there may be other airports, with and without control towers, within the surface area covered by the double tuna can.

You're going to find there is very little difference between the requirements for flight in Class C airspace and Class D airspace. Whether you're in the single or double tuna can airspace, the requirements are essentially the same. Let's examine the Class C requirements.

General Requirements–All operations in Class C airspace must comply with the previous regulation—FAR 91.129. In other words, the operating rules are essentially the same as in Class D airspace. This makes sense, since

Class B Airspace

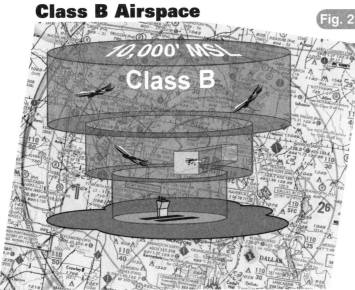

Fig. 23

Class B airspace may resemble an inverted wedding cake. Its multiple tier structure is designed to keep larger aircraft and small aircraft separated as they approach or overfly the primary airport. This is why an ATC clearance is required when operating anywhere within Class B airspace.

both Class D and Class C airspace have primary airports with operating control towers. They *should* have similar requirements for aircraft operations.

Traffic Patterns–If you're taking off or landing at a satellite airport within Class C airspace, you must comply with the FAA arrival and departure traffic pattern established for that airport. There's nothing new here. Just because the primary airport is a little bit busier, there's no reason why you should do anything different at one of the satellite airports than you would for Class D airspace.

Communication—Arrival or Through Flight–If you want to land at the primary airport in Class C airspace, or if you just want to fly through that airspace, you must establish and maintain two-way radio communication. But who 'ya gonna call? The double tuna can of airspace may be controlled by a tower, an approach control facility, or a combination of both. Read all about it on your sectional chart, which generally instructs you to contact Approach Control on a specific frequency within 20 nm of the primary airport for the Class C airspace (of course, you're required to establish and maintain two-way radio communication prior to entering Class C airspace).

Communication—Departing Flight–If you're departing the primary airport within Class C airspace, you must establish and maintain two-way radio communication with the tower prior to departure. If the controller hands you off to Departure Control, talk and listen to the departure controller until you're out of the double tuna can (Class C airspace). If you're departing a non-tower satellite airport lying within the surface boundaries of Class C airspace, you must establish and maintain two-way radio communication with the approach or departure control facility having jurisdiction over that airspace. Do this as

soon as practicable after departure. (An approach or departure control facility is usually the ATC facility having jurisdiction over Class C airspace.) In the rare event the satellite airport has an operating control tower, do exactly as you would do if you were departing the primary airport having an operating control tower. In other words, communicate with the tower at the satellite airport and follow their instructions.

Equipment Requirements–The minimum equipment required to operate within Class C airspace is a two-way radio and a transponder with altitude reporting capability (per FAR 91.215).

FAR 91.131 Operations In Class B Airspace

Class D airspace was small (a single tuna can). Class C airspace was slightly larger because there were bigger and faster airplanes there (a double tuna can). Class B airspace is the biggest of these tuna can stacks of airspace (Figure 23). It usually extends upward to 10,000 feet MSL and often has horizontal dimensions of many miles, as shown in Figure 23. This airspace is larger than Class C or D airspace because its primary airport has many very large and fast airplanes, such as Boeing 747s and 777s, and considerable IFR activity.

In some cases, Class B airspace (Figure 23) looks like several stacked cans of tuna. Actually it looks more like an inverted wedding cake with individual tiers or floors contributing to its structure. Extra tiers allow faster jet airplanes to make long arrivals and departures into and out of the primary airport while remaining within the protected airspace. The following are the requirements to take off or land at the primary airport or operate within the wedding cake airspace:

Operating Rules–First, you must follow all the rules of FAR 91.129 (Class D airspace) while in Class B airspace. In addition, before you can enter Class B airspace you'll need a *clearance* from the ATC facility having jurisdiction over that airspace. A clearance is essentially verbal *permission* for entry into this airspace.

This is different from the entry requirements for Class C or D airspace, which only required that you establish and maintain two-way radio communication before entry. And keep in mind that if you have a clearance to enter Class B airspace and then leave it for some reason, you need a new clearance to get back in. I experienced this one time when landing at North Las Vegas, which underlies the shelf of Las Vegas' McCarran International airport. While I had a clearance to enter Class B on my descent to North Las Vegas, I descended through one ring of Class B but would have flown into another, lower ring ahead if I hadn't purposely avoided that lower Class B shelf ahead.

Pilot Requirements–You need to be at least a private pilot to take off or land at the primary airport in Class B airspace. There are exceptions for student pilots, recreational pilots and sport pilots who meet the additional requirements of FAR 91.161(d), 61.94. 61.135 and/or 61.95.

Equipment Required – The minimum equipment required to operate within Class B airspace is a two-way radio with all the frequencies needed for communication with ATC, a transponder with altitude encoding capability and, for IFR operations, a functioning VOR receiver.

If, for any reason, it's necessary to conduct training operations within Class B airspace (such as an airline doing touch and goes or instrument approaches at a big airport), then the procedures established by ATC should be followed. In this instance, an airliner may receive a clearance to enter and leave Class B airspace with specific restrictions.

FAR 91.135—Operations In Class A Airspace

You move to the head of the class when you get an "A," and it's that way in airspace, too. Class A is the top (literally) of the heap. It's air so rare that you can only go there with an IFR clearance. How's that for exclusive? This is the fine wine of airspace.

So where do you find Class A airspace? It's all the airspace over the lower 48 states from 18,000 feet MSL up to and including FL 600 (Figure 24). That's the territory inhabited mostly by jets, and in the lower levels, turboprops. Occasionally you'll see a pressurized Cessna cabin class twin or a pressurized Navajo or Aerostar, but mostly it's the kerosene burners up there.

Class A Airspace

Class A airspace starts at 18,000' MSL and extends vertically to 60,000' MSL. It extends offshore and overlies the waters within 12 nautical miles of the coast within the 48 states and Alaska.

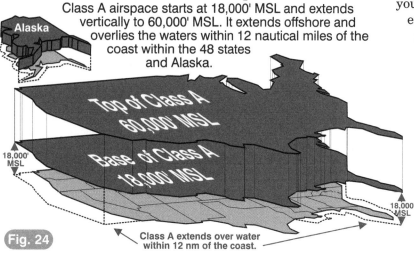

Fig. 24

Class A extends over water within 12 nm of the coast.

Altitudes (known as flight levels since they are all based on pressure altitude with the altimeters all set to 29.92 inches of Hg) in Class A airspace are the normal even-west and odd-east arrangement, but things change when you get to FL290. Above that level, aircraft must be specially equipped to fly in RVSM–Reduced Vertical Separation Minimums–airspace. To operate under RVSM, altimeters are made more sensitive, manuals must be written, crews must be trained, and FAA approval received. The flight levels at and above FL290 are also separated by 1,000 foot intervals with odd value eastbound flight levels (i.e., FL290, 310, 330, 350, etc.) and even value westbound flight levels (i.e., FL300, 320, 340, 360, 380, etc.).

Visual Flight Rules

FAR 91.155—Basic VFR Weather Minimums

Why in the world would we want to talk about VFR weather minimums in preparation for an instrument rating? You'll discover, once you become an instrument pilot, that there will be times that you just don't want to be in the clouds. Sometimes you have no choice, but other times you do, and you will need to know what the VFR weather minimums are for the airspace you're flying in so you can decide whether or not it's possible to cancel your IFR flight plan. After all, the inside of a clouds isn't all that interesting (it's like watching snow between TV channels, except that you may actually be watching snow). In fact, it's quite boring compared to what you see in VMC. On the other hand, you may find it more convenient to fly VFR for a portion of your flight. That's why, as an instrument pilot, you'll find that you have to make both IFR and VFR decisions.

For instance, you may have to decide if the current weather will require you or even allow you to use your instrument rating. It may not be VFR along your route, so IFR flight (or no flight at all) is required. On the other hand, you'll have to look at the capabilities of both yourself and your aircraft and decide if that mix is capable of safely handling the conditions that exist. An IFR rating is not a license to fly in any kind of weather. With a single-engine aircraft, there are many conditions you will just not be able to cope with. Icing and embedded thunderstorms are just two of the problems you'll want to avoid. Not that any sensible pilot flying any airplane ever deliberately seeks these things out. Normally aspirated aircraft may not be able to climb to some of the minimum enroute altitudes found in the western United States.

As we discussed above, there might be times you will file to one airport and then cancel and go on to your intended destination, which may not have an instrument approach. To do that, you'll have to remember minimum altitudes for flight and basic VFR minimums in the various classes of airspace. The flying business requires a constant accumulation of information. You aren't allowed to forget the things you've learned for previous certificates or ratings. Instead, you're expected to build on them and refine them to fit with your new capabilities.

Figure 25 is a summary of VFR requirements for the various classes of airspace. The exception noted as 91.155(b) allows you to operate an airplane at night clear of clouds and within a half mile of the runway in an airport traffic pattern when the visibility is at least one statute mile but less than the three normally required. This would allow you to perform your three night takeoffs and landings in what would be less than VFR conditions anywhere else. This could come in very handy if you need-

Basic VFR Weather Minimums in Controlled Airspace

Altitude or Airspace	Flight Visibility	Distance From Clouds
Class A	not applicable	not applicable
Class B	3 statute miles	clear of clouds
Class C	3 statute miles	500' below 1,000' above 2,000' horizontal
Class D	3 statute miles	500' below 1,000' above 2,000' horizontal
Class E .... Less than 10,000' MSL......	3 statute miles	500' below 1,000' above 2,000' horizontal
At or above 10,000' MSL...	5 statute miles	1,000' above 1,000' below 1 statute mile horizontal

Basic VFR Weather Minimums in Uncontrolled Airspace

Altitude or Airspace	Flight Visibility	Distance From Clouds
Class G .... 1,200' or less above the surface (regardless of MSL altitude)	91.155(b) allows you to operate an airplane at night clear of clouds and within a half mile of the runway in an airport traffic pattern when the visibility is at least one statute mile but less than the three normally required.	
Day, except as provided in FAR 91.155 (b)......................	1 statute mile	clear of clouds
Night, except as provided in FAR 91.155 (b)......................	3 statute miles	500' below 1,000' above 2,000' horizontal
More than 1,200' above the surface but less than 10,000 feet MSL: Day	1 statute mile	500' below 1,000' above 2,000' horizontal
Night	3 statute miles	500' below 1,000' above 2,000' horizontal
More than 1,200' above the surface and at or above 10,000 feet MSL	5 statute miles	1,000' above 1,000' below 1 statute mile horizontal

Fig. 25

ed to do a night IFR flight with passengers and needed to get night landing current. Of course, if you tell your passengers to wait by the runup area while you fly around and get current, don't expect them to be there when you get back. Passengers don't understand what *current* means. Some of them think it's a berry used to make a type of jam. All they hear is the word "runup," which to them probably sounded like you said, "*Run up* into the hills man, while you still have time to flee for your life."

FAR 91.157–Special VFR Weather Minimums

Special VFR operations pertain to the airspace defined by the upward extension of the lateral boundaries of a class B, C, D or E surface area around an airport (Figure 26). These operations may only be conducted with an ATC clearance, clear of clouds and with flight visibility of at least one statute mile. That's during the daytime. A special VFR clearance at night requires that you be instrument rated, current to fly IFR, and that the aircraft be equipped for flight under IFR. Why? Because it's difficult to see clouds at night. The chances are that without an instrument rating (thus the accompanying instrument skills),

you might fly into a cloud at night and not know how to handle yourself properly. This is night fright from not seeing white, and the outcome is often not right.

Special VFR can be very useful in departing an airport affected by a very localized weather phenomenon such as a marine layer. Remember, the SVFR clearance applies only to the vertical and horizontal dimensions of the surface-based controlled airspace and only up to 10,000 feet MSL. Operating special VFR can allow you to take off and fly out of the area as long as the visibility is at least one statute mile and you can remain clear of clouds. Check your *Airport/Facilities Directory* and sectional charts, though, because special VFR is not available at certain airports. "NO SVFR" in the legend or above the airport name

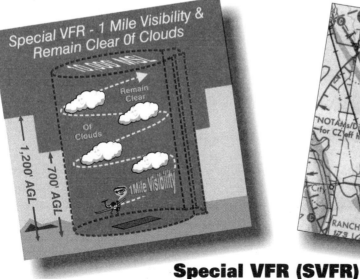

Fig. 26

Special VFR (SVFR)

A special VFR clearance applies only within the lateral limits of the Class E, D, C and B surface area (including any surface-based extensions) below 10,000 feet MSL. It allows you to fly with 1 mile visibility while remaining clear of clouds. The purpose of SVFR is to allow you to depart toward VFR weather or to land when the weather is less than basic VFR. A SVFR clearance at night requires that you be instrument rated and be current to fly IFR. The aircraft must also be legal for IFR flight, too.

(as in Figure 27, position A) means special's a no-go at that facility, and so are you unless you're ready and able to file IFR.

No Special VFR Allowed Here

Instrument Flight Rules

The initial section of these Part 91 regulations dealt with VFR flying in as much as it pertained to you, an aspiring instrument pilot. Now it's time to look at those specific regulations that you may have never seen during your private pilot training. These are the regulations that directly and exclusively affect those with an instrument rating (I'm optimistic that you'll soon have one, too) when they are making IFR flights. Some of these rules are similar to the VFR regulations you've already learned, but are a bit more stringent, such as the amount of fuel you're required to carry aboard the airplane. You'll also find that, unlike VFR flying, an instrument pilot is sometimes *required* to have an alternate airport for a particular flight. Ready to cover new frontier? Let's head em' up and move em' out, partner.

FAR 91.167—Fuel Requirements for Flight in IFR Conditions

To be legal flying IFR, you need enough fuel to fly to your destination, fly from that airport to your alternate airport (if one is required), and then fly for an additional 45 minutes at normal cruising speed (Figure 28). Of course, this is all based on weather reports, forecasts and the actual weather conditions. That's more fuel than you've been required to carry for VFR flight. The big question is, "When are you required to have an alternate airport when flying IFR?"

If the weather at your destination airport is forecast to be a ceiling of at least 2,000 feet above the airport elevation and a visibility of at least three statute miles for at least one hour before to one hour after your estimated time of arrival, then you do not need to list an alternate airport on your IFR flight plan. You do not need to carry the fuel required to fly to that alternate. In this case, you would need only the fuel to fly to your destination and 45 minutes reserve fuel. You can remember this as the "1-2-3" rule—at least one hour before to one hour after, two thousand foot ceiling and three miles visibility (Figure 28).

On the other hand, there's a big difference here between being practical (legal) and being realistic. It is possible to be legally stupid. It's like a friend of mine who took a college chemistry class (that's practical) hoping it would have a happy hour (that's not realistic). Suppose the forecasts indicate that you'll meet the 1-2-3 requirement for an IFR flight. But in looking at the forecast vs. actual weather for the last few hours, you see that wishes aren't coming true. Hopefully, you'll activate your common sense and take the path with the greater chance of survival by flight planning for an alternate airport.

The rules on alternates and fuel reserves are there for the protection of you and your passengers. If you don't list an alternate under these conditions and the weather goes from sweet to sour, you are the one who pays the price. And if you happen to survive the ordeal, the FAA may help you remember the experience by taking away your pilot's license for a while.

Any forecast of conditions "occasionally," "intermittently," "chance of," or "briefly" below 1-2-3 are considered

Fuelish Thoughts for Weather-Wise Pilots

"The forecast for ABC indicated no alternate was needed. As we approached the area, [we received vectors for] deviating around thunderstorms. ABC Approach advised that no one was getting into ABC due to the thunderstorm activity...[but] hopefully in 15 minutes, Approach would be able to accommodate arrivals. I told Approach that we had "minimum fuel" and could only accept a short delay...and needed to land as soon as conditions improved. After about 10 minutes, I told the controller that we needed [a circling approach] for Runway 20. As we were being vectored, the right low fuel warning light illuminated. On final approach, the controller stated that visibility was going down rapidly and it would be difficult to land on Runway 20. I told the first officer to declare an emergency because we had to land...due to low visibility [for Runway 20], regardless of the tailwind component.... We landed with about 450 lbs total fuel."

Both the *Air Traffic Control Handbook* and the *AIM* explain that a minimum fuel advisory is just that: an advisory. It does not indicate an emergency situation or imply a need for traffic priority. In order to receive traffic priority, pilots should declare an emergency. Even when an alternate has been determined, plans may still have to be changed, creating an additional demand on fuel supplies. An air carrier crew thought they had planned for all contingencies, but still were caught short.   **NASA Callback Report**

Fuel Requirements for IFR Flight

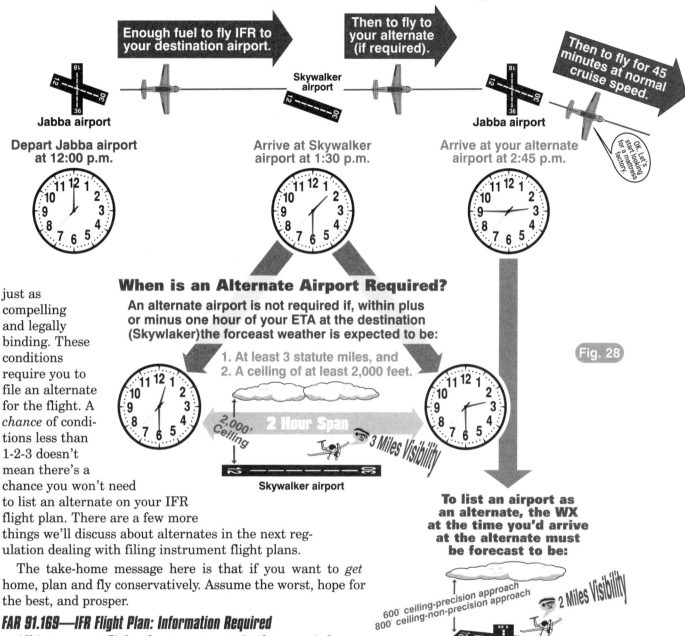

Enough fuel to fly IFR to your destination airport.

Then to fly to your alternate (if required).

Then to fly for 45 minutes at normal cruise speed.

OK. Let's start looking for a mattress factory.

Skywalker airport

Jabba airport

Jabba airport

Depart Jabba airport at 12:00 p.m.

Arrive at Skywalker airport at 1:30 p.m.

Arrive at your alternate airport at 2:45 p.m.

When is an Alternate Airport Required?

An alternate airport is not required if, within plus or minus one hour of your ETA at the destination (Skywlaker)the forceast weather is expected to be:

1. At least 3 statute miles, and
2. A ceiling of at least 2,000 feet.

Fig. 28

2,000' Ceiling

2 Hour Span

3 Miles Visibility

Skywalker airport

To list an airport as an alternate, the WX at the time you'd arrive at the alternate must be forecast to be:

600' ceiling-precision approach
800' ceiling-non-precision approach

2 Miles Visibility

Jabba airport

just as compelling and legally binding. These conditions require you to file an alternate for the flight. A *chance* of conditions less than 1-2-3 doesn't mean there's a chance you won't need to list an alternate on your IFR flight plan. There are a few more things we'll discuss about alternates in the next regulation dealing with filing instrument flight plans.

The take-home message here is that if you want to *get* home, plan and fly conservatively. Assume the worst, hope for the best, and prosper.

FAR 91.169—IFR Flight Plan: Information Required

All instrument flight plans must contain the same information that VFR flight plans require. That is:

1. The aircraft identification number, and if you are using an approved radio call sign such as "Cactus One," you'll have to provide that, too. You probably won't have to worry about radio call signs, since they're pretty much the exclusive province of air carriers and special operators (air ambulance, etc.).

2. The type of aircraft you are flying (the FAA doesn't want to see you write "fixed wing" here. Give them the type designator [BE36, C152, C172. SR22, AA1, PA34, etc.] as shown in FAA Order 7110.65).

3. The full name and address of the pilot in command.

4. The point and proposed time of departure. This time should be listed in Coordinated Universal Time (UTC) (even if you don't fly coordinated).

5. The proposed route, cruising altitude, and true airspeed at that altitude.

6. The point of first intended landing and the estimated time enroute (they're looking for the name of the airport, not "I intend to land on the numbers."

7. The amount of fuel on board, in hours and minutes. This estimate should be based on your known consumption rate at cruise. I say "known" because most of us know what our airplane really uses, and it's often not what the book says.

8. Alternate airport, if required.

9. The number of people on board the aircraft. That's not the number who *are* bored, it's the number (including you) *on* board whom they might have to rescue.

10. The color of the aircraft.

11. Any other information the PIC or ATC believes is necessary for ATC purposes.

All of this is what you've been used to filing for VFR flight plans, except for the need to file an alternate if your destination does not meet the 1-2-3 rule. As you can probably guess, if you need an alternate you can't just throw darts and pick any airport whose name you like. Your choice of alternate airport must meet specific weather and facility requirements.

Suppose you want to list an airport as an alternate and there's a non-precision approach (one without a glideslope) at that airport. To be legal as an alternate, the minimum forecast weather at the time you expect to arrive would be a ceiling of 800 feet and two miles visibility (which I'll refer to as *800-2* from now on). An airport with a precision approach (one with a glideslope) can have a minimum forecast as low as 600-2 as shown in Figure 28 (there is an exception to the 800-2/600-2 rule discussed on the next page).

Now, the 800-2 or 600-2 requirement is the weather forecast to exist at the time you would anticipate arriving at the alternate (not the ETA at your first destination airport). Suppose you plan on reaching your destination at 10 a.m. and it takes 30 minutes to travel to the alternate. To legally list this airport as an alternate, the minimum 800-2 or 600-2 weather must forecast for 10:30 a.m.

So, during the flight planning process, you'll need to check the weather at the destination to see if it meets the 1-2-3 requirement. If it doesn't, then you'll be required to pick an alternate airport for the flight and list it on your IFR flight plan. To list an alternate, you'll estimate your

time of arrival at this airport and check the weather forecast to see if the weather will be at least 800-2 or 600-2 at your ETA. Keep in mind that if you actually had to fly to the alternate, you'd use the landing minimums shown on the actual approach chart for that airport to tell you how low you could go and the minimum flight visibility required for the approach (each IFR approach chart has a specific minimum altitude and minimum visibility to be used for that particular procedure. In later chapters we'll chat about this in great detail).

As a final note, would you believe that you can list an airport as an alternate even if that airport doesn't have an instrument approach? It's true. Practically speaking, to do so you need to look at the airway nearest the airport and check for the lowest permissible altitude along the route, also known as the minimum enroute altitude (MEA). Then you'd check the area forecast and see if the forecast ceiling and visibility for that area would allow you to descend and land at the chosen airport in VFR conditions (that's why it's called the *area* forecast and not the *over Bob's house* forecast). If these conditions are met, then you could list this airport as an alternate on your IFR flight plan. If you have to make a missed approach at your destination, you'd arrange with ATC to fly to that alternate near the airway and descended on that airway to the lowest permissible altitude and then proceed in basic VFR conditions to a landing.

Please note that I'm not encouraging this strategy, because it doesn't have much cushion for you to sit on. Area forecasts attempt to estimate the weather for a fairly wide swath of territory, and say nothing about what it will really be like over BillyBob International. Given that it has to be VFR-good for BillyBob to really *function* as an alternate, this is a somewhat dicey ploy. Keep in mind that the alternate requirement is there for a reason, and not just to give the controller another line to type when entering your flight plan. You might have to use the alternate!

Using A GPS Approach at an Alternate Airport

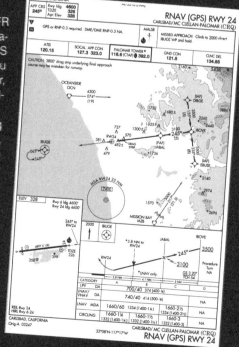

It's possible that the airport you've chosen to list as an alternate airport on your IFR flight plan has only a GPS approach. Unfortunately, because of potential GPS accuracy limitations, you can't base your flight planning to an alternate on the use of a GPS approach unless that airport has an instrument approach *other* than GPS that you could fly in the event of a GPS failure or accuracy limitation. This restriction, however, doesn't apply to Wide Area Augmentation Systems (WAAS), which are now considered standalone navigation systems (see Chapter 13, Page 13-15).

So, if you don't have an IFR approved WAAS unit, you can base your flight planning to the alternate on the use of the RNAV (GPS) Rwy 24 approach shown to the right, because Palomar airport also has a standard ILS approach. On the other hand, even though the chart shows "precision" LPV minimums (more on this in Chapter 13), the FAA says you must use the non-precision requirement (800 foot ceiling and two miles visibility) in deciding if the weather will be suitable at your time of arrival for listing this airport as your alternate (this is equally true for those with an IFR approved WAAS unit). Of course, if you had to actually fly to this airport after a missed approach at your destination, you'd descend to the lowest minimums allowed by your GPS equipment when flying the approach.

Why doesn't the FAA allow you to use 600-2 for flight planning purposes, when this approach offers precision glideslope minimums? The answer rests with how the DA or decision altitude is created for these approaches. Not all DAs allow the airplane to descend as low as the DAs found on most ILS approaches. Thus, use of 800-2 vs. 600-2 for forecast weather at your alternate ETA gives you a better chance of actually being able to land at the alternate upon your arrival there.

The Reasoning Behind 800-2 and 600-2

The reason for the 800-2 or 600-2 requirement at your alternate ETA is to help minimize the chance the weather will be below minimums and thus prevent a landing. Now, wouldn't that be nice? You travel to your destination and make a missed approach because the weather is too poor for a landing, then head off to your alternate airport only to find that the weather is below minimums there, too.

Does life get any better than that? You bet it does! Almost anything is better than that. If you're adhering to the minimum fuel requirement after missing the approach at your alternate, you'll have 45 minutes of cruise fuel to use in deciding what to do next. Keep in mind that you can use one-half of your cruise fuel allotment just climbing to altitude in higher-performance airplanes. Now isn't that nice, too? In reality you have less than 45 minutes in which to decide where to go next.

In fact, the FAA is sufficiently concerned about your having a very good chance of landing at your alternate that they've made the weather requirements for listing one on your flight plan even more stringent at some airports. For instance, at Palm Springs, CA, if you wanted to list the VOR-A approach (a non-precision approach) as an alternate, you can't just use the 800-2 requirement I mentioned above. Instead, if you plan to use this non-precision approach at Palm Springs, you'll need to have at least 1300-2 forecast at the time you'd arrive there (Figure 29, position Z).

How would you know that Palm Springs lists a non-standard alternate requirement if you don't read palms? You'd look at the booklet (or database) of approach charts that all instrument pilots use and check for the symbol indicating that non-standard alternate requirements exist at Palm Springs (Figure 29, position Y). This symbol is in the upper left hand corner of the approach chart and is shown as a black triangle with the white letter "A" inside. This means that non-standard alternate minimums exist for use of this approach at this airport. How would you know what those non-standard alternate minimums are at Palm Springs? You'd go to the front of the approach chart booklet (Section E) and read what it says under Palm Springs, as shown in Figure 29, position Z.

Why are the Palm Springs alternate minimums higher than standard? The most common reason airports have higher-than-normal alternate minimums is that the basic approach minimums are higher to begin with. In other words, some instrument approaches will allow you to descend to a low minimum altitude and land with a low visibility. Palm Springs isn't one of these airports (and it's not because of all the palm trees, either).

In fact, if you were making the VOR-A approach into Palm Springs as a destination airport, you'd have a minimum descent altitude of 1,100 feet and be required to have 1 1/4 miles visibility for landing. So it's natural to expect that listing Palm Springs as an alternate airport would require a pretty decent weather forecast (1300-3) at your ETA just to list this approach on your flight plan as an alternate. Now, if you're a little befuddled by the terminology listed here, don't worry. Once you read Chapter 11 on Understanding Approach Charts, the new lingo here will make a lot more sense to you.

Now let's have a serious talk about alternates. First, just because you list an airport as your alternate, does not mean you are required to go there if you cannot land at your intended destination. That brings up the subject of real alternates and paper alternates. The paper alternate is the one you list on your flight plan. That's the one you MUST have fuel to fly to and then to fly for an additional 45 minutes at normal cruise power. That's also the place the FAA is going to expect you to turn up if you should be having such a bad day in aviation that you first are unable to land at your intended destination and then have a complete communications failure.

If you've ever flown in the American Midwest in the winter, you're familiar with weather reports and forecasts that include a "chance of a 500 foot ceiling and one mile visibility" for a 500 mile radius or so. That pretty much rules out IFR flights in many single-engine aircraft and some light twins, because they do not carry enough fuel to

Non-standard Alternate Minimums

If an airport has non-standard alternate minimums (minimums other than 600-2 or 800-2), they will be found in Section E of the NACO (government) approach chart booklet. The presence of a black triangle containing the letter "A" on an approach chart indicates that non-standard alternate minimums exist for this airport.

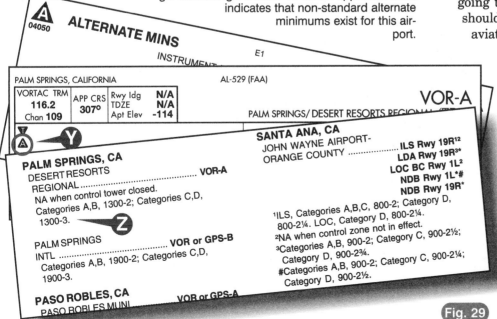

Fig. 29

make it to a legal alternate after flying to the intended destination while still maintaining a 45–minute reserve. The FAA does not have a sense of humor about this, and for good reason. Forecasts for bad weather are historically less accurate than those for good weather, and it's not uncommon for all those areas with a chance of 500 and 1 to deteriorate rapidly to less than the lowest landing minima shown on your approach chart.

This does not mean that you have to go all the way to that legal alternate if you can't land at your destination. That's what makes this what I unofficially call a *paper alternate*. The *real* alternate is the one you'll go to if, while proceeding to your destination, you decide the weather has deteriorated sufficiently that it's best to divert to somewhere else.

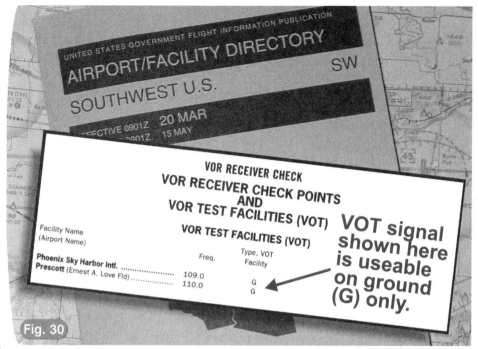

Fig. 30

FAA approved VOT checks are found in the rear section of the *Airport/Facility Directory*.

Perhaps you were planning to go to an airport that has only an NDB circling approach and relatively high approach minimums. Let's assume that there's a legal alternate airport with another NDB approach (one that meets the 800-2 requirement) 150 miles north that you can list on your IFR flight plan. There's also a big (airline) airport 30 miles away that has multiple ILS approaches with low minimums (this is a precision approach that allows you to land with as little as ½ mile visibility while bringing you to within 200 feet above the runway's touchdown zone, thus allowing you a good chance of landing in bad weather).

Let's also say that this big airport has a forecast of 800 overcast and 3 miles at the time you would arrive to use it, with a chance of 400-1 and snow showers. You can't technically list the big airport as a legal alternate (the chance of 400-1 within +/- one hour of your ETA nixes this). If, however, you have to make a missed approach at your destination, it might be wiser to fly to the big airport and shoot an approach there, since it offers you a good chance of being able to land. In other words, the big airport can't be your paper alternate but it certainly can be a real one.

Generally, when picking an alternate, you want to think *downhill, downwind,* and *VFR*. Downhill, which really pertains mainly to mountainous terrain, means you want to find an alternate at a lower altitude. Downwind makes the time expended getting to your alternate shorter. VFR indicates that if at all possible, you should be looking to fly toward improving weather for an alternate.

FAR 91.171–VOR Equipment Check for IFR Operations

If you are going to use your VOR equipment on an IFR flight plan it either has to be maintained, checked and inspected under an approved procedure, or it has to have been operationally checked within the preceding 30 days.

There are several ways to accomplish the VOR check, so let's talk about them in order of descending desirability. The first and most accurate method for testing VOR equipment is to use a test signal generated by a "certificated and appropriately rated radio repair station" or an

VOR Equipment Check for IFR Flight Using VOR Test Signal - VOT

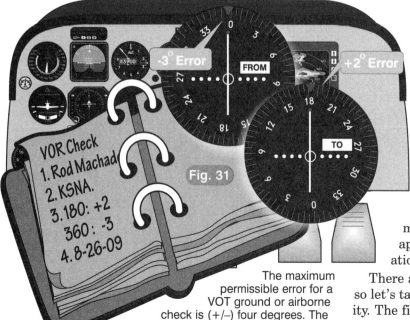

Fig. 31

The maximum permissible error for a VOT ground or airborne check is (+/–) four degrees. The results of this check must be logged and kept in the aircraft.

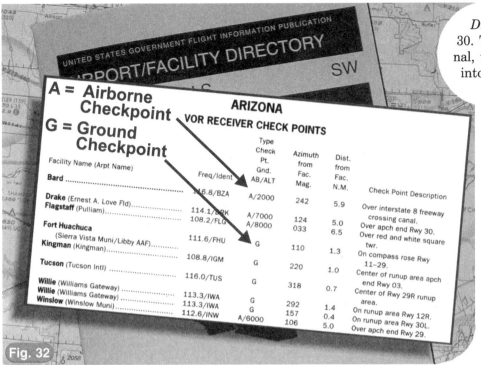

Fig. 32

FAA designated airborne and ground checkpoints are found in the rear section of the *Airport/Facility Directory*.

mation in the *Airport/Facility Directory (A/FD)* as shown in Figure 30. To conduct the test with a VOT signal, tune in the VOT frequency (tune it into your VOR receiver, not your NDB receiver) and center the course deviation indicator. The omni-bearing selector should read 0 degrees and the TO/FROM indicator should read "FROM." If the VOR receiver operates an RMI, that should point to 180. Some VOTs can be used while airborne, but these are few and far between and are listed in the *A/FD*. Whether using a repair station signal or a VOT signal, the maximum permissible error is plus or minus four degrees of 0 and 180 to get the needle to center. For a VOT check, this is the maximum permissible error whether accomplished on the ground or airborne (Figure 31).

Some airports have a designated spot on the airport for VOR check purposes. These checkpoints will also be found in the *A/FD*, which contains the frequency of a nearby VOR to be used and the bearing to be checked (Figure 32). There is a point on the airport where this check must be done, and you will also find this in the *A/FD*. Just tune the appropriate VOR, set the bearing and note any error. The permissible error for this check is also plus or minus four degrees (Figure 33).

You can also use airborne checkpoints designated by the FAA and listed in the *A/FD* and these have a maximum

FAA-operated VOT test signal. In the event you choose to use a repair station signal, you'll have to get the repair station to make an entry in the aircraft log *or other record* certifying the bearing transmitted by the repair station for the check and the date of transmission. This could be a pretty pricey way to get a VOR check done, but if you're having radio work done anyway, you might consider this option.

If there is an FAA-operated VOT test signal on or close to the airport of intended departure, you'll find that infor-

VOR Equipment Check for IFR Flight Using a Ground Checkpoint

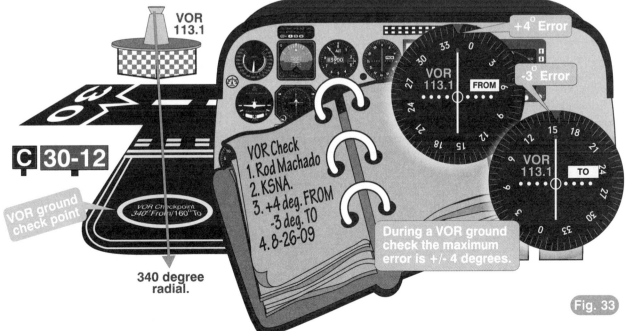

Fig. 33

VOR Equipment Check for IFR Flight
Comparing Two VORs on Same Frequency

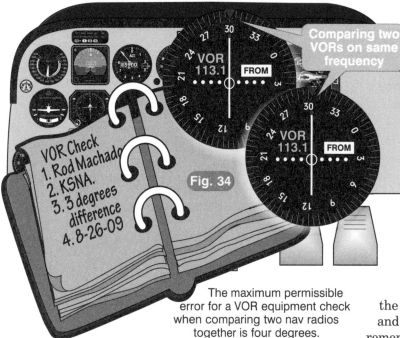

The maximum permissible error for a VOR equipment check when comparing two nav radios together is four degrees.

permissible bearing error of plus or minus six degrees. Obviously you're not going to be using airborne checkpoints to check your VOR for accuracy when you're flying IFR in IMC, right? This is something you'd typically do during a VFR flight. Imagine calling ATC and asking to be vectored to VFR conditions so you can check your VOR for accuracy. Asking for this is a sure way to let the controller know that your wheel is turning but the hamster's dead.

If none of these methods are available at or near your airport of departure, you can make your own checkpoint in flight. To do this, select a VOR radial that is the centerline of an established airway. Find a prominent landmark on your chart that lies under the selected radial and is at least 20 miles from the VOR (again, you'll have to do this in VFR conditions, perhaps some time in advance of the IFR flight you plan to make, unless of course you carry a spare hamster). Maneuver directly over this landmark at a reasonably low but legal altitude and note the VOR bearing shown on your receiver. The maximum allowable error between the indicated bearing and the published radial when using this test is plus or minus six degrees.

Now, if none of the above methods are available to you, and if you have two VOR receivers in the airplane, you can check the VOR receivers against each other as long as the two systems are totally separate except for the antenna (Figure 34). To do this check, tune both VOR receivers to the same ground station and note the indicated bearings to that station on each receiver. The maximum permissible error for this procedure is four degrees (not + or – 4 degrees, either). In other words, if the OBS says 340 on one unit with the needle centered, the other must say either 336

or 344 degrees with its needle centered. Either one would be a maximum difference of 4 degrees from the other. Notice that this is the only airborne check with a tolerance of four degrees. What you have really checked is the fact that the receivers are accurate within four degrees of each other, not their accuracy with respect to the ground station. Therefore, it's highly unlikely that any one of the VOR receivers is way out of tolerance.

No matter who makes the VOR checks and no matter what method is used to do those checks, a proper record of it must be kept. Remember, as far as the FAA is concerned, if it isn't recorded it didn't happen. The regulations require you to log (in the aircraft log, a stone tablet, or other medium of your choice) the signature of the person making the check, the place of the check, the bearing error and date of the check. An acronym to help you remember this is *SPED* for *signature, place, error* and *date*.

FAR 91.173–ATC Clearance and Flight Plan Required

If you are going to operate in less than basic VFR conditions (i.e., fly in IMC or fly IFR, either way is a correct way of saying this) in controlled airspace, you must file an IFR flight plan and have received an appropriate clearance from ATC. Now, this is when operating in controlled airspace. It's still legal to fly in uncontrolled airspace without an IFR flight plan or ATC clearance. All the folks east of the Mississippi will have a hard time finding uncontrolled (Class G) airspace at altitudes above 1,200 feet AGL, but it does still exist out west and often only in mountainous areas, as shown in Figure 35. As previously mentioned, I won't spend more time chatting about flying IFR in uncontrolled airspace because I consider it flying through a loophole rather than a healthy option that I'd like to see anyone exercise.

Class G "Uncontrolled" Airspace

Class G (uncontrolled) airspace existing more than 1,200 feet above the surface is more common in the western part of the United States.

FAR 91.175–Takeoff and Landing Under IFR

It would be hard to find a regulation that is discussed more in pilot lounges than this one. It's also hard to find a regulation that is more important to safety when flying IFR. That's because this is the regulation that tells you when it's legal to leave your minimum altitude on an approach and land your airplane. That's important in my book.

To understand this regulation, you need a few big picture details (I say this with caution, because Michelangelo was asked for the big picture and ended up painting an entire ceiling). First, instrument approaches are navigational courses (VOR, NDB, GPS, etc.) that take you to a runway or an airport having a runway (if an airport doesn't have a runway then you should check lost and found, the police department, or your mind).

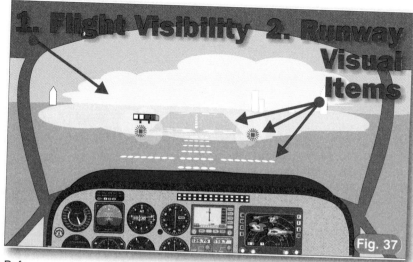

Before you can leave the minimum altitude on an instrument approach you must have the required minimum flight visibility shown on the approach chart as well as at least some reference associated with the runway or approach lights.

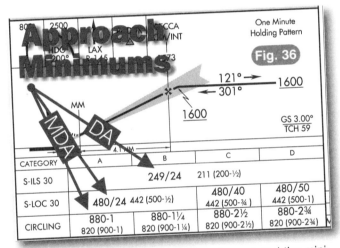

The minimum allowable altitudes for descent and the minimum visibility for an instrument approach are found in the lower part of the instrument approach chart.

All instrument approaches have two things in common. They have a minimum altitude that pilots descend to while looking for the airport and they have a minimum flight visibility that pilots must maintain when leaving the minimum altitude. These minimum altitudes (referred to as an MDA—*minimum descent altitude* or as a DA—*decision altitude*) along with the minimum required visibilities, are shown on the approach chart, as shown in Figure 36. These altitudes are also referred to as the *approach minimums* for that approach. That's the big picture, so now let's work on the details.

This regulation begins by stating that, unless otherwise authorized by the Administrator (that's the FAA), when an instrument letdown to a civil airport is necessary, you must use an instrument approach procedure prescribed for the airport in Part 97. That means that you can't take a bearing off the local radio station (such as K-DIE or K-BAM) and fly your own homemade approach. It doesn't matter how careful you have been in mapping it all out, it's illegal, risky, and non-insurable, so don't do it. Now, there are folks that have their own private approaches to their own private airports. That's the "otherwise authorized" part I mentioned. These approaches have all been surveyed and flight checked by the FAA at the owner's expense and they're conducted over a line of trampoline factories (OK, just kidding on the last one, but it's not a bad idea, right?).

Here's what the rest of this regulation says, in very simple form. It's the most important part, too.

When making an instrument approach and descending to a minimum altitude, you can't leave that altitude unless you have one or more items associated with the runway or approach lights in sight and have the required flight visibility as shown on the approach chart (Figure 37). That's it, in simple terms. Now for the details, because that's where the devil is.

When there is an MDA or a DA established for an approach procedure, a pilot can not operate below the MDA or continue an approach below the authorized DA unless three general conditions are met.

Condition 1

The airplane must *continuously* be in a position from which a descent to landing on the intended runway can be made at a normal rate of descent using normal maneuvers (Figure 38). This means that if at any time you feel your airplane has drifted too far off course and you're operating below the MDA or DA, then you must immediately fly the missed approach procedure (meaning that you'll climb, typically proceed to an intersection to hold, and then work with ATC to fly the approach again or fly to another airport and fly the approach there).

Condition 2

The flight visibility is not less than the visibility prescribed for the approach being used (Figure 39). Notice that it is the *flight* visibility that counts here, not the visibility reported by the tower or an electronic measuring device such as an RVR transmissometer. (We won't talk about commercial operator regulations, such as Part 121 or 135, which have slightly different rules to follow regarding the visibility required for a pilot to land.)

Condition 3

The pilot must have at least one of the following visual references in sight (meaning it must be distinctly visible and identifiable) for the intended runway of landing:

Bad Positions for Landing

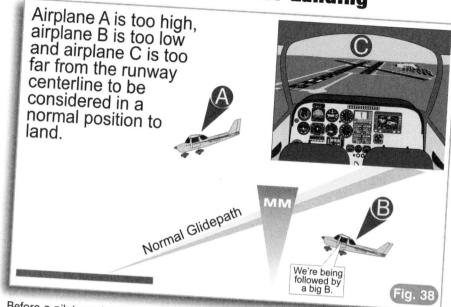

Airplane A is too high, airplane B is too low and airplane C is too far from the runway centerline to be considered in a normal position to land.

Before a pilot can leave the minimum altitude on any approach, he or she must be in a position to make a "normal" descent using "normal" maneuvers to land.

• *The approach light system* (except that the pilot may not descend below 100 feet above the touchdown zone elevation using the approach lights as a reference unless the red terminating bars or the red side row bars are also distinctly visible and identifiable. More on this shortly):

• *The threshold*
• *The threshold markings*
• *The threshold lights*
• *The runway end identifier lights*
• *The visual approach slope indicator*
• *The touchdown zone or touchdown zone markings*
• *The touchdown zone lights*
• *The runway or runway markings*
• *The runway lights*

We'll discuss this regulation in additional detail in Chapter 12—the chapter that deals with understanding instrument approach charts. But it's important here to notice that the last nine items are on the *runway* side of the landing threshold (Figure 40). The first item is the approach lighting system, and it can extend from 1,400 feet to 3,000 feet from the threshold. It should be obvious that you can use the approach light system to meet the visual and identifiable requirement for descending below the MDA or DA—at least you can go as low as 100 feet above the runway's touchdown zone elevation before having to see any one of the last nine items in continuing the approach. After all, the reason the approach lights extend so far from the threshold is to help you find the runway. Since there's a bit more to this regulation that should be of interest, I'll leave the red terminating bars and the red side row bars for Chapter 12, beginning on page 12-7.

Required Flight Visibility

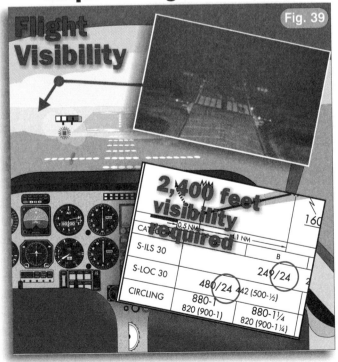

The minimum required in-flight visibility for this approach is found in the approach chart's minimums section. You'll learn more about this in Chapter 12.

The Runway Environment

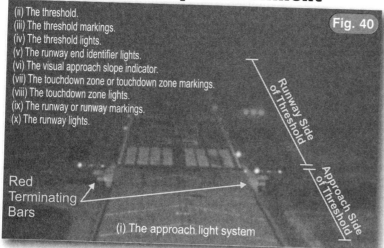

Fig. 40

(i) The approach light system

(ii) The threshold.
(iii) The threshold markings.
(iv) The threshold lights.
(v) The runway end identifier lights.
(vi) The visual approach slope indicator.
(vii) The touchdown zone or touchdown zone markings.
(viii) The touchdown zone lights.
(ix) The runway or runway markings.
(x) The runway lights.

Red Terminating Bars

Runway Side of Threshold

Approach Side of Threshold

Nine of the possible 10 items a pilot might see that are associated with the runway environment are on the landing side of the runway. The approach lights are on the approach side of the runway threshold.

FAR 91.177—Minimum Altitudes for IFR Operations.

This is the regulation that says you can't operate lower than the minimum altitudes shown on instrument charts (not even if you're wearing a thick helmet) unless you're authorized to do so by ATC. This means that if you're on an airway with a minimum enroute altitude of 8,000 feet, then you can't go below 8,000 feet unless ATC says so. When might ATC say so? When they have a minimum vectoring altitude or minimum instrument altitude (MVA or MIA) lower than the MEA, as they often have.

Suppose you wanted to fly IFR between two VORs or via GPS from waypoint to waypoint (or airport-to-airport as shown in Figure 41). There will be no minimum altitude posted for you to fly, since there is probably no airway between these routes. If so, you are required to maintain at least 1,000 feet above the highest obstacle within a horizontal distance of four nautical miles of the course to be flown. Now, this is the minimum altitude if you're operating in a non-mountainous area, such as somewhere in Kansas (OK, anywhere in Kansas). On the other hand, if you're operating in a mountainous area, then you must maintain a minimum of 2,000 feet above the highest obstacle within a horizontal distance of four nautical miles of the course to be flown.

Designated Mountainous Areas

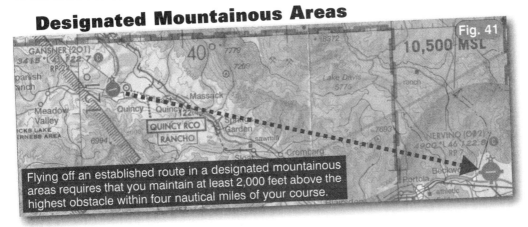

Fig. 41

GANSNER (2O1)

QUINCY RCO
RANCHO

10,500 MSL

Flying off an established route in a designated mountainous areas requires that you maintain at least 2,000 feet above the highest obstacle within four nautical miles of your course.

If you wanted to file a direct route between two points, how would you know what the highest obstacle was? You'd have to look at a topographical chart to find it. How would you know if you're operating within a mountainous area? You can look in the AIM and determine those areas designated at mountainous (Figure 42).

Is it realistic for a pilot to file IFR point to point, avoiding flight on a specific airway, just to minimize time enroute? And do the pilots who do it always know the height of the terrain over the long distance they'll fly? Well, if they don't and they list an incorrect altitude, the ATC computer normally issues an altitude that's at or above the controller's minimum vectoring or minimum instrument altitude for the routes to be flown. This assumes that the radar controller has minimum altitudes for the area in question. For most of the area across these United States, there are minimum radar altitudes (MVAs and MIAs). At least these altitudes act as a backup in the event the pilot isn't good with sectional/WAC charts or altitudes (or is so afraid of heights that he's incapable of looking at one posted on a chart).

Designated Mountainous Terrain in the U.S.

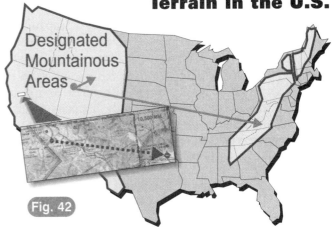

Designated Mountainous Areas

10,500 MSL

Fig. 42

§ 91.183—IFR Radio Communication

First, you, the PIC operating IFR, are required to keep a continuous watch on the radio frequency (*watch* means *listen,* since only Electromagnet Man can see a radio frequency). So, no turning down radio volumes when you want to rest (which, by the way, is one of the most common reasons for lost communication).

When not under radar control ("1234 Bravo, radar contact lost"), you are required to report to ATC the time and altitude when passing all designated reporting points (also known as *compulsory reporting points* on the IFR chart, or the reporting points given by ATC). If your airplane is under radar control, then you only need to report your time and altitude at any points ATC specifically requests.

Finally, you're required to report any unforecast weather you might encounter (doing so means everyone else flying IFR in the vicinity benefits, too) and any information that relates to the safety of flight (such as bird activity, alien landings, Elvis sightings, etc.).

FAR 91.185—IFR Operations: Two-way Radio Comm Failure

In today's air traffic environment, we all tend to take communications capability for granted. Given the reliability of solid state electronics, radio failure is almost a non-issue, except when it happens to you. And that's enough to make it an important issue to study.

The failure can happen on either side. ATC occasionally has major computer or other glitches that put it offline in more ways than one. And despite those dual nav radios, you can experience electrical or other failures that will leave you speechless.

Despite the importance of communication to the aviation equation, the modern day instrument system is built on the premise that pilots might be required to fly IFR *without* the use of an air traffic controller's radar or, in critical situations, without the availability of radio communication. That's why pilots are given IFR clearances. If radar goes kaput and/or pilots and controllers stop talking to each other, the clearance provides a place to go, a route to get there, and what to do when you arrive at that place.

At issue is what the pilot's responsibilities are when he or she loses radio communication with ATC. And don't think that this is something that only happens when a radio fails on board the aircraft, either. I've been in situations where the ATC frequency was so congested I couldn't get a word in edgewise (which always makes me edgy), yet

if I'd kept heading where I was heading, I would have scraped a mountain edgewise.

Perhaps you're starting to see an IFR clearance in a new light, which is bright. Bright of you, that is. The clearance is not just a flight plan; it's a *backup plan* that provides a safety net for you and ATC.

If you experience two-way radio communication failure in VFR conditions, or if VFR conditions are encountered after you experience it, the rules say to continue the flight under VFR conditions and land as soon as feasible. This makes sense in much the same way that it makes sense not to make fun of a carnival worker's misspelled tattoo (especially if his name is spelled "Blayde"). After all, if you can proceed and land in VFR conditions, it makes no sense to keep on going IFR without the ability to communicate.

On the other hand, suppose you encounter VFR conditions but are not sure you can stay that way? You might be above the clouds but unsure how far those clouds extend (a good reason to always have a thorough weather briefing and a printout of that weather depiction chart, right?). If that's the case, I'd stay VFR as long as I could but follow my IFR clearance to the destination, descend, and land according to the rest of this regulation.

If you experience two-way radio communication failure in IFR conditions then the very first thing to do is squawk 7600 on your transponder (7700 if you're experiencing an emergency). Next, you'll have to make decisions about three things: the route to fly, the altitude to fly, and when to fly the approach. Fortunately, the decisions have been made for you. You just have to know the rules.

1. What route should you fly?

The simple answer is, the route you've been given.

The right route is that assigned in the last ATC clearance you received. If you were being radar vectored at the

Lost Comm: What Route Do You Fly?

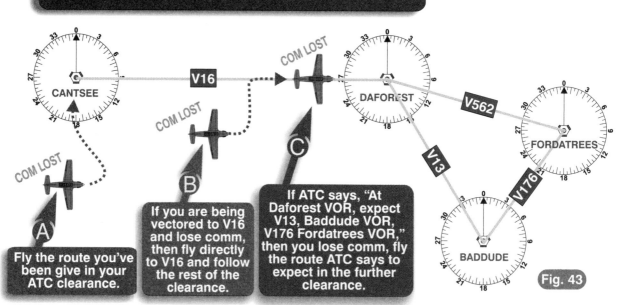

Fig. 43

Lost Comm: What Altitude Do You Fly?

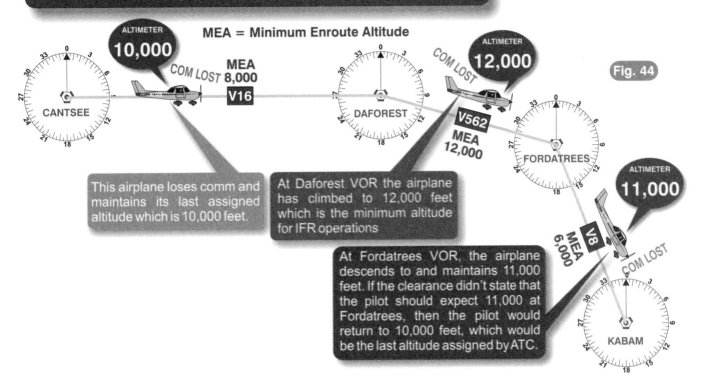

"2132 Bravo, expect V16 direct Daforest VOR, V562 direct Fordatrees VOR, V8 direct Kabam VOR, climb and maintain one zero thousand feet, expect one one thousand at Fordatrees VOR."

MEA = Minimum Enroute Altitude

Fig. 44

This airplane loses comm and maintains its last assigned altitude which is 10,000 feet.

At Daforest VOR the airplane has climbed to 12,000 feet which is the minimum altitude for IFR operations

At Fordatrees VOR, the airplane descends to and maintains 11,000 feet. If the clearance didn't state that the pilot should expect 11,000 at Fordatrees, then the pilot would return to 10,000 feet, which would be the last altitude assigned by ATC.

time of the communication failure, then fly a direct route from your present position to the place (fix, airway, navaid, etc.) specified in the vector clearance. This is one reason ATC tells you the reason for the vector when you're issued one.

What do I mean by a direct route? I mean a 90 degree intercept as long as it's navigationally feasible or pointing the airplane's nose directly at the place you were being vectored (no crosswind assumed, OK?).

On the other hand, suppose ATC advises you that you should expect a different route at some specific point or time. If you then experience two-way radio communication failure, fly that newer route at the specific time or when reaching that particular place.

For instance, let's say you're on a specific routing and ATC says, "2132 Bravo, when reaching Cantsee VOR, expect V16 direct Daforest VOR, V562 direct Fordatrees VOR." If you lose comm, then proceed to Cantsee VOR and follow the route ATC said you to expect (Figure 43). This is what ATC expects you to do, so make sure you do it.

What if you're preparing to depart an airport and the tower controller advised you to fly a specific heading after takeoff? There's a provision in the Aeronautical Information Manual, AIM (5-2-6(b)) that says a pilot may be instructed to fly a specific heading after takeoff but isn't necessarily told the purpose of that heading. In these instances, you're expected to associate departure headings with vectors to your assigned route. If you lose radio comm after takeoff, fly the route filed in your flight plan.

2. What altitude should you fly?

If you've had two-way radio communication failure, fly at the highest of the following altitudes:

a. The altitude or flight level assigned in the last ATC clearance received;

b. The minimum altitude for IFR operations; or

c. The altitude or flight level ATC has advised may be expected in a further clearance.

Suppose you're on a route with a minimum altitude of 8,000 feet and you've been assigned 10,000 feet (Figure 44). You would maintain 10,000 feet, since that's the altitude assigned in your clearance. If there is a short segment of your route that has a minimum altitude of 12,000 feet, then you would climb to 12,000 feet when appropriate (you'll learn about minimum airway altitudes in Chapter 15). Stay there or at the minimum airway altitude until these minimum airway altitudes allow you to return to 10,000 feet, your last assigned altitude.

If you've been told to expect a different altitude at a specific place or time and you subsequently lose contact, do what you were told to expect, because that's what ATC now expects.

3. When should you fly the approach (or leave the clearance limit, if appropriate)?

Here's what the regulation says, word for word, except where I've added some information in brackets to help make it clear. Once you read these two paragraphs, we'll go over each situation and analyze it carefully. Yeah, it's

Lost Comm: When Should You Fly the Approach?
Scenario 1

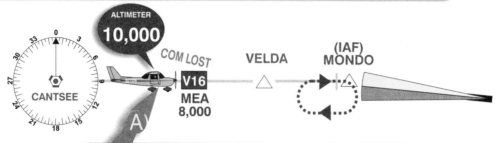

"2132 Bravo, is cleared to MONDO intersection via V16 direct MONDO, expect further clearance at 13:30, time now, 13:05."

ALTIMETER
10,000
COM LOST | VELDA | (IAF) MONDO
V16
MEA **8,000**
CANTSEE

With lost comm, airplane A should proceed to the IAF (the fix from which the approach begins) and hold until 13:30 (the EFC time), then fly the approach.

Fig. 45A

pretty detailed, somewhat like reading the fine print of an automobile rental contract. Then again, if you understanding this regulation you won't need the airplane-to-airplane collision damage waiver because you won't be bumping into another instrument pilot in the event of lost comm.

a. When the clearance limit is a fix from which an approach begins [an IAF or initial approach fix], commence descent or descent and approach as close as possible to the expect-further-clearance time if one has been received, or if one has not been received, as close as possible to the estimated time of arrival as calculated from the filed or amended (with ATC) estimated time enroute [the ETE filed in your IFR flight plan].

b. If the clearance limit is not a fix from which an approach begins [a fix short of the IAF], leave the clearance limit at the expect-further-clearance time if one has been received, or if none has been received, upon arrival over the clearance limit, and proceed to a fix from which an approach begins and commence descent or descent and approach as close as possible to the estimated time of arrival as calculated from the filed or amended (with ATC) estimated time enroute.

So what exactly does that mean?

When you receive your IFR clearance prior to departure, ATC will often clear you all the way to the destination airport. While enroute, however, ATC may change things and clear you to a point (an intersection, fix or navaid) short of the destination airport. This point is known as your *clearance limit*. While the destination airport is often your clearance limit, ATC sometimes has to restrict your movement along the route because it's the only way the controller can manage IFR traffic entering or leaving an airport complex. At issue here is what you should do if you've received a clearance limit short of the destination airport and experience lost comm. Here are the four situations in which this could apply to you.

1. You received a clearance limit and the controller issued you an *expect further clearance* (EFC) time.

In this example ATC has cleared you to an *initial approach fix* (IAF) that's 30 miles from the destination airport (Figure 45A, Airplane A). Your clearance for this example might read as follows:

2132 Bravo is cleared to MONDO intersection, expect further clearance (EFC) at 1330.

If you lost comm prior to reaching MONDO and didn't receive a clearance beyond this limit, you'd proceed to MONDO and hold until 1330 (Figure 45, Airplane A). This is, after all, the time at or beyond which the controller thought he could allow you to proceed to the airport, fly the approach, and land. So, at 1330, you'd begin your descent (or, if you're in a holding pattern, as close as possible to it, meaning you'd modify your holding pattern so that you're at MONDO heading inbound at 1330) and commence flying the instrument approach procedure. (Note: All approach charts have one or more IAFs. These are the intersections at which the approach officially begins. If you're at the IAF inbound, you're officially flying the instrument approach procedure.)

2. The controller gave you a clearance limit (which happens to be the IAF) but didn't give you a time to expect further clearance.

In this example (Figure 45B), the controller gives you MONDO (an IAF) as your clearance limit but doesn't give you a time to expect further clearance. This isn't an uncommon situation, either. Often, the controller may not know when he will have room for you beyond the IAF. He may be waiting for you to get close to the IAF to know what EFC time to give you. And he knows that if he gives you the wrong EFC time and you lose comm, it may make it very difficult for him to move all the traffic that has to be displaced to let you, a lost comm aircraft, fly the approach (more on this in a bit). The correct procedure here is to begin your descent as close as possible to the estimated time of arrival (ETA) that you calculated when you filed your IFR flight plan (the time calculated from adding the ETE to your departure time) as shown in Figure 45B, Airplane B.

It's quite possible your ETE has changed because of unforecast weather or previous ATC rerouting. That's

Lost Comm: When Should You Fly the Approach?
Scenario 2

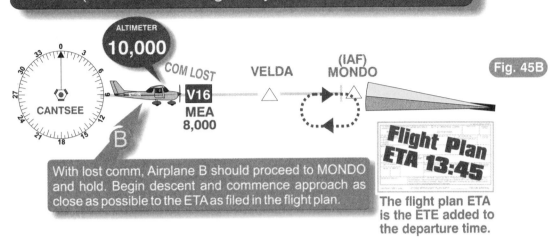

"2132 Bravo, is cleared to MONDO intersection via V16 direct MONDO. (**Note**: no EFC time given by controller in this clearance.)

With lost comm, Airplane B should proceed to MONDO and hold. Begin descent and commence approach as close as possible to the ETA as filed in the flight plan.

Flight Plan ETA 13:45

The flight plan ETA is the ETE added to the departure time.

Fig. 45B

why you should always advise ATC when your ETE changes significantly, and give them an update on your new ETE. Remember, ATC is counting on this estimate to determine when you'll leave the IAF and begin your descent for the approach under lost comm conditions. This is why, when filing an IFR flight plan, you want to file your ETE to the IAF along the route you plan to use and not file the ETE to the destination airport itself. Keep in mind that some IAFs can be as far as 50 nautical miles from the destination airport.

3. The controller gives you a clearance limit that's a fix short of the IAF and also gave you a time to expect further clearance.

Here, the controller clears you to a fix that is short of where the approach officially begins (i.e., the IAF) as shown in Figure 45C. Your clearance might read:

2132 Bravo is cleared to VELDA intersection, expect further clearance at 1330.

In this example, leave your clearance limit at the EFC and proceed to the IAF via the route shown in your clearance (Figure 45C, Airplane C). If you arrive at the IAF earlier than the ETE indicated in your flight plan (or as amended with ATC), hold in a standard holding pattern (or the published holding pattern). Leave the holding pattern, descend, and fly the approach when reaching the ETE (if you arrive at the IAF after your ETE is passed, then descend and fly the approach. No delay is necessary). Does this make sense to you? If not, think about it this way. When ATC issues this clearance limit and you subsequently lose comm, the only means the controller has of determining when you'll begin your descent and start flying the approach is when your ETE is reached. Sure, the

Lost Comm: When Should You Fly the Approach?
Scenario 3

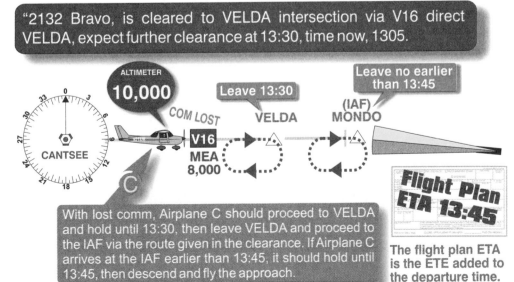

"2132 Bravo, is cleared to VELDA intersection via V16 direct VELDA, expect further clearance at 13:30, time now, 1305.

Leave 13:30

Leave no earlier than 13:45

With lost comm, Airplane C should proceed to VELDA and hold until 13:30, then leave VELDA and proceed to the IAF via the route given in the clearance. If Airplane C arrives at the IAF earlier than 13:45, it should hold until 13:45, then descend and fly the approach.

Flight Plan ETA 13:45

The flight plan ETA is the ETE added to the departure time.

Fig. 45C

Lost Comm: When Should You Fly the Approach?
Scenario 4

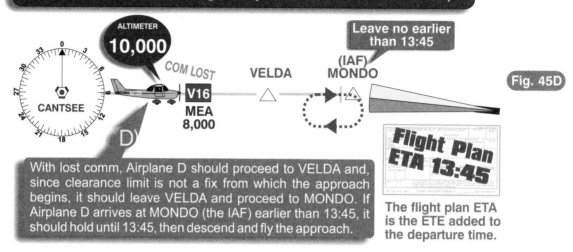

"2132 Bravo, is cleared to VELDA intersection via V16 direct VELDA. (**Note**: no EFC time given by controller in this clearance.)

Leave no earlier than 13:45

Flight Plan ETA 13:45

The flight plan ETA is the ETE added to the departure time.

With lost comm, Airplane D should proceed to VELDA and, since clearance limit is not a fix from which the approach begins, it should leave VELDA and proceed to MONDO. If Airplane D arrives at MONDO (the IAF) earlier than 13:45, it should hold until 13:45, then descend and fly the approach.

controller might have radar and can see your altitude readout, but this is real time. Estimating when (ETE) and where (IAF) you'll leave your altitude and fly the approach is based on the controller having an idea of your ETE.

As a second part of this example, suppose your clearance limit is short of the IAF and you didn't receive an EFC by the time you arrived at this point. Your clearance might read:

2132 Bravo is cleared to VELDA intersection.

In that situation, fly past the clearance limit and proceed to the IAF (Figure 45, Airplane D). From there you'd hold until the ETE as filed (or amended) in your flight plan expired, then complete the approach. If you arrive over the IAF and the ETE has already passed, keep on going. Leave your altitude and complete the approach.

So, is that what pilots do when flying IFR in the real world? The fact is that many pilots fly their given clearance directly to the airport and land because they don't remember the lost comm rules (but this doesn't make their actions right). Fortunately, given that most areas have radar coverage nowadays, controllers are very adept at getting other folks out of your way. Nevertheless, you can't go wrong by following the lost communication rules. So know them well because you need to know them and you'll most certainly be tested on them in the FAA knowledge exam and on the practical test.

FAR 91.187—Operation Under IFR in Controlled Airspace: Malfunction Reports

"Houston, we have a problem!" Hopefully, yours won't be as severe as the one that afflicted Apollo 13. As pilot in command of an airplane being operated IFR in controlled airspace, you are required to report as soon as practical to ATC any malfunctions of navigational, approach, or communication equipment occurring in flight (Figure 46). While you might think, "Hey, guys, you'll never guess what my altimeter is doing" makes for interesting conversation, what the controller really wants from you (because that's what the rules say he wants) is:

(1) Aircraft identification;

(2) Equipment affected;

(3) Degree to which the capability of the pilot to operate under IFR in the ATC system is impaired; and

(4) Nature and extent of assistance needed from ATC.

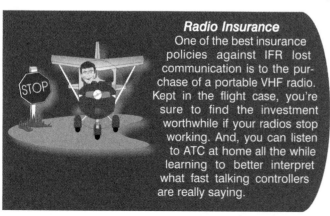

Radio Insurance
One of the best insurance policies against IFR lost communication is to the purchase of a portable VHF radio. Kept in the flight case, you're sure to find the investment worthwhile if your radios stop working. And, you can listen to ATC at home all the while learning to better interpret what fast talking controllers are really saying.

Malfunction Reports

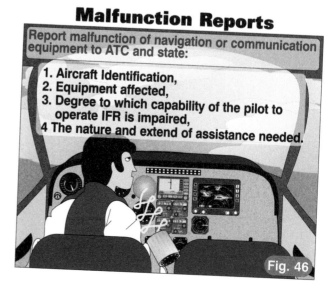

Report malfunction of navigation or communication equipment to ATC and state:

1. Aircraft Identification,
2. Equipment affected,
3. Degree to which capability of the pilot to operate IFR is impaired,
4. The nature and extend of assistance needed.

Fig. 46

FAR 91.205—Powered Civil Aircraft with Standard Category U.S. Airworthiness Certificates: Instrument and Equipment Requirements.

It doesn't get much more down than this, the mother of all rules. This is the one that says what instruments you need up and running in order to fly IFR.

Notice I said "up and running." Having your co-pilot hold the aircraft's sole altimeter in her lap does *not* constitute having it function.

To understand what instruments are necessary for IFR flight you need to know about those required for VFR flight, too, so let's review (Figure 47).

The instruments/equipment necessary for day VFR flight are:

Airspeed indicator

Altimeter

Magnetic direction indicator

Tachometer for each engine

Oil pressure gauge for each engine using pressure system

Temperature gauge for each liquid-cooled engine

Oil temperature gauge for each air-cooled engine

Manifold pressure gauge for each altitude engine

Fuel gauge indicating the quantity of fuel in each tank

Landing gear position indicator, if the aircraft has a retractable landing gear.

For small civil airplanes certificated after March 11, 1996, in accordance with Part 23 of this chapter, an approved aviation red or aviation white anti-collision light system (I would prefer an anti-collision force field if one were available, but it isn't). In the event of failure of any light of the anti-collision light system, operation of the aircraft may continue to a location where repairs or replacement can be made.

If the aircraft is operated for hire over water and beyond power-off gliding distance from shore, approved flotation gear readily available to each occupant and at least one pyrotechnic signaling device. As used in this section, "shore" means that area of the land adjacent to the water which is above the high water mark and excludes land areas which are intermittently under water.

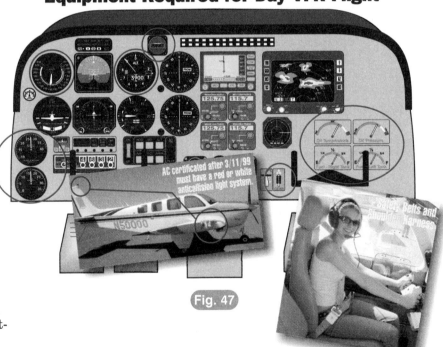

Equipment Required for Day VFR Flight

AC certificated after 3/11/99 must have a red or white anticollision light system.

Fig. 47

An approved safety belt with an approved metal-to-metal latching device for each occupant two years of age or older (fortunately, this doesn't apply to pilots who act younger than two years of age according to their pediatrician).

For small civil airplanes manufactured after July 18, 1978, an approved shoulder harness for each front seat. The shoulder harness must be designed to protect the occupant from serious head injury when the occupant experiences the ultimate inertia forces specified in FAR Part 23.561(b)(2). Each shoulder harness installed at a flight crewmember station must permit the crewmember, when seated and with the safety belt and shoulder harness fastened, to perform all functions necessary for flight operations.... (There are additional details listed in this reg that aren't pertinent to this chapter so I won't cover them. But if you're upset by this and your name is Blayde, give me a call and I'll personally interpret them for you. Just don't hit me.)

Don't worry. I think that stuff is optional equipment.

The instruments/equipment necessary for night VFR flight are: (Figure 48)

Equipment Required for Night VFR Flight

The instruments and equipment previously specified for day VFR flight

Approved position lights

An approved aviation red or aviation white anti-collision light system on all U.S.-registered civil aircraft. In the event of failure of any light of the anti-collision light system, operations with the aircraft may be continued to a stop where repairs or replacement can be made.

If the aircraft is operated for hire, one electric landing light (sorry, save those candles for the solstice).

An adequate source of electrical energy for all installed electrical and radio equipment (who moved my hamster?)

One spare set of fuses, or three spare fuses of each kind required, that are accessible to the pilot in flight (not the kind of fuses you light, but the kind that let the lights work).

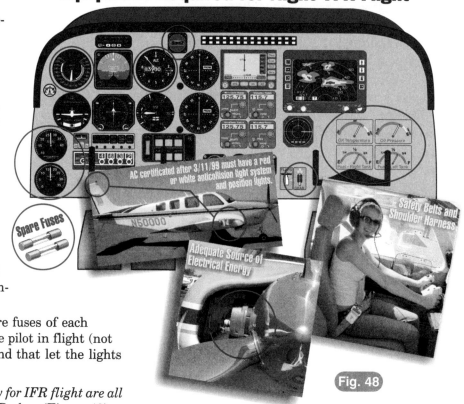

Fig. 48

The instruments/equipment necessary for IFR flight are all those required for day and/or night VFR plus: (Figure 49)

Two-way radio communication system and navigational equipment appropriate to the ground facilities to be used

Gyroscopic rate-of-turn indicator (there is additional information in this regulation that really isn't pertinent to general aviation airplanes).

Equipment Required for Day/Night IFR Flight

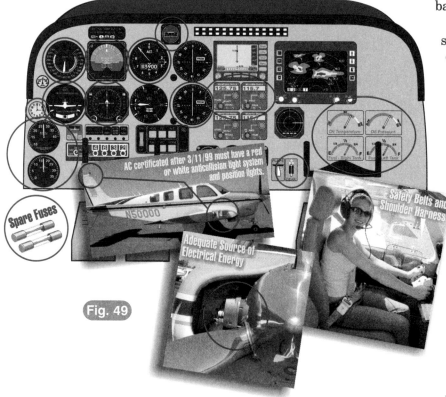

Fig. 49

(4) Slip-skid indicator

(5) Sensitive altimeter adjustable for barometric pressure

A clock displaying hours, minutes, and seconds with a sweep-second pointer or digital presentation

Generator or alternator of adequate capacity

Gyroscopic pitch and bank indicator (artificial horizon)

Gyroscopic direction indicator (directional gyro or equivalent)

For flight at and above 24,000 feet MSL (FL 240). If VOR navigational equipment is required under paragraph (d)(2) of this section, no person may operate a U.S.-registered civil aircraft within the 50 states and the District of Columbia at or above FL 240 unless that aircraft is equipped with approved distance measuring equipment (DME) (GPS can be used as a substitute for DME). When DME required by this paragraph fails at and above FL 240, the pilot in command of the aircraft shall notify ATC immediately, and then may continue operations at and above FL 240 to the next airport of intended landing at which repairs or replacement of the equipment can be made.

Now, I've tried to eliminate those ancillary parts of this regulation that don't pertain to you (all except for that Blayde, guy). So, grab a book of FARs if you want the details that don't pertain to you as a general aviation airplane pilot. Did you notice that the vertical speed indicator isn't a required instrument for IFR flight? It's the only one of the six panel instruments that can be missing or placarded as inoperative and not affect an IFR flight (at least as far as the regulations are concerned). If you'd like to know how to deal with inoperative instruments, read Postflight Briefing #8-1.

FAR 91.211—Use of Supplemental Oxygen

It is in your best interest, not to mention that of your passengers, to have full mental capability while piloting an airplane. Reducing oxygen flow to the brain is one of the quickest ways to diminish its ability and get us to act really weird as a result. To keep us from acting any weirder than we're genetically programmed to do, the regulations require the PIC (and any required flight crewmembers) to use supplemental oxygen when flying for more than 30 minutes above 12,500 feet up to and including 14,000 feet. If you go above 14,000 feet, you must use oxygen from the moment you exceed that altitude (Figure 50).

Over the years I've had pilots come up to me and say, "Hey, couldn't I be at 13,500 feet for 29 minutes, descend to 12,500 feet for a few seconds, then immediately climb back to 13,500 feet, thereby avoiding the use of oxygen?" Legally, the answer is yes. But a question like this makes me think that the pilot's brain has already suffered permanent damage from oxygen deprivation, privation (or perhaps libation).

So much for the crew. What about family and friends who are along for the fun? Hopefully, they're not asleep in back because you forgot to provide them with oxygen! According to the regulations, you, the pilot in command, are required to provide each occupant of the aircraft with supplemental oxygen when operating at altitudes above 15,000 feet MSL. The rule specifically states *provide,* not force them to use. Common sense dictates that it should be used, of course, but it's the old "You can lead a horse to water" situation. You will notice that if some of your passengers choose not to use oxygen above 15,000 feet, they may be very, very quiet. That's because they've probably dozed off or are unconscious, and if you're the type that hates being alone, prepare to get really lonely.

All these altitudes are MSL altitudes. Since you might someday fly a pressurized airplane, these rules also apply to cabin pressure altitudes. For instance, if you pressurize the cabin to an altitude simulating 13,000 feet, then you and the flight crew are required to use supplemental oxygen for that portion of the flight exceeding 30 minutes at that cabin altitude.

Oxygen is great for staying alive, but it also has a less desirable property. It helps things burn better, faster, and hotter. Anything flammable combined with oxygen can make for an unhappy ending. This includes petroleum products (lip balm and gloss are petroleum products!), hair sprays, alcohol, and perfumes. Add a touch of spark and these things will go up faster than an F-16 on afterburners. Make absolutely certain that any source of ignition is stifled before you let the oxygen flow go, Moe.

The airlines are always telling passengers to extinguish their cigarettes before putting on the oxygen mask (yes, they still smoke on some international flights). Frankly, I'm amazed that we need to tell anyone this. After all, who would smoke in an oxygen tent? Perhaps an even more appropriate question to ask is, who would do it a second time?

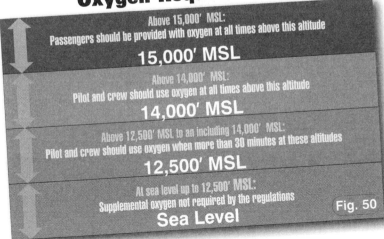

Oxygen Requirements

Above 15,000' MSL:
Passengers should be provided with oxygen at all times above this altitude

15,000' MSL

Above 14,000' MSL:
Pilot and crew should use oxygen at all times above this altitude

14,000' MSL

Above 12,500' MSL to an including 14,000' MSL:
Pilot and crew should use oxygen when more than 30 minutes at these altitudes

12,500' MSL

At sea level up to 12,500' MSL:
Supplemental oxygen not required by the regulations

Sea Level

Fig. 50

ATC Transponder and Altitude Reporting Equipment Requirement

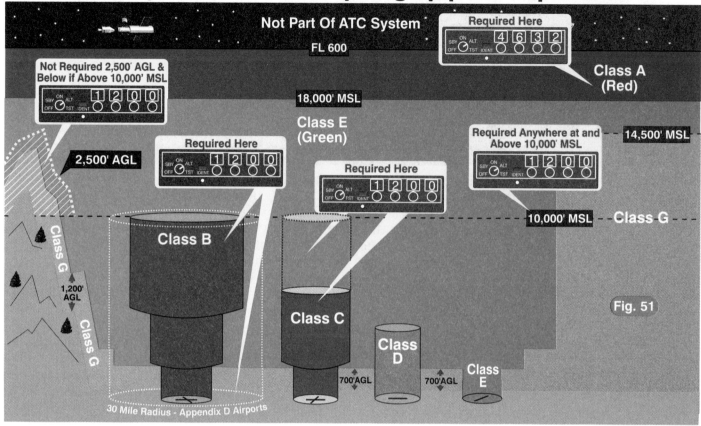

Fig. 51

FAR 91.215—ATC Transponder and Altitude Reporting Equipment and Use

Transponders are often known as Mode 3/A 4096 code capable transponders, though you can call yours anything you want. The 4096 is the number of codes that can be set on the unit (for the math-enabled among you, there are four "digit windows" each having eight possible numbers, or 8×8×8×8=4096). Most transponders also have Mode C or Mode S capability, otherwise known as having altitude reporting capability.

Transponders with Mode C capability are required while operating in any of the following areas: (See Figure 51.)

In Class A, Class B, and Class C airspace areas as well as in all airspace above the ceiling and within the lateral boundaries of Class B or Class C airspace upward to 10,000 feet MSL

In all airspace within 30 nautical miles of certain airports listed in appendix D, section 1 of FAR Part 91, from the surface upward to 10,000 feet MSL (known as the Mode C veil around Class B airspace as shown in Figure 52). These airports are identified from your aeronautical sectional charts by thin, circular magenta rings.

In all airspace of the 48 contiguous states and the District of Columbia at and above 10,000 feet MSL, excluding the airspace at and below 2,500 feet above the surface.

One last thing about this regulation. It requires you to keep your transponder turned on while in the airspace listed above, or in any controlled airspace. In addition to keeping it turned on, you must also operate it in Mode C (the altitude reporting mode) if you are so equipped.

You are probably wondering, "What do I do if my Mode C fails in flight or fails at some intermediate stop on a cross country flight?" Well, fear not. ATC can waive the Mode C requirement at any time. Simply call the Center or approach controller with your request. If you don't *have* a transponder, ATC wants at least a one-hour notice before they approve a flight in an area requiring a transponder.

Mode C Veil-Class B Airspace

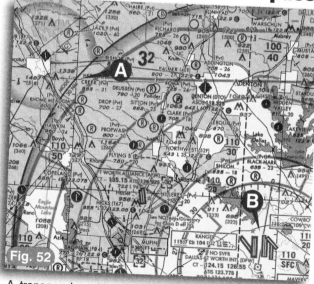

A transponder with Mode C capability is required anywhere within the solid magenta line shown at position A, (30 nm radius) surrounding the primary airport in Class B airspace (position B).

FAR 91.411—Altimeter System and Altitude Reporting Equipment Tests and Inspections

Let me make this regulation simple. You can't operate your airplane in controlled airspace under IFR unless, within the preceding 24 calendar months, each static pressure system, each altimeter instrument, and each automatic pressure altitude reporting system has been tested and inspected. You'll know you meet this requirement because the inspection will be logged in the aircraft logbooks, as shown in Figure 52.

FAR 91.413—ATC Transponder Tests and Inspections

You can't use an ATC transponder unless, within the preceding 24 calendar months, it has been tested and inspected. As with the pressure system checks, you'll know this requirement is met because the inspection will be logged in the aircraft logbooks, as shown in Figure 53.

NTSB Regulations

The National Transportation Safety Board (NTSB) is the agency responsible for aircraft accidents (Figure 54), incidents and overdue aircraft. Under certain conditions, you may have to notify them or file

Static System/Transponder Check

Fig. 53

GERDES AVIATION SERVICES
FAA Approved Repair Station G3RR399J

The Altimeter/Static and Transponder Systems have been inspected to
__20,000__ feet, and were found to comply with F.A.R. 43, Appendix E &F.
N Number __500GE__ Date __08-01-05__ Signature __Brian Gerdes__
FAA APPROVED REPAIR STATION G3RR399J
4012 W. Commonwealth Ave. Fullerton CA 92833   Office (714) 525-7545

For IFR flight, the transponder and the altimeter/static system must be tested, inspected and logged within the preceding 24 calendar months.

a report if you are involved in an aircraft accident in which any person receives serious injury or the aircraft receives substantial damage. Part 830 of the Board's regulations governs the reporting of accidents, incidents, and damage to aircraft, cargo, mail, or injury to required crewmembers.

NTSB 830.2—Definitions

Sometimes things mean just what I say they mean, nothing more and nothing less. So it was in Wonderland, anyway. In FAA-land, things mean what the FAA says they mean, and that extends to the terms *serious injury* and *substantial damage*. These things have very specific FAA definitions, and you need to know them because if either occurs, you have certain reporting requirements.

There are five specific definitions of a serious injury. Looking at them closely, they appear to be what you might see at any hockey game. A serious injury is any injury that:

Requires hospitalization for more than 48 hours, commencing within seven days from the date the injury was received

Results in the fracture of a bone (except simple fractures of the fingers, toes or nose)

Causes severe hemorrhages, nerve, muscle, or tendon damage

When Go Arounds Go Bad

AIR CALIFORNIA

Fig. 54

The pilot of this airplane was instructed to go around but delayed doing so. As a result, he let the airplane get too slow. The result was this non-fatal accident.

Involves any internal organ

Involves second- or third-degree burns, or any burns affecting more than five percent of the body surface

Substantial damage is defined as damage or failure that adversely affects the structural strength, performance, or flight characteristics of the aircraft and that would normally require major repair or replacement of the affected component. The following are NOT considered to be substantial damage for the purposes part of calculating your need to report:

Engine failure or damage limited to an engine if only one engine fails or is damaged

Bent fairings or cowling, dented skin, small puncture holes in the skin or fabric

Ground damage to rotor or propeller blades and damage to landing gear, wheels, tires, flaps, engine accessories, brakes, or wingtips

An accident is an occurrence in which any person suffers death or serious injury, or in which the aircraft receives substantial damage. An incident means an occurrence other than an accident, associated with the operation of an aircraft, which affects or could affect the safety of operations.

NTSB 830.5—Immediate Notification

The operator of an aircraft must immediately and by the most expeditious means available notify the nearest National Transportation Safety Board (NTSB) field office when an aircraft accident (serious injury or substantial damage) *or* any of the following listed incidents occur:

Flight control system malfunction or failure

Inability of any required flight crewmember to perform his or her normal flight duties as a result of injury or illness

Failure of structural components of a turbine engine excluding compressor and turbine blades and vanes

In-flight fire

Aircraft collide in flight

Damage to property, other than the aircraft, estimated to exceed $25,000 for repair or fair market value in the event of total loss (i.e., you land on a large house or a small Mercedes)

An aircraft is overdue and is believed to have been involved in an accident

NTSB 830.10—Preservation of Aircraft Wreckage, Mail, Cargo, and Records

This regulation says that if you are the operator of an aircraft involved in an accident or incident, it's your job to protect the wreckage and everything associated with that wreckage until the NTSB arrives and assumes responsibility. Avoid disturbing the wreckage. Do so only if it's necessary to help persons injured or trapped, to protect the wreckage from further damage, or to protect the public from injury. If you need to move the wreckage or anything associated with it, make notes, take photographs, or draw sketches to detail its original condition.

NTSB 830.15 Reports and Statements to Be Filed

The operator of an aircraft must file a report within 10 days after an accident or after seven days if an overdue aircraft is still missing. A report on an incident for which immediate notification is required shall be filed only as requested by an authorized representative of the Board.

Those are some of the important regulations necessary for flying safety. Of course, some of you may be thinking there's only one thing more boring than studying the FARs and that's listening to golf on the radio. OK, let me make this a little more exciting for you by introducing you to our next subject, airport operations.

Postflight Briefing #8-1

Inoperative Equipment: What Now?

Here's the situation. You walk out to the airplane and notice a piece of equipment is inoperative. Can you legally fly the airplane? The answer is: it depends. Of course, if the engine's inoperative, you're staying put. But what if it's the clock? or the vertical speed indicator? Or the number two communication radio? Let's find out.

Figure 55 shows a Pilot Decision Sequence chart useful for answering questions about inoperative equipment.

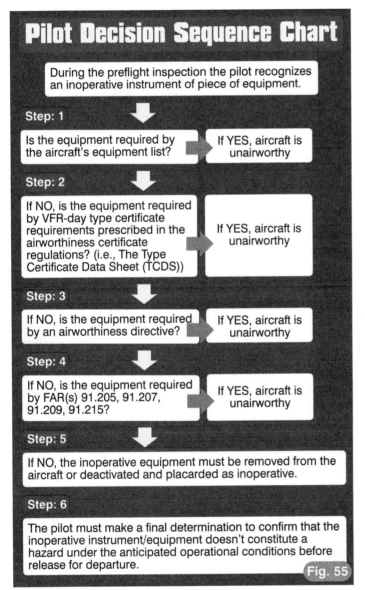

Fig. 55

The Aircraft Flight Manual

Fig. 56

might be able to provide an equipment list for that particular airplane's make, model and serial number. Contact the manufacturer to find out.)

Looking in section 6 of the *AFM* (the *Weight and Balance/Equipment List* section), you'll see a long list of airplane equipment (Figure 57). While different manufacturers vary the way this information is presented, all *AFMs* provide some means of identifying whether individual equipment is required or is optional for that airplane.

The Weight and Balance Equipment List

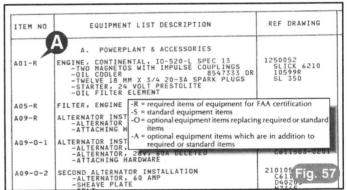

Fig. 57

Step #1:

Step #1 asks if the equipment is required by the aircraft's *equipment list*. Does your airplane have an equipment list? Probably so. If the airplane was manufactured after March 1, 1979, then the FAA says it must have an *Aircraft Flight Manual* (AFM), which includes an equipment list. Figure 56 shows the *AFM* that Cessna provides for the 1985 Cessna Centurion. (Note: for airplanes manufactured prior to this date, the airplane manufacturer

For instance, Cessna provides four designators next to each piece of equipment to identify whether it's a *required, standard,* or *optional* item for that airplane (see the shadow box in the center of Figure 57, position A).

In the top left corner of Figure 57, the first equipment item under the *Powerplant and Accessories* section is the engine. It has an *R* next to the designation *A01*. Therefore, the engine is a *required* item for original FAA certification of this airplane. Thank goodness they cleared this one up for us. Nevertheless, if the engine or any other *required* item is inoperative, you can't go flying until it's repaired or replaced.

Further down the list, under the *Electrical System* section, you'll see the designation *D25-S* for the electric clock (Figure 58, position B). This is a *standard* item which wasn't required when the airplane was originally certified. Therefore, it's not a mandatory part of this airplane's equipment list but it may be mandatory according to the other steps on our flow chart.

The Weight and Balance Equipment List

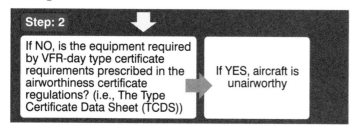

ITEM NO	EQUIPMENT LIST DESCRIPTION	REF DRAWING
D16-A-5	ALTITUDE ENCODER, BLIND -ENCODER	2101011-1 C744001-01
D16-A-6	ALTITUD -R = required items of equipment for FAA certification	1-3
D16-A-7	ALTITUD -S = standard equipment items -ENC -O = optional equipment items replacing required or standard -ALT items -CAB	8-5 13-10 0-0000
D16-A-8	ALTITUD -A = optional equipment items which are in addition to required or standard items -ENCODING ALTIMETER (LIGHTED) -ALTITUDE ALERTER -CABLES & MISC ITEMS	-5 2101013-21 43310-0000
D25-S	ELECTRIC CLOCK	C664508-0102
D25-O	ELECTRIC CLOCK, DIGITAL (NET CHANGE) -CLOCK/CHRONOMETER	0770776-3 C664511-01
D28-R	COMPASS, MAGNETIC	C660501-0102
D38-R	GAGE, FUEL QUANTITY, (IN LOWER DISTAL)	C6
D67-A	HOURMETER INSTALLATION	C667562-01.1

Fig. 58

One step below this is the designator *D25-O (Figure 58, position C)*. This indicates that a digital electric clock is an *optional* equipment item which is an *allowable replacement* for a standard or required item. In other words, no sundials, hourglasses, or ancient Aztec calendars are allowed as an optional means of measuring time in the cockpit.

And a few steps below that in Figure 58 is the designation *D67-A (.* This indicates that the hourmeter (A.K.A., the Hobbs meter) is an *optional* item for this airplane. According to this list, you can operate the airplane if the Hobbs meter isn't working (which is perfectly fine as far as most rental pilots are concerned).

Step #2:

Let's assume that Step #1 indicated that the inoperative equipment isn't mandatory. Step #2 asks if the equipment is required by the airplane's *VFR-day type certificate* or the airworthiness regulations as per FAR 91.213 (d) (2) (ii). If it is, then the airplane is unairworthy until that equipment is replaced or repaired. Here's what all this means.

There is something known as the *Type Certificate Data Sheet* (*TCDS*). This is a listing that shows the specific

equipment required for that particular type, make and model of airplane (Figure 59).

In fact, the *TCDS* lists the equipment required for that airplane based on its particular serial number. Some airplanes (a particular model of Cessna 150 for instance) don't require a propeller spinner. Yet, another model (a Cessna 152, for example) or the same model with a different serial number may require a propeller spinner be installed.

So the big question is: where does the average pilot find the *TCDS*? One source is the FAA's *Regulatory and Guidance Library* located at: http://rgl.faa.gov/. This is an excellent source of aviation information. Another source is a mechanic with an IA (Inspection Authorization). You can also call or visit the FAA to get this information.

The Type Certificate Data Sheet

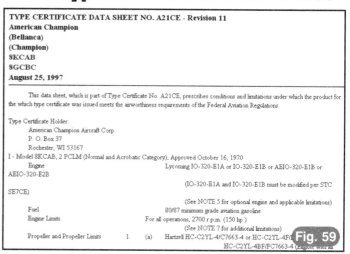

Fig. 59

Let's assume that you called the FAA and asked an inspector about an inoperative piece of equipment. If he or she looks over the *TCDS* and tells you that this equipment is required for your airplane, then it must be repaired or replaced before you fly. If it's not required, then you should proceed to Step #3.

Step #3

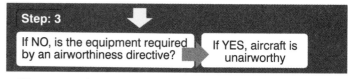

If you aren't grounded by Step #1 or 2, then Step #3 requires you to check and see if the equipment is required by an *Airworthiness Directive* (*AD*) as shown in Figure 60.

For instance, on some P210 models, an *AD* requires that you have either a dual vacuum system or an electric artificial horizon for *IFR* flight. If one vacuum pump became inoperative or the electric artificial horizon went belly up, the airplane is no longer airworthy for IFR flight until the inoperative instrument is repaired or replaced.

The big question that pilots face is how to know if and when an *AD* requires a specific piece of equipment to be operable in the airplane? Certainly the owner or operator

Airworthiness Directives

85-02-07 CESSNA: Amendment 39-4991. Applies to Models 205, 205A (S/Ns 205-0001 thru 205-0577); 206, U206, U206A, U206B, U206C, U206D, U206E, U206F, U206G, TU206A, TU206B, TU206C, TU206D, TU206E, TU206F and TU206G (S/Ns 206-0001 thru U20606827); P206, P206A, P206B, P206C, P206D, P206E, TP206A, TP206B, TP206C, TP206D and TP206E (S/Ns P206-0001 thru P20600647); 207, 207A, T207, and T207A (S/Ns 20700001 thru 20700773); 210G, 210H, 210J, 210K, T210K, 210L, T210L, 210M, T210M, 210N and T210N (S/Ns 21058819 thru 21064535); T210G, T210H, T210J, (S/N T210-0198 thru T210-0454) and P210N (S/Ns P21000001 thru P21000760) airplanes certificated in any category.

Compliance: Required within 100 hours time-in-service after the effective date of this AD, unless already accomplished.

To eliminate the possibility of loss of the fuel selector roll pin installation, accomplish the following:

(a) Visually inspect the fuel selector for free play. If free play exceeds 15 degrees, replace any components that exhibit loose or worn conditions, as necessary, to reduce the free play to this limit.

(b) Safety the fuel selector shaft to yoke roll pin installation by installing safety wire through the roll pin in accordance with Cessna Single Engine Customer Care Service Information Letter SE84-5.

(c) The airplane may be flown in accordance with FAR 21.197 to a location where this AD may be accomplished provided fuel tank selection during flight is not performed.

(d) An equivalent means of compliance with this AD may be used if approved by the Manager, Aircraft Certification Office, Federal Aviation Administration, 1801 Airport Road, Room 100, Mid-Continent Airport, Wichita, Kansas 67209; telephone (316) 946-4400.

This amendment becomes effective on March 6, 1985.

Fig. 60

of the airplane receives the *ADs*, but suppose it's a rental airplane? How would you know? After all, most pilots don't have easy access to *ADs*, do they? In some cases, they do.

For instance, you can look up all the *ADs* pertinent to an airplane on on the FAA's web site at: http://rgl.faa.gov/. You can even subscribe to these ADs while at this site, too. Unfortunately, reading an *AD* is often as easy as reading *Finnegan's Wake* on a moonless night, during an electrical storm while huddled down in a ship's swaying crow's nest. *ADs* are not always easy to understand. Once again, you're almost forced to consult a qualified mechanic to determine if the inoperative equipment is required for this flight.

Let's assume the mechanic tells you that he knows of no *AD* limiting flight with the referenced equipment inoperative. What next? You go to Step #4.

Step #4

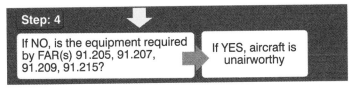

Step #4 requires you to reference FAR 91.205, 91.207, 91.209 and 91.215 to determine if the inoperative equipment is required for this flight. For instance, 91.205 is the *Instrument and Equipment Requirements* regulation. It lists all the equipment that must be on board for *Day VFR flight*, *Night VFR flight*, *Instrument flight*, etc. It's an easy regulation to understand and doesn't require a crypto-linguist to interpret. FAR 91.207, 91.209 and 91.215 reference ELT, aircraft lighting requirements and transponder/Mode C requirements, respectively.

Let's say that you've made it this far and Steps #1-4 do not prohibit flight based on the equipment that's inoperative. What next? It's time for Step #5.

Step #5

At this point you must either *remove* the inoperative equipment from the airplane or *deactivate* it. Hmmm. Let's examine the first option.

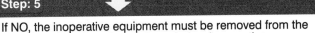

If NO, the inoperative equipment must be removed from the aircraft or deactivated and placarded as inoperative.

Equipment Removal

Suppose the landing light is inoperative. Can you remove the bulb from the airplane? The way to know what you can or cannot do to the equipment on the airplane is to check the definition of *preventive maintenance*. As a pilot you're allowed to perform preventive maintenance without being a licensed mechanic or being supervised by that mechanic. Preventive maintenance is defined in FAR 43, Appendix A (it's a long list so I won't print it here but you can find it in any good FAR source). Therefore, you're allowed to remove the landing light bulb in this instance (hopefully, you'll do this in accordance with the manufacture's maintenance manual).

Additionally, anytime a pilot performs preventive maintenance, he or she must make an entry in the *maintenance records* in accordance with FAR 43.9. Figure 61 shows what this entry should look like. In other words, you shouldn't have an entry that reads something like, *"Took out bulb, taped on a big flashlight with duct tape in its place and hooked string to the switch so I could activate it in flight. Looks good to me as long as you don't mind the rattlin' noise during flight. Signed: Bubba."*

Maintenance Record Entry

Placard (Minimum 1/8 inch high letters)

Landing Light Inoperative

PREVENTIVE MAINTENANCE ENTRY:

(DATE) Total time _____ hours. Landing light bulb removed in accordance with (manufacturer) maintenance manual, Chapter ____, _____page. Landing light switch placarded inoperative.

_____   _____
Pilot's Signature   Certificate Number

Placard (Minimum 1/8 inch high letters)

Landing Light Inoperative   **Fig. 61**

Next, you must write the word **INOPERATIVE** on a piece of tape with letters a minimum of 1/8th inch tall. Then place this tape over or near the inoperative piece of equipment (in case you're a comedian, don't even think about placing it on the pilot's forehead). In this instance, you should place the tape above or near the landing light switch (don't place it over the landing light cover on the outside of the airplane).

It's fair to say that anytime you remove an item from an airplane, it's best to consult a qualified mechanic first (and I'm not talking about the guy who works on your Toyota, either).

As a personal note, I'd leave the landing light installed and simply deactivate it. How do you do that? Read on.

Equipment Deactivation

In maintenance circles, deactivating a piece of equipment implies removing it from its power source. Suppose the airplane's gas heater is inoperative. This is a difficult item to remove, so you decide to deactivate the heater instead. Unlike a landing light (which you can deactivate yourself) the heater's deactivation isn't covered by the definition of preventive maintenance. A mechanic *must* be consulted. (Even if it's not required, I'd recommend that you always consult a mechanic anytime you decide to deactivate a piece of the airplane's equipment.)

Maintenance Record Entry

Placard (Minimum 1/8 inch high letters)

Aircraft Heater Deactivated

PREVENTIVE MAINTENANCE ENTRY:

(DATE) Total time _____ hours. **Aircraft Heater Deactivated** in accordance with (manufacturer) maintenance manual, Chapter ____, _____page. **Heater Switch** placarded inoperative.

_____   _____
Mechanic's Signature   Certificate Number

Placard (Minimum 1/8 inch high letters)

Aircraft Heater Deactivated   Fig. 62

Let's say, upon examination, the mechanic elects to cap the heater's fuel lines as a means of deactivating the device. FAR 43.9 requires that the mechanic make an entry in the maintenance records that looks something like that in Figure 62.

Additionally, you or the mechanic must still write the word **INOPERATIVE** on a piece of tape with letters a minimum of 1/8th inch tall. This tape must be placed over or near the inoperative piece of equipment (the *heater switch* in this instance).

Is that all there is to this? Nope, one more thing.

Step #6

Step: 6

The pilot must make a final determination to confirm that the inoperative instrument/equipment doesn't constitute a hazard under the anticipated operational conditions before release for departure.

If you remove or deactivate a piece of inoperative equipment, you (the PIC) must make a final determination that the equipment doesn't constitute a hazard under the anticipated conditions of flight.

Whew! Are we there yet?

Nope, you have one additional thing to consider.

How long can the inoperative equipment remain inoperative? FAR 91.405 says that the owner or operator of the aircraft shall have any inoperative equipment repaired, replaced, removed, or inspected at the next required inspection. For most airplanes, this refers to the *annual inspection*. If the airplane is operated for hire, then the next required inspection also refers to the next 100 inspection in addition to the annual inspection. (As a side note, the landing light is a required equipment item if the airplane is operated at night for hire.)

Despite the six steps mentioned above, your local FAA inspector may require an additional step(s) when removing or deactivating equipment. For instance, he or she may require a placard be placed in the airplane if the landing light is removed. The placard might read, "Day-VFR Flight Only." I suggest you make a call to your local FAA office just to make sure the work you're doing is acceptable to them.

Heck, it seems like it would be a lot easier to sell the airplane every time something stops working and buy a new one. Indeed, I realize that all this can be confusing. No argument here. But, there is some good that can come out of all this. If you follow these procedures, pilots will have a better idea about what equipment is or is not working when they enter an airplane.

So this is life in the big city when it comes to inoperative equipment. Yes, it's a bit troublesome, but if you're ever ramped check by the FAA, I wouldn't plan on using the old ruse, "Hey, the compass was working when I took off this morning." Difficult as it may be, it's better to jump through the hoops and make sure you're completely legal before hitting the airways.

Chapter 9
IFR Aviation Weather Theory

Introduction

What is it all about? Whether to be or not to be? Putting the right foot in and taking the left foot out? Nope. It's all about the weather. And that's no Hokey-Pokey when speaking of the reason for obtaining an instrument rating. It's all about being qualified to fly when the weather isn't severely clear.

When studying for your private pilot license, the basic strategy was, "Avoid the weather." Good weather, bad weather, just stay away from the stuff because it can only cause you grief after you brief.

Instrument pilots, on the other hand, learn how to fly in adverse weather while avoiding certain aspects of it that can cause them harm. That's what this chapter is about. You of course studied meteorology as a private pilot, but perhaps you've since learned that meteorology isn't the study of meteors. You are thus ready for a review of the basics and a thorough peek at what's behind the clouds. Studying meteorology is redundant you say? You took more than one high school English class in grammar, didn't you? I believe that an instrument pilot can't learn too much meteorology. Just like grammar, ain't you know? You don't need a weatherman to know which way the wind blows as long as you can figure it out yourself.

So let's begin our discussion with the basics.

Atmospheric Circulation—Finding the Air Apparent

OK, here's your short weather course. All weather is the result of the uneven heating of the earth's surface. Class dismissed.

OK, not quite so quick. But I believe I've made my point, however unevenly. It's the uneven heating of the earth's surface that causes air circulation. Had Hemingway lived longer, he would doubtless have recognized this crucial truth by writing a sequel to his famed novel and called it, "The Air Also Rises."

Air that circulates brings with it some of the general properties of the surface over which it formed, such as hot/cold/wet/dry. That means water can be transported by moving air. Water in the air means clouds can form when the air is sufficiently cooled. Cloud formation means that the heat energy originally used to evaporate the water in released back into the air. Sufficient released heat means rising air. This means thunderstorms can form.

Class dismissed now? We're getting there. That's the big picture. The rest is merely details, but some of them are pretty important details, so please stay tuned.

Have you ever seen someone do a fire walk on hot coals? Have you noticed that they don't walk, but run instead? The secret is to keep moving on a hot surface. The same applies to air. The movement of air is a never-ending story because this is how Mother Nature attempts to redistribute heat. As air moves, it creates the things we collectively refer to as weather. Think of it as the earth breathing. No breath means death.

Let's assume, for the sake of discussion, that our earth doesn't rotate (even though the earth may move for the firewalker). Figure 1 shows how the portion of the earth at the equator receives a great deal more solar heat than the area near the poles. Equatorial air, resting over a warmer surface, is eventually heated from below, just like our firewalker (but you don't hear the words, "ouch" and "mamasita" when the air moves). The air becomes less dense, and rises. Our weather engine is now in gear.

Up to a certain altitude in the atmosphere, called the tropopause, temperature decreases with altitude. Heated air rises, cooling as it does so, and continues upward-bound until it finds air of a similar temperature near the tropopause (position A). Once it's at equilibrium with the air around it, our restless parcel stops rising, but it doesn't stop moving.

Unable to ascend further, the air begins a journey north and south toward the poles, where it eventually cools and descends (position B). The airflow cycle in this simple illustration is completed when cold, descending polar air moves toward the equator, replacing the rising equatorial air (position C). This simple, single-cell circulation would be the way things were if the earth didn't rotate and Nature worked on earth as it does in textbooks.

Without earthly rotation, our discussion might end here (and my house would either be on fire on in deep freeze). The earth, however, rotates, which literally introduces a new twist into the calculations.

The Coriolis Force—How Air Gets All Screwed Up

When viewed from above the north pole, the counterclockwise rotation of the earth causes air to curve or twist

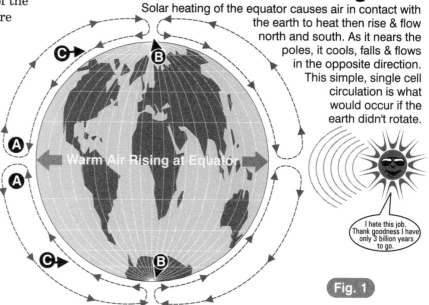

Single Cell Air Circulation for a Non-rotating Earth

Solar heating of the equator causes air in contact with the earth to heat then rise & flow north and south. As it nears the poles, it cools, falls & flows in the opposite direction. This simple, single cell circulation is what would occur if the earth didn't rotate.

Warm Air Rising at Equator

I hate this job. Thank goodness I have only 3 billion years to go.

Fig. 1

to its right (relative to the terrain) in the northern hemisphere (and to the left, as seen from the north pole, in the southern hemisphere). It kind of depends on which end is up. No matter which way the air moves, it will have a right curve or twist added to its direction of motion. j

Air is forced to curve by something known as the Coriolis force. It's the original air force, though it isn't a force in the way force is applied if a bat hits a ball. The Coriolis force, which sounds like something that happens if you don't pay your local loan shark, is an apparent force. No energy is expended in the making of this force. The earth rotates under a moving parcel of air, which gives the air the appearance of being deflected to the right of the direction in which it was moving. What appears to be magic is actually sleight of land.

Effect of Coriolis Force in the Northern Hemisphere

To demonstrate the effect of the Coriolis force, draw several lines along a straight edge over a rotating record. Make sure record rotates in the direction shown since this simulates the direction of earth's rotation as seen from over the north pole in the northern hemisphere.

As you can clearly see, the line always curves to the right in the direction of its motion because of the Coriolis force. A moving mass of air will also curve to the right in the direction of its motion in the northern hemisphere.

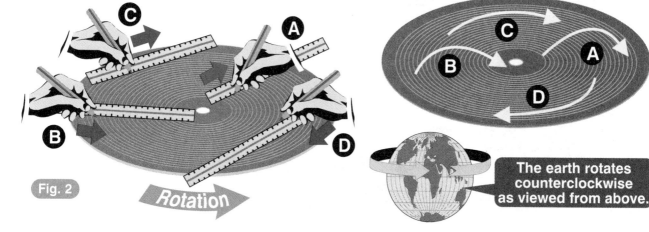

Fig. 2   Rotation

The earth rotates counterclockwise as viewed from above.

You can demonstrate the Coriolis force quite nicely, as shown in Figure 2. Take an old record (or a new CD of a singer you don't like) and spin it in the direction the earth rotates (counterclockwise) as if you're looking down from over the north pole. Have a friend hold a ruler one-half inch above the rotating record. Take a piece of chalk and move it along the straight edge of the ruler drawing a line on the rotating surface. Do it first from the exact center outward, as in position A. Then do it from the edge to the exact center, as in position B. Finally, do it in a sideways direction, as in positions C and D.

Single Cell Circulation to 30 Degrees North Latitude

Warm, rising air at the equator is curved to the right by the Coriolis force. As it travels northward at high altitudes, it cools and tends to bunch-up at the 30 degree north latitude position. (warm, rising air also moves south of the equator, but we're only concerned about northerly air movement right now).

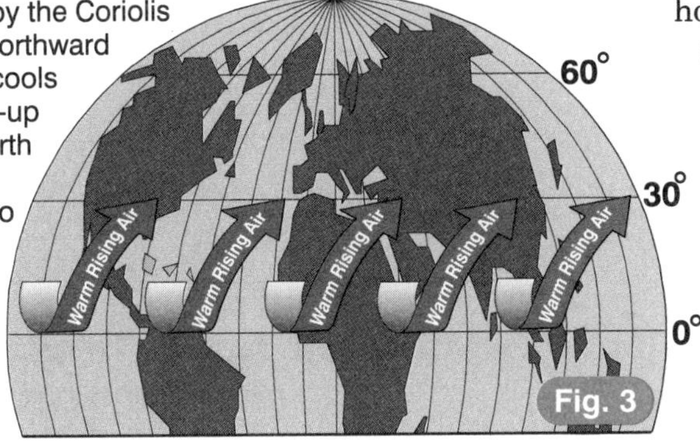

Fig. 3

Circulation of Air at 30 Degrees North Latitude

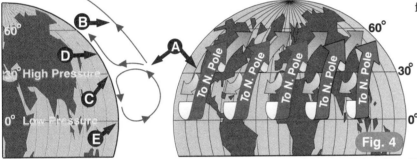

Fig. 4

High altitude, northeasterly flowing air bunches-up at 30° north latitude (position A). Some of this high altitude air continues northward (position B), while some of it falls, creating a permanent band of high pressure air around the globe at approximately 30 degrees of latitude (position C). The air at this latitude splits, some moving north (position D) and some moving south, back to the equator (position E).

Multi Cell Circulation of Air in the Northern Hemisphere

Fig. 5

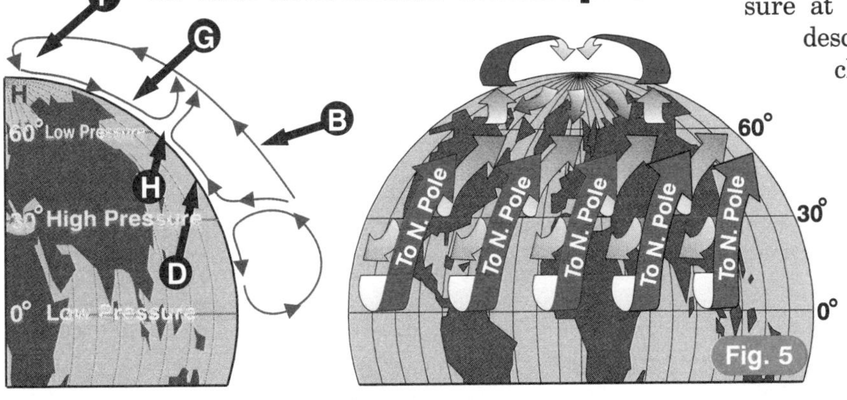

As high altitude air (position B) flows north, it finally reaches the North Pole (position F) where it cools, falls and flows southward (position G). The cold polar air flowing southward (position G) eventually makes contact with the warmer air flowing northward (position D). This warmer air flows up and over the cooler air, forming the polar front (position H). Three individual circulation cells are now apparent in both the northern and southern hemispheres (not shown here).

Now, let me throw you a curve by asking you to notice how the chalk path curves. Each path is curved to the right in the direction the chalk moved. No matter which way you moved that chalk, a right curve was apparently added to its motion. North of the equator, the Coriolis force curves the air to the right. South of the equator, the Coriolis force adds a left curve to the motion of the air. We'll limit our discussion to events in the northern hemisphere because that's where you probably live.

Remember, no matter which way the air moves in the northern hemisphere (right, left, sideways or diagonally), it will have an apparent right curve or twist added to it by the Coriolis force.

Now let's take a look and see how the Coriolis force alters the simple, single-cell atmospheric circulation previously presented in Figure 1. In the northern hemisphere, rising warmer air is curved to the right in an easterly direction by the Coriolis force (Figure 3). Eventually, the high altitude rising air moves in an easterly direction and starts to bunch up, much like a freeway crowded with cars. This bunching up occurs most noticeably at about 30 degrees north latitude. As the air rises, some of its heat is lost through radiation during the ascent.

Both bunching up and cooling cause some (not all) of this air to descend slowly at the 30 degree north latitude location, shown in Figure 4, position A. Bunching up increases the air mass above and thus causes a higher surface pressure at the 30 degree latitude position. As the air descends toward the surface, it warms, causing clear skies (usually) and warm surface temperatures. Some of this high pressure air flows southward toward lower pressure at the equator (position E). The rest of this warm, low altitude air at position D moves northward.

Some of the high altitude air that didn't descend at 30 degrees latitude continues to move northward toward the pole, as shown by position B in Figure 5. As it continues to cool, it falls, and travels southward from the North Pole (position F). At approximately the 60 degree north latitude (position G), this southward-moving colder air meets the northward moving warmer air (position D). These two air masses have

Wind Belts of the Northern Hemisphere

Surface winds, resulting from three individual circulating cells in the atmosphere, form three permanent wind bands across the northern hemisphere. Effects of the Coriolis force cause these winds to curve to their right in the direction in which they move.

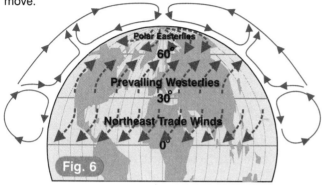
Fig. 6

different temperatures, and thus different densities. We know that things with different densities tend to not mix. This is why you shouldn't put your used motor oil down the gutter drain, especially if the drains run to the sea. Fish don't need lube jobs or tuna ups. Besides, they don't have grease fittings.

When very cold polar air bumps into cool tropical air, the result is a transition zone, shown at Figure 5, position H. This zone is known as the polar front (a front is simply a zone where air masses with different densities meet). Some of the northward-moving, cool air flows upward over the colder (denser) polar air (Figure 5, position H). This ascending air is carried northward, toward the pole, with the rest of the high altitude winds. Three separate cells of cir-

3D Multicell Circulation of Air

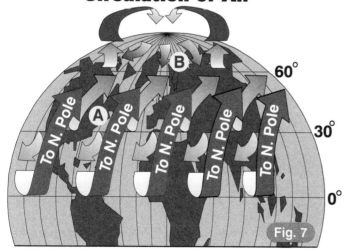
Fig. 7

Three wind belts are seen from above in 3-D perspective. Notice how warmer, northward moving air from 30° latitude (position A) confronts colder, southward moving air from the north polar region (position B). This confrontation is the source of much of the nasty weather we experience in the United States.

culation are now evident. It's sort of like aerial juggling. In a while we'll discuss fronts and their movement. Right now, just notice how winds in these three cells are affected by the Coriolis force.

Figure 6 depicts a profile of these three individual circulation cells. Between 0 and 30 degrees latitude, the northeast tradewinds blow. From 30 to 60 degrees, the prevailing winds are westerlies, and from 60 to 90 degrees the winds are the polar easterlies.

Notice that meteorologists always talk about winds in terms of the direction they blow from, not to! Meteorologists do this because winds, like people, are better understood when you know their origins. If winds come from the north, they're likely to be cold; from the south, they're likely to be warm. It's like an entrepre-

High and Low Pressure Centers on a Nonrotating Earth

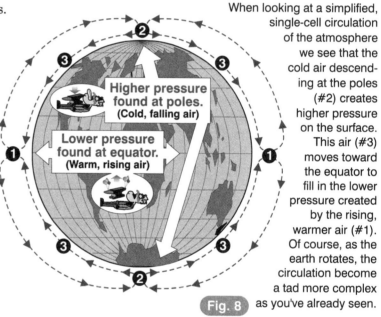

When looking at a simplified, single-cell circulation of the atmosphere we see that the cold air descending at the poles (#2) creates higher pressure on the surface. This air (#3) moves toward the equator to fill in the lower pressure created by the rising, warmer air (#1). Of course, as the earth rotates, the circulation become a tad more complex as you've already seen.
Fig. 8

neur pilot from redneck country who comes to the city and brings his culture with him. He starts an FBO in New York, then modifies all his airplanes so their stall horns play Dixie and takes an oath never to be caught dead in a Grumman "Yankee." Figure 7 depicts this circulation on a multidimensional level.

While the issue of air is weighing on your mind, let's see how it weighs on the earth.

Air Pressure and Vertical Air Movement

Air has weight. This weight exerts a pressure on the earth's surface in much the same way the high school bully exerted pressure on your chest when he sat on your rib cage during class (fortunately, the teacher would occasionally turn away from the blackboard and tell the thug to get back in his seat). Changing the air's temperature changes its density and the pressure it exerts on the earth's surface.

For example, along the equator there exist areas of warmer (less dense), rising air, as shown in Figure 8, position 1. Rising air certainly wouldn't create as much

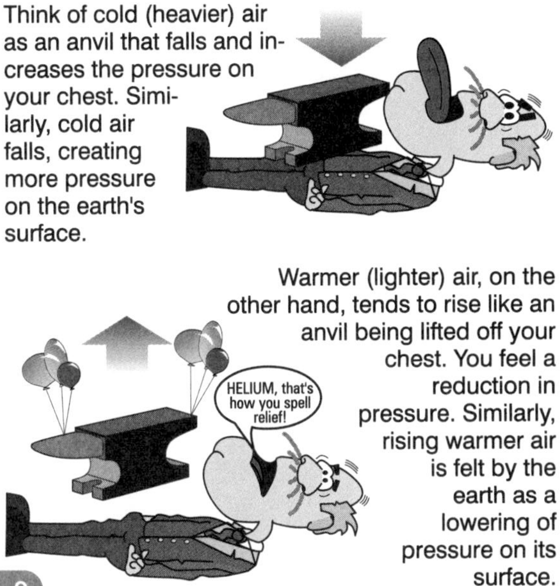

Air Movement and How It Affects Surface Pressure

Think of cold (heavier) air as an anvil that falls and increases the pressure on your chest. Similarly, cold air falls, creating more pressure on the earth's surface.

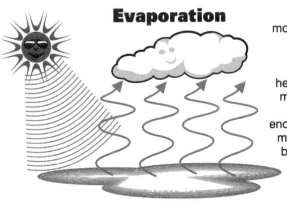

Warmer (lighter) air, on the other hand, tends to rise like an anvil being lifted off your chest. You feel a reduction in pressure. Similarly, rising warmer air is felt by the earth as a lowering of pressure on its surface.

HELIUM, that's how you spell relief!

Fig. 9

pressure on the surface as descending air. After all, one moves upward, while the other pushes downward. Warmer (less dense) rising air provides less push or pressure on the surface. We call large areas of warm rising air *low pressure centers*. Near the equator, it's quite common to find permanent belts of low pressure air wrapped around the earth.

Conversely, permanent *high pressure areas* exists at the poles (Figure 8, position 2). Auto salesmen gather in these high pressure areas, where colder (more dense) air descends, creating more pressure on the earth's surface. Now you know why cold air falls on your toes during those nocturnal refrigerator raids (unless you wear your shoes to bed). Think of cold air as that bully (or an anvil) resting on your chest, as shown in Figure 9. Gravity pulls the anvil downward as it does with cold air, increasing the pressure on your body. Let's attach helium balloons to the anvil, making it lighter. Now the anvil moves upward (off your chest), in

the same manner as rising warmer air moves upward off the earth's surface. Pressure at the surface decreases as warm air rises. Of course, as warm air rises, cold air moves in underneath to replace it. Thus, atmospheric circulation consists of high pressure air moving toward lower pressure air (Figure 8, position 3). This simple air circulation model is a fundamental key to understanding weather. It's a wind-wind situation for everyone.

Now that you understand major wind patterns, it's time to examine exactly what makes the wind blow.

Getting Water Into the Air

Weather as we know it (meaning clouds, rain, thunderstorms, etc.) wouldn't exist if there weren't a way of putting water into the air. Television meteorologists would all be forced to read the news, which means we'd hear things like, "Today, there's a 50% chance that a movie star will drink herself into a fog and produce occasional lightning." Weather is water. There's a good chance the room you're sitting in right now contains several pints of water suspended in the air. You can't see it, but it's there. It got there through one of two different processes—evaporation or sublimation. Either of these processes causes water molecules to absorb heat energy and enter the atmosphere.

Water exists in three states: solid (ice), liquid, and gas (water vapor). Changing from ice to water vapor (or water

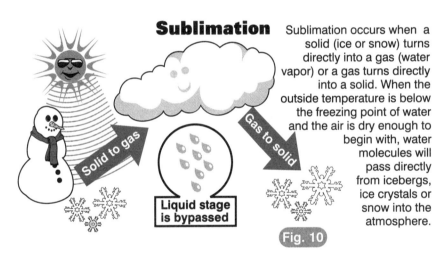

Sublimation Sublimation occurs when a solid (ice or snow) turns directly into a gas (water vapor) or a gas turns directly into a solid. When the outside temperature is below the freezing point of water and the air is dry enough to begin with, water molecules will pass directly from icebergs, ice crystals or snow into the atmosphere.

Solid to gas

Gas to solid

Liquid stage is bypassed

Fig. 10

vapor to ice) while bypassing the liquid stage is a subtle process known as sublimation. For instance, snow or ice can sublimate directly from a solid to the gaseous state. This increases the water vapor content of the atmosphere, as shown in Figure 10.

A more common means of adding water to the atmosphere is through evaporation. As water molecules absorb heat energy, they eventually become energetic enough to jump into the air (Figure 11). More heat means more evaporation. If the water lands on the hair of a TV evangelist, it's known as air-to-hair combat.

Given enough heat and a large enough water supply, the atmosphere can fill with water vapor. Fill is a relative term (first cousin, usually). For a given temperature,

Evaporation

Evaporation is the most common means by which water is added to the atmosphere. Solar heating causes water molecules to absorb heat energy. Given enough heat the water molecules eventually break free and enter the atmosphere.

Fig. 11

Water Holding Ability of Warm and Cold Air

A In warmer air, water molecules (large circles) vibrate and move faster. Thus, they tend not to stick together (as they like to do). This allows more water molecules to enter the air before it becomes completely saturated with water vapor.

B Cooling the air slows the speed & impact of colliding water molecules, allowing some of them to stick together, thereby returning to the liquid state in the form of a cloud (sky puddle). This leaves fewer unattached "invisible" water molecules in the now saturated air.

C As cooling continues, the smaller droplets grow and merge into larger "visible" droplets of water. The colder air is still saturated, but even fewer water vapor molecules remain in the air. Thus, colder air can hold less water vapor than warm air.

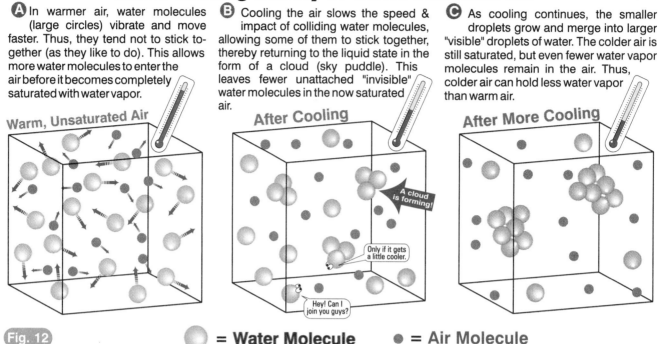

Fig. 12   ● = Water Molecule   • = Air Molecule

the air can only hold a certain amount of water, just as a theater has only so many seats. Air differs from a theater in having more or fewer seats depending on the temperature. Warmer air is like a large theater; it can hold a lot of water vapor. Cold air is like a small theater; it holds less water vapor for a given volume of air. The air is saturated when additional water vapor is unable to enter the air at a given temperature. Saturated air is very much like a packed theater, and there are only two ways more water can get in. Someone (Mr. Eau in seat 15-H) has to leave, or the temperature has to rise. (See *Air Science Facts* sidebar below.)

The Water Content of Warm and Cold Air

Anyone who has spent time along the eastern coast of Florida or the Texas Gulf coast knows what humidity is. I remember landing in Miami one time. I got out of the airplane and felt like a human Crockpot.

Why are summers usually more humid than winters? Summers are generally more humid because the air is warmer to begin with. Warm air has the capacity to hold more water than colder air.

To understand why warm air can hold more water vapor than cold air, you need to understand a little quirk about water molecules. Unlike air molecules, water mole-

cules like to cling to one another. They're insecure. This explains why you're more likely to find puddles of water than puddles of air on the ground. Of course, a dog standing nearby wearing a sheepish grin has a leg up on this theory, but you get the point, right?

Heating the air causes both air and water molecules to vibrate faster (Figure 12A). Water molecules that bounce and ricochet off each other with sufficient impact are less likely to stick together. Thus, you can put more water molecules into warmer air without them clinging to each other and forming clouds (sky puddles).

As the air cools, water molecules move slower and vibrate less (Figure 12B). Collisions between water molecules are now gentle enough to let them stick together. These clinging water molecules become visible, in the form of a cloud. In other words, the water molecules can't remain as vapor (gas), so they return to the liquid state in the form of something visible (a cloud). Additional cooling allows the water droplets to grow in size, as shown in Figure 12C.

The process of water vapor becoming visible is called condensation and it results in the formation of fog or clouds. When water vapor condenses it means that the air

Air Science Facts

Technically speaking, cold air doesn't hold less water because there's less room between cold air molecules. Flight instructors use this explanation because pilots fly airplanes, they don't design clouds. The fact is that water molecules constantly move between their liquid and gaseous phases. This process never stops but it does become lopsided. The rate at which water vapor leaves a liquid surface depends a lot on the temperature at the boundary of that surface. Therefore, if the temperature at the boundary between a puddle of water on the ground and the air above it is high, then water molecules become more energetic at the boundary and escape into the air (evaporation). The rate at which these water molecules escape is known as the vapor pressure. As the temperature decreases, water molecules have less energy and fewer escape from the puddle. The water molecules that are already in the air now tend to clump together in small microscopic droplets. As the temperature decreases, water molecules become less energetic and more clumping occurs. As air cools, the rate of evaporation decreases more quickly that does the rate of condensation (i.e., growing droplet size). Eventually, a certain temperature is reached (the dewpoint) where droplets form clouds with the possibility of precipitation.

How a Cloud Forms

On cold days a visible breath shaft is often seen when warm, moist air from the lungs is cooled by coming into contact with the cold, ambient (outside) air. As the air in the breath shaft cools, its water vapor condenses (returns to its liquid state), resulting in visible moisture in the form of a cloud (a mouth cloud).

Fig. 13

is saturated and can't hold any more water in vapor form. Now you know why cold air can hold less water vapor than warm air. It reaches its point of saturation sooner.

Keep in mind that the process of condensation is the opposite of evaporation. When it comes to water, what goes around definitely comes around.

This explains The Mystery of the Sweating Glass. Why does a glass get damp on the outside when you pour cool lemonade in it on a hot summer's day? Hot air, carrying lots of moisture, comes in contact with the cool surface of the glass. The suddenly chilled air can't hold its water. Your drink is a drip.

Do you recall your last flight on an air conditioned airliner? Cool, wasn't it? Dry, too. Very dry. Air conditioning cools the air and dries it, making your eyes feel like tiny shriveled raisins rattling around in oversized sockets. Contact lenses dry and stick like contact paper, making you wish for those good old days when everyone wore glasses with observatory-like lenses.

Two Ways to Be Cool

There are two ways to cool air and condense water vapor. First, you can put the air in contact with a cooler surface or environment. Second, you can lift the air and let it cool by expansion. Let's examine the first process.

First, you can bet than anyone named Francis went to Catholic school. You can also bet that any place in Minot, North Dakota in the winter is cold. Talk with anyone on those cold winter mornings and you'll see visible breath shafts (clouds) coming from their mouth, as shown in Figure 13. Warm air from their lungs contains a lot of moisture. As this

warm air comes into contact with the colder surroundings, the breath shaft becomes saturated with water vapor, condensation occurs, and a cloud forms. This is how clouds form by coming into contact with a cooler surface. (An added benefit is that if the person speaking to you ate onions, you can see it in time to get into your HAZMAT suit, and say, "I saw that coming.")

Fog formation is often based on air coming into contact with a cooler surface. Water vapor condenses, forming visible moisture in the form of clouds that touch the ground. But what about clouds that don't touch the ground? How do clouds form higher in the atmosphere?

If you lift air, you'll cool it. You'll have to go a bit farther than from your desktop to the top of your head to have any noticeable effect, so this isn't an experiment you can do at home. Rising air undergoes a decrease in pressure because of the decrease in weight (thus pressure) of the atmosphere above it. This is similar to the reduction in body pressure experienced when your friend taught you to swim and you ascended from the bottom of a swimming pool (once you finally let go of the big rock he told you to hold onto, of course). Air molecules expand when they are subject to less pressure. Since there is no other energy source available, the air molecules must use their own energy to expand. This slows them down, which results in a lower temperature. Air that rises always expands and cools. What happens to cooler air? It doesn't hold as much water as warmer air. Out of a high rise comes water. This creates visible moisture, which we call clouds, as shown in Figure 14.

Fortunately, the process of condensation is predictable and doesn't involve reading tea leaves or a tossed set of bones. In fact, we can even determine the temperature at which clouds begin to form. Before we can do this, however, we need to know something about the percentage of water in the air, otherwise known as the relative humidity.

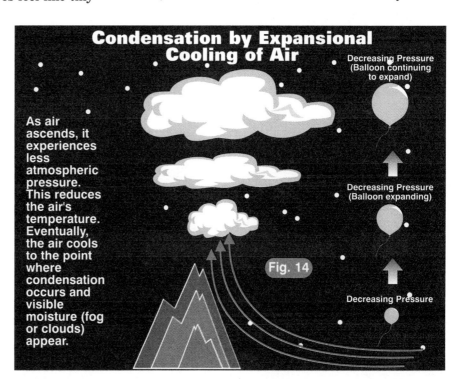

Condensation by Expansional Cooling of Air

As air ascends, it experiences less atmospheric pressure. This reduces the air's temperature. Eventually, the air cools to the point where condensation occurs and visible moisture (fog or clouds) appear.

Decreasing Pressure (Balloon continuing to expand)

Decreasing Pressure (Balloon expanding)

Decreasing Pressure

Fig. 14

Relative Humidity

Relative humidity is not a family member who's all wet; it's a measure of how much water vapor the air is holding in relationship to how much it could theoretically hold at its current temperature.

Rush hour in Los Angeles, California helps us visualize this. At 3 p.m., each moving automobile on the freeway is spaced about three car lengths behind the next. With greater space between vehicles, it's easy to slip in and move with traffic (especially when no weapons are involved). It might be said that the freeway currently holds only 25% (1 of a total capacity of 4) of the number of automobiles it's capable of holding. We might say the freeway's relative capacity is 25%.

But what happens at 5 p.m.? Space between automobiles decreases until bumpers are nearly touching. The freeway is now 100% saturated with cars. No more will fit. Nothing is moving. Its relative capacity is now 100%. If a car tries to get onto the freeway, another has got to go over the railing, which isn't so bad if your family car happens to be an Abrams Army tank.

Similarly, evaporation or sublimation can add only so much moisture to the air before things reach a saturation point. And when the air is saturated, you're not going to coax any more water vapor into it. Evaporation or sublimation is just one way air becomes saturated, and it's not even the most common way.

Cooling the air is the most common way for it to become saturated. Suppose air parcel A in Figure 15 contains only half the moisture it's capable of holding. We can say this parcel is 50% saturated, relative to the amount of moisture it can hold at its current temperature. Another way of expressing this is to say its relative humidity is 50%. The numerical value of 50% is relative to that particular parcel of air only.

What happens to the relative humidity when the air temperature decreases? Yes, the relative humidity goes up. It's just like the freeway losing a few lanes. It loses its capacity to handle traffic. When the temperature decreases, the air loses its capacity to hold water.

As air parcel B in Figure 15 is cooled, its water molecules start clinging to one another and begin to return to the liquid state. The air eventually becomes saturated and can't hold additional water molecules with further cooling. Parcel B's relative humidity has now increased to 100%, condensation occurs, and water molecules are forced out of the air.

Notice that the actual amount of water (vapor and liquid) in parcel B didn't change. Only the ability of the air parcel to hold additional water vapor was changed.

While relative humidity informs us about the air's capacity to hold water vapor, it doesn't allow us to predict when clouds will form. After all, relative humidity just tells us the state of the air right now, not what it will be in the future. There is, however, a meteorological value known as the dewpoint which provides us with cloud-predicting ability.

The Dewpoint

The dewpoint is the temperature to which a parcel of air must be cooled to become 100% saturated. It's a predictor of when condensation will begin for a particular parcel of air and is often determined by the use of a wet and dry bulb, hand-swung thermometer as shown in Figure 16. Assume a meteorologist says the air's dewpoint is 60 degrees Fahrenheit (F). If our thermometer shows the air's temperature is 75 degrees F, then we immediately know the air is not completely saturated. In other words, its relative humidity is less than 100%. But cool the air down to its dewpoint of 60 degrees F and the relative humidity increases to 100%. Condensation occurs, and fog or clouds form (that's condensation, not condescending, which is when folks belittle you in front of a cloud). This lead to the famed Rolling Stones lyrics, "Hey! You! Get off of my cloud."

Meteorologists refer to the actual temperature difference between the temperature and the dewpoint as the temperature/

Relative Humidity

The parcel of warm air (A) is holding 50% of the water vapor it's capable of holding. We say its *relative humidity* is 50%. As the air cools, its capacity to hold water vapor diminishes. Water molecules begin to stick together, condense and return to the liquid state (form a cloud). Remember, if water molecules are leaving the vapor state for the liquid state, you're not going to get more water vapor into the air (and that is that). Eventually the air cools to the point where it can't hold any more water. The *relative humidity* has increased to 100% as shown by parcel B.

Warm Air: Relative Humidity - 50%

The container of air at this temperature can actually hold an additional 10 water molecules in the vapor phase (for a total of 20). Relative to the 20 that are possible, the *relative humidity* is 50%.

Cold Air: Relative Humidity - 100%

As the air cools, its water holding ability decreases. Now it can't hold any more water in the vapor phase because the water molecules want to cling and form a cloud. Relative to this container, the relative humidity is now 100%.

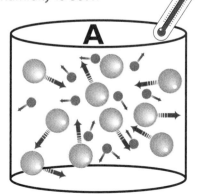

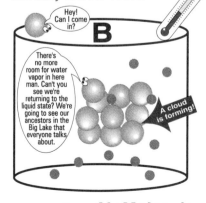

= Water Molecule   • = Air Molecule

Fig. 15

Courtesy NASA Collection

Fig. 16

The psychrometer is a device used to determine the dewpoint and relative humidity.

All Dew Determination

Dew point is determined by use of a wet and dry bulb thermometer—also called a psychrometer (Figure 16). Both are identical, mercurial thermometers. One measures air temperature; the other is encased in a wet sheath, permitting moisture to evaporate and cool the thermometer. Both thermometers are connected by small rope and are swung around for a few seconds. Then their temperatures are read.

Based on the readings from the two thermometers, the dewpoint, relative humidity and other measures can be calculated.

The first time I saw a weather specialist do this I thought he was a Bruce Lee protégé doing a nunchuka demo. In actuality, he swung them for a few seconds, took a reading, then retired with his data to the weather room.

It was a calculating move.

dewpoint spread. The process of condensation can actually begin about 5 degrees F (2.8 degrees C) before the air temperature cools to its dewpoint (otherwise stated as a temperature/dewpoint spread of 5 degrees).

Dewpoints are handy numbers for instrument pilots to know for several reasons. It's important to understand that the dewpoint is a great indicator of the atmosphere's water content. High dewpoint temperatures indicate a lot of water in the air. You can expect something known as mesoscale convective weather (discussed later) when dewpoints are above 60 degrees F. On the other hand, low dewpoint temperatures indicate little water in the air. The temperature/dewpoint spread also tells you whether the humidity is high or low as well.

Assume, for instance, you're planning an IFR flight to arrive at an airport about a half hour after sunset. Low clouds and low visibility already exist at the airport. What is the likelihood that the visibility will improve after sunset? Not much, right? Be aware that fog or low cloud formation can occur even with temperature/dewpoint spreads of as much as 6 degrees F. Visibility will drop quickly when the air begins cooling, and visibility is the most important factor in determining whether or not you're legal to land during an instrument approach.

Condensation and Cloud Formation

If clouds are present, does that mean it's going to rain? Definitely not. But if you have rain, or some other form of precipitation (hail, snow, etc.), clouds are definitely nearby. If you're driving along and see water coming from the sky without clouds, there's a good chance that your car's windshield cleaning mechanism is going haywire.

For significant precipitation to occur, clouds must generally be around 4,000 feet thick. Precipitation can take the form of rain, hail, snow, ice pellets or grains, or freezing rain. Essentially, precipitation is any or all forms of water particles, whether liquid or solid, that falls from the sky and reaches the ground. It is distinguished from clouds or dew in that it falls and makes contact with the earth's surface. When flying near any airport reporting precipitation of light or greater intensity, expect clouds to be at least 4,000 feet thick. This is an important clue when

considering whether or not it might be possible to climb on top of the clouds to avoid colder, freezing temperatures aloft.

Lapse Rates and Temperature Inversions

Suppose you decide to date a cheerleader in high school but are too cheap to pay for the entire meal and too inconsiderate to do anything but talk about yourself. When you ask her for another date, don't be surprised if she says, "No, no, never, never, no, no, way." No mystery here. Similarly, most weather mysteries are equally easy to solve, once you understand the relationship between lapse rates and temperature inversions.

The sun heats the earth. That's a fact. Very little of the sun's energy directly heats the air. That's also a fact. Then how does the air become warm? To incoming light, the atmosphere acts much like a pane of glass on a greenhouse (Figure 17). It lets solar radiation easily pass through without absorbing much heat itself. The heat is absorbed by the earth's surface. It's this heated surface that is primarily responsible for the atmosphere's heat content.

Solar Radiation and Heating of the Atmosphere

The earth's atmosphere acts like glass to incoming solar radiation. It lets the sun's ray pass through while absorbing relatively little heat. This allows most of the solar radiation to be absorbed by the earth's surface.

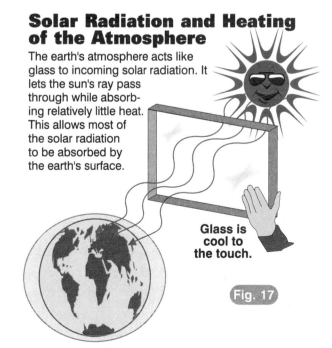

Glass is cool to the touch.

Fig. 17

As we learned in the beginning of this chapter, it's the surface of the earth that heats or cools the air directly. On clear days, when the earth absorbs an enormous amount of heat, the air in contact with the surface is warmed by touching (Figure 18), a sort of earthly hot flash. This occurs in much the same way that your ear becomes burned when you place a hot iron to it (as in "I was ironing when the phone rang"—this is known as an ear ring). As we move away from this heated surface, the air cools. We might say the temperature lapses or changes with an increase in altitude. Meteorologists call this the temperature lapse rate.

It may surprise you to learn that we can't predict precisely how the temperature will change in a given place on a given day as we go up in altitude. Even meteorologists don't know for sure, and they're paid to make good guesses. You were taught in private pilot school that the average or *standard atmospheric lapse rate* is a steady 3.5 degrees F (approximately 2.0 degrees C) per thousand feet. Not true! This is a misconception on the order of believing the posted mileage in new car sales literature. This literature states that your mileage will vary depending on how you drive. For example, if you drive with the engine running, you'll get less mileage. There are many variables affecting the rate at which temperature changes with altitude. Nevertheless, when it comes to estimating the level where a structural icing potential exists in clouds, the *standard lapse rate* is useful (more on structural icing later in this chapter).

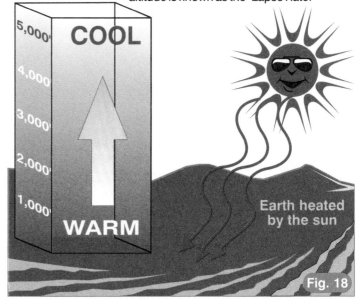

Temperature Change With Altitude

Air in contact with the surface is heated by conduction (touching). Closer to the surface, the air is warmer and, with an increase in altitude, the air cools. This change in temperature with a change in altitude is known as the "Lapse Rate."

COOL

5,000'
4,000'
3,000'
2,000'
1,000'

WARM

Earth heated by the sun

Fig. 18

To identify the rate of temperature change, weather specialists across the nation send up rawinsondes twice daily. Connected to a balloon, these devices provide information on wind, pressure, humidity and temperature.

Using this information, meteorologists are able to determine an exceptionally important measurement called the *ambient* (environmental) temperature lapse rate or ambient lapse rate for short. This lapse rate is essentially a vertical temperature profile of the atmosphere Its the temperature you'd read if you held a thermometer and climbed a long ladder thousands of feet vertically).

Temperature change with altitude varies considerably. It's anything but consistent. On a very hot day, the desert surface can reach temperatures of 150 degrees F as shown in Figure 19. Four to five feet above the surface the air temperature may be only 90 degrees F.

That's an incredible lapse rate! Airplanes entering this shallow, heated layer of air during landing might experience turbulence as well as a decrease in air density. The turbulence is caused by thermals or updrafts, which are small, rising parcels of warmer air that your airplane bumps into.

Above the heated layer of air, this super lapse rate reverts to a normal, less dramatic temperature decrease with altitude. The depth (height) of this superheated layer can increase during the day as warm air from below rises and mixes with the cooler air aloft.

Figure 20 depicts several temperature-altitude plots for a clear day. At 11 a.m., the temperature plot tilts to the left immediately above the surface, indicating a dramatic temperature drop with altitude (point A). This is the result of a super-high lapse rate found over very hot surfaces.

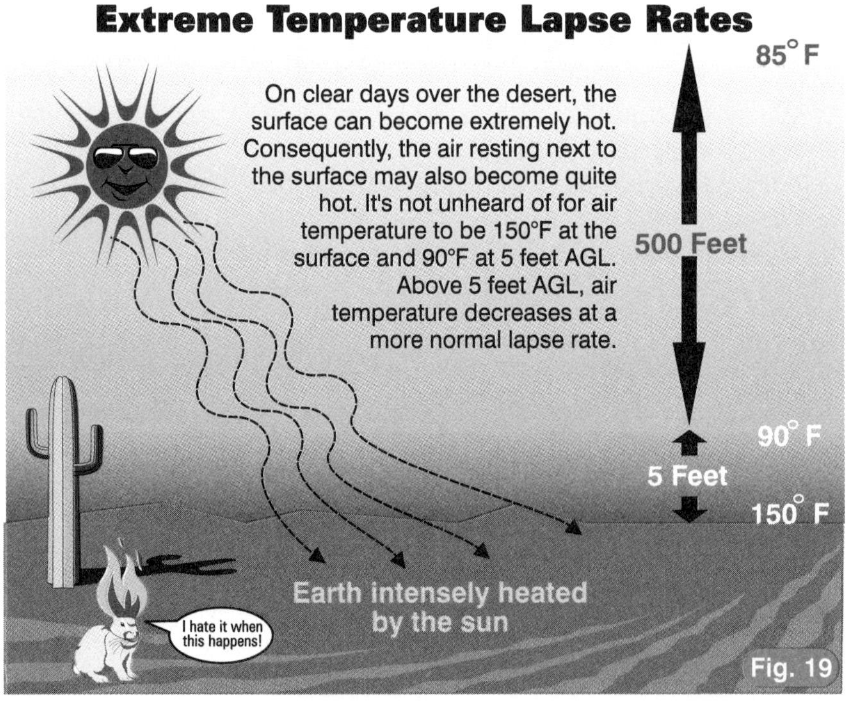

Extreme Temperature Lapse Rates

85° F

On clear days over the desert, the surface can become extremely hot. Consequently, the air resting next to the surface may also become quite hot. It's not unheard of for air temperature to be 150°F at the surface and 90°F at 5 feet AGL. Above 5 feet AGL, air temperature decreases at a more normal lapse rate.

500 Feet

90° F

5 Feet

150° F

I hate it when this happens!

Earth intensely heated by the sun

Fig. 19

As altitude increases, the temperature decreases at a more normal, less dramatic lapse rate (point B). Later, at 3 p.m., the surface temperature starts off warmer and a quick temperature drop is even more noticeable because of intense afternoon heating (point C).

Temperature Inversions

While it's common for air temperature to decrease with height, sometimes the opposite occurs. There are many occasions when the temperature actually increases as you ascend. This is called a temperature inversion, since the normal decreasing temperature lapse rate is turned upside down or inverted. There are two types of temperature inversions: a *surface inversion* and an *inversion aloft*.

Surface Inversion—A surface inversion, shown in Figure 21, is the most common type. It frequently forms around sunset and lasts until midmorning. A setting sun allows the surface temperature to drop quickly, especially on cloudless, calm nights. In the absence of a cloud cover, the earth cools quickly, in much the same way a heated waterbed cools when the covers are left off. There is nothing above the surface to absorb the radiant heat. Clouds, on the other hand, are

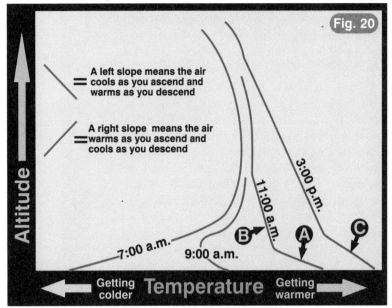

Temperature Profile of Superheated Surface Air

Fig. 20

A left sloping line indicates a temperature drop with altitude. Slope (A) and slope (C) both indicate the presence of a superheated layer of air close to the surface. The surface air of slope (C) starts off warmer because it's later in the afternoon. Above the surface, the air at slope (B) shows a normal lapse rate.

somewhat like blankets, in that they prevent rapid surface cooling. The water droplets in them absorb radiant heat from the surface. As they warm, they re-radiate this heat back toward the ground, which absorbs the heat energy again. This exchange continues all night long and keeps surface temperatures warmer than they would be on a clear night.

As the earth cools, the air next to it starts to cool. In situations where there is not a lot of mixing, the layer adjacent to the earth cools, while the air above remains at or near daytime temperatures. The result is a temperature inversion.

The base of a surface inversion (where the temperature starts to increase with height) is located at the surface (I'm just making sure this is clear). The top of the inversion occurs where the temperature lapse rate resumes its normal decrease with height. Typically, the top of surface inversions occurs within a few hundred feet of the ground.

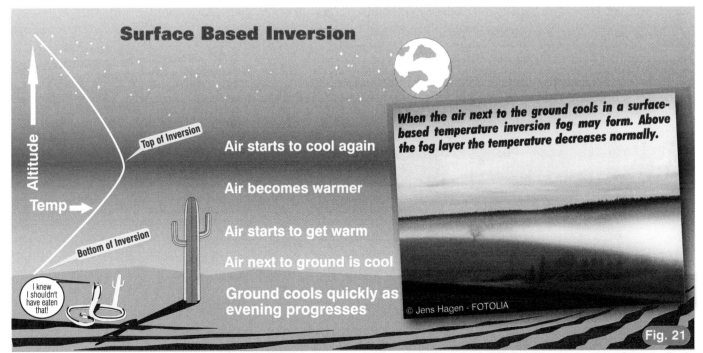

A surface inversion occurs as the ground cools and the air next to it also cools. The air at altitude still contains heat from earlier in the day. With a further increase in altitude the air resumes its normal decrease in temperature.

In case you think surface inversions involve sissy, wimpy little temperature changes, think again. Surface inversions can result in a temperature increase of 25 degrees F with a 250 foot increase in height above the surface (even larger temperature differences are possible).

Figure 22 shows several temperature/altitude plots for the late evening and early morning hours. At 6:30 p.m., a little after sunset in this profile, the temperature plot tilts to the right (position A). This means the temperature increases with an increase in altitude—up to a point—then the temperature plot bends back to the left (position B). Where the curve bends to the left, the air is the warmest (position B). This is the top of the surface inversion. Above the inversion, the air has a normal (decreasing temperature) lapse rate (position C).

The 5 a.m. temperature plot tells a similar story. The plot line starts at the far left of the diagram, indicating the surface temperature has cooled noticeably during the late evening and early morning (position D). As night progresses, the top of the inversion occurs at pro-

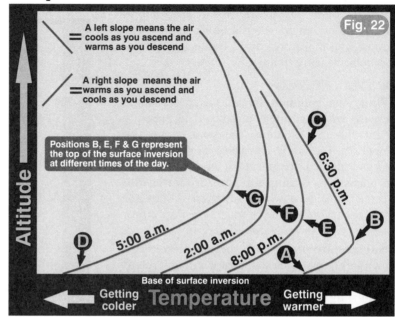

Temperature Profile of a Surface Inversion

Fig. 22

A left slope means the air cools as you ascend and warms as you descend

A right slope means the air warms as you ascend and cools as you descend

Positions B, E, F & G represent the top of the surface inversion at different times of the day.

Altitude

6:30 p.m.

5:00 a.m.

2:00 a.m.

8:00 p.m.

Base of surface inversion

Getting colder   **Temperature**   Getting warmer

A surface inversion starts at the surface and is characterized by an increase in air temperature with altitude (a right sloping line). The top of the inversion occurs where temperatures resume their normal decrease with altitude (a left sloping line). As day progresses into night the top of the inversion increases in height as shown by positions (E) to (F) to (G).

gressively higher altitudes (points E to F to G) as the layer of colder surface air grows. (Remember, Figure 22 is a microview of the atmosphere with an altitude scale in hundreds of feet.)

During winter in parts of Alaska, surface inversions can be quite impressive. Air at the surface can be minus 45 degrees F, while at 200 feet AGL the air temperature can be minus 5 degrees F. This is a 40 degree F temperature increase in 200 feet—a very dramatic temperature change (although probably not enough to cause your already frozen hair to crack if you climb a tree too quickly). Long nights and short days contribute to this type of dramatic surface inversion.

Without wind to mix the warm and cold air together, a surface inversion is more likely to form. Winds of about seven knots or greater can start mixing the warm and cold layers of air, causing the inversion to disappear. Little parcels of rising warm air (called *convective currents* because the motion is mostly vertical) from hotspots on the surface can help

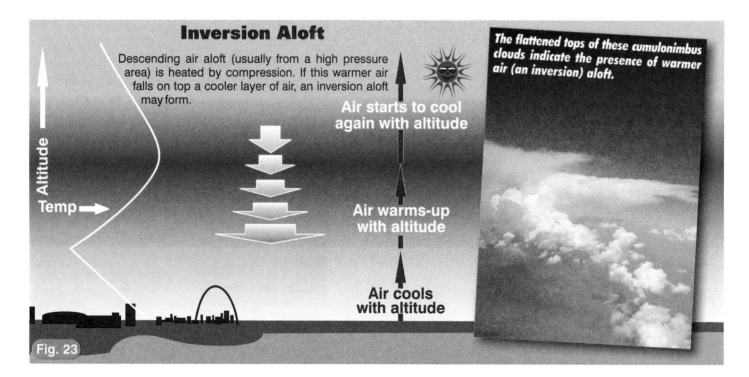

Inversion Aloft

Descending air aloft (usually from a high pressure area) is heated by compression. If this warmer air falls on top a cooler layer of air, an inversion aloft may form.

The flattened tops of these cumulonimbus clouds indicate the presence of warmer air (an inversion) aloft.

Air starts to cool again with altitude

Altitude

Temp

Air warms-up with altitude

Air cools with altitude

Fig. 23

Temperature Profile of an Inversion Aloft

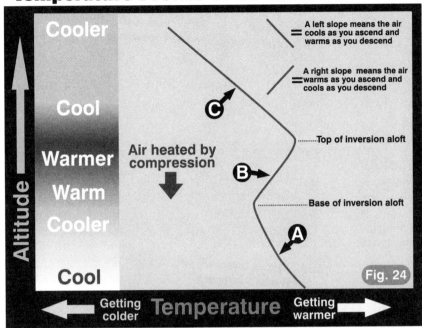

An inversion aloft is characterized by a temperature profile that starts decreasing at the surface (position A), increases (position B), then finally decreases again at the top of the inversion (position C). When air aloft is forced to descend (as in a high pressure area) it heats by compression. If warmer air comes to rest over a colder layer of air, an inversion aloft may form.

break up an inversion. This is why surface inversions forming over the desert seldom last past midmorning, which is the time when convective currents typically start forming and begin mixing the air.

Inversion Aloft—The other type of inversion is loftier, and called an *inversion aloft*. These inversions are caused by warmer air moving horizontally over colder air or by air aloft that is descending and heated by compression (Figure 23). Unlike surface inversions, these inversions are typically found at higher altitudes (thus the word aloft).

High pressure centers in the atmosphere consist of large masses of air descending at rates of hundreds to thousands of feet per day. As this subsiding air descends, it experiences the same effect divers experience when descending to the bottom of a swimming pool—an increase in pressure.

An increase in air pressure produces an increase in temperature for the same reason that PLAY-DOH (I mean the clay, not the child philosopher with ticklish feet, "Playtoe") becomes warm when it's kneaded. Compressing PLAY-DOH (or air) increases its temperature. The harder the dough is squeezed, the warmer it gets. If this descending layer of warm air comes to rest on a cooler layer of air, a temperature inversion can form. This type of inversion is sometimes called a *subsidence inversion*.

In the summer months, a subsidence inversion is more common in the western half of the country than in the eastern half. In particular, it's quite common on or near the Pacific Coast. When warm, high pressure air subsides (lowers) onto the cool, moist inflow of air from the ocean, an inversion aloft forms, as shown in the temperature-altitude profiles of Figure 24.

A pilot faces a decreasing temperature lapse rate when departing an airport beneath the inversion. The climb is initially made in cool air (position A). Upon entering the bottom of the inversion the air becomes warmer as altitude is gained (position B). At the top of the inversion, a decreasing temperature lapse rate is once again present (position C).

Effects of Temperature Inversions

Have you ever noticed smoke coming from a chimney in the early morning or evening hours? Sometimes this smoke ascends for a short distance then spreads out horizontally, as shown in Figure 25. The flattening of smoke is a sure indication of a temperature inversion (since it's often seen closer to the surface in the evening, it's probably a surface inversion).

Warm, rising puffs of smoke cannot ascend through the warmer air of an inversion. In a very similar way, the presence of a temperature inversion acts to flatten cloud tops. Layer-type clouds (otherwise known as stratus or

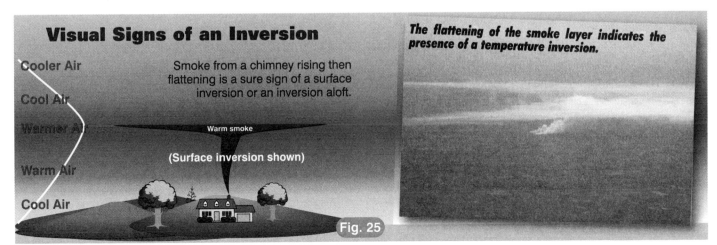

Stratus Clouds Are a Sign of a Temperature Inversion

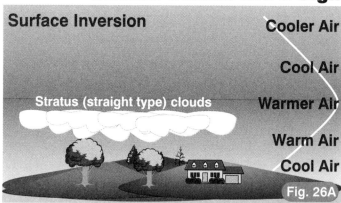

As warm parcels of air rise, expand and cool they may eventually form clouds. The inversion acts like a lid that keeps these rising parcels from ascending into the warmer air of the inversion. The parcels form clouds having *straight* tops, called *stratus* clouds.

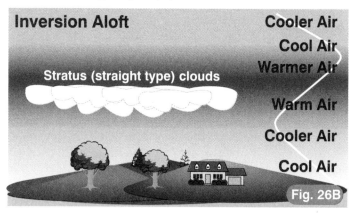

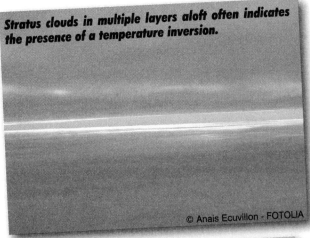

Stratus clouds in multiple layers aloft often indicates the presence of a temperature inversion.

© Anais Ecuvillon - FOTOLIA

Multiple haze layers can also indicate the presence of a temperature inversion.

horizontally-stretched type clouds) are another visible indication of a temperature inversion, as shown in Figures 26A and 27B (more on stratus clouds later).

What to Expect in an Inversion

The visible signs of an inversion should cue pilots to expect several possible flight conditions. First, temperature inversions mean an increase in the likelihood of cloud formation. Since cool air exists at the surface, the air might start to condense, forming fog or low clouds.

Second, visibility beneath an inversion can be quite low. Objects look farther away than they actually are. The mind equates something that is difficult to see with it being farther away. A natural response to this situation is to get closer to the item you're attempting to see.

Third, temperature inversions can indicate the presence of low-level wind shear. An inversion can allow a warmer, faster layer of air aloft to move, unrestricted by surface friction (Figure 27). Since warmer and colder air are of different densities, they tend to not mix (somewhat like professional wrestlers and professional chess players; each has a different "mental" density and they don't mix well). Given the proper conditions, the warmer air aloft can easily slip across the top of the cooler air, like skis on snow. Such a condition is conducive to the formation of a low-level jet stream. This is where air, within a few hundred to a few thousand feet above the surface, can be moving at speeds up to 100 MPH.

In the presence of an inversion, if surface winds are calm, and winds at a few hundred to a few thousand feet AGL are in the 25 knot range, be prepared for possible wind shear. Wind shear is a condition where the velocity and/or direction of the wind changes drastically over a

Wind Shear in a Temperature Inversion

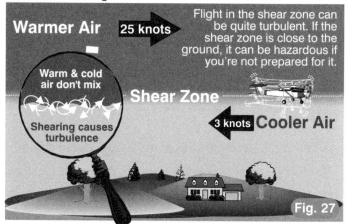

Wind shear in a temperature inversion can occur in the zone where warm air aloft and cold air below meet. The greater the difference in velocity between the warm and cold air, the greater the turbulence found in the shear zone (the warm and cold air in the shear zone don't mix well). It's possible to have sudden changes in airspeed when climbing or descending through wind shear.

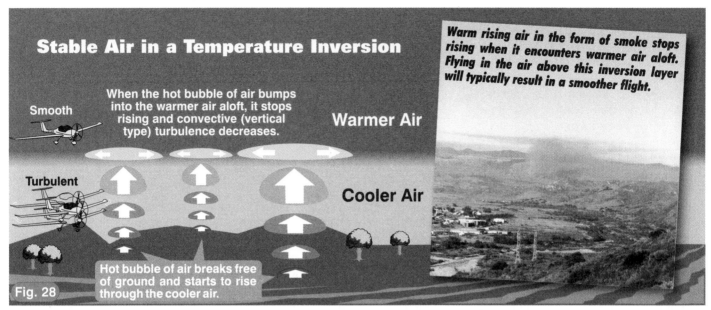

Stable Air in a Temperature Inversion

Smooth

When the hot bubble of air bumps into the warmer air aloft, it stops rising and convective (vertical type) turbulence decreases.

Warmer Air

Turbulent

Cooler Air

Hot bubble of air breaks free of ground and starts to rise through the cooler air.

Fig. 28

Warm rising air in the form of smoke stops rising when it encounters warmer air aloft. Flying in the air above this inversion layer will typically result in a smoother flight.

Stable air is air that suppresses vertical motion. In a temperature inversion, a warm bubble of air rises through the cooler air but can't rise into the warm air aloft (the bubble must be hotter than its surroundings for it to rise). Vertical air motion is suppressed. Therefore, temperature inversions are associated with stable air since they suppress the vertical motion of rising bubbles.

small distance. Wind shear can occur at all altitudes and in all directions and result in a sudden loss of lift. Large crab angles on approach to an airport that's reporting calm surface winds are another clue to the presence of this wind shear. In other words, if the tower reports the winds as calm, but you have to crab substantially to keep aligned with the runway, be prepared for strong wind shear as you descend (see sidebar below). I can think of no better time to add a few extra knots to the approach speed for safety. If you are descending into a low stratus cloud deck while inbound on an instrument approach, expect that your wind correction angle might change. So be prepared.

Fourth, temperature inversions indicate the presence of stable air. Stability is the tendency of the atmosphere to resist vertical motion. In much the same way an inversion impedes the vertical progress of a hot-air balloon, it also impedes the ascension of warmer air in the atmosphere, as shown in Figure 28 Little parcels of warm air attempt to rise, but they can't ascend into the increasingly warmer layers of air aloft (just like the smoke stops rising when it hits warmer air aloft). This means the atmosphere becomes smoother, because the warm parcels of air stop rising. A smoother, more comfortable ride is the net result.

This is especially true when you're flying within the warmer air that rests on top of the cooler air at the bottom of the inversion. At this point, there is probably very little air rising within the warmer air, and you are not likely to experience much turbulence.

Temperature inversions are very important weather signposts for instrument pilots. First, they indicate that convective clouds are not likely to form. After all, the air is stable because the inversion keeps a lid on warmer rising clouds. Let's say, that you're flying above the clouds and see extensive flat (stratified) tops at 10,000 feet. You can feel comfortable assuming that there are no thunderstorms within those clouds, given the low tops and stable nature of the air. In fact, without thunderstorm detection equipment, a pilot report indicating stratified tops at 10,000 feet or so would be sufficiently good evidence that you could depart without worrying about convective weather.

On the other hand, suppose the temperatures at altitude were all below freezing (yep, you can have temperature inversions with below freezing temperatures as we've just learned from our previous discussion on Alaska). If so, then knowing that the tops are regular and flat allows you

The Wind Shear Zone

When the reported winds at an airport are from a different direction and speed than you're experiencing while flying an approach, this could indicate the presence of an inversion and possible wind shear zone. So listen carefully for the airport's reported winds and take notice of your heading, crab angle and ground speed as clues for possible wind shear. This phenomena is common when operating in stratus-type clouds.

Wind at surface

Wind at altitude

to determine if it would be reasonable to attempt a climb through the clouds and into the clear air above. As you'll learn soon, airframe icing is likely while flying in the clouds at or below freezing temperatures. Getting above the clouds as quickly as possible means that typical airframe ice won't form or it means that no additional ice will accumulate on your airplane (more on airframe icing later). In this case, if the tops of the stratus clouds weren't too high, you might consider an IFR-to-VFR on top departure. Of course, your decision in this instance depends on several factors, airplane performance being the most important.

Professional commercial and instrument pilots know the most important tools for analyzing weather are visual clues, particularly haze layers, flattened cloud tops and smoke levels. These are all flags signaling the existence of a temperature inversion.

As the VOR is primary for navigational positioning, the thermometer is primary for meteorological understanding. Pay attention to the temperature when climbing or descending.

Perhaps Abraham Maslow summed it up best when he said, "To the man who only has a hammer in the toolkit, every problem looks like a nail." The more tools in your toolkit, the better chance you'll have of building a complete picture of the weather at hand. One of the tools you'll most certainly want is knowledge of how slight changes in the lapse rate affect atmospheric stability.

Atmospheric Stability: Warm Over Cold and Cold Over Warm

The atmosphere is stable when it resists the upward movement of air. It is unstable when it permits or amplifies this upward movement. In other words, stable air, if given an upward shove, sinks back to its original level. Unstable air, if shoved upward, continues to climb of its own volition.

Atmospheric stability can be roughly visualized in two different scenarios. Figure 29A consists of a warm layer of air resting on top of a colder layer of air. Do these two layers want to change places? In other words, will the cold air on the bottom want to rise up through the warm air on top? This is unlikely. Cold air is heavy (more dense) and warm air is light (less dense). It's a marshmallow on top of an apple. The atmosphere is stable, since these two layers are content to remain where they are.

This explains why, after sunset, the air is usually stable. As the earth cools, so does the air resting next to it. An upper layer of the atmosphere remains warm from heat acquired during daylight

Stable and Unstable Air

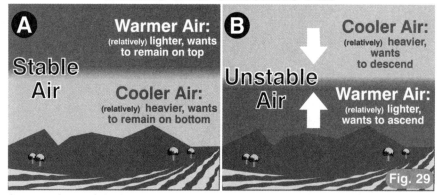

A warmer layer of air above a cooler layer of air is a stable condition. This is called a temperature inversion and it forms in stable air. These two layers don't want to change places. In unstable air, however, a warmer layer of air is found below a cooler layer of air. These two layers want to change places. This is an unstable condition and vertical motion (convection) occurs between these two layers.

hours. Cold (heavy) air is on the bottom and warmer (lighter) air on top, a very stable condition. We know this condition to be a temperature inversion, and it explains why inversions are associated with stable air.

Figure 29B shows a colder layer of air resting on top of a warmer layer of air. Does the warm layer of air on the bottom want to rise through the colder air above? You bet. Warm air rises, cold air falls. It's sort of like sitting on a balloon in the bathtub (you're on your own if you try this at home, especially if there's no water in the tub). Rise, gonna rise. You know that balloon wants to rise, and it will at the first opportunity. Warm air surrounded by cooler air will do exactly the same thing. Cold on top of warm is a very unstable condition.

As we've already seen with super lapse rates, a layer of air resting next to the heated surface of earth can become quite warm. The vertical motion of unstable air produces turbulence. It also produces good visibility as the rising air causes atmospheric mixing and helps disperse airborne pollutants.

A heated landmass results in air rising and clouds forming while no clouds form over the surface of much cooler waters.
Courtesy NASA JSIC

The earth isn't heated evenly. The air next to the earth's surface isn't heated evenly either. If it were, then entire layers of air in the atmospheric environment would move up and down together. In reality, layers of air don't do this. What actually happens is that some chunks of air become hotter than others. These air parcels break off from the surface and ascend individually, as small blobs of variable sizes. It's the original Lava Lamp. Dust devils or isolated thunderstorms are often visual evidence of this happening.

The Ambient Lapse Rate

I previously mentioned the *ambient* temperature lapse rate, which I also like to call the *environmental* lapse rate for clarity. This is the actual rate at which atmospheric temperature changes with altitude. In other words, it's the change you'd see on a thermometer if you carried one up into the atmosphere with you. It's the real world.

Many aviation books will tell you the average ambient lapse rate is 3.5 degrees F (2 degrees C) per thousand feet, and this number is often used in calculations. Even the FAA uses it. Fine and dandy, but as I pointed out earlier, it's a convenient fiction, an average that conceals a huge amount of variation, both horizontally and vertically.

The 3.5 degree figure might hold true in one instance, say for 10,000 or 20,000 feet over a town somewhere, then change to a different rate. It might remain true for 50,000 feet straight up over a shopping mall in Topeka, but be different if measured 15 or 50 miles away. The lapse rate is highly variable from place to place, time to time, and even moment to moment. You can guess at it, you can approximate it, but in the end if you want real information about the temperature lapse rate in the environment (the ambient conditions) you must actually measure it with a thermometer.

With an understanding of the environmental lapse rate under your seatbelt, you're ready to use your airplane's thermometer to make a rough approximation of atmospheric stability. On your next cross-country flight, take vertical temperature measurements every thousand feet of climb. Ask yourself, "Am I climbing into air that's becoming warmer or colder?" If you're climbing into warmer air (a temperature increase with altitude) then a temperature inversion is present. This is a stable condition (see Figure 29A), and no fancy calculations or advanced thinking are necessary. Enjoy your flight.

If you're climbing into colder air (the temperature decreases with altitude), then atmospheric stability is dependent on how quickly the temperature decreases. If the air cools quickly as you ascend, then the cold air is above you and the warmer air is below (see Figure 29B). You can be sure these two layers want to change places. Some instability is sure to be present.

In this sense, you've just learned how to do what meteorologists do with the rawinsonde lapse rate information they collect from these ascending instruments. Hopefully you'll understand this concept better than I understood how to fill out a job application when I was in high school. When I came to the part that said, "Salary expected?" I put "Yes."

Rising Parcels of Air

Let's consider those individual parcels of rising warm air we previously discussed. If they occur near a post, they're referred to as parcel post. No matter where they occur, a warm parcel-blob breaks away from the surface and rises into the cooler air aloft. As this air blob ascends it expands, as shown in Figure 30.

The air parcel expands much like a sealed bag of potato chips found in the back of your ascending airplane. Bags of potato chips, like air parcels, expand because atmospheric pressure decreases with a gain in altitude.

Basic physics decrees that as a parcel of air expands, it also cools. This is why the last time an aviation mechanic stuck an air hose in your nose (happens all the time at

The Meaning of Adiabatic Cooling

We've been speaking of air cooling from expansion as it's lifted, and heated by compression as it's forced downward. There is a more precise term for this process and it's called *adiabatic cooling* (or heating). Don't worry, adiabatic is not a Greek word meaning "you'll never understand weather if you live to be 100." It literally means "without gain or loss of heat." In other words, adiabatic cooling or heating occurs without having to take heat away or add it to the parcel.

Expanding a parcel of air by lifting will move its molecules farther apart, keeping them from bumping into one another and this creates less friction. Energy has been used in expanding the parcel, which causes the molecules to slow down a little. Thus, air temperature decreases. The parcel has cooled, yet no heat has been taken from it.

Conversely, compressing a parcel of air by downward motion moves its molecules closer together and increases their speed, which increases the air's temperature. No heat has been added to this parcel, yet it becomes warmed. Whenever you hear about adiabatic cooling or adiabatic heating you can assume it involves the lifting or falling of air and the resultant temperature change.

Expansion and Cooling of Rising Air

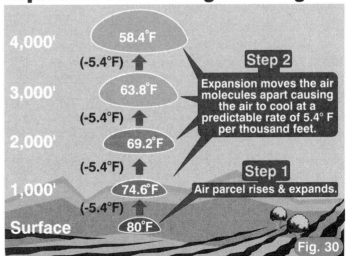

As long as a rising parcel of air doesn't start to condense & form a cloud, it will cool at a rate of approximately 5.4°F per every thousand feet of altitude gain. This is a constant that occurs everywhere on earth (similarly, as the unsaturated parcel descends it compresses and heats at a rate of 5.4°F per thousand feet altitude change).

Expansion and Cooling of Rising Air

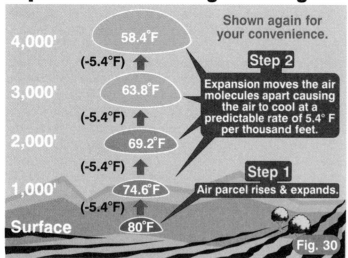

Shown again for your convenience.

Step 2
Expansion moves the air molecules apart causing the air to cool at a predictable rate of 5.4° F per thousand feet.

Step 1
Air parcel rises & expands.

4,000'   58.4°F
         (-5.4°F) ↑
3,000'   63.8°F
         (-5.4°F) ↑
2,000'   69.2°F
         (-5.4°F) ↑
1,000'   74.6°F
         (-5.4°F) ↑
Surface   80°F

Fig. 30

As long as a rising parcel of air doesn't start to condense & form a cloud, it will cool at a rate of approximately 5.4°F per every thousand feet of altitude gain. This is a constant that occurs everywhere on earth (similarly, as the unsaturated parcel descends it compresses and heats at a rate of 5.4°F per thousand feet altitude change).

places named Funny Man Bob's Mechanic and Joke Shoppe) you felt a chill in your proboscis. The expanding parcel of air cooled, and did so without actually having to give up any of its heat.

That's right. If you cause a parcel of air to expand or compress by moving it up or down, you'll cause it to become cooler or warmer because of how the pressure around the parcel changes. In other words, the air parcel is cooling or heating not because heat is taken away or being adding to it. It's changing temperature because of how the pressure around the parcel changes.

This change is known as the *adiabatic* process. Adiabatic literally means without gain or loss of heat. A parcel of air can cool down or heat up on its own, by expanding or compressing, without taking away or adding heat to it.

Here is an amazing fact of atmospheric physics:

A vertically moving parcel of air changes temperature at a constant rate of 5.4 degrees F (3.0 degrees C) for every thousand feet of movement as long as that parcel remains unsaturated (meaning that it doesn't form a cloud) as shown in Figure 30.

What does this mean to you? For all practical purposes, no matter where you are on earth (even the Bermuda Triangle!), if you lift a parcel of unsaturated air, it's going to cool at the dry adiabatic lapse rate of 5.4 degrees F for every thousand feet of altitude change, as shown in Figure 30. If you cause a parcel of air to descend, it's going to heat at the dry adiabatic rate of 5.4 degrees F (3.0 degrees C) for every thousand feet of altitude change. For now, we'll just concentrate on what happens when the parcel moves upward.

At this point I hear you saying, "Doesn't the rising parcel of air move through an atmosphere that also changes temperature?" Yes, it does. But the rate at which

the atmosphere (the ambient or environmental conditions) changes temperature is, you will recall, inconsistent. It's inconsistencies that make things interesting, including the weather.

Suppose we measure the ambient lapse rate with the airplane's thermometer, as shown in Figure 31. Our thermometer shows a decrease in ambient temperature as we gain altitude. Which will cool most quickly, the environment or the rising parcel of air? As the Kung Fu Master Kan would say to his disciple Caine, "Ahhhh, Grasshopper, read on."

The airplane's thermometer in Figure 31 shows that, at this spot, at this time, there is an ambient (environmental) temperature decrease of 6 degrees F per thousand feet. The parcel, shown resting on the surface, rises because it is one degree warmer (at 71 degrees F) than the surrounding air (70 degrees F). This differential can be caused by the air parcel lying over a portion of the ground that is warmer, perhaps because it's paved, or because it's rock as opposed to the soil of surrounding areas. For whatever reason, there's a difference in temperature, and the air is on the move. Fasten your seatbelt and hang on tight.

Keep in mind this air parcel is going to cool off at 5.4 degrees F per thousand feet, because that's a law and air is very law abiding. By 5,000 feet above the ground, it will cool to 44 degrees F (5.4 [drop per thousand feet] × 5 [thousands of feet] = 27; 71–27 = 44). The surrounding air, meanwhile, has cooled to 6 degrees F (5 [thousands of feet] × 6 [degree F drop per thousand feet] = 30; 70–30 = 40).

Environmental VS. Rising Air Parcel Lapse Rates in Unstable Air

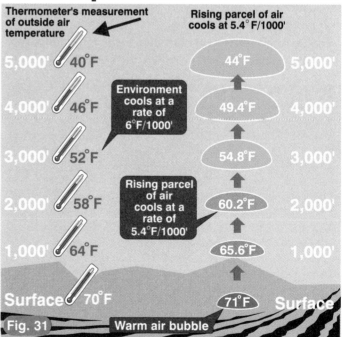

Thermometer's measurement of outside air temperature

Rising parcel of air cools at 5.4° F/1000'

5,000' 40°F   44°F   5,000'

4,000' 46°F   Environment   49.4°F   4,000'
                 cools at a
                 rate of
                 6°F/1000'
3,000' 52°F   54.8°F   3,000'

2,000' 58°F   Rising parcel 60.2°F   2,000'
                 of air
                 cools at a
                 rate of
                 5.4°F/1000'
1,000' 64°F   65.6°F   1,000'

Surface 70°F   71°F   Surface

Fig. 31   Warm air bubble

A warm bubble of air at the surface starts to rise because it is 1 degree warmer than its environment. As the bubble ascends, it cools at the constant rate of 5.4°F per thousand feet. The environmental lapse rate (as measured by a thermometer in the airplane) changes 6°F per thousand feet. As the bubble rises it remains warmer than the environment. Thus, the bubble continues to climb indicating that the air in the environment is unstable.

How Ordinary People Forecast Weather Before There Were Meteorologists

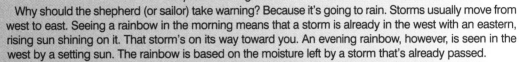

In Eric Sloane's book *Folklore of American Weather*, he describes how early Americans used their five senses to predict the weather. For instance, one piece of folklore says,

Rainbow in the morning,
Shepherd take warning;
Rainbow toward night,
Shepherd's delight.

Why should the shepherd (or sailor) take warning? Because it's going to rain. Storms usually move from west to east. Seeing a rainbow in the morning means that a storm is already in the west with an eastern, rising sun shining on it. That storm's on its way toward you. An evening rainbow, however, is seen in the west by a setting sun. The rainbow is based on the moisture left by a storm that's already passed.

Here's another bit of lore:
When the ditch offends the nose,
Look for rain and stormy blows.

Why? High pressure air, associated with good weather, tends to prevent odors from being released as quickly from sewage ditches, as well as cellars. A moist smelling cellar or offensive smelling ditch was often an indication of low pressure air which releases these odors. And low pressure air is associated with poor weather. Add this book to your collection.

As long as there is a temperature differential, our air parcel will keep moving. In fact, because the temperature differential is now greater than it was at ground level, the air packet will move even faster and accelerate its journey to equilibrium. When it gets there is all a matter of degree. The atmosphere depicted in Figure 31 is unstable, since it encourages upward motion of individual air parcels.

Let's examine a situation where the atmosphere (not the parcel) is cooling at a lesser rate of, say, 3 degrees F per thousand feet (Figure 32). Same starting conditions, but this time look what happens at just 1,000 feet AGL. The rising parcel has cooled to 65.6 degrees F, or to 1.4 degrees F cooler the same temperature as the surrounding air. It becomes cooler than the surrounding air and suddenly it's a sinker that would be the envy of any major league pitcher. The South may rise again; the air won't, at least not far, because in this instance the atmosphere is stable.

The important fact you need to take away from this explanation is that the ambient (environmental) lapse rate determines the stability of the atmosphere. Don't forget this concept! It's extremely important!

The next time you're on a flight, observe the thermometer during the climb. By noting the rate that temperature changes with altitude, you're measuring the environmental lapse rate in much the same way a rawinsonde does. If the environment cools quicker than 5.4 degrees F per thousand feet, as shown in Figure 31, then the atmosphere is potentially unstable, because a rising parcel of unsaturated air can't cool as quickly as the environment.

If the environment cools at a rate less than 5.4 degrees F per thousand feet, or even becomes warmer with altitude (as in a temperature inversion), the atmosphere is potentially stable. A rising parcel of unsaturated air will cool more quickly than its surroundings and tend to fall back to earth, as shown in Figure 32.

If the environment cools at exactly 5.4 degrees F per thousand feet, then a parcel of air will have the same temperature as its surroundings if it's physically moved up or down. The atmosphere would be neutrally stable. In other words, a parcel will neither climb nor descend on its own.

Hopefully, this far into the weather chapter, you're not confused like a neighbor of mine who always drank too much. One evening he put a dime in a parking meter then looked at the needle as it pointed to 60 and said, "Oh gosh, I can't believe it. I just lost 100 pounds."

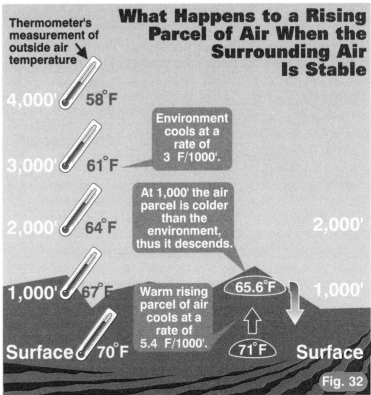

When the environment doesn't cool as quickly with an increase in altitude (i.e., remains warmer longer), it is more stable. In this example, the environment cools at only 3°F/1,000'. A warm, rising parcel of air cooling at an expected rate of 5.4°F/1,000' can only ascend to 1,000' before it becomes cooler than its environment. Thus, the environment (the surrounding atmosphere) is stable and the cooler air bubble now descends.

Saturated Parcels of Rising Air

So much for unsaturated air. Now, let's get wet.

Once these rising parcels cool to within a few degrees of their dewpoint, condensation occurs and clouds form. Now things get really interesting, because when clouds form, heat is released into the parcel as the water goes from invisible vapor to visible moisture. Think about it for a second—what is an ice cube if not a big drop of water with the heat removed? Same goes for water that materializes out of water vapor. In the course of rearranging themselves in a new formation, the water molecules shed heat. You can take my word for it, or take three years of physics. Your choice. This *latent heat*, as the physics people call it, is added to the temperature of the air parcel, thus changing the behavior of that parcel of air.

An air parcel that's busy chugging out clouds doesn't cool as quickly as one that isn't engaging in puffery. Not cooling quickly is just another way of saying that the parcel remains warmer. The process is still an adiabatic one, since no stove or refrigerator is involved (i.e., no heat added or removed) In other words, no outside heat energy is being added or taken away from the parcel. The moist parcel changes temperature based on the latent heat energy already contained within the water molecules of that parcel. Because of this latent heat energy, saturated parcels of air cool at rates between approximately 2 and 5 degrees F per thousand feet, depending on how much water vapor (thus, how much trapped heat) was in the air to begin with. Another way of saying this is the moist adiabatic lapse rate is between 2 and 5 degrees F per thousand feet (the average moist adiabatic lapse rate is about 3.5 degrees F per thousand feet).

Figure 33 shows what happens when a rising parcel of air becomes saturated. Let's assume a parcel of unsaturated air is pushed up the side of a mountain. As it ascends, it cools at the unsaturated rate of 5.4 degrees F per thousand feet. The environmental lapse rate, as measured by our airplane's thermometer, also happens to be 5.4 degrees F per thousand feet. At 1,000 feet, this air parcel's temperature is the same as the surrounding air (its environment). It has neutral stability, since the parcel neither wants to rise nor descend.

Unstable Air With Respect to a Condensing Parcel

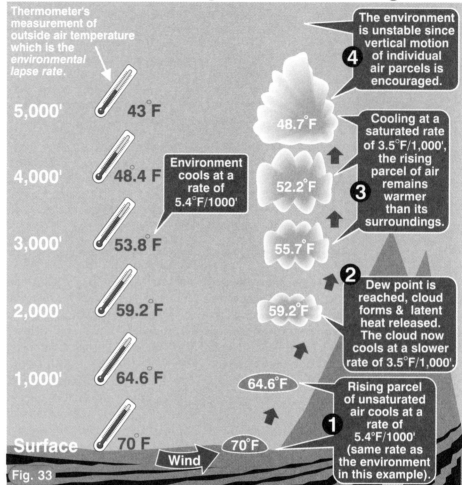

A rising parcel of unsaturated air (i.e., no cloud forming) being moved up a mountain slope cools at the same rate as the environment in this example (step 1). So far the atmosphere (the environment) is neither stable nor unstable; it's neutrally stable. When the parcel becomes saturated and a cloud forms (step 2), it releases its latent heat which warms the body of the rising parcel (the cloud). Thus, the cloud remains warmer than its environment since this particular cloud parcel cools at only 3.5°F/1,000' (step 3). The parcel now rises on its own without the help of wind. The atmosphere is considered unstable since it encourages the parcel to rise (once it's given a shove upward, of course).

Pushed aloft by The Force (the wind against rising terrain), at 2,000 feet the parcel cools to within a few degrees of its dewpoint and the moisture starts to condense. The parcel now becomes saturated. Latent heat is released, causing the rising air parcel to cool at a slower rate of only, let's say, 3.5 degrees F per thousand feet. Push this baby up the mountain just a tiny bit more and a big difference in temperature will arise between the parcel and the surrounding atmosphere.

At 3,000 feet, the parcel has only cooled another 3.5 degrees F, while the surrounding air temperature dropped by an additional 5.4 degrees F. There is now a 1.9 degree F differential at 3,000 feet, and the air parcel is already doing the Loco-Motion. It rises on its own because it's warmer than the surrounding air. There may not be a free lunch, but there is a free ride. While the atmosphere was neutrally stable with respect to the unsaturated parcel of air, it is now unstable due to saturation of the rising parcel. To learn more about atmospheric stability please read Postflight Briefing #9-2.

Blowing in the Wind

Put a little water on your hand and blow on it, as shown in Figure 35. What does it do? It should cool your hand as the moisture evaporates (if it doesn't you've been eating too many Jalapeño peppers!). Heat, taken from your hand, is used in evaporating the saliva (that's why your hand feels cool—it lost some of its heat). Blowing simply accelerates this process. This heat (known as the *latent heat of vaporization*) is now trapped as energy in the water vapor above your hand. It's in a different energy state known as latent heat.

Try not to become overwhelmed by this concept of different forms of energy (energy states). Remember, whenever you put gasoline in your tank you're converting ancient vegetables and dinosaur lips into movement energy. Your automobile is nothing more than a fancy energy converting device much like that of the atmosphere.

Think of evaporation as a process opposite that of condensation. While evaporation puts *water* into the atmosphere, condensation gives the *water* back. If evaporation takes *heat* away, condensation must give *heat* back. The heat given back is known as *latent heat* (the *latent heat of condensation* to be precise). When water vapor condenses, latent heat is given back to the parcel, making that parcel slightly warmer.

An Experiment to See How Heat Energy Changes Its Form

Put a little saliva on your hand

Blow on saliva to accelerate the evaporation process

Parcel of moist air forms above your hand which contains heat taken from your hand & water from your saliva

Moist Air = Water + Heat

Spot on hand is now cool from heat loss during evaporation

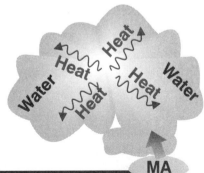

Rising moist air (MA) that forms a cloud is converted back into water (which becomes visible) & heat (which warms the cloud)

Clouds and Atmospheric Stability

When an air parcel moves within unstable air, its direction is upward. Cloud formations tend to accumulate vertically, as you can see in Figure 34. Cumulus clouds accumulate. As these clouds build, they eventually release their condensed water in the form of intermittent, showery-type precipitation. It's not unusual to see rain appear beneath a cumulus and, shortly thereafter, disappear.

Since cumulus clouds form in unstable air, there is a lot of vertical motion in the atmosphere. Dirt, dust, haze, and other pollutants are drawn upward and redistributed to neighboring areas. That's why cumulus clouds normally correlate with decent-or-better visibility. All this vertical motion, of course, produces turbulence, which is a common phenomenon near or under cumulus clouds. Figure 34 also lists the conditions typically encountered when cumulus clouds are present.

When an air parcel moves in stable air, the resulting motion is more horizontal than it is vertical. The parcel of air doesn't develop the temperature difference with its environment that encourages vertical motion. If an air parcel is given a shove up the side of a mountain, it can eventually cool enough to condense and form a

Cumulus Clouds

These are trees, not clouds.

Cumulus Clouds are associated with:

1. Unstable air
2. Good visibility
3. Showery type precipitation
4. Turbulent conditions

Fig. 34

cloud. Then, when given an opportunity, the parcel of air sinks back to its original level on the other side of the mountain. During the process stratus, or horizontally-stretched type clouds, develop as shown in Figure 35.

Stratus clouds are the result of water vapor condensing in air parcels that have little vertical movement. For instance, if the atmosphere becomes warmer with height (such as in an inversion), parcels of warm air are prevented from rising. Since these air parcels can't move vertically, they tend to be flat on top and any cloud tops present will take on a straight or stratified appearance.

It's no accident that stratus clouds often signal the presence of a temperature inversion. Limited vertical air movement in stable air means poor visibility. Pollutants, dust, dirt, and haze become trapped under the inversion much like dirt under a carpet. Any precipitation associated with stratus clouds is usually in the form of a continuous type of drizzle, because stratus clouds typically contain smaller water droplets than those found in cumulus clouds and the clouds usually cover a wider area for a longer period of time. Figure 35 depicts the conditions typically found when stratus clouds are present.

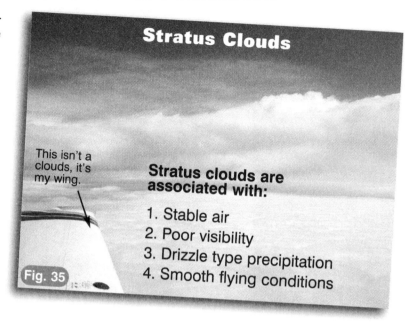

Stratus Clouds

This isn't a clouds, it's my wing.

Stratus clouds are associated with:

1. Stable air
2. Poor visibility
3. Drizzle type precipitation
4. Smooth flying conditions

Fig. 35

CLOUD FAMILIES

Everyone has some kind of family, even if you're a test tube baby (in which case you may have a Bunsen burner for an uncle). Clouds have families, too. There are four of them: high, middle, low and those with extensive vertical development.

High clouds are cirriform and include cirrus, cirrocumulus, and cirrostratus. They are almost entirely composed of ice crystals. Their base heights range from about 16,500 to 45,000 feet, in the middle latitudes.

Low clouds are the stratus, stratocumulus, and fair weather cumulus cloud types. Low clouds are almost entirely water, but at times the water may be supercooled. Low clouds at subfreezing temperatures can also contain snow and ice particles. Their base heights range from near the surface to about 6,500 feet in the middle latitudes.

Middle clouds are the altostratus, altocumulus and nimbostratus cloud types. These clouds are primarily water, much of which may be supercooled (water that is colder than 32 degrees F but isn't frozen; it will often freeze instantly if given something to freeze on, such as a nice passing airplane). Their base heights range from about 6,500 to 23,000 feet in middle latitudes.

Clouds with extensive vertical development include towering cumulus and cumulonimbus. These clouds usually contain supercooled water above the freezing level. When a cumulus grows to great heights, the water in the upper part of the cloud freezes into ice crystals and forms a cumulonimbus cloud. Bases heights of cumuliform cloud bases range from 1,000 feet or less to above 10,000 feet.

Nearer My Cloud to Thee, But How High Are You?

Just how high up *is* that cloud. Good question. Sometimes you can get an ATIS answer, but there's a way to figure out for yourself the approximate height of the bottoms of cumulus clouds.

Because atmospheric pressure affects the dewpoint, it will decrease approximately 1 degree F for every thousand foot altitude gain. Couple this with the understanding that a rising parcel of unsaturated air cools at a rate of 5.4 degrees F per thousand feet (2.5 degrees C per thousand feet), and you get the dewpoint and temperature converging at a rate of 4.4 degrees F per thousand feet.

So what? Well, when the temperature and dewpoint come together, water vapor condenses in the parcel and clouds form. To *estimate* the height of the cloud bases, simply find the difference between the temperature and dewpoint and divide this by 4.4 degrees F (or 2.5 degrees C if using Celsius). The number you get is the height of the cloud bases in thousands of feet.

This method of estimating is only reliable with cumulus clouds, since they are usually formed by lifting and thus subject to the effects of changing lapse rates.

Determining Bases of Cumulus Clouds From Surface Temperature & Dew Point

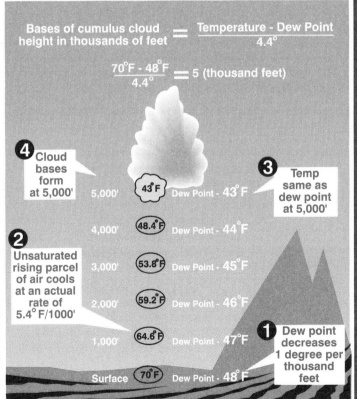

$$\text{Bases of cumulus cloud height in thousands of feet} = \frac{\text{Temperature - Dew Point}}{4.4°}$$

$$\frac{70°F - 48°F}{4.4°} = 5 \text{ (thousand feet)}$$

4 Cloud bases form at 5,000'

2 Unsaturated rising parcel of air cools at an actual rate of 5.4° F/1000'

3 Temp same as dew point at 5,000'

1 Dew point decreases 1 degree per thousand feet

5,000'	43°F Dew Point - 43°F
4,000'	48.4°F Dew Point - 44°F
3,000'	53.8°F Dew Point - 45°F
2,000'	59.2°F Dew Point - 46°F
1,000'	64.6°F Dew Point - 47°F
Surface	70°F Dew Point - 48°F

You can estimate the bases of cumulus clouds by using the formula listed above. The dewpoint decreases approximately one degree Fahrenheit for every thousand feet of altitude gain. The actual temperature lapse rate in a rising air parcel for non saturated air is 5.4°F/1000'. Given this information, we can estimate where the temp and dew point will come close enough to form cloud bases (the 4.4° value in the denominator is the air parcel's lapse rate with 1° subtracted from it for a decrease in the dew point).

Weather-wise pilots understand that water in the atmosphere is the enemy. When the atmosphere contains lots of moisture, there is great potential for atmospheric mischief once lifting gets going. For instance, the area around Texas has a great deal of water vapor in the air. The area around the Texas panhandle is called Tornado Alley because some of the world's nastiest thunderstorms swoop through this area. The Gulf of Mexico adds so much water vapor to the air that a fast-moving cold front from the north often provides enough lift to create squall lines (lines of thunderstorms) hundreds of miles long. In other words, the fast moving cold front acts like a snow plow in that it scoops or pushes up large parcels of moist air that eventually become warmer than the atmosphere surrounding them. The results are nasty, ornery thunderstorms that cause increases in bed sales because pilots need some place under which to hide when mom's not home.

Understanding the difference in lapse rates between the environment and a rising parcel of air is perhaps the most important concept to comprehend. You're well on your way to being a real meteorological monster if you understand this concept. Before you get too carried away with yourself, though, I must warn you that like most scientific models, the parcel concept is an attempt to make a simple statement about a remarkably complex real world. It works, in general, as a generalization and provides useful insights. Just keep in mind that it is a simplification of a complex reality.

Just as important as temperature differences in determining weather are differences in atmospheric pressure. For years you've listened to the nightly weather report and nodded when the weatherperson spoke of highs and lows and falling barometers. Now you're about to find out that "high low" is not a greeting, and get the lowdown on what these terms really mean.

High and Low Pressure Areas

One time I was in a pro golf tournament and the pressure was really on. Folks from all over the country watched me. I was about to take the most important shot of my life. When I finally putted, my ball ran up and hit the clown's mouth and bounced into the moat. I guess I couldn't handle the pressure. Of course, we speak of pressure metaphorically as compelling us to act or move in a certain, almost predictable way (like miss a once-in-a-lifetime golf shot). Atmospheric pressure causes air to do the same thing—to move in a certain way.

As you might have noticed from our discussion of temperature and air parcels, there is a ceaseless, restless attempt to equalize any differentials in the atmospheric system. This applies to pressure differentials, as well. Pressure differences are another way in which the atmosphere gets moved around, helping to create wind and weather.

Our atmosphere is composed of mega-billions of air molecules. Each air molecule is affected by gravity. This is why air has weight.

At the earth's surface, air pushes down with a pressure of 14.7 pounds for every square inch, as shown in Figure 36. That's a lot of pressure. The next time you tell someone that you're under a great deal of pressure, you won't be lying, even if you're lying down.

While gravity provides a constant tug on the air, the atmosphere still experiences variations in the pressure it exerts on the earth's surface. Sometimes individual sections of air are forced upward or downward. Mechanical or thermal forces are often responsible for this movement. Regardless of the cause, small changes in atmospheric pressure can still be felt at the surface of the earth.

We've previously learned that air over the North Pole is cooled and sinks. As the cool, descending air pushes on the surface, its weight is felt as higher atmospheric pressure. Conversely, at the equator air is heated by warm surface temperatures, and it rises. Rising air reduces the pressure it exerts on the surface, creating extensive areas of low pressure around the globe.

Variations in temperature, over water and land, cause changes in atmospheric pressure. Wherever there's a differential in the atmosphere, be alert, because I guarantee you something will happen to try to equalize it. In the case of pressure, the air moves from areas of higher pressure to areas of lower pressure. This is the reason we have wind. Were there no differences in pressure across the earth's surface, you could get a really good deal on a sailboat. Of course, you'd also need to find a really good deal on a set of oars.

Sea and Land Breeze Circulation

Everyone knows it's usually breezy by the sea, but hardly anyone knows why.

Figure 37 shows a typical daytime sea breeze. Remember, it's called a *sea breeze* because that's the direction from which the air blows (from the sea). The sea

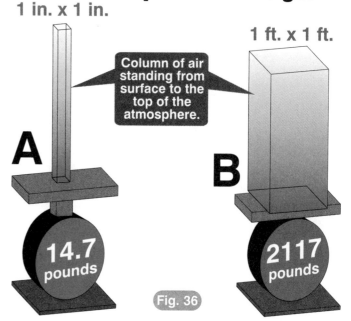

The Atmosphere Has Weight

Air has weight. One square inch of air (scale A) standing from the earth's surface to the top of the atmosphere weighs 14.7 pounds. It also produces 14.7 pounds per square inch of pressure on the surface. A square foot of air (scale B) standing the same height weights 2,117 pounds and produces 2,117 pounds per square foot of pressure on the surface.

breeze forms because land warms faster than water. Heating the land heats air lying next to it, causing the air to rise. This creates a small land-based low pressure area. Air rising over the land eventually cools by expansion and moves toward the ocean, where it begins to settle. It continues to cool (becomes heavier) as it makes contact with the cool water, thus forming an area of high pressure over the ocean. Higher pressure over the ocean forces air to move toward land, creating a breeze from the sea. A single-cell circulation pattern is established.

Later in the evening, after the land has had a chance to cool, airflow near the beach reverses direction (Figure 38).

After sunset, the ocean retains more of the day's heat than the land. Land isn't generally heated to the depth water is, so it has less heat to lose and cools more rapidly. In the late evening hours, the low pressure center that was once over land is now over the water. High pressure now exists over the land where the air has cooled. A land breeze (blowing from the land) forms and airflow moves toward the water. The original single-cell circulation pattern is reversed.

These two types of airflow—land and sea breezes—are miniature models of atmospheric circulation. Magnify them thousands of times and they become the large high and low pressure centers talked about by meteorologists.

How a Sea Breeze Forms

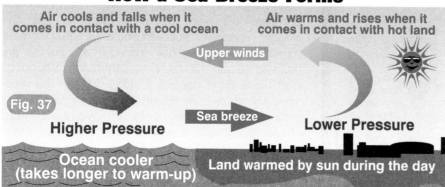

As land is heated by the sun during the day, the air next to the surface becomes warm and rises. Water takes longer to heat because water can absorb more solar energy before a temperature increase occurs. Therefore, during the day, the ocean remains cooler than the land. Air over the ocean that's in contact with the cool water also cools and falls, creating higher pressure. Airflow is from the water toward the land where the pressure is lower (thus it's called a *sea breeze*).

How a Land Breeze Forms

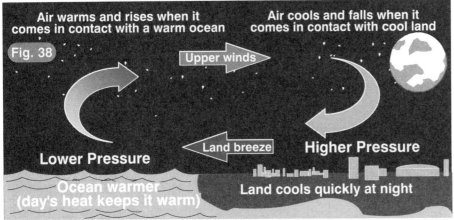

The ocean heats to a greater depth than the land during the day. Thus, at night, the ocean remains warmer than the land. Descending high pressure air over the land moves toward the rising low pressure air over the ocean. Since the breeze is from land it's called a *land breeze*.

descend and rise slowly, descending at rates from a few centimeters per second to thousands of feet per day. Within these slowly moving oceans of air, smaller air parcels move up and down, playing out any of the previously discussed stability scenarios.

It's important to remember that these high and low pressure oceans of air are the environments that smaller parcels of air move within. The environment is constantly changing (albeit slowly) because high and low pressure air moves. If the environment is slowly changing, atmospheric stability also changes. This is one reason why the atmosphere can be stable one day and unstable the next. Tempest fugit, and stability, too.

Keep in mind that the terms *high* and *low* are relative. One man's ceiling is another man's floor. A low pressure center can exist simply because there are several higher pressure centers around it, as shown in Figure 39. Here's another way of thinking about the concept of pressure centers being relative to one another. You can spend a lot of time working out, pumping iron to look tough. Or you can just hang out with a bunch of sissies and weaklings and look tough by comparison. It's all relative. If the area surrounding a parcel of air becomes slightly cooler, this makes the central parcel of air warmer, thus lower in pressure by comparison. Air would then flow in the direction of this lower pressure, as shown in Figure 39.

Keeping It in Perspective

Keep high and low pressure areas in their proper perspective. High and low pressure centers are large masses of air—sometimes thousands of miles across—that

Highs and Lows on Weather Maps

On weather maps, high pressure and low pressure systems are represented by a series of contour lines (see Figure 40). High pressure centers are cooler and denser masses of air. Moving downward and outward, they rotate in a clockwise direction. Low pressure centers are typically warmer, less dense masses of air. Air moves inward and upward and rotates counterclockwise in a low pressure system. Right now you must be thinking, "Why does the air circulate counterclockwise in a low?" Perhaps you're wondering why your head is spinning counterclockwise, instead. As long as your name isn't Linda Blair, in a moment I'll stop the mental spinning by telling you why air spins this way.

The contour lines surrounding the highs and lows are called *isobars*. These are not where isos go to drink. An isobar is a line connecting areas of equal barometric pres-

The Rotation of Highs and Low Pressure Areas

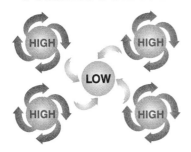

High and low pressure areas are measured by comparison. If the center of an air mass is slightly lower in pressure it makes the surrounding areas higher in pressure. Similarly, if the surrounding areas are slightly higher in pressure it makes the center area lower in pressure. **Fig. 39**

Pressure Centers on Weather Maps

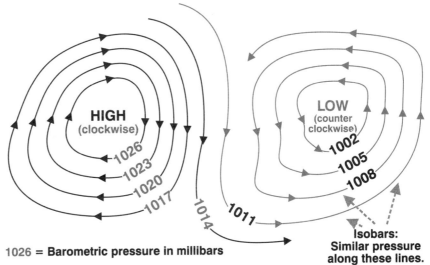

1026 = **Barometric pressure in millibars**

Pressure centers on weather maps are created by barometric pressure readings from weather stations across the United States. The lines shown above are called *isobars*. The prefix *iso* means *equal* and *bar* represents *barometric pressure*. Therefore, anywhere along the isobar the pressure is the same. **Fig. 40**

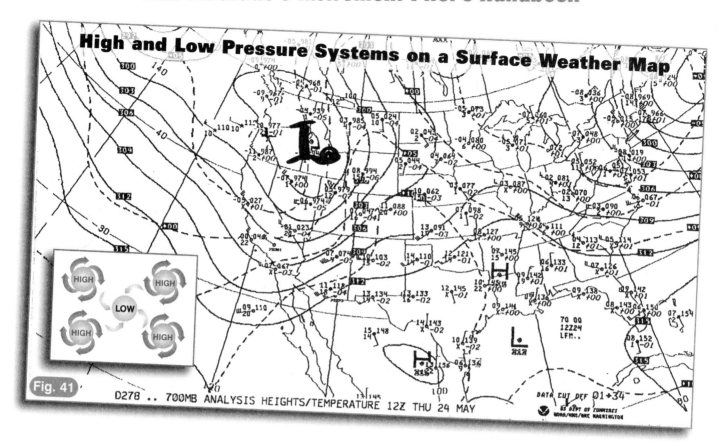

High and Low Pressure Systems on a Surface Weather Map

Fig. 41

D278 .. 700MB ANALYSIS HEIGHTS/TEMPERATURE 12Z THU 24 MAY

sure. This is similar to the contour lines on an aeronautical sectional chart connecting areas of equal altitude. *Iso* means equal, and *bar* represents barometric pressure. Weather computers can automatically draw lines connecting areas with similar surface pressure. The result is a pattern like the one shown in Figure 41, which depicts atmospheric pressure distribution on a typical surface weather map.

Placed along each isobar in Figure 40 is a pressure value, stated in millibars (thousandths of a bar, which is the international unit of pressure). The isobar in the very center of the high pressure system connects all areas having a pressure of 1,026 millibars. Moving toward lower pressure (anywhere away from the high's center), the pressure decreases until the isobar connects pressure of 1,002 millibars in the center of the low. Figure 41 shows how these patterns appear on a surface weather map.

Perhaps you've been feeling a little uncomfortable with Figures 40 and 41? Perhaps you wonder why the air doesn't flow directly from the high to the low as it does in a vacuum cleaner hose? Don't worry. I'm going to explain this next. As a result, you'll become a celebrity of aviation knowledge, perhaps ending up with your name in lights (all without having to change your name to "Don't Walk").

Circulation in Highs and Lows: Going With the Flow

Air should flow directly from the high to the low because of something known as a pressure gradient force. This is a fancy term for your common sense knowledge that things run downhill. The pressure gradient force is the basic pushing force exerted on the air, causing it to move from higher to lower pressure, as shown in Figure 42.

So why doesn't air do what it should? It would, if it could. But it doesn't, because of the Coriolis force. As the descending high pressure air settles and spreads outward, the Coriolis force adds a right curve to its motion (Figure 42B). This explains the clockwise circulation shown in Figure 42E. The low pressure system, on the other hand, has air converging toward it. As air moves inward toward the center of the low, the Coriolis force also curves it to the right (Figure 42C). Eventually, the air is forced into a counterclockwise circulation around the low as shown in Figure 42D.

Because of these two forces—pressure gradient and the Coriolis force—air circulation around a high or low flows parallel to the isobars instead of across them, as shown in Figure 42E. It's enough to make your air stand on end.

Surface friction also has an effect on winds operating within 2,000 feet of the surface. This has a tendency to decrease wind speed as air is tugged on by mountains, trees, and other terrain features. But as the air slows down, it is less affected by the Coriolis force. This means the right curve added to the air diminishes slightly. This gives the wind the appearance of turning slightly left of the isobars within 2,000 feet of the surface (it's really turning right a bit less), as shown in Figure 43. Over water, where there is less surface friction, wind curves left of the isobars by 10 to 15 degrees. Over land, with greater friction, wind can curve 25 to 45 degrees left of the isobars.

Surface friction explains why weather maps depicting winds for high altitudes (more than 2,000 feet AGL) show isobars aligned differently from maps showing surface isobars. Figure 44 depicts this difference with a constant pressure chart for 10,000 feet MSL and one for the surface.

Why Air Doesn't Flow Straight

The pressure gradient (difference in pressure over distance) would cause air to flow *directly* from a high pressure area to a low pressure area if it were not for something known as the Coriolis force.

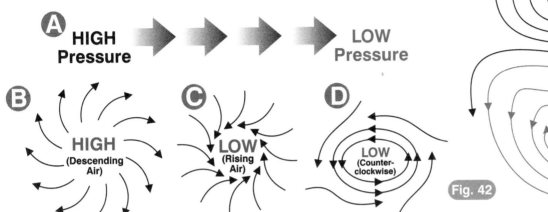

As air descends and diverges from the high, a right curve is added to its motion by the Coriolis force. A clockwise pattern of circulation is eventually established.

As air converges toward the center of the low, it's curved to the right by the Coriolis force.

Eventually, a counter-clockwise circulation is established by air converging from all sides of the low.

Any parcel of air that moves is acted upon by two forces: the pressure gradient force (the push from high to low) and the Coriolis force (the right twist in the direction it moves). Therefore, instead of flowing straight; air flows parallel to the isobars rather than across them.

As you'll see later, surface winds can give a false appearance of what the wind a few thousand feet above the surface is doing. Windshear is common when surface winds are calm and the wind at higher altitudes (a few thousand or even a few hundred feet AGL) is moving quickly.

Sometimes pilots are like surface winds—they give false appearances. It's similar to my high school friend who tried to appear wealthy at only 17 years of age. Once, he took a classmate out for dinner and asked her what she'd like to eat. She said, "Oh, I guess I'll have the steak and

Effect of Surface Friction on Winds

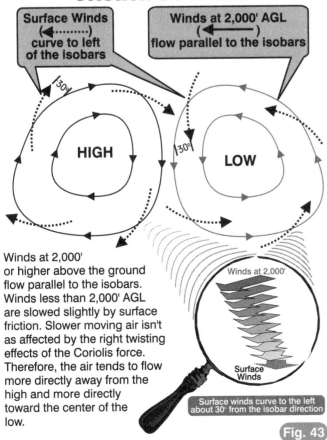

Winds at 2,000' or higher above the ground flow parallel to the isobars. Winds less than 2,000' AGL are slowed slightly by surface friction. Slower moving air isn't as affected by the right twisting effects of the Coriolis force. Therefore, the air tends to flow more directly away from the high and more directly toward the center of the low.

Surface Winds vs. Winds at 10,000' MSL

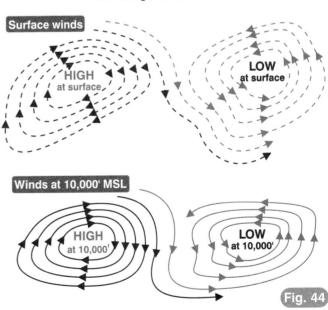

Examination of these wind patterns indicates that the surface winds flow in a slightly different direction than winds at altitude (10,000' MSL). Surface friction causes this difference to be 10° to 15° over water and as much as 25° to 45° over land with 30° being typical (depending on how rough the terrain is).

Taking Advantage of High Altitude Winds

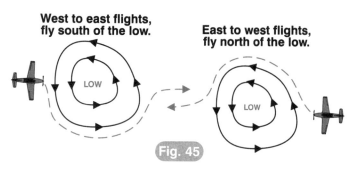

West to east flights, fly north of the high.

East to west flights, fly south of the high.

West to east flights, fly south of the low.

East to west flights, fly north of the low.

Fig. 45

Wind Correction Angles in Highs and Lows

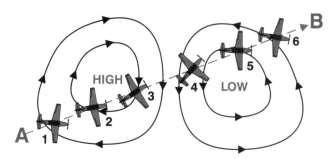

Our airplane desires to maintain a ground track from (A) to (B). Flying toward a high pressure area requires a wind correction to the right of the desired ground track (Airplane 1 and 2). Flying away from a high is like flying toward a low. Thus, a left wind correction is required (Airplane 3 and 4). Flying away from a low is like flying toward a high, thus requiring a right wind correction angle (Airplane 5 and 6).

Fig. 46

Determining the Location of a Low

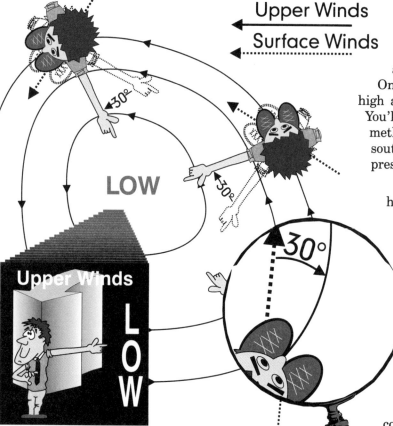

Upper Winds
Surface Winds

You can determine the location of a low pressure system by standing with your back to the wind and sticking out your left hand. Rotate 30° to the right to compensate for the wind's left shifting tendency due to surface friction. You're now approximately aligned with the isobars above the friction level. Your left hand now points toward the general location of the low pressure system.

Fig. 47

lobster combo." Her looked at her and said, "Well, guess again." Not everything is as it appears to be. Winds are no exception.

The Answer is Flowin' in the Wind

Sharp pilots on long cross-country flights know how to take advantage of high altitude airflow to gain a tailwind and avoid a headwind. On west-to-east flights, plan to fly north of the high and south of the low, as shown in Figure 45. You'll have a tailwind most of the way using this method. On east-to-west flights, plan on staying south of the high and north of the low. This is called pressure pattern flying.

Pilots can tell whether they're approaching a high or low based on the relationship between their wind correction angle and their ground track. For instance, in Figure 46 the airplane is flying a ground track from position A to B. Airplane A flies into a high pressure area. Thus, in positions 1 and 2, a wind correction to the right is required to maintain the plane's ground track. As the airplane flies away from a high, it must be flying toward a low. Approaching a low requires an increasing left wind correction, as shown in positions 3 and 4. Flying out of a low, the airplane moves toward another high with the expected wind correction angle to the right of the ground track, as shown in positions 5 and 6.

You will always make a wind correction to the right when approaching a high, and to the left when approaching a low. If you ever want to determine the position of a low pressure center, stand with your back to the wind, rotate 30 degrees to the right (to compensate for the

Isobar Spacing and Wind Speed

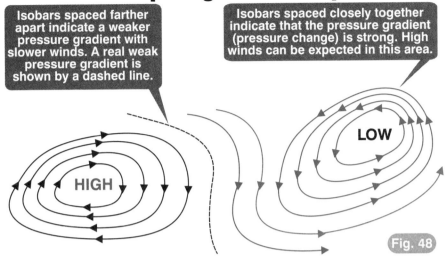

Isobars spaced farther apart indicate a weaker pressure gradient with slower winds. A real weak pressure gradient is shown by a dashed line.

Isobars spaced closely together indicate that the pressure gradient (pressure change) is strong. High winds can be expected in this area.

Fig. 48

effects of ground friction) and stick out your left hand. It will point in the direction of the low, as shown in Figure 47.

As high pressure air descends, it eventually makes contact with the surface. Since it can't penetrate the ground, it spreads out in all directions. Meteorologists call this divergence. As we've already learned, the air spreads out from the center of the high and the Coriolis force causes it to curve to the right, thus setting up a clockwise circulation.

Low pressure air converges near the center of a low. Having nowhere else to go laterally as it converges from all directions, it begins to rise. Interestingly, convergence in the low accelerates the air. In much the same way a spinning ice skater picks up speed by bringing his or her arms in toward the body, wind speed in a low increases because air converges (is brought in) toward its center. This explains why wind velocities are generally higher around a low than a high.

Notice how the isobars are spaced in Figure 48. They are more closely spaced around the low than the high. Closely spaced isobars indicate a rapid pressure change. Rapid pressure changes mean faster winds. Isobar comparison around the high and low provides you with a good indication of wind speed in that system.

Weak pressure gradients (areas where there isn't much horizontal pressure change) are shown by dashed lines, as shown above the high in Figure 48. Expect light winds in this area.

Weather Associated With Highs and Lows

In addition to wind direction and speed, high and low pressures centers have their own weather associated with them. As high pressure air descends, it tends to warm up slightly, decreasing the relative humidity. Clouds are less likely to form with decreasing relative humidity, and clouds that are present are likely to dissipate. Highs are generally associated with clear skies.

Lows, on the other hand, have rising air that expands and cools. If the air within the low approaches its dewpoint, condensation occurs. If this happens, clouds appear

and the weather usually gets worse. Air that condenses in a low pressure system releases its latent heat, which adds to the heat content of the low pressure system. The low pressure area is now slightly warmer, causing it to rise faster. This further increases the chance that the weather in a low pressure area will continue deteriorating.

Remembering that you make a left wind correction when flying toward a low, you can use the Rule of L—left, low, lousy—to help remind you what weather to expect.

Keeping It in Perspective

Let's back off for a second in order to air it out and see the big picture. Large masses of air circulate around high and low pressure areas. Within these large masses, which heat or cool due to rising and falling air, individual parcels of air can in turn rise and fall, driven by changes in the environmental lapse rate.

Once again, you can see that the stability of the atmosphere is affected by several interacting variables.

Song of the Sky

Guy Murchie's book *Song the Sky* is one of my favorite books about the subtleties of weather. I'm here to sing its praises. Years ago, as a student pilot, I thought I understood the full effect of an important atmospheric phenomena, at least until Guy Murchie deepened my understanding with a few observations that I had never considered. The coriolis force is a good example.

1. The Craft

SHE WAS BUILT like a whale, for cargo and comfort. Ninety-four feet long and full-bellied, with wide tail flukes that could ease her nose up or down at the merest nudge of her controls. Her sinews and nerves were four and a half miles of steel cable

Murchie says, "A mighty planetary force is obviously at work here, causing everything from spinning tops to draining bathtubs to turn one way more easily that the other in each hemisphere. This is because the earth beneath the sky is forever turning 'out from under' whatever is upon it, whether air or water or solid moving object."

Solid moving object? Really? Read on.

"It is why the arctic rivers cut faster into their right banks than their left ones, why the Trans-Siberian Railroad has to replace more right than left rails on each stretch of one-way track. It is why the Germans' Big Bertha gun in World War I, firing on Paris from seventy miles way, had to aim a mile to the left of the target so the three-minute trajectory of its shells would be corrected."

Song of the Sky is an apt title that correctly describes Guy Murchie's appreciation of nature's mechanics and beauty. This was the book that helped accelerate and deepen my understanding of Mother Nature's workings by collecting, connecting and conveying ideas that often take a lifetime to assemble on our own. Save yourself the time. Add *Song of the Sky* to your reading list by checking out a used book store in town or online. You won't regret it.

Ridges and Troughs

Pressure patterns can take on unusual, elongated shapes, much like the derrieres of professional TV viewers. To the novice, these pressure patterns are just pretty; to the trained eye, they're pretty important. Figure 49 shows an extended area of a high and a low pressure center.

An elongated area of low pressure is known as a trough (pronounced TROFF). The pressure along this line is lower than the pressure on either side. Notice how the isobars show counterclockwise circulation at the trough line but don't form a closed circulation pattern. A trough frequently delineates the boundary between two different pressure centers. Just as pigs gather at a pig trough, storms gather at an atmospheric trough.

Perhaps the best way to think about a trough is to consider it, metaphorically, to be like a valley (Figure 50). The floor of the valley is lower than the mountains bordering it. Given the chance, water would easily flow into this valley. In a similar way, a trough allows air to converge (to flow into it). Of course, the air doesn't really sink into the trough, it just flows toward the lower pressure and rises. The concept of a trough simply makes it easier for meteorologists to visualize the way air flows.

An elongated area of high pressure is known as a ridge and is shown in Figure 50. The pressure is higher along the center of the ridge than it is on

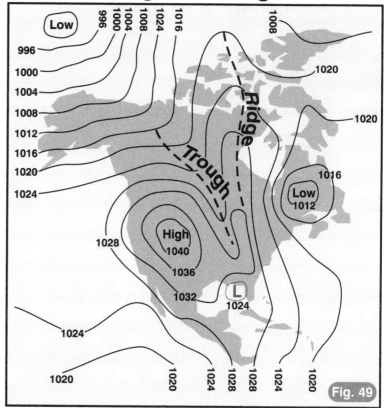

Troughs and Ridges

A trough is an extended area that's lower in pressure than the area on either side of it. Circulation is counterclockwise but not closed since the isobars aren't connected. A ridge is an extended area of pressure that's higher than the pressure on either side of it. Circulation is clockwise and, like the trough, isn't closed because the isobars aren't connected.

Troughs and Ridges

Ridge contains diverging air (moving downward)

Trough contains converging air (flowing into & up)

Fig. 50

A trough is a "V" or "U" shaped, extended area of low pressure. Think of it being similar to a valley or depression that draws air into it in much the same way a low pressure area draws air into it. This drawing-in or "convergence" causes air to ascend and, depending on its stability, might be the source of poor weather. A ridge, on the other hand, can be thought of as a "V" or "U" shaped, extended mound of descending, high pressure air. Good weather is usually associated with a ridge.

either side. Think of a ridge as a mountain of piled up, heavy, descending air. The circulation of air along the isobars at a ridge line is clockwise, but the isobars don't form a closed circulation. In other words, they still have descending air but it doesn't follow typical clockwise circulation around a specific center point. Ridges exhibit characteristics similar to highs, with descending air and a minimum of cloudiness and precipitation.

But highs and lows are associated with more than the horizontal flow of air. These pressure centers attract or repel massive moving wedges of air known as frontal systems.

Frontal Systems

A while back, a pilot flew the wrong way on the downwind leg at a controlled airport. He heard the tower controller say, "Attention all aircraft in the pattern, use caution, there's some nut flying the wrong way on the downwind leg." The pilot immediately picked up his mic and said, "It's not just one nut, there are five nuts flying the wrong way." I guess you could say the real nut and the other pilots had a little confrontation. Likewise, air masses of different densities bumping into one another can also cause a confrontation. We call this confrontation a *front*, which is the battleground where these air masses meet.

Frontogenesis is about frontal formation (as Genesis, the first book of the Old Testament, describes how the universe formed). It's about two air masses, having different properties, bumping into one another and battling it out.

At first glance, you'd think the air would just sort of mix itself together and everything would even out. It doesn't work that way, though, because the differences in temperature result in air masses of differing density. Things of different densities, such as oil and water, don't mix readily.

The zone of transition between air masses of different densities is called a front. Think of it as the place where the weather action is, and often the place you as a pilot don't want to be. This is one kind of action you can definitely live without.

Frontal systems start with large air masses. These masses of air take on the characteristics of their source region (the land or water over which they originate). This occurs in much the same way people take on aspects of the local culture of the state in which they live. That's why my friend from Texas just loved armadillos. It is, after all, the state animal. Of course, he didn't care much for me when I mentioned that his state animal looked like a "rat on a half shell." That's my tail.

Fronts, like people, are often very different. Figure 51 depicts the source regions for the different air masses that affect weather in the United States. Continental polar air masses come from where Santa Claus lives—near the North Pole. These are dry, cold air masses. Maritime polar comes from the same latitudes, but the air is moister because it originates over water. Maritime tropical air masses are born over heated, moist tropical waters, meaning they are warm and full of water vapor. This also means there is a tremendous amount of latent heat energy trapped inside the air (look out for thunderstorms). And continental tropical air masses are typically hot, dry, and unstable at low levels. The instability makes for bumpy flying but good visibility. Rain showers are virtually nonexistent as afternoon relative humidity drops to 10% or less.

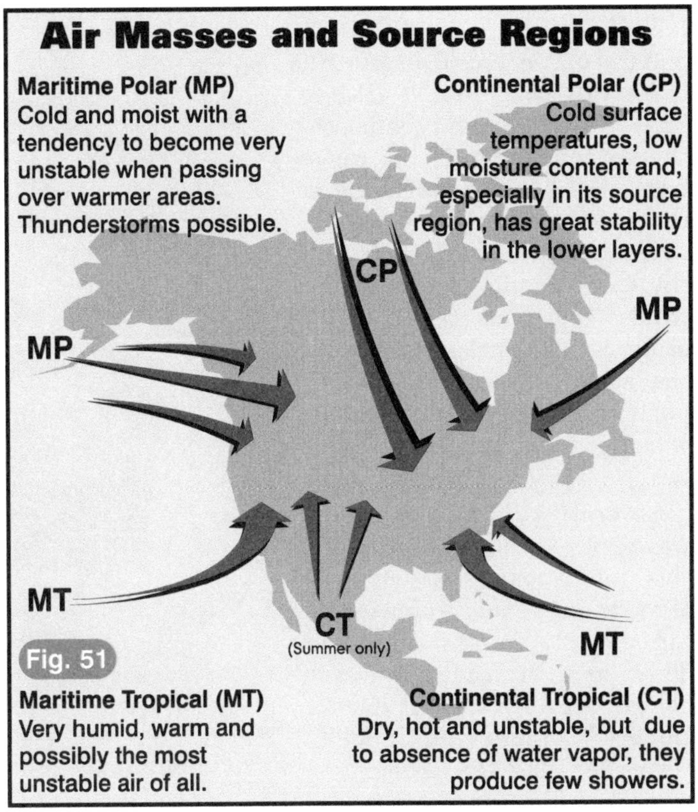

Fig. 51

The Cut Off Low

The Cut-Off low pressure area seen to the left is a swirl of stratocumulus clouds west-southwest of the Straits of Gibraltar. This is all that remains of a North Atlantic cyclone which has been cut-off from the westerlies.

This occurs when a low pressure center, that normally moves along with the jet stream, become separated from the west to east belt of high altitude winds. Often the low becomes separated because of a dip in the jet stream or a deep upper level trough.

Having nothing to steer this low pressure area, it can sit and spin for days. The result is often damp, dreary weather along with periods of rain or snow. The cut-off low often won't leave a region until it is caught up by the westerly winds.

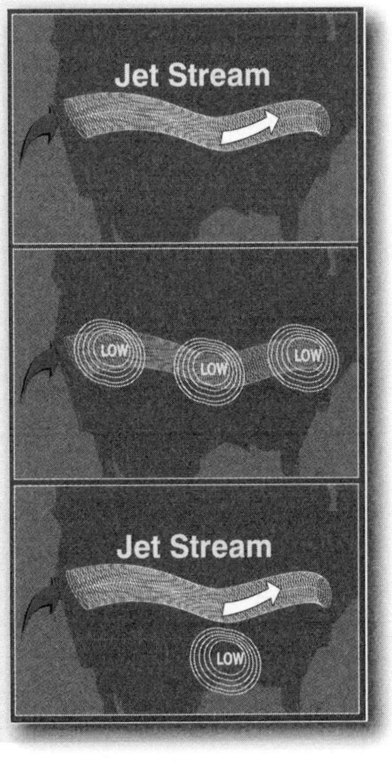

The Polar Front

A cap of dense, cold air sits over the north polar region (Figure 52A). This undulating, amoeba-shaped mass of cold air comes from the cool air descending at the poles. Moving southward, this cap of cold air flows from the east, forming a band of winds known as the polar easterlies. The polar front is the zone between the cold polar easterlies and the warmer prevailing westerlies.

Several protrusions or waves of cold air occur along this frontal zone. There can be three to seven long waves existing globally at any one time. These long, protruding waves of cold air are anything but stationary. Plunging and retreating like the probing tentacles of an octopus, these waves advance southward in one area and retreat northward in another. It's this advance and retreat that we, as ground observers, experience as frontal movement.

The Polar Front

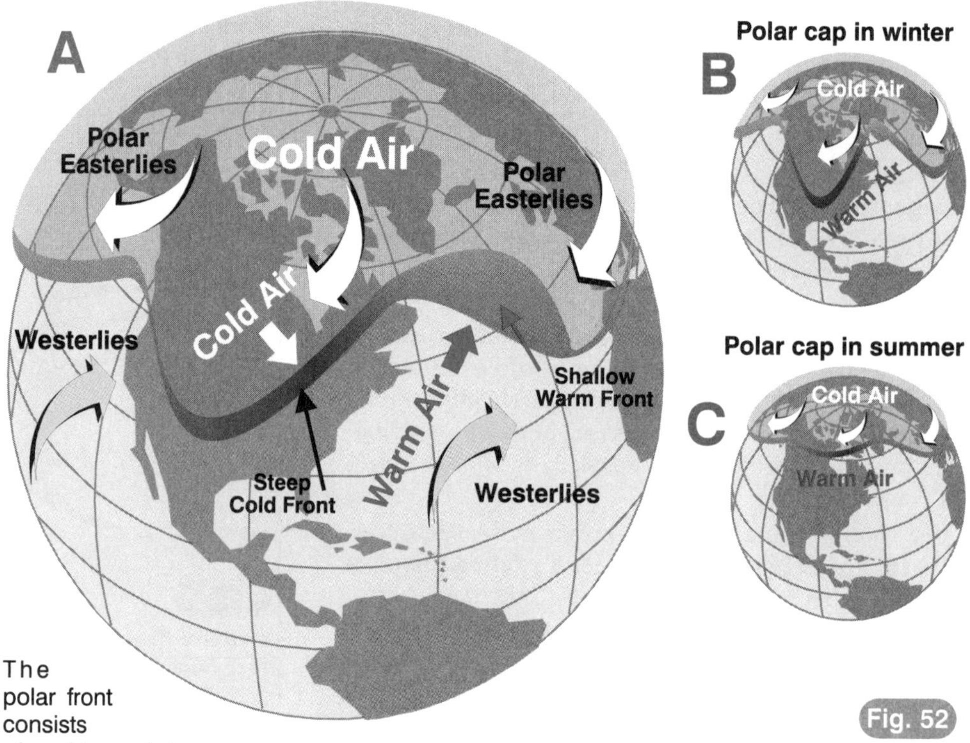

A

Polar Easterlies

Cold Air

Polar Easterlies

Cold Air

Westerlies

Cold Air

Shallow Warm Front

Warm Air

Steep Cold Front

Westerlies

Polar cap in winter

B

Cold Air

Warm Air

Polar cap in summer

C

Cold Air

Warm Air

Fig. 52

The polar front consists of a cold cap of air centered over the North Pole. Air over the pole descends and is cooled by a cold source region. Moving southward, this descending, high pressure air curves to the right, forming winds known as the polar easterlies. This mass of air is responsible for much of the weather we experience in North America. Cold air overtaking the warmer air of the westerlies forms steep-sloped cold fronts as shown by Globe (A). Warmer air replacing receding cooler air forms shallow-sloped warm fronts as shown in Globe (A). In the summer months the polar front doesn't extend as far south as it does in winter as shown by Globes (B and C).

During winter, a long cold wave of this air can plunge down into the tropics, as shown in Figure 52B. A cold wave advancing southward in one area can allow the introduction of warm tropical air moving northward. Winter weather is characterized by a longer, more protruding polar front, as shown in Figure 52B. The polar front is less wave-like in the summer (Figure 52C).

If you're really interested in how small storms form along the polar front see Postflight Briefing #12-1.

Different Types of Fronts

As a plunging long wave of cold air moves southward, it overtakes warmer, moister air. Hello, cold front (Figure 53, position A). Blue triangles represent the direction of cold front movement. Warm tropical air fills in the receding side of the long cold wave, forming a warm front (position B). Warm fronts are represented by red half circles. As cold and warm fronts advance and retreat, weather constantly takes on new faces. Sometimes the warm and cold air butt up against one another and neither moves. This is called a stationary front (position C). Sometimes the cold front catches up to and lifts the warm air ahead of it forming an occluded front (position D). Many pilots find all of these to be an affront, since they frequently mean poor flying conditions.

Pressure falls as fronts approach. If you've ever spent time with a barometer, you will have seen this effect first-

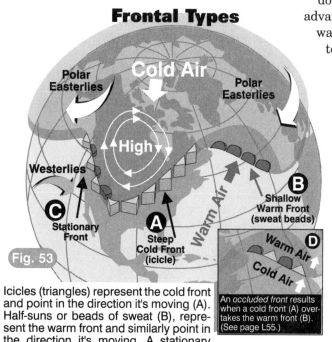

Frontal Types

Polar Easterlies

Cold Air

Polar Easterlies

High

Westerlies

Warm Air

Shallow Warm Front (sweat beads)

B

C

Stationary Front

A

Steep Cold Front (icicle)

D

Warm Air

Cold Air

An *occluded front* results when a cold front (A) overtakes the warm front (B). (See page L55.)

Fig. 53

Icicles (triangles) represent the cold front and point in the direction it's moving (A). Half-suns or beads of sweat (B), represent the warm front and similarly point in the direction it's moving. A stationary front is indicated by icicles and beads of sweat on opposite sides of a frontal line (C). Beads of sweat and icicles pointing in the same direction indicate that the faster moving cold front has overtaken and undercut the slower moving warm air (D). This is called an *occluded front*.

Front Found Along a Trough

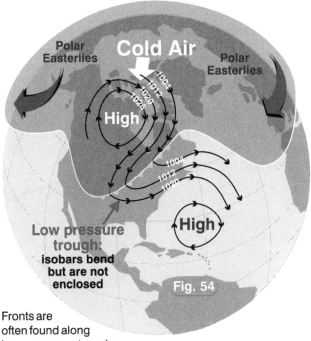

Fig. 54

Convergence in a Low Pressure Trough

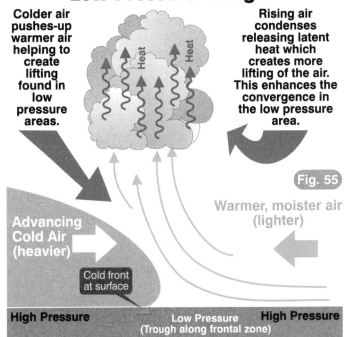

Fig. 55

Fronts are often found along low pressure troughs. According to our definition, a trough is an extended "V" or "U" shaped area of low pressure. Circulation in a trough is counterclockwise but not closed (i.e., the isobars don't connect). As you can see, the trough shown above meets these requirements. Because of the convergence in a trough, it's usually associated with bad weather (such as the cold front within it).

hand. You should also work on your social life. Pressure falls because fronts are often found along low-pressure troughs. Figure 54 depicts this process. Notice that the cold front lies in a trough along the border between two high pressure areas. As the front approaches, the pressure falls. It increases after frontal passage, since a high pressure area lies behind the front. But, why is the area along the front associated with a trough or area of low pressure?

Figure 55 shows the cold front air mass approaching a warmer air mass. Cold air is heavy, so it easily slips under the warmer air. As it does, it lifts the warmer air (which usually contains a lot of moisture). Given sufficient lift and lapse rate, it condenses and releases its latent heat. Heat released into the air enhances upward movement, intensifying the low pressure along the front. Simply stated, the frontal zone itself helps intensify the trough's low pressure. (While there are other reasons for trough formation, this gives you a basic understanding of how troughs form and what they do).

Remember, the trough is a line where the pressure is lower than on either side of the line, and where the isobars form a counterclockwise curvature but don't form a closed circulation. Along the cold front in Figure 54, the isobars are elongated

diagonally in a downward and upward direction. Air flows in a counterclockwise circulation but it's not the typically smooth, circular flow of a low pressure center. In other words, the isobars look pinched and bent along the trough axis.

Polar cold fronts tend to move toward the low pressure trough, as shown in Figure 56. Keep in mind that high and low pressure centers move, so their associated troughs move. You can think of the front being drawn along with the trough much like a horse is drawn to a carrot. Many variables affect the intensity of a low pressure trough—high altitude winds, intensity of upper-level convergence, latent heat of the air, to name just a few. Your job is to gain

Polar Front Moves Toward Low Pressure Trough

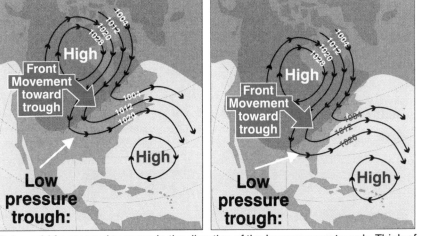

Polar cold fronts tend to move in the direction of the low pressure trough. Think of the trough as drawing the frontal system into it as water might be drawn into a trough or depression on the earth's surface.

Fig. 56

enough knowledge about weather to make some basic predictions.

This is why I went to school to study psychology—to allow me to predict human behavior. A friend of mine used to fly for TWA. One day he's departing London's Gatwick airport when he spies another jet that looks like it's a little too close for comfort. "Gatwick Approach," he says, "who's that guy on my right?" The controller, with his spiffy British accent replies, "Well sir, if he has sunglasses on, then that's your copilot." Unless you've graduated from the Tony Soprano School of Comedy, you should have predicted a similar response.

Don't worry, you'll become equally good at predicting weather by understanding a few more basic weather principles.

Discontinuities Across a Front

Recall that a front is a boundary or transition zone separating air masses having different properties. As you cross a front, these properties change or become discontinuous. When in an airplane, temperature is one the most easily recognized discontinuity across a front.

Pilots flying across a front are likely to notice a sharper temperature change at lower altitudes than higher ones, where air tends to become more homogenous. Since relative humidity varies with the moisture content of the air, as well as the temperature of the air, you should also expect changes in dewpoint with frontal passage.

There is always a change in wind direction associated with a frontal passage. Figure 57 shows an airplane flying from A to B across a cold front. On the east (right) side of the cold front the wind is from the left, requiring a left crab angle to maintain a straight ground track. On the

Wind Shift Across a Front

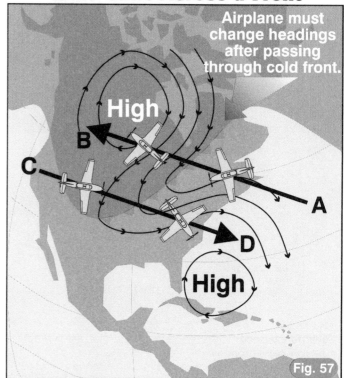

One of the indications of frontal passage is a wind shift. The airplane above, flying from position (A) to (B) and from (C) to (D), must change its heading to the right to stay on course.

west (left) side of the cold front the wind is from the right, requiring a right crab angle to maintain a straight ground track. Wind shifts from left to the right are an additional way pilots know they are crossing a frontal area. Direction of travel is irrelevant. Notice that a pilot flying from C to D still experiences a wind shift from left to right.

A stationary observer on the ground will notice a shift in wind with frontal passage. By the time the cold front in Figure 57 moves past position A, the wind will shift from a southerly (from the bottom of the page) to a northwesterly (from top of page) direction.

Aside from temperature, dewpoint, and wind shift, a falling-then-rising barometer is another good indication of frontal passage. As the front approaches, barometric pressure lowers. In other words, the altimeter settings for local airports along your flight path are reporting consistently lower altimeter settings. Altimeter settings rise as the high pressure air behind the front approaches.

Cold Front Characteristics

A cold air mass overtaking a warm air mass is called a cold

Typical Cold Front Size and Shape

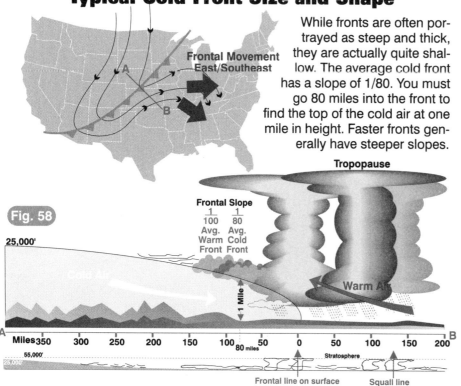

While fronts are often portrayed as steep and thick, they are actually quite shallow. The average cold front has a slope of 1/80. You must go 80 miles into the front to find the top of the cold air at one mile in height. Faster fronts generally have steeper slopes.

front. Cold air, being heavier than warm air, moves along the surface pushing warmer air up in a bull-dozer-type action. Because of its consistency and surface friction, the leading edge of the cold air tends to stick to the surface forming a steeply sloped frontal edge, as shown in Figure 58. Faster moving cold fronts have steeper frontal slopes than slower ones. The steeper slope and faster speed of the front is one reason why the most critical period for wind shear occurs just as or just after a cold front passes the airport.

Of course, frontal steepness is relative. To me, a set of stairs leading up to a children's slide is steep. To a mountain climbing friend, the face of Yosemite's El Capitan is steep (at least that's what he told me when he invited me to sign his brand new body cast). Cold frontal slopes range on a meteorological scale of 1/50 (that's steep) to 1/150 (not too steep) and average about 1/80. A slope of 1/80 means that 80 miles behind the point where the cold front is at the surface, the top of the cold air would be 1 mile above the ground (Figure 58). Of course, these ratios are far smaller than the 10,000 to 1 gear ratio found in most restroom towel dispensers.

Figure 58 shows a cross sectional view of the cold front. The diagram is exaggerated for clarity, since the cold air is nowhere near as tall, relative to its length, as it is in this picture. A more realistic vertical versus horizontal view of this front is shown at the bottom left of the diagram. With tops of the cold air ranging up to 25,000 feet, the cold front occupies a relatively small vertical slice of the atmosphere.

In the northern hemisphere, strong cold fronts are usually oriented northeast to southwest and move toward the

Cold Fronts and Squall Lines

Cb - Cumulonimbus (cumulus cloud with rain)
Cu - Cumulus cloud
As - Alto stratus (higher stratus cloud)
Ns - Nimbo stratus (stratus with rain)

Fast moving cold fronts may generate a line of thunderstorms up to and beyond 150 miles in advance of the actual front. This line of thunderstorms is called a *squall line* and contains some of the nastiest weather pilots can imagine.

Descending Cold Air 25,000'

Rising Warm Moist Air

Fig. 59

Miles 150   100   50   0   50   100   150
Front on Sfc.   Squall Line

east and southeast as shown in Figure 58. They are often followed by colder and drier weather. The cloudiness and weather associated with the front depends on the degree of stability and moisture content of the air mass ahead that's being lifted by the front.

Keeping It in Perspective

Earlier we talked about how parcels of air are lifted within their environment. Keep in mind that it's not the environment that's lifted, it's a parcel that's somehow pushed upward. Cold fronts provide an excellent means of lifting these parcels. Of course, the longer and steeper the front, the larger the number of parcels lifted. Therefore, the effects of stability or instability of the air are more widespread.

Two Types of Cold Fronts

Cold fronts can be divided into two general types—fast-moving and slow-moving.

Fast-moving cold fronts have been clocked in excess of 60 MPH (52 knots), which means you can be doing the legal freeway speed limit in some states and get run over by a speeding cold front. On average, they usually move at half that speed. Their speed is generally faster in winter than in the summer months.

Most of the cloudiness and precipitation associated with a cold front is located along and ahead of the area where warm and cold air meet, as shown in Figure 59. Because of the cold front's high speed, this weather is often the most hazardous that pilots encounter. Couple a fast-moving, steep-sloped cold front with unstable, moist air and you have the possibility of cumulonimbus (nimbus means rain) clouds, scattered thunderstorms, and rain showers in advance of the front, as shown in Figure 59.

This cold front weather is sure to make you happy that you're on the ground taking the picture and not in the air.

2© Steven Gibson - FOTOLIA

Squall Line Thunderstorms

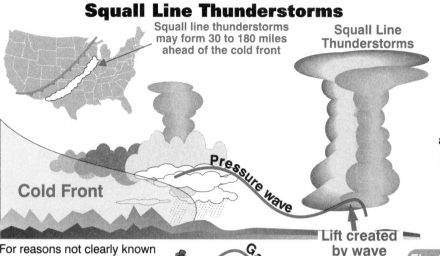

Squall line thunderstorms may form 30 to 180 miles ahead of the cold front

Squall Line Thunderstorms

Cold Front

Pressure wave

Lift created by wave

Fig. 60

Garden hose

For reasons not clearly known to meteorologists, squall lines sometimes form in advance of a rapidly moving cold front. One theory has it that the cold front and its pressure system might generate a wave form (also known as a *gravity wave*) that moves in advance of the actual front. This is similar to the wave generated when you shake a garden hose. The wave travels along the hose. In a similar manner, pressure waves might travel ahead of the cold front generating lift and creating thunderstorms in the unstable air.

Fast-moving cold fronts can generate squall lines 30 to 180 miles in advance of and parallel to the front, as shown in Figure 60. *Squall lines* are lines of thunderstorms containing some of the most turbulent weather known to pilots.

Some meteorologists speculate that an isolated wave form may cause prefrontal lifting in the warm, moist air preceding the cold front. Think of this prefrontal wave (called a *gravity wave*) as the form appearing in a long garden hose that's given a good shake. This ripple of energy moves along the hose. A wave of air, moving in advance of the cold front, can generate enough prefrontal lifting (lifting in advance of the actual front) to form clouds and even instigate squall line thunderstorm weather. (See Gravity Wave sidebar page 9-41.)

Slow-moving cold fronts, on the other hand, generally generate less-hazardous weather. Slower moving cold air forms a shallower slope, with less intense lifting of air (see Figure 61). Precipitation and cloud formation occurs in a broad band behind the cold front's surface position. Because the lifting is less intense, stratiform clouds are more likely to form if the air is relatively stable. Fog can also form in the rainy area.

Unstable air, on the other hand, creates cumulus clouds and thunderstorms. Either way, the weather is confined to a narrow band along the front, as shown in Figure 62. This is similar to the way our high school principal would confine all the class tough guys to the last row during school assembly. These guys were so tough that they didn't just roll a package of cigarettes up in their shirt sleeves. Instead, they'd have an entire carton rolled up in there. And matches. And ashtrays.

Slow Moving Cold Fronts and Stable Air

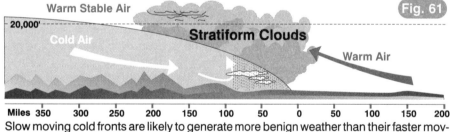

Warm Stable Air

Fig. 61

20,000'

Cold Air

Stratiform Clouds

Warm Air

| Miles 350 | 300 | 250 | 200 | 150 | 100 | 50 | 0 | 50 | 100 | 150 | 200 |

Slow moving cold fronts are likely to generate more benign weather than their faster moving cousins. With a shallower slope, less intense lifting occurs. If stable air is being lifted, stratiform type clouds may occur over a large area.

Slow Moving Cold Fronts and Unstable Air

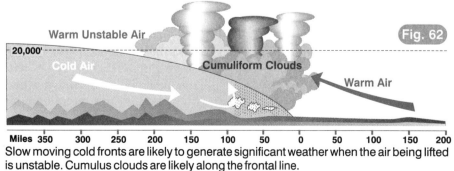

Warm Unstable Air

Fig. 62

20,000'

Cold Air

Cumuliform Clouds

Warm Air

| Miles 350 | 300 | 250 | 200 | 150 | 100 | 50 | 0 | 50 | 100 | 150 | 200 |

Slow moving cold fronts are likely to generate significant weather when the air being lifted is unstable. Cumulus clouds are likely along the frontal line.

Stratiform clouds associated with stable air in a slow moving cold front.

Cumuliform clouds associated with the unstable air of a slow moving cold front.

Warm Fronts and Moist Stable Air

Warm fronts consist of warmer air overriding and replacing cooler air in the retreating part of the wave cyclone. Warm front slopes are very shallow, thereby producing less dramatic lifting as compared to a cold front. Additionally, warm fronts move slower (about 15 MPH on the average). Warm frontal weather is, therefore, distributed over a larger area for a longer time.

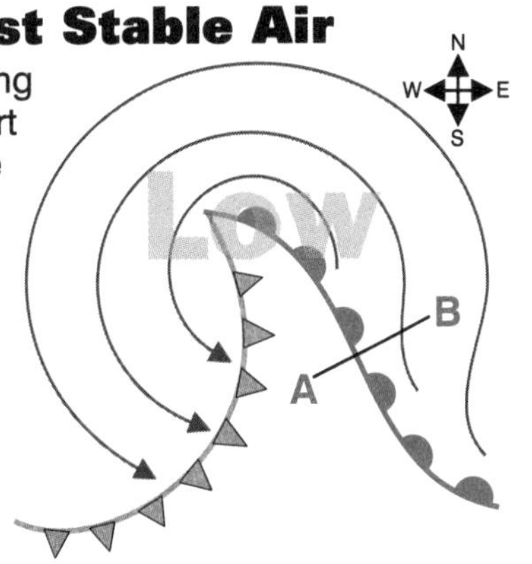

Fig. 63

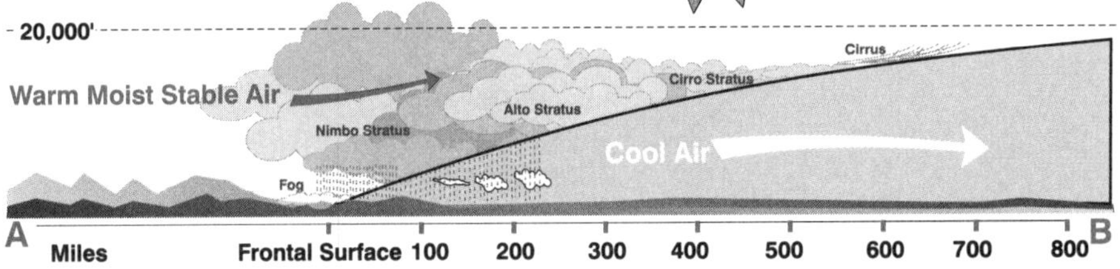

Stratiform clouds associated with warm fronts and moist stable air.

Warm Fronts

Warm fronts are typically associated with the small wave patterns moving along the polar front, as shown in Figure 63. Retreating cool air in the upper part of a small frontal wave is replaced by warmer, moister air from the south. Being heavier and denser, the retreating cool air is tugged by surface friction as it moves. Warm front orientation is more north-south or northwest-southeast, with the frontal position moving in a northeasterly direction, as shown in Figure 63.

Tugging creates a long, shallow slope over which warm air rises gradually as it replaces the cooler air. Because cool air is reluctant to give way to lighter, warmer air, warm fronts usually move at 15 MPH (13 knots) or half the speed of the average cold front. Warm front slopes typically range between 1/50 to 1/200, with an average of 1/100. A shallower slope means that warm frontal weather is distributed over a larger area than that of a cold front.

If the rising warm air is moist and stable, stratiform-type clouds develop in the warm front. The sequence of cloud formation encountered in advance of the warm front is cirrus, cirrostratus, altostratus and nimbostratus.

Precipitation increases gradually with the approach of the warm front and usually continues until it passes. This sequence is depicted in Figure 63. It's not unusual to have thunderstorms embedded in the stratus cloud mass if the air being lifted by the warm front is warm, moist, and conditionally unstable, as shown in Figure 64.

Widespread precipitation ahead of a warm front often causes low stratus and fog to form. The precipitation raises the humidity of the cold air to saturation. This and other related effects produce low ceilings and poor visibilities over a wide area. The warm frontal zone itself often has wide areas with ceiling and visibility reports of zero.

If the retreating cold air has below-freezing temperatures, the precipitation can take the form of freezing rain or ice pellets (freezing rain is extremely dangerous to pilots because its accumulates rapidly). Freezing rain occurs because raindrops from the warmer air aloft freeze as they fall into the colder air below. In fact, freezing rain or ice pellets are usually good indicators that there's warmer air aloft. The same can be said of heavy, wet snow, too. The snow is heavy because it becomes wet as a result of warmer temperatures aloft.

Warm Fronts and Moist Conditionally Unstable Air

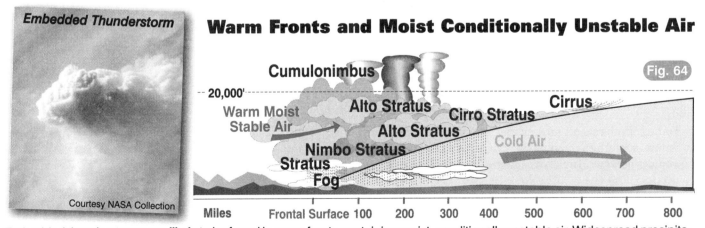

Embedded Thunderstorm

Courtesy NASA Collection

Fig. 64

Embedded thunderstorms are likely to be found in warm fronts containing moist, conditionally unstable air. Widespread precipitation is also likely to be found ahead of the warm front which generates fog and low stratus clouds. The frontal zone is also likely to have extensive fog and stratus because of high humidities induced from precipitation ahead of the front.

Stationary Fronts

Sometimes the opposing forces exerted by air masses of different densities are of similar strength and little or no movement occurs between them. With little or no movement at the air mass boundary, a stationary front forms, as shown in Figure 65. Wind on either side of the boundary blows parallel to the front rather than across it.

Stationary Front on Surface Weather Map

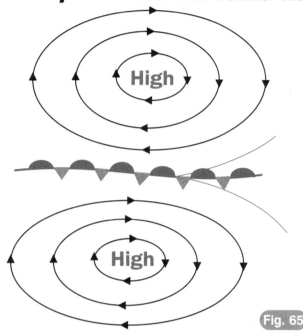

Fig. 65

When opposing air masses of different densities meet and no movement occurs, a stationary front forms. Wind on either side of the front blows parallel to the front's boundaries.

While stationary fronts are seldom (precisely) stationary, they usually move at a rate of less than 5 knots. The type of weather that forms is similar to that of a warm front, but it's less intense because very little lifting of warm air over cold occurs. An annoying feature of stationary fronts is that their weather patterns usually persist for several days, driving VFR pilots to new depths of frustration. Frankly, there's nothing worse than having bad weather persist for days, as it often does in Europe.

Leavin', On a Jet Stream

The jet stream consists of one or more tubes of very fast moving air flowing west to east across the United States (other places, too, but we'll start close to home). The jet stream does several things. High altitude winds direct storm track movement across the United States, as well as providing tailwinds to pilots moving in an easterly direction.

To best understand how the jet stream forms, we need to know something about the tropopause, which is the boundary between the troposphere (where all our weather occurs), and the stratosphere (where very little weather occurs). This boundary surrounds the earth like skin surrounds an onion. The tropopause is shown in Figure 66. Temperatures decrease until reaching the top of the troposphere. Above the tropopause, however, temperatures remain steady and then start to increase.

The Tropopause

The tropopause is like a thin skin covering the troposphere. It's found at lower altitudes over the poles and higher altitudes over the equator. Height varies because of the direct effects of air expanding by heating and shrinking by cooling.

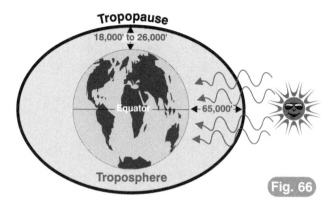

Fig. 66

The tropopause tends to bulge at the middle of the earth as a one-a-day Hostess Twinkie man might bulge at the beltline. Normally, the tropopause is located around 30,000 feet MSL in the northern latitudes and bulges at the equator to altitudes of 65,000 feet MSL. It bulges because the warmer air near the equator expands slightly. As we move northward the air cools and shrinks slightly, thus lowering the height of the tropopause. Typical polar tropopause levels can be expected at 18,000 to 26,000 feet MSL.

Occasionally, breaks occur in the tropopause. You are not responsible for these, so you don't have to pay for them. Think back to the last time you witnessed a big, big fellow sit on a waterbed (this guy's so big that when he gets on a scale it says, "Please, one at a time!"). You winced because this fellow's weight caused a large bend or bulge in the mattress. If it bulges too much and tears, water—under pressure—shoots out and swirls around the tear zone, as shown in Figure 67. Uneven weight distribution on the mattress causes a shearing or tearing effect in its thin skin.

Waterbed and the Jet Stream

When too much stress is applied to the mattress of a waterbed, it bulges then finally ruptures, sending water swirling in all directions. In a similar manner, too much stress on the troposphere (it's like a thin rubber mattress) might cause a similar rupture, allowing air to swirl. This might propagate something known as the jet stream.

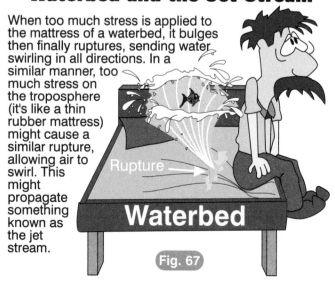

Fig. 67

The Jet Stream

Think of the warmer air to the south standing taller than the colder air to the north. The differences in these heights stretch and eventually tear the tropopause in a manner similar to someone sitting on a water bed and stressing its mattress. At the point of tear, a large difference in temperature exists. This causes air to swirl in a circular manner as shown below. Warmer air rises upward toward the tropical or southern part of the tropopause. Then it cools and descends at the northern part of the polar tropopause. This circular motion is primarily responsible for the formation of the jet stream.

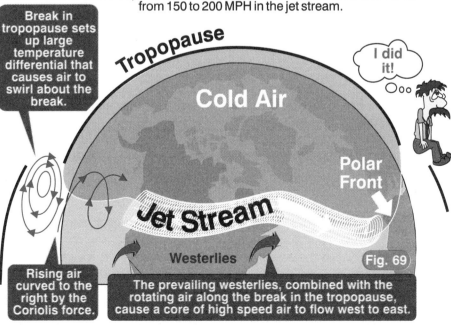

Fig. 68

In a similar manner, a strong vertical temperature gradient can cause large differences in pressure, resulting in a bulge or tear in the tropopause. Pressure differences occur because warmer air expands and cooler air shrinks. Given enough vertical expansion and shrinkage in the troposphere, a break in the tropopause occurs. Air spills around the tear, as shown in Figure 68.

Figure 69 shows warm, tropical air rising at the break in the tropopause. This warm air circulates upward and northward toward the cold polar air. Then it circulates downward as it's cooled. As it circulates upward and downward, it's curved to the right by the Coriolis force. This gives the air a west-to-east rotating motion. The jet stream's tube of fast-moving air is further coaxed into a west to east motion by the prevailing westerlies.

Jet streams are usually found along or near the polar front, and can have winds in excess of 200 MPH. If you could get your non-turbocharged Cessna 172 up that high (you can't—take pictures if you do) and tried to fly against the jet stream, you'd actually travel backwards at cruise speed!

Jet streams are important because they help meteorologists track the west-to-east migration of wave cyclones and their associated storms. These wave cyclones (and their associated low pressure systems) tend to follow the jet stream's winds at higher altitudes. Jet streams can also modify pressure centers near the surface.

Think of a jet stream as a ceiling fan that forces air earthward and forms a high pressure center. At other times, jet streams act like the ventilator fans found in our ceilings. These fans create a sucking action that creates a

Jet Stream Movement

The jet stream contains high speed, high altitude winds flowing from west to east. The flow of this stream normally follows the polar front and, at times, modifies the direction of polar frontal movement. It's not unusual to find winds from 150 to 200 MPH in the jet stream.

Jet stream accompanied by high altitude clouds across Newfoundland.

Three Stages of Thunderstorm Formation

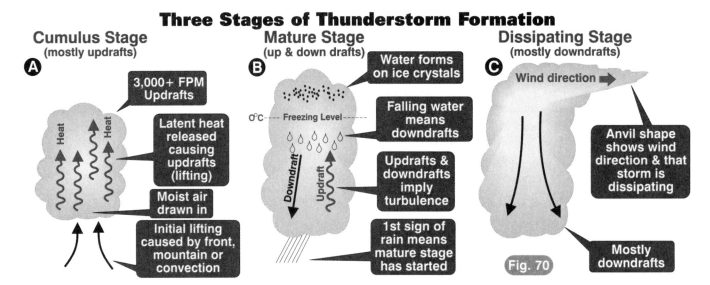

Cumulus Stage (mostly updrafts)

Ⓐ

3,000+ FPM Updrafts

Heat   Heat

Latent heat released causing updrafts (lifting)

Moist air drawn in

Initial lifting caused by front, mountain or convection

Mature Stage (up & down drafts)

Ⓑ

Water forms on ice crystals

0°C ---- Freezing Level ----

Falling water means downdrafts

Downdraft   Updraft

Updrafts & downdrafts imply turbulence

1st sign of rain means mature stage has started

Dissipating Stage (mostly downdrafts)

Ⓒ

Wind direction →

Anvil shape shows wind direction & that storm is dissipating

Fig. 70

Mostly downdrafts

miniature low pressure center. Jet streams can increase low pressure centers on the earth's surface, modifying local weather patterns. The exact reasons for this are beyond the scope of this book. Suffice it to say that meteorologists pay very close attention to the jet stream when forecasting weather.

Studying the jet stream (admittedly advanced for a private pilot) is like playing the slots in Las Vegas. Even if you don't win, it makes putting coins in your washing machine a lot more fun. Playing with ideas about the jet stream makes studying weather a lot more fun, because it helps explain many things that would otherwise seem a complete mystery. And if all else fails, you can always blame almost anything on the jet stream.

Thunderstorms

Thunderstorms are Mother Nature's bad boys. I mean really bad boys, too. This is definitely not how you want to light up your life. Let me make one thing very clear here. As an IFR pilot you do not—DO NOT!—knowingly fly through thunderstorms when flying IFR. No one—nope, not even the big boys—does so unless that person is involved in atmospheric or psychiatric research. Even then, it's only with a fully paid life insurance policy and hefty armored reinforcement of the plane's structure. Your job as an IFR pilot is to avoid thunderstorms, and that's that. There's no wiggle room here.

Are we paying attention now?

Good, because thunderstorms can and do cause pilots lots of grief. Along with ice, thunderstorms are something every pilot in every size of airplane is taught to avoid when flying IFR. Remember, it's not a question of "My plane isn't big enough to do that." In the case of thunderstorms, nobody's plane is big enough, though I have to admit that Ercoupes are really small airplanes. My friend has an Ercoupe with a small sign on the wing that says, "If found, please drop in mailbox. Postage guaranteed."

That's not to say that if you're caught in a thunderstorm, you are absolutely fillet of soul. Let's just say your survival opportunities languish.

A thunderstorm is one of the most impressive displays of raw power in existence. Around 40,000 of these light-

ning-bolt, thunder-belching creatures roam the planet every day. Your job is to avoid them.

If you could purchase a Mattel thunderstorm kit, it would include three items: moisture, unstable air, and some type of lifting force. It would also be marked, "Not for sale to pilots. Use only with adult supervision. Contains big trouble."

Moisture is a necessary ingredient of thunderstorms simply because it contains trapped energy, in the form of latent heat. The more moisture available in the air, the taller the thunderstorm monster can grow.

All the moisture in the world, however, won't help thunderstorm growth if the air is stable. A strong temperature inversion (very stable air) acts like a lid on cumulus clouds and stunts their growth. In the presence of unstable air, building cumulus clouds can heat up well beyond the temperature of their surroundings, creating conditions ripe for thunderstorm formation.

Finally, thunderstorms, like people, sometimes need a good kick in the pants (a push) to commence the growth process. A lifting force, in the form of wind blowing up a mountain, frontal lifting, surface heating, or convective activity is often sufficient to start thunderstorm formation.

The (Not So Secret) Life of a Thunderstorm

Thunderstorms get a life, but it isn't long. Their life cycles generally range from 20 to 90 minutes. They usually form in clusters of two or more cells (misery loves company), each in various stages of development.

Thunderstorm cells have three stages: cumulus, mature, and dissipating. You can think of these as the beginning, middle, and end of a brief but very electric story. Come on baby, light my ire. Let's examine each stage.

Cumulus Stage—The first stage of a potential thunderstorm is the cumulus stage. Although cumulus clouds don't always become thunderstorms, the initial stage is always a cumulus cloud, as shown in Figure 70A. Air parcels, given an initial shove by a lifting force (front, mountain, or convective heating), form a small cumulus cloud in the unstable air. As the cumulus cloud grows, updrafts draw in more moist air from below. Latent heat

Space View of Thunderstorms

Reaching tens of thousands of feet into the atmosphere, thunderstorms are Mother Nature's ultimate heat engines.

Courtesy NASA Collection

Mature Stage - Wet Downburst

It rains when the water within a thunderstorm can no longer be supported by updrafts, indicating the mature stage of the thunderstorm.

Courtesy NASA Collection

is released as this moisture condenses. This makes the cloud warmer and accelerates its growth. The cumulus stage is characterized by updrafts that can exceed 3,000 feet per minute, redefining the term "booster shot."

Mature Stage—Unlike people, thunderstorms are their nastiest when mature. This stage is characterized by updrafts, downdrafts, turbulence (sometimes severe), low-level wind shear, hail, ice, rain, and lightning. No wild left behind. This is the most dangerous stage of a thunderstorm's life cycle.

Toward the end of the cumulus stage, just before the mature stage, there is a lot of water in the cloud. The cloud droplets are very close together and give the cloud its crisp, well defined appearance. As more low-level, moisture-laden air is drawn into the cloud, the condensation process continues, producing additional cloud droplets in the updrafts (in other words, the rate of precipitation growth is increased where air currents carry water droplets upward and increase the size of those droplets).

Soon the cloud droplets begin bumping into each other and start combining, growing larger and larger. In fact, it takes about one million tiny cloud droplets to produce a

respectable size raindrop. Gravity pulls on these droplets just as it does your airplane (and beltline). So, what's holding all of them up in the cloud? The only thing keeping the raindrops aloft is the updraft. As long as they are not too heavy, they are held aloft. The faster the updraft velocity, the larger the raindrops.

Eventually, a point is reached where the raindrops become so heavy that the updraft can no longer support their weight and they begin to fall. Yet, they're still growing as they collide with other cloud droplets. Once they get bigger than 5 millimeters, atmospheric drag breaks them apart into two smaller raindrops. Your first visual clue that the thunderstorm has reached the mature stage will be rain at the surface (see graphic above).

Falling water creates downdrafts, because rain-drops tend to drag air along with them as they fall. The greater the rainfall rate, the greater the downdrafts. If you don't believe this, try an experiment the next time you're in your home-based karaoke club system—your shower. Run the water and notice how air currents swirl as droplets shoot from the shower head. This same principle is responsible for the downdrafts found within the cumulus

Atmospheric Gravity Waves

Atmospheric gravity waves ripple the surface of the Indian Ocean and are mirrored by wave clouds directly above in the atmosphere.

Courtesy NASA

Like a shaken garden hose, the "gravity" wave moves along causing the air to rise (and form these clouds) and fall in an undulating pattern.

Historic NWS Collection

Lifting Forces for Airmass Thunderstorms

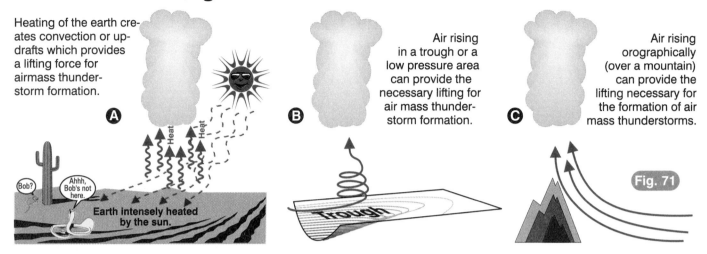

Heating of the earth creates convection or updrafts which provides a lifting force for airmass thunderstorm formation.

A

Bob?

Ahhh, Bob's not here.

Earth intensely heated by the sun.

B Air rising in a trough or a low pressure area can provide the necessary lifting for air mass thunderstorm formation.

Trough

C Air rising orographically (over a mountain) can provide the lifting necessary for the formation of air mass thunderstorms.

Fig. 71

cloud. If you experience lightning while in the shower, change shampoo brands and stop taking the hair dryer in with you.

With its combination of updrafts and downdrafts, the mature stage offers the greatest amount of turbulence and wind shear. Hail is likely at any time during this stage.

It's not unusual for thunderstorms to grow to 25,000 to 35,000 feet. In certain parts of the country they can tower to 50,000 to 60,000 feet, extending into the tropopause.

Airline pilots try to avoid being anywhere near thunderstorms. It's dangerous and often very uncomfortable for passengers. It can be really bad for the airplane, too.

Dissipating Stage—Throughout the mature stage, downdrafts develop and updrafts weaken. Ultimately, downdrafts are all that's left in the once-mighty thunderstorm cell. But don't be fooled. Although aged on a meteorological scale, this geriatric cloud still packs a powerful wallop of gusts and turbulence.

The dissipating stage is often characterized by an anvil top (Figure 70C). Without continued vertical development, the thunderstorm's top is blown over by high-altitude winds. The upper part of the cloud resembles a blacksmith's anvil which points in the direction the storm is moving. This should serve as a reminder that any nearby pilots will get pounded.

These same winds begin to disassemble the cloud's structure. With most of the water gone, the cloud is composed almost entirely of ice crystals. This changes the cloud's appearance. The crisp, sharp edges now look soft and fuzzy. Rain at the surface is now light.

Thunderstorm Types

The lifting action required for thunderstorm formation can be furnished by any of four sources: heating from below (creating convective currents), lifting by a front, air movement up a mountain, or convergence of air. Typically, thunderstorms form in air masses, in fronts, or over mountains.

Air Mass Thunderstorms—Air mass thunderstorms generally form within a warm, moist air mass and are not associated with fronts. They are usually classified as con-

vective (heated from below) or orographic (mountain-induced) thunderstorms. They are usually isolated and widely scattered enough that pilots can safely navigate around them. The most important characteristic of an air mass thunderstorm is that it moves very slowly, making it relatively easy to avoid. What makes them tricky is that they are very hard to forecast.

During the afternoon or early evening, land masses can provide enough heating for air to begin rising and condensing. Figure 71A illustrates this process. With enough moisture and instability, thunderstorms form. Troughs or areas of decreasing pressure can also provide the necessary lifting for thunderstorm formation, as shown in Figure 71B.

Orographic Thunderstorms—Orographic thunderstorms occur when moist, unstable air is forced up mountain slopes, as shown in Figure 71C. When heating from below works in conjunction with other lifting forces (orographic lifting, for instance), airmass thunderstorms tend to increase in frequency, especially during afternoon and early evening.

Frontal Thunderstorms

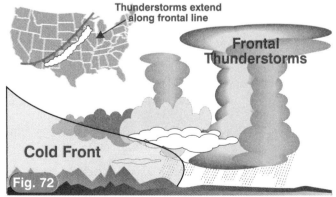

Thunderstorms extend along frontal line

Frontal Thunderstorms

Cold Front

Fig. 72

Tremendous lifting occurs along the boundaries of a fast moving cold front. Given unstable air and a fast moving cold front, you could have thunderstorms stretching for hundreds of miles ahead of the front. This may require that you either sit out the storm or plan an extensive deviation (best to sit it out!).

Embedded Thunderstorms

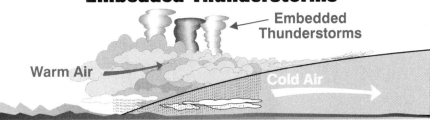

Embedded Thunderstorm

Courtesy NASA Collection

Embedded thunderstorms are likely to be found in warm fronts containing moist, conditionally unstable air. They present a problem in that you may fly under the stratus clouds of the warm front and encounter extensive areas of downdrafts associated with the thunderstorms. Fortunately thunderstorms associated with warm fronts are the least severe of frontal thunderstorms. **Fig. 73**

Sometimes thunderstorms are scattered along mountain peaks and safe passage around them is possible. When the conditions are right, however, you can have entire mountain ranges obscured by orographic thunderstorms. It's not unusual to have violent thunderstorms preventing passage for substantial distances in mountain ranges such as the Rockies.

Frontal Thunderstorms—Because fronts vary in slope and speed, thunderstorms associated with them vary considerably in intensity. Faster moving fronts usually produce the nastiest thunderstorms.

Thunderstorms associated with cold fronts are normally the worst, except for those found in squall lines. Both of these are associated with movement. Frontal thunderstorms usually form in continuous lines, as shown in Figure 72, and are relatively easy for pilots to identify.

As an IFR rated pilot, you'll often find yourself trying to circumnavigate thunderstorms along a fontal line. You won't, and I repeat, WON'T fly through a frontal line in solid IFR conditions when thunderstorms are present. Your author's decision on this is final, which your flight could be if you act out of line by flying through that line.

Unfortunately, circumnavigation is often impractical, given that a frontal line can extend several hundred miles and be packed with thunderstorms along the entire front. Unless you can get out of the clouds, perhaps on top of a lower layer of obscuring clouds and avoid the thunderstorms visually, your best bet is to park the airplane, have a soda, and tell tall tales to older and wiser pilots waiting on the surface for frontal passage. I've done this on several occasions when thunderstorms loomed along my flight path.

One time I landed at a small town in Nebraska to wait out the weather. I dropped in at a shack-like restaurant for a shack snack. I should have known better. I've now learned to look at the telephone keypad to see if the numbers 9 and 1 are worn down. If so, I starve so that I might continue living.

Thunderstorms can also be found in warm fronts. The gentleness of warm frontal lifting produces stratiform type clouds. These clouds can hide thunderstorms, as shown in Figure 73. These hidden pilot pokers are called embedded thunderstorms. These are not sleeping beauties. Embedded thunderstorms are not easily visible, and they present real hazards to IFR pilots. What you don't see can hurt you. Fortunately, because of the shallow lifting, thunderstorms associated with warm fronts are usually the least severe of all frontal-type thunderstorms.

Warm occlusions can also produce thunderstorms. Rapid lifting of warm air occurs along the upper cold front which sets off thunderstorm development, as shown in Figure 74. These thunderstorms are usually more severe than those found in warm fronts. And, in a similar fashion, they are usually embedded in stratiform clouds.

Squall Lines

As if one thunderstorm weren't enough (it is), these electric shows sometimes appear in extended lines—sort

Thunderstorms in a Warm Occlusion

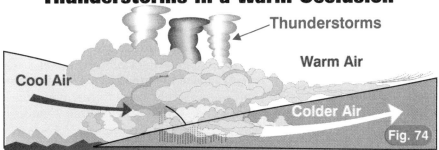

View of Thunderstorms From Space

Courtesy NASA Collection

The rapid lifting of warm air by the upper (overriding) cold front can set off thunderstorm development. This type of thunderstorm is usually more severe than those found in warm fronts and has the additional hazard of being embedded (hidden) by the stratus cloud mass.

Squall Line Thunderstorms

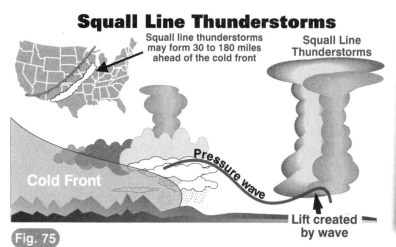

Squall line thunderstorms may form 30 to 180 miles ahead of the cold front

Squall Line Thunderstorms

Pressure wave

Cold Front

Lift created by wave

Fig. 75

Squall Line from Space

Courtesy NASA Collection

of a chorus line of trouble. Squall lines are associated with the most severe of weather conditions—large hail, destructive winds, tornadoes. Squall lines often develop 30 to 180 miles ahead of and roughly parallel to a fast-moving cold front, as shown in Figure 75.

Squall lines frequently accompany cold fronts, but a cold front is not an absolute requirement for their existence. Low pressure troughs, easterly waves, or atmospheric convergence can also produce squall lines. Keep in mind the difference between a squall line and a squall. In meteorology lingo, a squall is a defined sudden increase in wind speed of at least 16 knots with the speed rising to 22 knots or more for at least one minute. There's a big difference between a squall line and a squall.

Thunderstorm Turbulence

As an instrument pilot, you should be convinced by now that thunderstorms are not a party you want to attend. Most thunderstorms have the capability to produce extreme turbulence, updrafts and downdrafts that far exceed the capability of most light aircraft to cope. You don't want to be in the clouds if there are thunderstorms nearby. You certainly don't want to fly into a thunderstorm on purpose—or accidentally, either. With a little knowledge, a lot of respect and a dose of patience, you can often safely circumnavigate these airborne bullies when flying IFR.

Should you manage to accidentally stumble into one of these monsters, the FAA recommends that you fly straight ahead, set power for the recommended turbulence penetration speed (normally at or below your maneuvering speed—Va) and attempt to maintain a level *attitude* (instead of trying to hold altitude and possibly overstressing the airplane). Flight at and below Va means that your airplane will stall before experiencing excessive loads on the wings, and it's much better to be stalled than to have no wings—you can recover from a stall, right?

One of the significant hazards produced by thunderstorms is something known as the first gust, which is illustrated in Figure 76. During the mature stage, when rain begins falling from beneath the cell, a massive gust of cold air shoots down to ground level and spreads out in a horizontal direction. Winds of 20 to 50 knots and higher, within 150 feet of the ground, have been reported. Although most intense within 10 to 15 miles from the storm, the effects of these winds have been known to travel distances of 50 miles from the generating cell. In fact, years ago the Strategic Air Command (no, not Stargate Command) had a policy that its pilots weren't allowed to depart or approach an airport when a rain downburst was sighted within 15 miles of the runway complex. If it was good enough for SAC it should be good enough for YOU, because their airplanes are bigger than yours.

If you are on the ground or at least 15 miles away (where you

The Thunderstorm's First Gust

Fig. 76

Roll Cloud

First gust, windshear, turbulence & rapid wind changes up to about 3,000' above ground level.

10 to 15 miles

Dust

Winds up to 100 knots at 150' AGL

Pilots may experience rapid changes in airspeed when encountering the first gust of a thunderstorm.

The first gust from a mature thunderstorm contains many hazards. With winds of 20 to 50 knots at 150 feet above ground level, this gust may cause dangerous airspeed changes close to the surface. Blowing dust, flailing trees and a sudden downburst of rain might sometimes provide a visual clue to the presence of first gust hazards.

Virga Over Denver

Fig. 77

How Virga Forms

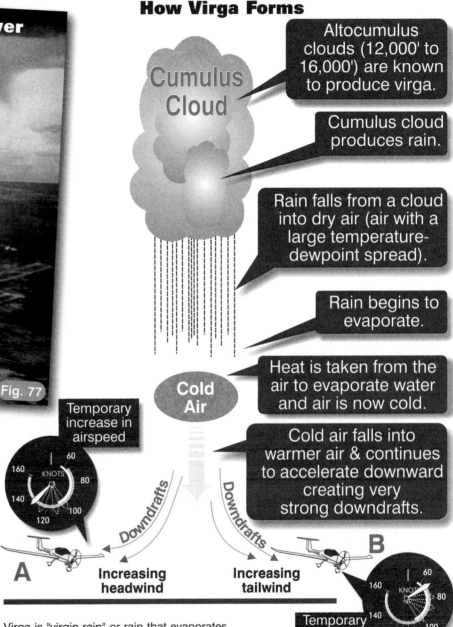

Altocumulus clouds (12,000' to 16,000') are known to produce virga.

Cumulus cloud produces rain.

Rain falls from a cloud into dry air (air with a large temperature-dewpoint spread).

Rain begins to evaporate.

Heat is taken from the air to evaporate water and air is now cold.

Cold air falls into warmer air & continues to accelerate downward creating very strong downdrafts.

Cumulus Cloud

Cold Air

Temporary increase in airspeed

Downdrafts

Downdrafts

A — Increasing headwind

B — Increasing tailwind

Temporary decrease in airspeed

Virga is "virgin rain" or rain that evaporates before being touched by the ground. It's sometimes associated with a severe downdraft phenomenon known as a "microburst." Microbursts produce downdrafts containing winds up to 150 knots that typically last from two to five minutes. Unlike a thunderstorm's downburst, which can cover areas of 10 miles or more, the microburst usually covers an area less than two and a half miles at the surface. An airplane attempting to take off into or land into a microburst might experience a temporary increase in indicated airspeed (A) as it flies into an increasing headwind. As it flies through the core of the microburst it may experience an increasing tailwind (B) which temporarily lowers its indicated airspeed.

Fig. 78

should be), the passage of a gust front resembles a miniature cold front. As the front passes, the wind shifts and becomes strong and gusty; temperatures drop sharply; and because the air in the downdraft is cold and heavy, surface pressure rises. This cold air can linger close to the ground for several hours after the thunderstorm dissipates.

Seasoned pilots expect rapid changes in both wind direction and velocity under these conditions. They watch for several signs of the first gust when thunderstorms are present. They keep an eye out for the first signs of rain beneath the cell (and use the other eye to make sure the copilot doesn't pick their pockets). Rain usually indicates rapid changes in wind direction or velocity, also known as wind shear. Rising dust and flailing trees also indicate the presence of this gust.

Before the arrival of a gust, the very best place to be is on the ground. Think carefully about taking off or landing in the presence of a reported or anticipated thunderstorm. Sometimes it's better to wait for the storm to dissipate or move before taking off; if you're already off, head for a thunderstorm-free destination for landing. Patience is the most often rewarded virtue in aviation. Those without it become some doctor's patient, and their planes often become a scrap metal dealer's delight.

Virga

Virga (Variable Intensity Rain Gradient Aloft) is virgin rain. It's called virgin because the rain doesn't touch the ground (Figure 77). Virga occurs when rain falls from a cumulus cloud (usually an altocumulus cloud) and evaporates before hitting the surface.

Think of virga as a "do not disturb" sign. As rain falls into the drier and warmer air beneath the cloud, it evaporates, as shown in Figure 78. You know it takes heat to evaporate water. Where does this heat come from? It

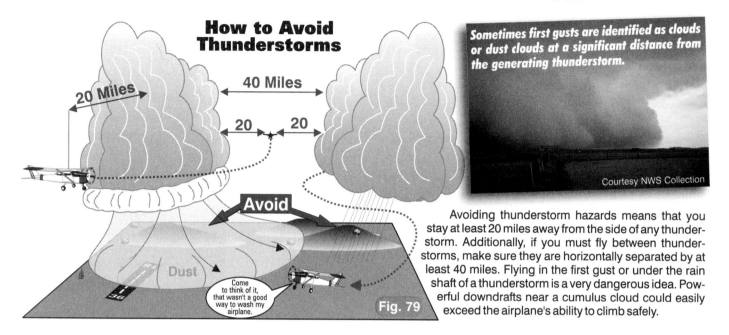

How to Avoid Thunderstorms

Sometimes first gusts are identified as clouds or dust clouds at a significant distance from the generating thunderstorm.

Courtesy NWS Collection

Fig. 79

Avoiding thunderstorm hazards means that you stay at least 20 miles away from the side of any thunderstorm. Additionally, if you must fly between thunderstorms, make sure they are horizontally separated by at least 40 miles. Flying in the first gust or under the rain shaft of a thunderstorm is a very dangerous idea. Powerful downdrafts near a cumulus cloud could easily exceed the airplane's ability to climb safely.

comes from the air the rain falls through. This makes the air cold. The cold air falls, picking up speed as it descends. You can expect moderate turbulence and high-velocity downdrafts beneath virga.

My advice to you is to avoid flying directly underneath and near virga. You're thumbing your nose at the gods of turbulence and wind shear if you decide otherwise. If you see either virga or the downburst from a thunderstorm near the airport, I'd recommend making friends with your car or the airport café until the phenomena dissipate.

Thunderstorm Avoidance

No one wants to get beat up. That's why some folks study karate, kung fu, or tai chi. Of course, karate and kung fu work pretty well on an assailant. Tai chi works well, but only if the assailant moves real slowly (even if it's the more formal version of this art, known as "Coat and tie chi"). What instrument and commercial pilots also need is some form of defense against thunderstorms. It should come as no surprise to you that the best means of defense is avoidance.

When flying *near* or *around* thunderstorm cells, avoid each one by at least 20 miles (Figure 79). That may seem like a lot, but it isn't. Thunderstorm cells have tentacles of turbulence reaching out many miles. While turbulence is more frightening to pilots than it is structurally damaging to airplanes (assuming you're flying at or below maneuvering speed), it should be avoided. Besides, it bothers passengers and makes them think you don't know how to fly smoothly.

Flying between two cells is recommended only if enough distance separates them. Most pilots use a minimum of 40 miles separation between big cells for this minimum distance. Also, avoid flying directly underneath a thunderstorm cell. Once the cell becomes mature and rain falls, you can expect substantial downdrafts in the core of the rain shaft. Small airplanes don't have sufficient power to even think about out-climbing these downdrafts.

The question is, how you avoid thunderstorms when you're flying under instrument conditions? Well, there are really only two practical ways to do this. You either have lightning detection equipment (Stormscope, Strike Finder, etc.) or you have airborne radar. Yes, you can gain the assistance of Center's or Approach Control's radar, but there are definite limits on what these radar units can tell you.

Perhaps you're curious how IFR pilots handled thunderstorms before radar or lighting detection equipment was widely available for smaller airplanes. It's no secret. These pilots avoided thunderstorms visually. They'd either visually circumnavigate cells during the day, or at night they'd look for the lightning strikes and avoid those. In many cases, flying near or around thunderstorms meant being able to climb on top of a cloud deck (or remain below it) in order to see the storms and avoid them. If pilots couldn't do this, they didn't fly (well, sometimes they still did, but such people were often eliminated from the gene pool at an early age and thus left few survivors to carry on the tradition).

Lightning

Lightning is a phenomenon associated with every thunderstorm. Without lightning, you'd have no thunder, which would make for a pretty poor thunderstorm. While not much of a problem during the day, lightning is a real thriller at night. The most important thing to understand about lightning is that it seldom affects airplanes in flight.

What it does affect is you, the pilot. A reduction in night vision occurs when your pupils close as a reaction to the intense light display (Figure 80). It's not unusual for pilots to experience varying degrees of night blindness from lightning many miles away. Turning the white cockpit lights up as bright as possible is usually the best remedy for acclimating yourself to future flashes. This simply gets the eyes used to an elevated light intensity.

I wouldn't recommend wearing your sunglasses when lightning is present, either. You probably won't be able to

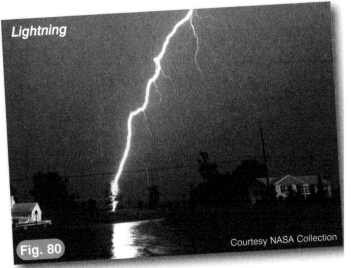

Lightning

Courtesy NASA Collection

Fig. 80

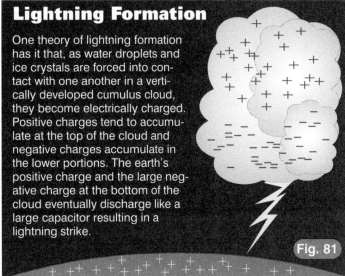

Lightning Formation

One theory of lightning formation has it that, as water droplets and ice crystals are forced into contact with one another in a vertically developed cumulus cloud, they become electrically charged. Positive charges tend to accumulate at the top of the cloud and negative charges accumulate in the lower portions. The earth's positive charge and the large negative charge at the bottom of the cloud eventually discharge like a large capacitor resulting in a lightning strike.

Fig. 81

see the panel in the dark, even with the panel lights on. And don't try what one pilot did, which was to punch one glass lens out of his sunglasses. He said that if lightning struck, it would only affect one eye. Then, of course, he'd have to reinsert one lens and remove the other. The only thing brilliant about that idea is the lightning strike itself. Figure 81 explains the mechanics of lightning formation.

Now that you know a bit about thunderstorm formation, you'll certainly want to learn more about how to differentiate a harmless cumulus cloud from one that will grown into a thunderstorm. That's why you should read Postflight Briefing #9-3.

Microbursts

No, a *microburst* isn't an immediate expression of joy by the patron of a microbrewery when receiving his first beer of the day. Instead, it's a small scale but very intense downdraft of air that spreads outward from its center in all directions when reaching the surface. The wind shear produces both vertical and horizontal components, and you can bet it's hazardous to all types and categories of aircraft. No one is immune from its effects and the hazards are greater when encountered at low altitudes.

The problem with these little devils is that they're difficult to predict, see, or detect. This is the result of several factors, including the typically small size of a microburst and its short lifespan, as well as the fact that that a microburst can occur over areas without surface precipitation. No conventional detection systems detect microbursts very well.

When attempting to predict the chance of a microburst, you'll want to keep an eye out for any of the low or middle layer convective cloud types. Keep in mind, however, that microbursts commonly occur within the heavy rain portion of thunderstorms, and in much weaker, benign appearing convective cells that have little or no precipitation reaching the ground (virga, remember?).

Figure 82 depicts the life cycle of a microburst as it descends in a convective rain shaft. It's important to keep in mind that the microburst intensifies for about 5 minutes after it strikes the ground. A few of its primary characteristics are:

Size: The microburst downdraft is typically less than 1 mile in diameter as it descends from the cloud base to 1,000–3,000 feet above the ground. In the transition zone

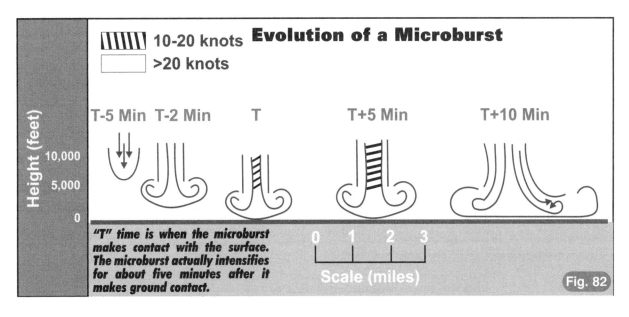

Evolution of a Microburst

IIIIII 10-20 knots
☐ >20 knots

Height (feet)

T-5 Min   T-2 Min   T   T+5 Min   T+10 Min

10,000
5,000
0

"T" time is when the microburst makes contact with the surface. The microburst actually intensifies for about five minutes after it makes ground contact.

0   1   2   3

Scale (miles)

Fig. 82

Microburst Encounter During Takeoff

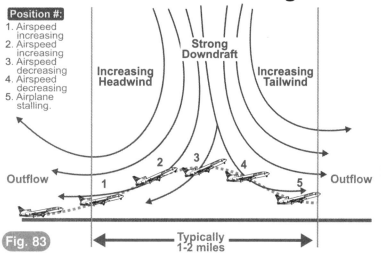

Position #:
1. Airspeed increasing
2. Airspeed increasing
3. Airspeed decreasing
4. Airspeed decreasing
5. Airplane stalling.

Strong Downdraft

Increasing Headwind   Increasing Tailwind

Outflow   Outflow

Fig. 83   Typically 1-2 miles

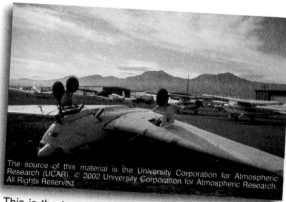

This is the type of accident that occurs when an airplane experiences wind shear as a result of a microburst. This particular accident happened in Boulder, Colorado.

near the ground, the downdraft changes to a horizontal outflow that can extend to approximately 2½ miles in diameter.

Intensity: The downdrafts can be as strong as 6,000 feet per minute. Horizontal winds near the surface can be as strong as 45 knots resulting in a 90 knot shear (headwind to tailwind change for a traversing aircraft) across the microburst. These strong horizontal winds occur within a few hundred feet of the ground.

Visual Signs: Microbursts can be found almost anywhere that there is convective activity. They may be embedded in heavy rain associated with a thunderstorm or in light rain in benign-appearing virga. When there is little or no precipitation at the surface accompanying the microburst, a ring of blowing dust may be the only visual clue to its existence.

Duration: An individual microburst will seldom last longer than 15 minutes from the time it strikes the ground until dissipation. The horizontal winds continue to increase during the first 5 minutes, with the maximum-intensity winds lasting approximately 2–4 minutes. Sometimes microbursts are concentrated into a line struc-

ture, and under these conditions activity may continue for as long as an hour. Once microburst activity starts, multiple microbursts in the same general area are not uncommon and should be expected.

There's little doubt that microburst wind shear creates a severe hazard for aircraft within 1,000 feet of the ground, particularly during the approach to landing and landing and takeoff phases. The impact of a microburst on aircraft that have the misfortune of encountering them is shown in Figure 83. The aircraft may encounter a headwind (performance increasing) followed by a downdraft and tailwind (performance decreasing), possibly resulting in terrain impact. Thanks, but no thanks. I don't like being grounded.

This is all the more reason to be vigilant when the conditions are conducive to microburst formation. If necessary, you can delay a departure or even delay your landing. Declaring a missed approach could be the wisest course in such circumstances. You don't want to get caught close to the ground in a microburst condition. Finally, keep in mind that the difference between a microburst and a thunderstorm's downburst is one of size.

Delta Flight 191's Deadly Microburst Encounter in 1985

On August 2, 1985 at 1805:52 Central Daylight Time, Delta Airlines Flight 191, a Lockheed L-1011, crashed while approaching to land on Runway 17L at the Dallas Fort Worth International Airport. While passing through a rain shaft beneath a thunderstorm, Flight

Photo Source: NTSB

191 entered a microburst which the pilot was unable to traverse successfully. The airplane struck the ground about 6,300 feet north of the approach end of Runway 17L, hit a car on a highway north of the runway killing the driver, struck two water tanks on the airport, and then broke apart. Except for a section of the airplane containing the aft fuselage and empennage, the remainder of the airplane disintegrated during the impact sequence and a severe fire erupted. Of the 163 persons aboard, 134 passengers were killed while 26 passengers and three cabin attendants survived.

The NTSB determined that the probable cause of the accident was the flight crew's decision to initiate and continue the approach into cumulonimbus clouds which they observed to contain visible lightning; the lack of specific guideline procedures and training for avoiding and escaping from low altitude wind shear, and the lack of definitive real-time wind shear hazard information. This resulted in the aircraft's encounter at low altitudes with microburst-induced severe wind shear from a rapidly developing thunderstorm located on the final approach course.   *NTSB Abstract*

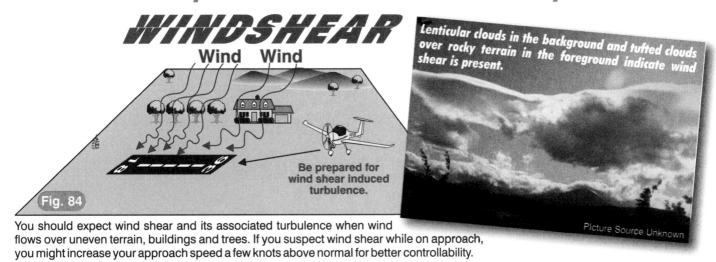

WINDSHEAR

Wind   Wind

Be prepared for wind shear induced turbulence.

Fig. 84

Lenticular clouds in the background and tufted clouds over rocky terrain in the foreground indicate wind shear is present.

Picture Source Unknown

You should expect wind shear and its associated turbulence when wind flows over uneven terrain, buildings and trees. If you suspect wind shear while on approach, you might increase your approach speed a few knots above normal for better controllability.

Turbulence and Wind Shear

Nothing bothers people more than an unsettling force they can't see. That's why the kids in our family always ran when we heard grandma do the Bruce Lee karate call—awwaeeeeaaahhhh. We didn't have to see her to know the damage her kung fu would do. Pilots experience the same thing with turbulence—it's there, but they don't know where. There are, however, several ways to anticipate and avoid turbulence and wind shear. Let's start with an understanding of wind shear, and find out when and where it might occur.

Wind shear occurs when wind makes a rapid change in direction or velocity (or both). If you're standing by the roadside and a truck goes by, your pants or skirt start to wiggle. One instant, the wind was calm; in the next, it changed in direction and/or velocity with truck passage. If it was a big enough and fast enough truck, the wind shear might have ripped your pants clean off and taken a toupee along with it (another Kodak moment).

Wind shear and its associated turbulence can become a factor during landing, when winds flow over uneven ter-

rain. Figure 84 shows how this might occur. Like water flowing over rocks on a creek bed, wind is upset, tumbled and churned as it flows over buildings, trees and other structures near the runway.

Often, wind shear is felt as hardly more than a bump in low-wind conditions. But given enough wind speed, say 10 to 15 knots, turbulence can be quite noticeable. Anticipating bumpiness, most pilots add a few knots to their approach speed (perhaps 5 knots or more) for better controllability during landing. Of course, they'll make sure the extra speed doesn't cause them to run out of runway. Knowing where to expect turbulence prevents you from being shocked when it appears.

Convective currents are the most common form of turbulence you're likely to encounter in flight. As we've already seen, convective activity is often responsible for the start of thunderstorm formation. On a smaller scale, it becomes quite noticeable at low altitudes during approach to landing, as shown in Figure 85.

Mountain Waves

If you believe a mountain wave has something to do with flapping your hands at hikers, then you must also

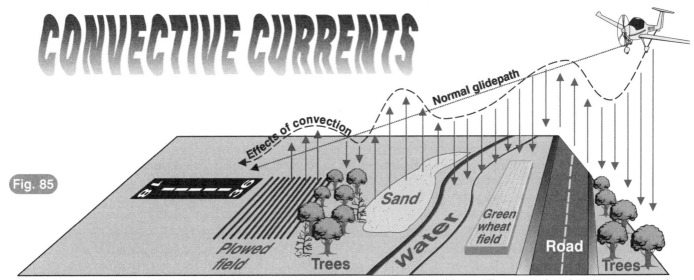

CONVECTIVE CURRENTS

Normal glidepath

Effects of convection

Fig. 85

Plowed field   Trees   Sand   Water   Green wheat field   Road   Trees

Convective currents caused by differences in terrestrial heating are quite common. Where different terrain exists, it's not unusual for pilots to experience considerable up and down drafts while on approach. Perceptive pilots can identify these convective currents by observing that plant life and water generally absorb heat and create downdrafts. Terrain, on the other hand, generally radiates heat & creates updrafts.

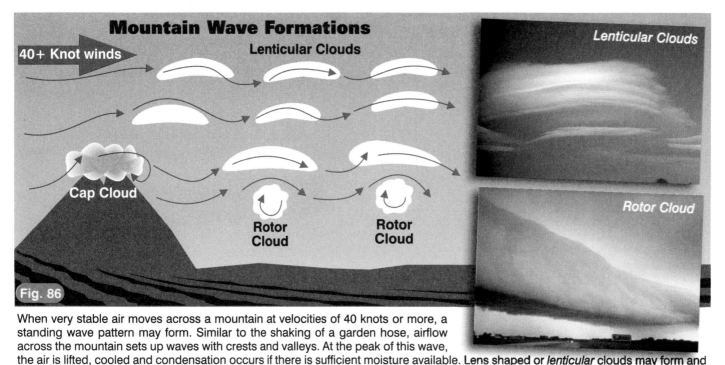

When very stable air moves across a mountain at velocities of 40 knots or more, a standing wave pattern may form. Similar to the shaking of a garden hose, airflow across the mountain sets up waves with crests and valleys. At the peak of this wave, the air is lifted, cooled and condensation occurs if there is sufficient moisture available. Lens shaped or *lenticular* clouds may form and appear to stand in one position. Underneath the lenticular cloud small rotor clouds may appear. Rotor clouds contain massive turbulence.

believe that using your car key on your home's front door could start the place up. You undoubtedly know that a mountain wave is something much more interesting.

Throw a pebble in a still pond and wave patterns radiate outward, eventually traveling across the entire pond. If we move water over a pebble, a curve is added to the flowing stream. When air moves over a larger pebble—a mountain range, for example—it also has a curve added to its motion, as shown in Figure 86. Given enough wind speed and large enough mountains, these wave patterns can travel hundreds of miles from their generating source.

Very stable air, moving above the level of surface friction, usually flows in a laminar or smooth, layered pattern. But when it encounters a large enough obstacle (a mountain range, for example) a standing or mountain wave pattern is established in the mass of moving air. The standing wave is very similar to the wave which appears when a long rope is given a good shake at one end (the gravity wave discussed earlier). The wave pattern appears to travel the length of the rope, eventually dissipating in a flip at the end. Mountain waves do something very similar.

As wind, usually with a velocity of 40 knots or more, encounters a sufficiently large mountain, a perturbation or shake-of-the-rope occurs. A wave pattern is induced in the once smooth-flowing (laminar) air. This pattern sets up a series of waves, in the downwind direction, with valleys and peaks that remain stationary. Given enough moisture in the stable air, condensation (from air cooling as it rises) occurs at the peaks of these waves.

Directly over the mountain top, a *pileus* or *cap* cloud occurs above the rough mountain surface. Farther downwind almond or lens-shaped clouds form at the wave crests. These clouds are called *lenticular* clouds because of their lens shape.

The formation of lenticular clouds is shown in Figure 86. As moist air rises on the upwind side of the wave, it cools and condenses, producing a cloud. On the downwind side of each wave crest, the air sinks and warms, resulting in the cloud droplets evaporating. Lenticular clouds differ from other clouds not only in shape, but because they appear not to move. This is because the air is rushing through them as they continually form on their western edges and evaporate away on their eastern edges. This is why they are sometimes called standing wave clouds.

When the air between the cloud-forming layers is too dry to produce clouds, lenticular clouds will form one above the other. Sometimes, when a strong wind blows perpendicular to a tall mountain range, the wave pattern extends up into the stratosphere. This produces a dramatic display resembling a fleet of UFO's. It is typical for mountain waves to form 100 miles or more downstream from the mountain barrier.

Directly underneath the lenticular clouds, a small rotor cloud can frequently be found below mountain peak altitudes. Rotor clouds result from the frictional effects of the surface and a lifting action from the rising crest of air. Air velocity is slowed near the surface yet flows faster at higher altitudes. This adds a rolling motion to tubes of air similar to the forward motion of a baker's rolling pin. Long cigar-shaped clouds form, each containing severe turbulence. These clouds should be avoided just like food physicists avoid mixing pasta with antipasto so as to prevent a large food explosion. Violent turbulence will also be found in the up- and downdrafts associated with lenticular clouds.

Pilots must be especially cautious when flying near or around mountain waves. Many varieties of turbulence appear in these wave patterns. Keep in mind that mountain waves can and do form in dry air. The problem is that

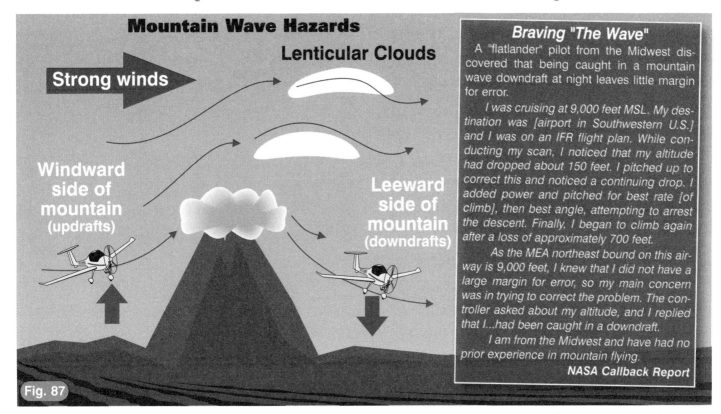

Mountain Wave Hazards

Strong winds

Lenticular Clouds

Windward side of mountain (updrafts)

Leeward side of mountain (downdrafts)

Fig. 87

Braving "The Wave"

A "flatlander" pilot from the Midwest discovered that being caught in a mountain wave downdraft at night leaves little margin for error.

I was cruising at 9,000 feet MSL. My destination was [airport in Southwestern U.S.] and I was on an IFR flight plan. While conducting my scan, I noticed that my altitude had dropped about 150 feet. I pitched up to correct this and noticed a continuing drop. I added power and pitched for best rate [of climb], then best angle, attempting to arrest the descent. Finally, I began to climb again after a loss of approximately 700 feet.

As the MEA northeast bound on this airway is 9,000 feet, I knew that I did not have a large margin for error, so my main concern was in trying to correct the problem. The controller asked about my altitude, and I replied that I...had been caught in a downdraft.

I am from the Midwest and have had no prior experience in mountain flying.

NASA Callback Report

Approaching the mountain on the windward side (the upwind side) you could encounter strong updrafts. On the leeward side (the downwind side), it's possible to encounter strong downdrafts that your airplane might not be able to out climb.

you can't see them. In other words, telltale lenticular clouds are not visible. With the lack of clouds in dry, fast moving air, pilots sometimes expect little or no hazard when approaching a mountain. Smart pilots, however, understand that winds in excess of 25 knots at mountaintop altitudes are sure to bring some degree of turbulence as well as up- and downdraft hazards.

Approaching a mountain on the windward side (the upwind side), as shown in Figure 87 you might find yourself climbing at several thousand feet per minute with power completely reduced. While this produces one heck

of a ride, it's not as dangerous as approaching a mountain from the leeward side (downwind side) with insufficient altitude.

Approaches to mountains with strong winds present should be made with caution, because the strong downdrafts can easily exceed the ability of a light airplane to climb. One way to minimize the risk if you are uncertain of conditions is to approach the ridge at a 45 degree angle. If downdrafts are encountered, you need only make a 90 degree turn to avoid the mountain instead of a 135 degree turn, as shown in Figure 88.

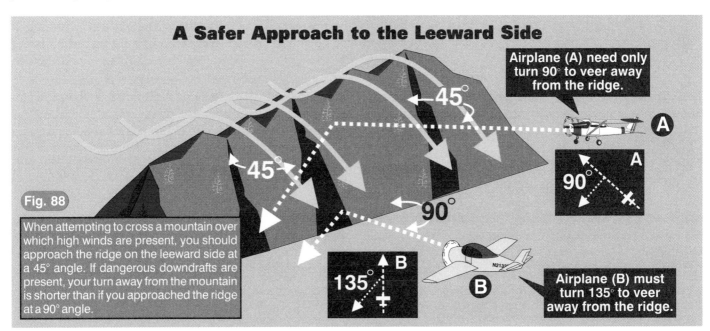

A Safer Approach to the Leeward Side

Airplane (A) need only turn 90° to veer away from the ridge.

45°

45°

90°

A

90°

Fig. 88

When attempting to cross a mountain over which high winds are present, you should approach the ridge on the leeward side at a 45° angle. If dangerous downdrafts are present, your turn away from the mountain is shorter than if you approached the ridge at a 90° angle.

B

135°

Airplane (B) must turn 135° to veer away from the ridge.

Temperature Inversions and Wind Shear

Temperature inversions are common on the surface during clear, calm nights with little or no surface winds. Strong winds, however, can exist just above the inversion. Because air of different temperatures doesn't mix well, the warmer air on top tends to slide over the colder air below (Figure 89). This sliding, shown in Figure 90, becomes even more apparent when strong pressure differences exist, causing high wind speeds in the warmer air aloft.

If winds move in excess of 25 knots at 2,000 to 4,000 feet above the surface, you should expect wind shear in the zone where the warm and cold air meet. Differences in wind velocities cause a tearing or churning of the air, producing eddies or turbulence in the shear zone. Pilots climbing or descending at slow speeds might find the wind shear bad enough to induce a stall at altitudes close to the ground.

If the inversion occurs within a few hundred feet above the ground, wind shear can be a significant hazard. Imagine approaching an airport in a strong temperature inversion. Surface winds are calm at the airport, but you notice the winds at your altitude are quite strong. This often becomes apparent because of the rather large crab angle required to remain aligned with the runway. A

Temperature Inversion Turbulence

The haze layer below indicates the presence of a temperature inversion with the accompanying possibility of wind shear.

Fig. 89

noticeable difference between your airspeed and ground speed is another clue to the possibility of wind shear.

Suppose you encounter a sudden tailwind while descending from D to F through an inversion, as shown in Figure 90. Differences in wind velocity might cause you to lose a slight amount of airspeed as you descend into a tailwind (Airplane E). A sudden tailwind acts like a burst of wind from behind the airplane. Airspeed is momentarily lost until the airplane is accelerated by the tailwind, then it returns to the previous speed as shown by Airplane F. This event becomes even more serious when the airplane is close to its stall speed and the temperature inversion is close to the surface. It's possible for the airplane to stall without sufficient room for recovery.

Suppose you were climbing through an inversion into a headwind as shown by Airplanes A, B and C. A sudden headwind, while climbing through the inversion, might cause a temporary increase in airspeed as shown by Airplane B. While this isn't as serious as a loss of airspeed, the turbulence it produces can startle a pilot (much like how I was startled when a friend of mine bought a cheap home that advertised solar heating; it turns out the place had no roof).

Be cautious. Anticipate wind shear within the first few hours after sunset. Also anticipate it before and after sunrise. These are the times when temperature inversions are most common. The presence above the inversion of winds in excess of 25 knots, with calm surface winds, is a good sign that wind shear may be lurking. Add a few knots onto your approach speed to reduce the danger of a wind shear induced stall.

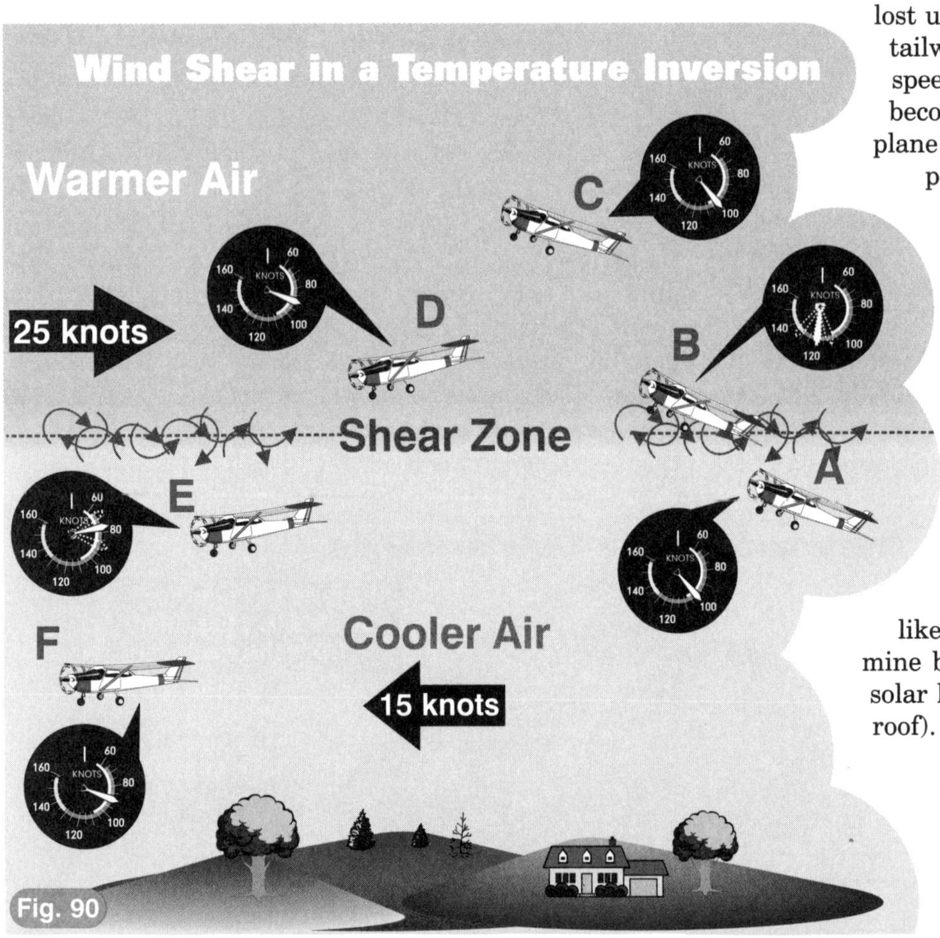

Wind Shear in a Temperature Inversion

Warmer Air

25 knots

C

D

B

A

Shear Zone

E

Cooler Air

F

15 knots

Fig. 90

Wind shear in a temperature inversion can cause sudden changes in your airplane's indicated airspeed. Airplane A is climbing through the inversion into an increasing headwind. At position B the indicated airspeed temporarily increases. As the airplane adjusts to the new wind direction, the indicated airspeed returns to normal at position C. Airplane D is descending into an increasing tailwind. At position E the indicated airspeed temporarily decreases, then returns to normal at position F. These indicated airspeed changes are more pronounced in heavier airplanes with large differences in wind speed.

Fog

Fog is a cloud that touches the ground. Fog comes in on little cat's feet, and casts its gloomy pall over the airport, putting an end to the day's aviating for VFR pilots and sometimes even for IFR-rated pilots. Fog is one of the most frequent causes of reduced surface visibilities and it can represent a challenge for all pilots.

Fog presents a serious problem because it can form in a very short time. I've seen airports go from three miles visibility to less than one-half mile in just a few minutes because of fog. Many pilots have raced an approaching fog bank to the airport only to lose the race. Figure 91 shows the reduced visibility experienced in fog.

Remember that the dewpoint is the temperature at which water will condense out of the air. The dewpoint is a function of humidity, and the number is so crucial that it's one of the things you will hear on the ATIS broadcast. Small temperature/dewpoint spreads are conducive to fog formation. That's why fog is common in colder months. It can, however, form any time the air contains enough moisture, condensation nuclei, and cooling temperatures.

Unfortunately, there are a lot of ways to brew up a batch of fog. Cooling the air to its dewpoint is the most common means of fog production. Adding moisture to air near the surface also aids in fog formation. Precipitation from fronts is a common way moisture is added to the air. Fog is classified by the way it forms. Let's examine some of the different types of fogs.

Radiation Fog—This isn't the type of fog that forms in the one-time Pacific nuclear testing areas, the Bikini Atolls (or the most popular place there, known as the No-Bikini Atoll). Radiation fog is what happens when the ground radiates its heat away. On clear, calm nights, terrestrial radiation of heat cools the ground. This allows the air resting next to the surface to cool quickly. As air is cooled and approaches its dewpoint, water vapor condenses and forms a shallow layer of fog. Radiation fog is very common at night and in the early morning hours. Figure 92 shows an example of radiation fog.

Radiation Fog

Radiation fog forms when the ground radiates its heat away and the air in contact with the ground cools by conduction.

Fig. 92

Courtesy FAA

Areas of high humidity (rain soaked ground and vegetation) are especially conducive to the formation of radiation fog. This is why golf courses are common places for this type of fog. I've driven by these courses early in the morning and seen golf clubs popping out the top of a 6 foot layer of radiation fog. All you can see are funny little hats (with propellers on them if they are worn by pilots) floating on the top of a 6 foot layer of fog.

I've even seen control towers standing above a shallow radiation fog layer at the airport. It's VFR for the controller but IFR for taxiing pilots. On other occasions, I've made an instrument approach to an airport, descended to the lowest allowable minimum descent altitude and found myself still above the fog layer. That's no fun. Bodies of water, despite their moisture potential, aren't a likely place for radiation fog to form. Bodies of water don't cool as quickly at night (compared to land), making radiation fog unlikely.

Winds up to about 5 knots tend to mix and deepen the layer of fog. Higher winds tend to disperse radiation fog. Solar heating of the earth after sunrise tends to dissipate radiation fog. Despite a fog layer, some solar heating makes it to the surface. This warms the ground, which helps dissipate the fog from below. Radiation fog also dissipates around its periphery first, where it's the thinnest. Of course, all this assumes a high-altitude cloud layer isn't preventing a reasonable amount of solar heat from reaching the surface.

Some people speak of fog burning off rather than dissipating. There really is no fire involved here as there is in a typical Machado home barbecue (that's because Machado cooked steaks are made up of 5% meat, 95% lighter fluid). So keep in mind the next time you hear the FSS specialist mention a time at which the fog will burn off that it's a fluid situation.

Advection Fog – Convection means to move something vertically; advection means moving it sideways. Advection fog is fog that forms elsewhere and comes to visit you. Sometimes called sea fog, advection fog is most common in coastal areas, though it can form in inland

Diminished Visibility in Fog

Fig. 91

Fig. 93   Courtesy NOAA Collection

Fig. 94   © Kerry Werry - FOTOLIA

areas as well. As warmer, moist air comes in contact with the ocean's surface, air temperatures decrease and water vapor condenses as shown in Figure 93 and 94. With slight heating, the air pressure over the land lowers, drawing advection fog inland. Advection fog deepens when winds increase to about 15 knots. Winds above this speed tend to lift fog layers into low stratus or stratocumulus-type clouds. (Stratocumulus clouds are a mixture of both stratus and cumulus clouds.)

Advection fog can form quite rapidly and cover extensive areas. Many a pilot has found only a deep white fog where the airport was supposed to be, even though the airport was reporting VFR conditions just a short time earlier. Of course, plan B is to always have a fog-free airport nearby. Remember, good pilots always have a plan B and even a plan C.

Upslope Fog – When warm, moist air is forced up the slope of a mountain and condenses, it forms upslope fog (Figure 95). Technically, this cloud is considered fog because it touches the surface of the mountain. Upslope fog depends on wind for its existence. Therefore, it's not

dependent on terrestrial cooling. This means that upslope fog can form under a higher layer of clouds that usually prevent terrestrial cooling. Expect to see upslope fog in the winter and spring on the eastern side of the Rocky Mountains.

Precipitation-Induced Fog – Warm rain, falling through cooler air, can bring the air to the point of saturation, forming fog. Commonly associated with warm fronts, precipitation-induced fog can occur in slow-moving cold fronts and stationary fronts. Couple this fog with the conditions that produce it—warm, cold and stationary fronts—and you get a double whammy of hazards.

Ice Fog – Ice fog forms under conditions similar to those that cause radiation fog, except the air temperature is way below freezing (Figure 96). Instead of fog, you wind up with water sublimating directly into the air as ice crystals. We're talking temperatures around –25 degrees F as being favorable for its formation. This happens mostly in the Arctic region but it is not unknown in the middle latitudes. Ice fog can be quite blinding to someone when flying into the sun. If your instructor is sending you to the Arctic regions on your solo cross countries, you might want to check and see if he's upset with you over something.

Fig. 95   © FOTOLIA

Fig. 96   Courtesy NOAA Collection

Steam Fog

Steam fog on Lake Superior. Air temperature is six below zero. Courtesy NOAA Collection

Fig. 97

Steam Fog – Anyone who has seen a heated swimming pool early on a cool morning has witnessed steam fog (Figure 97). As dry, cold air passes over a body of warm water, moisture evaporates rapidly from the surface. Condensation takes place as the cold air is quickly saturated. Water droplets often freeze, falling back into the water as ice crystals. Steam fog is conducive to low level turbulence and icing.

Keep in mind that the reduced visibilities associated with fog will be one of the biggest challenges you face as an IFR pilot. You can navigate all types of serious weather for hundreds of miles only to find that you can't see the airport at the missed approach point on your instrument approach. Fortunately, you'll soon learn how the approach lighting system associated with an ILS approach allows you to transition and land with as little as one-half mile visibility. This is very important in terms of increasing your chances of landing as an instrument pilot. Nevertheless, always plan to have an alternate plan just in case the visibility is too low. I always had a plan in case I was rejected when I asked a girl out for a date in high school. One time I asked a young lady for a date and she said, "I wouldn't go out with you if you were the last man on earth."

My plan? I replied, "If I were the last man on earth I'm pretty sure I'd be way too busy to go out with you anyway." It's good to have a plan.

I See Icing

Aside from thunderstorms, structural icing is an instrument pilot's biggest in-flight worry. Icing is something that should leave any pilot cold. Why? Because test data show that ice, snow, or frost having a thickness and roughness that's similar to medium or coarse sandpaper on the wing's leading edge or upper surface can reduce lift by as much as 30% and increase drag by as much as 40%. Even a mere hint of frost can disrupt the airflow over the wings, creating loss of lift. That's why it should be removed before flight (and not with cold water shot from a hose, either).

And it's not just a matter of how much ice. Non-pilots often think the danger from ice has to do with it weighing the plane down until it sinks. It's cold comfort to know the truth, which is that the major danger from ice has to do with its ability to disrupt the aerodynamics of flight, something that can be accomplished with surprisingly little ice accumulation.

Keep in mind that your airplane was probably tested without ice as part of the aerodynamic equation. The FAA and aircraft manufacturer say the plane will fly as built. Add ice and you've just become an unsalaried test pilot under unknown conditions. Maybe a little ice on the leading edge won't keep you from staying up in the air. Then again, maybe it will.

Believe it or not, this is one area where the standard lapse rate of 2.0 degrees C (3.5 degrees F) is useful. You can use it to estimate where the freezing level begins before an IFR flight. Assume that your field elevation is 1,350 feet MSL with a temperature of +8 degrees C. At what MSL altitude would you find the freezing level? Put away your abacus and do this one in your head. With a lapse rate of 2 degrees C per thousand feet, you'll have to rise 4,000 feet above the field to reach the freezing level. Adding this altitude onto the field elevation means the freezing level can be found at approximately 5,350 feet MSL. Now, onto the specifics of ice.

The best strategy for dealing with structural icing is to not have it happen. While it's generally not good to avoid serious issues, this is one case where that's the optimal approach. But to avoid structural icing, you've got to know something about it. Voila, that's why you have me. So let's examine the cool details of the subject.

Chilling Ice Capades

This "chilling" statement reflects the gravity of the situation encountered by an instructor and student in an ice-encumbered Cessna 172. Knowing the limitations of one's aircraft and having a respect for the forces of nature are two universal lessons learned by the instructor who submitted this report.

The [Cessna 172] began to accumulate light rime ice in cruise at 10,000 feet.... Icing became increasingly heavier until...we were having difficulty maintaining altitude. Departure [said] he needed us to maintain 10,000 feet. I told him we were picking up ice and requested vectors [to the] ILS Runway 35 at XXX... We checked in with the Tower [and we were] cleared to land. Icing was moderate at that point. We had full throttle at 70 KIAS and [we were] descending 400 feet per minute. We were unable to maintain approach minimums, and at one point Tower said, "You probably know this, but I'm getting an altitude alert...." We briefed the approach and knew we were going to have to find the runway regardless of the weather... We saw the approach lights at about 400 feet AGL, almost 500 feet below the localizer approach minimums. We landed without incident (with two inches of ice). The approach and tower controllers were extremely helpful.

Causes: We took off into forecast icing conditions.... I thought if we could get up high enough (10,000 feet) we could fly over the icing layer... Even a very thin layer of ice on the leading edge and upper wing surfaces can cause a dramatic loss of lift and increase in drag. With two inches of ice, these pilots were lucky to be near an airport.   **NASA Callback Report**

The Two Conditions for Ice Formation

Two conditions are necessary for structural ice to form and stay on your airplane. First, the airplane must be flying through some visible water such as rain or cloud droplets. Second, the temperature at the point where the moisture makes contact with the airplane must be 0° C or colder. Avoid either one of these conditions and you avoid ice.

Sounds easy. Stay where the air temperature is above zero. Not so simple, Simon. Cool it. Which is exactly what can happen to your airfoil, where aerodynamic cooling takes it down to 0° C despite the ambient temperature being a few degrees warmer. So don't count on a precise 0° C or lower to anticipate icing. Besides, when was the last time you calibrated your airplane's thermometer? On some airplanes, the thermometers are old enough to have advanced degrees.

Clear and Rime Ice—Quality vs. Quantity

Unlike shoes in a shoe store, icing comes in two basic types. Clear and rime. The type of ice that forms often has to do with the presence of supercooled water droplets. These are droplets that are cooled well below their freezing point because of their motion and their travels in the clouds that produced them. Once supercooled water droplets hit a collecting surface, part of the drop freezes instantaneously. Because of the latent heat of fusion released by the freezing droplet, the remaining portion freezes more slowly. Aerodynamic effects determine how the remaining portion of the drop freezes. As a result, you're likely to see two basic types of structural ice form.

Clear ice forms when, after initial impact, the remaining liquid portion of the drop flows over the aircraft surface gradually freezing as a smooth sheet of solid ice. This type forms when drops are large, as in rain or in cumuliform clouds.

Figure 98 is an example of clear ice, which is hard, heavy, and tenacious. Even if your airplane has deicing equipment (boots, for example), the removal of this type of ice is often difficult (OK, it's not always perfectly clear, either).

When droplets are small, such as those found in stratified clouds or in light drizzle, it's possible for rime ice to form. The liquid portion remaining after initial impact freezes rapidly, before the drop has time to spread over the aircraft surface. The small frozen droplets trap air between them, giving the ice a white appearance, as shown in Figure 99.

Compared to clear ice, rime ice is lighter in weight and its weight is of little significance. Its irregular shape, however, and rough surface make it very effective at decreasing the aerodynamic efficiency of airfoils, thus reducing lift and increasing drag. Rime ice is brittle and more easily removed than clear ice.

Mixed Clear and Rime Icing

In cooking school I learned that mixing two distinctly different things doesn't always give you what you expect. For instance, you can't mix an oatmeal breakfast with a roast beef dinner and expect to get a meat meal that lowers your cholesterol. On the other hand, you can mix clear and rime ice together and get a version of both.

Mixed structural icing occurs when drops vary in size or when liquid drops are intermingled with snow or ice particles. This mixture can form rapidly and, as ice particles become embedded in clear ice, it builds in a very rough accumulation that sometimes takes on a mushroom shape on leading edges.

Icing Intensities

As an instrument pilot, it's important for you to understand that all clouds at subfreezing temperatures are potential ice makers. The amount and rate of ice accretion, however, depends on the drop size, drop distribution and aerodynamic effect of the airplane. On some occasions, ice may not even form despite a cloud meeting the criteria for ice formation. This may lead you to believe that because you didn't get ice in one cloud at subfreezing temperatures you won't get it in others. Nothing could be farther from the truth.

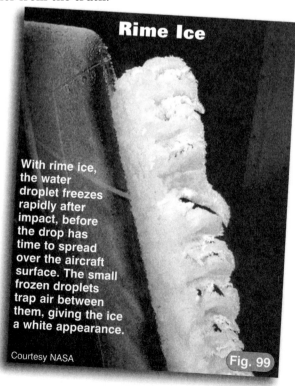

Courtesy NASA — Fig. 99

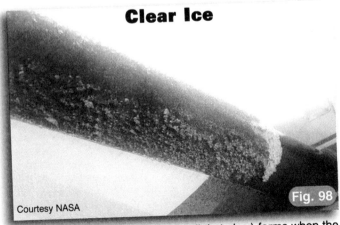

Clear ice (OK, sometimes it's not all that clear) forms when the liquid portion of the drop remaining after initial impact flows over the aircraft surface gradually freezing as a sheet of solid ice.

Icing Forecasts

Here's the good news about icing. You can visit the Aviation Weather Center at the NWS and view the current icing potential (CIP) forecast. The CIP and FIP provide measures of the icing potential at all locations in the continental U.S. using a 100 point scale and color codes.

Courtesy NASA

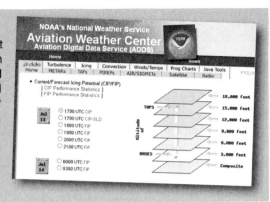

If there are many large, supercooled water droplets present, the potential for hazardous icing exists. On the other hand, an equal or lesser number of small droplets favors a slower rate of icing. You'll often find small water droplets in fog and low level clouds. Drizzle or very light rain is good evidence of the presence of small drops in such clouds; but in many cases there is no precipitation at all. The most common type of icing found in lower level stratus clouds is rime.

On the other hand, the abundance of water and large drop size found in thick extensive stratified clouds (i.e., altostratus and nimbostratus) produce continuous rain and could produce serious icing. These clouds and the systems that produce them may cover thousands of square miles and make an extended flight hazardous.

In thick, stratified clouds the concentrations of water is normally greater with warmer temperatures. Thus, the heaviest icing will usually be found at or slightly above the freezing level where the temperature is never more than a few degrees below freezing. In layer type clouds, continuous icing conditions are rarely found to exist more than 5,000 feet above the freezing level, and are usually two or three thousand feet thick.

At this point you might consider it a good idea to begin a climb the moment you begin picking up ice in stratiform clouds in hopes of getting above the level where ice forms. If so, chill out for a moment. I suggest you think very carefully before doing this. Trying to climb in smaller, underpowered airplanes with ice already on the wings is very risky business. What I'd call ice-y dicey. As you climb, the slower airspeed and larger angle of attack increases the time and surface areas exposed to ice. Most small airplanes are not fit to climb in icing conditions, especially when the pilot isn't sure he or she can get to a point where ice formation stops. And even if it does stop, this doesn't mean you'll get rid of the ice that's already on the airplane.

Climbing is the wise choice only when you can with a high degree of certainty get safely get above the cloud tops, where ice can't and won't continue to form. This implies that you know where the cloud tops are. Hopefully, you'll have recent pilot reports to provide you with this information.

On the other hand, if you can descend to lower levels where the temperatures are above freezing, this is a much better option. Then again, the 180 degree turn when you begin picking up ice is an equally valid response to ice formation. Of course, if you're in the family F-18, ice will hardly send a chill down your empennage, given the power of that airplane.

In cumuliform clouds, the upward currents produce conditions favorable for the formation and support of many large water drops. In case you don't believe this, just think about the raindrop size and rainfall intensity that's normally associated with thunderstorms and the showers they produce. When your airplane enters the heavy water concentrations found in cumuliform clouds, the large drops break and spread rapidly over the leading edge of the airfoil, forming a film of water. If temperatures are freezing or colder, the water freezes quickly to form a solid sheet of clear ice. A good rule is to avoid cumuliform clouds under these conditions. This means, however, that there will be fewer, if any, pilot reports of icing with which you can better determine its rate and frequency of formation in flight.

Keep in mind that the updrafts in cumuliform clouds can carry large amounts of liquid water far above the freezing level. On rare occasions, icing has been encountered in thunderstorm clouds at altitudes of 30,000 to 40,000 feet, where the free air temperature was colder than minus 40° C. You don't expect ice to form at these low temperature, since any water is usually in the solid state. Your expectations to the contrary, supercooled water droplets have been observed at temperatures colder than –40° C (normally, supercooled water drops are most abundant in clouds at temperatures between 0° C and –15° C with deceasing quantities at colder temperatures).

Weathering the Weather

As an aspiring instrument rated pilot, you already know that weather is a serious force to be reckoned with. You don't need to get a Ph.D. in meteorology to be a good pilot, but you do need to understand and apply a basic knowledge of weather to fly safely.

Weather is a contributor to far too many aviation accidents. Most occur not because something came out of nowhere and smote the poor pilot, but because the pilot didn't properly anticipate what the weather would be, and plan accordingly.

Pilots as a group tend to be strong personalities. That's why they're called pilots in command. However, when it comes to the weather, a little bit of humility will go a long way toward keeping your skin (and that of your aircraft) intact. "Know before you go," is the fundamental concept with which I hope you blow out of this chapter.

Just remember, the answer is blowin' in the wind.

Advanced Weather Concepts

On a local level, you can get by with a basic understanding of fronts, rain forecasts, and fog warnings. As an instrument-rated pilot, however, you'll need a much deeper understanding of how weather systems move across the country. Welcome to advanced weather for the advanced pilot. You may or may not have covered the following items during your private pilot training. Either way, you can only improve your understanding of the meteorological process as you attend to the following discussion of wave cyclones, jet streams and the like.

Ignorance on any subject, much less weather, never rewards but always punishes. Don't be like the fellow in a quiet community who was amused by the black rubber hose that city personnel placed across his street one day. No knowing what it was, he decided to back over it a few hundred times each day before he went to work. Two months later he discovered the city was installing an interstate in his once tranquil front yard.

Wave Cyclones [Frontal Waves]

Not all fronts are found along low pressure troughs. Sometimes they form as small waves along one of the three to seven larger waves of the polar front. These smaller waves (also known as wave cyclones because they rotate in a counterclockwise manner) move along the polar front in an easterly direction. They are blown that way by the prevailing westerlies. Let's examine this process.

(The word *cyclone* indicates low atmospheric pressure having a counterclockwise rotation. Small wave cyclones are also simply called storms because they bring inclement weather).

Discontinuities along the polar front can appear and cause small wave cyclones (sometimes referred to as frontal waves) to form. Figure 100 (on the right hand page) depicts this process. Wave cyclones usually form in slow-moving cold fronts or stationary fronts, as shown Figure 100A. Airflow on each side of the stationary front is parallel to the actual front. Thus, there is little or no reason for the front to bend or twist.

Any small disturbance in the stationary frontal pattern, caused by uneven heating, irregular terrain or high altitude winds (the jet stream), can start a wave-like bend in the front as shown in Figure 100B. If the wave-like bend is big (energetic) enough, warm air can start to rise over the retreating colder air. This often leads to condensation, and the release of latent heat into the atmosphere which intensifies the low pressure system (in other words, makes the air want to rise more quickly).

As the low pressure deepens, atmospheric pressure decreases. Counterclockwise circulation bends the front, which advances the cold air and forms a cold front, as shown in Figure 100C (position 1). As warmer air slides up and over the receding colder air, a warm front forms as

shown in Figure 90C (position 2). As fronts form, the entire wave cyclone (the storm) moves in an easterly direction, along with the prevailing westerlies.

Advancing cold air (cold front) usually moves faster than retreating cool air (the zone of which is the warm front). Think of the cold air as falling or sliding underneath the warm air. Things that fall are accelerated by gravity. Retreating cooler air tugs at the ground as the warmer air slides up and over it. This tugging or sticking to the ground slows the advancing warm front. Retreating cool air acts like I did during my first visit to the dentist—I got splinters under my fingernails as my mother tried to tug me off the porch.

Figure 100D shows the faster-moving cold front catching up to and overtaking the slower warm front. Meteorologists call this an occlusion, and it is depicted by warm front and cold front symbols moving in the same direction.

Since these fronts overlap, pilots find that an occluded front contains a combination of warm and cold frontal weather, as shown in Figure 100D. Once the occlusion forms, frontal movement slows down. The low pressure area diminishes in intensity because warm air is no longer rising and condensing over the colder air. In the final stage, shown in Figure 100E, the occlusion dissipates and the two fronts form a stationary front once again. Remnants of the low spin off and usually dissipate in forgotten whirling eddies.

Sometimes multiple storm systems (several wave cyclones) form along the polar front, as depicted in Figure 101. It's not unusual for three, four, or more of them to appear. These move eastward, with the flow of the westerlies, and in the same direction as the high altitude jet stream (which blows from west to east).

Wave Cyclone Weather Patterns

Small frontal systems that occur in wave cyclone patterns offer a large scale mixture of the most interesting weather (a wave cyclone is the storm system that typically contains fronts, a low pressure system and counter-

Storm Systems Move Eastward

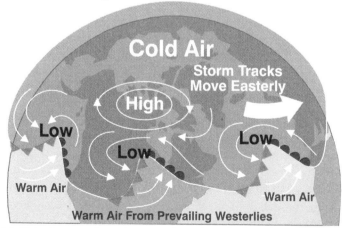

Multiple storm systems (wave cyclones) can be found moving eastward along the polar front. Warm air from the prevailing westerlies and high altitude winds move these storms.

Fig. 101

SHORT WAVE (STORM) FORMATION

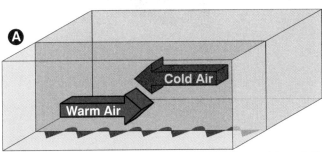

A Frontal waves may form along a slow moving cold or stationary front.

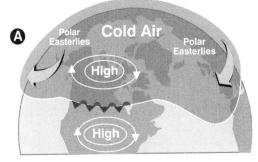

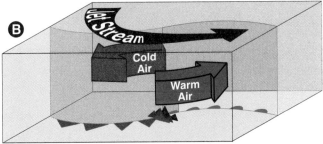

B The jet stream or a geographical feature may cause a bend in the front.

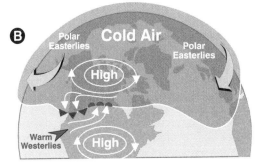

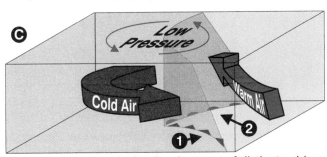

C Low pressure forms in the development of distinct cold and warm fronts.

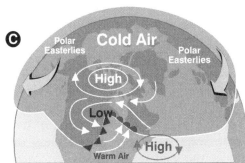

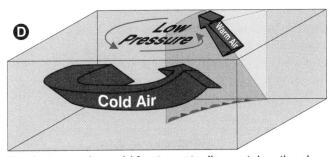

D The faster moving cold front eventually overtakes the slower warm front.

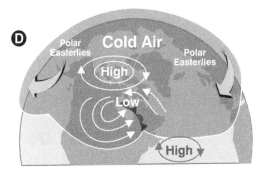

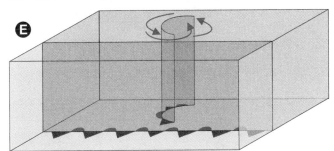

E The frontal occlusion eventually dissipates.

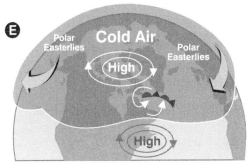

Fig. 100

Weather Experienced in a Wave Cyclone

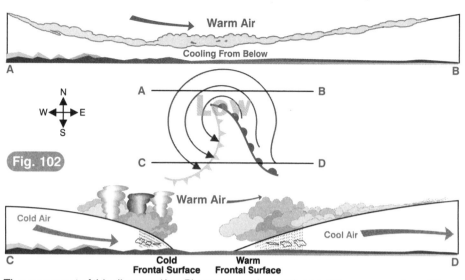

Fig. 102

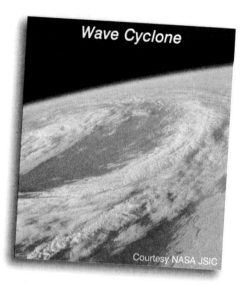

Wave Cyclone

Courtesy NASA JSIC

The upper part of this diagram (A to B) represents the north part of the wave cyclone. Warmer air is above you in this part of the wave, implying that you may experience showers or snow flurries, depending on the temperature of the air below. If you were stationary on the surface south of the low, the fronts would pass from (C to D). The warm front passes first, followed by clearing skies, then the cold front and finally clearing skies and cold air.

clockwise—cyclonic—circulation). Figure 102 shows one of these wave cyclones in full formation. North of the low pressure center, clouds lower and thicken, producing rain or snow usually lasting 12 to 24 hours. If the storm's warmer air is above you (along path A to B), precipitation usually takes the form of showers or snow flurries, depending on the temperature of the air below.

South of the low (along path C to D), you'll experience the approach of a warm front with lowering stratus, nimbostratus (stratus clouds with rain). With passage of the warm front, the weather clears and the air warms up. Finally the cold front arrives, typically bringing cumulonimbus clouds (these cloud types have the greatest turbulence) and thunderstorms. Cold air, clearing skies, and gusty winds follow the cold front.

In time, one frontal system may catch up and overlap with the other in a wave cyclone. This overlapping is knows as an occlusion. Two varieties of occlusion are typical: cold occlusion and warm occlusion.

Cold Occlusions

In wave cyclones, cold fronts usually catch up to and overtake slower moving warm fronts. This overtaking produces what is known as a cold-type occluded front or a cold occlusion.

Cold occlusions occur when the air ahead of the warm front is less cold than the air behind the overtaking cold front, as shown in Figure 103. The cold front overtaking the warm front lifts the warm air up and over the retreating cool air. Essentially, the warm front is lifted entirely off the surface by the undercutting cold front.

The hollowed-out warm front symbols in Figure 103 represent the lifting of the warm front by the colder air. Weather ahead of the occlusion is similar to that associated with warm fronts, while weather near the surface position is similar to that of cold fronts.

As the occlusion develops, warm air is lifted higher and higher. Finally the cloud system associated with the warm front disappears. The weather and cloud system now

Cold Occlusion

A cold occlusion occurs when the cold front overtakes and lifts up the preceding warm front. The warm air is lifted entirely off the surface by the cold front. Weather ahead of the occlusion is similar to that in a warm front. Near the surface, the weather is similar to that of a cold front.

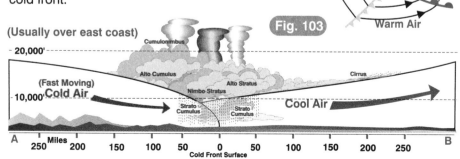

Fig. 103

A Weak Occlusion

Courtesy NASA JSIC

Warm Occlusion

A warm occlusion occurs when the Pacific cold front pushes the warmer air up and over the retreating Arctic air mass. The Pacific air mass, not being as cold as the Arctic air mass, similarly moves up the same slope. Weather associated with the warm occlusion is similar to that of a warm front, while tropical cold front weather occurs near the upper cold front boundary.

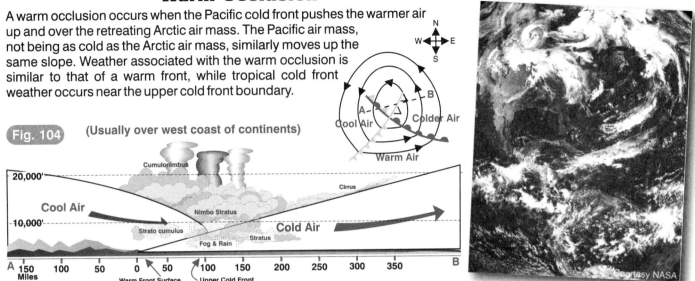

Fig. 104 **(Usually over west coast of continents)**

resembles that of a cold front. Cold occlusions form predominantly over continents or along the east coast and are more common than warm occlusions.

Warm Occlusions

Warm-type occluded fronts (or *warm occlusions*) are usually found in the northwestern United States. They begin with cold air masses from the Pacific overtaking a retreating colder air mass from the Arctic. Warmer air is caught between these moving air masses. This process is shown in Figure 104.

The retreating Arctic air mass is colder than the approaching Pacific air mass. The Pacific cold front pushes the warmer air up and over the retreating Arctic air mass. The Pacific air mass is cool, but not as cold as the Arctic air mass, and it moves up the same slope as well. At this point the Pacific cold front becomes an upper cold front. Weather in the cross sectional area from (A) to (B), shown in the insert, is shown in Figure 104.

The structure of the warm occlusion (Figure 104) shows an open-type cold front symbol. This indicates that the Pacific front is no longer in contact with the surface. Weather associated with a warm front occlusion has characteristics of both warm and cold fronts. The cloud sequence ahead of the occlusion is similar to that of a warm front, while tropical cold front weather occurs near the upper cold front boundary.

Are we having fun yet? Remember, it takes a lot of study to become intimately familiar with weather. It's not something you're expected to master before you become a private or even an instrument pilot. The study of weather is an ongoing process for pilots. Try to learn a little about it every day. It's similar to the study all bachelors should do before they begin doing their own wash. As a bachelor I bought a box of detergent and on its side it said, "Use All!" I did. Frankly, half a box would have worked just fine.

Postflight Briefing #9-2

The Adiabatic Chart

As an instrument pilot you should have some idea about how the adiabatic chart used by meteorologists is constructed. So let's construct one. First, the adiabatic chart, Figure 105, is a composite of expected lapse rates and actual lapse rates. The graph begins with a grid providing a measure of height on the vertical axis and temperature on the horizontal axis (Figure 106). Next we add the dry adiabats, shown as thin black dashed lines (Figure 107). The dry adiabats are nothing more than sloping lines representing the dry adiabatic lapse rate of 5.4 degrees F per thousand feet. These lines slope to the left because the temperature decreases (leftward movement on the grid) as altitude increases (vertical movement on the grid). A

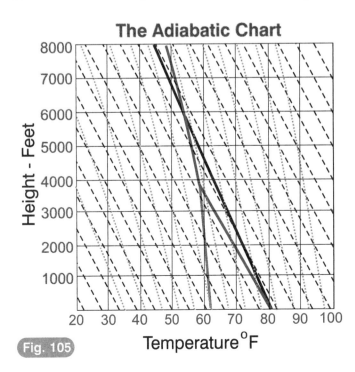

The Adiabatic Chart

Height - Feet

Temperature °F

Fig. 105

The Adiabatic Chart

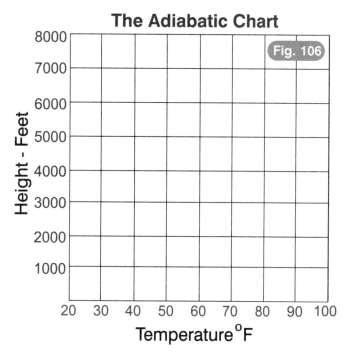

The Adiabatic Chart (Dry Adiabats)

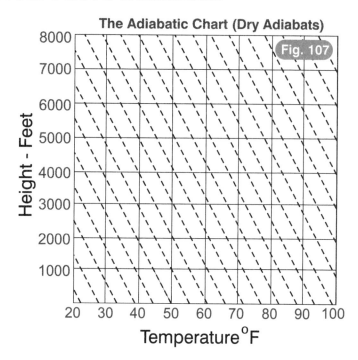

rising parcel of unsaturated air would cool at a rate that's parallel to any one of these lines.

Next we add the moist adiabats, shown as thin blue dotted lines (Figure 108). Moist adiabats represent how saturated air changes temperature as altitude increases. Remember, when air becomes saturated and forms a cloud, latent heat is released. Because heat is released to the saturated air parcel, the temperature of that rising parcel doesn't cool as quickly. Therefore, the moist adiabat doesn't slope to the left as much as the dry adiabat (keep in mind, the great the leftward slope of any line, the greater the temperature loss with altitude. After all, if the line were vertical, this would mean the temperature stays the same with a gain in altitude). A rising parcel of saturated air would cool at a rate parallel to the nearest moist adiabat line shown on the chart.

Figure 109 shows both the dry and moist adiabats on the adiabatic chart. Here's how to make sense of this chart, as it stands now. If you raised a parcel of air and it remained unsaturated, it would cool at 5.4 degrees F per thousand feet. This means that the cooling would exactly parallel the black dashed line (the dry adiabat). As soon as the parcel became saturated and formed a cloud, the rate of cooling would parallel the blue dashed line (the moist adiabat).

Now let's play meteorologist and do what they do (and I don't mean check to see if the newspaper came wrapped in plastic so they will know whether or not to forecast rain for that day). Let's send up a rawinsonde and take a temperature sounding of the atmosphere. After all, to find out how stable the atmosphere is we need to know the ambient (environmental) lapse rate. Let's say that our airborne

The Adiabatic Chart (Moist Adiabats)

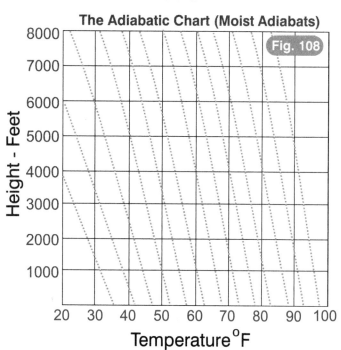

The Adiabatic Chart

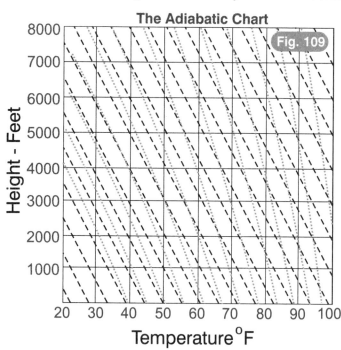

The Ambient Lapse Rate

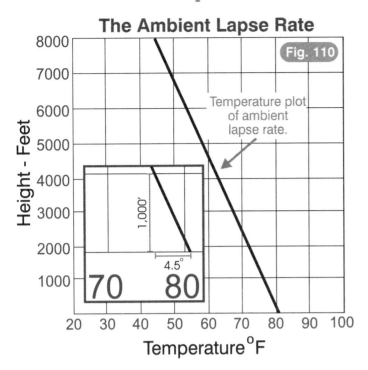

Temperature plot of ambient lapse rate.

thermometer measures an ambient temperature decrease of 4.5 degrees F per thousand feet. Let's plot that lapse rate as a heavy black line as shown in Figure 110.

To see how stable or unstable the atmosphere is, let's compare our ambient lapse rate with the dry adiabats (Figure 111). Let's initially raise a parcel of unsaturated air starting at 3,000 feet represented by the small red dot on the ambient lapse rate line (Figure 111A). As we raise that parcel, it will cool at a rate that's parallel to the dry adiabat line. As you can see, according the diagram,

because the slope of the rising red arrow is to the left of the ambient lapse rate line, the parcel cools more quickly than the ambient lapse rate. The parcel won't rise, indicating that the atmosphere is stable.

Figure 111B shows that the ambient lapse rate as measured by a rawinsonde indicates a temperature inversion exists (the middle portion of the thick black line slopes to the right, indicating an increase in temperature with altitude, thus an inversion). Now let's raise a parcel of unsaturated air beginning at 3,000 feet (represented by the red dot). As you can see, the red arrow indicates that the air parcel would cool at the dry adiabatic lapse (parallel to the dry adiabat line). The red arrow's slope is obviously way to the left of the thick black line (representing the ambient lapse rate), thus the rising parcel would remain cooler than the surround air. The atmosphere in the inversion this instance would be stable.

Figure 111C shows the ambient lapse rate in an unstable atmosphere. Let's raise a parcel of unsaturated air beginning at 3,000 feet. The red arrow shows that the parcel cools at the dry adiabatic lapse rate, thus paralleling the dry adiabat. Yet, the slope of the red arrow is to the right of the thick black line (the ambient lapse rate). This means that the rising parcel doesn't cool as quickly as the ambient air. Thus, the parcel will remain warmer than the surrounding air. The atmosphere, in this instance, is considered unstable. The ambient lapse rate in this example cools about 6.0 degrees F per thousand feet. This is called a *super adiabatic lapse rate*. While rare aloft, it is very common near the ground on hot days. This explains thermals and convective bumps near the surface.

What happens when air is forced to rise and becomes saturated because it reaches its dewpoint? This is where

The Adiabatic Chart (Dry Adiabat Comparison)

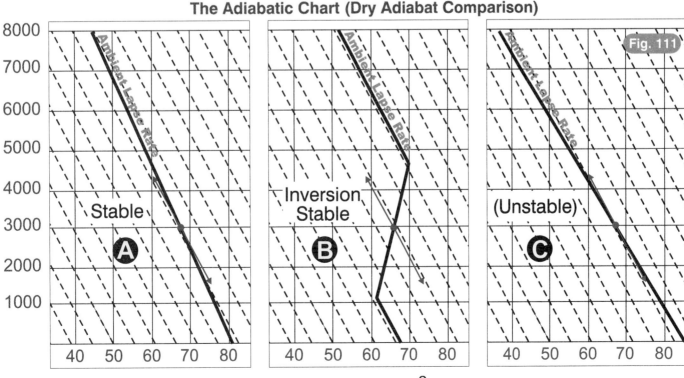

Temperature °F

The Adiabatic Chart

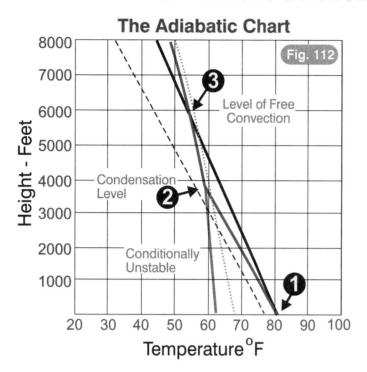

the surrounding air and the parcel continues to rise on its own. Thus, the origin of the term "free convection." In this example the atmosphere is unstable.

Keep in mind that a saturated air parcel in free convection is losing moisture by condensation as it rises. Taking this into account, along with the colder air at higher altitudes, explains why the moist adiabatic line (blue dotted line) slopes or leans toward the dry adiabatic line (think black dashed line). Eventually, the rising air parcel cools to the temperature of the surrounding air, either because it loses a lot of its moisture or runs into warmer temperatures aloft (such as at the tropopause) and free convection ceases.

Once again, keep in mind that the parcel method of understanding stability has its limitations. It assumes that there is no energy exchange between the parcel and the surrounding air. In other words, it assumes a perfect adiabatic process. This is true in a perfect world but does have its limitations in our atmosphere, where some mixing takes place. Nevertheless, the parcel method should give you a good handle on understanding the adiabatic process.

the moist adiabats become useful. Figure 112 shows the adiabatic process in saturated air. Let's assume that an atmospheric sounding indicates that the ambient lapse rate is 4.5 degrees F per thousand feet as indicated by the thick black line. The thin dashed line (I've only drawn one on this chart) represents the dry adiabatic lapse rate. The thin blue dotted line represents the moist adiabatic lapse rate. The dewpoint of the air at the surface in this example is 62 degrees F and is represented by the thick blue line. As you know, the dewpoint decreases at 1 degree F (approximately .5 degrees C) per thousand feet. The thick blue line on the chart represents this sloping decrease of 1 degree F per thousand feet starting at 62 degrees at the surface. Finally, the red line represents the temperature decrease of a rising parcel beginning at the surface.

The parcel starts out at about 81 degrees F (position 1). It is initially forced upward, perhaps by being blown up the side of a mountain, and decreases at the dry adiabatic lapse rate since it's initially unsaturated. Because the red line at this position slopes to the left of the thick black line (the ambient lapse rate) it remains stable.

Eventually, however, the parcel cools to its dewpoint, which is the intersection between the dewpoint line (the thick blue line) and the red line (position 2). At about 4,000 feet, the air reaches its condensation level and becomes saturated. Heat is now released to the parcel and it cools at the moist adiabatic rate of 2.5 degrees F per thousand feet (as indicated by the sloping think blue dotted line), thus remaining slightly warmer in the process. The parcel (the red line) decreases temperature at a rate that parallels the nearest moist adiabat (the thin blue dotted line). At 6,000 feet, the rising parcel of saturated air is the same temperature as the ambient air (this is the point where the red line intersects the thick black line as shown in position 3). This point is known as the *level of free convection*. Above this level the parcel becomes warmer than

Postflight Briefing #9-3

A Convective Question

Now that you know a bit about thunderstorms, you'll need to know a little more about how to detect them. Sure, lightning, strong gusts along with intense rain showers are all good indicators of thunderstorm activity, but what about those times when you're aloft and can't directly evaluate these items. In particular, what about those times when cumulus clouds are in the process of becoming a thunderstorm? What may appear to be a harmless cumulus cloud might actually be a thunderstorm in training. Therefore, the question is: *What criteria distinguish a convectively harmless cumulus cloud from one that can damage an airplane?*

This is a question all instrument pilots must be able to answer. On one hand, the answer is pretty simple. A pilot must avoid any cloud having a significant chance of severe turbulence or even the slightest chance of destructive turbulence. On the other hand, the sister question to the first is not so easy to answer: How can a pilot tell if this level of turbulence exists in a convective cloud?

The fact is that these are important questions to instrument rated pilots, questions in need of answers. So let me offer you the response I typically offer my fellow pilots when asked these questions.

Let's begin with how airplanes are built. Airplanes certificated under Part 23 prior to September 14, 1969 were required to withstand vertical sharp edge gusts of 30 feet per second (FPS) at Vc, which is the *velocity of cruise* or the beginning of the airspeed indicator's yellow arc. Beech Bonanza aircraft are typical of airplanes in this category. Those certificated on or after this date were required to withstand vertical sharp edge gusts of 50 FPS at Vc. The newer Rockwell Commander is an airplane falling into this category. This doesn't mean, however, that airplanes in the pre- '69 category can't withstand vertical gusts of greater intensity. This was just the minimum vertical gust requirement necessary according to the regulations at the time.

Now let's talk about water.

As you've already learned, to keep large volumes of water suspended it in the atmosphere it takes a lifting force, otherwise known as *updrafts*. The more water suspended within a cloud the greater the lifting force or updraft that's required to keep it there. When the amount of water suspended exceeds the lifting force that suspends it, the water falls. We call this rain and measure the amount in *inches per hour*.

It doesn't have to rain, however, for us to measure the amount of water suspended inside the cloud. We can merely identify the amount of water in a cloud using radar and say that if it did rain, then the rainfall rate would be a specific amount, calibrated in inches per hour.

Given this observation, it's logical to say that a cloud with a rainfall rate (or potential rainfall rate) of .5 inches per hour has less updraft action than a cloud with a rainfall rate of 2 inches per hour. We can conclude that the larger the rainfall rate (or potential rainfall rate), the stronger the updrafts found inside a cloud.

As you undoubtedly know, radar energy is reflected by solid objects, not clouds themselves. The water suspended in a cloud is a solid object, but the cloud itself isn't. The more water suspended within the cloud, the greater the ratio of radar energy returned for a given amount sent out by the radar unit. The amount of this reflected radar energy, referred to as *reflectivity* or *Z*, is calibrated in the form of a quantity known as *dBZ* or *decibels of Z*.

Now things are about to get really interesting.

Years ago Project Rough Rider (and subsequent government studies) established a correlation between the amount of water suspended in a cloud and the vertical gusts found within that cloud (measured in feet per second) as shown in Figure 113. If we can equate rainfall rates with radar reflectivity or dBZ's, we can make some interesting assumptions using the results of the Rough Rider study.

It turns out that rainfall rates producing radar reflectivity ranging from 16 to 29 dBZ's (known as a *Level 1* radar return) generate a 100% probability of light turbulence and a 10% chance of moderate turbulence. Light turbulence is defined as vertical gusts from 0-19 FPS and moderate turbulence is defined as vertical gusts from 20 to 34 FPS.

Rainfall rates producing radar reflectivity ranging from 30 to 39 dBZ's (known as a *Level 2* radar return) generate a 100% probability of light turbulence, a 40% chance of moderate turbulence, and a 2% chance of severe turbulence. Severe turbulence is defined as vertical gusts from 35 to 49 FPS.

Rainfall rates producing radar reflectivity ranging from 40 to 49 dBZ's (known as a *Level 3* and 4 radar return) generate a 100% probability of light turbulence, a 90% chance of moderate turbulence, a 10% chance of severe turbulence, and a 3% chance of destructive turbulence. Destructive turbulence is defined as vertical gusts of 50 FPS and higher.

Now you know the answer to the question, "What criterion distinguishes a convectively harmless cumulus cloud from one that can damage an airplane?" The answer is: *Any convective cloud with a radar reflectivity of 40 dBZ's (a Level 3 radar return) or higher needs to be avoided and treated as an immediate threat to your safety aloft.*

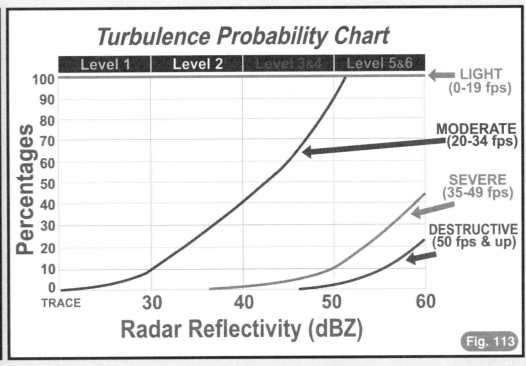

Turbulence Probability

The turbulence probability chart provides you with a statistical means of estimating the probability of turbulence based on the amount of water in a cloud.

For instance, if a cloud has sufficient water to reflect radar energy to a value of 40 to 49 dBZs, then there is a 3% chance of destructive turbulence (at the higher 49 dBZ value), a 10% chance of severe turbulence (at the higher 49 dBZ value), and a 100% chance of light turbulence in that cloud.

Because of this potential for severe and destructive turbulence, pilots always avoid cloud areas/masses containing 40 dBZ and higher.

Turbulence Probability Chart

Level 1 — Level 2 — Level 3&4 — Level 5&6

Percentages (vertical axis: 0, 10, 20, 30, 40, 50, 60, 70, 80, 90, 100)

Radar Reflectivity (dBZ) (horizontal axis: TRACE, 30, 40, 50, 60)

LIGHT (0-19 fps)
MODERATE (20-34 fps)
SEVERE (35-49 fps)
DESTRUCTIVE (50 fps & up)

Fig. 113

Airborne Weather Radar Display Levels

Airborne Display Level/Color	Display Level	VIP Level	dBZ Appx.
5-6 Magenta	Extreme	Level 6	50 to 59 dBZ
	Intense	Level 5	
3-4 Red	Very Strong	Level 4	40 to 49 dBz
	Strong	Level3	
2 Yellow	Moderate	Level 2	30 to 39 dBZ
1 Green	Weak	Level 1	16 to 29 dBZ
0 Black	These display descriptions are for *airborne radar* and differ from the NWS, Center and Approach Control screen weather display. **Fig. 114**		

The National Weather Service has established six storm levels. Airborne radar manufacturers adopted these levels along with the color codes shown above. These are the colors seen on modern airborne radar displays.

The 3% chance of destructive turbulence is simply too significant to ignore. While the chances are small, the outcome is eternal. Figure 114 shows how different dBZ's of reflectivity are color coded on airborne radars. It is any wonder that the Level 3 radar return is identified as red as shown in Figure 115? Red means danger, right? Airline pilots avoid all areas having red on their radars and so should you.

Sharp pilot that you are, I'm sure you're wondering why I would not suggest the mandatory avoidance of a Level 2 radar return when flying a pre 1969-certificated airplane. After all, a Level 2 return has a 40% chance of 20

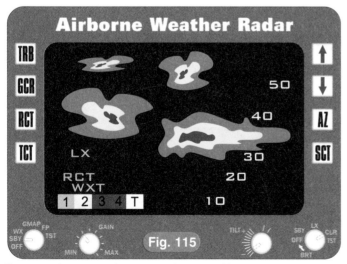

Fig. 115

Because the areas shown in red on an airborne radar represent Level 3 storm returns, all pilots should avoid these areas. Because the highest level of turbulence probability also applies to lesser storms levels, the yellow and green areas surrounding the red areas should also be avoided by thunderstorm distance recommendations.

to 34 FPS gusts, which can exceed the certificated stress limit of this airplane when it is flown at Vc (the top of the green arc or Vno). Consider the following idea.

Airplanes typically cruise at high altitudes which means that the higher they fly, the lower their IAS. In my A36 Bonanza, at lower altitudes I can cruise at more than 170 knots indicated (about 5 knots over Vc). At 10,000 feet, I'm indicating about 145 knots in cruise (which is about 5 knots above the "gross weight" maneuvering speed). When cruising at higher altitudes, the A36 should be able to withstand sharp edge gusts a little greater than 30 FPS without experiencing any problems (not that I look forward to or even desire to experience this, of course). What about the 2% chance of severe turbulence? Well, this also implies that there is a 98% chance of not experiencing severe turbulence. We have to choose our risks and this one doesn't disturb me that much given the following preference.

Whenever possible, I always try to avoid flying in or near Level 2 radar returns, regardless of when the airplane was certificated. If you're flying IFR and you want to obtain full utility from your airplane, you may often fly in or near areas containing Level 2 returns. I wouldn't, however, enter a Level 2 return if I thought there was any chance of it evolving into a Level 3 or greater return. How would I make this assessment? There are many clues. One of the best is the presence of any Level 3 or greater returns within the same airmass. If these exist, it's reasonable to assume that the airmass is unstable enough to hatch Level 3 and greater convective weather.

There's a very important point to be made here that is subtle but significant. If red (Level 3) exists anywhere in a mass or area of clouds, then the statistical turbulence associated with that Level 3 area applies to all the lesser levels, too. In other words, just avoiding the red area in a radar return and flying through the yellow or green area of that return isn't safe. Project Rough Rider established that the lesser levels will also have the same probability of turbulence associated with the highest level of return in that mass or areas of cells.

At this point I know you're wondering it's possible for you to identify the strength of radar returns when you don't have radar. There are several ways to do this, all of which require that you use OPR's (*Other People's Radar*).

It's perfectly acceptable for you to ask the controller to solicit a pilot report for you from another radar-equipped airplane under his or her control. You can simply ask if there is anyone with radar showing a Level 3 or higher radar return headed in your direction of flight. There is, however, a better way to obtain this information thanks to modern technology.

For instance, it's now quite common for airplanes to have uplinked, real time NEXRAD radar available in the cockpit (Figure 116). Though it's sometimes called "real time," this is a misnomer. NEXRAD radar updates can be five to six minutes old when received in the cockpit. In a sense, the NEXRAD information you see in the cockpit

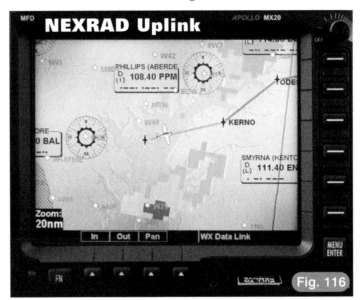

Fig. 116

NEXRAD weather uplink for the cockpit provides pilots with information similar to that found on airborne weather radar displays. The uplink service provider, however, may color code dBZ levels differently from that what is used on airborne weather radar. Yellow on some displays might identify areas with 40 dBZs or higher. So make sure you check you manufacturer's handbook.

can be ancient history when it comes to thunderstorm development. Given this limitation, we can still derive some very valuable information from cockpit based

NEXRAD radar when we use dBZ values to assess the information.

If you're using NEXRAD, you want to identify the color representing 40 dBZ's (Figure 117). These are the areas representing Level 3 radar returns. You want to avoid them and all the sub-levels associated with that radar return. As I've already stated, the Rough Rider study indicated that the highest level of anticipated turbulence within the storm applies to all the sub-levels within the storm (i.e., the Level 1 and 2 portions, too). So if an area of Level 3 radar returns is present, the entire area should be avoided.

The real issue here is that pilots shouldn't use uplinked NEXRAD in IMC to pick their way through convective weather in the way someone with airborne really real-time weather radar might attempt the feat. In other words, NEXRAD isn't a *tactical device* as is on-board weather radar. Instead, pilots should be using this information to decide whether they to remain in VMC and visually avoid the storms, when and where to make major route changes or tap into additional sources of information such as that provided by Stormscope/StrikeFinder devices, pilot reports, Center radar, Approach radar, FSS radar and so on.

If you understand the relationship between dBZ's and the probability of turbulence associated with radar returns, you're now in a position to make better, safer weather decisions when flying IFR.

NEXRAD Weather as Seen on Your Home Computer

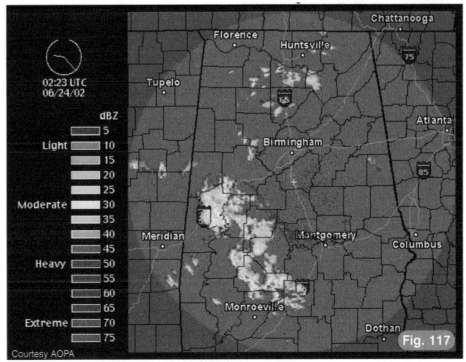

Updated: 2:23 AM UTC on June 24, 2002 change

NEXRAD weather information is available via the internet through your home computer. When making go-no/go decisions about convective activity using NEXRAD, make sure you examine the weather provider's dBZ calibration values. In this example, 40 dBZs is shown as an orange area.

Center's WARP Weather Information

There was a time not too long ago when Center's radar scope would only portray precipitation symbolically as *slashes* and *Hs*. That's changed with the advent of NEXRAD. Now both Center and Approach control can see precipitation on their screens using WARP and STARS technology. No, don't think Star Trek here. This is different. Let's begin with Center's WARP system first.

WARP stands for Weather and Radar Processor. This system makes NEXRAD weather information available to the Center controller in the form of three distinct color bands as shown in Figure 118. These color bands are royal blue, checkered cyan and cyan, with each corresponding to the specific storm levels shown in Figure 119.

Center's WARP Wx Presentation

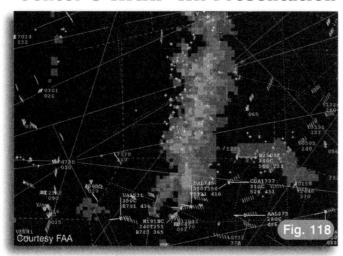

Courtesy FAA
Fig. 118

A Center controller sees weather derived from NEXRAD information portrayed as one of three different colors: *royal blue*, *checkered cyan* and *cyan*. Each color represents different precipitation intensity levels.

As you already know, you want to avoid any Level 3 storm or higher, period! This corresponds to any area with checkered cyan or cyan on the controller's screen. Controllers no longer in terms of storm levels (i.e., Level 1, 2, 3, etc.). Instead, they speak in terms of precipitation intensity. It's up to you to know how to interpret these intensity levels.

Looking at Figure 119, it's clear that Heavy precipitation refers to a Level 3 storm or above. Therefore, if a controller reports *Heavy* precipitation in your direction of flight, you'll most certainly want to avoid this area.

Precipitation reported as *Moderate* is considered a Level 2 return and can border on Level 3 intensity. As I stated previously, you should try to avoid Moderate levels of precipitation (a Level 2 return) whenever possible regardless of the certification date of your airplane. Unless you're sure that the Moderate precipitation won't become Heavy (evolve from a Level 2 to a Level 3 storm), then it's best to avoid Moderate levels of precipitation whenever possible.

WARP Precipitation Levels

Air Traffic Control Center's Wx Display Terminology			
Airborne Display Level/Color	**Reported by ATC as:**	**Storm Level**	**dBz** Appx.
5-6 Cyan	**Extreme** 2" to 16" Rainfall Rate/Hour	Level 6	50 to 59 dBZ
		Level 5	
3-4 Checkered Cyan	**Heavy** .5" to 2" Rainfall Rate/Hour	Level 4	40 to 49 dBZ
		Level 3	
2 Royal Blue	**Moderate** .175" to .5" Rainfall Rate/Hour	Level 2	30 to 39 dBZ
1 Not Shown Fig. 119	**Light** (not shown on WARP) .01" to .1" Rainfall Rate/Hour	Level 1	16 to 29 dBZ

Center controllers no longer refer to weather radar returns as storm levels (i.e., Level 1, 2, 3, etc.). Instead, they refer to radar returns as one of three different precipitation intensity levels: *moderate*, *heavy* and *extreme*.

The WARP system doesn't show *Light* precipitation. Therefore, the Center controller will be less likely to identify the entire boundary of a storm system. What does that mean to you? As the Project Rough Rider study indicated, the statistical probability of turbulence applies to the entire boundary of the storm system, not just the Level 3 areas (Heavy precipitation) and above. So the controller may not be able to provide you with a complete idea of the extended boundaries of a storm system.

WARP also has the ability for overlaying lightning strikes as shown in Figure 120. If you ask the controller for information on lightning activity in your area and you identify the presence of lightning, you'll have an immediate confirmation on the existence of thunderstorm activity. Remember, if the controller sees lighting symbology on his screen, then you can bet there's thunderstorm activity, too (unless an amateur is attempting to fix his solid state TV while standing in his swimming pool).

Keep in mind that WARP is nothing more than NEXRAD information that can be as much as 6 minutes old by the time the controller receives it. Six minutes is about how long it takes the NEXRAD imagery to be processed and distributed. Therefore, when you're asking the Center controller about any weather displayed on his or her screen, that same weather might be six minutes old. In the life of a thunderstorm, a lot can happen in six minutes. The storm, for instance, can grow to a Level 3 or 4 condition (Heavy precipitation) from an apparently benign Level 2 return (Moderate precipitation).

When WARP isn't available (most likely because of technical problems with NEXRAD imagery), then the Center's *narrowband* Air Route Surveillance Radar can display precipitation returns either with slashes or Hs or a combination of both. This "slash" and "H" symbology is the means that Center had for displaying precipitation returns long before they went to WARP. Figure 121 shows slashed lines

WARP Lightning Strike Overlay

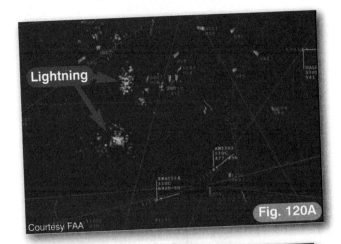

Fig. 120A

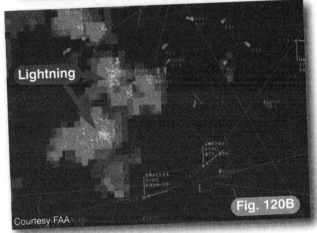

Fig. 120B

Narrowband Radar "Slash" Symbology

Fig. 121

When using narrowband radar weather depictions, the slashes (hatched lines) identify areas of weather radar returns greater than 30 dBZ.

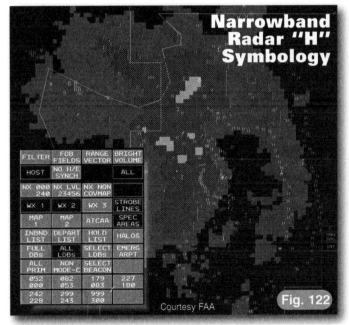

Narrowband Radar "H" Symbology

Fig. 122

When using narrowband radar weather depictions, the H's identify areas of weather radar returns greater than 40 dBZ.

NX 000 240	NX LVL 23456	NX NON COVMAP	
WX 1	WX 2	WX 3	STROBE LINES
MAP 1	MAP 2	ATCAA	Fig. 123

The Center controller can selectively isolate the slashes and Hs or allow them both to identify weather on their radar screen.

Center controllers can superimpose lightning strikes (Figure 120A) over NEXRAD imagery (Figure 120B) on their screens. It is interesting to note that lightning is occurring within the Level 3 (heavy precipitation) returns, reaffirming that thunderstorms are associated with Level 3 (and higher) returns.

(sometimes called "hatched" lines by controllers). The slashed lines represent weather radar returns greater than 30 dBZ. That can mean an area of Level 2 returns or greater. You don't know how much greater, though. There could be a Level 3, 4, 5, or 6 storm present in the area. When the "H" symbol is present, it outlines areas that are greater than 40 dBZ (Figure 122).

If the Center controller advised you that WARP information wasn't available, you could ask him or her for information on the slashes and Hs shown by their narrowband weather information. Any area surrounded by an H is an area to avoid. Center controllers must typically activate individual buttons to display the slashes, the Hs and the slashes and Hs together (the WX#1 key, the WX#2 key, or the WX#3 key, respectively) as shown in Figure 123. If both slashes and Hs are being displayed, then avoid the Hs and use caution for the slashes since the border between them and the Hs indicate a Level 2 return.

In this instance, the best way to let the controller know you're interested in slashes and Hs, is to say something like, "Sir (or ma'am, and don't get these mixed up or you'll end up in a holding pattern somewhere), will you activate your Weather #3 key and tell me the positions of the slashes and Hs's relative to my airplane and its direction of flight?"

Airport Surveillance Radar [Approach Control] Weather Info

The newest approach control facilities provide weather imagery on their radar screens using a system known as STARS (Standard Terminal Automation Replacement System). This is the FAA's latest advancement in computer systems for controlling traffic in the terminal (approach) environment. STARS is capable of providing the approach controller with six distinct levels of weather information, as shown in Figure 124. This is unlike Center's WARP information, which groups storm levels into three groups as previously seen, while leaving out Level 1, or light precipitation.

STARS, through symbology, provides information on each storm level that's available (see Figure 125. When talking to an approach controller about weather, you can ask for information about Level 1 (light precipitation), Level 2 (moderate precipitation) and Level 3 (heavy precipitation). You're not really all that interested in whether it's a Level 3 or Level 6 return, because as we discussed

ASR's STARs Wx Presentation

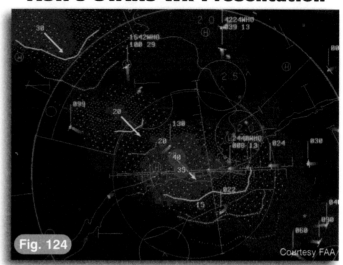

Fig. 124 Courtesy FAA

With STARS (standard terminal automation replacement system), Approach controllers can identify six distinct levels of weather information.

ASR's STARs Wx Levels

Approach Control's (ASR) Wx Display Terminology

Airborne Display Level/Color	Reported by ATC as:	Storm Level	dBz Appx.
	Extreme 2" to 16" Rainfall Rate/Hour	Level 6	50 to 59 dBZ
		Level 5	
	Heavy .5" to 2" Rainfall Rate/Hour	Level 4	40 to 49 dBZ
		Level 3	
	Moderate .175" to .5" Rainfall Rate/Hour	Level 2	30 to 39 dBZ
Fig. 125	Light .01" to .1" Rainfall Rate/Hour	Level 1	16 to 29 dBZ

STARS uses the same three precipitation descriptors that WARP uses (moderate, heavy, extreme) but also uses a "Light" designation since Level 1 returns are shown.

earlier, you'll avoid flying into the clouds in all areas with Level 3 and higher returns. If three strikes, you're out.

Weather information generated by STARS isn't based on NEXRAD, either. It's based on the actual radar returns from that approach control's radar unit. This means that, unlike Center's WARP with the weather presentation being as much as six minutes old, STARS doesn't have any noticeable weather delay (OK, about 10 seconds between what's out there and what the controller sees). What the controller sees is what's happening at the moment. This is as real-time as weather gets.

As a final note, keep in mind that ATC radar can't detect turbulence. You know that turbulence can be expected to increase as the rate of rainfall or intensity of precipitation increases. If you're operating IFR in the clear air near a thunderstorm, you should expect to experience severe or greater turbulence. You might not experience nasty turbulence, but you should know it could very well be lurking. That means if you're visually circumnavigating thunderstorms on an IFR flight plan, you should avoid them by at least 20 miles and with great caution.

The Wisdom of Captain Allan Englehardt

Photo by Elvis A. Brathwaite

I had just finished teaching a seminar on IFR flying when a young man came up to talk with me. He said that he had passed his FAA checkride for the instrument rating a few months earlier and confessed to me that he lacked confidence in his skills regarding how to fly his Cessna 182 in bad weather. He then asked if I might be available for some flight instruction and would it be OK if he called me when bad weather was forecast. He suggested that if there was a forecast for icing or possibly even a squall line of thunderstorms, that I could teach him how to deal with these situations.

Needless to say, this pilot didn't get it. While the instrument rating is nice to have and will permit flights on days that would otherwise be impossible for VFR-only pilots, thunderstorms and icing conditions just can not be dealt with safely in most any single-engine airplane, except by staying on the ground.

Finally, I told the young man that I would have other things to do on days with such forecasts and I suggest that he find something else productive and safe to do on these days, too.

Captain Allan Englehardt
Airline captain, designated pilot examiner
National flight instructor of the year

Captain Allan Englehardt

Chapter 10
IFR Weather Charts

Who you gonna call? Weatherbeaters, also known as the friendly folks at your non-local Automated Flight Service Station (AFSS), is one way to get an official weather briefing. But it's not the only way. You can also use the Internet and a few approved software packages to obtain an official weather briefing. In this chapter we'll discuss the details of weather briefings, the charts and the text reports and forecasts needed to determine if the

Aviation Weather Services

One time, many moons ago, I picked up the phone on a lonely Saturday night and called 411. I asked the operator if she had a number for a Rod Machado in her listings. She said she didn't. So I told her to copy my number down, because I wasn't getting anywhere near enough phone calls. Then I told her to give it out to as many girls as possible.

You can get some pretty good information by dialing 411. Unfortunately, this isn't information that instrument pilots can use, at least when flying. That's because we need weather information, not phone numbers.

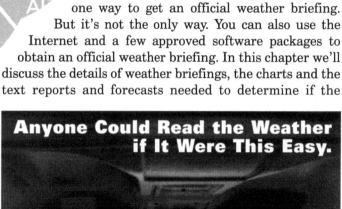

weather passes the common sense test as well as meeting the requirements for safe IFR flight.

Dialing (800) WX- BRIEF in most areas of the country connects you to the nearest AFSS facility serving up weather. If you prefer to call a specific AFSS, you can look it up in your local *A/FD (Airport/Facility Directory)* (see Figure 1). If you hear a recording of Bob Marley's *I Can See Clearly Now* when you call, hang up. You've got the wrong number, and it is not necessarily going to be a bright, bright sunshiny day.

Personal computers have become an increasingly popular way of obtaining a weather briefing that meets your legal requirements for preflight preparation. The FAA currently offers online access to the weather database via a service called Direct User Access Terminal service (DUATS). It's

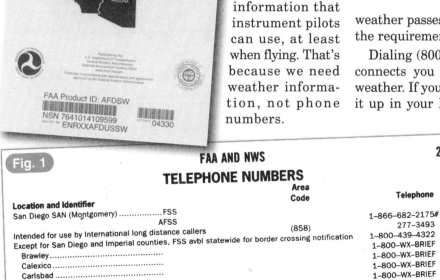

Fig. 1

Phone numbers for the automated flight service station and national weather service offices can be found in the Airport/Facility Directory.

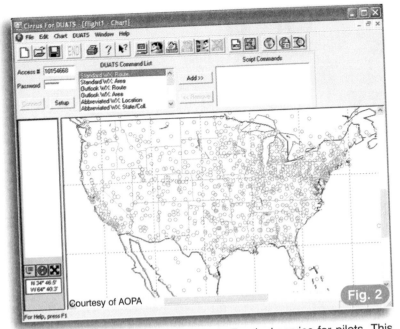

Courtesy of AOPA   **Fig. 2**

DUAT is the FAA's Direct User Access Terminal service for pilots. This service provides direct internet access to weather briefing, flight planning, and flight plan filing information, allowing you to obtain a self briefing and file a flight plan prior to flying. The service is free to pilots having a current medical certificate.

one of several computer-based systems providing official weather briefings, NOTAMs, flight-plan filing and related services (Figure 2). All you need is a personal computer, and access to the Internet. Several commercial weather vendors sell software and access to either government or private weather databases. These programs allow you to file an official VFR and IFR flight plan via computer as well as plan your flight based on the specific performance capabilities of your airplane. Some even provide a means to download NACO (National Aeronautical Charting Office) IFR charts. Is that service, or what?

There are other means of acquiring unofficial weather information. While they don't count as a full, formal briefing that meets your legal obligation, sometimes all you need is a quick look to understand just how smart it would be to stay ground bound. Newspaper weather forecasts, many Internet sites (including The Aviation Digital Data Service [ADDS] operated by the National Weather Service), the Weather Channel and local news broadcasts all contain weather information with varying degrees of detail. And there are many shareware or freeware computer programs (for both PCs and Macs) that automatically aggregate weather information from several sources and present it in a graphically pleasing and easily understood format that often includes charts, satellite photos, and radar images. You just tell the program the places you want to know about, and it does the rest, even updating the information regularly without being prodded.

The Telephone Briefing

If you can visit a Flight Service Station for your weather briefing, that's all the better. With all the consolidation that has taken place, the opportunity to walk in and play Face the Briefer has diminished considerably, but do it if

you can. You'll find some very helpful briefing specialists there to interpret weather information for you, and it really helps to *see* what the weather is by viewing maps and charts showing fronts, high and low pressure areas, jet stream flows, and surface observations. Of course, you can surf the ADDS site during a telephone briefing and view the same basic charts he or she uses, too.

How does an IFR briefing differ from the VFR briefings you've received up until now? Well, the format is basically the same. The information you receive, however, is often much more extensive. While briefers realize that VFR pilots really need to avoid bad weather, and will discourage them in subtle ways when things are nasty, IFR pilots are assumed to be prepared to tackle the bad stuff. Here's how it will go once you've gone live.

The FSS briefer says, *Good morning, this is Hawthorne Flight Service.*

You respond by saying, *Good morning. I'm an instrument pilot planning an IFR flight. 2132 Bravo, a Cessna 210, leaving John Wayne at 1100 Zulu. Cruising 8000 feet, direct San Jose. Estimate two hours and 15 minutes enroute. Request a standard weather briefing.*

This is an acceptable order in which to provide the required information to the FSS specialist. Of course, if you actually make your request this way, expect a slight pause while the specialist recovers from having actually received the correct information in the correct order without having to beg for it.

In addition to the *standard* briefing (the one the specialist would naturally provide you) there are two additional types of briefings you can request, the *abbreviated* and the *outlook* briefing. Let's review all three.

A *standard briefing* contains all the important weather items of concern, as well as additional essential information. These items include adverse conditions, weather syn-

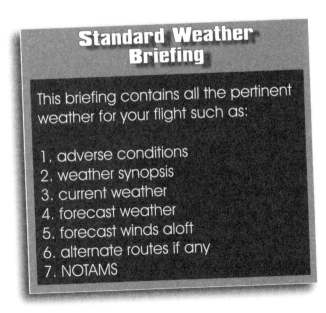

Standard Weather Briefing

This briefing contains all the pertinent weather for your flight such as:

1. adverse conditions
2. weather synopsis
3. current weather
4. forecast weather
5. forecast winds aloft
6. alternate routes if any
7. NOTAMS

An Early Weather Bureau Office

Circa 1900 Historic NWS Collection

National Weather Service History

Did you know that in 1870 President Ulysses Grant signed a joint resolution creating the Weather Service? This was the precursor to the National Weather Service we know today. Originally, "Observer Sergeants" of the Army Signal Service made the first systematized weather observations in 1870. Hand drawn analysis was the primary method to forecast weather at the turn of the 20th century.

In 1925, with the Navy's cooperation, the Weather Bureau made the first routine weather observations by airplane. In 1932 kites were being replaced by airplane observations.

Before computers were available to produce weather models, forecasts were produced by hand. It wasn't until May of 1955 that the first operational numerical weather prediction model was produced by computer. In the mid to late 1960's, forecasters began using computer generated numerical forecasts to enhance their own forecasting ability.

opsis, current weather, forecast weather, forecast winds aloft, alternate routes if any and NOTAMs. NOTAMs include items concerning airports, navigation aids and hazards, all of which contain information that's essential for safe flight.

A standard briefing is the entire enchilada, from the tortilla to the *pico de skyo*. It's everything, and it assumes you have and know nothing. Always request a standard briefing if you haven't collected any weather information prior to your first call.

If you're calling to update or supplement previously acquired weather information, ask for an *abbreviated briefing,* and state the specific information you need. Each type of information has its own rate of change. METARs (hourly surface reports) change hourly, while TAFs (terminal aerodrome forecasts) are produced four times a day (once every six hours). If all you want is an update on the weather at your proposed destination, you don't need to sit through the entire enchilada. You can taco just what you need and skip the rest.

Ask for an *outlook briefing* if you are calling the FSS for weather information six or more hours in advance of your proposed departure time. I usually call the night before a

flight, to obtain a general idea about the weather the following day. It's difficult for meteorologists to predict weather accurately more than 24 hours in advance. An outlook briefing is general information, intended to give you a notion of what's out there, and some sense of whether the weather is so bad (or good) that you should definitely cancel (or plan) your flight. A standard briefing is still necessary as departure time grows closer. Whatever you do, don't ask for a "good weather briefing" because there's no such official phrase. Besides, the specialist is likely to say, "Sorry, but the weather is not that good today."

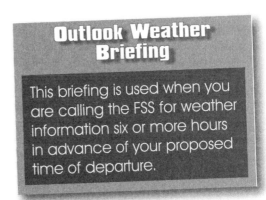

Outlook Weather Briefing

This briefing is used when you are calling the FSS for weather information six or more hours in advance of your proposed time of departure.

Abbreviated Weather Briefing

This briefing contains the weather information you need to update or supplement a previous weather briefing.

Once you're given the FSS specialist the necessary information, get ready to copy. The briefer is about to do his/her thing. You will receive at least the following information, in this order (omitting items where there is no relevant information, of course):

1. *Adverse conditions*

You will first be advised of major items that might cause you to say "Whoa, Briefer. That's enough. I thank you, my passengers thank you, good day and goodbye." This might include such things as runway closure at your departure or destination airport due to a 777 with a collapsed gear

What's a Legal Weather Briefing?

You are legally required to have a weather briefing before any non-local flight.

Seems easy, until you ask yourself (or someone else) one simple question: What's a weather briefing, and who can give one? The rules (FAR 91.103) state that "Each pilot in command shall, before beginning a flight, become familiar with all available information concerning that flight." Should something unpleasant happen, you will have a very hard time convincing the FAA that you didn't get a weather briefing because weather wasn't information that concerned you.

Until fairly recently, the only way to get anything approximating a weather briefing was to call a Flight Service Station. All such calls are recorded both manually and on tape, so it was always possible to prove a pilot was (or wasn't) properly briefed. Many pilots now obtain a briefing via computer from one of several private weather services. Whether or not this constitutes a legal weather briefing for purposes of meeting the letter of the law depends on that service's ability to prove you actually obtained the weather.

If you obtain a weather briefing via computer, make sure the service you're using keeps a record of the briefing. Call them and ask if you're not sure. If they don't, then it's best to leave a paper trail to protect yourself. Calling your friendly local (or not-so-local) FSS is a sure way to establish having received a briefing.

Besides, some of them have really great music-on-hold.

on the runway, six inch hailstones, a hurricane in progress, unacceptable IFR conditions, etc.

2. *Synopsis*

This is the general weather pattern covering the major weather systems and air masses influencing weather in the area where the proposed flight will take place.

3. *Current conditions*

Current surface observations for the departure and destination airports and pilot reports of enroute conditions.

4. *Enroute forecast*

The briefer will take you from departure and climbout through landing, summarizing the forecast for the period you'll be airborne. That's why the time of departure and estimated time enroute are important information to communicate when requesting a briefing.

5. *Destination forecast*

The forecast weather for the estimated time of arrival (ETA).

6. *Winds aloft*

You will be given the winds at the altitude closest to your proposed flight altitude for which there are measurements, which is at 3,000 foot intervals through 12,000 feet. Some briefers will do minor math and interpolate, giving you something between the 6,000 and 9,000 figures if you're planning to fly at 8,000 feet.

7. *NOTAMs*

Notices to Airmen are information of an advisory or cautionary nature. They can include everything from a runway being closed to a navaid being dysfunctional or temporary flight restrictions (TFRs).

8. *ATC delays*

These will be pretty rare for pilots flying to anything other than major metropolitan airports. If you are headed for O'Hare or JFK, the briefer will tell you of any holds due to flow control or other measures designed to keep the traffic humming.

That's it.

Or is it? The briefer will usually conclude by asking you if there's anything else you'd like to know. Speak now or forever hold your wings, unless you call back. Now is the time to ask any questions you might have, though I must remind you that, "Should I go?" is not a question to which they will respond with anything other than vague mumblings such as, "Does your airplane have a rollbar?" You're the pilot in command. You make the big decisions.

Briefers are trained by the FAA to disseminate weather information. They're very skilled at reading charts and forecasts and relaying that information to pilots. They are not meteorologists nor are they the PIC. They don't forecast weather, or decide what it means in relation to your aircraft, skill, and risk assessment. They only talk to you about the weather facts.

Fuelish Thought for Weather-Wise Pilots

As summer drifts into fall, weather patterns become unsettled in many areas of the country, and unforecast storms may suddenly appear. Pilots may be required to deviate well off intended routes, and this in turn may cause carefully planned fuel reserves to vanish. Add an additional delay for holding, and a pilot's options can become limited, as this commuter Captain reports:

The forecast for ABC indicated no alternate was needed. As we approached the area, [we received vectors for] deviating around thunderstorms. ABC Approach advised that no one was getting into ABC due to the thunderstorm activity...[but] hopefully in 15 minutes, Approach would be able to accommodate arrivals. I told Approach that we had "Minimum Fuel" and could only accept a short delay...and needed to land as soon as conditions improved.

After about 10 minutes, I told the controller that we needed a circling approach for Runway 20. As we were being vectored, the right low fuel warning light illuminated. On final approach, the controller stated that visibility was going down rapidly and it would be difficult to land on Runway 20. I told the First Officer to declare an emergency because we had to land...due to low visibility [for Runway 20], regardless of the tailwind component.... We landed with about 450 lbs total fuel.

Both the *Air Traffic Control Handbook* and the *AIM* explain that a minimum fuel advisory is just that: an advisory. It does not indicate an emergency situation or imply a need for traffic priority. In order to receive traffic priority, pilots should declare an emergency. Even when an alternate has been determined, plans may still have to be changed, creating an additional demand on fuel supplies. An air carrier crew thought they had planned for all contingencies, but still were caught short.   **NASA Callback Report**

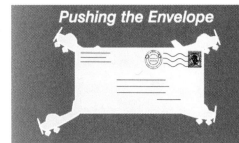

Pushing the Envelope

"When it comes to testing new aircraft or determining maximum performance, pilots like to talk about "pushing the envelope." They're talking about a two dimensional model: the bottom is zero altitude, the ground; the left is zero speed; the top is max altitude; and the right, maximum velocity, of course. So, the pilots are pushing that upper-right-hand corner of the envelope. What everybody tries not to dwell on is that that's where the postage gets canceled, too."

Admiral Rick Hunter, U.S. Navy.

And good talk it is! They will tell you all about the highs, lows, squiggles, and squirts comprising the aviation weather map. All you have to do is listen. Unfortunately, too many folks don't listen. For example, suppose a comedian made the following PA announcement at the airport, "Flight 58 has no engine, the crew showed up in their pajamas, and we'll be boarding in 15 minutes." You can bet that 90% of Flight 58's passengers would race to board the plane. So listen carefully when the briefer speaks.

Briefers are sort of the Dear Abby of flightdom. They will answer almost any question (about aviation, that is; questions about your love life should still be directed to Dear Abby or maybe the 411 operator). They'll tell you about Customs, search and rescue, ATC services, preferred routes, and why the computer will take a flight plan for one route and not another. They'll look up phone numbers for aviation facilities (no, not your phone number, either), read the NOTAMs, provide information about TFRs, military training routes, restricted areas, and other special use airspace.

They will do almost anything they can to get you almost any information you want about the aviation system. Just ask and ye shall receive.

Other Sources of Weather Information

There is, the proverb says, more than one way to skin an airplane, and there are lots of other places to get information about which way the clouds blow.

NEWSPAPERS–My friend liked to read his local newspaper because the reporters worked for the mafia. These guys could print the news before it happened. One headline read, "Tomorrow at 3 o'clock, a guy named Dominick is going to accidentally walk into someone's fist." Most newspapers provide you with at least some valuable information about weather. For instance, most newspapers publish a weather map showing major weather systems around the country, and many carry a satellite picture that helps provide a look at what the weather's doing. Weather-wise pilots study weather on a daily basis. Examine the weather chart and/or satellite photo provided by the paper every day. These charts are a lot more accurate than they were several years ago, and spending a few minutes a day seeing what the weather is doing will contribute greatly to your weather education.

Pilots Automatic Telephone Weather Answering Service (PATWAS). This telephone service is a continuous recording, made by a human, of meteorological information for pilots. A PATWAS message is recorded and updated at a minimum of every five hours, beginning at 0600 and ending at 2200 local time. PATWAS is not intended as a sub-

stitute for a briefing by an FSS specialist. It is, however, useful as a preliminary briefing, to help in making those go or no go decisions. Sometimes you hear all you need to know from this general summary. Phone numbers for PATWAS are available in the *Airport/Facility Directory (A/FD)*.

Telephone Information Briefing Service (TIBS) – *TIBS* is a continuous telephone briefing service consisting of prerecorded weather and/or aeronautical information. It's offered by automated flight service stations and provides weather briefings for an area or a route. It also provides airspace procedures and special aviation announcements. Using your Touch Tone phone, you can select from several weather menus of prerecorded information. TIBs service is provided 24 hours a day and is updated as conditions change. Look in the A/FD for TIBs phone numbers.

Transcribed Weather Broadcast (TWEB) – A *TWEB* is a prerecorded broadcast of weather and aeronautical information by some FSSs. Broadcast continuously over selected navigation stations (like VORs and NDBs), TWEBs contain information on route-oriented weather and route forecasts. They usually provide information for a corridor 25 miles to either side of a specified route along which certain broadcasting navaids are located (VOR airways, for instance).

Figure 3 shows a VOR frequency box with a small black circle containing a reverse bold T in the corner of the navaid frequency box. This means that a TWEB broadcast is available on that VOR. Some TWEB broadcasts can be

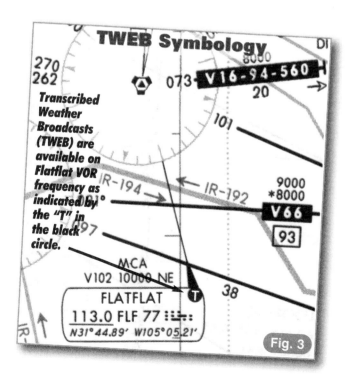

Fig. 3

accessed by telephone. These broadcasts are intended to supplement your
in-flight weather information and are
not intended as a substitute for a specialist-provided briefing.

TWEBs broadcast information
includes a synopsis, adverse conditions, TWEB route forecast. winds
aloft, radar reports, surface weather
reports, density altitude warnings for
any field at or above 2,000 feet MSL,
PIREPs, alert notices (if applicable) and
closing statements. (Don't you wonder
why the FSS didn't throw in a holiday
greeting and birthday wishes, too?)

*Hazardous In-flight Weather
Advisory Service* (HIWAS)–HIWAS is a
continuous broadcast of in-flight weather advisories. Similar to TWEBs, HIWAS
can be received over certain VOR and
NDB stations as indicated by a small
black circle in the containing a reverse
bold H in the navaid frequency box (Figure 4). The purpose of HIWAS is to keep you abreast of any hazardous weather such as thunderstorms, icing, strong winds, etc. These advisories of hazardous forms of weather are SIGMETs, convective SIGMETs, AIRMETs, AWWs, CWAs, and urgent PIREPS (all of which will be discussed shortly).

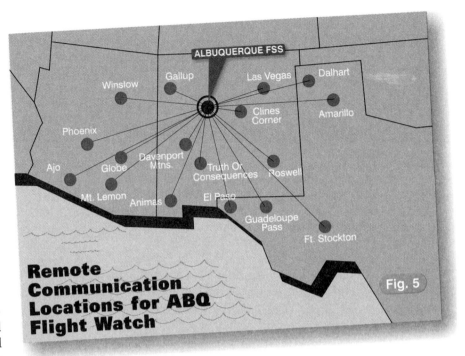

Remote Communication Locations for ABQ Flight Watch   Fig. 5

The unique thing about HIWAS as well as TWEBs is that you can simply turn up the volume on your VOR and listen to this continuous weather broadcast while traveling to your destination. This keeps you informed without having
to repeatedly contact a Flight Service Station. It's interesting to note that, given the plentiful use of GPS for navigation, pilots hardly seem to find a use for their VOR units anymore. Well, listening to HIWAS is a good reason to keep
your VOR equipment operating and tuned to a nearby navaid.

In a geographical area where HIWAS has been implemented, you might hear a HIWAS alert on an ATC frequency
(such as Approach or Departure Control). The alert notice might sound like this:

*Attention all aircraft. Hazardous weather information (SIGMET, Convective SIGMET, AIRMET, Urgent Pilot
Weather Report, or Center Weather Advisory) for (geographical area) available on HIWAS, Flight Watch, or Flight
Service frequencies.*

HIWAS

Fort Stockton chart excerpt

Fig. 4

Upon hearing this one-time alert, you should make plans to contact the
FSS to find out if this information is applicable to you. At least listen to
the nearest VOR over which HIWAS is broadcast for a description of the
particular weather information contained in the alert notice.

As with all prerecorded in-flight broadcasts, HIWAS is not intended as a
substitute for a specialist-provided briefing. Take advantage of these in-
flight weather advisories by keeping the volume up slightly when using a
TWEB or HIWAS broadcasting navigation station. When you hear any voice
transmission, turn up the volume to listen to the incoming broadcasts.

Enroute Flight Advisory Service (EFAS) – Enroute Flight Advisory
Service, otherwise known as *Flight Watch,* is one of the most amazing
sources of in-flight weather information available to pilots (of course, an
XM satellite display of cockpit weather is easily the equivalent of EFAS).
It's basically a clearinghouse for timely and meaningful weather information useful to pilots in the air. Flight Watch consists of trained specialists at selected FSSs who have attended additional weather courses in
order to be able to better assist pilots in flight. The Flight Watch frequency is the same everywhere below 17,500 feet—122.0 MHz. Service is
available from 6 a.m. to 10 p.m. local time, for aircraft flying between
5,000 feet AGL and 17,500 feet MSL. The specific service area (Figure 5)
can be found in the *A/FD.* This service is strictly a weather information
service. It's not intended for changes of flight plan information, radar
information, or any other non-weather related conversations.

Weather Without Reservations

It was autumn, and the Indians on the remote reservation asked their new Chief if the winter was going to be cold or mild. Since he was an Indian Chief in a modern society, he had never been taught the old secrets, and when he looked at the sky, he couldn't tell what the heck the weather was going to be.

Nevertheless, to be on the safe side, he replied to his tribe that the winter was indeed going to be cold and that the members of the village should collect wood to be prepared.

But also being a practical leader, after several days he got an idea. He went to the phone booth, called the National Weather Service and asked, "Is the coming winter going to be cold?"

"It looks like this winter is going to be quite cold indeed," the Meteorologist at the weather service responded.

So the Chief went back to his people and told them to collect even more wood in order to be prepared.

One week later he called the National Weather Service again. "Is it going to be a very cold winter?" he asked.

"Yes," the man at the National Weather Service again replied, "it's going to be a very cold winter."

The Chief again went back to his people and ordered them to collect every scrap of wood they could find.

Two weeks later he called the National Weather Service again. "Are you absolutely sure that the winter is going to be very cold?"

Absolutely," the man replied. "It looks like it's going to be one of the coldest winters ever."

"How can you be so sure?" the Chief asked.

The weatherman replied, "The Indians are collecting firewood like crazy."

Pilot Reports (PIREPs)–Years ago, a flight instructor told me that while on a dual cross-country flight, his student tried to give Flight Watch a "PIRATE." Had the instructor not stopped the student, the conversation might have gone as follows: "Ahh, Oakland Flight Watch, this is 2132 Bravo, I'd like to give a PIRATE."

"OK 32 Bravo, what would you give this pirate?"

"Oh, ahh, I'd like to give him his leg back. Over."

Fortunately, the instructor pulled the mic plug before his student could damage his career.

As you know, it's not PIRATE, it's a PIREP or *pilot report*. These reports provide information on current conditions as reported by pilots up there, in the air. PIREPs are aviation's version of reality TV. This is the original Survivor show. PIREPs are made to the FSS, EFAS or an ATC facility, and they can be of immense assistance in helping you to make a go/no-go decision, or to avoid problem areas once you're airborne.

When contacting EFAS or the FSS, in flight or before takeoff, you will usually be provided current pilot reports as part of the weather briefing. If they aren't forthcoming, ask for them. These reports give you a good idea of how well reality is conforming to the forecast that day.

In many instances, PIREPs have allowed me to make a decision to go when the forecast painted a very bleak picture. PIREPs become especially important in understanding what's happening in areas where weather reporting stations are few and far between.

Whenever you contact the FSS, EFAS, or ATC, give them a pilot report. Pilots don't do this often enough. Even if the weather is clear, report it. I make it a point to listen to Air Route Traffic Control Center whenever I'm on a cross-country flight, whether or not I'm signed on for radar service. Believe me, if there's nastiness ahead, you'll hear it. My rule is that when the male pilots' voices hit a high C or above, it's time to re-evaluate my options. This is one of those cases where it's not just what they say, but how they say it, that counts.

Weather Reports

There are many weather reports available from the National Weather Service and private weather services to aid pilots in flight planning. Knowing what to ask for and how to use the information is an important pilot skill, and it's particularly critical for IFR pilots.

The available weather products are of two basic types, *observations* and *forecasts*. Observations are historical. They are the weather conditions that occurred at the time the observation was taken. Forecasts are weather estimates for several hours (sometimes days) into the future. Like all estimates, weather forecasts are subject to change. Sometimes, considerable change. If you've ever remodeled your house and remember what the original estimate was, and what you finally paid, you understand exactly what I'm saying. Keep in mind at all times that a weather observation is like a fish—it starts to deteriorate as soon as it's caught. The fresher the better, for both.

Let's examine the weather reports you'll need for successful and safe IFR flight planning. Unless the weather report has the word "forecast" or "prognosis" in it, then it's probably an observation.

You and only you are responsible for making your go/no-go decisions. It takes training to make good weather decisions. Weather charts are part of this training. There are many times when you'll have access to weather charts without the benefit of a briefer. Knowing how to interpret these charts is very important. Even if there *is* a briefer at the other end of the chart, you remain responsible for understanding the information and acting on it, which means you need to know which end of the chart is up.

Most of the weather charts I'm going to describe are on the instrument pilot knowledge exam. I have added additional practical information where appropriate. You'll find that a few charts include partial legends. These legends help interpret some (but not all) of the chart's symbols. So, for purposes of the FAA knowledge exam, you'll need to memorize some basic chart symbology. As you'll soon see, many of the chart's symbols can be generalized to

Additional Sources of Weather Information

Flight Information Service–Broadcast or FIS-B

If you don't hear the George Jetson sound of the future yet, then listen closely. The latest and greatest development in aviation technology is called Automatic Dependent Surveillance-Broadcast—ADS-B for short. With it comes a wonderful form of uplinked cockpit weather called FIS-B (not to be confused with Frisbee, though both involve things that fly). To understand how FIS-B works you need to know a little about ADS-B. You also need to know your alphabet, so viewing a couple of episodes of Sesame Street would be a good idea.

ADS-B is cutting edge technology that is already present in the cockpits of many airplanes. It's a revolutionary new way of identifying and controlling air traffic. The concept is so simple, you have to think, "Why didn't I think of that?" Ready? Instead of bouncing radar waves from a ground-based antenna off of flying airplanes, then trying to interpret the ghostly signals, why not just let the airplanes do the talking directly?

See, I told you it was simple. I mean, who knows better where it is than your airplane? So why not get it to cough up the info, rather than trying to divine it from radar returns that don't provide much information? ADS-B uses conventional Global Navigation Satellite System (GNSS) technology and a relatively simple broadcast communications link as its fundamental components. It does this with a universal access transceiver (UAT). Garmin's GDL 90 is an example of a UAT that interfaces with a multi-function cockpit display. This UAT is remotely mounted in your airplane and designed to transmit, receive, and decode ADS-B messages sent from other airplanes and from ADS-B ground stations (called GBTs). This data link broadcasts your aircraft's position, velocity, projected track (all derived from GPS) and flight identification to other ADS-B equipped aircraft in your area, as well as to GBTs (see figure to the right). No plane, no gain. No interpreters needed.

ADS-B - Automatic Dependent Surveillance Broadcast

GNSS Constellation

Communications Satellite

Downlink to ATC Center

AC to AC

A/C Position Speed, Etc. Info

Ground Link to ATC

The interesting thing about the GBTs is that they can send weather information such as NEXRAD weather radar images, METARs, TAFs, TFR information and so on directly to your plane via a data uplink. It's like a private TV channel, just for *you*. This means you'll have access to full time weather in real time without having to call the AFSS, as shown below, left. Of course, you'll need some sort of multifunction display to show this information in the cockpit. Who knows, eventually maybe you'll be able to get old Star Trek episodes enroute.

To use ADS-B and FIS-B, your airplane will need to establish a two-way data link with the ground using a UAT. This isn't a cheap proposition in terms of equipment at the moment, but in time costs will decrease, making the technology more accessible for all pilots. The FAA says that ADS-B will eventually replace its aging radar network, making ADS-B mandatory for all airplanes. The transition should take approximately 20 years, according to FAA sources.

As an aside, it's not necessary to have ADS-B in order to receive uplinked weather information in your cockpit. There are many weather providers that currently provide this service. For instance, you can purchase a Garmin 496 GPS unit and activate its weather service. Do so and you'll have weather, terrain and airport info.

MountainScope screenshot (c) 2007 by PCAvionics, PCAvionics.com Courtesy of PCAvionics

Weather Advisories

Center Weather Advisory (CWA)

A *Center Weather Advisory* (CWA) is an aviation warning that can be used to anticipate and avoid adverse weather conditions in the enroute and terminal environments. CWAs are created primarily for use by air traffic controllers, but they're not secrets. In fact, they're available online. Each CWA is an accumulation of the latest monitoring, analysis and interpretation of real time weather. In my opinion, it doesn't get much better than this.

Courtesy FAA

Now, technically speaking and according to the FAA, the CWA is not a flight planning product. Then again, neither is looking out the window according to the FAA, but I've found both very useful in helping me understand what the weather is like from the Center's perspective. After all, a CWA is issued by the meteorologist at the Center. Since the CWA reflects current conditions expected at the time of issuance and/or is a short-range forecast for conditions expected to begin within two hours of issuance, it certainly has flight planning value and you should use it.

CWAs are valid for a maximum of two hours. If conditions are expected to continue beyond the two-hour valid period, a statement will be included in the CWA. A CWA may be issued in the following three situations:

1. As a supplement to an existing in-flight aviation weather advisory for the purpose of improving or updating the definition of the phenomenon in terms of location, movement, extent, or intensity relevant to the ARTCC area of responsibility. Let's say, for example, that a SIGMET for severe turbulence had been issued by the Aviation Weather Center (AWC) in Kansas City, Missouri, and the outline covered the entire ARTCC area for the total four-hour valid time period. Three tornados, however, have appeared in one relatively small area. No sense keeping that a secret. The forecaster will issue a CWA covering only the affected portion of the ARTCC area.

2. When an in-flight aviation weather advisory has not yet been issued but conditions meet the criteria, based on current pilot reports, and the information must be disseminated sooner than the AWC can issue the in-flight aviation weather advisory. In the case of an impending SIGMET, the CWA will be issued as urgent (UCWA) to allow the fastest possible dissemination.

3. When in-flight aviation weather advisory criteria are not met but conditions are or will shortly be adversely affecting the safe flow of air traffic within the ARTCC area of responsibility.

Example of a CWA:

> **ZME1 CWA 081300**
> **ZME CWA 101 VALID UNTIL 081500**
> **FROM MEM TO JAN TO LIT TO MEM**
> **AREA SCT VIP 5-6 (INTENSE/EXTREME) TS MOV FROM 26025KT. TOPS TO FL450.**

This CWA was issued by the Memphis, Tennessee (TN), ARTCC. The 1 after the ZME in the first line denotes this CWA has been issued for the first weather phenomenon to occur for the day. It was written on the eighth at 1300Z. The 101 in the second line denotes the phenomenon number again (1) and the issuance number (01) for this phenomenon. The CWA is valid until the eighth at 1500Z. The area is bounded by Memphis, TN, to Jackson, MS, to Little Rock, AR, and back to Memphis, TN. Within the CWA is an area with scattered VIP 5-6 (intense/extreme) thunderstorms moving from 260 degrees at 25 knots. Tops of the thunderstorms are at FL450.

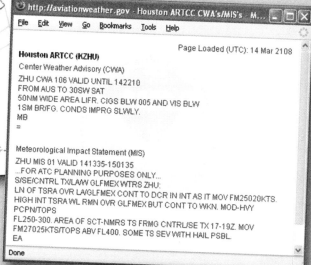

You can have direct access to CWAs by visiting the National Weather Service web site at:

http://aviation weather.gov/products/cwsu/

In Chapter 16 on flight planning, we'll talk a little more about using the Center Weather Advisory.

METAR Weather Reporting Format

```
METAR  KINK  081955Z  32014G20KT  1/2SM  R30R/2400FT  DZ FG  OVC006  13/12  A3004
SPECI  KMKC  081936Z  20014G24KT  1/2SM  R34/2600FT  +SN BLSN FG  VV008  00/M03  A2898
METAR  KBOI  081953Z  23008KT  5SM  SCT015  19/13  A2994  RMK SLP156 T01930128
METAR  KLAX  081955Z  01013G20KT  3SM  HZ  SKC  18/11  A2995
```

Fig. 6

other charts. I'll specifically advise you when a chart's legend is available for a specific chart on the exam.

Aviation Routine Weather Reports [METAR]

METAR (pronounced *ME–TAR;* the complementary chart would be UJANE) observations are taken hourly at many reporting stations located across the country. These reports indicate the weather conditions at the time the observation was made. Other than a pilot report, a METAR observation is as close as you can get to the actual weather conditions without sticking your finger or head out the window.

Not only do these reports provide a current weather observation, they also allow you to sense a trend in the weather by observing several of the past hourly reports. Figure 6 shows a typical METAR for several airports (those reports preceded by the letters *SPECI* are special, unscheduled reports as a result of a significant weather change. An example would be when the ceiling goes above or below 1,000 feet or when the visibility goes above or below three miles).

You'll notice that these weather reports consist of abbreviations. This is a carryover from the days when weather data was sent via Teletype, which moved only slightly faster than pony express. (Nevertheless, encoded (abbreviated) weather reports are actually a mixed blessing if you can uplink real-time cockpit weather information on your MFD or GPS display. Reading encoded METARs and TAFs is often faster and more efficient this way. This is a good reason to know the abbreviations.) On the other hand, some personal computer software will automatically decode the abbreviations, providing you with a description of the weather in English (call your local aviation software dealer—and no, you can't use your personal computer on the instrument or commercial pilot knowledge exam to interpret weather symbols for you).

Interpreting the METAR requires an understanding of the individual sections contained within the report. Figure 7 is a breakdown of these sections. Let's take a closer look at each one.

To help you understand the order in which a METAR presents the weather, take a look at the following letter sequence: STWVRWCTDA. This stands for *Should Tina Walk Vera's Rabbit Without Checking The Dog's Appetite?* Each letter represents a particular segment of the weather contained within the METAR as follows:

S　Station identification
T　Time in Zulu or UTC
W　Wind direction and velocity
V　Visibility
R　Runway visual range (if reported)
W　Weather
C　Clouds
T　Temperature
D　Dew point
A　Altimeter setting

By remembering this sentence/letter sequence, you'll become an object of ridicule in your village but gain the ability to remember the order in which the METAR information is presented. This is also a great party trick, especially if it's a gathering of MIT or Cal Tech engineering grad students. Keep in mind that a METAR won't report what *isn't* happening, nor will it report a segment if the measuring equipment (such as a barometer) is not functional. By knowing what should be there, you'll easily identify any missing section. Let's jump into interpreting the METAR.

Station–The letter S in Figure 7 represents the first section of the METAR. It is a four-letter/number designation

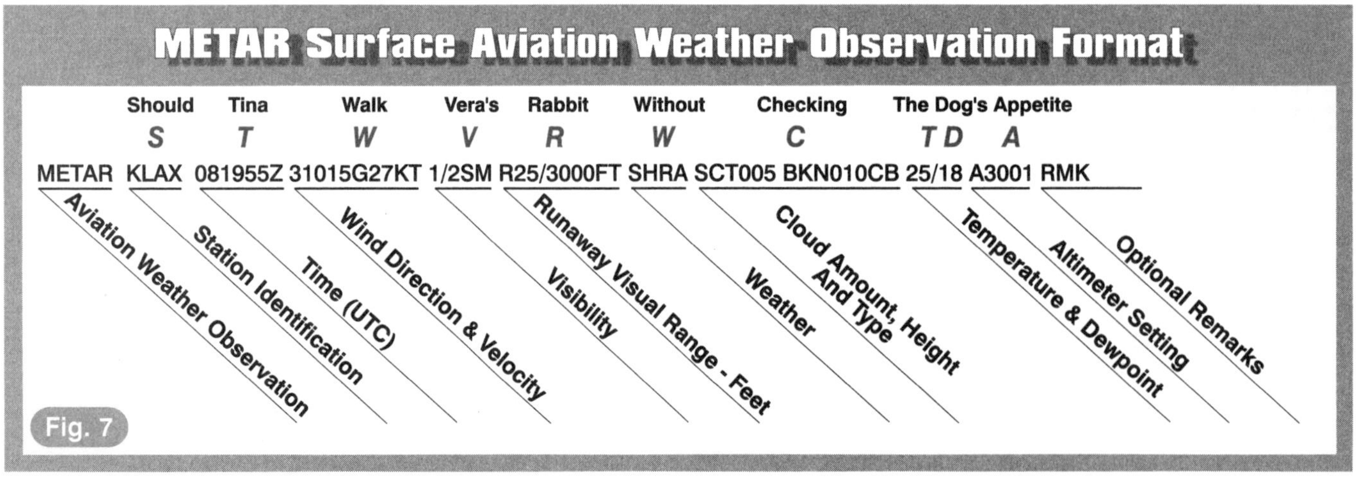

METAR Surface Aviation Weather Observation Format

	Should	Tina	Walk	Vera's	Rabbit	Without	Checking	The Dog's Appetite	
	S	T	W	V	R	W	C	TD	A
METAR	KLAX	081955Z	31015G27KT	1/2SM	R25/3000FT	SHRA	SCT005 BKN010CB	25/18	A3001	RMK

Aviation Weather Observation / Station Identification / Time (UTC) / Wind Direction & Velocity / Visibility / Runaway Visual Range - Feet / Weather / Cloud Amount, Height And Type / Temperature & Dewpoint / Altimeter Setting / Optional Remarks

Fig. 7

Weather Codes

Qualifiers		Weather Phenomena		
Intensity or proximity 1	Descriptor 2	Precipitation 3	Obscuration 4	Other 5
- Light Moderate (no qualifier) + Heavy VC means: in the vicinity *(METAR: between 5 & 10 sm of observation point(s) TAF: between 5 to 10 sm from center of runway complex)*	MI Shallow BC Patches PR Partial DR Low Drifting BL Blowing SH Shower(s) TS Thunderstorm FZ Freezing	DZ Drizzle RA Rain SN Snow SG Snow grains IC Ice crystals PL Ice pellets GR Hail GS Small hail &/or snow pellets UP Unknown Precip	BR Mist (≥5/8sm) FG Fog (<5/8sm) FU Smoke VA Volcanic ash DU Dust SA Sand HZ Haze PY Spray	PO Dust/sand whirls SQ Squalls FC Funnel cloud(s)/ +FC Tornado/ waterspout SS Sandstorm DS Duststorm

Fig. 8

for the station or airport reporting the observation. KLAX is the designator for Los Angeles International Airport (*K* is the international designator that precedes almost all U.S. location identifiers. The exceptions are Alaska locations, which start with *PA* and Hawaii locations, which start with *PH*). You'll learn some of these airport letter designations for your local area as you go along (some of them are easy to guess). The only time you need to be really worried is if you irritated an airline desk agent when checking in for a flight and he checks your bag with a KIM tag, which stands for "Keep it moving."

Time–The letter T in Figure 7 is the date and time the weather observation was made. For instance, at KLAX, the observation was taken on the 8th day of the month at 1955 Zulu (also referred to as UTC or Coordinated Universal Time). Weather reports are always given in Zulu time. This is the time in Greenwich, England and not the time certain African tribes use. Using UTC calibrates all the weather reports to one time zone. All you need do is convert from UTC to your local time zone when interpreting weather reports.

Wind–The letter W in Figure 7 identifies the wind direction, velocity, and any gusts. The first three digits represent the wind direction in degrees, relative to true north (wind is reported relative to magnetic north in computer-generated voice messages from ATIS, ASOS and AWOS broadcasts and when given by controllers). The next two digits are the wind velocity in knots (identified by the letters KT). The G followed by a number represents the wind gust in knots. For instance, a wind report of 31015G27KT indicates that the wind is 310 degrees at 15 knots with gusts to 27 knots. Gusts are reported when a 10 knot fluctuation occurs between the wind's peaks and lulls. A calm wind is reported as 00000KT (four zeros doesn't mean that the machine that generates the wind at the airport is broken, either). The letters *VRB* may be used if the wind speed is 5 knots or less. If the wind's direction varies by 60 degrees or more and the speed is greater than 6 knots, then variable wind direction values follow the reported wind. For instance, a 280V350 following the wind report indicates that the winds are 280 degrees variable to 350 degrees. The two extremes in direction will be included in clockwise order.

Visibility–The letter V in Figure 7 stands for visibility. Surface visibility is measured in statute miles and fractions thereof. A space divides whole miles and fractions and the letters SM follow the visibility to indicate statute miles. In Figure 7, the reported surface visibility is 1/2 mile. If you fly internationally, you should be aware that the U.S. is an exception in reporting prevailing visibility as the greatest visibility equalled or exceeded throughout at least one-half of the horizon circle, but not necessarily contiguous. (Be advised that this can mean sections of the circle equaling one-half or more of the circle. In other words, these sections don't have to be touching each other.)Significant differences in any sector from the prevailing visibility or a differing tower visibility will be stated in the remarks (RMK) section of the METAR.

Runway Visual Range–The letter R in Figure 7 stands for runway visual range (RVR). RVR is an electronically measured value used to determine the distance (in hundreds of feet) down a runway that a pilot can see high intensity runway lights. This value is important to all instrument pilots. Figure 7 shows the RVR along Runway 25 (R25) is 3,000 feet. An M or P prefix before the RVR indicates its value is below the minimum value measurable or above the maximum value measurable by the system (respectively). The numbers following the slash indicate the RVR in feet (FT).

Weather–The letter W in Figure 7 represents the weather phenomena presently found at the airport. Figure 8 lists the weather codes used in reporting the weather phenomena. These codes contain five columns. The first two columns contain qualifiers (intensity or proximity and a descriptor of the weather). The last three columns contain the actual weather phenomena, such as precipitation, obscuration, etc. Up to three separate groups of weather phenomena may be included in the report; the most dominant weather is reported first. Various forms of precipitation—rain, snow, hail—reaching the surface are combined into a single group.

For instance, moderate rain and snow (these are two types of precipitation) present at the airport, are reported as SNRA (snow is the dominant precipitation and is reported first). Both are types of precipitation and are reported as one group. The absence of a + or – sign in front of the precipitation indicates that it's moderate in intensity.

Moderate rain, fog and volcanic ash are three separate groups of weather phenomena and are reported as three separate groups: RA FG VA. If light rain, fog, and volcanic ash were reported, it would look like the following: –RA FG VA. If light drizzle, hail and a sandstorm were reported it would look like the following: –DZGR SS (remember,

METAR Weather Reporting Format

```
METAR  KINK  081955Z  32014G20KT  1/2SM  R30R/2400FT  DZ FG  OVC006  13/12  A3004
SPECI  KMKC  081936Z  20014G24KT  1/2SM  R34/2600FT  +SN BLSN FG  VV008  00/M03  A2898
METAR  KBOI  081953Z  23008KT  5SM  SCT015  19/13  A2994  RMK SLP156 T01930128
METAR  KLAX  081955Z  01013G20KT  3SM  HZ  SKC  18/11  A2995
```

Fig. 6

light drizzle and hail—both are types of precipitation—are grouped together). It would also be a hail of a weather report. Talk about the rolling stones!

The obscuration or second section of the weather phenomena in Figure 8 is only reported in the weather grouping if the visibility is less than seven miles. The presence of smoke (FU) at the airport won't be listed in the weather grouping if the visibility is seven miles or greater.

In Figure 7, the letters SHRA represent showers (SH) and rain (RA). This is spoken as *moderate rain showers*. If it were light rain showers it would be abbreviated as –SHRA.

Clouds–Now to cloud the picture. The letter C in Figure 7 represents the cloud coverage, height, and type.

Cloud cover is either SKC (sky clear), indicating no clouds; FEW (reporting more than 0 to 2/8), SCT (scattered), representing coverage of between 3/8 and 4/8 of the sky; BKN (broken), which indicates the sky is between 5/8 and 7/8 covered by clouds; or OVC (overcast) which is complete sky coverage (8/8 coverage). (Automated reporting systems use the letters CLR to indicate no clouds are reported below 12,000 feet.)

A three-digit number following the cloud coverage represents the height of the cloud base in hundreds of feet

AGL. Three zeros indicates that the cloud height is less than 50 feet AGL.

Cloud types are provided when towering cumulus (TCU) or cumulonimbus (CB) are observed.

Sometimes weather phenomena based at the surface hide all or part of the sky. This is considered an obscuration. When the sky is obscured and cloud details cannot be assessed, but information on vertical visibility is available, the cloud group is replaced by a five-character group. The first two characters are the letters VV followed by the vertical visibility in units of hundreds of feet. VV004 means the vertical visibility is 400 feet (ATIS reports still broadcast the term *indefinite* as in "indefinite 400 feet obscured").

Sometimes an obscuration doesn't obscure the entire sky. In this situation, partial obscurations are reported by the amount of obscuring phenomena (FEW, SCT, BKN), followed by three digits (e.g., BKN001). In the remarks, the obscuring phenomenon precedes the amount of obscuration and the three digits (e.g., FU BKN001, which means that the smoke layer, at 100 feet AGL, is obscuring 5/8 to 7/8 of the sky.)

From your study of airspace, you know that a minimum of a 1,000 foot ceiling is required for operations within surface-based controlled airspace. In the METAR, the lowest layer of clouds reported as broken or overcast, or any reported vertical visibility into obscuring phenomena is considered the official ceiling.

In Figure 7, the METAR indicates the presence of a scattered layer of clouds at 500 feet, a broken layer of clouds at 1,000 feet (the ceiling), and CB's (cumulonimbus clouds) are present.

Temperature/Dewpoint– The letters T and D in Figure 7 represent the reported temperature and dewpoint in degrees Celsius. This is reported to the nearest whole degree using two digits (e.g., 6 degrees C is reported as 06). Sub-zero values are prefixed with an *M* (e.g., 03/M02. In Figure 7, the temperature is 25 degrees C and the dewpoint is 18 degrees C.

Remarks Appended to METARS

Remarks	Definition
Sky and Ceiling	
FEW CU	Few cumulus clouds.
BINOVC	Breaks in overcast.
LWR CLDS NE	Lower clouds northeast.
CIG 14V19	Ceiling variable between 1,400 feet and 1,900 feet.
Obscuring Phenomena	
FG7	Fog obscuring 7/10 of the sky.
BLSA3	Blowing sand obscuring 3/10 of the sky.
THN FG NE	Thin fog northeast from reporting station.
Visibility	
VSBY S1W1/4	Visibility south is 1 mile, west is 1/4 mile.
SFC VSBY 1/2	Surface visibility is 1/2 mile.

Remarks	Definition
Weather and Obstruction to Vision	
RAB30	Rain began 30 minutes after the hour.
RAE30	Rain ended 30 minutes after the hour.
OCNL DST LTG NW	Occasional distant lightning NW of reporting station.
T OVHD MOVG NE	Thunderstorm overhead, moving northeast.
Wind	
WND 27V33	Wind variable between 270 degrees and 330 degrees.
PK WND 33048/22 ("PK WND" is used whenever the peak winds exceed 25 knots)	Peak wind within the past hour from 330 degrees at 48 knots occurred 22 minutes past the hour.
Pressure	
PRESSR	Pressure rising rapidly.
PRESFR	Pressure falling rapidly.

Fig. 9

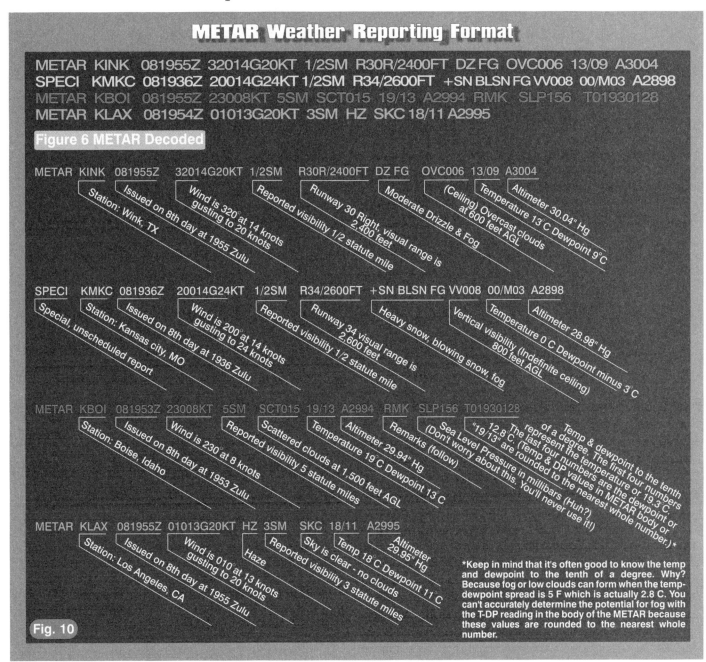

METAR Weather Reporting Format

METAR KINK 081955Z 32014G20KT 1/2SM R30R/2400FT DZ FG OVC006 13/09 A3004
SPECI KMKC 081936Z 20014G24KT 1/2SM R34/2600FT +SN BLSN FG VV008 00/M03 A2898
METAR KBOI 081955Z 23008KT 5SM SCT015 19/13 A2994 RMK SLP156 T01930128
METAR KLAX 081954Z 01013G20KT 3SM HZ SKC 18/11 A2995

Figure 6 METAR Decoded

METAR KINK 081955Z 32014G20KT 1/2SM R30R/2400FT DZ FG OVC006 13/09 A3004

Station: Wink, TX
Issued on 8th day at 1955 Zulu
Wind is 320° at 14 knots gusting to 20 knots
Reported visibility 1/2 statute mile
Runway 30 Right, visual range is 2,400 feet
Moderate Drizzle & Fog
(Ceiling) Overcast clouds at 600 feet AGL
Temperature 13°C Dewpoint 9°C
Altimeter 30.04" Hg

SPECI KMKC 081936Z 20014G24KT 1/2SM R34/2600FT +SN BLSN FG VV008 00/M03 A2898

Special, unscheduled report
Station: Kansas city, MO
Issued on 8th day at 1936 Zulu
Wind is 200° at 14 knots gusting to 24 knots
Reported visibility 1/2 statute mile
Runway 34 visual range is 2,600 feet
Heavy snow, blowing snow, fog
Vertical visibility (Indefinite ceiling) 800 feet AGL
Temperature 0°C Dewpoint minus 3°C
Altimeter 28.98" Hg

METAR KBOI 081953Z 23008KT 5SM SCT015 19/13 A2994 RMK SLP156 T01930128

Station: Boise, Idaho
Issued on 8th day at 1953 Zulu
Wind is 230 at 8 knots
Reported visibility 5 statute miles
Scattered clouds at 1,500 feet AGL
Temperature 19°C Dewpoint 13°C
Altimeter 29.94" Hg
Remarks (follow)
Sea Level Pressure in millibars (Don't worry about this. You'll never use it!)
"19/13" are rounded to the nearest whole number.)*
The last four numbers represent the temperature or 19.3°C. 12.8°C. (Temp & DP values in METAR body or "19/13" are rounded to the nearest whole number.)*
Temp & dewpoint to the tenth of a degree. The first four numbers are the dewpoint or

METAR KLAX 081955Z 01013G20KT HZ 3SM SKC 18/11 A2995

Station: Los Angeles, CA
Issued on 8th day at 1955 Zulu
Wind is 010 at 13 knots gusting to 20 knots
Haze
Reported visibility 3 statute miles
Sky is clear - no clouds
Temp 18°C Dewpoint 11°C
Altimeter 29.95" Hg

*Keep in mind that it's often good to know the temp and dewpoint to the tenth of a degree. Why? Because fog or low clouds can form when the temp-dewpoint spread is 5 F which is actually 2.8 C. You can't accurately determine the potential for fog with the T-DP reading in the body of the METAR because these values are rounded to the nearest whole number.

Fig. 10

Altimeter–Hi! Or in this case, high. The letter *A* in Figure 7 represents the altimeter setting for that location. Without this, you could be accused of having a bad altitude. The altimeter setting is always prefixed with an A, indicating the altimeter setting in inches of mercury. All four digits of the pressure are listed. Simply insert a decimal after the second digit (or before the third digit—your choice). In Figure 7, the altimeter setting is 30.01 inches of Hg.

At the end of the METAR you will sometimes find supplementary information in the form of remarks (RMK). This is where the briefer can customize the observation by adding supplemental information. Figure 9 shows a few of these remarks (see the *Aeronautical Information Manual* or *Aviation Weather Services Advisory Circular AC 00-45E* for more information on remark codes). Don't be overwhelmed. Some of these codes are rarer than a wealthy flight instructor. You'll learn them as you encounter them.

Look at the following remark, for example: RAB05E30SNB30E45. This means that rain began at 5 minutes past the hour and ended at 30 minutes past the hour, snow began at 30 minutes past the hour and ended at 45 minutes past the hour. If the remark began with RAE42SNB42, then the rain would have ended at 42 minutes past the hour while the snow began at 42 minutes past the hour. The remark TSB05E45 means a thunderstorm began at 5 minutes past the hour and ended at 45 minutes past the hour. Finally, the remark FZDZB42 WSHFT 30 FROPA means that freezing drizzle began at 42 minutes past the hour and a wind shift began at 30 minutes past the hour with the frontal passage. If you see the remark DONTGO, use your own judgment.

Figure 10 shows the decoding of the METAR found in Figure 6.

Automatic Weather Observing Programs

Automatic weather observing stations will soon serve as the nation's primary surface weather observing network. These weather-watching computers-in-a-can transmit weather information (temperature, pressure, dewpoint, winds, cloud heights, etc.) directly to you in flight.

It's a little eerie, at first, to get a weather report untouched by a human from observation to delivery. I mean, how do you know the station isn't making up the observations, like a college student in first year chem lab? What if they band together and take over the Weather Channel?

Reality is, these units have extensive internal checks to make sure their sensors are making sense. And the existence of these automated weather observers means we now have reliable weather information from far more reporting points than the human-staffed system could ever provide. And the information is available nonstop, around the clock.

We'll discuss two types of automatic weather observing systems, the Automatic Weather Observing System (AWOS), and the Automatic Surface Observing System (ASOS). The Automatic Weather Sensor System (AWSS) is essentially identical to ASOS so it won't be discussed here.

AWOS–*Automatic Weather Observing System* units are installed at many airports across the country where weather reports were previously not available. Consisting of various sensors (Figure 11), a processor, a computer-generated voice system, and transmitter, these stations broadcast minute-by-minute, real-time, local weather information directly to pilots. AWOS/ASOS transmissions are receivable within 25 nautical miles of the transmission site, at or below 10,000 feet AGL. The transmissions can also be received on the airport. Frequencies for AWOS can be found near the airport data on the sectional chart, as shown in Figure 12, position A and in the *A/FD* as shown in Figure 13.

Four basic levels of AWOS stations are available:

1. AWOS-A reports only altimeter setting.

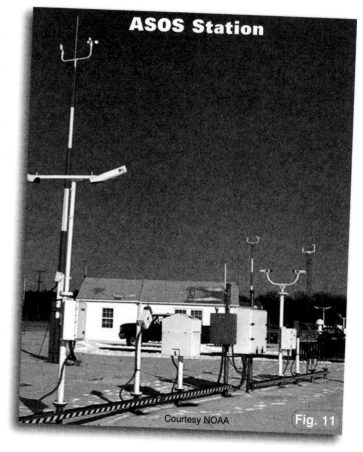

ASOS Station

Courtesy NOAA

Fig. 11

2. AWOS-1 usually reports altimeter setting, wind data, temperature, dewpoint and density altitude.

3. AWOS-2 provides the information provided by AWOS-1 plus visibility.

4. AWOS-3 provides the information of AWOS-2 plus cloud-ceiling data.

A typical ASOS or AWOS voice-transmitted observation might sound something like the following:

"Denver, Denver Front Range airport, automated weather observation. One eight three three Zulu. Sky conditions six thousand five hundred scattered. Visibility greater than one zero. Temperature two two Celsius.

Where to Find AWOS Frequencies

Fig. 12

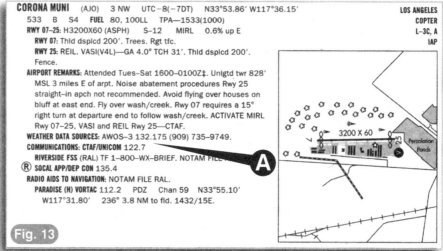

CORONA MUNI (AJO) 3 NW UTC-8(-7DT) N33°53.86' W117°36.15'
533 B S4 FUEL 80, 100LL TPA—1533(1000)
RWY 07–25: H3200X60 (ASPH) S–12 MIRL 0.6% up E
  RWY 07: Thld dsplcd 200'. Trees. Rgt tfc.
  RWY 25: REIL. VASI(V4L)—GA 4.0° TCH 31'. Thld dsplcd 200'. Fence.
AIRPORT REMARKS: Attended Tues–Sat 1600–0100Z‡. Unlgtd twr 828' MSL 3 miles E of arpt. Noise abatement procedures Rwy 25 straight–in apch not recommended. Avoid flying over houses on bluff at east end. Fly over wash/creek. Rwy 07 requires a 15° right turn at departure end to follow wash/creek. ACTIVATE MIRL Rwy 07–25, VASI and REIL Rwy 25—CTAF.
WEATHER DATA SOURCES: AWOS–3 132.175 (909) 735–9749.
COMMUNICATIONS: CTAF/UNICOM 122.7
RIVERSIDE FSS (RAL) TF 1–800–WX–BRIEF. NOTAM FILE RAL.
Ⓡ SOCAL APP/DEP CON 135.4
RADIO AIDS TO NAVIGATION: NOTAM FILE RAL.
  PARADISE (H) VORTAC 112.2 PDZ Chan 59 N33°55.10' W117°31.80' 236° 3.8 NM to fld. 1432/15E.

LOS ANGELES
COPTER
L–3C, A
IAP

3200 X 60
Percolation Ponds

Fig. 13

Dewpoint one niner Celsius. Wind three five zero at zero three. Altimeter two niner seven eight. Remarks, density altitude seven thousand five hundred."

Despite its reliability, the AWOS unit is still a machine and for that reason it might not be telling you the whole truth. For instance, the entire airport might be surrounded by clouds with a single, solitary hole over the ASOS, AWSS, or AWOS-3 weather unit. You can bet that little puppy reports *all clear*. The entire airport may be shrouded in fog while the ceilometer (cloud height measuring device) reports no clouds at the airport. Fortunately, the visibility would provide a clue to the presence of fog. When a human weather observer supplements mechanical weather observations, these problems disappear. Use a little common sense when using an automated observation of the weather to make your decisions.

ASOS (*Automatic Surface Observing System*)-ASOS is not something you put on spaghetti. Instead, it's sort of an AWOS on steroids. In addition to basic weather measurements, it also reports precipitation type and intensity as well as the occurrence of freezing rain. Situated at airports and other observing points nationwide, these automated stations provide minute-by-minute reports on the ever-changing weather. The intent is eventually to put about 1,700 of these stations into service.

One of the unique benefits of the automated system is that pilots can listen to computer-generated voice observations while airborne (some computer voices sound like Darth Vader with a cold). These transmissions, like those of AWOS, are usually receivable within 25 nautical miles of the airport below 10,000 feet AGL.

Figure 14, position B shows an *A/FD* excerpt for Oceanside airport, showing that ASOS observations can be heard on 127.8 MHz or by calling the listed phone number.

ASOS reports are similar to the METAR format that we've already studied. There are a few subtle differences. One of those is that automated stations cannot report clouds that are above 12,000 feet. The ASOS will report *CLR* (meaning no clouds are reported below 12,000 feet)

Finding ASOS Frequencies

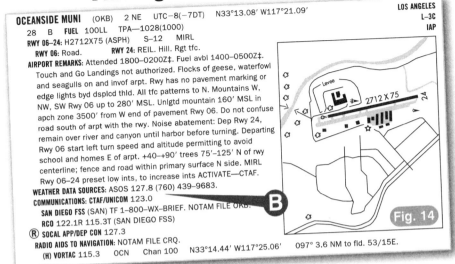

Fig. 14

instead of the *SKC* value shown in a METAR. There could be a solid overcast at 15,000 feet, but the ASOS can't see it. Out of sight, out of RAM. Keep this little idiosyncrasy in mind whenever you see an observation annotated as AUTO, COR (for CORrected) or in the remarks you see AO1 or AO2 (AO1 or AO2 indicates the level of sophistication of the precipitation discrimination sensors associated with the ASOS unit. AO2, being more sophisticated, can discriminate between different liquid and frozen precipitation—rain, snow, etc.).

Remember, if you see or hear of something missing from a ASOS report, it doesn't mean it's not there. It just means that the ASOS unit can't or didn't detect it.

Figure 15 shows two ASOS weather observations. You can tell these are automatic-type surface observations because the letters AUTO (meaning AUTOmated) and/or COR are located directly after the location of the date/time identifier (no, AUTO doesn't mean someone stood on an automobile to make the observation, either). As you can clearly see, the ASOS observations are provided in the same format as the METARs we've already studied. There's nothing new to be learned here. Simply read the ASOS observations as you do the METAR. (See Figure 9 for a sampling of the codes for the remarks (RMK) found at the end of the ASOS (METAR) observation.)

The ASOS observation for KABC shows AUTO right after the date/time group and the letters AO2 in the remarks section. This indicates that no human oversight backed up or augmented the ASOS report. Some locations have a human observer (sometimes Otto) augment the ASOS report. Whenever the human observer augments or adds to the ASOS report, the AUTO is deleted, because now

ASOS Reports

Fig. 15

METAR KABC 121355Z AUTO 21016G24KT 180V240 1SM -RA FG BKN015 OVC025 06/05 A2990 RMK AO2 PK WIND 20032/25

METAR KINK 130900Z COR 03005KT 21/2SM +SHRA OVC015 15/14 A3000 RMK AO2

The word *AUTO* or *COR* (for *COR*rected) appearing in the METAR indicates that this report was derived from some type of an automatic surface weather observation unit (ASOS, AWOS, etc.). When the ASOS report is augmented by a human observer, the word *AUTO* or *COR* is deleted.

it is a manual observation. However, the remarks section will still show either an AO1 or an AO2.

Personally, I am inclined to place greater faith in automated weather reports when a human being oversees the process (but not if he has to stand on an automobile, of course). Even though the current automated weather detectors are very sophisticated, they're still machines. So don't expect them to behave properly all the time. For the same reason, I don't completely trust those automated blood pressure machines found at shopping malls and airports. I heard of a pilot who put in his quarter, stuck in his arm and when his reading came up as 450 over 360, it wouldn't let him go. He had to drive home with the machine still attached to his arm (just kidding). Remember, machines can't detect all the weather, and if it says AUTO there's nobody check to see if the thing has broken its RAM dam and lost its mind.

Whither the Weather?

Having the current weather for airports along your route is valuable. But this is just one fry short of a Happy Meal if you're planning tomorrow's flight. Weather changes from day to day, hour to hour, minute to minute. It also changes while enroute. Pilots need a means of predicting this change.

Since most pilots aren't proficient with Ouija boards (no matter what they may claim), most of them look into the future through more conventional means such as one of several aviation forecasts that try to predict the future.

I should note that this is a somewhat thankless task. If the forecast is wrong, everyone complains. If it's right, nobody compliments. Undaunted, the forecasters persevere, using ever bigger and better computers to try to know which way the wind will blow.

Aviation Terminal Forecasts (TAF)–A TAF provides a description of surface weather you can expect to occur at an airport. TAFs are an excellent means of identifying the weather you can expect upon arrival at an airport. You can compare forecasts for airports along your route to obtain a better idea of how the weather is expected to change. When used in conjunction with METARs, TAFs provide a good idea of the present weather and how it's expected to change.

TAFs are forecast weather for a 24 hour period. They are issued four times daily (once every six hours at 0000Z, 0600Z, 1200Z and 1800Z). Much of the weather coding is similar to the METAR weather format (I knew that would make you happy). Since it's relatively simple to read, we won't need a memory-type acronym to interpret TAFs. If there are any major differences in the codes used by TAF compared to METAR, I'll let you know. Let's examine the TAF weather shown in Figure 16.

Station: (KLAX)

Same form and format as the METAR.

Date Forecast Issued: (091140Z):

The report was issued on the 9th day (09) at 1140 Zulu (UTC).

Aviation Terminal Forecast [TAF]

```
TAF
KLAX 091140Z 091212 22020KT 3SM -SHRA BKN020
      BECMG 1619 33015KT FM0300 35014KT 2SM TSRA OVC015
      TEMPO 0612 1SM +RA PROB40 0809 1/2SM FG
```
Fig. 16

Time of Forecast: (091212)

This forecast's date and valid times are indicated by the six-digit number sequence (091212). The first two numbers represent the date and the second two numbers represent the time the forecast period begins (1200Z). The last two numbers represent the ending time of the forecast period (1200Z). The forecast is valid from 1200Z on the 9th to 1200Z on the 10th (a 24 hour period). If midnight UTC is the beginning time period of the forecast it will be coded as 00. If it is the ending time, it is coded as 24. Therefore, a 24 hour forecast beginning and ending at midnight UTC would be indicated as 0024.

Forecast Winds:

(22020KT)

This is presented in the same format as the METAR. Figure 16 shows winds forecast to be from 220 degrees true direction at 20 knots. Winds will always be indicated, regardless of their velocity.

Forecast Visibility:

(3SM)

This is the prevailing visibility expected in statute miles, up to and including six miles. Expected visibilities greater than six miles are forecast as *P6SM* (*plus six statute miles*).

Forecast Weather:

(-SHRA)

The same five categories used in a METAR are used in a TAF for reporting weather phenomena, as shown in Figure 8. The letters -SHRA represent only operationally significant weather that's forecast for the implied time period. In other words, light rain showers are forecast starting at 1200Z.

Forecast Cloud Conditions: (BKN020)

This is the same as the METAR format. In this example, broken clouds are forecast at 2000 feet AGL. As in the METAR, ceiling layers are designated by the lowest layer that's BKN, OVC or shows VV (vertical visibility) into an obscuration.

Expected Changes: (BECMG, FM, TEMPO, PROB)

When gradual changes in the prevailing conditions are expected (usually over a period not to exceed two hours), the abbreviation *BECMG* (becoming) is used. BECMG is followed by four digits. The first two digits indicate when the change is expected to begin and the last two digits indicate when it's expected to be completed. The weather conditions that follow are expected to change at a gradual rate over the depicted time period. Any weather condition forecast prior to BECMG which is not revised following the change time period is expected to remain the same. For example, our report showing *1619* after BECMG means that from 1600Z to 1900Z the wind is expected to change to 330 degrees at 15 knots and all other weather is expected to remain the same.

FM is followed by a four-digit number which indicates the beginning time of a self contained portion of the forecast. This is used when a *rapid* (significant) change in weather (usually occurring in less than one hour) is expected. In our report the sequence of FM0300 indicates that from 0300Z the following weather conditions should occur: winds 350 degrees at 14 knots, two miles visibility, thunderstorms and rain, and an overcast ceiling of 1,500 feet. Weather that's omitted in the FM group isn't significant to aviation.

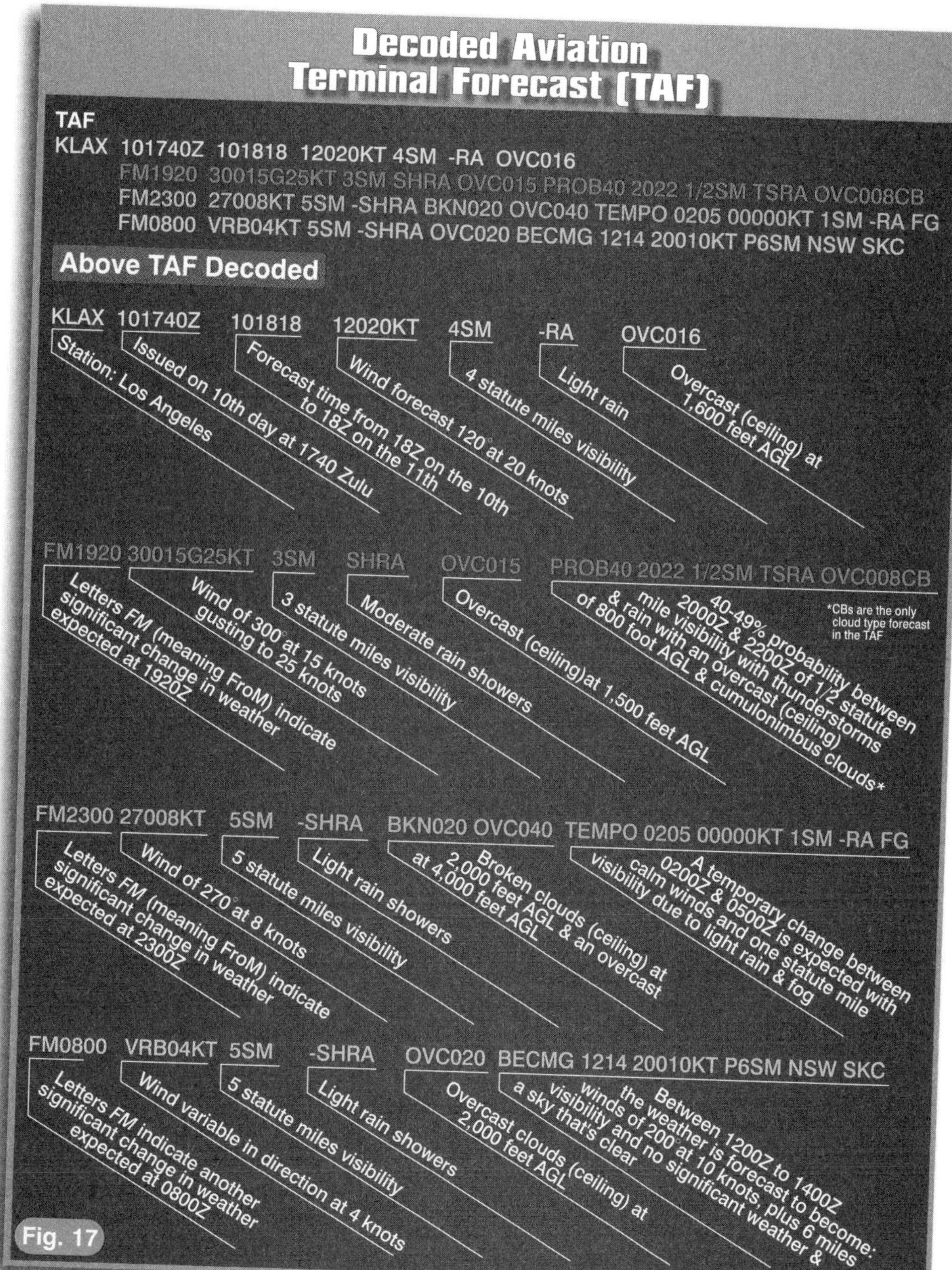

TEMPO indicates that fluctuations (temporary and usually lasting less than one hour) from the predominant weather conditions are expected. TEMPO is followed by a four digit number (0612) indicating the period during which these variations are expected. In our report, a temporary condition of one-mile visibility and heavy rain is expected to occur between 0600Z and 1200Z. There's only one tempo. No up-tempo or down-temp for jazz fans.

PROB (PROBability) is used when the likely occurrence of any weather phenomenon falls in the 30 to 39% (PROB 30) or 40 to 49% (PROB 40) range of expectation. If the probability of the condition is 50% or higher, the terms *BECMG, TEMPO* or *FM* are used. In our report, the sequence PROB40 0809 1/2SM FG indicates that between the hours of 0800Z and 0900Z there is a 40 to 49% proba-

bility of 1/2 mile visibility in fog. Figure 17 shows a detailed analysis of an airport's TAF.

Remember, TAFs are issued once every six hours. Make it a point to check the latest TAF to obtain the most current forecast information. I make it a point to check the METAR against the TAF. If the TAF said that this hour was to be clear but the METAR showed clouds, then that particular TAF might be too optimistic. That would make me less inclined to place a great deal of trust in the accuracy of the rest of the TAF. Once something isn't right, you're less inclined to trust it any of it. That's why I never trust motel signs. One sign read, "Free color TV." Well, I nearly got arrested when taking it out to my car.

Fig. 17

Aviation Area Forecasts (FA)

Remember the anxiety you felt when you went to a drive-in theater and drove off without unhooking the speaker? Five blocks away you heard, "Attention, attention, the snack bar will be closing in 15 minutes." OK, perhaps this never happened to you, but you might feel a similar sensation when looking at the area forecast. It consists of a lot of words without vowels. As I mentioned previously, this is part of the carryover from those days when Teletypes were slow and words were abbreviated to speed things up. With just a little practice, you'll be interpreting these reports as fast as Einstein whipping through nonlinear differential equations. After all, what's the difference?

The *aviation area forecast (FA)* is a general forecast often covering a region that includes several states. It's your key to finding the expected weather enroute and at airports not having aviation terminal forecasts (not every airport has a terminal forecast, which makes the area forecast your only forecasting tool). Figure 18 shows a typical area forecast.

FAs are issued three times daily for six specific areas in the lower 48 United States. They are 12 hour forecasts with an additional 6 hour outlook. As with other weather reports and forecasts, times are in Zulu. Unlike the aviation terminal forecast, however, the area forecast presents its cloud heights in MSL rather than AGL (unless noted by an AGL or ceiling designation). This is logical, once you think it through, since the forecast isn't for a specific spot, but rather a huge area over which there is often considerable variation in terrain height. In the area forecast, a ceiling is identified by *CIG* (which means ceiling). Figure 20 shows a few of the common contractions, definitions and variability terms used in the FA and other weather reports and forecasts.

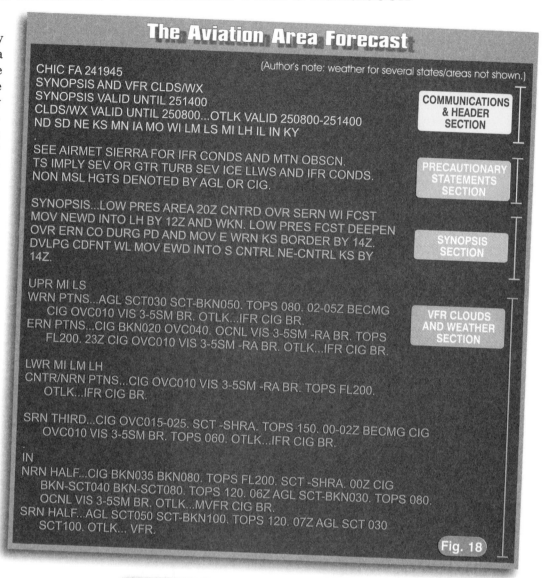

Fig. 18

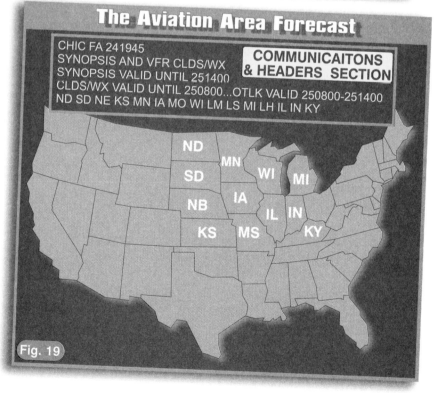

Fig. 19

Categories

Category	Definition
LIFR - *Low IFR* - ceiling less than 500 feet and/or visibility less than 1 mile.	
IFR - Ceiling 500 to 1,000 feet and/or visibility 1 to less than 3 miles.	
MVFR - *Marginal VFR* - ceiling 1,000 to 3,000 feet and/or visibility greater than 5 miles.	
VFR - No ceiling or ceiling greater than 3,000 feet and visibility greater than 5 miles.	

Remarks appended to VFR items

Remarks	Definition
VFR CIG ABV 100	Ceiling greater than 10,000 feet and visibility greater than 5 miles.
VFR NO CIG	Cloud coverage less than 6/10 or thin clouds and visibility greater than 5 miles.
VFR CLR	Cloud coverage less than 1/10 and visibility greater than 5 miles.

Examples of categorical groupings

Example	Definition
LIFR CIG	Low IFR due to low ceiling only.
IFR F	IFR due to visibility restricted by fog.
MVFR CIG H K	Marginal VFR due both to low ceiling and to visibility restricted by haze and smoke.
IFR CIG R WND	IFR due both to low ceiling and to visibility restricted by rain, wind expected to be 25 knots or greater.

Contractions

Contraction	Designator	Definition
CLR	CLR	Sky clear
SCT	SCT	Scattered
BKN	BKN	Broken
OVC	OVC	Overcast
OBSCD	X	Obscured
PTLY OBSCD	-X	Partly obscured
CIG	C	Ceiling

Area coverage of showers and thunderstorms

Adjective	Coverage
Isolated	Single cells (no percentage)
Widely scattered	Less than 25% of area affected.
Scattered	25% to 54% of area affected
Numerous	55% or more of area affected

Fig. 20

Variability Terms

Variability terms are often included in the remarks and indicate how often a change might occur in ceilings, sky cover, weather, etc.

OCNL ... means *occasional* and indicates that there is a greater than 50% probability that the associated weather condition will occur, bit for less than 1/2 of the forecast period.

CHC ... means *chance* and indicates that there is a 30% to 50% probability that the associated weather condition will occur.

SLGT CHC ... means *slight chance* and indicates that there is a 10% to 20% probability that the associated weather conditions will occur.

The FA consists of four sections:

1. *Communications and header section*
2. *Precautionary statements section*
3. *Synopsis section*
4. *VFR clouds and weather section*

Let's examine the FA in Figure 18. The first section of the FA was issued for the Chicago area (the C following CHI indicates that this forecast contains clouds and weather). This forecast was issued on the 24th day of the month (24) at 1945Z. Underneath this line is *SYNOPSIS AND VFR CLDS/WX*, which tells you what's in this forecast in case you don't already know. The next line states that the SYNOPSIS is valid until 1400Z on the 25th day of the month (251400). The line underneath indicates the CLDS/WX section is valid until 0800Z on the 25th (a 12-hour period from the time the forecast begins). Note that the synopsis is valid for 18 hours while the VFR clouds and weather section is valid for only 12 hours. The OTLK (outlook) information is valid from 0800Z on the 25th to 1400Z on the 25th (that's a six-hour period).

Following this are the states/areas making up the forecast area. North Dakota, South Dakota, Nebraska, Kansas, Minnesota, Iowa, Missouri, Wisconsin, Lake Michigan, Lake Superior, Michigan, Lake Huron, Illinois, Indiana, Kentucky are covered in this area forecast, as shown in Figure 19.

As you can plainly see, vowels are left out of the report where possible to condense it for transmission. Fortunately, weather briefers (which isn't underwear you put on when getting the weather) read it to you in real English.

The precautionary statements section, in Figure 18, is next. These statements are included in all area forecasts. Any IFR conditions, mountain obscuration, turbulence, or icing that are present or expected to occur will be covered in something called an AIRMET (AIR METeorological advisory). As you'll soon see, these are advisories of significant weather phenomena and should be of concern to you. Keep in mind that hazardous weather (IFR, icing, and turbulence) are not included in the area forecast. You must refer to AIRMETs and other in-flight aviation weather advisories for this information (we'll discuss these shortly).

The next statement indicates that thunderstorms imply possible severe or greater turbulence, severe icing and low-level wind shear and IFR conditions. The last statement indicates that all heights in the area forecast are MSL unless otherwise noted.

The synopsis section of the area forecast is the *big picture* of what's going on. It is a brief summary of the location and movements of fronts, pressure systems and circulation systems for an 18 hour period. Figure 21 shows how you might mentally picture this synopsis (but don't tell anyone other than another pilot or your three-year-old that you have a picture of a synopsis in your head. They won't understand, and might report it to the authorities).

The VFR clouds and weather section contains a 12-hour specific forecast, followed by a six-hour categorical outlook. This gives us a total forecast period of 18 hours. You'll find that the VFR CLDS/WX section is several paragraphs long. Much like a flight instructor's car, it's often broken down by states or by well known geographical areas. A general description of clouds and weather which covers an area greater than 3,000 square miles and is significant to VFR flight operations follows each of the listed geographical areas.

To interpret the area forecast, it's best to start with the synopsis section, which is frank and to the point. According to the synopsis shown in Figure 21, at 2000Z an area of low pressure is centered over southeastern Wisconsin and is forecast to move northeastward into Lake Huron by 1200 Zulu and weaken. The low pressure is forecast to deepen over eastern Colorado during the period and

The Aviation Area Forecast

SYNOPSIS...LOW PRES AREA 20Z CNTRD OVR SERN WI FCST MOV NEWD INTO LH BY 12Z AND WKN. LOW PRES FCST DEEPEN OVR ERN CO DURG PD AND MOV E WRN KS BORDER BY 14Z. DVLPG CDFNT WL MOV EWD INTO S CNTRL NE-CNTRL KS BY 14Z.

SYNOPSIS SECTION

Fig. 21

move east into the western Kansas border by 1400 Zulu. The developing cold front will move eastward into south central and northeast central Kansas by 1400 Zulu.

After you've looked over the synopsis, the forecast weather for individual states or specific locations in the VFR CLDS/WX section will make more sense to you. Keep in mind that surface visibility and obstructions to vision are included in the area forecast only when the forecast visibility is expected to be six statute miles or less. Precipitation, thunderstorms and sustained winds of 20 knots or greater are always included when forecast. Specifically, the abbreviation *WND* is included in the outlook if winds, sustained or gusty, are expected to be 20 knots or greater.

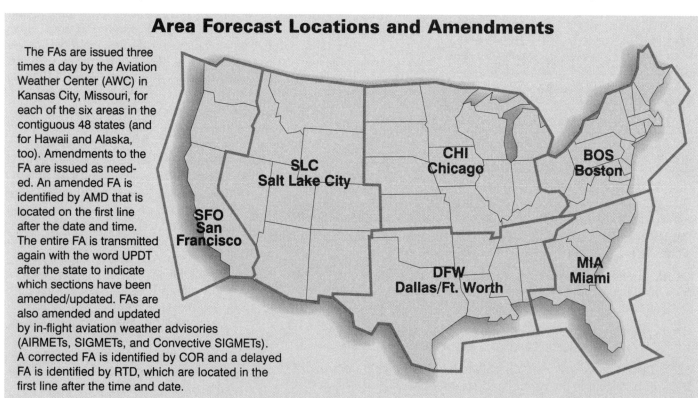

Area Forecast Locations and Amendments

The FAs are issued three times a day by the Aviation Weather Center (AWC) in Kansas City, Missouri, for each of the six areas in the contiguous 48 states (and for Hawaii and Alaska, too). Amendments to the FA are issued as needed. An amended FA is identified by AMD that is located on the first line after the date and time. The entire FA is transmitted again with the word UPDT after the state to indicate which sections have been amended/updated. FAs are also amended and updated by in-flight aviation weather advisories (AIRMETs, SIGMETs, and Convective SIGMETs). A corrected FA is identified by COR and a delayed FA is identified by RTD, which are located in the first line after the time and date.

Winds Aloft Forecast
Fig. 22

FD WBC 151745
BASED ON 151200Z DATA
VALID 1600Z FOR USE 1800-0300Z. TEMPS NEG ABV 24000

FT	3000	6000	9000	12000	18000	24000	30000	34000	39000
ALS			2420	2635−08	2535−18	2444−30	245945	246755	246862
AMA		2714	2725+00	2625−04	2531−15	2452−27	265842	256352	256762
DEN			2321−04	2532−08	2434−19	2441−31	235347	236056	236262
HLC		1707−01	2113−03	2219−07	2330−17	2435−30	244145	244854	245561
MKC	0507	2006+03	2215−01	2322−06	2338−17	2448−29	236143	237252	238160
STL	2113	2325+07	2332+02	2339−04	2356−16	2373−27	239440	730649	731960

Winds Aloft Forecasts (FD)

There are certain moments in your life that you just don't forget. I once asked a passenger to look and see if the strobe light was on. He said, "Yes, no, yes, no, yes, no...." I guess he was a little confused about how strobe lights work. The way to keep from being confused about how wind affects your airplane is to know how fast and from what direction it blows. This is extremely important for properly estimating fuel consumption, not to mention figuring out whether you'll get to your meeting on time. Fortunately, there is a forecast that provides you with an estimate of winds for up to 24 hours in advance. It's known as the *winds aloft forecast.*

Winds aloft forecasts are very useful to pilots. These forecasts are issued twice daily and are valid for 6, 12, or 24 hours. Each forecast is issued with a valid time for its use. Figure 22 shows a typical winds aloft forecast.

Winds are forecast for true altitudes starting at 3,000 feet and additional 3,000 foot increments up to 12,000 feet (we won't worry about higher altitudes for the moment). Winds less than 1,500 feet above the reporting station's surface are not forecast. In other words, if your airport lies at 5,000 MSL, the 6,000 foot winds aloft forecast will be blank for the area around the airport (it doesn't mean that there is no wind up there today, however). Temperature is not forecast for altitudes within 3,000 feet of the surface.

Winds aloft are provided in knots and their direction is always in reference to true north, as are other weather reports and forecasts. Figure 22 depicts the forecast winds at 6,000 MSL above AMA (Amarillo, Texas) as 2714. Unlike METAR or TAF, the first two numbers of this four-digit value represent the wind direction in tens of degrees; you need to add a zero onto these numbers to get the wind direction. The last two numbers represent the wind's velocity. The wind at AMA is forecast to be from 270 degrees at 14 knots. At 6,000 MSL above MKC the wind is forecast to be from 200 degrees at 6 knots with a forecast temperature of +3 degrees C.

The – or + after the winds represents a negative or positive temperature value that follows the four-digit wind value. Winds aloft temperatures are in degrees Celsius. At 9,000 feet MSL over DEN (Denver, CO), the winds are forecast to be from 230 degrees at 21 knots with a temperature of –4 degrees C. If winds are expected to be light and variable the identifier *9900* is used. This doesn't mean wind from 990 degrees, with no velocity (we can't have a wind with an unknown direction and no speed). Technically, it means that the winds are less than 5 knots. Calm winds are identified by 0000.

Forecast temperatures are useful for several reasons. Many pilots use them to predict where temperature inversions will occur. Any time you see the forecast temperature increasing (or not decreasing as much) with altitude, you know you have a stable air situation. Warmer air aloft could act as a lid, trapping industrial pollutants, so visibility may be restricted.

If you want the winds at an altitude between those listed, it's time to interpolate. This is not something done so everyone can understand what's being said when there's a speech given at the UN. It's the process of meeting the numbers halfway. Break out the Cray supercomputer. Actually, the math is easy, and you can probably do it either in your head or, if that's full, on your fingers. If the altitude you'll be flying at is halfway between two forecast levels, the wind and temperature will be about halfway between the numbers given for those two levels. Add the two wind (or temperature) numbers and divide by 2.

Bingo. I told you it was easy, not like calculus.

Actually, halfway is about all you'll ever need to figure. If you're nearer than that to one forecast level or another, use that level and you'll be close enough for rock 'n roll. If you believe there is a significant difference between the winds at 6,000 feet and the winds at 6,750 feet and that this can be forecast with great precision, then you might also believe that the state put signs reading "Highway Patrol Next Exit" on the freeway so you can turn yourself in when you do something wrong.

One of the important items to check during cross-country flight planning is the altitude that will provide the most favorable (or at least the least adverse) winds. After studying the winds aloft forecast, you can decide on an altitude giving you less of a headwind or more of a tailwind. Sometimes it's advantageous to spend additional time climbing in order to catch a tailwind.

E6-B Winds Aloft Cruising Altitude Selection Tool

Have you ever had to choose a cruising altitude based on variable wind directions and speeds? Certainly you'd want the altitude yielding the highest groundspeed for your course on any IFR flight, right? How do you make that choice? Instead of casting your fate to the winds (so to speak), why not try a more scientific method, such as using the wind side of the E6-B computer? Here's how to do it.

1. Assume these are the winds aloft forecast for today's flight.

Winds Aloft
3,000 Feet - 310 degrees @ 22 knots
6,000 Feet - 340 degrees @ 15 knots
9,000 Feet - 030 degrees @ 10 knots
12,000 Feet - 010 degrees @ 40 knots

2. Let's assume your true course is 260 degrees and true airspeed is 156 knots. On the clear plastic portion of the circular scale, plot the wind forecast for each altitude shown above. Do this by placing the grommet (the center) on the airspeed arc labeled 100. Place the wind direction under the true index by rotating the circular scale. Then mark the wind velocity up from the 100 arc. We'll begin by plotting the wind for 3,000 feet as shown below.

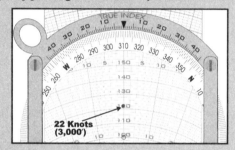

22 Knots (3,000')

3. Next we'll plot the wind for 6,000 feet.

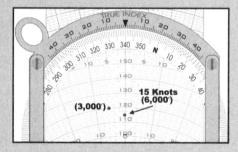

15 Knots (6,000')
(3,000')

4. Then we'll plot the wind for 9,000 feet

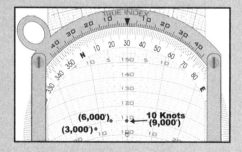

(6,000') 10 Knots (9,000')
(3,000')

5. Finally, we'll plot the wind for 12,000 feet.

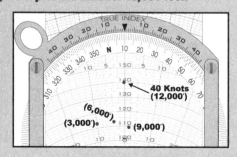

40 Knots (12,000')
(6,000')
(3,000') (9,000')

6. Now rotate the circular scale to place the true course (260 degrees) under the true index as shown below and to the right. To determine the wind's effect on your groundspeed, position the 156 knot true airspeed arc under each wind dot. The groundspeed for that wind is under the grommet. Let's test each wind dot. The figure to the right indicates that the wind at 3,000 feet produces a groundspeed of approximately 141 knots

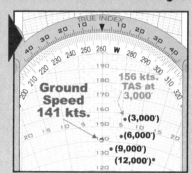

Ground Speed 141 kts.
156 kts. TAS at 3,000'
(3,000')
(6,000')
(9,000')
(12,000')

7. The figure to the right indicates that the wind at 6,000 feet produces a groundspeed of approximately 153 knots.

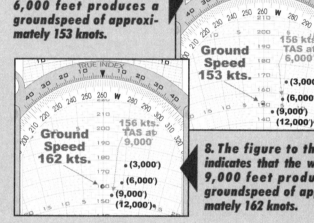

Ground Speed 153 kts.
156 kts. TAS at 6,000
(3,000')
(6,000')
(9,000')
(12,000')

Ground Speed 162 kts.
156 kts. TAS at 9,000
(3,000')
(6,000')
(9,000')
(12,000')

8. The figure to the left indicates that the wind at 9,000 feet produces a groundspeed of approximately 162 knots.

9. The figure to the right shows that the wind at 12,000 feet produces a groundspeed of approximately 164 knots.

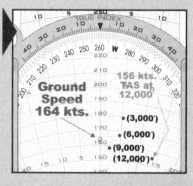

Ground Speed 164 kts.
156 kts. TAS at 12,000
(3,000')
(6,000')
(9,000')
(12,000')

10. It seems that the best groundspeed (164 knots) occurs at an altitude of 12,000 feet. Since you can get a groundspeed of 162 knots at 9,000 feet your first thought might be that this is the obvious option. Keep thinking. You need to weigh the benefits of climbing an extra 3,000 feet just to go two knots faster (maybe—remember, we're talking forecasts and guesses and interpolation here, not scientific certainty). Take a look at your performance charts and examine the difference in fuel consumption between these altitudes. Consider that flying at higher altitudes suggests the use of supplemental oxygen (i.e., recommended for flights above 10,000 feet during the day or 5,000 feet at night). My experience tells me that when wind changes speed more than four knots per 1,000 feet, you're likely to encounter wind shear. Between 9,000 feet and 12,000 feet, the wind changes 30 knots, which works out to a 10 knot change per 1,000 feet. It's safe to say that it will be bumpy between these altitudes. This is one more reason you might elect to stay at 9,000 feet instead of 12,000 feet. This is a handy little technique for use during preflight planning or even while in flight.

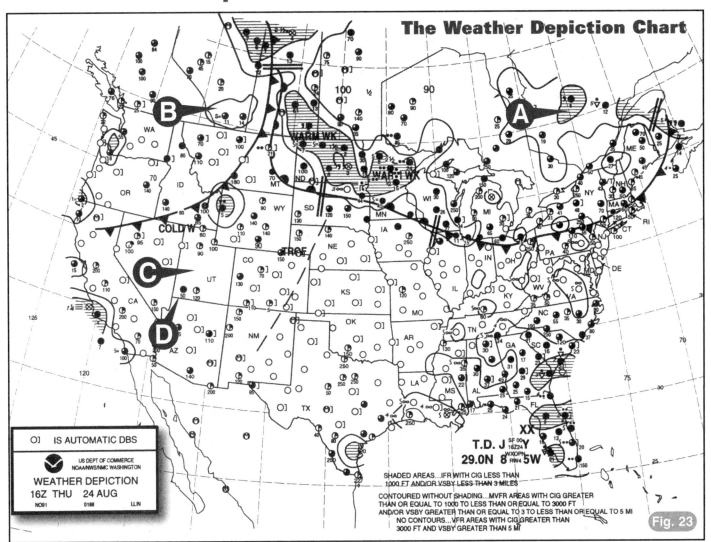

The Weather Depiction Chart

Fig. 23

Weather Charts: Getting the Big Picture

OK, you don't like numbers, and you're not real big on words. Fortunately, when it comes to weather, you haven't been left out in the cold. Much of the complexity of weather makes a lot more sense presented as pictures, which is the way weatherpeople have been looking at the weather for decades.

There are a number of weather charts that can prove to be very informative and useful. Accessing them was easy when there was a Flight Service Station on almost every airport corner. If you have a personal computer, it's now even easier, because the charts are available from a variety of sources electronically (and in color, too). You can brief yourself from the comfort of your home (assuming it's not a mobile home because, if it is, then it's likely that a tornado is bearing down on you right now and that means a little less comfort for you). And if you are fortunate enough to be near one of the remaining Flight Service Stations, stop in for a look at some of the following charts. It's a great way to literally get the picture.

Weather Depiction Chart

The *weather depiction chart* (Figure 23) is prepared from METARs. It provides pilots with a broad overview or a bird's eye view (which doesn't mean it shows you the locations worms and cats) of weather conditions. It's an excellent place to begin your briefing and determine the general weather conditions upon which to base your flight planning. The chart is issued every three hours, beginning at 0100Z.

The weather depiction chart has lots of good information. Perhaps most important is the graphical view it gives you of where VFR and IFR conditions prevail.

The weather depiction chart always comes with a means of decoding a few of its symbols. A decoding key is located in the bottom right hand corner of the chart. For instance, any area that is shaded is IFR (ceilings less than 1,000 feet and/or visibility less than 3 miles, position A). Contoured areas without shading are areas of marginal VFR (MVFR) weather with ceilings greater than or equal to 1,000 feet to less than or equal to 3,000 feet and/or visibility of three to five miles (position B). Areas without contours are areas of VFR with ceilings greater than 3,000 feet and visibilities greater than five miles (position C).

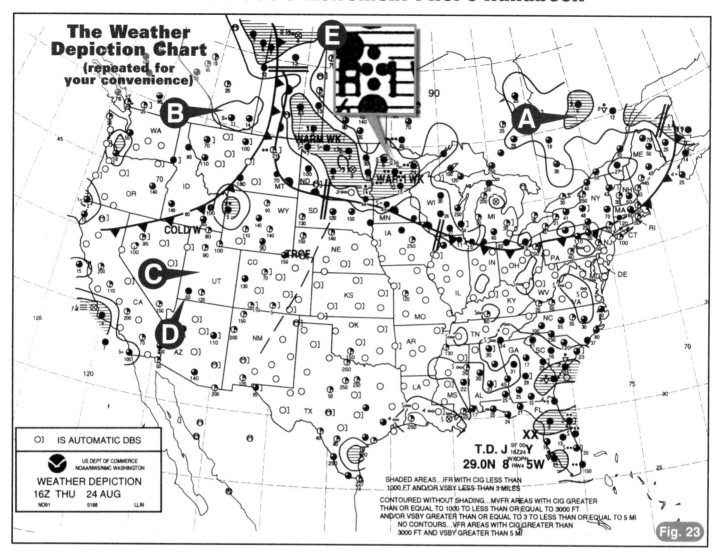

Fig. 23

Numbers and symbols surrounding the individual stations inform you about cloud heights, coverage, and weather and obstruction to vision. A key for this chart's symbols is shown in Figures 24 and 25. (Note: the code shown on the actual weather depiction chart above is provided to you on the knowledge exam.) You have to wonder why the FAA doesn't show and define most of the other symbols they use on the chart, as well. After all, they could put them in a box place somewhere over the Pacific or Atlantic Ocean. Other than a few flying fish, there aren't too many pilots needing weather depiction information out there. For instance, in the southwest corner of Utah (position D) the station circle is completely darkened in. Using the key in Figure 24, you can tell that the sky is overcast.

Cloud height is determined the same way it is with the METAR and TAF data, by adding two zeros to the numbers underneath the station circle, as shown in Figure 25. This tells us that the height of the overcast with the numbers 50 under the station circle is 5,000 feet. Visibility and precipitation is shown to the left of the station circle. In north central Minnesota, the station showing four dots in a diamond pattern indicates the area of heaviest precipitation (Figure 23, position E insert). Four dots indicate continuous rain that was heavy at the time of the observation (Figure 25).

Another nice thing about the weather depiction chart is that it shows the location of frontal systems using symbols similar to those on the surface weather map. Before your detailed flight planning begins, take a look at the weather depiction chart. Ask yourself these questions: Where are there VFR or MVFR conditions in the

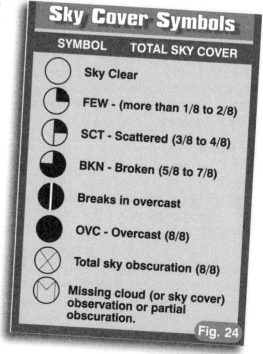

Sky Cover Symbols

SYMBOL	TOTAL SKY COVER
	Sky Clear
	FEW - (more than 1/8 to 2/8)
	SCT - Scattered (3/8 to 4/8)
	BKN - Broken (5/8 to 7/8)
	Breaks in overcast
	OVC - Overcast (8/8)
	Total sky obscuration (8/8)
	Missing cloud (or sky cover) observation or partial obscuration.

Fig. 24

direction I'm headed? In an emergency, at least you'd know where the better weather conditions are, and you could head in that direction if need be. Which way is the front moving? The weather is sure to become worse in the direction of frontal travel.

The great value of the weather depiction chart lies in the frequency of its issuance. You only get that advantage, however, if you're using the latest product. Just as you look on a box of cookies for the expiration date (don't you?), check when the weather depiction chart was issued. If it's stale, wait for a fresh one. And under no circumstances should you eat the weather report. That is *not* what is meant by "be a good consumer."

Weather Depiction Plotting Symbols

PLOTTING SYMBOL	MEANING
⊖ 8	Few clouds, base 800 feet, visibility more than 5
12	Broken sky cover, ceiling 1,200 feet, slight rain showers, visibility more than 5
5 ⊙ 0	Thin overcast with breaks, visibility 5 in haze
▲ 20	Scattered at 2,000 feet, clouds topping ridges, visibility more than 5
2= ○	Sky clear, visibility 2, light fog
1/2 ≡ ⊗ 3	Total sky obscuration, visibility ½, fog, vertical visibility into obs 300 feet, fog determined by automated system
2= ⊗ 2	Total sky obscuration, vertical visibility into obs is 200 feet, visibility 2, light fog
1/4 ✳ ⊗ 5	Total sky obscuration, vertical visibility into obs is 500 feet, visibility ¼ intermittent snow
1 ⚡ ● 12	Overcast, ceiling 1,200 feet thunderstorms, rain showers, visibility 1
•	Intermittent rain (not freezing), slight at time of observation.
••	Continuous rain (not freezing), slight at time of observation.
⋮	Intermittent rain (not freezing), moderate at time of observation.
⋰	Continuous rain (not freezing), moderate at time of observation.
⋮	Intermittent rain (not freezing), heavy at time of observation.
⋰	Continuous rain (not freezing), heavy at time of observation.

Fig. 25

Varieties in Weather Depiction Charts

This DTN Weather Depiction Chart prepared for AOPA shows IFR, MVFR and VFR areas as easy-to-see color coded station models. Also shown are with frontal systems and pressure centers. There is no station model information for the specific type of weather at a station, as there is in the NWS's weather depiction chart shown in Figure 23.

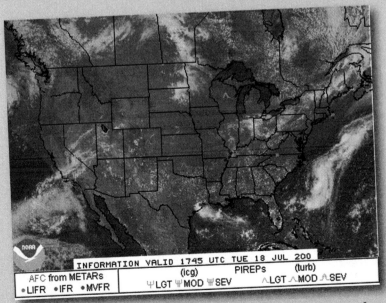

The National Weather Service offers a slightly different product that shows areas of IFR, MVFR and VFR superimposed on a satellite photo. PIREP information on icing and turbulence also appear.

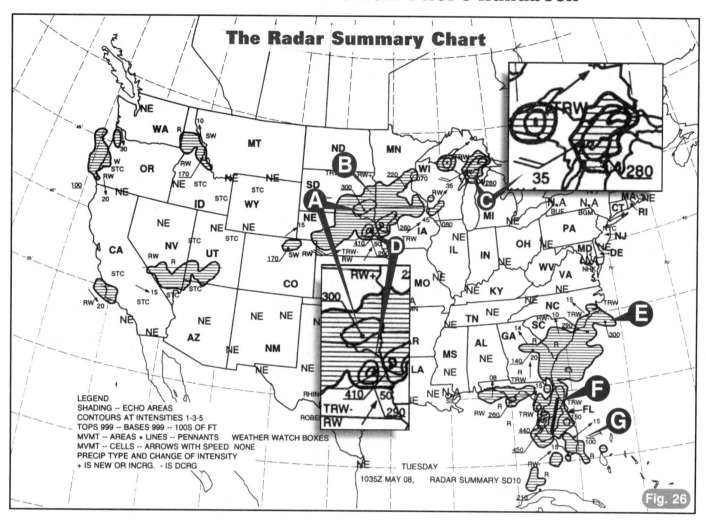

Fig. 26

Radar Summary Chart

The radar summary chart, shown in Figure 26, is issued 16 times during a 24-hour period (some private weather services offer it 24 hours a day). It presents the location of radar echoes resulting from precipitation (usually water or hail) suspended in clouds. Since radar energy is incapable of reflecting off clouds, this chart does not directly show cloud locations, though you can surmise that where there's rain, there are clouds.

The absence of a radar return obviously doesn't mean that there are no clouds. Radar energy goes right through a cloud. It takes *precipitation-size* water drops to show up on radar in the form of a precipitation echo. If enough suspended water is present, the radar will show its location. Keep in mind that it also takes updrafts to suspend water. And strong updrafts are associated with thunderstorms. If the radar shows enough water, there's a strong possibility thunderstorms are present.

By examining the radar summary chart, you'll be able to determine the location of precipitation echoes, their intensity, intensity trend, configuration, coverage, echo tops, bases and movement.

Figure 27 provides a legend with which to interpret the symbols on the radar summary chart. This won't be available on the knowledge exam, so there are a few items you need to memorize.

Radar Summary Chart Legend

VIP LEVEL	ECHO INTENSITY	PRECIPITATION INTENSITY	RAINFALL RATE In/hr STRATIFORM	RAINFALL RATE In/hr CONVECTIVE
1	WEAK	LIGHT	LESS THAN 0.1	LESS THAN 0.2
2	MODERATE	MODERATE	0.1 - 0.5	0.2 - 1.1
3	STRONG	HEAVY	0.5 - 1.0	1.1 - 2.2
4	VERY STRONG	VERY HEAVY	1.0 - 2.0	2.2 - 4.5
5	INTENSE	INTENSE	2.0 - 5.0	4.5 - 7.1
6	EXTREME	EXTREME	MORE THAN 5.0	MORE THAN 7.1

450
Highest precipitation top in area in hundreds of feet MSL. (45,000 FEET MSL)

* The numbers representing the intensity level do not appear on the chart. Beginning from the first contour line, bordering the area, the intensity level is 1-2, second contour is 3-4, and third contour is 5-6.

SYMBOLS USED ON CHART

SYMBOL MEANING
R   RAIN
RW   RAIN SHOWER
HAIL   HAIL
S   SNOW
IP   ICE PELLETS
SW   SNOW SHOWER
L   DRIZZLE
ZR, ZL   FREEZING PRECIPITATION
NE   NO ECHOES OBSERVED
NA   OBSERVATIONS UNAVAILABLE
OM   OUT FOR MAINTENANCE
STC S   STC ON - all precipitation may not be seen
ROBEPS   RADAR OPERATING BELOW PERFORMANCE STANDARDS
RHINO   RANGE HEIGHT INDICATORS NOT OPERATING

SYMBOL MEANING
+   INTENSITY INCREASING OR NEW ECHO
−   INTENSITY DECREASING
           NO SYMBOL NO CHANGE IN INTENSITY
35   CELL MOVEMENT TO NE AT 35 KNOTS
           LINE OR AREA MOVEMENT TO EAST AT 20 KNOTS
LM   LITTLE MOVEMENT
MA   ECHOES MOSTLY ALOFT
PA   ECHOES PARTLY ALOFT

SYMBOL MEANING
           LINE OF ECHOES
SLD   8/10 OR GREATER COVERAGE IN A LINE
WS999   SEVERE THUNDERSTORM WATCH
WT999   TORNADO WATCH
LEWP   LINE ECHO WAVE PATTERN
HOOK   HOOK ECHO

RAINFALL RATES SHOULD BE USED WITH CAUTION

Fig. 27

Arrow A indicates strong to very strong echoes (area within second contour) with echo tops to 30,000 feet MSL (as indicated by the *300* value above the bent line below the number value).

Arrow B shows weak to moderate echoes (area within first contour) with rain showers increasing in intensity (as indicated by *RW+*).

Arrow C indicates an area of echoes moving toward the northeast (the arrow points in that direction) with strong to very strong echoes and echo tops to 28,000 feet MSL.

Arrow D depicts intense to extreme echoes within the smallest contour. Echo tops reach 29,000 feet MSL. A cell in the northeast corner of Nebraska is moving northeast at 50 knots (a single arrow refers to a single cell and that arrow points northeast. The speed of that cell is located at the tip of the arrow).

Arrow E indicates that the highest echo tops are at 30,000 feet MSL, with weak to moderate echoes, thunderstorms and rain showers (as indicated by the letters *TRW*), and cell movement is toward the northeast at 15 knots.

Arrow F shows a line of echoes (as shown by a solid black line) with the highest echo tops at 45,000 feet MSL. No movement of the line is indicated here.

Arrow G tells us that that the echo bases are at 10,000 feet MSL (shown by a line "above" the numerical value) and cell movement is toward the northeast 15 knots. Weak to moderate echoes are present along with rain (indicated by the letter *R*).

The radar summary chart is helpful to VFR pilots because it provides clues on where the air is convectively active, or the weather is severe. The greater the suspend-ed precipitation, the greater the intensity of the updrafts required to suspend it. When you have echoes with three contours (indicating intense or extreme echo intensity), then you have a greater chance of extreme turbulence and its associated problems. The taller a thunderstorm, the nastier it generally is. Precipitation heights provide you with a rough idea of just how strong the echo (or areas of echoes) is.

As an IFR pilot, you need to know that the radar summary chart is also a good indication of how convective the air might be. The presence of echoes should be your clue to look at other charts and weather reports to get an idea of the thunderstorm potential of the air.

Without lightning detection equipment or airborne weather radar, you shouldn't be flying IFR in the clouds unless you are absolutely sure that those clouds don't contain thunderstorms. This, of course, is just common sense, but it's also sense that seems to be uncommon among far too many instrument pilots. Keep in mind that the presence of a Level 1 or 2 echo (a single contour) doesn't necessarily mean thunderstorms are present or that they could even form. To know if a thunderstorm is present, you'd need to have an indication of lightning or see the letter "T" on the chart. On the other hand, it's a good bet that any Level 3 storm (second contour or higher) indicates the presence of thunderstorms.

Finally, keep in mind that unlike other charts, the radar summary chart can show the lines and cells of hazardous thunderstorms. If you see a solid line (Arrow F), you've got thunderstorms. In regard to thunderstorms, perhaps the wisdom of Mark Twain is applicable when he said, "It's better to be cautious 100 times than to die once."

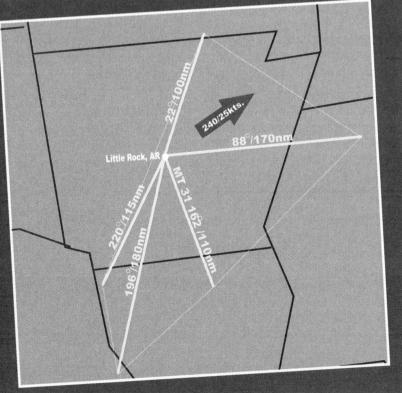

Radar Weather Report (SD)

Thunderstorms and general areas of precipitation including rain and snow can be observed by radar. A radar weather report, or SD as it's also known, may be transmitted as a separate report, or it may be included in a scheduled weather broadcast by the FSS. While you may not have an occasion to use these reports often, it's important to know how to interpret them.

The following is an example of an SD:

LZK 1133 AREA 4TRW +/+ 22/100 88/170 196/180 220/115 C2425 MT 31 AT 162/110

The SD is interpreted as follows: Little Rock (Arkansas) radar weather observation taken at 1133 Zulu. An area of echoes of 4/10 coverage, containing thunderstorms and heavy rain showers, increasing in intensity. The area is defined by points (referenced from the LZK radar site at 22 degrees and 100 nautical miles; 88 degrees and 170 nautical miles; 196 degrees and 180 nautical miles; 220 degrees and 115 nautical miles. Cells within this line are moving from 240 degrees at 25 knots. (These points are plotted on a map. By connecting the points with a straight line, you'll have an outline of the area of echoes. The maximum tops (MT or MTS) are located at 31,000 feet MSL and are at 162 degrees and 110 nm from LZK.

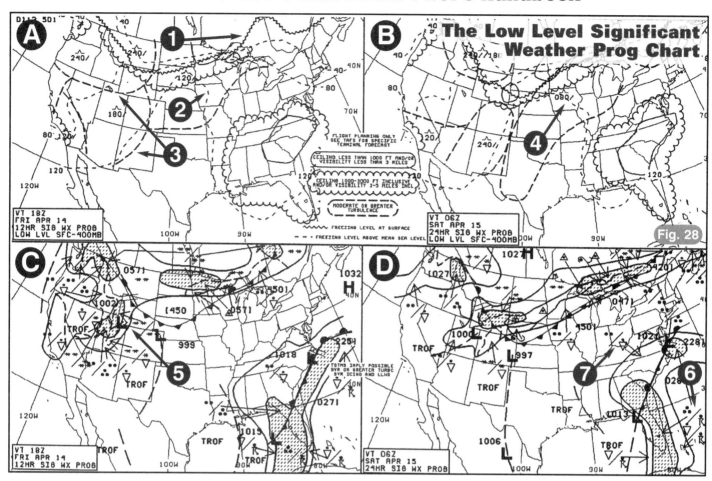

Low-Level Significant Weather Prognostic Chart

A friend of mine phoned each of his upcoming dinner guests to tell them that he had good news and bad news for the get together. "The good news," he said, "is that I've just purchased new living room furniture to make your visit more comfortable."

"What's the bad news?" asked one guest.

"The bad news," my friend said, "is that you'll have to wear plastic leisure suits to make sure you don't ruin it."

Essentially, my friend gave his guests a *prognosis* or a future outlook of the amount of fun they could expect to have at dinner. While the terminal area forecast, area forecast and winds aloft forecast are all a textual prognoses of the weather, the *low-level significant weather prognostic chart* does the same thing in picture form.

The low-level significant weather prognostic chart—the *prog chart,* as it's usually referred to by those not wishing to carry supplemental oxygen—is a graphic version of the area forecast, though it differs slightly from the written version, as shown in Figure 28. While the area forecast pro-

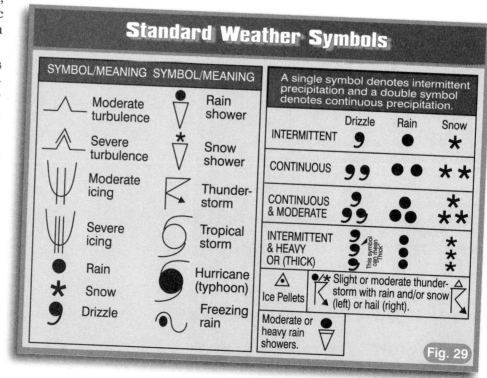

vides weather for one of six forecast areas in the United States, the prog chart provides a picture forecast for the entire continental U.S. The prog chart consists of four panels. The upper panels are 12-hour (left panel, A) and 24-hour (right panel, B) predictions of significant weather from the surface to the 400 millibar pressure level (that's 24,000 feet). The lower panels (panels C and D) are 12- and 24-hour predictions of surface weather. Prog charts are issued four times daily, approximately once every six hours.

A key, located between both upper charts, helps with interpreting the weather symbols. For instance, all areas surrounded by solid lines are areas with ceilings less than 1,000 feet and/or visibilities less than three miles (these are IFR conditions and the code is similar to that used on the weather depiction chart). The areas surrounded by scalloped lines are not seafood harvesting zones. They're areas of marginal VFR conditions consisting of 1,000 to 3,000 foot ceilings and/or 3 to 5 mile visibilities. Areas outside scalloped lines are forecast to have ceilings greater than 3,000 feet and 5 miles visibility.

Panels A and B of the significant weather prog chart have zig-zag lines, which indicate the location of the freezing level at the surface (panel A, position 1). Dashed lines on the same panel indicate freezing levels at altitude (panel A, position 2). Freezing levels are important for instrument pilots, since they want to avoid flying in the clouds when the temperatures are near or below freezing, lest they pick up ice and turn their aircraft into a giant

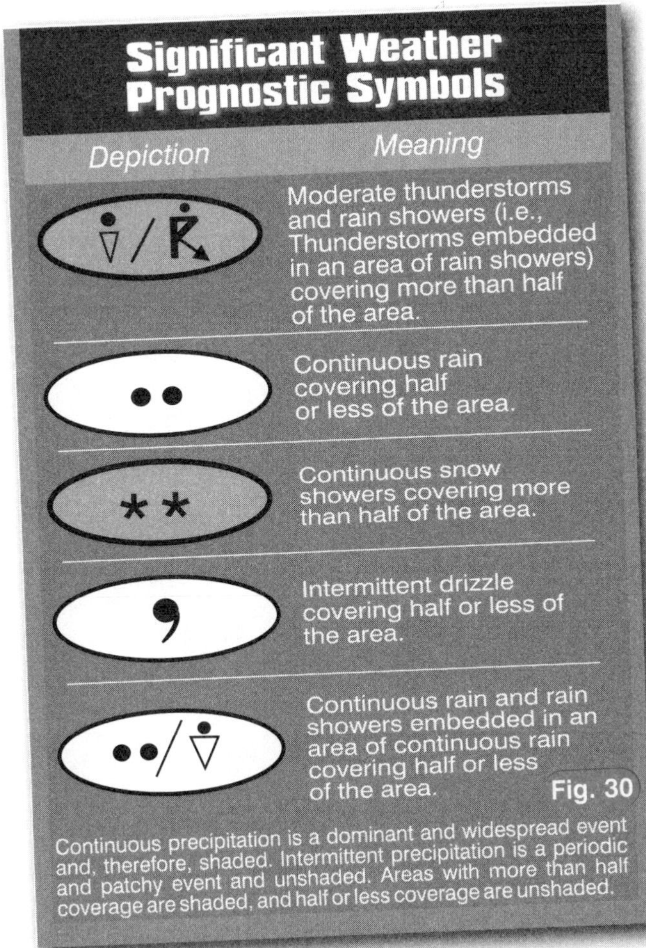

snow cone. You'd have to be pretty low on the IQ index not to see how useful the prog chart is to an instrument pilot. In fact, the pilot who wouldn't find this chart useful is probably the type of person who, when asked during a job interview if he lives alone, replies by saying, "Ahh, does silverware count?"

An additional and very useful feature of the significant weather prog chart is its forecast of turbulence. The long thick dashed line surrounding California, Arizona, and parts of New Mexico and Colorado indicates moderate or greater turbulence is forecast during the 12-hour period (panel A, position 3). (Use the key between panels on the prog chart.) Within the area surrounded by the long dashed line is the number *180* with what appears to be a witch's hat symbol above it and a small short diagonal line to the right. The 180 means this turbulence is forecast from the surface up to 18,000 feet. In the 24-hour significant weather prog (panel B, position 4) the 080 indicates that moderate turbulence is forecast for this area from the surface to 8,000 feet during the forecast period. A blank to the right of the diagonal line (i.e., the "/" to the right of 080/) indicates the base of the turbulence when it doesn't begin at the surface. By comparing the 12- and 24-hour significant weather prog, you can visualize the direction of weather movement during the next 24 hours. (Figure 29 and 30 show additional symbols used in this chart. These figures aren't provided on the instrument pilot knowledge exam.)

The 12- and 24-hour surface prog (panels C and D) provides you with the expected location and movements of fronts, pressure systems, and their generated weather. The 12 hour surface prog (panel C) forecasts a low pressure center over northern Utah (panel C, position 5). The unshaded area within the solid line that circles several western and northwestern states indicates that the forecast precipitation will cover half or less of this area. The symbol (**/**) and its arrow pointing to the shaded area of the Utah low indicates *continuous* to *continuous and moderate* snow is forecast (use the key in Figure 29 to help with this interpretation). By comparing panels C and D, you see that the low is forecast to move northeastward into Wyoming. According to Figure 30, the shaded area surrounding the low indicates that the continuous snow (the precipitation) is still expected to cover more than half of the area during the latter part of the forecast period.

In the 24 hour surface prog chart, the west coast of Florida is expected to have continuous and moderate rain (three dots) and slight or moderate thunderstorms with rain indicated by the thunderstorm symbol (ℝ) with a single dot above (panel D, position 6). (I think a good thunderstorm symbol is a tiny picture of a pilot's face with a Don King hairdo and smoke trails coming off his clothes.)

The area in the upper part of North Carolina (panel D, position 7) is expected to have rain showers (a single dot above a triangle indicates either *showery precipitation* or *rain showers,* while two dots indicates *continuous rain*). According to Figure 30, since the entire area is enclosed by a solid line, the precipitation is expected to cover less than half of the area.

Significant Weather Prognostic Symbols

Depiction	Meaning
▽̇ / ℝ̇	Moderate thunderstorms and rain showers (i.e., Thunderstorms embedded in an area of rain showers) covering more than half of the area.
••	Continuous rain covering half or less of the area.
✱ ✱	Continuous snow showers covering more than half of the area.
⸴	Intermittent drizzle covering half or less of the area.
••/ ▽̇	Continuous rain and rain showers embedded in an area of continuous rain covering half or less of the area.

Fig. 30

Continuous precipitation is a dominant and widespread event and, therefore, shaded. Intermittent precipitation is a periodic and patchy event and unshaded. Areas with more than half coverage are shaded, and half or less coverage are unshaded.

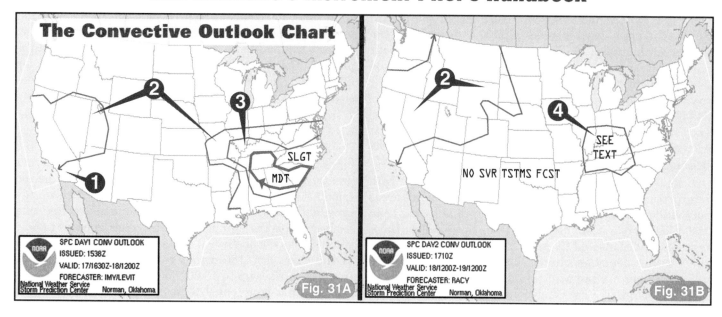

The Convective Outlook Chart

SLGT
MDT

SPC DAY1 CONV OUTLOOK
ISSUED: 1538Z
VALID: 17/1630Z-18/1200Z
FORECASTER: IMY/LEVIT
National Weather Service
Storm Prediction Center   Norman, Oklahoma

Fig. 31A

NO SVR TSTMS FCST

SEE TEXT

SPC DAY2 CONV OUTLOOK
ISSUED: 1710Z
VALID: 18/1200Z-19/1200Z
FORECASTER: RACY
National Weather Service
Storm Prediction Center   Norman, Oklahoma

Fig. 31B

By comparing panels C and D, it appears that the poor weather on Florida's western coast will move eastward. Panels A and B, however, suggest that all of Florida will still have ceilings of 1,000 to 3,000 feet and/or visibilities of 3–5 miles.

Convective (Severe) Weather Outlook Chart

The *convective outlook chart* is a preliminary outlook for thunderstorms, specifically *severe* thunderstorms (severe thunderstorms are defined as thunderstorms with 3/4-inch hail or larger and/or wind gusts of 50 knots or greater and/or tornadoes). Covering two consecutive days (Figure 31), this is basically a map of where not to go. It is issued in two panels, labeled (surprise) Day 1 (Figure 31A) and Day 2 (Figure 31B). The Day 1 panel is a 24-hour forecast for areas expected to have thunderstorms. It's issued five times daily, starting at 0600Z, and is valid from 1200Z that day until 1200Z the following day. It's issued again at 1300Z, 1630Z, 2000Z and 0100Z, with each issuance valid until 1200Z the following day.

The Day 2 panel contains the same information as the Day 1 convective outlook except that it's issued twice daily, beginning at 0830Z. It's updated at 1730Z and covers the time from 1200Z the following day to 1200Z the next day.

Both panels in the convective outlook chart qualify the levels of severe thunderstorm risk as SLGT, MDT and HIGH. They also show the areas where general thunderstorms (non-severe) are expected to exist. Figure 32 shows how to interpret these different levels of risk.

This convective outlook chart is used as an advanced flight planning tool to identify and avoid those areas where thunderstorms are forecast. A

line with an arrowhead (Figure 31A, position 1) delineates an area of probable, general (non-severe) thunderstorm activity. Facing in the direction of the arrow, thunderstorm activity is expected to the right of the line. If other than general thunderstorm activity is forecast (i.e., severe thunderstorms), the terms SLGT, MDT or HIGH will be used to indicate the expected risk of severe thunderstorm coverage. Severe weather outlook areas and tornado watch areas are also shown on the chart. Just to be clear here, severe thunderstorms are defined as thunderstorms with 3/4-inch hail or larger and/or wind gusts of 50 knots or greater and/or tornadoes. A non-severe thunderstorm is still a thunderstorm and it should be avoided. Period! Don't let the nice fluffy term "non-severe" fool you since, practically speaking, there is no such thing as a non-severe thunderstorm to a pilot in an airplane.

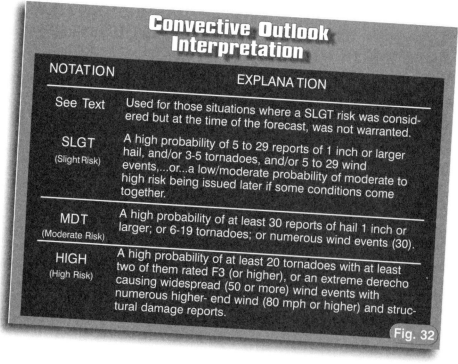

Convective Outlook Interpretation

NOTATION	EXPLANATION
See Text	Used for those situations where a SLGT risk was considered but at the time of the forecast, was not warranted.
SLGT (Slight Risk)	A high probability of 5 to 29 reports of 1 inch or larger hail, and/or 3-5 tornadoes, and/or 5 to 29 wind events,...or...a low/moderate probability of moderate to high risk being issued later if some conditions come together.
MDT (Moderate Risk)	A high probability of at least 30 reports of hail 1 inch or larger; or 6-19 tornadoes; or numerous wind events (30).
HIGH (High Risk)	A high probability of at least 20 tornadoes with at least two of them rated F3 (or higher), or an extreme derecho causing widespread (50 or more) wind events with numerous higher-end wind (80 mph or higher) and structural damage reports.

Fig. 32

From Figure 31, it's clear that general thunderstorms (non-severe) are forecast for the western and north-western corner of the United States. central plains (Figure 31 A and B, position 2). An area where a *slight risk* of severe thunderstorms exists is in the eastern Gulf Coast states (Figure 31A, position 3).

Convective Outlook (AC)

In addition to the convective outlook chart, there is also the convective outlook text as shown in Figure 33. This is a textual notation of forecast thunderstorms and you are referred to it by the convective outlook chart as shown in the Day 2 panel in Figure 31B, position 4. The *SEE TEXT* reference is used for those situations where a slight risk of thunderstorms was considered but at the time of the forecast, did not warrant an actual depiction of "SLGT" on the outlook chart.

Convective Outlook

MKC AC 291435
CONVECTIVE OUTLOOK...REF AFOS NMCGPH94O.
VALID 291500Z-301200Z
THERE IS A SLGT RISK OF SVR TSTMS TO THE RIGHT OF A LINE FROM 10 NE JAX 35 NNW AYS AGS 15 E SPA 30 NE CLT 25 N FAY 30 ESE EWN.
   GEN TSTMS ARE FCST TO THE RIGHT OF A LINE FROM 55 ESE YUM 30 NE IGM 15 S CDC 30 SW U24 25 ESE ELY 40 W P38 DRA 50 SW DRA 50 NW NID SAC 30 E ACV 25 E ONP 40 E BLI.
      ...SEVERE THUNDERSTORM FORECAST DISCUSSION...
.SERN U.S...
   COOL FRONT CONTS SC/NC BORDER. VERY MOIST AND UNSTBL AMS ALONG AND S OF FRONT E OF APLCHNS WITH CAPES TO REACH TO 4000 J/KG WITH AFTN HEATING. ALTHOUGH WIND PROFILES ARE WK...COMB OF FRONTAL CNVGNC COUPLED WITH SEA BREEZE FRONT WILL INITIATE PULSE SVR TSTMS VCNTY AND S OF FRONT THIS AFTN/EVE. PRIMARY SVR EVENTS WILL BE WET DOWNBURST TO PUSH SWD FROM CNTRL RCKYS EWD TO MID ATLC CST. E OF APLCNS FRONT NOW LCTD VCNTY WND DMG.
      ...GENERAL THUNDERSTORM FORECAST DISCUSSION...
...GULF CST AREA INTO SRN PLNS...
   SFC FNT CURRENTLY LOCATED FM THE CAROLINAS WWD INTO PARTS OF OK WL CONT TO SAG SLOWLY SWD ACRS THE SRN APLCNS/LWR MS VLY THRU THE REMAINDER OF THE PD. S OF THE BNDRY...A VRY MOIST AMS RMNS IN PLACE AS DWPNTS ARE IN THE MID TO UPR 70S. WHILE SOME CLDNS IS PRESENT ACRS THE AREA...SUF HEATING SHOULD OCR TO ALLOW FOR MDT TO STG AMS DSTBLZN DURG THE LATE MRNG/ERY AFTN. AS A RESULT...SFC BASED CAPE VALUES SHOULD BE AOA 2000 J/KG THIS AFTN. BNDRYS FM OVERNIGHT CNVTN AS WELL AS SEA BREEZE CIRCULATIONS SHOULD BE SUF TO INITIATE SCT TO NMRS TSTMS ACRS THE AREA. MID TO UPR LVL FLOW IS RELATIVELY WK...SO THIS SUG ORGANIZED SVR TSTM ACTVTY IS NOT LIKELY.

Fig. 33

Winter Weather Warning

This "chilling" statement reflects the gravity of the situation encountered by an instructor and student in an ice-encumbered Cessna 172. Knowing the limitations of one's aircraft and having a respect for the forces of nature are two universal lessons learned by the instructor who submitted this report.

The [Cessna 172] began to accumulate light rime ice in cruise at 10,000 feet.... Icing became increasingly heavier until...we were having difficulty maintaining altitude. Departure [said] he needed us to maintain 10,000 feet. I told him we were picking up ice and requested vectors [to the] ILS Runway 35 at XXX.... We checked in with the Tower [and we were] cleared to land. Icing was moderate at that point. We had full throttle at 70 KIAS and [we were] descending 400 feet per minute. We were unable to maintain approach minimums, and at one point Tower said, "You probably know this, but I'm getting an altitude alert...." We briefed the approach and knew we were going to have to find the runway regardless of the weather.... We saw the approach lights at about 400 feet AGL, almost 500 feet below the localizer approach minimums. We landed without incident (with two inches of ice). The approach and tower controllers were extremely helpful.

Causes: We took off into forecast icing conditions.... I thought if we could get up high enough (10,000 feet) we could fly over the icing layer....

Even a very thin layer of ice on the leading edge and upper wing surfaces can cause a dramatic loss of lift and increase in drag. With two inches of ice, these pilots were lucky to be near an airport.

NASA Callback Report

Surface Analysis

The surface analysis chart (Figure 34) shows the location of pressure patterns and fronts. This chart is based on reported weather data and is issued every three hours. Individual reporting stations and their associated weather are depicted on the chart. Additional decoding information for the station model on this chart can be found in the FAA's *Aviation Weather Services Handbook* (AC 00–45E).

Even without a detailed understanding of this chart's symbols, you can derive some interesting information from it. Think of the surface analysis as a very large visual portrayal of hundreds of METARs. Although this chart's information may be older than the individual METARs, it can provide you with a big picture of the weather for individual stations along your route. For instance, the chart shows the temperature/dewpoint spread over a large area. From this you can get a good feel for the likelihood of fog or low cloud forming before and after sunset.

Orientation of the isobars (spaced at four-millibar intervals) and the pressure patterns gives you an idea of surface winds. Cloud coverage at the time the chart was constructed is identified by the fill of the individual station

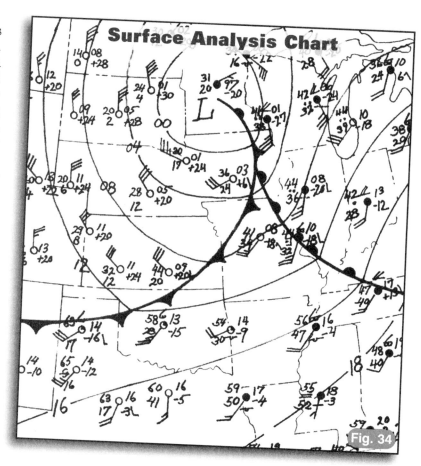

Surface Analysis Chart

Fig. 34

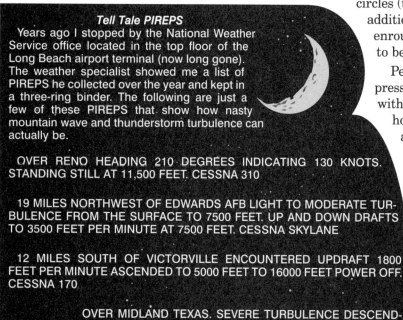

circles (the chart, however, doesn't show cloud height). In addition, you can determine the types of clouds existing enroute. Much, much more useful weather material is to be found on the surface analysis chart.

Personally, I like comparing the present location of pressure systems and fronts using the surface analysis with the predicted future locations on the 12- and 24-hour prog chart. This tells me where these fronts are now and where they're likely to be in the future. Just be glad that meteorologists don't play around too much when constructing these charts. If they did, you can bet that someone would surely draw a front chasing a little airplane ahead of it that's racing to the nearest airport and a caption coming from the cockpit that reads, "Mommy!"

The Constant Pressure Chart

Constant pressure charts are depictions of upper atmospheric soundings, made by radiosonde ascensions. These charts provide you with information for several pressure levels in the atmosphere. You should look at the 850mb (5,000 feet) and 700mb (10,000 feet) constant pressure charts to assess atmospheric moisture conditions. Figure 35 shows a 700mb constant pressure chart.

Reporting stations are shown as small circles on the chart (Figure 36A). To the left of these circles are two very important numbers. The top left

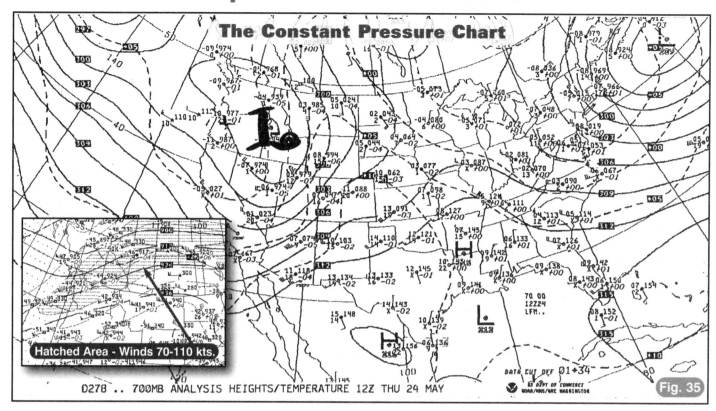

The Constant Pressure Chart

D278 .. 700MB ANALYSIS HEIGHTS/TEMPERATURE 12Z THU 24 MAY

Fig. 35

number is the temperature at this pressure level, and underneath the temperature is the temperature/dewpoint spread. At 10,000 feet, eastern Montana (position A) has a temperature of +5 degrees Celsius and a temperature/dewpoint spread of 10 degrees Celsius. Moving westward, the temperature drops to 3 degrees Celsius and the temp/dewpoint spread is now 4 degrees Celsius. Station models are filled in solid whenever the temperature/dewpoint spread is 5 degrees or less, indicating areas of high

moisture content (or, it could also mean the meteorologist had a leaky pen. OK, that won't happen).

Continuing farther west, toward eastern Washington (position B), the temperature decreases to –4 degrees Celsius and the spread is now 1 degree Celsius. This indicates that the air is moist enough to condense and produce visible moisture. Couple this moist air with temperatures between –15 degrees Celsius and 0 degrees Celsius, and you can count on some nasty icing potential. Compare the current constant pressure chart with older ones to get an idea if the air is becoming wetter or drier. Figure 36B provides more information on chart symbols.

The constant pressure chart is also useful to help determine wind direction, by referencing the depicted isobars. Areas of strong winds (70 to 110 knots) are identified by hatching (shading as shown by the insert in Figure 35). Hatching is not the place where your chickens come to lay eggs, and in those kinds of winds it's unlikely they stay to lay anyway.

Constant Pressure Chart Symbols

TT ⌐HGT T-D Hc(LV,M) LV - not plotted M - missing	**TT:** Temperature degrees Celsius **HGT:** Height in meters **T-D:** Temp-dewpoint spread (X means air extrm. dry) **Hc(LV,M):** Plot of surface pressure height change that occurred in last 12 hours **Circle:** Black when T-D is 5 degrees or less **Wind:** 10 knots/barb, 50 knots/flag
22 479 ● 4 LV 850 mb	**TT:** 22 degrees Celsius **HGT:** 1,479 meters, or 5,000 feet pressure altitude **T-D:** 4 degrees Celsius (thus dewpoint is 18°Celsius) **Hc(LV,M):** Not plotted **Circle shading:** T-D is less that 5 degrees **Wind:** Light and variable
09 ⌐129 ○ 17 -03 700 mb	**TT:** 9 degrees Celsius **HGT:** 3,129 meters, or 10,000 feet pressure altitude **T-D:** 17 degrees Celsius (thus dewpoint is -8°Celsius) **Hc(LV,M):** Plotted pressure height decreased 30 meters in last 12 hours **Circle:** T-D greater than 5 degrees Celsius **Wind:** from 010 degrees at 20 knots
-19 558 ○ X +03 500 mb	**TT:** -19 degrees Celsius **HGT:** 5,580 meters, or 18,000 feet pressure altitude **T-D:** Greater than 29 degrees Celsius **Hc(LV,M):** Plotted pressure height increased 30 meters in last 12 hours **Circle:** T-D greater than 5 degrees Celsius **Wind:** from 210 degrees at 60 knots
-46 919 ○ +10 300 mb	**TT:** - 46 degrees Celsius **HGT:** 9,190 meters, or 30,000 feet pressure altitude **T-D:** not plotted **Hc(LV,M):** Plotted pressure height increased 100 meters in last 12 hours **Circle:** T-D greater than 5 degrees Celsius **Wind:** from 270 degrees at 30 knots

Fig. 36A

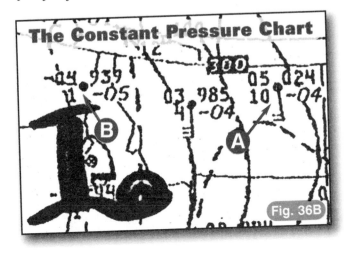

The Constant Pressure Chart

Fig. 36B

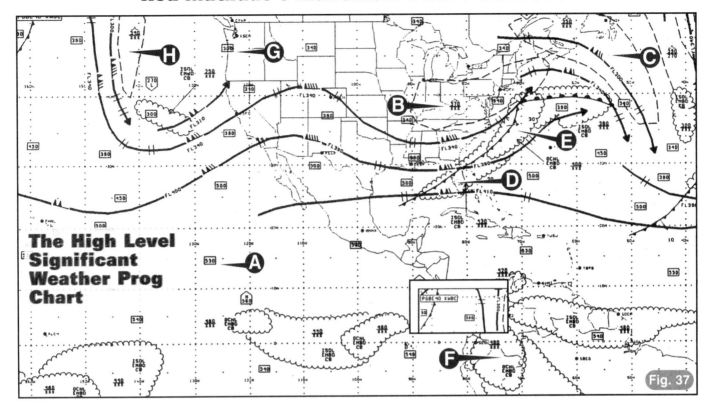

Fig. 37

High-Level Significant Weather Prog Chart

When you want an overview of the flying conditions above 24,000 feet (FL240) use the *high-level sig weather prog* chart (Figure 37). The high-level significant weather forecast pertains to the layer from 24,000 to 60,000 feet (FL240–FL600). It's issued four times a day with valid times of 00Z, 06Z, 12Z, and 18Z. On this chart you'll find information about jet streams, cumulonimbus clouds, turbulence, and tropopause heights. Surface fronts are also included to add perspective, along with other conditions like tropical cyclones, squall lines, volcanic eruption sites, and sandstorms and dust storms.

Tropopause heights are enclosed by rectangles and plotted in hundreds of feet (Figure 37, arrow A). The centers of high and low heights are identified with *H* and *L* respectively along with their heights and enclosed by polygons.

Areas of moderate or greater turbulence are enclosed by bold dashed lines with intensities identified by symbols (the witch's hat, remember?). The vertical extent of turbulence layers is specified by top and base heights in hundreds of feet. Turbulence bases that extend below the layer of the chart are identified with *XXX*. Top and base heights are separated by a line (Figure 37, arrow B). Height values are pressure altitudes. For example, *370/XXX* identifies a layer of turbulence from below FL240 to FL370. This is an area of moderate turbulence as indicated by a single witch's hat above the *370* value.

Figure 37 shows cumulonimbus areas are identified with *CB* and characterized by coverage and tops. As you know by now, cumulonimbus clouds (CBs) are thunderstorm clouds. Areas of CBs that meet specific criteria are enclosed by scalloped lines. What criteria? Widespread CBs within an area or along a line with little or no space between individual clouds, and CBs that are embedded in cloud layers or concealed by haze or dust. The prog does not display isolated or scattered CBs (one-half or less coverage) which are not embedded in clouds, haze, or dust. Coverages are identified as isolated (ISOL), occasional (OCNL), and frequent (FRQ). Isolated and occasional CBs can be further characterized as embedded (EMBD). Coverage values for the identifiers are: isolated—less than 1/8; occasional—1/8 to 4/8; and frequent—more than 4/8. CB tops are identified in hundreds of feet, using the standard top and base format previously discussed.

The identification and characterization of each cumulonimbus area will appear within or adjacent to the outlined area (and pointed to by a small arrow from the identification information). For instance, about one inch below the arrow referencing the letter D is the term *ISOL EMBD CB*. This indicates that in the area surrounded by scalloped lines and referenced by the thin arrow pointing directly from the letters, there exists a chance of isolated embedded thunderstorms. The value *430/XXX* to the right of this term indicates that these thunderstorms have tops of 43,000 feet and extend to or beyond the lower limit of the chart (24,000 feet MSL). The area referenced by arrow E depicts occasional cumulonimbus clouds with 1/8 to 4/8 coverage and bases below 24,000 feet and tops at 40,000 feet.

Jet streams with a maximum speed of more than 80 knots are identified by bold lines. Arrowheads on the lines indicate the orientation of each jet stream. Double hatched lines positioned along the jet core identify changes of wind speed. These speed indicators are drawn at 20-knot intervals and begin at 100 knots. Wind speed maximums along the jet core are characterized by wind symbols and altitudes. A standard wind symbol with pen-

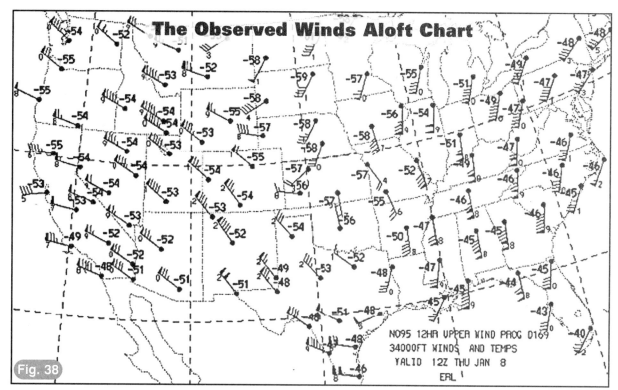

The Observed Winds Aloft Chart

NO95 12HR UPPER WIND PROG D169
34000FT WINDS AND TEMPS
VALID 12Z THU JAN 8
ERL

Fig. 38

nants (50 knots for each flag) and barbs (10 knots for each barb) is placed at each pertinent position to identify velocity. The altitude in hundreds of feet prefaced with *FL* is placed adjacent to each wind symbol.

For example, the jet stream velocity symbols to the lower right of arrow G, Figure 37, indicate a speed of 90 knots. (Note: The FAA still mixes the height values of MSL and FL. Apparently the chief meteorologist—he's the one that wears a puffy cloud hat and always leaves a few letters out of all the words he uses—still hasn't made up his mind whether MSL or FL is the correct one to use.)

Observed Winds Aloft Chart

Who doesn't like pictures, especially if it's a picture of the winds aloft? This is what the observed winds aloft chart accomplishes, as shown in Figure 38. The legend is shown in Figure 39. This is a four-panel, twice daily (1200Z and 000Z) chart that depicts the winds and temperatures at *the second standard level*, and at 14,000, 24,000 and 34,000 feet—just in case your Piper Cub is turbocharged and has JATO (jet assisted takeoff) bottles on each wing.

OK, what's the *second standard level*? This is the altitude for a reporting point that's between 1,000 and 2,000 feet AGL at that station. What's its purpose? The second standard level helps meteorologists determine any low-level wind shear and ground frictional effects on lower atmospheric winds. Looking at the winds at this second standard level altitude might help you anticipate how your airplane will be affected during an instrument approach. Meteorologists compute

the second standard level by finding the next thousand-foot level above the station elevation and adding 1,000 feet to that level. For example, the next thousand-foot level above Oklahoma City, OK, (station elevation 1,290 feet MSL) is 2,000 feet MSL. The second standard level for this station is thus 3,000 feet MSL (2000 feet + 1000 feet), or 1,710 feet AGL.

Wind direction and speed are shown by arrows, the same as on the forecast charts, and are drawn to the nearest 10-degree increment (you make the call as to whether it's from the 100s, 200s, or 300s degree sector). The second digit of the two or three degree reference is shown at

Plotted Winds and Temperatures

Plotted	Interpretation
	12 degrees Celsius, wind 060 degrees at 5 knots
	3 degrees Celsisu, wind 160 degrees at 25 knots
	0 degrees Celsius, wind 250 degrees at 15 knots
	-9 degrees Celsius, wind 260 degrees at 50 knots
	-47 degrees Celsius, wind 060 degrees at 115 knots
	-11 degrees Celsius, wind calm or light and variable

Fig. 39

the tail of the arrow. For instance, if you see a 9 at the tail of the arrow in Figure 39, this means the winds are from either 090 degrees, 190 degrees, or 290 degrees. Looking at the direction the arrow is pointing makes this an easy determination. Each full arrow feather represents 10 knots of wind, half a feather represents 5 knots, and a pennant indicates a 50 knot wind.

I guess the National Weather Service doesn't want to make it too easy to determine those winds. I wondered when their motto changed to "If you want the weather you've got to work for it...like we do." A calm or light and variable wind is shown as *LV* and a missing wind as *M*, both plotted to the lower-right of the station circle. The station circle is filled in when the reported temperature/ dew-point spread is 5 degrees Celsius or less. Observed temperatures are included on the upper two panels of this chart (24,000 feet and 34,000 feet). A dotted bracket around the temperature means a calculated temperature.

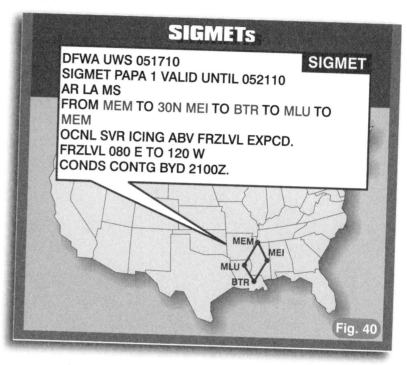

SIGMETs

DFWA UWS 051710
SIGMET PAPA 1 VALID UNTIL 052110
AR LA MS
FROM MEM TO 30N MEI TO BTR TO MLU TO MEM
OCNL SVR ICING ABV FRZLVL EXPCD.
FRZLVL 080 E TO 120 W
CONDS CONTG BYD 2100Z.

SIGMET

Fig. 40

In-flight Aviation Weather Advisories

Most people want to protect things that are of value to them. Take me, for instance. I like to protect my hearing. That's why I once walked over to my neighbor's house and asked him to turn down his stereo. It was simply too loud. When he asked why I wanted it turned down, I replied that I was trying to use power tools at home and I couldn't hear when they were working. He got the point. Pilots like to protect their hearing as well as the rest of their body when airborne. That's why they make it a point to understand what in-flight advisories are and how they're disseminated.

In-flight aviation weather advisories are forecasts that advise pilots of potentially hazardous weather—some of which might have been forecast, and some of which might have arrived as a complete surprise to everyone involved. These advisories are provided to the FSS and are normally included in a standard weather briefing. Always make it a point to ask the briefer for any in-flight advisories. In-flight advisories may also be obtained through TWEB and HIWAS broadcasts over specific VORs and NDBs. EFAS (Flight Watch) also has the full listing of in-flight advisories, so you can easily access them in flight via a radio call.

There are three types of advisories: SIGMETS, AIRMETS, and convective SIGMETS. All of these should cause you to pay immediate and full attention, because they are warnings of weather that could be anywhere from unpleasant to downright dangerous. When any of these warnings are posted for your area of potential flight, it's time to get out the cautious calibrator when figuring out whether to change plans or change planes (say, from a 172 to a 737 being piloted by someone else).

SIGMET (WS)

A *SIGMET* is an advisory of non-convective weather (non-thunderstorm type weather) that is potentially hazardous to all aircraft, big and small. SIGMETs are issued

when any of the following occur or are expected to occur: severe icing not associated with thunderstorms, severe or extreme turbulence or clear air turbulence (CAT) not associated with thunderstorms, dust storms, sandstorms, and volcanic ash that lowers surface visibilities to less than three miles and any volcanic eruption (something we pilots are not trained to handle and would prefer to see on a TV screen rather than our windscreen).

Any of these items certainly affects both large and small airplanes, but it's safe to assume that if it's bad for the big boys, it's really bad for you. SIGMETS are named by the phonetic alphabet (that's not the alphabet you use when talking on the phone) using designators from November through Yankee, excluding Sierra, Tango and Zulu (these three are AIRMET designators). By knowing the specific phonetic name and number of a SIGMET or AIRMET, you can call the FSS or EFAS and determine if it has been canceled, continued, amended, or updated.

Figure 40 shows a typical SIGMET and the area it affects. This SIGMET was issued for the DFW area at 1710Z on the 5th day of the month and is valid until 2110Z on the same day. The letters *UWS* (Urgent Weather Sigmet) are included in the first issuance of a SIGMET. SIGMETs have names for identification. This SIGMET is named Papa 1, indicating that this is the first SIGMET issued in that specific area. Issuances for the same weather phenomena will be sequentially numbered using the original name (Papa 2, Papa 3, etc.) until the need for caution ceases.

The SIGMET in Figure 40 is for Arkansas, Louisiana, and Mississippi. From MEM to 30 miles north of MEI to BTR to MLU to MEM, you can expect occasional severe icing above the freezing level (remember, these three-letter identifiers are all VORs in the affected area). The freezing level is from 8,000 feet eastward to 12,000 feet westward. Conditions continuing beyond 2100Z. (The maximum forecast period of a SIGMET is four hours.)

AIRMET [WA]

AIRMETS warn of significant weather but describe conditions at intensities lower than those that trigger SIGMETs. They are intended for all pilots in the preflight and enroute phase of flight to enhance safety.

AIRMETs are issued once every six hours on a scheduled basis, with unscheduled amendments issued as required. Each AIRMET issuance contains AIRMETs still in effect, significant conditions not meeting AIRMET criteria, and an outlook for conditions expected after the AIRMET valid period. AIRMETs are valid for a period of six hours. AIRMETs contain one or more of the following weather phenomena when they occur or are forecast to occur: moderate icing, moderate turbulence, sustained winds of 30 knots or more at the surface, ceilings less than 1,000 feet and/or visibilities less than 3 miles affecting more than 50% of the area at one time, as well as extensive mountain obscuration.

To help you better identify the meaning of an AIRMET, each one has a fixed alphanumeric designator. If you see AIRMET *Sierra,* this stands for IFR and mountain obscurations; AIRMET *Tango* stands for turbulence, strong surface wind and low-level wind shear; and AIRMET *Zulu* stands for icing and freezing level heights. Here's how this designation works.

The upper portion of Figure 41 shows an AIRMET and the area it affects. It was issued for the Dallas/Ft. Worth forecast area on the 5th day of the month at 1445Z. The *T* following DFW indicates the type of AIRMET. In this instance it means Tango (for turbu-

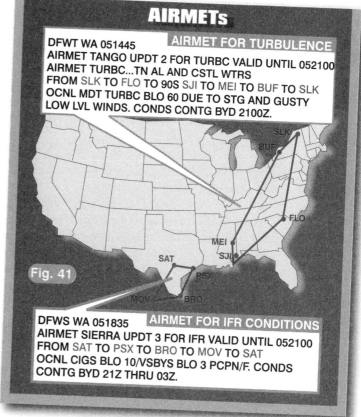

AIRMETs

AIRMET FOR TURBULENCE

DFWT WA 051445
AIRMET TANGO UPDT 2 FOR TURBC VALID UNTIL 052100
AIRMET TURBC...TN AL AND CSTL WTRS
FROM SLK TO FLO TO 90S SJI TO MEI TO BUF TO SLK
OCNL MDT TURBC BLO 60 DUE TO STG AND GUSTY
LOW LVL WINDS. CONDS CONTG BYD 2100Z.

Fig. 41

DFWS WA 051835   AIRMET FOR IFR CONDITIONS
AIRMET SIERRA UPDT 3 FOR IFR VALID UNTIL 052100
FROM SAT TO PSX TO BRO TO MOV TO SAT
OCNL CIGS BLO 10/VSBYS BLO 3 PCPN/F. CONDS
CONTG BYD 21Z THRU 03Z.

lence). AIRMET Tango is updated and is valid until 2100Z on the 5th day of the month and applies to the area around Tennessee, Alabama and the coastal waters. The area described in the AIRMET is expected to have moderate turbulence below 6,000 feet MSL due to strong and gusty low-level winds. These conditions are expected to continue beyond the AIRMET's valid time of 2100Z.

AIRMET Sierra in the lower portion of Figure 41 is on its third update. The *S* following DFW indicates AIRMET Sierra (which indicates IFR conditions or mountain obscuration). As you know, mountain obscuration is nothing more than clouds covering the mountains. This is Mother Nature's way of letting incautious pilots play peekaboo.

The bordered area shown is expected to have occasional ceilings below 1,000 feet and visibilities below three miles in precipitation and fog. Conditions are expected to continue beyond 2100Z through 0300Z.

The *Z* following SFO (San Francisco) represents AIRMET Zulu (Figure 42). AIRMET Zulu indicates a forecast for icing, which is very important to every IFR pilot. In the bordered area defined by the AIRMET, you can expect light, occasional moderate rime icing in clouds and precipitation between the freezing level and Flight Level 180. The freezing level is forecast to be between 6,000 and 8,000 feet. Sounds like fun, doesn't it? Not really.

Do you recall the precautionary statements section of the area forecast? It said to see AIRMET Sierra for IFR conditions and mountain obscuration. This is why you always need to check for AIRMETs that may affect your flight.

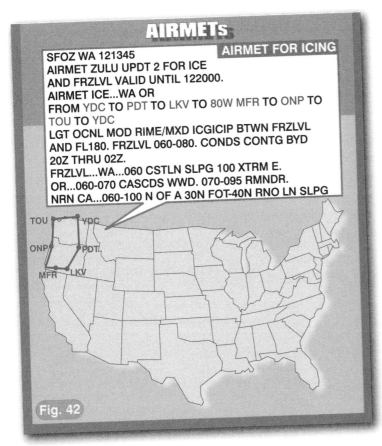

AIRMETs

AIRMET FOR ICING

SFOZ WA 121345
AIRMET ZULU UPDT 2 FOR ICE
AND FRZLVL VALID UNTIL 122000.
AIRMET ICE...WA OR
FROM YDC TO PDT TO LKV TO 80W MFR TO ONP TO
TOU TO YDC
LGT OCNL MOD RIME/MXD ICGICIP BTWN FRZLVL
AND FL180. FRZLVL 060-080. CONDS CONTG BYD
20Z THRU 02Z.
FRZLVL...WA...060 CSTLN SLPG 100 XTRM E.
OR...060-070 CASCDS WWD. 070-095 RMNDR.
NRN CA...060-100 N OF A 30N FOT-40N RNO LN SLPG

Fig. 42

Convective SIGMETs (WST)–Another version of the SIGMET is the *convective SIGMET* (WST). These are the granddaddies of in-flight advisories and report things that are hazards to all aircraft. These are the baddest of the bad boys, the things with which no pilot in his or her right mind chooses to mix. You can hurt yourself even *thinking* about some of this stuff.

A convective SIGMET is an advisory associated with convective activity such as severe thunderstorms. Any convective SIGMET implies severe or greater turbulence, severe icing, and low-level wind shear. Sound like fun? You like one-way trips? A convective SIGMET may be issued as a result of any of the following nastinesses—severe thunderstorms due to surface winds of 50 knots or greater, hail at the surface of ¾ of an inch or more, tornados, embedded thunderstorms, a line of thunderstorms, or thunderstorms of VIP level 4 or more affecting 40% or more of an area of at least 3000 square miles. A convective SIGMET is the FAA's way of saying that something is about to hit the fan, and if you don't want to get messed on you'll steer clear.

Figure 43 is an example of a convective SIGMET. This SIGMET was issued on the 22nd day of the month at 1855Z. It is the 20th consecutive SIGMET (20C) issued on this day in the central U.S. The SIGMET references a line in the vicinity of GLD to CDS. It forecasts a line of thunderstorms developing by 1955Z and moving eastward at 30 to 35 knots through 2055Z. Hail to one and one-half inches is also possible. That's pretty serious weather. You'd better be on the ground wearing a hard hat and a roll bar if you experience hail that size. Whistling "Hail to the Chief" might help, too. Or whistle in the kitchen and make it "Hail to the Chef."

Convective SIGMETs also contain an outlook. This is a forecast for thunderstorms that are expected to require convective SIGMET issuance two to six hours into the future. The convective SIGMET outlook in Figure 43 indicates isolated strong thunderstorms will develop over

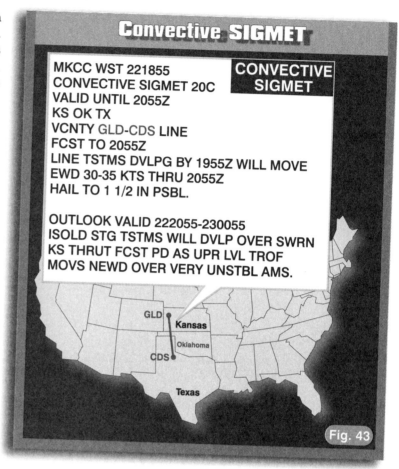

Convective SIGMET

MKCC WST 221855
CONVECTIVE SIGMET 20C
VALID UNTIL 2055Z
KS OK TX
VCNTY GLD-CDS LINE
FCST TO 2055Z
LINE TSTMS DVLPG BY 1955Z WILL MOVE
EWD 30-35 KTS THRU 2055Z
HAIL TO 1 1/2 IN PSBL.

OUTLOOK VALID 222055-230055
ISOLD STG TSTMS WILL DVLP OVER SWRN
KS THRUT FCST PD AS UPR LVL TROF
MOVS NEWD OVER VERY UNSTBL AMS.

Fig. 43

southwestern Kansas through the forecast period as an upper level trough moves northeastward over very unstable air.

Pilot Reports (PIREPs)

As mentioned earlier, pilot reports provide pilots with some of the best real-time weather information available. This is the word from the mouths and mics of those who've been there before you. It's as real and real-time as you're going to get.

PIREPs provide an excellent means of determining current weather between reporting stations. FSS and Flight Watch, as well as other ATC specialists, long for pilots to give reports of weather and other items of interest, par-

Reporting Turbulence In PIREPs

Turbulence reports should include location altitude, or range of altitudes, aircraft type, and should include whether you're in clouds or clear air. Also include the degree of turbulence, intensity, and duration (occasional, intermittent, and continuous) as determined by the pilot. It is essential that the report is obtained and disseminated when possible in conformance with the U.S. Standard Turbulence Criteria Table as follows:

Light. *Occupants may feel slight strain against seat belt. Unsecured objects may move slightly.*

Moderate. *Unsecured objects are dislodged. Occupants feel definite strains against seat belts and shoulder straps.*

Severe. *Occupants forced violently against seat belts or shoulder straps. Unsecured objects are tossed about. Food service and walking are impossible.*

Extreme. *Aircraft is tossed violently about, impossible to control. May cause structural damage.*

Reports of CAT (clear air turbulence) or chop can be used to further describe the type of turbulence. (Note CAT is a higher-altitude phenomenon—experienced typically by jet traffic—and not normally associated with cumuliform clouds.)

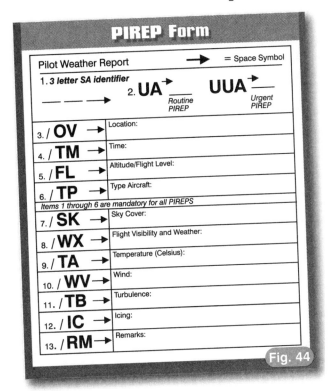

PIREP Form

Pilot Weather Report ——▶ = Space Symbol

1. *3 letter SA identifier*

— — — ——▶ 2. UA—▶ ___ UUA—▶

Routine PIREP / Urgent PIREP

3. / OV ▶	Location:
4. / TM ▶	Time:
5. / FL ▶	Altitude/Flight Level:
6. / TP ▶	Type Aircraft:

Items 1 through 6 are mandatory for all PIREPS

7. / SK ▶	Sky Cover:
8. / WX ▶	Flight Visibility and Weather:
9. / TA ▶	Temperature (Celsius):
10. / WV▶	Wind:
11. / TB ▶	Turbulence:
12. / IC ▶	Icing:
13. / RM▶	Remarks:

Fig. 44

Key for Encoding Pilot Reports

1. 3-letter station identifier - nearest weather reporting location to the reported phenomena

2. UA - Routine PIREP, UUA is an urgent PIREP

3. /OV - **Location**: Use 3-letter NAVAID idents only
   a. *Fix*: /OV ABC or OV/ABC090025 (the first three numbers are the radial from the VOR and the last three numbers are the distance. In this example the PIREP concerns the area near the 090 degree radial of the ABC VOR at the 025 or 25 nautical mile position).
   b. *Fix to fix*: /OV ABC-DEF, OV/ABC-DEF120020

4. /TM - **Time**: 4 digits in UTC (Zulu) (e.g. /TM 0915)

5. /FL - **Altitude/Flight Level**: 3 digits for hundreds of feet, if not known use UNKN (e.g. FL085 is 8,500 feet and FL310 is 31,000 feet).

6. /TP - **Type aircraft**: 4 digits maximum, if not known use UNKN (e.g. /TP C150, /TPB747).

7. /SK - **Cloud layers**: Describe as follows:
   a. Cloud amount.
   b. Height of cloud bases in hundreds of feet.
   c. Height of cloud tops in hundreds of feet. If unknown, UNKN is used
   d. (e.g. /SK SCT038-TOP080)- means a scattered layer exists at 3,800 feet MSL and the tops are at 8,000 feet MSL. (Remember this is a pilot report and pilots use their altimeter to measure height above sea level so all reported clouds heights are MSL.) (e.g. /SK BKN-OVC055-TOPUNKN - means a broken to overcast cloud base starts at 5,500 feet MSL and its tops are unknown.

8. /WX - **Weather**: Flight visibility (FV) reported first in METAR format, precipitation, restrictions to visibility, etc. Standard weather symbols are used and intensity reported same as in METAR (e.g. /WX FV02SM -RA HZ means that the flight visibility is 2 miles in light rain and haze).

9. /TA - **Air temperature in Celsius**: If below zero prefix with an "M" (e.g. /TA M08). Temperature shall also be reported if icing is reported.

10. /WV - **Wind**: Direction and speed in 6 digits. Wind direction less than 100 degrees is preceded by a zero. (e.g. /WV 27045KT - means the wind is from 270 degrees at 45 knots.)

11. /TB - **Turbulence**: Use standard contractions for intensity and type (use CAT - Clear Air Turbulence or CHOP when appropriate). Include altitude only if different from FL, (e.g. /TB LGT-MDT BLW 060 - means that the turbulence is light to moderate below 6,000 feet MSL. A report showing /TB EXTRM means extreme turbulence is reported at the altitude identified in position 5 above).

12. /IC - **Icing**: Describe using standard intensity and type contractions. Include altitude if different than FL (e.g. /IC LGT-MDT RIME).

13. /RM - **Remarks**: Use free form to clarify the report. /RM LRG FLOCK OF GOOSEY LOOKING BIRDS HDG GNLY NORTH OF AIRPORT MAY BE SEAGULLS, FORMATION LOUSY AND COURSE ERRATIC....

Fig. 45

ticularly any unforecast conditions you might encounter. Pilot reports don't have to relate to just weather information. Reports of flocks of birds, balloons, and other items affecting flight are all helpful.

I remember seeing the following pilot report distributed by a Midwest FSS (decoded for your convenience). *Pilotless airplane (Aeronca Champ) last seen heading northeast of Goodland at 3,000 feet.*

It seems the airplane was being hand propped without a qualified pilot aboard (or apparently off-board, either). The engine started and, with the throttle set too high, the airplane zoomed off through a field and became airborne (it would have given the pilot a crewcut, but at the time the plane had no crew). The plane remained airborne for a little more than an hour before slamming into a farmer's field. Shouldn't this be called a *nonpilot* report or a *no-pilot-aboard* report?

Pilot reports are officially coded, which cleans them up and removes the screams and other extraneous comments, and they are then disseminated through the ATC system for use in flight planning. The official format for this coding is shown in Figure 44. Figure 45 shows how PIREPs are encoded. Let's examine a few reports.

Is It Worth the Gamble?

Most folks wouldn't invest $1,000,000 to make $1, but they would invest $1 to make $1,000,000. This is known as the Lotto. Why then would some folks invest one million hours of the rest of their lives just to get home (or rush to be home) an hour sooner?

Figure 46 shows a typical pilot report. It is a routine PIREP (UA meaning *routine,* not United Airlines; UUA means *urgent*)/ from Oklahoma City to Tulsa/ at 1800Z/ at 12,000 feet (FL means *flight level* and is used for any altitude)/ reported by a Beech 90. (The type of aircraft is important. If a 747 reported light turbulence it could mean moderate or severe for a small airplane.)/ The base of the first cloud layer is at 1,800 feet MSL broken with tops at 5,500 MSL (since a pilot reported this he or she is referencing the altimeter which displays height in MSL

A Typical Pilot Report (PIREP)

KTUL UA /OV KOKC-KTUL /TM 1800 /FL 120
/TP BE90 /SK BKN018-TOP055/OVC072-TOP089 /CLR ABV
/WX FV03SM RA /TA M9 /WV 08021KT /TB LGT 055-072
/IC LGT-MDT RIME 072-089.

Fig. 46

values. This means, for example, that if the ground elevation is 1,295 feet MSL, then the 1,800 foot MSL ceiling is 505 feet above ground.)/ The base of the second overcast cloud layer is at 7,200 feet MSL and tops are at 8,900 feet MSL/ and the weather is clear above the upper layer/ weather type: flight visibility is three miles in moderate rain/ temperature is –9 degrees Celsius/ the wind is from 080 degrees at 21 knots (pilots can determine wind direction and velocity from the cockpit by using a sophisticated GPS system)/ turbulence is *light* between 5,500 feet and 7,200 feet/ there was light to moderate rime icing between 7,200 feet and 8,900 feet.

Pilot reports are quite useful. They are, however, most meaningful when first issued. Conditions can change with time. Be very suspicious of pilot reports more than an hour old.

Putting It All Together

The secret to successful flight planning is in anticipating the weather's behavior.

The first thing you need to know and understand is that this is not yet a precise science. Despite satellites, megacomputers, and all manner of technology we still cannot forecast the weather with anything like perfect precision. So all forecasts and briefings should be treated as statements of what's likely to happen, all the while knowing it is never *certain.* Don't be lulled into complacency because the lines demarcating a zone of bad weather just miss your destination, or because a forecast says conditions will be OK for an easy IFR approach.

The second thing you need to know is your weather limits. One man's comfortable IFR flight is another man's hours of terror. This has to do with airplane size and capability, equipment, training, experience, and risk aversion (or lack thereof). Every IFR flight involves a calculation of all these variables, and your result may (and probably should) differ from that of the person standing next to you at the briefing counter. Know your limits. Stick to them. If a little voice says, "Don't go," don't go. Bringing fear to yourself or your passengers is the act of an inconsiderate pilot, not a wise one.

To make a good decision, you've got to get the picture. Like a football team, if you go into a game without a game plan or overall strategy, the outcome is unlikely to be a winner. It's easy to get overwhelmed by all the weather information that's available. Without some basic plan for approaching and digesting the data that's raining down, you can easily get snowed.

One strategy for gathering the essential information is to compare and contrast key weather products. Sometimes putting two things side-by-side yields information that neither offers when viewed separately. Here are some of my favorite show-and-tells.

Surface Map and Weather Depiction Chart–Looking at the surface weather map tells you where the fronts and pressure systems are. Comparing this with the weather depiction chart provides you with a picture of what effect these fronts and pressure centers are having on surface weather. Figure 47 shows a typical comparison.

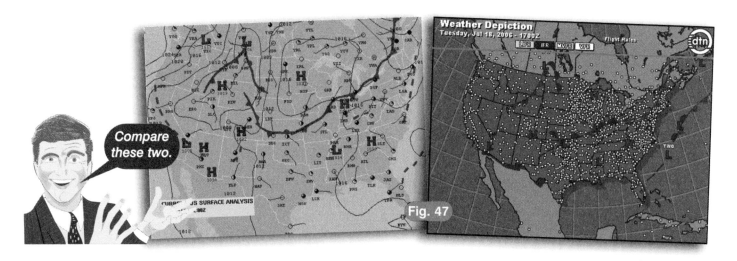

Compare these two.

Fig. 47

Weather Depiction Chart and Radar Summary Chart–With this comparison, shown in Figure 48, you get an idea of the convective activity associated with areas of IFR, MVFR, and VFR conditions. If an area of MVFR conditions is associated with large, fast moving echoes (meaning thunderstorms), you might want to reconsider planning a flight in this direction. Thunderstorms mean turbulence and rain showers. Keep in mind that the weather depiction chart will generally be a few hours older than the radar summary chart.

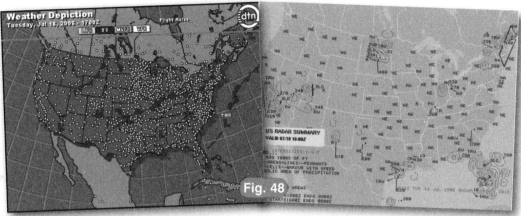

Fig. 48

Area Forecast and Prog Charts–Since the area forecast is a textual description and the prog chart is a picture, comparison provides you with a complete, big picture description of forecast weather (Figure 49).

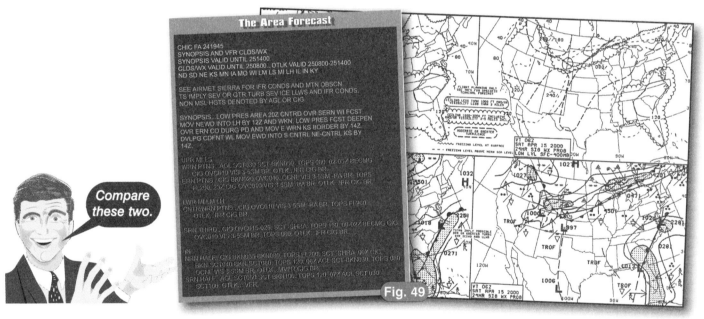

Fig. 49

Weather Depiction and Prog Charts–Since the weather depiction chart shows the location of fronts and pressure systems, you can see which way these systems will move by comparing them against the 12- and 24-hour surface prog chart, as shown in Figure 50. You'll also get an idea about what kind of weather (IFR? MVFR? VFR?) will develop along the front by referring to the prog chart.

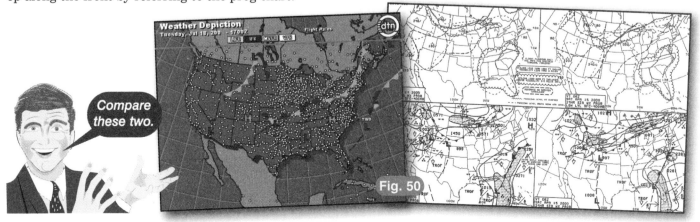

Fig. 50

METARs/Surface Map–Compare individual METARs with the surface weather map, as shown in Figure 51. This provides you with an understanding of surface weather around and between your departure and destination airports. If the surface weather map's reporting stations are all darkened-in along your route, this means you might be flying above a layer of clouds even though the destination airport is reporting clear conditions. Look at the isobars and, using your knowledge about clockwise and counterclockwise airflow around highs and lows, decide on a route that increases the likelihood of a tailwind. Remember, the surface weather map information can be up to three hours old.

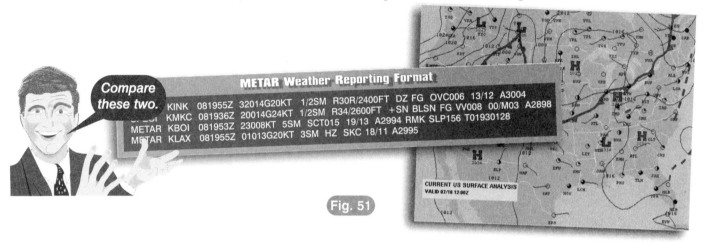

Fig. 51

Finally, examine the winds aloft forecast for temperatures and the selection of a favorable cruising altitude. Then examine the convective SIGMETs for thunderstorms, SIGMETs for any severe conditions and any AIRMETs for IFR conditions, turbulence, or pertinent icing conditions, as shown in Figure 52.

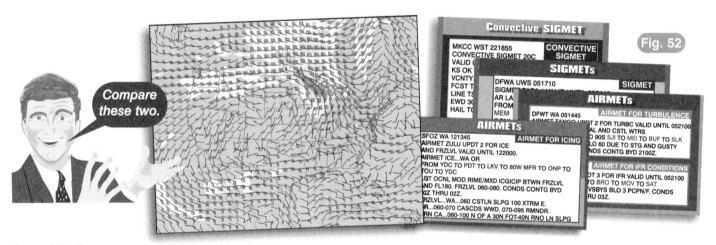

Fig. 52

Sunny Side Up

A pilot's skill at handling weather is based on his or her weather sense. Developing weather sense takes time and effort. To do it well means doing it often. Unlike flying, there is weather every day, and also unlike flying, it's free. On any given day, you can brief for a pretend flight, examine the weather in other parts of the country, compare what the weather was yesterday to what it is today and compare both of those to the forecasts.

Starting with the basic charts and concepts, you slowly learn to make use of more sophisticated information, and you get better at compiling all that information into a view that's accurate.

Pilots must continually educate themselves about how weather works. You aren't born with weather forecasting in your veins, and developing your capabilities requires that you make an effort to hone your skills. Unfortunately, not all pilots do this. As a result, they're often disappointed at their inability to understand, much less predict, the weather. They wind up taking someone else's advice, waiting for a briefer to tell them what to do, or (ultimately) putting themselves and their passengers in peril because they didn't understand the information they were given.

With work, you'll eventually develop the ability to sense when the forecast isn't quite on the mark. This is the real weather sense. It's almost a subconscious awareness that the sum of all the information doesn't add up to the total of the forecast.

So make it a point to check the weather every day, even if you're not flying. Call the FSS or PATWAS, look at the newspaper weather chart, check your personal computer, or take a look outside and compare what's happening today to what happened yesterday. This is how pilots develop weather sense. It's a sense that will offer you many years of safe flying.

Chapter 11
Understanding Approach Charts

The Origin of Approach Charts

Many years ago when aviation was in its infancy, pilots slowly realized that they couldn't fly visually all year round. Even during those seasons when the weather was typically good, a local fog bank or low clouds might make flying unthinkable, rendering wings as useless modern day elevator operators.

Crafty pilots (which is all pilots) of course worked to overcome the limitations imposed by clouds and poor visibility. Pilots don't like limitations. A few thought they could plow through clouds solely by a postural sense of feel, and with that "seat of the pants" flying was born. Unfortunately, it was soon proved that seat-of-the-pants flying often resulted in not knowing which end was up, which caused many pilots to upend, and thus end up plowing earth.

Others tried flying low to visually track landmarks such as telegraph lines. Most got the message that this wasn't a good idea. If he'd been born earlier, Johnny Cash could have sung, "Because you're mine, I'll fly the lines."

A few pilots even tried following railroad tracks in low visibility conditions. This was known as "making tracks," or doing the locomotion. And it often caused a commotion, especially if the vertical visibility was only 100 feet or so, since the pilots then had to fly that low to know where to go. That was OK until they encountered the first enroute tunnel, for which they only bored a hole big enough to accommodate the train, not the plane. The result was tunnel vision, in which the airplane disappeared, creating a form of plane drain.

Starting in the 1930s, captain Elrey B. Jeppesen began collecting notes about the fields into which he operated. Elrey studiously collected terrain and obstruction information, field lengths, and topological information. Soon, other pilots were asking for copies of Captain Jeppesen's notebook. The captain knew a business when he saw one, and in 1934 the IFR chart publishing enterprise was born. From its humble start, that business grew into today's international charting giant, Jeppesen-Sanderson. Not long after that, the U.S. government decided to follow suit, and the government is today the only major national competitor of Jeppesen-Sanderson. The focus of this book will be entirely on U.S. government charts.

Approach Charts Today

Approach charts now consist of sophisticated graphics appearing on rectangular pieces of paper, or images on electronic cockpit displays. These charts are remarkable displays of communications capability—truly chart art. They combine graphics and a small amount of text to convey an amazing amount of information in a confined space. These charts provide you a means of departing the enroute structure and making a safe approach and landing—all while having little or no visibility out the window.

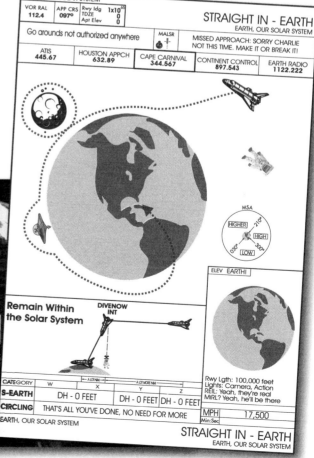

Space Shuttle Approach Chart? Not Really.

Your success and safety as an IFR pilot depends on your ability to really understand IFR approach charts. There is a tremendous amount of information to be gleaned, but it's accessible only to those who invest the time and effort needed to become fluent in chart. It's not a hard language to learn, and it's one you definitely need to know.

Here is where our adventure begins. We're going to follow in the footsteps and wing wash of Captain Jeppesen. I'm going to teach you to fully understand approach charts, much as Captain Jeppesen might have explained it to one of his peers before handing over a hand drawn copy of his treasured notebook. Don't worry, no pilots will be harmed in the making of this explanation, because it will describe an existing chart that's been built in the current era, by people who are really skilled at what they're doing.

We'll start by finding an airport in need of an instrument approach. Sound good? Let's go.

How the FAA Builds an Approach Chart

Let's say you and a thousand other people have taken a fancy to Riverside, California (although, somebody must have pulled its plug, because there's no river that I can see on either side of Riverside). Let's also assume that there is no IFR approach into Riverside (there is, but let's pretend it's just you and me, dressed up as Captain J). Fortunately, the FAA frequently pays attention to the needs of the flying public, so it's possible that your community could convince them to build an instrument approach to Riverside airport, even if it isn't beside a river.

Here's how, in a very basic way, the FAA might go about creating an instrument approach to this airport. Once you understand this process, you'll understand the basic language and symbology used on most instrument approach charts. And just to keep things fun, I'm going to use the famous "LOBSTER" technique of education here. This means I'll be *leaving out boring stuff that's esoteric* and *recondite*. This should keep you from having to enroll in anti-depression therapy because you've read one-too-many FAA technical manuals on subjects like this.

How might the FAA begin building an instrument approach? Logic tells you that they'd certainly start by visiting the airport, flying a few visual sorties across and near the runway, and then setting up shop on the field and snapping to it with their protractors, maps and rulers.

Logically, that was a good guess. It is, however, incorrect. The FAA is staffed by a team of people who specialize in doing these things without looking! That's right. The terminal instrument procedures (TERPs) specialist who does much of the work constructing an approach will most likely have never been anywhere near the airport. It's the Stevie Wonder school of approach chart making.

Wait, it gets better. It's entirely possible this person has never been in any airplane, let alone an airplane like yours. In fact, the only pilot this specialist may have ever come close to is on a hot water heater or stove. Are you scared? Don't be. None of this really matters, because the TERPs specialists are armed with unbelievable amounts of detailed topographic and other information, and they are mega-skilled at applying the FAA's stringent geometric criteria as set out in the TERPs manual (FAA Order 8260.3B). These people know more about your local airport and its surrounding terrain than you do, even if you were born next to the runway.

Think about it for a second. Constructing an instrument approach is really a matter of saying, "OK, how do you get from this place to that place with sufficient clearance from all natural and unnatural objects, and with a reasonable amount of leeway built in?" How much clearance and how much leeway, under a wide variety of tightly-defined circumstances, is what the TERPs manual is all about. The TERPs manual says, in its own way, "If the ground is pretty flat for five miles in all directions, and the pilot is following this type of electronic navigation signal, you need that amount of clearance minimum from any obstacles. But, if the ground rises above this height within three miles, you must find a path with this amount of clearance in all directions and on top of that, the pilot has to remain at an even greater height until she or he has the airport in sight under certain specified weather minimums."

Electronic Flight Bag and the Paperless Cockpit

The EFB or portable electronic flight bag is a term used to describe essential piloting information that is now viewed on a personal computing device. These devices might be tablet PCs, laptops, PDAs or other forms of electronic display. The information presented can range from weather, to checklists to approach charts. Since many pilots are using EFBs in the cockpit, the essential question becomes, "Can IFR charts, both approach and enroute, be presented solely on EFBs, thus preventing the pilot from having to carry paper charts?"

According to the FAA's advisory circular, AC 120-76A that deals with certifying these devices for use in a cockpit, the answer is yes, but with many conditions. First, the FAA has stipulated that there are three classes of EFBs. The first two are essentially considered to be PEDs or portable electronic devices covered by FAR 91.21 and may need to be turned off during some phases of the flight to prevent electronic interference. Class 3 EFBs, can be used as the sole source of IFR charting information. While there are many requirements for an EFB to meet Class 3 criteria, as of this writing, most of the EFBs we use in general aviation airplanes do not meet these requirements. Therefore, the pilot is still required to have paper copies of the IFR charts needed for the flight.

On the other hand, there's nothing that says you can't print the IFR charts you intend to use for this flight, stow them, then refer solely to the EFB for charting information. Of course, you'd only do this if you, as PIC, consider the use of the EFB to be safe for flight.

The TERPs manual makes very exciting reading. Get yourself a plotter and a copy of the TERPs and you've got your own Hairy Plotter book. But first make sure you really have absolutely nothing else to do on Saturday night, not even the dishes.

TERPs specialists (real ones) might begin constructing the instrument approach by examining topological maps of the area, as well as local data on terrain and obstructions. Then they'd find the nearest electronic navaid (usually an NDB or VOR station) and examine how this facility could be used to safely steer and lower pilots from the enroute structure, leading them as close as possible to a runway or the runway centerline. Now, with GPS satellites flying overhead, it's not even necessary to have a nearby navaid for an airport to have an instrument approach.

Once the initial process is complete, an FAA flight inspection team heads out to fly the newly designed approach and see if theory and reality are on the same planet, let alone the same plane. Of course, to keep from having to constantly replace inspectors, they first do the testing in VFR conditions.

It's during this process that they catch things the maps don't show, along with the occasional cold or flu. I'm speaking of things like coniferous trees squatting along the approach path that have grown a few hundred feet since Lewis and Clark last updated the local topographical information. Or the new microwave repeater antenna, or the Empire State Burger building that's popped up near the airport, none of which were ever mentioned to the FAA or put in any database.

Depending on what the field team finds, the approach sometimes literally has to go back to the drawing board, and in rare instances the refs may blow the whistle and declare the approach dead. There are situations where no amount of twisting and turning will permit construction of an approach that meets the TERPs criteria. And that's one rulebook that has no exceptions. Meet it or beat it.

In most cases, though, either the original concept or a slight modification makes the grade, and the approach is approved and published. A chart is born. The entire process, start to finish, can take years to complete, though the typical time is shorter.

Granted, I've used the lobster here to simplify the process, but it's darn close to what I've described.

The Big "Approach Chart" Picture

Now that you've seen the general process in action, let's see how Captain Jeppesen might have drawn the approach if it were 70 years later and he was using techniques similar to that employed by the TERPs specialists. Here's the paper charting format or layout that we'll use. It's the one used by the U.S. Government's National Aeronautical Charting Office (NACO). We'll call it the NACO format because the Billy Bob format doesn't seem appropriate, and it's nice when things have authentic names (Figure 1).

An approach chart should be laid out in a way that makes it most useful to you, the pilot. That's why we place information on this chart in the order in which you're most likely to use it while flying an instrument approach—from the top down. As you fly an approach, you'll generally find the information you need in descending order on the chart. Before you even begin flying this approach you'll want to brief yourself on important information associated with this procedure. That's why there are three horizontal *briefing areas* found at the top of the chart.

The first briefing area contains procedural information (from left to right) like the type of approach, the navaid frequency, identification, direction, important runway information as well as the official approach name and the name of the airport.

The second briefing area provides you with takeoff/departure/alternate information, notes, limitations, approach lighting (if available) and the textual missed approach description.

The last briefing area contains the essential communications information for this approach.

Below the briefing areas you'll find the *plan view*. The plan view provides you with what a bird normally sees when it looks down (and I don't mean newspaper, either).

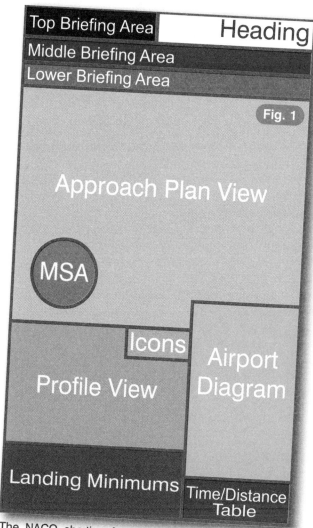

The NACO charting format allows you to obtain the information needed to fly an instrument approach in a logical order by reading from the top down.

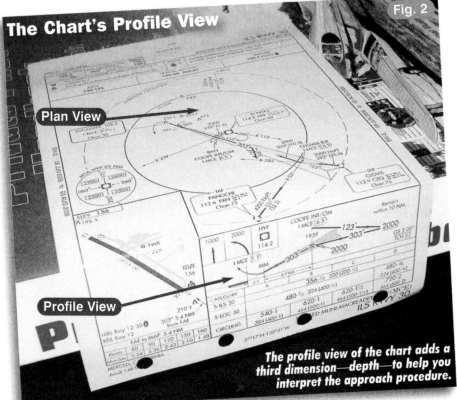

The Chart's Profile View

Fig. 2

Plan View

Profile View

The profile view of the chart adds a third dimension—depth—to help you interpret the approach procedure.

ures or the rare sports icon who is actually good with figures. By icons, I mean basic symbols representing concepts like climb to, turn right or left, fly this route, etc. Icons like these offer an immediate review/reminder of what to do when you approach the runway (where the MAP or *missed approach point* is usually located) and can't see it well enough to land the airplane.

At the very bottom of the chart you'll find the landing minimums, typically consisting of minimum descent altitudes (MDAs) and minimum in-flight visibility requirements. As we previously discussed in the FAR chapter, the MDA is the lowest altitude to which you may descend while guided entirely by instruments. To fly lower you must have the required visibility minimum shown on the chart, as well as an identification of the runway environment (we'll discuss this in more detail later in this chapter).

Why aren't these altitudes shown in the profile view? Perhaps the simple reason is that there's no room. It's like being a bachelor who eats only pizza and ends up with an apartment crowded with pizza boxes. One night I literally ran out of room in my apartment, so I skipped my evening pizza meal. The company got so concerned that they sent the truck around to see if I was OK. These approach minimums are so important that they deserve and get their own place on the chart.

The time/distance table, located at the bottom of the chart, has nothing to do with the number of drachmas it takes to make one yen. Instead, it provides you with an additional source of information on the location of the missed approach point. If you have neither the required visibility nor the runway environment in sight, you must make a missed approach at the missed approach point (we'll just call this the MAP from now on). The time/distance table provides you with information on how to identify or find the missed approach point. For instance, some MAPs are defined by timing your flight from a particular point along the approach course. You'll find the time it takes to fly to the missed approach point here, based on a range of groundspeeds.

Did you sense how the information you'll need to fly an instrument approach is found in a descending order on the approach chart? (If you're reading this in the library, you might want to answer silently, lest the librarian throw the book at you and then throw you out). It's pretty obvious, right? After all, landing minimums aren't placed at the top of the chart because you must fly the approach before you can land. Of course, a good pilot always briefs the approach before flying it. This means he or she looks the

This is a two-dimensional, big picture overview of the instrument approach procedure. There is even *minimum sector altitude* (MSA) information to help you better understand how terrain and obstacles in the area could affect you (more on the MSA later).

But why should you be satisfied with only a two dimensional understanding of the area when you'll be moving vertically, in the third dimension on this approach? Good question, and you should be glad I asked it. This is where the *profile view* comes into play. You might say that if you bent the approach chart near the middle at the line separating the profile view from the plan view, you'd have some semblance of depth information on this chart (Figure 2).

While that isn't what you should do, the profile view does add a third dimension by providing you with the minimum altitudes you're allowed to fly along the most important part of the approach course. Perhaps this is the same reason mug shots of a bad guy have both a head on and a profile view. It just gives depth to his face, meaning that if he has a big nose, it will be easy to identify him. That way, if the guy steals a small seagoing vessel, the police could just look for a sailboat that changes direction whenever he lies down in it.

In the hope that most, if not all, approaches for airplanes end with a landing at the airport, there is an *airport sketch* located either to the right or left of the profile view. (Some instrument approaches for helicopters end up at an oil rig in the Gulf of Mexico. You don't want to fly one of these in an airplane, even if you need a lube job and a burrito.)

Above the profile view is a small section for *icon*. No, icons aren't pictures of your heroes like famous sports fig-

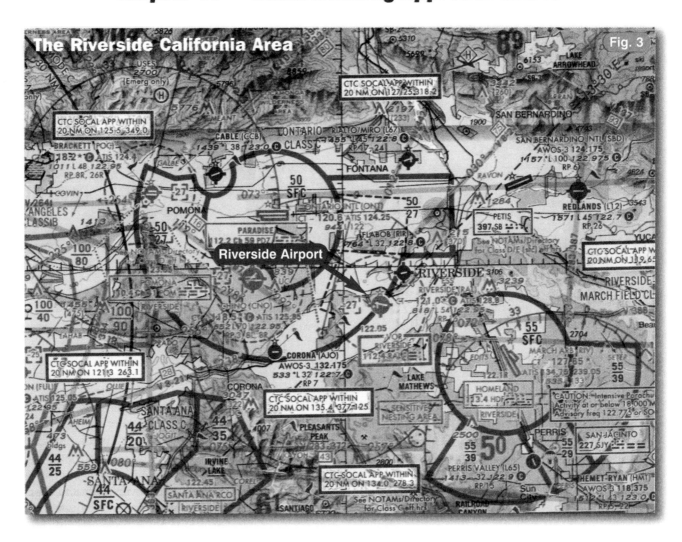

The Riverside California Area — Fig. 3

Riverside Airport

---

entire procedure over way before the approach is begun (and this doesn't mean he does it briefly, or in his underwear).

OK, is that enough of a big picture for you? I hope so. Admittedly, that was more a mural than a picture, but it's worth knowing that there's a lot of thought and strategy that goes into an instrument approach procedure. With that knowledge tucked into the folds of your mighty, supercharged brain, let's get on with the details.

I Want to Fly a VOR Approach to Riverside So I Can Be Happy

And I want you to be happy. So, we'll create an approach for your amusement and plane pleasure.

Perhaps our first consideration when constructing any approach is to make sure we have a nearby navaid to use in navigating to the airport. After all, you can't keep stopping and asking for directions to Riverside, because there are no gas stations up there. (If we're using GPS as the navaid, we can bypass worrying about finding a local navaid and just concern ourselves with the issue of terrain, which we'll discuss in a moment. For your education, however, let's leave GPS approaches for later).

Looking at the sectional chart excerpt covering Riverside airport (Figure 3), one of the first things we notice is that there is a VOR station located right on the field (as indicated by the small white dot to the left of the

blue aerodrome circle, Figure 4). How convenient, right? In the absence of this convenience, we might be able to use an off-field VOR, such as the Paradise VOR, located southwest of Riverside airport. Of course, there are limits to

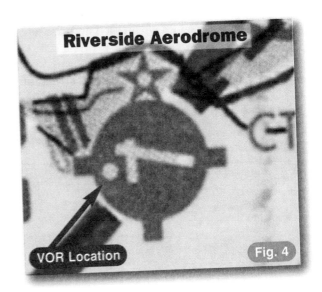

Riverside Aerodrome

VOR Location

Fig. 4

how far a navaid (VOR or NDB for instance) can be from the airport and still be used to create an approach, but we don't have to worry about this for Riverside.

Approaches to a Specific Runway

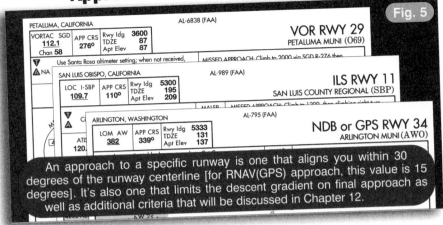

An approach to a specific runway is one that aligns you within 30 degrees of the runway centerline [for RNAV(GPS) approach, this value is 15 degrees]. It's also one that limits the descent gradient on final approach as well as additional criteria that will be discussed in Chapter 12.

If there were no nearby navaid, it's possible one might be installed if funds were available for the project (I mean FAA funding, not pilots chipping in on their own, which would mean that no navaid would be arriving anytime soon). On the other hand, remember my comment about GPS. This technology provides the FAA with the means of building an instrument approach to nearly any airport on earth. Since we have a VOR on the field, however, let's do it the old-fashioned way and use the existing navaid to create our Riverside approach.

It's always nice if we can design an approach that aligns a pilot directly with a runway centerline. I know you like to do turns. They may, in fact, be your specialty. But when you're at the minimum descent altitude in clouds and poor visibility, you may be ready to twist and shout, but you don't really want to turn, turn, turn. It's difficult and a bit riskier to transition from instruments to visual flying while you're also turning to line up with a piece of asphalt.

When an approach takes you straight-in to a specific runway, you'll see approaches with titles like VOR Rwy 29, ILS Rwy 11, and NDB or GPS Rwy 34 as shown in Figure 5. To be classified as an approach to a specific *runway,* the approach course must align within 30 degrees of the runway direction. (This value is actually 15 degrees if it's a precision GPS approach.)

If, because of the position of the navaid, obstructions, runway, or other reasons the approach course can't be aligned

within 30 degrees or less of a *specific runway*, then that procedure becomes an approach to an *airport,* instead of an approach to a runway. Approaches to airports have letters instead of runway numbers in their titles as shown in Figure 6 (e.g., VOR-A, NDB or GPS-C, LDA-C, etc.). An approach to an airport typically requires you to circle to land on a specific runway. Thus, these approaches have what is known as circle-to-land minimums instead of straight-in landing minimums. We'll discuss each criterion for which an approach becomes a circling approach in Chapter 12.

Riverside has two runways, Runway 9-27 and 34-16, as shown in Figure 7. This isn't because the construction folks had some extra asphalt left over. Additional runways are typically built at airports where there are frequent and considerable variations (often seasonal) in the prevailing winds. Now, it would be nice if we could design an approach using the longest runway and the one most often aligned with the prevailing winds. It happens that Runway 9-27 is the longest of the two runways, so let's use it for our approach. What if we build our approach to Runway 9, but the winds favor Runway 27, 16, or 34 on the day we decide to fly this approach? This isn't really as important as it seems. If the winds favor a different runway, we can make a provision on the approach chart that will allow us to circle to land on any of these runways. This would usually involve slightly higher minimums than those for a straight-in type of approach.

Approaches to an Airport

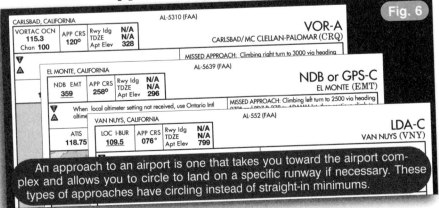

An approach to an airport is one that takes you toward the airport complex and allows you to circle to land on a specific runway if necessary. These types of approaches have circling instead of straight-in minimums.

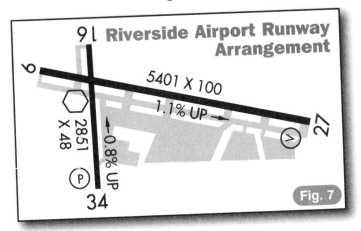

Fig. 7

What's important here is for you to see how it's possible for pilots to use one approach to take them to a point where they can maneuver (circle) to land on any runway that offers more favorable wind alignment. In many instances, however, airports have more than one instrument approach procedure, which allows you to choose one more appropriate to the current wind direction (which makes these type of approaches a wind-wind situation for all pilots).

Terrain Considerations

By looking at Riverside airport and its relationship to local terrain on the sectional chart (Figure 8), we can get a basic idea of how best to build our approach. Mountainous terrain lies to the north, east and south-

west of the airport. Let's copy the major topographical features onto a separate sheet of paper (about the size of the plan view) that will be the beginning of our approach chart, as shown in Figure 9.

As we've already concluded, it would be best to attempt building the approach course so that it lies in the same direction as the runway. What's the runway direction at Riverside? Is it 90 degrees? Well, not quite. In reality, the runway can lie in a direction located anywhere between 86 degrees and 95 degrees and still be called Runway 9. This doesn't mean that the runway has a kink in it, either. The FAA simply rounds off between these values. And that's why you have to be careful playing golf with a TERPS specialist, because he'll shoot a 95 and write 90 on his scorecard.

Runway 9 at Riverside actually has an alignment of 89 degrees. For reasons of terrain, the location of other airports, and airspace considerations, we'll choose a direction of 097 degrees for the inbound course (later, you'll see that when we create a procedure turn for course reversal, the choice of a 97 degree inbound course was the best option here). Remember, as long as the inbound course lies with-

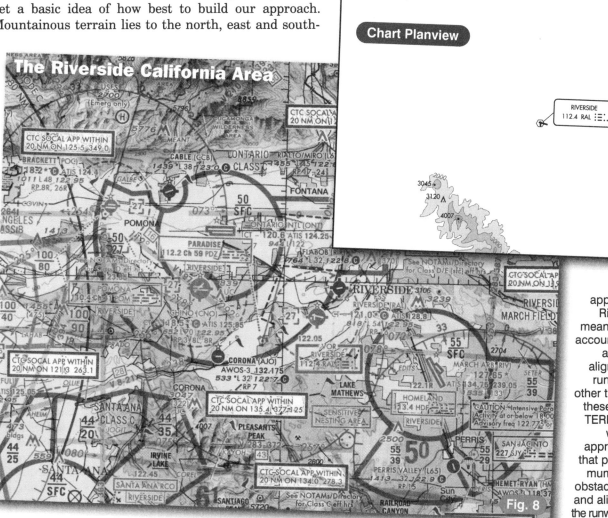

Fig. 8

Fig. 9

Building an approach to the Riverside area means taking into account the terrain as well as the alignment of the runway, among other things. Given these criteria, the TERPS specialist will select an approach course that provides optimum terrain and obstacle clearance and alignment with the runway centerline.

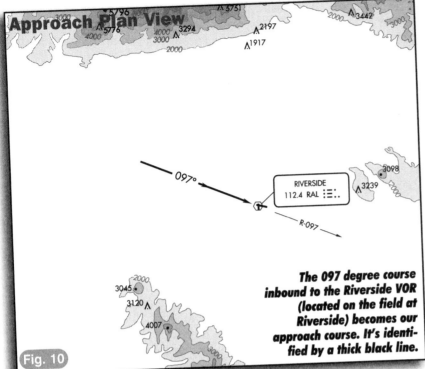

Approach Plan View

097°

RIVERSIDE
112.4 RAL

R-097

The 097 degree course inbound to the Riverside VOR (located on the field at Riverside) becomes our approach course. It's identified by a thick black line.

Fig. 10

The bottom briefing area provides the necessary communications information in the sequence it will usually be needed for the approach and landing. Before you begin flying an approach, you normally listen to the airport's ATIS, then call Approach Control (if you haven't already done so), call the tower, and then, after landing, talk to Ground Control. Additional frequencies can be found when and where space is available at the far right of this strip, such as the Riverside FSS frequency (in case you're lonely or need to call the FSS for some reason).

Getting Reversed on Course

As it stands now, our instrument procedure consists of the 097 degree course to (or the 277 degree radial from) the Riverside VOR. The question to ask is, "How might you get on the approach course to fly it and let down to the airport?" (This is a case where a letdown is good, not depressing.)

Yes, you *could* be radar vectored onto the approach by ATC, and you probably will be. But when approach plans are drawn, the assumption is that you will navigate on your own. TERPs specialists assume that all

in 30 degrees or less of the runway direction, TERPs criteria allow us to call it a straight-in approach to Runway 9 (this is why a TERPS specialist might slice a golf shot 29 degrees to the right and claim that it went perfectly straight).

So let's draw this inbound course (our approach course) as a very thick black line (Figure 10). Let's also assume that all instrument approach charts will have a *true north up* orientation (this is always beneficial, since any latitude and longitude references are then parallel to the chart's borders, and the pilot always knows which end is up). Since we're creating an approach chart, let's also give the approach an official name and list the pertinent airport and communications information available to us about Riverside airport as shown in Figure 11.

As you can see, the top briefing area provides the primary navaid (that's Riverside VOR) frequency used to fly the approach course as well as the approach course direction and airport-runway information. The touchdown zone elevation (TDZE) is the highest useable landing surface within the first 3,000 feet of the runway. (This is the area where commercial airline pilots are expected to land their airplanes. That sure beats aiming for the *last* 3,000 feet of the runway, right?) The middle briefing area provides a tiny picture of the approach lighting system (if one exists) that you might expect to see as you approach the missed approach point.

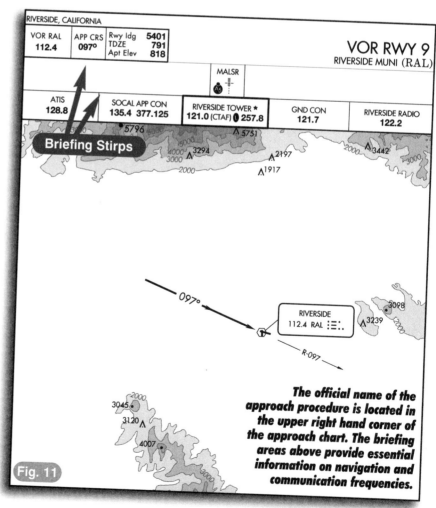

RIVERSIDE, CALIFORNIA						
VOR RAL 112.4	APP CRS 097°	Rwy ldg 5401 TDZE 791 Apt Elev 818				VOR RWY 9 RIVERSIDE MUNI (RAL)
			MALSR			
ATIS 128.8	SOCAL APP CON 135.4 377.125	RIVERSIDE TOWER ★ 121.0 (CTAF) 257.8		GND CON 121.7	RIVERSIDE RADIO 122.2

Briefing Stirps

097°

RIVERSIDE
112.4 RAL

R-097

The official name of the approach procedure is located in the upper right hand corner of the approach chart. The briefing areas above provide essential information on navigation and communication frequencies.

Fig. 11

the approach controllers might be eaten by aliens, and that all you'll have to work with is what's up and running when the flying saucer departs (without the teacup). This isn't a frequent occurrence, but these folks really like to plan ahead. Later they'll do the rest of the body. (OK, that joke is just for me.)

This is a very prudent approach to the approach. If the radar and controllers are both up and running, you have plenty of help to get you onto the approach structure. If they aren't, you still have all you need to get yourself down safely using your own navigation. You will see throughout our discussions of instrument flying that to the extent possible, redundancy and robustness are built into the IFR system.

Self-navigation means that if you were coming in from the west, you could fly to the VOR by intercepting and tracking inbound on the 097 degree course to the airport. Easy.

Too easy? OK, what would happen if you were arriving from the east? What, all flights from the east must land somewhere else? I wouldn't say that out loud, especially if I were in a library. Never fear. If you were approaching Riverside VOR from the east, you could fly to the VOR. No problem. But then you'd find yourself flying in the distinctly wrong direction unless you had a means of getting turned around on the approach course. As a student, I specialized in getting mentally turned around without anyone's help, but that's not precisely what I mean in this case. I'm interested in how you would arrive at Riverside VOR from the east, and then make a course reversal to end up inbound on the Riverside 097 degree course. It just so happens that there is a TERPs provision for this. In fact there are three ways of doing the deed, but we'll discuss just one for now. It's called a *procedure turn*. Here's how it works.

In the case at hand (or in the air), you would fly outbound on the 277 degree radial (the opposite of 097 degrees) for some distance and somehow turn around to reestablish yourself on the 097 degree inbound course. Hmm. But "some distance" and "somehow" are a bit vague, and flying IFR is about precision, so let's look at the details, which are carefully spelled out. How would you turn around? The best and easiest method is to make a 45-degree turn off the course, fly for a minute, then make a 180-degree turn back to intercept the course, and then track the final approach course inbound to the airport. This is known as the "45-180" type of procedure turn, and it's shown in Figure 12. There is, however, nothing mandatory about the 45-180 combo. As long as you get yourself turned around within the permissible area, you can do almost anything that winds up with you facing in the right direction.

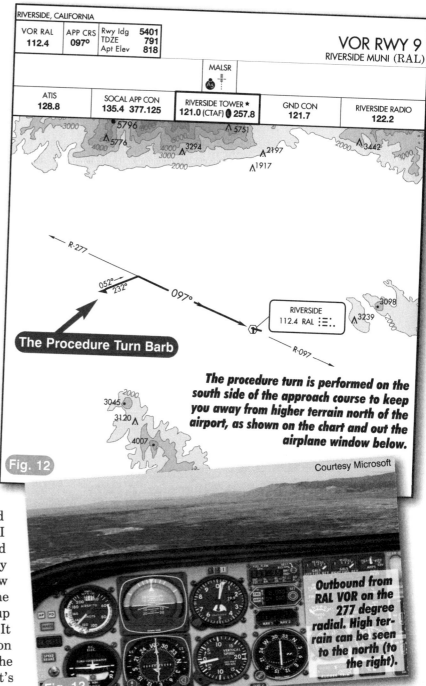

The procedure turn is performed on the south side of the approach course to keep you away from higher terrain north of the airport, as shown on the chart and out the airplane window below.

Courtesy Microsoft

Outbound from RAL VOR on the 277 degree radial. High terrain can be seen to the north (to the right).

There's a lot to be said for consistency, though, so I recommend sticking with the 45-180 combination. Flying outbound on the 277 degree radial (R-277) from Riverside, you'd turn left to a heading of 232 degrees and fly for one minute, then turn right 180 degrees (to a heading of 052 degrees) to intercept the 097 degree course, then fly that back to the airport. That's the procedure for the procedure turn. We'll do this particular procedure turn on the south side of the approach course, for a couple of reasons. First, that's what the chart says to do. Second, higher terrain north of the airport (Figure 13) suggests a strong reason for why the procedure turn is on the south side of the approach.

All fine and dandy, but where does the pilot initiate the procedure turn? Any place he wants? When a passenger

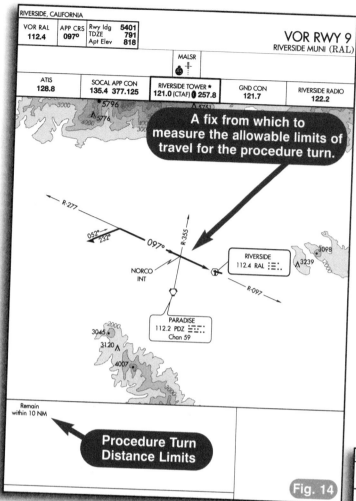

A fix from which to measure the allowable limits of travel for the procedure turn.

Procedure Turn Distance Limits

Fig. 14

the procedure turn must remain (NORCO in our example). This limit is normally 10 nautical miles. For now, let's agree that this will work for our VOR approach to Runway 9 at Riverside. Of course, this distance limit means nothing if you aren't aware of it. Fortunately, the "let's hide the procedure turn distance from the pilot" gag is no longer a favorite pastime of TERPs specialists. That's why this information is usually found in the chart's profile view (Figure 15).

Since NORCO is the place where the procedure turn officially begins, we'll also label it as the *initial approach fix* or IAF (IAFs are always labeled on approach charts with the letters IAF in parentheses). In case you're wondering why you need to identify an initial approach fix, think back to the FAR section that discussed lost communications procedures. Recall that you are required, under certain circumstances, to proceed to the fix from which an approach begins (page 8-34). The IAF is this place, and there are often several IAFs shown on approach charts.

Before we can decide on the minimum altitudes for the procedure turn, we need to assess the terrain for height and obstructions. You don't want your procedure turn to place you at the same altitude used by dirt bikes, do you? We want to be practical about this. We don't want nor do we need to have the procedure turn done at

says, "Are we there yet?" At the point of no return? Because of your enviable brain power, you're probably thinking that a pilot might get in trouble if he just kept flying outbound on that 277 degree radial and began his procedure turn a hundred miles from the VOR. You're right (proving once again that *Ginko biloba* actually works). That's why procedure turns always come with distance and speed (200 knots IAS) limitations in reference to a specific point on the approach structure. Anything beyond is no man's land; go there and "no man" is guaranteed to land.

Flying a procedure turn at the speed of sound would surely result in a sound—the sound of an airplane boring into the side of a mountain somewhere. It might be boring for the airplane, but certainly not for the pilot, to whom it would be totally terrifying. So let's establish that far-out point by creating an intersection on the approach course. There are several ways we can do this, but the simplest is to find a nearby VOR and use a cross radial. It happens that Paradise is nearby (I mean the Paradise VOR), so let's use its 355 degree radial and a very thin black line to establish an intersection that we'll call NORCO, as shown in Figure 14.

Procedure Turn Limitations

A TERPs specialist will look at the nearby terrain and establish a limit from a specific fix or point within which

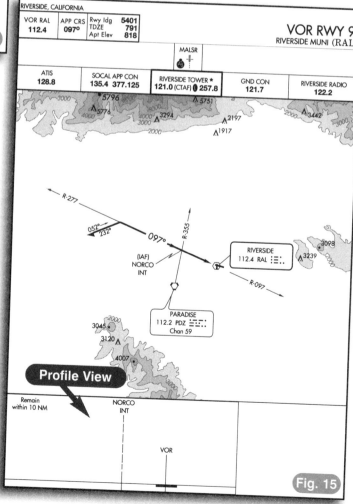

Profile View

Fig. 15

Holding Patterns in Lieu of a Procedure Turn

OK, the 45-180 barb-type procedure turn is a very popular means of course reversal, but it's not the only way to get the job done. And that's good, because it's not always possible for a TERPS specialist to use it at a given airport. One reason is that this procedure requires a great deal of space. The oval area used by these course reversals can make them impractical. Any higher terrain that intrudes can require an unreasonably high procedure turn altitude. This, in turn, increases the required rate of descent on final, which has definite limits under the TERPs standards.

Enter the holding pattern used in lieu of a procedure turn.

The holding pattern shown to the right is an excellent means of course reversal because it uses much less space to get pilots reversed and on course. Given that instrument pilots know how to enter a holding pattern, they can easily cross the fix from which the holding pattern begins, enter the pattern via one of the three methods described in Chapter 6, reverse course and be set up to fly the approach course inbound.

The one major difference about the holding pattern versus the 45-180 barb-type procedure turn is that the holding pattern must be flown exactly as shown on the chart. Freelance efforts to create your own holding pattern will *not* be applauded by ATC. If you need to express yourself creatively, take up ceramics—*after* you land. While you can technically do any type of course reversal when the 45-180 is used (i.e, you could do a 90-270 degree turn if it brings you great pleasure), you must fly the holding pattern as given, such as using one minute legs as shown above.

On the other hand, everything else we'll discuss about procedure turns still applies to the holding pattern.

As a side note, in Chapter 12, you'll learn that the 45-180 barb-type procedure turns aren't used in GPS approaches.

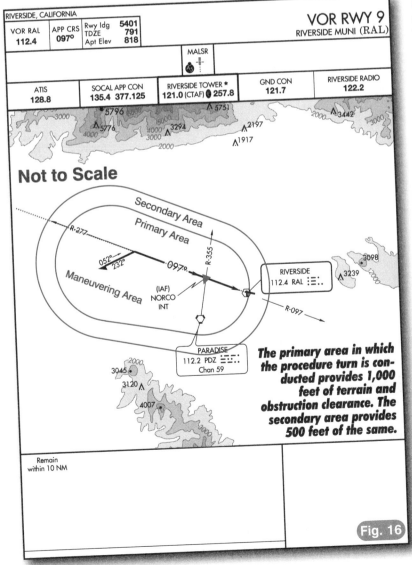

an altitude that keeps us above all obstructions south to the Mexican town of Hasta la Vista Bebe. We only need an altitude that keeps us safe at a reasonable distance, while turning, based on the maximum procedure turn speed of 200 knots IAS.

So what geometric area would be reasonable within which to should provide terrain and obstruction clearance? TERPs specialist use a modified geometric race-track like pattern consisting of primary and secondary areas of protection to make this assessment. While we won't cover this in great detail here (read Chapter 14 of *Rod Machado's Instrument Pilot's Survival Manual* for more detail on these and other charting issues), you can get an idea of how this plays out in Figure 16. The procedure turn area must provide the pilot a minimum of 1,000 feet of terrain and obstruction clearance within the primary area and 500 feet within the secondary area (the secondary area tapers to zero protection at the border).

Perhaps the most important take-away idea from this figure is to always make sure you do your procedure turn on the proper side of the approach course (the maneuvering side where the barb is). Even if you're a TV evangelist with a terrain-specialized guardian angel, you don't want to do your procedure turn on the wrong side of the approach course. First, your reinforced hair won't protect you in a collision of this magnitude. Second, for all you know, nobody has even considered that side. Could be dragons there. Consider it marked "Abandon ye all hope who enter here." Dante go there.

Looking at Figure 17 (and using other topological charts that I haven't shown), a TERPs specialist would probably find that there are no obstacles standing at an altitude greater than 2,000 feet along the westward-extending approach course (which is officially referred to as the *approach procedure track*) for the anticipated distance of the procedure turn. Therefore, the charting specialist would add 1,000 feet onto the terrain and obstruction clearance height of 2,000 feet and make this value 3,000 feet, the minimum altitude for the procedure turn.

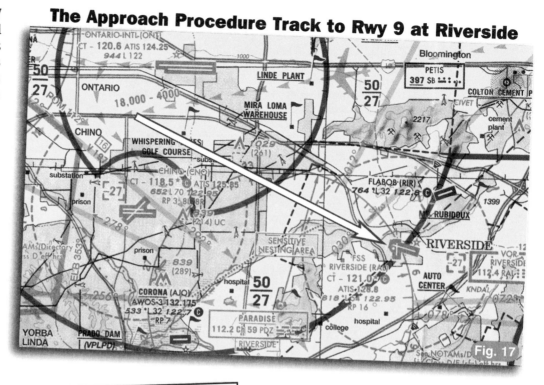

The Approach Procedure Track to Rwy 9 at Riverside

Fig. 17

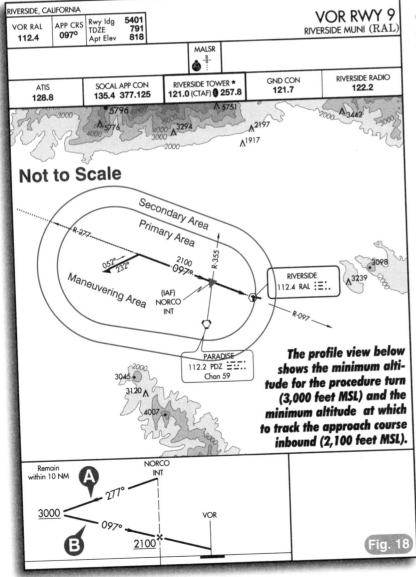

The profile view below shows the minimum altitude for the procedure turn (3,000 feet MSL) and the minimum altitude at which to track the approach course inbound (2,100 feet MSL).

Fig. 18

Figure 18 shows the chart's profile view indicating a minimum of 3,000 feet for the procedure turn. The line under 3,000 feet means that this is a *minimum* altitude. You can remain higher if you like, but you can't go any lower (not even if you have a TV evangelist hair helmet).

Once you've completed the course reversal and are established inbound to the VOR on the approach course, you can descend to a minimum altitude of 2,100 feet (where the TERPs specialist has determined there are lower obstacles along this route) if you wish, as shown in the profile view. Take a second to look at the symbology in the profile view. The thick, downward, right-to-left sloping line leading outbound from NORCO (Figure 18, position A) signifies the procedure turn and its minimum altitude of 3,000 feet. The approach course line (downward, left-to-right sloping) leading inbound to NORCO (Figure 18, position B) signifies completion of the procedure turn (when you're established on the 277 degree radial inbound to RAL VOR), thus allowing a lower altitude of 2,100 feet prior to reaching NORCO intersection.

Now, I hope you like to get down, too. This doesn't mean dancing. It's almost always wise to descend to the lowest altitude permissible on any given portion of an instrument approach. First, because you don't want to have to make a last-minute plunge for the asphalt (or concrete). Second, because the closer you get to the runway vertically, the better chance you have of seeing the asphalt or concrete and being in a position where you can safely descend and land on it. That

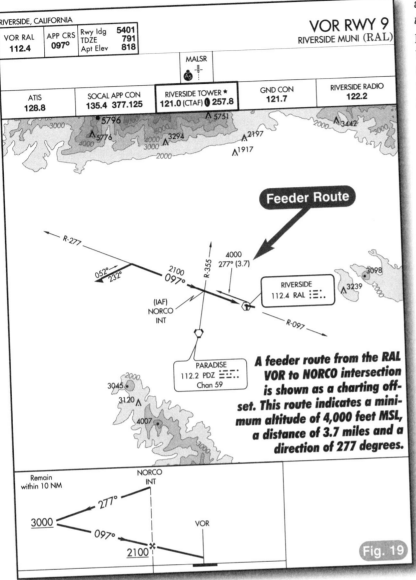

always contain the *altitude, direction* and *distance* necessary to make a transition from one point to the next on a chart. These routes are typically identified by a medium thick black line and have altitude, direction and distance information listed nearby. In Figure 19, the feeder route from the Riverside VOR is offset slightly (known as a *charting offset* to make it clear what you're supposed to do here) from the main approach course and indicates a minimum altitude of 4,000 feet and a direction of 277 degrees for 3.7 nautical miles to NORCO intersection (distances on feeder routes are placed in parenthesis to prevent confusion with altitude values, just as I've placed this sentence in parentheses to identify it as a separate but important thought).

Now that we've created the basic instrument approach structure, we should consider an additional and alternative method of getting onto the approach course at Riverside. Said another way, we need to build more feeder routes so we can transition from other navaids, intersections and airways onto our approach course at Riverside. We've already created a procedure turn, which allows us a means of course reversal in case you arrive at Riverside VOR from a direction other than that of the inbound approach course. For instance, what would happen if you are on a nearby airway or at a nearby navaid and want to transition onto the approach? Let's find out.

The nearest NDB is named PETIS (Figure 20). It would be nice if we could have a transition from this NDB to the approach structure. After all, it's in the best interests of all

is the objective, isn't it? You don't want to fly an instrument approach and not land because you didn't get low enough. Imagine saying to your passengers, "The four planes ahead of us landed, but they were 2000 feet lower, which might be why they could see the airport. I just didn't want to get down today."

Feeder Routes

There's one little problem we need to address before continuing to draw our chart. What is the minimum altitude a pilot should fly from Riverside VOR to NORCO intersection? This isn't covered in our profile view, right?

Figure 19 provides the answer. A TERPs specialist will evaluate the local terrain and decide on a safe altitude for the route from Riverside VOR to NORCO via the Riverside VOR 277 degree radial. Then he'll create something known as a feeder route, to make the transition clear to the pilot. Think of a feeder route as feeding you onto the initial approach structure via the IAF. Feeder routes

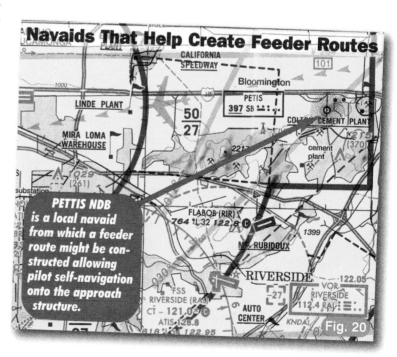

instrument pilots to have as many feeder route transitions on the chart as possible. Remember, the assumption is always that you will have to do your own navigation, with no choice for getting from enroute to approach other than via feeder routes (look ma, no radar!). Does the radar really stop working on occasion? You bet it does. Nothing's foolproof. Someone could spill their mocha milk-a grande supremo coffee on the circuitry, causing circuitry seizure in a puff of mocha milka java smoka (it would take a skilled electrician who uses Maxwell's equations to fix it, too).

On one occasion in Southern California, the local TRA-CON was nearly evacuated because of an approaching wildfire. It was out of the fire for the controllers, and into the frying pan for the pilots. In situations like that, pilots would be given instructions to fly certain transitions onto the approach structure, then cleared to fly the instrument approach, all without the aid of a radar controller. Yes, boys and girls, once upon a time it was *all* done that way.

You could, for example, be instructed to proceed to the Riverside VOR at 5,000 feet, and then be cleared for the VOR Runway 9 approach to Riverside. Given this clearance, as far as the controller is concerned you'll fly to the Riverside VOR at 5,000 feet, then track outbound on the 277 degree radial and descend to 4,000 feet, descend to 3,000 feet once past NORCO, fly the procedure turn, and once established inbound on the 097 degree course to Riverside, descend to 2,100 feet and complete the approach. The system works without radar because controllers can keep airplanes separated by the use of pilot position reports, as they did in the early days of aviation (and I don't mean last Tuesday, either).

By reviewing local terrain information and the availability of nearby navaids, a TERPs specialist can construct several feeder routes to help pilots transition onto the approach course. One example is the feeder route from PETIS, shown in Figure 21. It looks like a bearing of 200 degrees and a minimum altitude of 5000 feet for 7.5 nautical miles will work, given the local obstructions and terrain. Since the transition begins at the NDB, it is flown by ADF bearing to the Riverside VOR and not a radial or course to the VOR. You just have to use a little common sense to figure this out.

It's possible and even likely that if you were in the vicinity of PETIS NDB, the controller would request that you proceed direct to the NDB, and then clear you for the VOR Runway 9 approach to Riverside. If that happened, you'd fly direct to PETIS, track the 200 degree bearing to Riverside VOR and descend to 5,000 feet, turn and track outbound on the 277 radial from Riverside VOR and descend to 4,000 feet until reaching NORCO, then descend to 3,000 feet, fly the procedure turn and then, once established inbound on the approach course, you'd descend to 2,100 feet and fly the approach (more on this last part later). And you'd do it all on your own, without having the controller there to give you radar vectors onto the approach course.

It's important to remember that only medium thick lines (i.e., feeder routes) and maximum thick lines (initial approach segments and approach procedure tracks) have altitudes and distances associated with them. This means you can fly these routes on your own using your own navigation. Said another way, a route shown on the approach chart isn't flyable using your own navigation if that route is associated with only a very thin line (a thin line, one that is .007 inch thick, is typically used to identify an intersection or show a VOR radial/course).

For example, given the completeness of our chart at this time, the 355 degree radial from Paradise VOR (thin line, Figure 21) isn't flyable because it doesn't have medium or maximum thickness. More important, it doesn't have an altitude, direction, and distance associated with it. That's because the Paradise VOR 355 degree radial forms NORCO intersection. Just think of the medium (.01 inch thick) and maximum (.02 inch) thick lines as advertising signs. They provide you with information. They say you can fly these routes using your own navigation. It's kind of like a sign outside Bubba Bob's restaurant that says, "Eat at Bubba's. 5,000 flies can't be wrong." That tells you something. It says don't eat there unless you've had a tetanus shot.

Feed Me More Feeder Routes

Since we're constructing feeder routes, we should try to establish one from the Paradise VOR onto the approach structure via NORCO intersection. After all, the Paradise VOR is a major VOR in the Los Angeles basin (pilots love saying they've flown over Paradise) and it has several major airways passing through it, as shown in Figure 22. By examining local terrain and obstructions, a TERPs specialist will create a feeder route using the 355 radial from Paradise and having a minimum altitude of 3,200 for a distance of 3.5 nautical miles, as shown in Figure 23. Because this is now a flyable route, it gets its own medium thick line with and arrow. About all it lacks is a merit badge. Or, if it misbehaves, a demerit badge.

Of course, bright student that you are, you may be wondering why we didn't create a route from the Paradise VOR to the Riverside VOR, instead of creating a route that goes to NORCO intersection. After all, there's already a feeder route that starts at the Riverside VOR. Wouldn't it just be better to go from PDZ VOR to Riverside VOR and fly the depicted feeder route outbound? Not necessarily. First, it's always better to have feeder routes onto the approach structure begin at major intersections or navaids on the chart. This provides a pilot with more choices, makes his and everyone else's job easier, makes the world a happier place, causes flowers to bloom better, and birds to sing louder. In other words, isn't it better to have 10 freeway onramps in a big city instead of just one?

The second reason is that TERPs specialists design transitions to the approach structure so that pilots don't turn more than 120 degrees to become established on the connecting segment (in fact, 120 degrees is the maximum allowable limit for turns made when transitioning from one electronically navigated route to another). Heading from PDZ to Riverside VOR, then tracking outbound on the approach course requires a turn of approximately 130 degrees. It's just a lot cleaner and simpler to establish the PDZ transition directly to NORCO intersection.

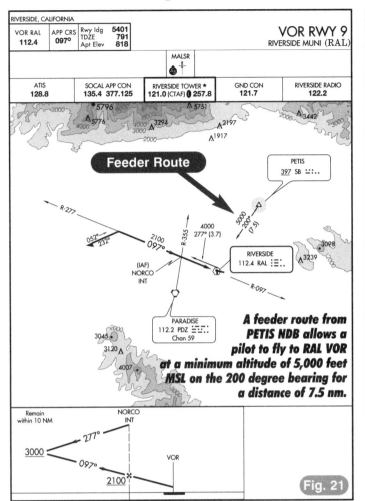

A feeder route from PETIS NDB allows a pilot to fly to RAL VOR at a minimum altitude of 5,000 feet MSL on the 200 degree bearing for a distance of 7.5 nm.

Fig. 21

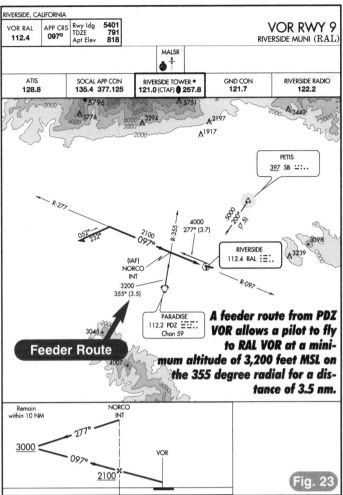

A feeder route from PDZ VOR allows a pilot to fly to RAL VOR at a minimum altitude of 3,200 feet MSL on the 355 degree radial for a distance of 3.5 nm.

Fig. 23

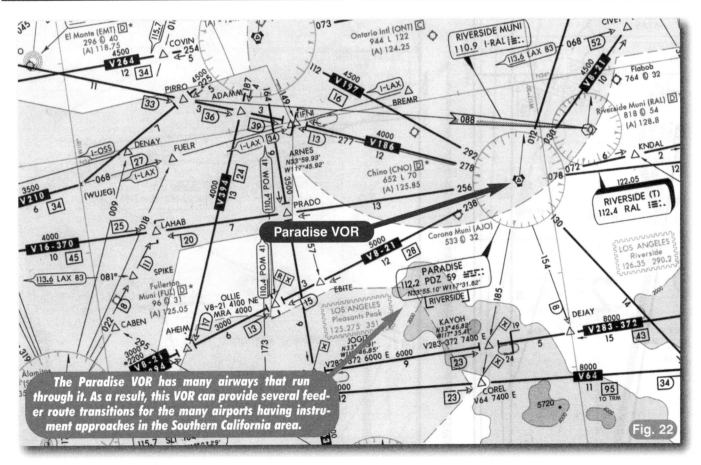

The Paradise VOR has many airways that run through it. As a result, this VOR can provide several feeder route transitions for the many airports having instrument approaches in the Southern California area.

Fig. 22

The Five Segments of an Instrument Approach

Instrument approaches consist of five parts or segments, each with its own symbols, rules, customs and quirks. The five segments are the feeder route, initial approach segment, intermediate approach segment, final approach segment and missed approach segment, as shown in the figure on the right.

Each segment is designed to allow you to safely and comfortably accomplish the specific objective of approaching an airport in IFR conditions. In much the same way that a staircase allows descent one step at a time, instrument approaches lower you in an orderly and progressive fashion. In aviation, it's a five-step program. If you understand the specific purpose of each instrument approach procedure segment, you will better understand how to execute the procedure.

The basic idea of all the segments making up an instrument approach is to take you from wide, expansive airways that are miles in width to fine, precision-like navi-

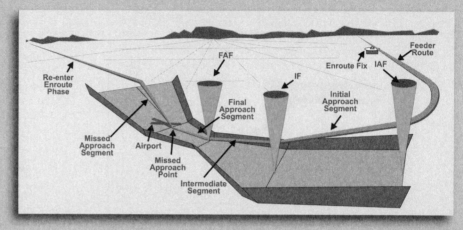

gational tunnels. Vertical and horizontal tolerances, speeds, and margins of safety all become smaller and more critical as you approach the runway. The various segments are designed with this in mind. They take you from the lofty-above and return you back to the surly bonds of earth. And they do it step by step, with forgiveness for excursions growing ever more stingy. As you get close to the runway, you lack slack.

Approach segments are flown in a specific sequence, as shown in the figure above. Size may not matter, but order definitely does. Starting with the feeder route, the aircraft is taken to an initial approach fix (IAF). IAFs are usually identified on the plan view of the approach chart. Initial approach segments start at the initial approach fix (IAF), and proceed to the intermediate fix (IF). IAFs are labeled with the letters (IAF), intermediate fixes are labeled with the letters (IF) on U.S. approach charts. The intermediate segment takes you to the final approach fix (FAF). While the initial approach segment may give you 1,000 feet of terrain and obstruction clearance, obstacle clearance may be as low as 500 feet on the intermediate segment. I told you tolerances would get tight.

When the final approach fix (FAF) exists, it is identified by a Maltese cross in the profile view of the chart. This is the place where your final descent to the lowest minimum altitude permissible on the approach begins. When the missed approach point (MAP) is reached, if you can't meet the legal landing criteria then the missed approach segment takes you to the missed approach holding point.

According to Figure 23, we now have three feeder routes shown on the chart's plan view. One begins at Paradise VOR, the other at Riverside VOR and the last at PETIS NDB. Each leads you to a point where you can intercept the approach course outbound (the Riverside 277 degree radial) and fly the procedure turn before proceeding inbound.

In Catholic school, a nun once asked me to use "ominous" in a sentence. I stood up and said, "Ominous guy." Later, in the emergency room, as I regained consciousness, I understood what ominous really meant. While it might not be ominous if an approach chart didn't have additional feeder routes to help you transition from the enroute to the approach structure, it would certainly be a shame. So let's do what TERPs specialists do and build additional feeder routes onto the approach structure, where possible. Before we can do this, we need to solve the problem of charting scale.

How Terrain and Obstructions are Depicted on the Plan View

The relief features associated with terrain on the approach chart's plan view are depicted when that terrain exceeds 4,000 feet above the airport elevation. Terrain may also be depicted if, within six nautical miles of the airport reference point (ARP), the terrain rises to 2,000 feet or more above the airport. Terrain meeting these criteria is shown because it should be of interest to the pilot (especially if that pilot's airplane doesn't have a force field).

Normally, terrain will be depicted by five or less tints of brown, with consecutively darker tints representing higher terrain elevation contours. Contour levels of 1,000 feet are used in this presentation.

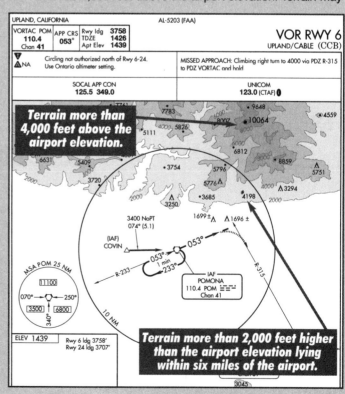

Charting Scale

Charting scale sounds like something plumbers might do while looking at the inside of your pipes, or maybe something best known to concert pianists. It is, in fact, what the approach chart manufacturers (not the TERPS people, but the folks like Jeppesen or NACO that actually produce these charts) often place on a chart so that you will have a better chance to see the pertinent parts of the approach procedure.

Let's make the plan view scale used by our instrument chart similar to that used by sectional charts, which is a ratio of 1:500,000 (which also happens to be the odds of a pilot not exaggerating the smoothness of his last landing). This allows our chart to display most (if not all) of the important navaids and feeder routes used for transitions onto the approach structure. This means that the symbols shown on the approach chart are relative in position and size, which helps you make better visual estimates of time to navaids and intersections.

However, since TERPs doesn't make a provision for providing a mileage scale on the plan view, we should have some means of estimating mileage. So let's create a 10 nautical mile ring and center it somewhere near the middle of the plan view. This means we can place the ring around either an IAF (or FAF, which we'll discuss shortly) on the approach procedure track, since these fixes typically default toward the center of the plan view, as shown in Figure 24. This provides us with some means of estimating distance. For instance, if your airplane travels at 120 KIAS, then you're covering two nautical miles a minute. That means you can fly from the edge of the ring to the center in about five minutes under a no-wind condition.

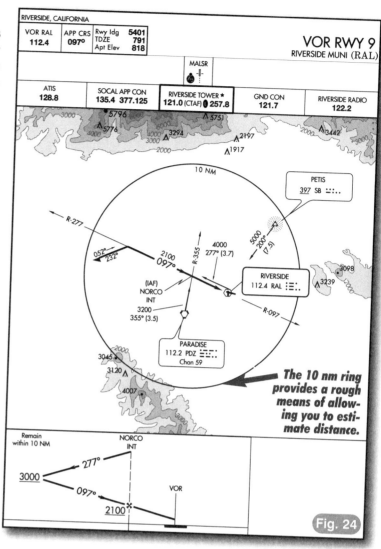

Fig. 24

The Enroute/Feeder Facilities Ring

On some NACO charts, there are intersections and navaids lying way beyond the plan view borders that provide transitions to the approach structure. If that intersection or navaid is no more than .25 inch beyond the border, we can fudge and place it right next to the border. Chart makers allow us to do this. Unfortunately, not all intersections and navaids lying beyond the plan view's boundaries can be shown this way.

To show facilities that lie beyond the chart's border, chart builders create an enroute and/or feeder facilities ring surrounding the solid inner ring as shown on the ILS Rwy 22 approach chart on the right. Notice that the inner *solid* ring, normally 10 miles in radius, is now 15 miles in radius and everything within it is to scale. Chart builders can take liberties to modify the radius of this ring to make the chart more functional and useful to the pilot. Outside the solid (15 mile) ring, you'll notice that no topography or obstructions are shown. The enroute and the feeder facilities rings contain intersections and/or navaids providing either airway or feeder route transitions onto the approach structure. The intersections or navaids on these outer rings are not shown to scale. Some charts may have only one of these rings (enroute or feeder) as appropriate if only enroute or feeder facilities are involved for transitions.

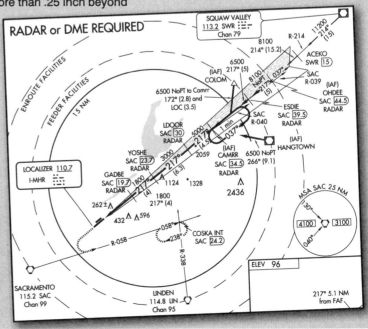

The IFR Area Chart

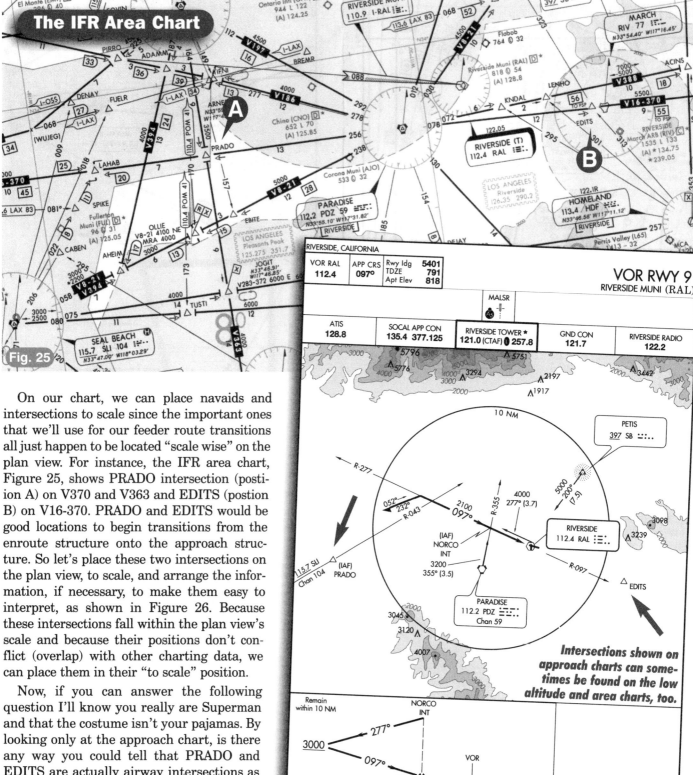

Fig. 25

RIVERSIDE, CALIFORNIA			
VOR RAL **112.4**	APP CRS **097°**	Rwy ldg **5401** TDZE **791** Apt Elev **818**	VOR RWY 9 RIVERSIDE MUNI (RAL)

ATIS **128.8**	SOCAL APP CON **135.4 377.125**	RIVERSIDE TOWER ★ **121.0 (CTAF) ❶ 257.8**	GND CON **121.7**	RIVERSIDE RADIO **122.2**

Intersections shown on approach charts can sometimes be found on the low altitude and area charts, too.

Fig. 26

On our chart, we can place navaids and intersections to scale since the important ones that we'll use for our feeder route transitions all just happen to be located "scale wise" on the plan view. For instance, the IFR area chart, Figure 25, shows PRADO intersection (position A) on V370 and V363 and EDITS (postion B) on V16-370. PRADO and EDITS would be good locations to begin transitions from the enroute structure onto the approach structure. So let's place these two intersections on the plan view, to scale, and arrange the information, if necessary, to make them easy to interpret, as shown in Figure 26. Because these intersections fall within the plan view's scale and because their positions don't conflict (overlap) with other charting data, we can place them in their "to scale" position.

Now, if you can answer the following question I'll know you really are Superman and that the costume isn't your pajamas. By looking only at the approach chart, is there any way you could tell that PRADO and EDITS are actually airway intersections as seen on IFR enroute/area charts? No, you can't. Nevertheless, it's reasonable to assume that these "freestanding" intersections on the approach chart plan view are indeed airway intersections. It happens that the approach chart plan view doesn't show low-altitude Victor airways because there's a practical limit to what can be placed on a chart due to chart clutter. There's nothing wrong, however, with assuming that these freestanding intersections shown on the plan view may also appear on the local low-altitude IFR enroute chart.

Now let's apply altitude, direction, and distance information to these feeder routes, as well as insert a medium thick line to create routes you can fly using your own navigation. Figure 27 shows these feeder routes. Let's also make the point where the 043 degree radial from PRADO intersection crosses the VOR approach course into Riverside an intersection named UPLAN (Figure 27). Creating an official "five-letter named" intersection means you can navigate to it more easily because it's most likely in your navigational (i.e., GPS) database. Giving the intersection a name also helps pilots and ATC more easily reference the airplane's position, letting ATC know where you are or where they'd like you to be. When ATC asks you for your position you can say that you're five miles from UPLAN, which is a lot better than saying, "UGuess," or "I'm over my present position, now."

If you were inbound to or outbound from the Paradise VOR on V16-370 and the controller cleared you for the VOR Runway 9 approach to Riverside via the EDITS intersection (sometimes stated as the EDITS transition), here's what you'd do. You'd fly to EDITS, and then turn in the shortest direction to track inbound to the Riverside VOR on the 274 degree course. Once again, you have to use a little common sense here. Since the feeder route is offset a bit to avoid covering the nearby "R-097" symbology, the route still implies that it points in the direction of Riverside VOR, and the only logical place it can take you is the Riverside VOR. You don't fly parallel to the 274 degree course to Riverside VOR. This would be taking the chart symbols literally. It's similar to someone telling you to go jump off a bridge—they don't expect you to take up bungee jumping. So you'd fly the route from EDITS for 8.2 nautical miles until reaching the VOR and, while doing so, descend to a minimum altitude of 5,000 feet (assuming ATC didn't give you any altitude restrictions). From Riverside VOR, you'd do the same thing we previously discussed when flying the feeder route from this position.

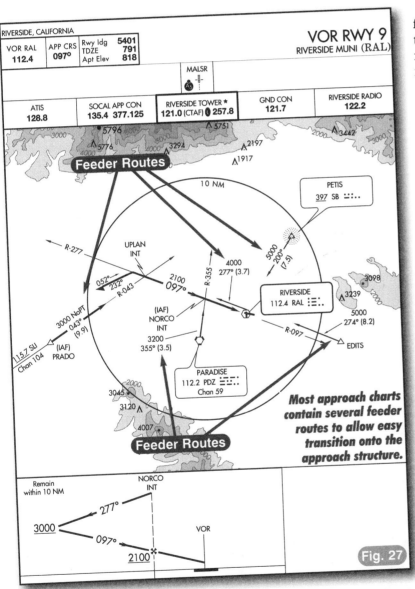

Most approach charts contain several feeder routes to allow easy transition onto the approach structure.

Looking at PRADO intersection, we see the feeder route with a new term, *NoPT*, listed next to the minimum altitude of 3,000 feet. NoPT means *no procedure turn*. If you're at PRADO intersection and the controller clears you for the approach via UPLAN transition, you'd track outbound on the 043 degree radial from SLI VOR, intercept the 097 degree course to Riverside VOR, then fly the approach course inbound.

You wouldn't need to fly the procedure turn, which is good because you probably can't have it. The procedure turn is used to help reverse direction on the approach course, but there's no need to reverse direction here. On routes where the procedure turn isn't allowed (by the FARs) or expected (by ATC) you'll see the term NoPT. Just say no and don't fly the procedure turn when flying these routes. It's not allowed, expected, or appreciated. Controllers do not like surprises. That's why many of them don't go to their own birthday party. They like control, and if you do what they don't expect you to do, you're making them lose control.

Like ATC, no one likes the unexpected, which is why I was shocked when my grandfather told me I was adopted. In shock, I said, "I was?" and he replied, "Yeah, but they brought you back."

Suppose you were at a very high altitude over PRADO intersection and couldn't lose altitude as quickly as needed to descend to the posted minimum feeder route altitudes. When this happens, and it does (maybe because the prior controller kept you at 20,000 feet before the handoff because you surprised her), it's permissible to ask ATC for permission to do a procedure turn. The controller will usually grant your wish, even if her name isn't Genie. If so, then you'd fly to UPLAN, then to NORCO, make a right turn (always do your procedure turn on the side where the barb is located) to intercept and track outbound on the 277 RAL radial and complete the procedure turn.

You absolutely must, without fail, ask for permission to do a procedure turn when NoPT is shown on the route. When NoPT isn't shown on a route (e.g., the route from RAL VOR to NORCO), then you are absolutely required to do the procedure turn. Of course, this assumes that a procedure turn even exists on a specific approach at the airport. If the approach procedure in question doesn't have a procedure turn then the lack of any "NoPT" on a route won't mean a thing. I'm assuming you've already made this common sense assumption.

MSAs—Minimum Sector Altitudes

Before we leave the plan view, there's one more thing we need to know for our approach chart. We need to provide you with some general idea of the minimum safe altitude above the terrain and obstacles in the Riverside area in case you have an in-flight emergency, where this information suddenly becomes really valuable. For instance, suppose you are picking up ice and simultaneously experience a loss of communication with ATC. Of course, given this type of emergency, it's reasonable to think that you might have taken a peek into King Tut's tomb and are now a victim of its legendary curse. Don't look in there next time. That notwithstanding, if you decide to begin an immediate descent but are not in communication with ATC, you could sure use a known safe altitude for the area in which you're located. Enter the MSA or *minimum sector altitude*, as shown in Figure 28.

The MSA provides you with 1,000 foot terrain and obstruction clearance for a radius of 25 nautical miles from the facility shown in the center of the MSA symbol. It doesn't guarantee you navigation or communication capability (in an emergency similar to the one I mentioned above, you might not be immediately concerned with navigating or communicating, either). At Riverside, a TERPs expert will look at the local terrain and obstructions then divide up the area into sectors (like pie slices, if necessary, each no less than 90 degrees in spread) and provide a minimum safe altitude for each area. (In Chapter 13, you'll learn that the GPS approaches don't offer sectors. Instead, they offer an MSA or minimum safe altitude as it would more appropriately be called since there are no sectors involved. See Figure 31.)

If, for instance, you were northwest and within 25 nautical miles of the Riverside VOR and had to make an emergency descent, you'd want to descend no lower than 11,100 feet until you had another means of identifying the height of the terrain and obstructions below you. More precisely, south of the VOR between the depicted bearing of 030 degrees and 300 degrees to the Riverside VOR (as seen in MSA symbol), an MSA of 6,800 feet applies.

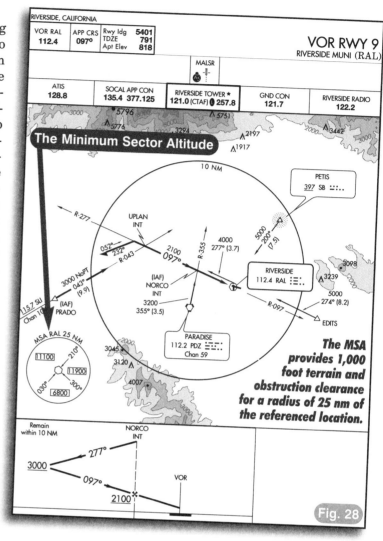

Fig. 28

Figures 29 and 30 show how this terrain might appear when looking out all three windows while flying a heading of 030 degrees and 120 degrees, respectively.

East of the Riverside VOR, between bearings 210 and 300 degrees to the station, the MSA is 11,900 feet. Keep in mind that the MSA has nothing to do with the approach/departure controller's minimum vectoring altitude (MVA) or the Center controller's minimum instru-

At RAL VOR, Hdg 030 Degrees: Terrain Viewed from Left, Front and Right Windows

Fig. 29

At RAL VOR, Hdg 120 Degrees: Terrain Viewed from Left, Front and Right Windows

Fig. 30

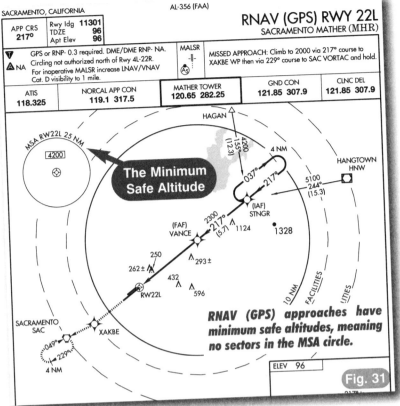

SACRAMENTO, CALIFORNIA   AL-356 (FAA)

APP CRS 217°	Rwy Idg 11301 TDZE 96 Apt Elev 96	RNAV (GPS) RWY 22L SACRAMENTO MATHER (MHR)

GPS or RNP- 0.3 required. DME/DME RNP- NA. Circling not authorized north of Rwy 4L-22R. For inoperative MALSR increase LNAV/VNAV Cat. D visibility to 1 mile.

MALSR

MISSED APPROACH: Climb to 2000 via 217° course to XAKBE WP then via 229° course to SAC VORTAC and hold.

ATIS 118.325	NORCAL APP CON 119.1 317.5	MATHER TOWER 120.65 282.25	GND CON 121.85 307.9	CLNC DEL 121.85 307.9

The Minimum Safe Altitude

RNAV (GPS) approaches have minimum safe altitudes, meaning no sectors in the MSA circle.

ELEV 96

Fig. 31

ment altitude (MIA). A controller, having a detailed video map, can easily have MVAs that are much lower than the MSAs. The MSAs are for large slices of the airspace pie and may contain a larger area of terrain and obstructions. A controller's MVA, on the other hand, is usually for a smaller area and only deals with obstructions within that space. It's kind of like focusing or specializing in a specific area, which I did as a bachelor when I became a lifeguard at our apartment's Jacuzzi.

As a final note on MSAs, chart builders try to build the MSAs at a navaid that's located in the middle of the plan view. This is fine, but for an MSA to be useful to you, the MSA must center on some type of navaid to which you can establish a bearing. Otherwise, there would be no way to identify sectors showing variable MSA values. For instance, you wouldn't have an MSA centered on a marker beacon, because they aren't directional. You could have one centered on a locater outer marker, however, because an NDB is involved there.

There are occasions where the MSA for the entire area of the circle is the same, as shown at Mather Field in Sacramento (Figure 31). The point about which the MSA is centered on this RNAV (GPS) chart is a waypoint that rests on the beginning of Runway 22L. In these instances, since the MSA isn't cut into different pie slices (no quadrants) it's appropriate to call the MSA the *minimum safe altitude* since only one altitude value is established.

The MAP or Missed Approach Point

Now that we've constructed the plan view, we're ready to work on the bottom portion of the chart. This is where you'll find the profile view, the airport sketch, the minimums section and the time/distance table. Before we can continue, however, I need to provide you with a little deeper understanding about how we fly an instrument approach. I promise that this will be more fun than the time my high school geology instructor told me I needed a deeper understanding of rocks and minerals. I ended up digging the hole for his backyard swimming pool.

Descent Below MDA: The Thrill is Gone, Baby

A pilot on her first IFR flight after passing the instrument check believed she had planned for every contingency. When it became necessary to divert to an alternate airport after reaching cruising altitude, she and her pilot spouse in the right seat handled the diversion well...except for one small detail.

It was my first IFR flight since receiving my instrument rating. Conditions at departure and arrival airports were VMC (current and forecasted), but I was determined to file IFR to gain experience.... Upon reaching enroute altitude, I tuned in the ATIS for the destination. I was shocked to hear "300 feet overcast, 1 mile in fog." My personal minimums were written down in advance and an attempt in this low IMC was out of the question—particularly since a missed approach would require holding over the ocean in a single-engine aircraft.

My spouse suggested that we try our alternate. ATIS there reported 800 feet broken and 2 miles. I asked my spouse to get out the alternate approach plates. My spouse is a private pilot and instrument student, and in flight was asking a lot of questions. It was my spouse's first time in IMC. I informed ATC that I wanted to go to the alternate, which was immediately granted.... Approach gave us vectors for the VOR approach... and instructed me to maintain 2500 feet until established, cleared for the approach, report FAF inbound.

The clouds started at 2,000 feet MSL. I intercepted the approach course and started the descent. We entered the clouds and held the MDA (640 feet). We reported the FAF. I worried as time passed that we would not see the airport.... Nav indication 'TO' and GPS indicated airport still ahead. We broke out of the clouds to find 800 foot broken conditions around the airport. I saw the airport and landed safely. Spouse was thrilled and really impressed. I, too, was elated.

It wasn't until hours later, as we continued our trip in a rental car and reviewed the flight, that I realized I had descended to MDA before the FAF. This occurrence was caused by inexperience, but I could have (and will in the future) do better cockpit coordination, review all possible plates for myself beforehand, and walk my spouse through my plans on the ground, to avoid (minimize) questions at critical times.

NASA Callback Report

Once we've completed the procedure turn (if it was necessary) and we're inbound on the approach course, we're in a position to descend to the lowest minimum descent altitude allowed for this procedure. In other words, we descend as low as possible on the approach course to get close to the runway both vertically and laterally. This gives us the best chance of seeing what we're hoping to see.

That means that we need to establish an altitude lower than 2,100 feet MSL (the minimum altitude for crossing NORCO intersection inbound), as shown in Figure 32 and 33. We also need to establish a point where the inbound approach course to the runway (or airport) officially ends. This is the point where, if we don't have the required visibility and the runway environment in sight, we need to make a missed approach. The missed approach procedure involves climbing to a safe altitude and (often) holding at a nearby intersection or navaid until you and ATC come up with a mutually agreeable plan on what to do next. Before we can establish our missed approach point, we need to identify something known as the final approach fix (FAF).

Take a look at the Maltese cross on the dashed vertical line identifying NORCO intersection in Figure 32. The Maltese cross identifies the FAF or final approach fix (I'll refer to it as the FAF from now on). The FAF identifies the point where you must look at the minimums section of the approach chart to identify your MDA or minimum descent altitude for this approach. This is like being a young flight instructor and checking the balance on my bank account. It was easy to find, because I knew when I found a decimal point, my balance would be to the right of that spot.

While we haven't discussed the minimums section yet, you can clearly see that there are no more altitudes shown on the profile view after NORCO. You now know to go to the minimums section to find them (hold on, we'll get there soon).

The FAF is also very important because it's the place from which we officially measure the distance to the missed approach point. Let's discuss the missed approach point, and you'll see how the FAF is involved.

TERPs specialists always try to create a missed approach point that's as close as possible to the runway

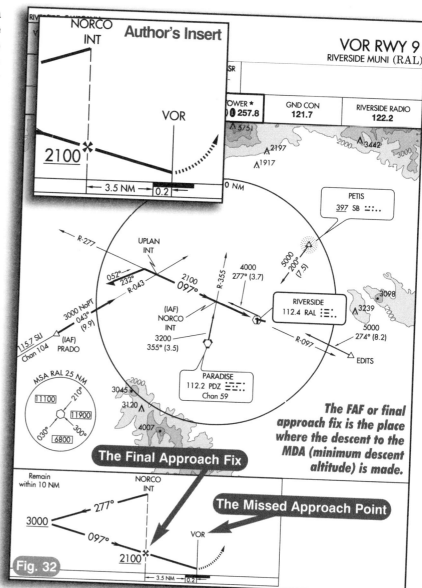

Inbound to RAL at NORCO

The airplane above is located at NORCO intersection at 2,100 feet (the #2 nav omni display shows a centered needle with a FROM triangle indicating that the airplane is on the PDZ 355 radial). Since the airplane is at the FAF, it's now in position to start its descent to the next lowest altitude, the minimum descent altitude.

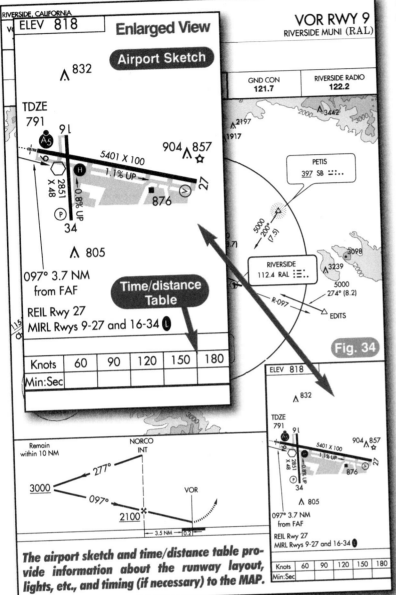

The airport sketch and time/distance table provide information about the runway layout, lights, etc., and timing (if necessary) to the MAP.

beginning of an upward curving dashed line represent the missed approach point and what you're supposed to do when you come to it and need to make a missed approach.

While we're at it, let's label the distances from the FAF (NORCO intersection) to the missed approach point and place these values at the bottom of the profile view (see my insert in the top left hand side of Figure 32). The distance from Riverside VOR to the runway threshold is 0.2 nm, and the distance from the runway threshold to the FAF is 3.5 nm. This gives a total distance of 3.7 nm from the FAF to the missed approach point. Why label this distance? Some missed approaches are determined by timing from the FAF, which means you would need to know this distance and the airplane's groundspeed to identify the missed approach point.

In this case, the approach uses the TO/FROM flag reversal of VOR passage to identify the missed approach point, so we don't need to time the approach.

Let me show you how this all ties together by creating the airport sketch and time/distance table on our chart.

Airport Sketches and Time/Distance Tables

Figure 34 shows our approach chart with its airport sketch and time/distance table (found underneath the airport sketch box). The airport sketch provides you with a picture of the airport layout as well as data and symbols to help identify the runways, their lengths, their slope, displaced thresholds, pictures of approach and runway lighting symbols (see the *Approach Lighting System* legend on Page 12-9, Figure 11, Chapter 12) as well as a tiny picture of the actual approach lighting established for a specific runway (if approach lighting exists for that airport).

Of course, the FAA assumes that you'll be wearing reading glasses with lenses the size of the Hubble telescope just to see the individual ink molecules used for each letter and number on the chart. Notice that the tiny picture of the approach lighting at the beginning of Runway 9 in the airport sketch is also shown in the center of the middle pre-approach briefing area, located near the top of the approach chart (refer to Figure 28 to see this). Right now, the most important thing to notice is the arrow-tipped black line coming from the left and pointing toward the six-sided VOR symbol on the chart. This arrow represents the actual direction of the approach course in relation to the airport layout. As you can see, the Riverside VOR is located to the right of the runway. Looking at this representation provides a good idea of what you can expect to see out your window as you approach the missed approach point.

Below the airport sketch box is the time/distance table. On those approaches where time from the FAF is used to identify the missed approach point, you'll find that time

threshold. This makes sense. If the missed approach point were not close to the runway threshold, it would defeat the purpose of the instrument approach, which is to put you in the most favorable position to land. At Riverside, the VOR is situated on the airport near the runway, so let's make the VOR the missed approach point. This is also is a common sense idea, since a change from "TO to "FROM" in the VOR's ambiguity indicator makes it real easy for you to identify when you're crossing the missed approach point.

Other ways of identifying missed approach points are by DME indications, NDB passage, arrival at DA or timing along the approach course. The most important point here (besides the missed approach point, of course) is that there is always some definitive, unambiguous way of identifying when you're at the missed approach point.

Since the approach course in the profile view of Figure 32 is represented by the maximum thick line, we'll let this line continue to the missed approach point, where the approach course officially ends. From here, we'll let the

listed here as shown in Figure 35. For this VOR approach to Runway 30 at Long Beach, the distance from the FAF to the missed approach point is four nautical miles. At 90 knots groundspeed, it will take 2 minutes and 40 seconds to get there. As noted above, since the missed approach point on our Riverside VOR Runway 9 approach is identified by VOR passage, no *time* values will be listed in the time/distance box (Figure 34). In fact, the lack of time values in this box is an immediate indication that the identification of the missed approach point doesn't involve time (I don't mean that the clocks stop moving here, but at least you're not required to begin timing when you cross the FAF).

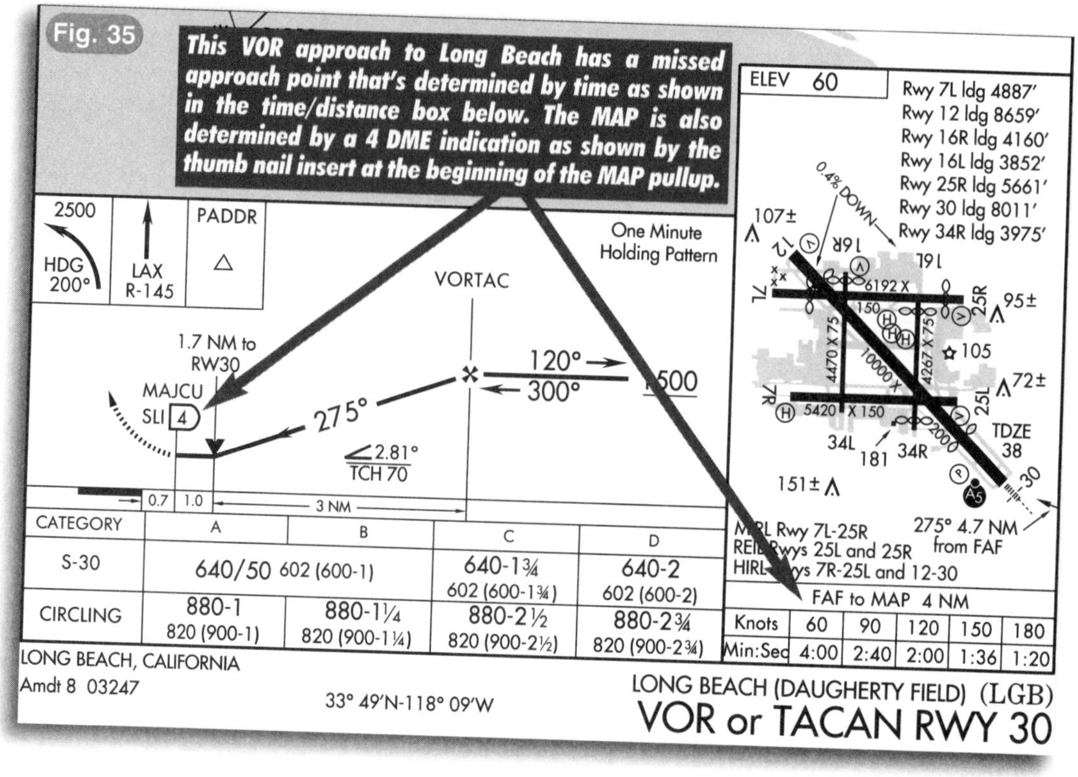

The Landing Minimums Section

Now that we've made our way to the missed approach point, we need to consider just how low we are allowed to go in the process of getting there. So, for the last part of our approach chart construction we'll concentrate on creating the landing minimums section. Here's a macro perspective on what this section is all about.

First, do you remember that tiny little itty-bitty picture of the approach lighting system at the beginning of Runway 9 on the airport sketch? Good, because that's how tiny the real approach lighting system will look if you stay at 2,100 feet and don't descend to the lowest allowable minimums on this approach. Remember, the basic objective of an approach chart is to provide you with a means of getting as close to the runway threshold in both a horizontal and vertical direction as possible, without hitting anything.

Until now, we've concentrated mainly on bringing you close to the runway in a horizontal direction. That's why our approach course takes you right next to the runway threshold. The question now is, "How close can you get vertically to the same runway?" In other words, what is the minimum descent altitude permissible for this particular approach? Obviously you're restricted to a minimum of 2,100 feet until reaching NORCO. Given that the airport elevation is 818 feet MSL, if you didn't descend further, you'd be 1,282 feet above the airport when you arrived at the missed approach point. This is unreasonably high for a pilot to identify the runway and descend straight-in for landing. There must be some lower altitude to which you can safely descend. There is. It's called the *MDA* or *minimum descent altitude*.

MDAs—Minimum Descent Altitudes

The TERPs manual says that the lowest permissible MDA for VOR approaches of this type must provide at least 250 feet of obstacle clearance. To determine what this MDA should be for a specific approach, a TERPs specialist looks at the local terrain and finds the highest obstacle within a specific distance (as specified in the TERPS manual) to the right and left of the inbound approach course past NORCO intersection. What distance would this be? Well, that's a bit complicated. It involves geometry and math that really aren't relevant to an instrument pilot here. Besides, one fellow at our FBO (the one who was just terrible at math) said, "Yeah, math is tough all right. That's why five out of four people have trouble with it." Suffice it to say that if you keep your course deviation indicator near the center of the display index you easily remain within the area where there is sufficient obstacle protection.

A full-scale deflection of your CDI means you may be beyond the obstacle-protected area by one inch or one mile. You just can't tell with a full-scale deflection of the CDI. That's why pilots are wise to execute a missed approach if and when their CDI is at or is approaching a full-scale deflection in these situations. This is one of many reasons you should try to keep that needle centered all the time and never be satisfied with any significant deviation. If you'd like more detailed and advanced information on how approach charts are constructed, take a look at my *Instrument Pilot's Survival Manual*.

Let's say we look carefully at the local topographical charts (along with other pertinent information on obstructions), and determine that there's an obstacle in the approach area topping out at 991 feet MSL (that's roughly 200 feet AGL in this area). Adding 250 feet onto this value gives us 1,241 feet MSL. According to TERPs

Fig. 35

This VOR approach to Long Beach has a missed approach point that's determined by time as shown in the time/distance box below. The MAP is also determined by a 4 DME indication as shown by the thumb nail insert at the beginning of the MAP pullup.

LONG BEACH, CALIFORNIA
Amdt 8 03247
33° 49'N-118° 09'W

LONG BEACH (DAUGHERTY FIELD) (LGB)
VOR or TACAN RWY 30

Chapter 11 - Understanding Approach Charts   11-25

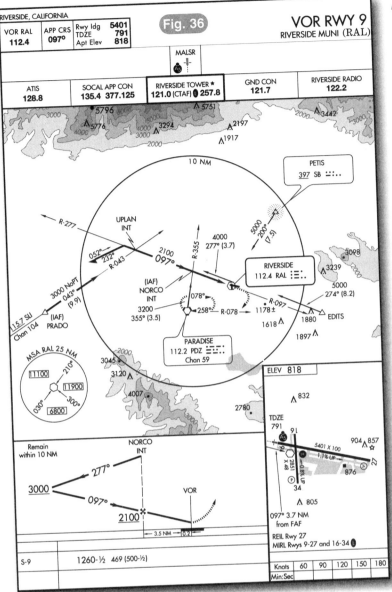

The Minimum In-Flight Visibility Requirement

As you've already learned in the FAR chapter, in order to legally descend below the MDA, you must have the required minimum in-flight visibility established by TERPs as well as one or more specific items in the runway environment (FAR 91.175). These visibility minimums will always be shown in the minimums section of the approach chart. The minimums section of the Riverside VOR Runway 9 approach (Figure 36) indicates that you need ½ mile in-flight visibility to legally descend below the MDA and land at Riverside. This is a relative low visibility minimum for a VOR approach, and TERPS allows it because Runway 9 has a sophisticated approach light system (you'll learn more about approach lights and their value in the next chapter).

But just because you can see the runway or its environment doesn't mean you have the minimum half mile of in-flight visibility, either. After all, you could be almost on top of the VOR looking down at the runway below and see it perfectly because you're only a few hundred feet above it, indicating that you have a few hundred feet of vertical visibility. But vertical visibility isn't enough here. You need to have a half mile (that would be 2,640 feet) of in-flight visibility in the direction in which you'll point your airplane for landing—and, unless you're flying a drill bit, you don't point directly downward to land, do you? That means you need a half-mile of in-flight visibility out the forward window where you look during landing. You do look out the forward windows when landing, don't you? If your instructor is in the right seat, you don't look to see if he's smiling as an indication of having the proper visibility for landing, do you? That's a novel but not necessarily legal idea.

criteria; initial MDA values are always rounded up 20 feet, so this gives us an MDA of 1,260 feet MSL for a straight-in Runway 9 VOR approach (Figures 36 and 37). Therefore, when crossing NORCO intersection inbound at 2,100 feet, you'd begin a descent to 1,260 feet and fly at this altitude until crossing over the VOR as indicated by a TO/FROM flag reversal. Hopefully you'll see the runway or the runway environment before reaching the missed approach point.

Here's one of the most important questions about instrument approaches. Suppose you're approaching the VOR and can actually see the approach lights or the runway lights through the clouds. Does this mean you can land? The answer is, a big fat NOT NECESSARILY! At this point, it's perfectly reasonable for you to say, "Ahh, can we be a little more vague about that?" OK, here's the skinny on the topic.

At MDA on the RAL VOR Rwy 9 Approach

Fig. 37   Courtesy Microsoft

HAT—Height Above Touchdown

Now, take a look at the numbers to the right of the landing minimums (Figure 38). The number 469 is known as the HAT or the *height above touchdown* value. For any straight in landing minimum (1,260 in this instance), the approach chart will always provide you with your height above the TDZE. Runway 9's TDZE is 791 feet MSL and when you add 469 feet onto this, you get 1,260 feet MSL (yes, even if you're one of the five out of four who have trouble with math). The numbers in parentheses to the right of the HAT are military minimums. You won't need these values unless you're in the military, so we won't speak of these values here.

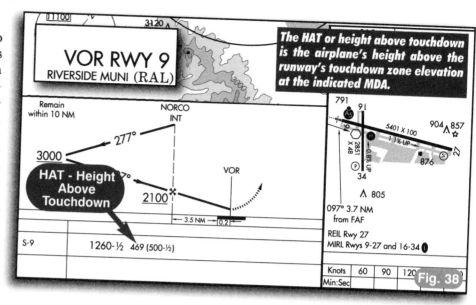

The HAT or height above touchdown is the airplane's height above the runway's touchdown zone elevation at the indicated MDA.

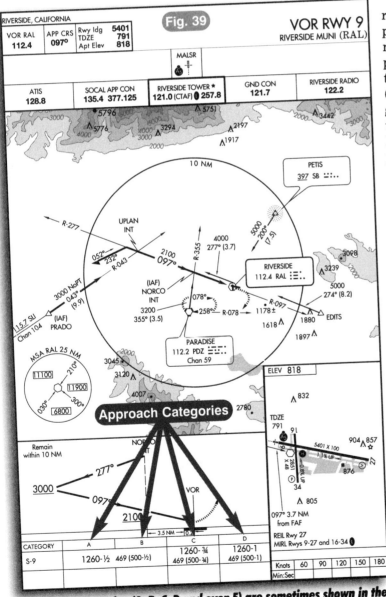

Approach categories (A, B, C, D and even E) are sometimes shown in the minimums section of the approach chart. Higher categories have higher approach minimums in terms of either minimum descent altitudes or minimum required visibilities for landing.

There is one other little problem we need to solve regarding charted minimums. We aren't the only pilots who are going to use this approach chart to make instrument approaches. Pilots of different airplane—big ones and small ones—will also be using this chart. It's even possible that a C5 Galaxy pilot (one of the largest airplanes in the world, as suggested by the word "galaxy" in its name) can use this chart to make an instrument approach (please keep in mind that I said that the *C5* and not the pilot was one of the "largest" in the world, although the latter could be true, too).

The problem here is that bigger airplanes typically approach at higher speeds because they usually have higher stall speeds, and thus require more room to maneuver than smaller airplanes. If an airplane were flying faster on the approach, it would seem reasonable to assume that its pilot would need to see the runway environment sooner than a pilot flying a slower airplane.

Think about it this way. If you were flying this approach at 15 knots (as could be done in a blimp, and yes, blimps fly instrument approaches, too) you'd have nearly all day to look for the runway environment. You wouldn't need much in-flight visibility because you could literally fly over the end of the runway look down from a height of 469 feet (the HAT), identify the threshold and descend gently for landing. You can't do the same thing if you are approaching in an airplane at 91 knots or a little less, can you? No, you can't. You are not a blimp, so disabuse yourself of that notion pronto. That's why our approach to Riverside requires a minimum of one-half mile of in-flight visibility. If you're in a bigger airplane and/or flying the approach at a faster speed, you might need more in-flight visibility to safely maneuver and land the airplane. That's why the FAA established what is known as *approach categories* that influence the minimum visibilities for an approach as shown in Figure 39.

Aircraft Approach Categories

Figure 39 shows our minimums section divided into four categories (A, B, C, and D) with different straight-in minimums displayed for the C and D categories. Airplanes fall into one of five different types of approach categories (approach charts, however, typically display only the first four categories). Each category is based on a value obtained by multiplying 1.3 times the airplane's power-off stalling speed in the *landing configuration* or Vso (since the airplane is landing, it was deemed wise by the FAA to use the stall speed in the landing configuration as the reference here). An airplane falls into Category A if 1.3 Vso is less than 91 knots; Category B is this value is between 91 knots but less than 121 knots; Category C if this value is between 121 knots but less than 141 knots; Category D if this value is between 141 knots but less than 166 knots and Category E if this value is 166

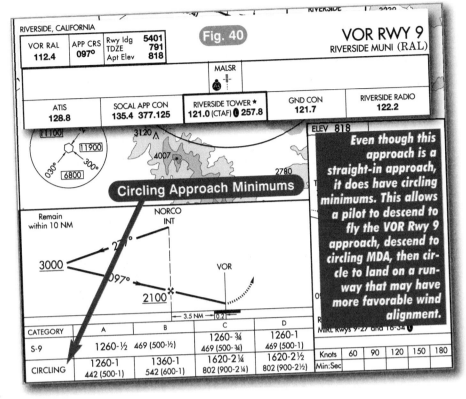

knots or more. It's very important to note that if you plan on operating at a speed greater than the upper limit of the speed range for your airplane's category, you should use the minimums for the category of speed that will be used. If your airplane falls into Category A, but you plan on approaching at 105 knots, you should use the Category B minimums shown on the approach chart. Or, heaven forbid, if you attach a rocket engine to your Cessna 152, you'll use Category E minimums—"E" standing for orbital "escape" velocity in this instance.

Figure 39 indicates that the MDA values are the same for all the approach Categories, but Category C and D require in-flight visibility minimums of ¾ and 1 mile, respectively, to legally descend below the MDA and land. It's up to the TERPs specialists to decide when and where higher minimums apply based on TERPs criteria. In the case of Riverside, it was considered safe to give Category B airplanes the same landing minimums as Category A airplanes.

Circling to Land

Before we can complete our VOR approach chart to Riverside, we need to deal with one more important issue. What happens if the VOR Rwy 9 approach is the only instrument approach into Riverside and the wind is blowing from 270 degrees? You certainly don't want to land with a tailwind if you can avoid it. After all, you might have started your descent from the MDA a little late and be higher than normal on the approach. Couple this with a tailwind and you may have diminished your chances of being able to bring the airplane to a stop on any runway shorter than that used by the space shuttle.

In this instance, it would be better to descend to a slightly higher MDA that would allow you to remain clear of obstructions while circling to land on Runway 27. TERPs specialists make a provision for circling to land by providing circling minimums, as shown in Figure 40.

Circle-to-land minimums are usually greater than straight-in landing minimums because you're likely to cover more area when circling. This means that there are likely to be more obstacles of varying heights. Thus the need for increasing the minimums. A TERPs specialist can identify the circling area in which you're supposed to remain by drawing arcs of specific radii from each runway threshold and connecting those arcs by tangents, as shown in Figure 41. For Category A airplanes, the radius is 1.3 nautical miles; the radius becomes larger with each approach category, as shown. It should be obvious to you why you'd want to use higher category minimums if you were approaching at speeds above those specified for your airplane's original category. Within the circling area described, you're guaranteed a minimum of 300 feet of obstacle clearance.

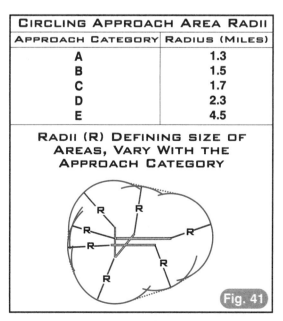

CIRCLING APPROACH AREA RADII	
APPROACH CATEGORY	RADIUS (MILES)
A	1.3
B	1.5
C	1.7
D	2.3
E	4.5

RADII (R) DEFINING SIZE OF AREAS, VARY WITH THE APPROACH CATEGORY

Fig. 41

HAA—Height Above Airport

Looking at Figures 40 and 41 (repeated here for your convenience), the circling area increases noticeably with each higher approach category. There's something else you need to notice here. Since a circling approach allows you maneuver around the airport instead of flying toward the runway for which the approach was designed, you're no longer interested in your HAT in regard to a specific runway. Instead, you should be more interested in your height above the airport elevation. After all, if you're now circling to land on Runway 27 or any other runway, you don't care what your height above Runway 9's touchdown zone elevation is, right? You should be more concerned with how high you are above the airport elevation, since you'll be circling around the airport. Thus, for circling approaches, the minima numbers before the parentheses are based on HAA or *height above airport* values, not HAT values. This means that the HAA for the Category A circling minima is 442 feet. If you add this value to the airport elevation (818 feet MSL) you obtain 1,260 feet MSL.

To see this in action, let's imagine that you're inbound on the approach course just outside NORCO intersection at 2,100 feet. The radar controller has cleared you for the VOR Runway 9 approach to Riverside and tells you to contact the tower at NORCO.

After making that contact, Riverside tower says that the winds have shifted and are now out of the west from 290 degrees at 15 knots. You are instructed to circle-to-land, *north* of the airport, for Runway 27. This means that, if you're a Category A airplane, you'll descend to a minimum of 1,260 feet MSL (the circling minimums MDA). If, at or before reaching the missed approach point, you have the required visibility and runway environment in sight, you'll maneuver to stay to the north side of Runway 9, per your clearance. Practically speaking, you'll make a right hand traffic pattern to land on Runway 27, perhaps maneuvering just to the downwind at or before reaching the missed approach point position. (Hopefully you'll have the required in-flight visibility of one mile and the runway environment in sight before reaching the MAP. Otherwise you'll have to make a pretty tight turn to begin your maneuvering.)

Of course, if you only have one mile of visibility, you'll want to remain within one mile of the runway (Figure 42). Why? Based on what you now know of how obstruction clearance is provided on a circling approach for Category A airplanes, maneuvering more than 1.3 miles from the runway centerline (Figure 41) could put you in an area of dangerous obstructions. This is an important concept, especially when you're circling to land under similar

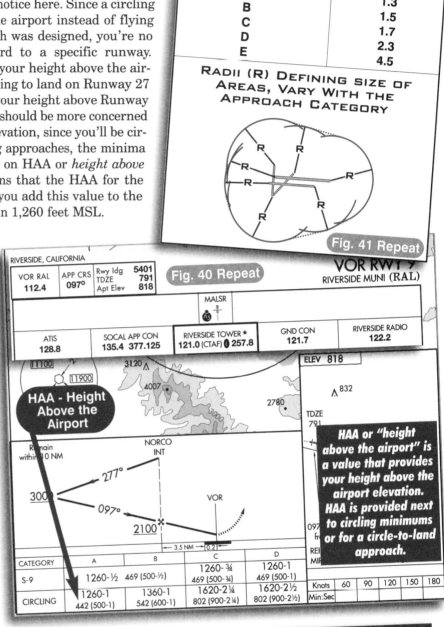

CIRCLING APPROACH AREA RADII

APPROACH CATEGORY	RADIUS (MILES)
A	1.3
B	1.5
C	1.7
D	2.3
E	4.5

RADII (R) DEFINING SIZE OF AREAS, VARY WITH THE APPROACH CATEGORY

Fig. 41 Repeat

RIVERSIDE, CALIFORNIA   **VOR RWY 9**
RIVERSIDE MUNI (RAL)

Fig. 40 Repeat

VOR RAL 112.4	APP CRS 097°	Rwy Idg 5401 TDZE 791 Apt Elev 818

ATIS 128.8	SOCAL APP CON 135.4 377.125	RIVERSIDE TOWER ★ 121.0 (CTAF) ◯ 257.8	GND CON 121.7	RIVERSIDE RADIO 122.2

ELEV 818

HAA - Height Above the Airport

HAA or "height above the airport" is a value that provides your height above the airport elevation. HAA is provided next to circling minimums or for a circle-to-land approach.

CATEGORY	A	B	C	D
S-9	1260-½ 469 (500-½)	469 (500-¾)	1260-¾ 469 (500-¾)	1260-1 469 (500-1)
CIRCLING	1260-1 442 (500-1)	1360-1 542 (600-1)	1620-2¼ 802 (900-2¼)	1620-2½ 802 (900-2½)

Knots	60	90	120	150	180
Min:Sec					

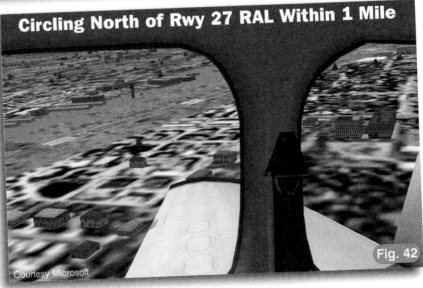

Circling North of Rwy 27 RAL Within 1 Mile

Courtesy Microsoft   Fig. 42

instances and the in-flight visibility is, let's say, two miles. You might think, "Well, I'm at the circling MDA but because of the better visibility, I'll make a wider pattern." If you're doing this at night and exceed the circling obstacle protected boundaries, you could find yourself stuck in a tree, mountain, or antenna (if you want to add another antenna to your airplane, this *is not* the way to do it).

It's possible that the approach chart will restrict your circling behavior in some way. The left side of the pre-approach briefing area in Figure 43 prohibits circling north or Rwy 9-27 for category D airplanes. Apparently the approach speed of these airplanes could allow them to move too close to higher obstructions in this area (Figure 44). It's important to say, however, that if the controller doesn't restrict your circling to any part of the airport, then you may circle to land as you see fit (as long as there isn't some sort of charted circling restriction indicated on the approach chart. You'll learn about these in Chapter 12).

Finally, what would you do if, while circling to land on a runway, you lost sight of that runway? No, I don't mean a rear passenger put his hands over your eyes and said, "Guess where?" (in which case you have every right to banish this person to the baggage compartment). The scenario I have in mind is one where you penetrate a lower layer of clouds and suddenly find yourself out of visual contact with the runway.

Here's the rule for just such an occasion: *first, make a climbing turn toward the landing runway, then follow the published missed approach procedure.* Making a climbing turn toward the landing runway (Runway 27, thus 270 degrees, in our previous example) always keeps you closer to the middle of the airport and helps you avoid straying from the area that protects you against obstacle encounters. Once the turn is made, follow the missed approach procedure as published.

A Restriction to Circling

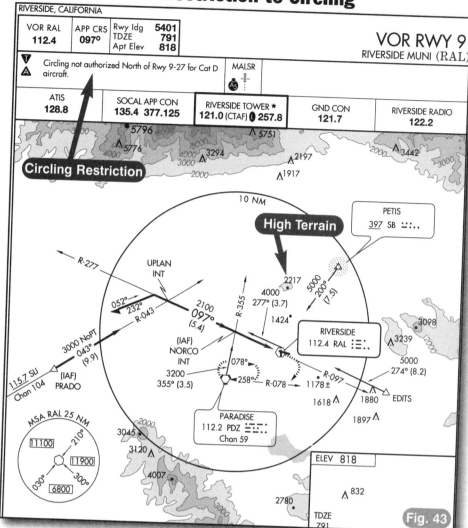

When terrain or obstructions restrict circling in specific areas of the airport, a note will often be placed in the briefing area at the top of the chart, as shown above. In this instance, circling is restricted north of the airport in Category C airplanes. This makes sense, since larger, faster airplane might be exposed to danger from higher terrain north of the airport (see Figure 44).

Higher Terrain North of Riverside Airport

The higher terrain north of the airport is clearly seen here. The speed at which Category D aircraft maneuver could easily allow them to maneuver too close to this terrain, thus exposing them to danger.

Figure 45 shows the nearly completed approach chart, just as Captain Jeppesen might have drawn it if he'd had the information a modern-day TERPS specialist has. There are a few incidental items shown, such as the amendment number at the bottom left and the lat/long information, at the bottom middle of the chart. The latitude and longitude information represent the airport reference point (the geographic center of the airport). You can read about the amendment number in the accompanying sidebar on the right.

Something's Missing

All good things must come to an end, and so it is with the approach. There are basically two possible outcomes of any approach. As Yoda would have put it, "Land, or land not." If you can't meet the legal minimums to land, you need a way out, which is why there is always a missed approach procedure.

From the looks of our topographical chart (Figure 46), it's clear we'd like avoid turns to the left, since the spinner on the nose of our airplane isn't shaped like a drill bit. There are mountains to the north and they'll leave us alone if we leave them alone. Since we'd like to have a place for the airplane to hold at after beginning the missed approach, it seems that a right turn toward the PDZ VOR would be a good option.

The reason for having a missed approach holding point is that you must now make a few important decisions about what you want to do next. For some reason (most likely poor visibility), you weren't able to land at this airport on your first attempt. You must now make a choice about whether to try another approach at this airport or head to another airport with more favorable weather. The third choice of wishing you were on a beach in Maui sipping a cool drink with a tiny umbrella in it isn't an option at the moment.

Since a TERPs specialist would have access to the most current and detailed obstruction information, let's place a few of obstruction symbols on the approach chart plan view to help us best decide on a logical missed approach procedure. Figure 47 shows a red box surrounding the additional obstructions added to the chart. From the looks of the 1,178 foot terrain ahead and to the right of the 097 degree radial. (Dots

The "Nearly" Completed Approach Chart

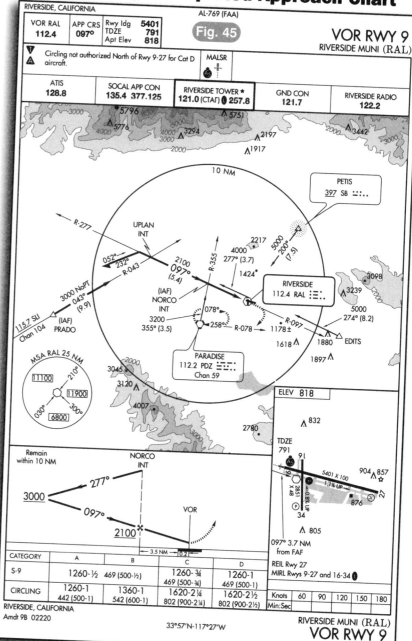

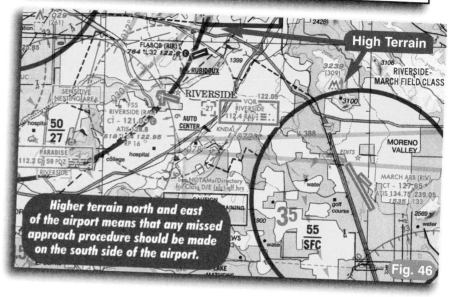

Higher terrain north and east of the airport means that any missed approach procedure should be made on the south side of the airport.

Fig. 46

Chart Amendment Numbers

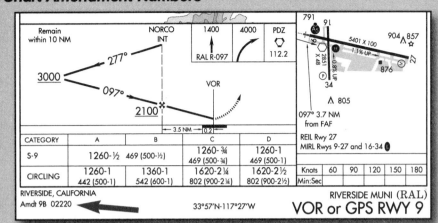

A lot of pilots don't realize it, but technically, instrument charts are just a graphic illustration of Part 97 of the Federal Aviation Regulations. That's right, your chart is the law! Any change to an FAR requires that a formal amendment be made, and approach charts are no exception. In the figure to the right, the bottom left side of the chart shows the amendment number, 9B followed by the numbers 02220. The amendment number indicates that this chart has had at least nine amendments since its conception. The B indicates that this is the second charting amendment issued against the original 9th charting amendment.

When checking FDC NOTAMs before a flight, you can check to see if your chart is current by check looking for FDC notams referencing the IFR chart you plan to use at your destination with the amendment number posted on the NOTAM. For instance, suppose an FDC NOTAM for Riverside said:

(FDC 6/7523) - INSTRUMENT APPROACH PROCEDURE CHANGED VOR OR GPS RWY 9,
RAL RIVERSIDE MUNI, RIVERSIDE, CA. AMDT 10...
INCREASE CIRCLING CAT A MDA 1,300/HAA 482, CAT B MDA 1,400/HAA 582.
WIE UNTIL PERM

The amendment number on the NOTAM is "AMDT 10." Thus, your chart isn't current and needs updating or replacing. The amendment number on the chart in your hands should be at least equal to or greater than the FDC NOTAM amendment number.

The numbers 02220 on the bottom of the approach chart provide you with the year and date of the last chart revision or when this chart was originally added to the book of charts. For instance, our chart was last changed in 2002 on the 220th day of the year.

Designing The Missed Approach Procedure

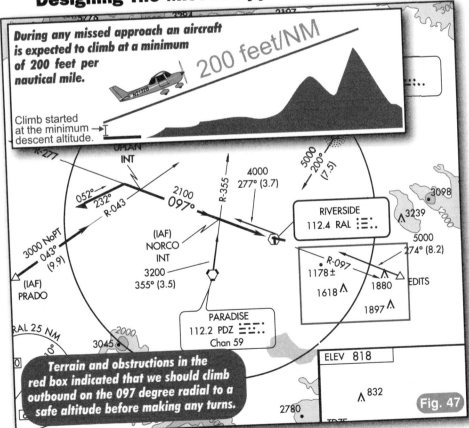

During any missed approach an aircraft is expected to climb at a minimum of 200 feet per nautical mile.

Terrain and obstructions in the red box indicated that we should climb outbound on the 097 degree radial to a safe altitude before making any turns.

represent terrain, unless your pen leaks ink. The +/- indicates an approximate terrain value and has nothing to do with where to connect the wires to the mountain.) It seems that we should maneuver to climb outbound on this radial to at least a safe minimum altitude before making the turn toward the PDZ VOR.

If we had all the detailed topographical information a TERPS specialist had, we'd probably decide that a minimum altitude of 1,400 feet would be best before beginning the turn. TERPs criteria require that all missed approaches have a minimum climb gradient of 200 feet per nautical mile to the missed approach holding altitude. This means that for every mile forward you progress you'd need to climb at least 200 feet. If you're climbing at a ground speed of 90 knots, then you're traveling at 1.5 nautical miles every minute. Therefore, with a 200-foot per nautical mile climb gradient requirement, you'll need to climb at a minimum *rate* of 300 feet per minute. It appears that any airplane meeting this minimum climb requirement would easily be able to clear all the obstacles in the immediate departure path (any airplane that couldn't meet this climb criterion would now be called a car).

A climb to 1,400 feet before turning right and flying to the PDZ VOR should provide adequate obstruction clearance in the missed approach path. Now, the question is, how do we portray this missed approach information on the chart? Let's do it by adding this information to the approach briefing area, the plan view, and the profile view.

Briefing Areas and Icons

The entire missed approach procedure description can now be read in the right side of the middle briefing area, at the top of the chart (Figure 48, position A). This makes it easy for you to review prior to beginning the approach. Given that the missed approach instructions are so important, let's also show the missed approach turn and holding position on the plan view by a dashed line (Figure 48, position B). Our plan view depiction shows that a (climbing) right turn is made to the PDZ VOR and the airplane is to hold east, on the 078 degree radial. Now, let's add a few easily recognized icons that a pilot can quickly review at the missed approach point to help him recall the missed approach procedure. We'll add these to the top right side of the profile view (Figure 48, position C).

The icons indicate that you're to climb on the 097 degree radial to 1,400 feet, then turn right and fly direct to the PDZ VOR and hold as shown at 4,000 feet MSL. Neat, eh? You have three separate sources of missed approach information both in textual and symbolic form. You'd almost get the impression that TERPs specialists think that the missed approach is pretty important. I think they're right, even if they do cheat at golf.

Cleared to Proceed

Well, the chart is done, just as it would have been by Captain Jeppesen if he'd only had today's satellite maps and imagery, GPS technology, laser surveying, electronic databases, and the wealth of knowledge and experience embedded in the TERPs.

You now know a lot about how instrument approaches are constructed, and are on your way to understanding how to fly many types of approaches, too. While we used one type of approach as an example in this chapter,

The Completed Approach Chart

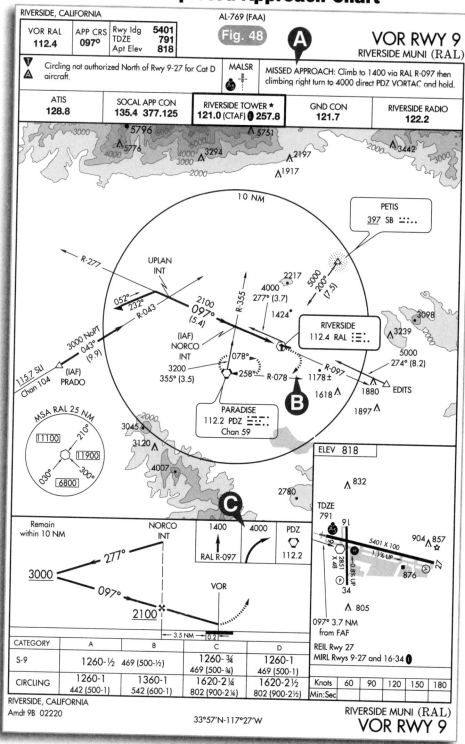

everything you learned about approach charts is applicable to other kinds of approaches. Sure, there are differences, and some charts have specific symbology we haven't touched on. Nevertheless, the core understanding you've just acquired about charts will provide you with 95% of the information needed to interpret all other charts.

The last 5% is details. In the next chapter we'll talk about the different approaches you're likely to fly as an IFR pilot, and their accompanying details.

Chapter 12
Approach Chart Analysis

There are times when you look at something and it just doesn't please the eye. This was especially true with my grandfather. One day he looked at the Hawaiian shirt I was wearing and said to everyone within earshot, "Look at that shirt. That's living proof there's a family in Berkeley without curtains." Ouch. OK, it was a Honolulu lulu of a shirt, but I liked it.

On the other hand, given how excited you are about flying instrument approaches, I doubt you'll ever come across an instrument approach plate you don't love seeing once you master all the intricacies associated with these charts. At first glance, an instrument approach chart can be a bit daunting, but it's just a matter of learning to read and understand Chartese, the shorthand language of charts. So, let's get started.

Bound Approach Chart Booklets

Instrument approach charts created by the government are contained in the U.S. *Terminal Procedures Publications* (TPP). TPPs contain 24 bound volumes of instrument charts, produced by the government's National Aeronautical Charting Office or NACO for short. These charts are also available on CD in vector graphics, which makes them easily uploaded to your electronic flight bag Tablet PC (Figure 1). You can even download NACO instrument approach charts from many web sites for free. Jeppesen also produces instrument approach charts, but we'll stick to covering NACO charts in this book. If you'd like to learn more about Jeppesen charts, then take a look at my advanced instrument book, *Rod Machado's Instrument Pilot's Survival Manual*.

Inside each NACO booklet, you'll also find departure procedures(DPs and SIDs), standard terminal arrival routes known as STARs (you don't have to live in Hollywood to use them), airport sketches, and non-standard departure minimums. We'll cover each of these items, one-by-one, so don't panic. There is a lot of commonality between approach charts, and I don't want you to pop your skullcap when you first see different approaches and all the details associated with them. Remember, approach charts are designed to fit the briefing format discussed in the previous chapter. That means you'll always find communication information in the briefing area section, feeder route information in the plan view, minima infor-

Flightprep's Motion LS800 Tablet PC

Tablet PCs are becoming the medium of choice for viewing instrument approach charts.

Courtesy: www.flightprep.com

Fig. 1

mation in the minimums section and so on. In fact, here's a bold claim (written in italic and I'm not even Italian). After reviewing the ILS chart info (the first section in this chapter), you should be able to look at nearly any approach chart and understand how to fly that approach. How's that for quick language learning? You'll know Chartese long before I habla Italian.

So let's begin with the big picture. The approach charts we'll cover in this section will be the ILS, Localizer, VOR, and NDB charts, as well as some slight variations of these charts. We'll save the GPS/RNAV charts for the next chapter.

The ILS or Instrument Landing System Approach

Figure 2 shows the ILS approach to Runway 30 at Long Beach, California (I don't know why they call it Long Beach when it has such a short one). From the top, the first three rows in the briefing section contain information in line with what was presented in Chapter 11, with a few notable exceptions.

First, not all airports are named the same as the city in which they reside. That's why NACO places the city name in the top left hand corner of the chart (position A) and the airport name directly under the type of instrument approach (position B).

Next, to the left of the middle briefing area are two black triangles containing the white letters *T* and *A* (position C). These symbols refer to the presence of nonstandard takeoff minimums and nonstandard alternate minimums, respectively. We'll cover nonstandard takeoff minimums in Chapter 14 (IFR departures) and nonstandard alternate minimums in Chapter 16 (flight planning).

Looking at the plan view in Figure 2, you can see the feathered symbol representing the localizer portion of the ILS in position D (it doesn't feel feathery when you touch it. Sorry. If you're disappointed, then touch a chicken.). You also see the outer and middle marker beacons for the approach (position E). The middle marker, labeled *MM* (sweet, eh?) is clearly identified. The outer marker *OM* on this approach just happens to be collocated with a nondirectional beacon (NDB) that transmits on a frequency of 233 KHz. Thus, BECCA intersection can be officially identified by both the outer marker (OM) and a nondirectional beacon, which is also referred to as a compass locator (L) when it's associated with the

markers of an ILS approach. Thus, a combination of outer marker (OM) and NDB compass locator (L) is known as a LOM or *outer compass locator*. If the compass locator was collocated with the middle marker, it would be called a LMM or, *middle compass locator*.

There's actually a third way to identify BECCA intersection. If you look carefully, you'll see a thin line representing the 200 degree radial (R-200) from Seal Beach VOR running through the intersection. Radials or bearings running through intersections on the plan view indicate that these may also be used as an alternate means of identifying that intersection.

In Figure 2, the SLI 200 degree radial can be used to identify BECCA intersection (position F). Similarly, the

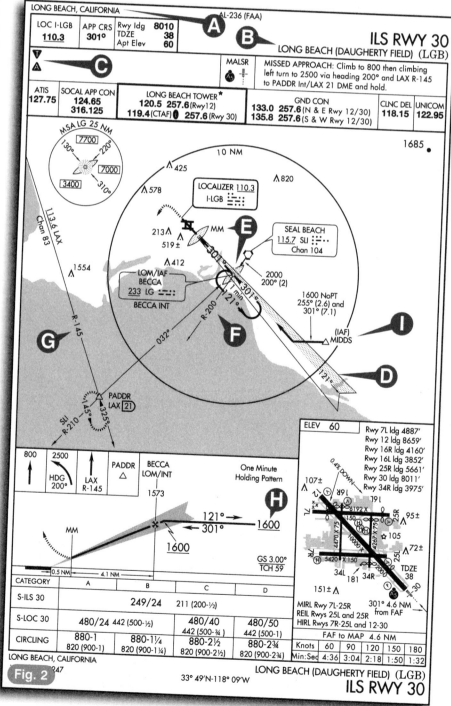

Fig. 2

LAX 145 degree radial (position G) and the SLI 210 degree radial can be used to identify PADDR intersection located to the bottom left of the plan view. Since PADDR is the missed approach holding fix, consider what happens when you have only one VOR/ILS indicator in the airplane (or only one that works because the other one was purchased from some guy in a van). If you execute the missed approach, you may be asked to hold at PADDR. If that happens, you'll have to keep switching between the SLI and LAX VORs. I'm sure your CFII will teach you how to do this fancy, rapid-fire handwork (which usually involves enrolling you in a Wing Chun kung fu class). Fortunately, TERPS specialists typically put all the frequencies needed for holding on the plan view, to make your job easier. This is certainly the case here, with the LAX frequency shown along the 145 degree radial.

Since we've already discussed feeder routes that lead you onto the approach structure, how would you transition onto the ILS approach if you were at or approaching SLI VOR? (sorry, but saying, "I'd pout until my flight instructor took over and did it himself," is not an acceptable answer). Recalling our earlier discussion, you'd need to find a medium-thick line having altitude, direction, and distance associated with it. Looking carefully (with your electron microscope), you'll see that there is such a line on the 200 degree radial from SLI VOR (Figure 3, position A). Because of the small space, the information associated with this feeder route is referenced by an arrow from the bottom right of the route.

In this case, you'd fly at a minimum of 2,000 feet for 2 miles on the 200 degree radial from SLI VOR until crossing the localizer. Then you'd enter the holding pattern and reverse course. This is a holding pattern used in lieu of a procedure turn and its use is mandatory because the letters *NoPT* are not shown on the route.

From Seal Beach VOR (there are no seals at Seal Beach, either), you'd fly to BECCA, make a teardrop entry then track the localizer inbound and descend to the next allowable altitude. You typically would not need to or be expected to make an additional circuit in the holding pattern when reversing course here. However, if you find yourself too high and need more time to descend and/or set yourself up for the approach, you could ask the controller for an additional turn in the holding pattern. If you just decide to make turns in excess of the teardrop entry and don't ask ATC's permission, this would be a turn for the worse. ATC doesn't expect you to do more than the entry. So don't do it without asking, lest you overstress the controller, causing him to retire early at Casa del Wingnut.

When approaching BECCA from SLI on the 200 degree radial, and after you cross the localizer, you could descend to 1,600 feet, the minimum altitude for the holding pattern as shown in the chart's profile view (Figure 2, position H). We'll soon talk about what to do once you're inbound on the localizer, so stay tuned.

How would you transition onto the approach structure if you were at MIDDS intersection (Figure 2, position I)? Remember, intersections shown standing alone on an

Feeder Route from SLI VOR

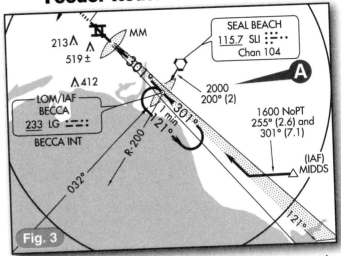

Sometimes feeder routes that take you onto the approach structure are difficult to identify on the chart, as shown by the route from SLI VOR to the outer marker.

approach chart are usually intersections found on the IFR enroute chart (Figure 4, position A). You could be heading toward MIDDS intersection on an airway and be cleared for the ILS Runway 30 approach to Long Beach. This means you'd need to know how to get from MIDDS onto the approach course (the localizer, in this instance).

How would you make this transition? Looking at MIDDS, there is a thick line routing that leads you to the localizer. A minimum altitude of 1,600 feet is associated with that routing. The means by which you'd navigate this short route isn't apparent, is it? Is this the punishment you get for touching a chicken? No. When a heading is shown for a route and no electronic means of navigating that route is apparent, the route is flown on your heading indicator. In other words, this is a *dead reckoning* route, except that you're not expected to correct for wind drift when flying it. That's right amigo. If you were at MIDDS and cleared for the approach, you'd fly a heading of 255 degrees for 2.6 nautical miles until intercepting the localizer. Then you'd track the localizer inbound.

Feeder Route from MIDDS

Intersections found standing alone on approach charts are usually found on the IFR enroute chart.

Cleared Confusion

On many occasions, ATC will vector you to a published route on an instrument approach. This will often be the main approach procedure track itself at which the airplane in positions Z and Y is heading, but sometimes it will be a route leading to the approach procedure (position X). In both situations, pilots are sometimes confused as to how low they can go when ATC issues those magic words, *cleared for the approach*. So here's the skinny on this important point.

According to FAR 91.175h(2), when radar vectors are used to take you to a portion of an instrument approach procedure, you will most likely not be operating on any published route (one showing a minimum altitude, direction and distance) as shown by all three airplanes (positions Z, X and Y). When this happens and you receive an approach clearance, maintain the last altitude you were given until you are established on a segment of a published route or instrument approach procedure, provided that ATC hasn't assigned you a different altitude in the interim.

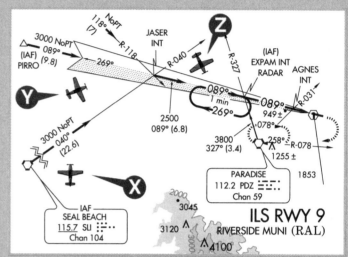

This means you shouldn't change from the altitude ATC last gave you during the vector until your airplane is on a feeder (flyable) route that shows a minimum altitude, direction and distance. In the case of the airplane in position Z, this altitude is 2,500 feet from JASPER; for the airplane in position Y, this altitude is 3,000 feet from PIRRO and in the case of the airplane in position X, this altitude is 3,000 feet from SLI VOR.

Once established on this route, you may descend to the published altitudes shown. These altitudes allow you to descend within each succeeding route or approach segment as you make your way to the airport. Of course, if ATC assigns a different altitude for any portion of that ensuing route, then you should follow ATC's directive.

Upon reaching the final approach course or fix, you may either complete the instrument approach in accordance with the published instrument procedure or continue a surveillance or precision radar approach to a landing, if you've made arrangements for such an approach. As a final note, if ATC vectors you across an approach course and an approach clearance hasn't been issued, you should maintain your last assigned heading and query the controller.

Dead Reckoning IFR Routes

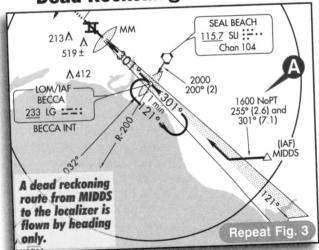

A dead reckoning route from MIDDS to the localizer is flown by heading only.

Dead reckoning segments are usually short and are built with enough tolerance so that even in strong winds you won't drift into obstacles or higher terrain. If this weren't the case there'd have to be a note next to MIDDS (Figure 3, position A) saying, "Wear helmet when approaching from MIDDS." After intercepting the localizer, you'd initially track the localizer by flying 301 degrees for 7.1 nautical miles until reaching BECCA intersection. The letters *NoPT* on the MIDDS routing indicate that no procedure turn (i.e., reversing course in the holding pattern) is allowed on this approach without specific permission from the controller. After all, why would you want to reverse course, when you're already on the inbound

course at the desired minimum altitude? When cleared for the approach from MIDDS intersection without restrictions, you simply fly the dead reckoning route, intercept the localizer, track it inbound, intercept the glideslope and start down on the approach. Where would you expect to intercept the glideslope? Let's find out.

The profile view shown in Figure 5, position C indicates that the minimum holding pattern altitude is 1,600 feet. The gray sloping area in this view represents the glideslope. This picture clearly shows that the glideslope is intercepted at

The ILS Chart's Profile View

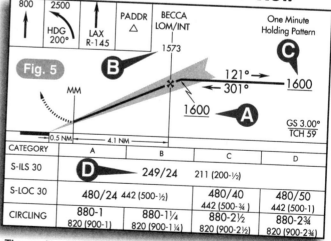

The profile view of the ILS chart shows the glideslope intercept altitude (1,600 feet, position A), the altitude at which the glideslope crosses the outer marker (1,573 feet, position B) and the minimum holding altitude (1,600 feet, position C).

Checking the Glideslope for Accuracy

The Captain of an air taxi cargo flight discovered that diamonds aren't every pilot's best friend.
After getting established on the ILS, I was cleared for the approach. I had only been on the localizer for about 15 seconds before I got the Glideslope (GS) indication. The GS needle moved from the bottom towards the "diamond" (that indicates ON the GS), and stopped on the "diamond." Assuming I was on the GS, I started my descent. Decision height intercept altitude was 1,500 feet and I was coming up on 1,000 feet when Tower gave me an altitude alert and advised me to climb back to 1,500.
When the avionics shop checked the GS, they found the GS needle physically sticking on the "diamond," which is a plastic piece protruding on the GS scale (not a painted mark). This was leaving NO GS warning flags to indicate a problem. Just a picture-perfect ILS with a not-so-perfect possible outcome had we been in weather down to minimums!

NASA Callback Report

1,600 feet before reaching BECCA intersection. At 1,600 feet, you intercept the glideslope and begin your descent. To make this clearer, the 1,600 foot value at the glideslope interception point has a zig-zag arrow next to it (Figure 5, position A). This identifies 1,600 feet as the official glideslope intercept altitude. Take notice of the 1,573 foot value just below the letters BECCA (Figure 5, position B. This is the altitude at which you should cross BECCA intersection if you're on the glideslope. With your glideslope needle centered, your altimeter should read 1,573 feet at BECCA because this is the altitude at which the glideslope officially intercepts BECCA intersection. If that's not your number, don't reach up and twist the altimeter's knob to make it agree.

This altitude is a practical means of checking your glideslope and/or altimeter setting (and your mind) for accuracy. If your altimeter is set incorrectly or your glideslope is reading in error, you'll see it here. If a serious error exists, then update your altimeter setting. If that's not the problem, you might want to execute a missed approach and try another approach (even if you're wearing a thick helmet or a headset with a mattress on it).

Consider the following situation. If, during a radar vector onto the localizer, ATC can't get you where they want you altitude-wise, you could end up tracking the localizer inbound at an altitude that puts you way above the glideslope. Or, you might be cleared for the approach via your own navigation (say from over SLI VOR) and you just can't descend quickly enough to 1,600 feet to intercept the glideslope from below. You would be high and might have to intercept the glideslope from above (otherwise known as the *High and the Mighty* technique). The problem with this is that false glideslope signals can sometimes lurk, calling with their siren songs (siren songs aren't really sung with sirens, you know) from beyond the actual glideslope.

These erroneous glideslopes require excessive descent rates to maintain. By checking your altitude as you cross the outer marker, as well as checking your descent rate against what you'd normally expect for the approach, you can tell if you're flying a false glideslope signal. If your approach path is aerodynamically similar to that flown by a falling manhole cover, you're probably tracking a false glideslope. Intercept from below and you never need worry about false glideslope signals.

Here is where things become really interesting. While all the approaches we've discussed so far have MDAs, the ILS doesn't. Instead, it has something known as a *DA* or *decision altitude* (sometimes still referred to as *DH* or *decision height*). This is the lowest altitude to which you're allowed to descend before making a decision to either continue the approach (if you meet the landing minimum requirements) or make a missed approach. The missed approach point on an ILS is always the DA shown in the minimums section.

DA for the straight-in ILS Runway 30 approach is 249 feet (Figure 5, position D). Approach chart designers try and build the approach so that DA is reached at or close to the same time you reach the middle marker. It's kind of like a good cook trying to complete the meal by the time the dinner guests are hungry, which was always easy for me since Pop-Tarts take only a minute to prepare. If the two match—the DA and MM in this instance, not hungry guests and Pop-Tarts—then you have the best of both worlds. This allows you to have an aural warning that you're approaching this decision point. (If you get an oral warning, it had better be coming from your dentist.) Sometimes this placement works, sometimes it doesn't. In the case of Long Beach, it appears that the missed approach (the upward sloping dashed line) begins at the middle marker, telling us that the middle marker and DA are in about the same spot.

Let's learn a little more about how ILS minimums, specifically the required visibility, play a part in this approach.

Visibility Minimums for the ILS Approach

Notice that to the right of the S-ILS-30 DA is the RVR value of 24 (Figure 5, position D), meaning 2,400 feet (RVR, or runway visual range, is an electronically derived estimate of the visibility in hundreds of feet that a pilot should have horizontally down the runway from the approach end—supposedly—in a moving airplane). Special instruments known as *transmissometers* assess this value and report it to ATC. To legally descend below DA (or MDA) and land the airplane, you must have the required in-flight visibility shown on the approach chart.

The fly in the "approach" ointment here is that RVR is an electronically derived assessment of the visibility (in hundreds of feet) a few feet off the ground, most often beginning at the approach end of the runway. It's not nor can it even be considered to be the flight visibility measured horizontally (or nearly so) between your position at DA

ILS DA Section

The Captain of a DeHaviland Dash 8 on approach into an East Coast airport reports a different sort of "conditional clearance":

We had briefed for the ILS approach. We were tracking inbound on the localizer and Approach Control kept us high (above glideslope) before clearance for the approach. I elected to fly the approach manually to facilitate intercepting the glideslope from above. We contacted the tower at the final approach fix [FAF]. Not long after the FAF, I heard the tower issue a caution to the aircraft ahead of us that there was a ship in the channel with a height of 150 feet. The tower controller then issued the same "Caution, ship in channel, 150 feet in height," to us. At this point we were over halfway between the FAF and the runway. While concentrating on flying the approach, in the back of my mind I was trying to consider the significance of the caution. We continued the approach and made contact with the approach lights just above the normal decision altitude of 218 feet. After landing...we looked over the approach chart and realized the "conditional DA" [359 feet] for tall vessels may have applied. I did not know what height constitutes a "tall vessel." It is not written anywhere that I could find. I asked clearance delivery and they did not know, but they checked and told us it was 85 feet or higher. Oops!

We were clearly remiss in not catching the "conditional" DA during the briefing, but there were several issues that "set the trap" for us. First, there was no mention of ships in the channel until we were well inside the FAF. Second, the Controller did not use the terminology "tall vessels," which gave us an ambiguous caution message.

The reporter recommends that ATC use the phraseology, "Tall vessels in approach area," which is the wording found on both NACO and commercial approach plates. This terminology would likely have triggered recognition among the flight crew that the higher, "conditional" decision altitude was required.

NASA Callback Report

and the runway threshold itself. This is a problem. Why? In Figure 5, notice that the missed approach point coincides approximately with the middle marker position, which is 0.5 nm from the runway threshold (1 nautical mile equals approximately 6,080 feet). That's approximately 3,000 feet from the runway threshold. When you reach a DA of 294 feet on this approach, the only way to know the flight visibility between your position and the runway threshold that happens to be 3,000 feet ahead of you is to estimate it yourself.

This is why the FAA is very specific in saying that you must have the required "flight" visibility shown on the approach chart to descend below DA and to land. So where's the required flight visibility on this chart? The answer is, it's the RVR but only after you convert it to a value useful to you as shown in Figure 6.

In the time/distance table shown, an RVR of 2,400 feet equates to ½ statute mile visibility (yes, flight visibilities are always measured in statute miles despite the chart distances being in nautical miles. Perhaps the FAA thinks that people are better at estimating a statute mile over a nautical one—except for people flying airships). To legally descend below the DA on this approach, you need ½ statute mile of forward visibility (1/2 mile x 5,280 feet/statute mile), which equates to approximately 2,600 feet (Figure 7). Obviously we're talking about forward visibility in the direction of the runway here, not upward in the direction of the constellation Taurus, the Bull, which would be a lot of bull if you think about it. You must also maintain this visibility all the way to touchdown. If you have less than ½ statute mile visibility at any time during your descent to land, then a missed approach is mandatory, as well as just plain smart, too.

As an additional point here, if the RVR equipment at the airport were inoperative, the tower would estimate the visibility. This works out fine since you, the pilot, are always thinking of visibility in terms of fractions of miles, not in terms of RVR. Right about now you're probably wondering, "Why have RVR if you make your own estimate of flight visibility at DA?"

Good question, grasshopper. It appears your college philosophy class is finally paying off. RVR does offer a horizontal assessment of the flight visibility a pilot should experience in the touchdown zone of the runway. This assessment often, but certainly not always, correlates to the visibility found at DA. I say *often*, because it's not always true. The FAA says that commercial operators like the airlines (they operate under Part 121 of the FARs) and air taxi pilots (they operate under Part 135 of the FARs)

RVR Conversion Table

RVR (feet)	Visibility (statute miles)
1,600	1/4
2,400	½
3,200	5/8
4,000	3/4
4,500	7/8
5,000	1
6,000	1 1/4

Fig. 6

RVR, as stated on approach charts, can be converted to fight visibility indicating the required distance a pilot must see from the cockpit to legally land the airplane as a Part 91 operator.

can't even begin an approach if the RVR is reported to be less than that shown on the approach chart. This doesn't apply to Part 91 operators (that's you since you operate under Part 91 of the FARs).

It is possible, however to find yourself at DA with the required flight visibility shown on the chart while the RVR indicates a smaller value. If that happens, you can legally land as long as you maintain the required flight visibility as seen from your cockpit. Be advised here that if three Part 91 pilots ahead of you executed a missed approach because they couldn't see the runway but you managed to land, you may have some explaining to do if an FAA inspector starts asking questions. In other words, there's a good chance that you actually did land without the required flight visibility. It's doubtful that any excuse you offer will satisfy an inspector in these instances. And saying, "Well, my X-ray vision allowed me see the runway" never works unless you're wearing a cape (then again, if you wear a cape and have X-ray vision, why would you need an airplane to fly?).

Finally, wise student that you are, you're probably wondering how a pilot can be 3,000 feet from the runway in the case of the ILS at Long Beach and be required to have only a minimum of ½ statute mile forward visibility for landing. After all, this means you'll be (3,000-2,600=400) 400 feet shy of seeing the runway from this position. Fear not. The FAA has thought of everything.

As you've already learned, all ILS approaches have an approach lighting system (ALS) that often looks like giant flattened, but well lit Christmas trees that point toward the landing threshold. The purpose of these lights is to help you transition from DA to a safe landing (Figures 8 and 9). Given that approach lights on an ILS typically range from 2,400 feet to 3,000 feet in length, they act as a visual extension of the proper direction for runway alignment, even when you can't see the actual runway. Now you know why FAR 91.175 allows you to descend below DA or MDA without having the runway in sight, as long as you have the approach lights in sight.

In this instance, it's legal to leave DA at Long Beach and use the approach lights to help you transition for landing. Looking at them should provide nearly the same horizon information you'd get if making a visual approach to the same runway. I say *nearly* because nothing beats the real thing. According to FAR 91.175(C)(3)(i), you can use the approach lights for descent if you can't see anything on the approach side of the runway, but there is a limit on how low you can go using these lights as a reference. If you don't have at least one or more of the other nine items

1/2 Mile Flight Visibility From the Cockpit

The picture above shows what one-half mile flight visibility looks like from the cockpit at decision altitude. Believe me when I say that one-half mile isn't much when looked at from DA at approach speed.

At the MM and approaching DA at LGB with 1/2 mile flight visibility during daytime, the approach lights help you find the runway threshold and transition more easily to VFR flight.

While at the MM and approaching DA at LGB with 1/2 mile flight visibility, the approach lights are more clearly visible than the runway threshold, especially at night.

listed in FAR 91.175(C)(3) (those things found of the *approach side* of the runway), then you can't go any lower than 100 feet above the TDZE, unless the red terminating bars or red side row bars are visible.

As you've already learned, these red bars are associated with the ALSF 1 & 2 approach lighting systems. Since these red bars are close to the runway threshold or are strategically placed (as in the case of the ALSF-2 approach lighting system), it's legal to continue your descent to landing knowing that the runway is directly ahead of the red bars (red is important here because red doesn't affect your night vision). Then again, it's assumed here that you'll always have the required visibility for landing, so there should be no excessive risk when descending below 100 feet above the TDZE while using these red bars as a reference. Nevertheless, keep in mind that what's legal to do isn't always what's wise to do.

The only practical reason you might use these bars as a reference for a continued descent is in heavy rain or when the runway is obscured by snow. These phenomena make it difficult to find the runway while still having the required forward visibility. As you can see, if the approach lights were inoperative on this approach, this would present a mighty big problem. That's why you'll want to read the sidebar titled *Inoperative Components* on page 12-15. It will tell you what to do if any of the approach's critical components are inoperative for an approach procedure. Be prepared to find large increases in your visibility minimums if the approach lighting goes kaput.

Finally, how do you know what type of approach lighting (if any) exists? How do you know if anything exists at an airport? Look in a legend somewhere, which works for airplane stuff but not for Bigfoot, UFOs, and the Loch Ness squid. Here's how this works. First, by looking at the airport sketch (or the approach light symbol in the middle part of the briefing area) in Figure 10 you'll see a small symbol at the end of

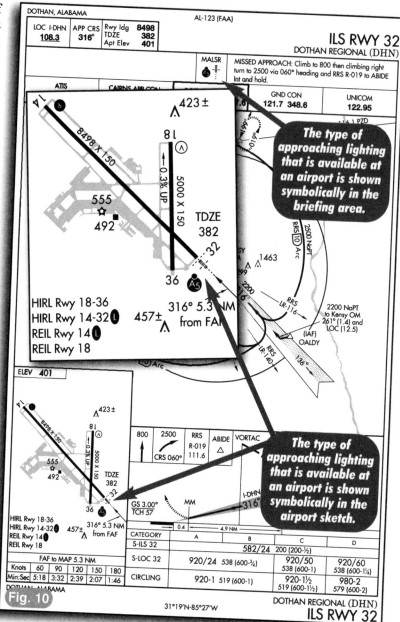

NACO charts typically use a small symbolic representation of the approach lighting system and a circular symbol to identify the type of approach lighting available for that runway. Use of the NACO legend shown in Figure 11 allows easy identification of that symbol.

each runway where the airport's visual aids exist (this includes approach lights and VASIs, too). Each symbol corresponds to an approach lighting symbol found in the legend included in the NACO chart booklet (Figure 11).

In the case of the ILS Rwy 32 to Dothan Regional, Runway 32 has a MALSR (the dot above the A5 symbol indicates that sequenced flashing lights—strobes to those old enough to remember what a disco ball is—are part of the lighting system). The reverse bold (white on black) of any symbol indicates pilot-controlled lighting for that lighting system exists. That means the lights are self-service. Activate them by clicking your mic 7 times in 5 seconds to turn on all the available lighting.

One last thing on the subject of approach lights. Not all pilots like having the strobe lights (the sequenced flashers

or the RAILs) in action. They're intense, and some people find them intensely distracting instead of immensely helpful. If you want the controller to turn these lights off, just use the phrase, "Kill the rabbit." Yes, really, that's the standard terminology, recognized in towers and approach control facilities throughout the land, though we can expect the PETA protestors to object.

My friend Rick Crose (one of the nicest controllers you'll ever meet) tells the story of a Learjet pilot flying practice approaches who called at the outer marker late one night and said, "Orlando Tower, Lear 321, outer marker, bag the bunny."

Rick thought that was funny, and turned off the strobes. On the next approach, the Lear pilot called at the marker and said, "Orlando Tower, Lear 321, outer marker, snare the hare."

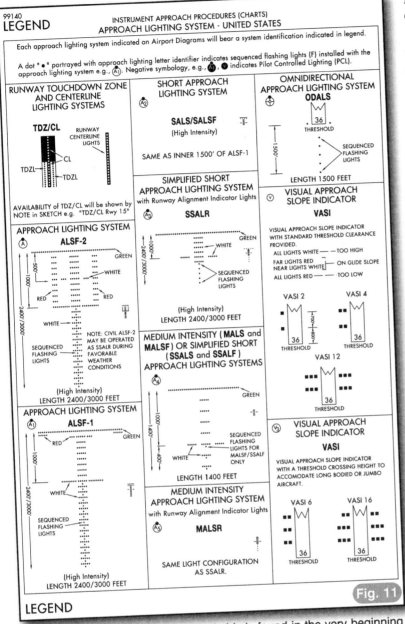

NACO's legend for an airport's visual aids is found in the very beginning of the approach chart booklet.

marker, the airplane's glideslope antenna would cross the threshold at 59 feet AGL.

Now, for those of us in smaller airplanes, the vertical difference between where the glideslope antenna is mounted and where the pilot is seated doesn't amount to enough to worry about. They don't call them "small airplanes" for nothing. The vertical difference does become important if you're flying a widebody (that's a jet, not the pilot's shape). For the really big boys, it's essential to know the TCH because there could be a large distance between the place where the pilot sits and the location of the glideslope antenna.

In some instances, a pilot might want to fly slightly above the glideslope, depending on the airplane, to keep from striking the landing gear or the bottom of the airplane on some object short of the runway. Just as in the store, "you break it, you buy it" is the applicable policy, and approach lights and ILS antennas are *really* expensive. Nobody wants to phone home and tell the chief pilot they just ate three approach lights or an ILS shed at LAX. And you can imagine how much fun this would be for the passengers in the rear of the airplane. It would mean the airlines would have to add another class of airline service, giving them first class, coach, economy and grinding.

Below the slanting gray glideslope symbol are the lateral distances from the LOM and MM to the runway threshold. It's 4.1 nm from BECCA to the MM and 0.5 nautical miles from the MM to the runway threshold. The total distance from BECCA to the runway threshold is 4.6 nm (see, you *do* use math in aviation). Why is this important? Because on some ILS approaches, it's possible to fly the approach without using the glideslope (otherwise known as a *localizer approach*) and doing so often requires that you identify the missed approach point by timing from the FAF.

Rick thought that was funny too, but he wanted to beat the pilot at his own humor game. On the next approach, Rick was ready. The moment he heard the Lear pilot key his mic and say, "Orlando Tower," Rick reached for the strobe switch and turned it off. But not before hearing the pilot yell out, "Bang! Bang! Bang!"

Rick doesn't say a thing, and then the pilot continues his transmission with, "Lear 321, outer marker, that was a good shot, wasn't it?"

Now you've seen the light.

Essential Glideslope Details

In the bottom right-hand corner of the profile view (Figure 12, position A), you can see that the glideslope angle for this approach is 3 degrees and the *TCH* or *threshold crossing height* of the glideslope is 59 feet. If your airplane remained on the glideslope past the middle

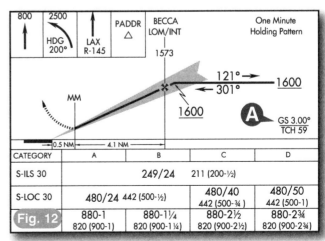

The profile view provides essential information on glideslope intercept altitudes, TCH's, distances to runway, etc.

Below the S-ILS 30 minimums for the ILS Rwy 30 approach to Long Beach, is another set of minimums (Figure 13, position A). These are localizer minimums, (S-LOC 30) meaning that you fly this approach without use of the glideslope, using the localizer for lateral guidance only. In this instance, you no longer descend to a DA (decision altitude), since no glideslope is involved. Instead, you descend to an MDA or *minimum descent altitude*, which is always the name of the minimums associated with a non-precision approach. The MDA for the S-LOC 30 at Long Beach is 480 feet. As you already know, some approaches have missed approach points determined by time. The MAP on this localizer approach to Long Beach is based on timing from the FAF (Figure 14). This is one reason

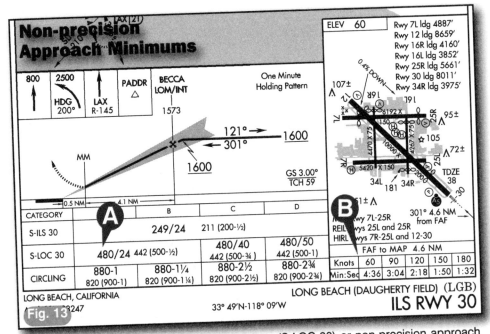

Below the ILS minimums you'll find the localizer (S-LOC 30) or non-precision approach minimums (position A). In the case of Long Beach above, the MDA is 480 feet and the required flight visibility is 1/2 mile (2,400 feet RVR converted).

why you always want to start timing when you cross over the FAF (BECCA in this instance) regardless of whether or not you're using the glideslope. Read more about how to do this in the sidebar on The 6 Ts.

One reason you might have to do a localizer approach and not the full ILS would be if the glideslope transmitter became inoperative. Perhaps someone accidentally backed into it with a car, or stole a critical part of its electronics in a silly attempt to make a vintage 1945 TV set work again. Just kidding on the last one. The truth is that sometimes electronics just fail and you have to be prepared to handle the problem if it arises.

The missed approach point for most non-precision approaches (approaches flown without use of a glideslope)

is normally found at the runway threshold (or near it). You can confirm this by looking at the time/distance table in the bottom right of Figure 13, position B. The distance from the FAF or final approach fix to the MAP is 4.6 nm. The FAF for non-precision approaches is always located where you find the Maltese Cross in the profile view (Figure 15). (For precision approaches, the FAF is the point where you intercept the glideslope and begin your final descent for landing.) This is the fix where you begin your final descent to the MDAs shown in the minimums section of your approach chart.

At 90 knots groundspeed, it will take 3 minutes and 4 seconds to travel from the FAF to the MAP, as shown in the time/distance table. That's why instrument pilots always start their stopwatch at the FAF when the approach has a MAP based on time (this is usually part of the *six-T* sequence discussed in the 6T Sidebar). At the end of 3:04 (that's time, not scripture), if you don't have the required visibility and at least

The Non-precision "Localizer" Approach

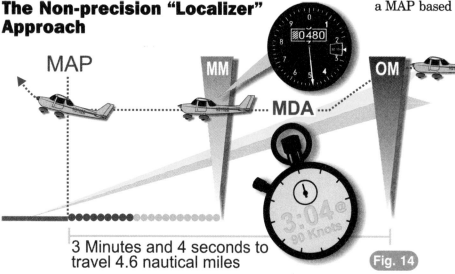

3 Minutes and 4 seconds to travel 4.6 nautical miles

Non-precision approaches may have their missed approach point determined by timing from the final approach fix. This is the case with the Long Beach localizer approach shown in Figure 13.

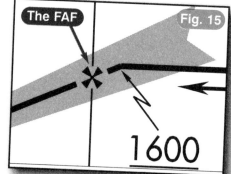

The FAF or final approach fix is identified by the Maltese Cross.

Time for Ts? A Verbal Checklist at the FAF

As an aspiring instrument pilot you'll most likely hear your CFI saying something about T's. No, he's not T-zing you here, either. There is a memory aid pilots use when when flying instrument approaches or in holding patterns. The memory aid is called the 6 T's and they stand for: TIME, TURN, TWIST, THROTTLE, TALK and TRACK.

Suppose you're inbound to OCN VOR in the holding pattern (Figure 16, position Z). You're cleared for the approach. The missed approach point on this approach is determined by timing from the VOR. So when you're over the FAF, which is the Oceanside VOR for the VOR-A approach to Oceanside, you've got to remember to do several little things. This is where the 6-T memory aid comes in.

The first thing you'll do when crossing the FAF is to TIME by either noting the time or clicking the button on your stop watch. At 90 knots ground speed (Figure 16, position Y), you should reach the MAP in 2 minutes and 16 seconds.

Next you'll TURN to a heading of 096 degrees (Figure 16, position X), which is the direction of the course outbound from the VOR and inbound to the airport.

Next you'll TWIST, meaning that you'll twist your VOR's OBS to a new value of 096 degrees.

Next you'll THROTTLE, meaning that you'll reduce the throttle to an appropriate value so as to begin a descent to the circling MDA of 1,140 feet (Figure 16, position W).

Then you'll TALK by reporting to the tower that you're inbound, or, in the case of Oceanside, you'll make a radio report to the pattern traffic that you're inbound on the VOR approach.

Finally, you'll TRACK, meaning that you'll turn slightly to ensure that you intercept the 096 degree radial outbound from the station.

Now, some approaches don't require that you time because their missed approach points are based on some navigational reference such as GPS, DME or reaching a DA, such as with an ILS. And some approaches don't require that you make a turn or even rotate the OBS at the FAF. But that's OK. The 6-T memory aid is still useful in that it's always good practice to run through the entire sequence when you're at the FAF on any instrument approach, even though you won't need to do any or all of the Ts.

For instance, on an ILS, when I'm at the final approach fix I'll still note my time. Why? If for some reason I'm asked to make a circling approach to another runway (assuming this ILS approach chart has circling minimums) I may need to identify the missed approach point by time. The ILS Rwy 30 approach to Long Beach is a good example.

Suppose you were descending on the glideslope past BECCA (Figure 13 on the previous page) and suddenly have your glideslope fail (not likely but a good example, nevertheless). Since the ILS to LGB has non-precision minimums (i.e., localizer minimums) you could continue the approach to the localizer MDA of 480 feet. The problem here is that the missed approach point for the localizer is determined by time to the runway threshold from the FAF. If you did your six T's at the FAF, you're now able to continue as a localizer approach. This is why it's always good to run through the six T's at the FAF, even if you're flying the full ILS approach.

When flying holding patterns, you will find the 6 T's a useful reminder to begin a turn to the specific entry heading; start the time upon entering the holding pattern entry (this T is out of sequence but it's a good reminder, nevertheless); twist the VOR omni bearing selector to track the inbound leg of the holding pattern; throttle to the specific holding airspeed; talk to the controller to report entering holding; and track the inbound course. In fact, the 6 T's should be used when reaching an intersection, regardless of whether or not a turn is required.

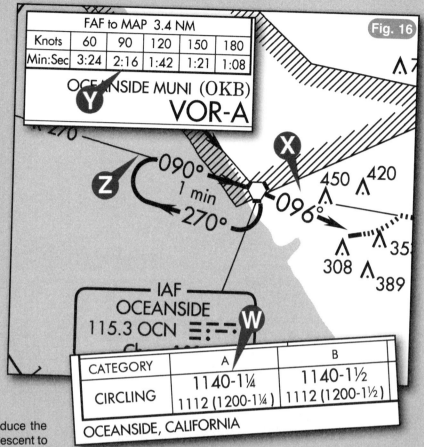

one of the required items listed in FAR 91.175 in sight, then you're required to execute the missed approach procedure.

Just to clarify an important point here, a missed approach means you must do one thing first: climb. It's just like being at a party and asking a girl to dance. If she says no, then you make your missed approach and move away to safer ground. Although one time I asked a girl to

dance and she said, no. I persisted. She finally said yes and we danced, then I noticed she kept getting taller. I finally discovered she had a wooden leg and I was twisting her in the wrong direction. A missed approach will often take you to a holding fix. From there, you and the controller will either work out the routing for another approach at the airport or a route to another airport, perhaps the one you filed as an alternate in your flight plan.

Making an Early Missed Approach

All missed approaches are designed to protect you from obstacles. This protection is not as fantastic as you might think. The missed approach protected area consists of an upwardly sloped plane that ascends uniformly at the rate of one foot vertically for each 40 feet horizontally (40:1) (Figure 17). This sloped surface starts at the missed approach point. It extends outward 15 miles

Fig. 17

for a straight-out missed approach. This climb plane translates into a gradient of 152 feet per nautical mile. Regulations require that no obstacles penetrate this upward sloping surface. When the missed approach is initiated, however, you are expected to climb so as to remain above (not at) this 40:1 sloped surface. Thus, you are expected to climb at least 200 feet per nautical mile unless otherwise noted. This means you will have an additional increasing altitude buffer of 48 foot/nm above the extended missed approach surface.

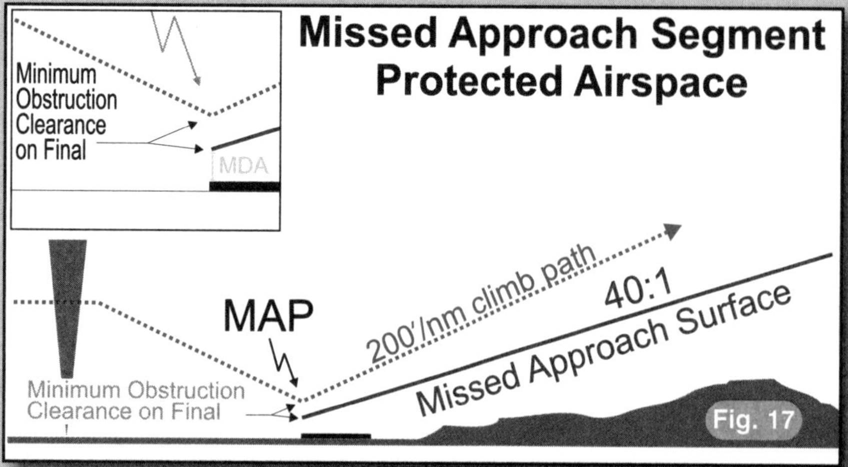

At 120 knots ground speed, or 2 miles per minute, you will need to climb at a minimum of 400 feet per minute to maintain that ever-increasing altitude buffer above the missed approach surface.

The altitude protection you start with above the missed approach surface is based on being on final approach at the MDA for the particular approach procedure being used (Figure 17).

If you make a missed approach on an ILS prior to reaching decision altitude or a non-precision approach prior to reaching the missed approach point, start a climb and proceed to the point where the missed approach would normally begin before making any turns. Since the missed approach point on an ILS is based on being at decision altitude while on the glideslope, you might have a difficult time finding this point. Fortunately, there is a way to handle this difficulty. The solution lies in understanding that the glideslope normally (not always) intersects the middle marker at decision altitude. So it's a safe bet to begin your climb and overfly the middle marker before making any required turns. If the marker equipment doesn't work, doesn't exist, or isn't installed on the aircraft, you can approximate the position of the ILS missed approach point by time. You need only start your timer at the FAF and fly to the non-precision missed approach point (and that's why it's good to do the 6T's covered in the previous sidebar at the FAF when flying an ILS approach). So proceed to the missed approach point (or somewhere close to it) before beginning any turns.

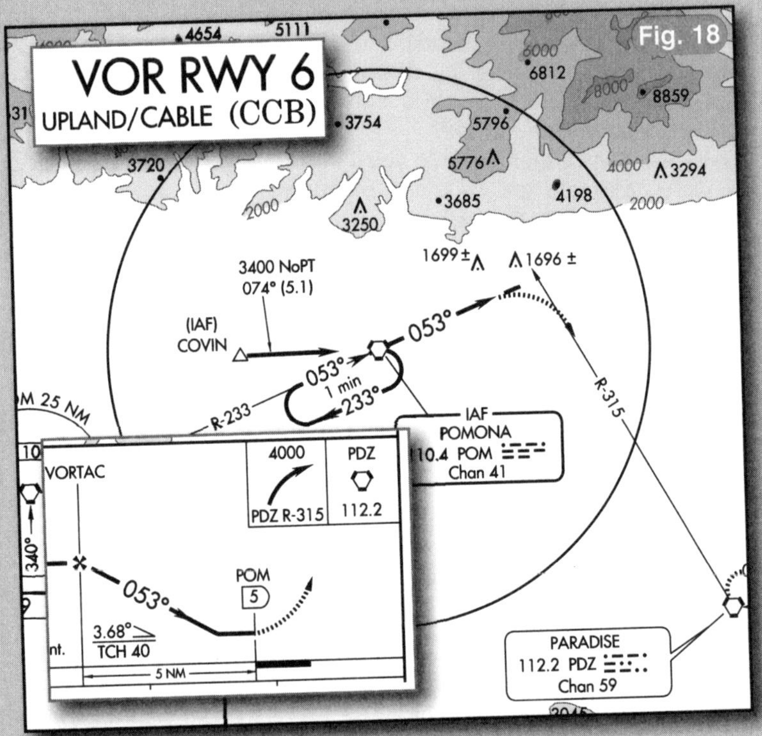

Figure 18 is the VOR Rwy 6 approach to Upland/Cable airport. As you can see, the missed approach

point is on the runway threshold. The missed approach requires that a turn be made to intercept the 315 radial to PDZ VOR. If you didn't fly to the missed approach point and turned to intercept the radial early, you'd be cutting diagonally across uncharted space and might end up with a space between your teeth if you hit something.

Now, in the immortal words of rock and roll legend Chubby Checker, let's add a slight "twist" to this approach. Suppose you've been cleared for the ILS Runway 30 approach at Long Beach and want to fly the non-precision portion of this approach. In other words, you won't fly the glideslope but will, instead, track the localizer and descend to the MDA. (This is a subtle point but it's worth noting. Some airports have a separate published localizer approach. Long Beach doesn't. Therefore,

if you ask for the Runway 30 Localizer approach into Long Beach the controller may say that there is no such published approach, and he'd be correct. If no separate localizer approach chart is published and you want to fly this type of approach, then ask to fly the ILS and use the non-precision minimums.)

At the FAF, you begin your six Ts and, after contacting the tower, you're told to circle to land on Runway 12. What altitude can you now descend to? Yes, this now becomes a circling approach, which is also a non-precision approach because it doesn't require use of the glideslope. If you fit into the Category A minimum section (Figure 19, position A), then you descend to an MDA of 880 feet and now need 1 sm of in-flight visibility for this approach.

More than likely, you'll hear the approach controller provide the circle-to-land instructions long before you reach the FAF, but it's possible to hear a controller issue this instruction when you're inside the FAF (although this would be bad form and might confuse a pilot in much the same way my dad used to confuse me as a kid when he told me to pick up my feet when I walked. How can you do that without tipping over?).

Most of the time ATC will let you know that pilots are circling to

Circling Approach Minimums

CATEGORY	A	B	C	D
S-ILS 30	249/24	211 (200-½)		
S-LOC 30	480/24 442 (500-½)		480/40 442 (500-¾)	480/50 442 (500-1)
CIRCLING	880-1 820 (900-1)	880-1¼ 820 (900-1¼)	880-2½ 820 (900-2½)	880-2¾ 820 (900-2¾)

LONG BEACH, CALIFORNIA   33° 49'N-118° 09'W

Fig. 19

ELEV 60

Rwy 7L ldg 4887'
Rwy 12 ldg 8659'
Rwy 16R ldg 4160'
Rwy 16L ldg 3852'
Rwy 25R ldg 5661'
Rwy 30 ldg 8011'
Rwy 34R ldg 3975'

MIRL Rwy 7L-25R
REIL Rwys 25L and 25R
HIRL Rwys 7R-25L and 12-30

FAF to MAP 4.6 NM

Knots	60	90	120	150	180
Min:Sec	4:36	3:04	2:18	1:50	1:32

LONG BEACH (DAUGHERTY FIELD) (LGB)
ILS RWY 30

Below the ILS minimums you'll find the circling approach minimums (position A). In the case of Long Beach above, the circling MDA is 880 feet and the required flight visibility is one statute mile.

land before you even begin the approach. It's nevertheless possible (although very unlikely) to be cleared for the ILS Runway 30 approach and have just begun your descent on the glideslope when you hear that you are cleared to circle to land north of the airport on Runway 25 right. If so, this is no longer a precision approach because you're no longer flying the glideslope down to a DA.

Instead, you would descend to the circling MDA of 880 feet, level off, and fly to the MAP (or you could descend on the glideslope and level off at the MDA. It's not necessary to stay on the glideslope now, since you're descending to an MDA). As a matter of practice, always start timing as you cross the FAF on a precision (ILS) approach. That way, if you are asked to circle you'll have a time reference established and can transition safely to the circling MDA.

What's circling to land all about? The typical reason pilots are instructed to circle to land is that the airport's active runways doesn't have its own instrument approach. In other words, a wind shift may require the controller to change the landing runway. In the case of Long Beach, if the active runway is 30 and the wind shifts in favor of Runway 12, there's a problem because there is no approach to Runway 12. Some airports have approaches to alternate runways. Long Beach doesn't. So the only way you're going to get there is to perform the maneuver known as *circle to land*. For those under the impression this involves something with a compass and a protractor, let's talk a bit more.

How do you circle to land? Well, you often have a lot of discretion, and no guidance (at least none of the electronic kind). A circling approach is IFR improv in the sky; strictly

When Circling Goes Bad

The "What's that tree doing there?" phrase is one of the nine early warning signs that a circling approach has gone bad.

pilot nav. You're on your own, Buckaroo. Think how exciting this is when you're operating in very low visibility, at an airport you've never seen before. Does it give you a hint when I tell you that commercial airlines are uniformly *prohibited* by regulation from making circle-to-land approaches? And it's not because those pro pilots can't fly in a circle, either (often, it's their signature maneuver). It's just easy to bend an airplane on local obstacles, despite a pilot's skill, while circling close to the ground.

My advice is to avoid straying away far from the runway complex. Remember, Stan, you've got no plan. This is freelance flight, and keeping the airport tight and in sight would be a really good idea. Remember, too, that you don't really know what's Out There. Think of it as one of those ancient maps, in which areas beyond the immediate town were marked, "Here there be Dragons." I would certainly never get farther from the airport than the minimum required landing *visibility*. For instance, the Category A circling visibility minimum at Long Beach is 1 sm (Figure 20, position A). I'd stay within one mile of the runway complex, knowing it would enhance my chances of survival. Think of this as circling to land with the Darwin option.

If you need a minimum of one mile visibility and have that, why go where the dragons live? You *know* you have one mile of visibility; you *don't* know if you have 1.1 or 1.5 miles of see-through space.

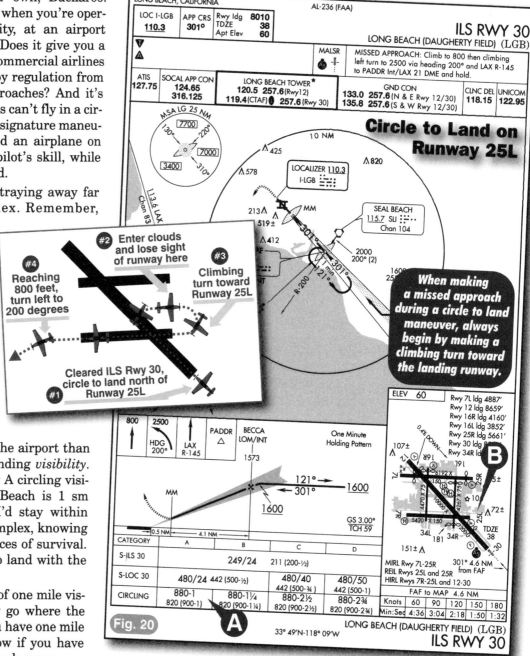

Apparently short on excitement in their lives, some pilots up the ante by opting for a circle-to-land approach *at night*. This is also known as *declining* the Darwin option. Circling to land at night under very low visibility conditions is downright risky. It's easy to lose sight of the runway, and because of the difficulty in identifying a horizon, it's even easier to lose control of the airplane. More than one pilot who wasn't skilled at flying by the seat of his pants was unable to circle while keeping an eye on the runway and control the airplane at the same time. These aren't pretty accidents.

When circling to land, when should you leave the circling MDA and begin your descent for landing? My advice is to wait until you're aligned (or nearly so) with the runway and have identified a good VASI signal. Fortunately, many airports have VASIs on their instrument runways. You just need to make sure you don't mistake the flashing

lights of a cop car for the VASI. This should be easy, because the VASI lights shouldn't be chasing a bad guy along a road or pulling over speeders. If you see a lot of flashing lights at the edge of the runway, the betting at the airport café on the ultimate success of your circling approach went against you.

Sometimes the controller will issue limitations on a circle-to-land procedure. For instance, the approach controller might say, "2132 Bravo, cleared for the ILS Runway 30 approach, circle to land Runway 25L, circle north of Runway 25L." The controller is telling you that he or she *knows* where there are dragons on the south side of the runway. Listen and live.

Finally, suppose you fly into a cloud and lose sight of the runway while circling to land? Oops! It happens. Now you really have your head in the clouds. What should you do? Light candles? Set up a nativity scene on the panel?

When restrictions to circling exist at some airports, this will often be found in the briefing area of the approach chart.

Contact a priest? Give me a call? No. You should fly the missed approach procedure shown on the approach chart. ILS Runway 30 chart (Figure 20).

But what happens if you're turning from right base to final approach for Runway 25L while circling to land at Long Beach and then lose sight of the runway? In this instance, you'd be on the north side of the Runway 25L heading in an easterly direction for a right downwind. The secret here when beginning the missed approach off a circle-to-land clearance is to make *a climbing turn toward the landing runway* (Runway 25L in this instance) and climb

to 800 feet. When reaching 800 feet, you should then follow the rest of the missed approach instructions, meaning you should now turn to a heading of 200 degrees and intercept and fly the LAX 145 radial to PADDR intersection. A climbing turn toward the landing runway always keeps you near the center of the runway complex and away from outlying peripheral obstructions, as well as clear of dragons.

Know before you go. Have in mind exactly which way you are going to turn and what you are going to do to execute a missed approach before starting a circle-to-land approach. Set personal limits, and stick to them. Remember, Darwin is watching.

Some approach charts even carry circle-to-land limitations, as shown in the middle of the briefing area at San Luis in Figure 21, position A. This is because some obstructions, such as mountains close to one side of the runway, are more permanent than others.

Now that you have the ILS approach under your belt, let's examine a slight variation of the ILS approach chart.

Inoperative Components

The landing minimums shown on your chart are based on the concept that everything's up and running in terms of landing system electronics and visual aids (such as VASIs). This is the best-case scenario. If everything is working, you get the best "deal" in terms of landing minimums.

Lose something and in most cases the rules change, as shown in the Inoperative Component Table below. This chart is found at the very beginning of your NACO chart booklet. This chart has four sections, defining different types of approaches with the specific inoperative component/aid listed below and the approach category and required visibility modification shown to the right.

For instance (looking at the top left of the chart, position A), suppose the ALSF-I approach lighting system is inoperative. If your airplane fits either approach category, then you must add ¼ mile to the visibility shown in the approach minimums section of your chart.

Suppose the same component is missing but your approach chart only requires a minimum of 1,800 RVR as indicated in its minimums section. If that's the case, then Section 2 of the Inoperable Component Table applies and the minimum flight visibility for all categories of aircraft increases to 4,000 feet RVR (position B), which translates to an in-flight visibility of ¾ of a statute mile. Pay attention to the difference between increasing the visibility *to* a specific value and increasing the visibility *by* some specific value. For the non-precision approaches shown in Section 3, if the particular approach you're flying has an inoperative MALSR, you must increase the visibility by ½ statute mile (position C). If, the MALS is inoperative for this same approach, you must increase the visibility by ¼ statute mile (position D).

Suppose more than one component on an ILS is inoperative? Perhaps the guy who does the maintenance on the ILS graduated magna cum lucky from maintenance school and happened to miss several classes on "electrons." He just isn't that good at keeping the electrical equipment up (and that's because he keeps knocking it over with his elbow). If that's the case, use the highest minimum required by any single component that is unusable. For instance, in Section 2, if the MALSR system was out and the RVR was also out, the highest visibility increase between the two would be to increase your landing minimums to 4,000 feet or ¾ mile in-flight visibility (position E).

As you can see, not all inoperative components require an increase in visibility minimums. For instance, the marker beacons on an ILS, if inoperative, don't affect your minimums. Nevertheless, a compass locator or precision approach radar (PAR) may be substituted for an inoperative OM or MM. If DME is installed with the ILS, then it may also be used in lieu of an OM.

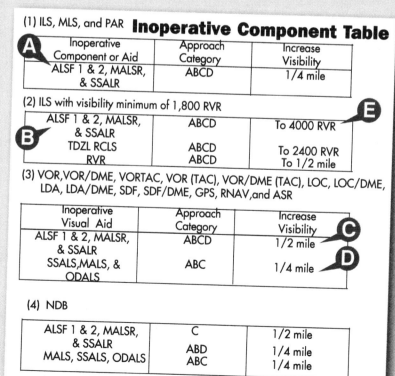

Inoperative Component Table

(1) ILS, MLS, and PAR

Inoperative Component or Aid	Approach Category	Increase Visibility
ALSF 1 & 2, MALSR, & SSALR	ABCD	1/4 mile

(2) ILS with visibility minimum of 1,800 RVR

Inoperative Component or Aid	Approach Category	Increase Visibility
ALSF 1 & 2, MALSR, & SSALR	ABCD	To 4000 RVR
TDZL RCLS	ABCD	To 2400 RVR
RVR	ABCD	To 1/2 mile

(3) VOR, VOR/DME, VORTAC, VOR (TAC), VOR/DME (TAC), LOC, LOC/DME, LDA, LDA/DME, SDF, SDF/DME, GPS, RNAV, and ASR

Inoperative Visual Aid	Approach Category	Increase Visibility
ALSF 1 & 2, MALSR, & SSALR	ABCD	1/2 mile
SSALS, MALS, & ODALS	ABC	1/4 mile

(4) NDB

Inoperative	Approach Category	Increase Visibility
ALSF 1 & 2, MALSR, & SSALR	C	1/2 mile
MALS, SSALS, ODALS	ABD	1/4 mile
	ABC	1/4 mile

The ILS Approach with a Teardrop Procedure Turn

Figure 22 is the ILS Runway 32 approach to Dothan Regional in Alabama. The first things attracting attention in the plan view are the DME arcs and the teardrop course reversal. The teardrop procedure turn is different from the typical barb-type 45-180 procedure turn. While the barb type procedure offers ample opportunity for innovation in execution, the teardrop course reversal must be done exactly as shown. No wiggle room here. The reason is that the obstacle-protected area for the teardrop reversal is much smaller than that for the 45-180 barb-type course reversal. Let's look at the teardrop procedure turn first, and then we'll see how the DME arcs are used.

Starting from over Wiregrass VOR (I bet there's no wiregrass down there, either), there is a teardrop transition from the VOR onto the localizer. If you were approaching the VOR via an airway and ATC cleared you for the approach via the teardrop transition, you'd fly outbound on the 155 degree radial and descend no lower than 2,200 feet as soon as you crossed the station. No minimum altitudes are shown in the plan view for the teardrop procedure turn, but they can be found in the profile view (as can all altitudes associated with routings having a maximum thick line).

The secret to flying this teardrop course reversal is to not let your instructor fly it. Instead, fly outbound within 10 nautical miles of the VOR then turn left to intercept the localizer. You can use either DME or timing to remain with the 10 mile limit. Since this approach doesn't require DME (it's not listed in the title) and if you don't have DME onboard (you should know if you do), then timing from over RRS VOR is the only practical way not to exceed the 10 nautical mile procedure turn limit. This is easy if you fly outbound route at 120 knots, since you'll cover 2 nautical miles a minute if 120 is your groundspeed. Just don't fly outbound more than 5 minutes at this speed before starting your turn inbound.

When flying outbound, you are obviously not required to intercept the DME arc during the turn, either (there is no assumption that you have DME equipment). You only need to ensure that you don't go beyond the 10-mile limit. The teardrop procedure turn isn't a DME arc transition, it's a turning transition onto the approach structure.

According to the profile view in Figure 22, once you've turned inbound on the localizer you are to maintain 2,200 feet, since this is the glideslope intercept altitude. If you were flying the localizer portion of this approach only

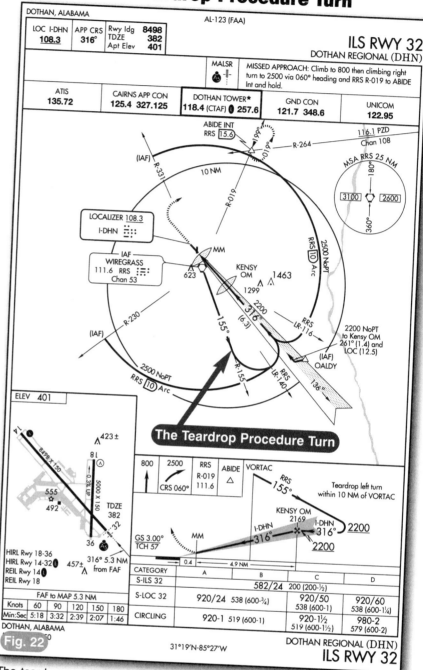

The teardrop procedure turn must be flown as charted to keep pilots away from obstacles residing outside a relatively small protected area. This unique course reversal allows pilots to get lower than would normally be allowed on a typical course reversal.

(perhaps because the glideslope is reported as inoperative on the ATIS), you'd maintain 2,200 feet until crossing KENSEY then commence your descent to an MDA of 920 feet.

As I've mentioned before, the missed approach point on a localizer approach is often located at the runway threshold. To be precise, however, the exact location of the missed approach point is found underneath the airport sketch in Figure 22. It's located 5.3 nm from the FAF. Looking at the mileages underneath the profile view, 4.9 miles plus 0.4 miles equals 5.3 miles, which just happens to be the runway threshold in this instance.

DME Arc Transitions Via Victor Airways

The 230 and 331 degree radials (positions A and B, respectively) from Wiregrass VOR are airways that create IAFs for the beginning of the DME arcs shown in Figure 22. In fact, any radial that intersects a DME arc on an approach chart and creates an IAF will be found to be an airway on a low altitude enroute chart.

Consider this. In some homes, the father wears a tie to dinner. At my uncle's place, he didn't wear a shirt to dinner, which made his tie look really funny. OK, you saw that coming, right? Pilots might not be as quick to catch where the DME source is for DME arcs on an approach chart. Notice that the DME arcs on this approach are generated from the VOR. This makes sense since a localizer can only generate DME signals along its single course.

This localizer frequency box is also missing the letters *Chan*. If you always thought that *Chan* marked the presence of an FAA-approved Chinese takeout nearby, keep thinking. *Chan* shows that the localizer has a DME channel. No *Chan*, no channel, no DME, and definitely no takeout.

Suppose you were inbound to Wiregrass VOR on Victor 7 (the 331 degree radial from RRS VOR) from the northwest as shown in Figure 23, position B and were cleared for the VOR approach via the DME arc. As you begin your *left turn* onto the arc, you circle to the right around the VOR and can descend to 2,500 feet on the arc.

Some people might be tempted to descend to the minimum enroute altitude (MEA) of the airway on which they're flying, which in this instance is 2,400 feet outside SKIPO intersection (we'll cover MEAs in the chapter on enroute charts). In some instances, the airway MEA can be a lot lower than the DME arc minimum altitudes. This is why, when cleared for any DME arc transition, you need to look ahead (especially if you're not psychic—or psychotic) and descend to no lower than the minimum DME arc altitude if that altitude is higher than the airway minimum altitude. This is known as having the right altitude attitude.

As you continue to circle, you'll eventually reach something known as the LR or *lead radial*. The lead radial on the DME arc you're flying is the 116 radial from RRS. When you cross this radial, you're close enough to the localizer course that you should begin a standard-rate turn to intercept the localizer and track it inbound. Since

Intercepting DME Arcs for the Approach

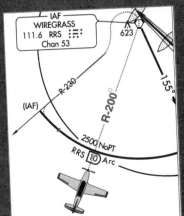

Let's take a minute for a bit of minutiae that's not so minute. Suppose you're 20 miles south of Dothan airport (it's just north of Wiregrass VOR), heading directly to Wiregrass VOR, inbound on the 200 degree radial. ATC gives you these instructions, "2132 Bravo, you're cleared for the ILS Runway 32 approach to Dothan (Figure 22) via the one zero mile arc southwest of Wiregrass VOR. Maintain 4,000 feet until established on the approach."

What would you do here? If you said, "I'd intercept the 10 DME arc on my present course, turn right and descend to 2,500 feet and fly the approach," you'd be incorrect (even though it seems correct). The fact is that it's only legal to use a DME arc for the approach transition if you begin flying the arc at the IAF. In this instance, you're intercepting the arc at somewhere other than an IAF. The only portion of the DME arc that's an IAF is that point made up of the 230 radial from RRS. You can't legally intercept the DME arc from your present position. The only way to legally fly this clearance is to proceed to the VOR and turn outbound on the 230 degree radial, which is an airway (see Figure 23, position A), and fly it to the IAF then turn left and fly the arc (of course, you could always request the teardrop course reversal if you so desire).

And no, you can't ask the controller to let you intercept the arc from where you are starting, either. It's not within the scope of the regulations to allow this. The controller *can* give you a radar vector onto the arc. This would be perfectly legal, but it's entirely at the controller's discretion.

Nevertheless, this isn't a clearance a controller is likely to initiate, because controllers are aware of these rules. A more frequent scenario is that a pilot asks to intercept a DME arc at other than an IAF, oblivious to the fact that you must begin the intercept from an IAF unless you're vectored onto the arc from somewhere else. Now you are in the small minority of pilots who understand how this works, and you won't be one of those asking to do the impossible.

The Radar Vector Approach Clearance

On some occasions, when radar vectoring is available at an airport, ATC will vector you onto the approach course instead of letting you fly the full route clearance (i.e., the feeder routes onto the approach structure). A typical approach clearance would be, *2132 Bravo is four miles southeast of BECCA. Turn left heading 330 degrees. Maintain two thousand until established on the localizer. Cleared ILS Runway three zero approach. Contact the tower 119.4 at the marker.*

The approach clearance (be it a *radar vectored* or *full route clearance* type) normally contains several standard items. When you know what to expect, the anxiety is lessened. First, the controller will usually issue a position report, to help you identify and confirm

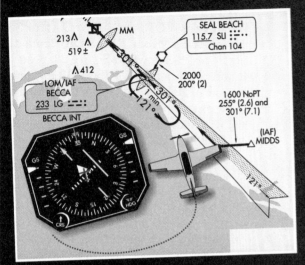

your location. Be alert for discrepancies. If a disagreement exists with the controller's position assessment, do not just sit there fat, dumb and lost. Immediately challenge the controller. And not to a wrestling match, either. This is a serious disagreement, and you two need to work it out real quickly. Tell the controller where *you* think you are. Maybe he's looking at the wrong blip, or she forgot that she'd switched to a different position after coffee break. Whatever the issue, it has to be resolved before you proceed.

The position report also alerts you to how fast things will happen. If you are two miles from the final approach fix, things will happen much more quickly than if you were five miles from the same fix.

Second, if you're being radar vectored, the controller will provide the approach course intercept heading. Start turning the airplane to the intercept heading as soon as it's reasonable for you to do so. This allows more time to set up for the intercept and prevent overshooting. A seasoned IFR pilot learns to prioritize heading, altitude and airspeed control when the approach clearance is issued. Remember that you can be at almost any altitude and still fly the approach course. However, if you don't fly specific headings, you'll never find the approach course and will be left forever wandering (and wondering). After receiving the approach clearance and establishing heading, altitude becomes the next priority, followed by airspeed control.

Third, the controller will provide altitude restrictions for the approach. In the clearance above, you were instructed to maintain 2,000 feet until established on the localizer. Once on the localizer you may descend to the lower altitudes shown for that approach routing/structure. If you're at 4,000 feet and the controller says to intercept the localizer at or above 2,000 feet, then you have the option of maintaining your present altitude or descending to 2,000 feet. It's your choice, but I typically prefer to get down early, if possible.

When controllers clear you for the approach, and do not provide any altitude restrictions, you should maintain your last assigned altitude until established on a segment of the published instrument procedure, which typically means some feeder route. Feeder routes and the approach course will always have an altitude, direction and distance listed on the chart. In many cases, the routes will also be shown by a heavy black line with an arrow pointing in the route's direction. These are routes that can be flown without the aid of radar, since they provide the information needed to get to the approach course and avoid terrain.

Keep in mind that any time you're radar vectored onto the approach structure, a procedure turn (be it the barb-type of a holding pattern used in lieu of a procedure turn) isn't required or expected. As I've said before, controllers like control, and dislike surprises. Don't give them any, lest you find yourself on a one-way vector to a galaxy far, far away.

---

both DME arcs have the letters NoPT associated with them, no procedure turn is allowed on the inbound course. Yes, this is pretty obvious, since the only procedure turn is a teardrop course reversal at the VOR and the localizer doesn't go to the VOR, does it? The FAA leaves nothing to chance for those folks who just love doing procedure turns.

Suppose you flew the ILS, reached DA and didn't meet the requirements of FAR 91.175 and had to make a missed approach? What would be the first thing you'd do? We've already agreed that giving the controls to your flight instructor and begging him to take over isn't an option. You would climb, of course. Think of it this way. You're flying a missed approach because something didn't work out as planned. At that instant, the ground is no longer your friend, and Priority One is putting distance between you and terra firma.

In case you haven't guessed by now, all missed approaches begin with a climb (if they don't, then someone who likes pencils has been messing with your charts. Hunt them down). The briefing area of Figure 22 shows that you'd climb to 800 feet, then make a climbing right

turn to 2,500 feet via a 060 degree heading to intercept the 019 RRS degree radial, and hold at ABIDE as shown. The dotted ground track in the plan view gives you a basic idea of where your airplane should travel in the process, with the holding pattern similarly described by dotted lines.

The Localizer Directional Aid Approach

Now I'm going to give you the straight goods on a crooked approach.

When I first heard the show title, "Walker, Texas Ranger" I thought it was about a lawman who used a walker to chase down (walk down?) really slow criminals. Well, the localizer direction aid kind of sounds like a localizer that's too old to get the job done on its own, doesn't it? It isn't. As you've previously learned, the localizer directional aid (LDA) approach is essentially a localizer that's similar to the localizer associated with a standard ILS approach. Just like a regular localizer, it's between 3 and 6 degrees wide. It's differs primarily in not being perfectly aligned with the approach runway. This is why it's called a localizer "directional aid." Since it's not aligned with the runway it just aids you in getting there.

The Localizer Directional Aid (LDA)

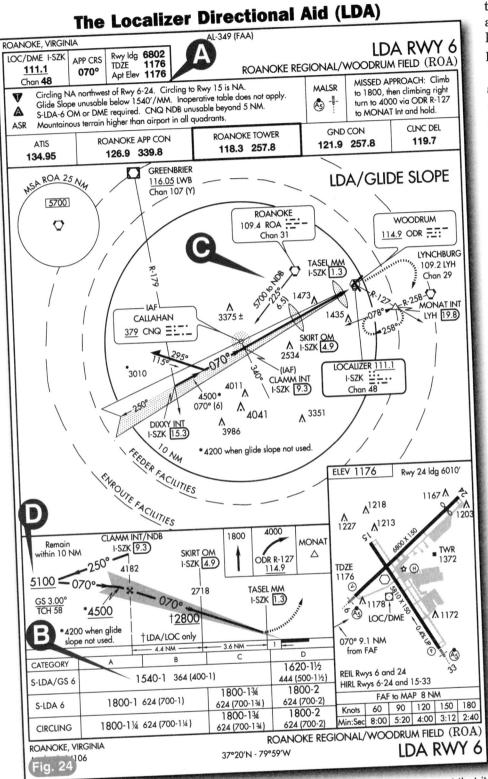

Fig. 24

The Localizer Directional Aid is similar to the localizer in use and accuracy except that it is often not part of a complete ILS approach and it's not aligned with the runway.

the very few LDAs accompanied by a glideslope. Let's examine it closely (feel free to move as close to the page as you'd like).

Briefly, the first thing you should notice is that there are several not-so-brief notes in the briefing area. Circling is not applicable northeast of Runway 6-24 (Figure 24, position A). Nor is circling to land to Runway 15 allowed. A clue to the reasoning behind these restrictions lies in the last note in the strip regarding higher terrain around the airport in all quadrants (the person who wrote the notes would probably like to have mentioned that more than one pilot tried converting a mountain-perched picnic bench into a wooden runway, without success). The glideslope is unusable below 1,540 feet, which just happens to be the decision altitude for the S-LDA/GS 6 approach (Figure 24, position B). Yes, according to the picture in the profile view, this is a decision altitude that has you making your decision (to land or make a missed approach) prior to reaching the middle marker.

The plan view shows a single feeder route from Roanoke (ROA) VOR to Callahan NDB via the 225 degree radial (Figure 24, position C). If you were cleared for the approach from ROA, you'd track outbound on the 225 degree radial until reaching the NDB (which is located within the electronic coverage area of the localizer. In other words, the localizer needle will begin moving toward the center when you're at the NDB even though the NDB doesn't appear to lie directly on the localizer). What would you do from here? Calling your instructor on his cell phone for instructions isn't an option.

The profile view shows that from the Callahan NDB, you'd track outbound on the localizer (remember, you'll have reverse localizer sensing in a direction of 250 degrees unless you're using a properly adjusted HSI), and descend to 5,100 feet (Figure 24, position D). The profile shows that you should remain with 10 nm of CLAMM (or the NDB, since the profile view considers them to be at nearly the same location by the designation CLAMM

In the case of the Roanoke's LDA Runway 6 approach (Figure 24), the approach is about 10 degrees misaligned with the runway (which is not because the installer took a drink before he installed it). Looking at the course arrow in the airport sketch (the black arrow indicating the direction of the inbound course), you get a good idea about the course offset that's to the right side of Runway 6. This approach happens to be a bit unusual in that it's one of

The Localizer Directional Aid (LDA)

This is the glideslope intercept altitude. As the note with the asterisk in the profile view says, you may descend to 4,200 feet prior to reaching CLAMM if you plan on flying the non-precision (localizer-only) approach (Figure 24, position F).

If you're flying the glideslope, you'll intercept it and fly the approach down to DA, which is 1,540 feet for a Category A aircraft (Figure 24, position G). Notice that the required flight visibility is 1 statute mile for the full LDA/GS approach. On the other hand, if you elect to fly the non-precision approach, you'll descend to 2,800 feet as the cross symbol indicates (Figure 24, position H). The cross is just a reference symbol. It doesn't mean you'll need special help (from above) when flying this portion of the approach since your instructor refuses to answer his cell phone. Unlike the ILS approach to Long Beach, this airport doesn't have RVR capability. If it did, the approach minimums would be in RVR values. Instead, the TERPS specialist just lists the standard, in-flight, statute mile visibility required for the approach.

OK, time for a pop quiz, even though you may not be someone's pop. Is 2,800 feet as low as you can go when flying the non-precision approach using only the LDA/LOC? Looking at the minimums section, you see that there's a lower MDA of 1,800 feet. Who gets *that*? Is it reserved for pop pilots and other entertainment stars? Nope. You, too, can have it. To descend below 2,800 feet, you need to identify the stepdown fix marked by SKIRT OM (Figure 24, position I).

To identify SKIRT you'll need either operable marker

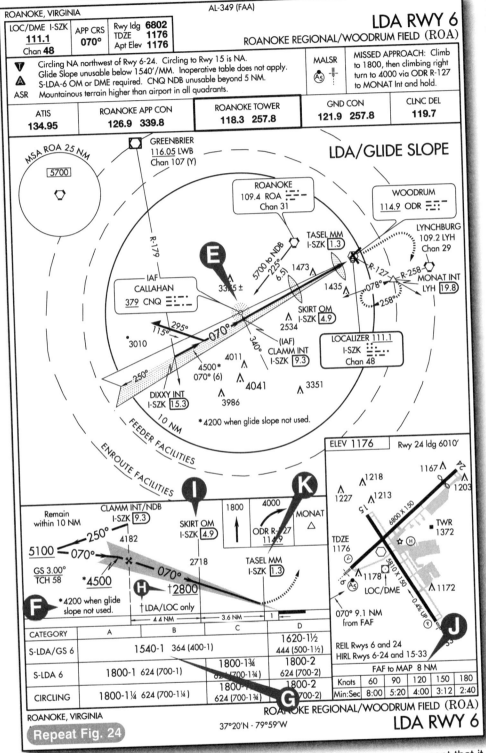

The Localizer Directional Aid is similar to the localizer in use and accuracy except that it is often not part of a complete ILS approach and it's not aligned with the runway.

INT/NDB). Remember, the procedure turn distance limitation shown in the profile view applies to the point where the procedure turn *begins,* unless otherwise stated in the profile view. In this profile view, the procedure turn begins at CLAMM intersection or the NDB (Figure 24, position E).

Once you've completed the procedure turn on the north side of the localizer you'll be headed inbound. When established on the localizer, descend no lower than 4,500 feet.

beacon equipment, DME or IFR approved GPS. How do you know? Common sense wins again. There's no other way to identify SKIRT intersection. The plan view doesn't show any radial from ROA VOR being present to identify the intersection. In the plan view, notice that the localizer frequency has DME (but no Chinese takeout), since it shows *Chan 48.* In the profile view, the DME mileage thumbnail shows a distance value of 4.9 nm. When your blue marker beacon light activates or when your DME reads 4.9 nm, you've successfully identified SKIRT and may descend to the lowest MDA allowed, which is 1,800 feet. Rock on, Pops.

What's the required minimum flight visibility to leave an MDA of 1,800 feet and land this airplane? Yes, it's 1 statute mile (which is not the distance you can see a statue from your airplane) for a Category A airplane. From now on, we'll just assume all our airplanes are Category A. Ask yourself where the missed approach point is for the localizer approach. Studious student that you are, I suspect you've already looked at the time/distance table below the airport sketch to find that it's 8 nm from the FAF (Figure 24, position J). Looking at the profile view, 8 nm from the FAF puts you at TASEL intersection (9.3 DME-1.3 DME=8 DME).

Since a DME thumbnail is shown as an identifier for TASEL (Figure 24, position K), you can identify the missed approach point by either a DME reading of 1.3 miles (assuming you have DME in your airplane, not in someone else's airplane, of course) or by timing the approach from the FAF to TASEL. At 90 knots ground-speed, you'll need 5 minutes and 20 seconds to reach the missed approach point (you're covering 1.5 miles per minute). As a general rule, if time is shown in the time/distance table at the bottom of the airport sketch, it's a sure bet that the approach, or at least one part of it (the non-precision part) has a missed approach point based on time.

Perhaps the most important thing to mention about this approach is that when you're at the missed approach point on either the precision or non-precision approach, the runway and the approach lighting system will probably be found somewhere to your left rather than out the front window. So, under a no-wind condition, don't be a dim bulb looking straight ahead for the bright lights. Look left and be right.

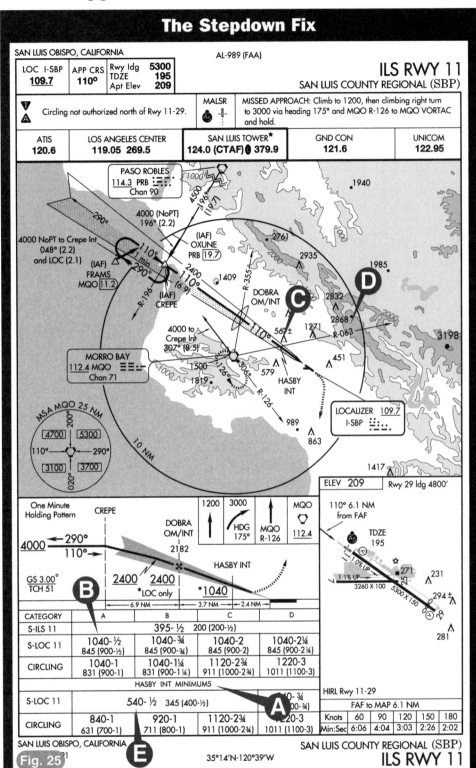

The Stepdown Fix

SAN LUIS OBISPO, CALIFORNIA   AL-989 (FAA)

ILS RWY 11
SAN LUIS COUNTY REGIONAL (SBP)

| LOC I-SBP 109.7 | APP CRS 110° | Rwy ldg 5300 | TDZE 195 | Apt Elev 209 |

Circling not authorized north of Rwy 11-29.

MALSR

MISSED APPROACH: Climb to 1200, then climbing right turn to 3000 via heading 175° and MQO R-126 to MQO VORTAC and hold.

| ATIS 120.6 | LOS ANGELES CENTER 119.05 269.5 | SAN LUIS TOWER* 124.0 (CTAF) 379.9 | GND CON 121.6 | UNICOM 122.95 |

Fig. 25

SAN LUIS OBISPO, CALIFORNIA   35°14'N-120°39'W

SAN LUIS COUNTY REGIONAL (SBP)
ILS RWY 11

ELEV 209   Rwy 29 ldg 4800'

TDZE 195

FAF to MAP 6.1 NM

Knots	60	90	120	150	180
Min:Sec	6:06	4:04	3:03	2:26	2:02

HIRL Rwy 11-29

Profile table

CATEGORY	A	B	C	D
S-ILS 11		395-½ 200 (200-½)		
S-LOC 11	1040-½ 845 (900-½)	1040-¾ 845 (900-¾)	1040-2 845 (900-2)	1040-2¼ 845 (900-2¼)
CIRCLING	1040-1 831 (900-1)	1040-1¼ 831 (900-1¼)	1120-2¾ 911 (1000-2¾)	1220-3 1011 (1100-3)

HASBY INT MINIMUMS

S-LOC 11	540-½ 345 (400-½)			
CIRCLING	840-1 631 (700-1)	920-1 711 (800-1)	1120-2¾ 911 (1000-2¾)	1220-3 1011 (1100-3)

Stepdown Fixes

It's important to identify the value of the stepdown fix in the Roanoke LDA Runway 6 approach. Approach procedure designers do their best to get the pilot as low as possible when close to the runway. That's why it's possible to have a single stepdown fix (one only) inside the FAF on a non-precision approach. The ILS Runway 11 approach to San Luis is another example of how much lower you can go when a stepdown fix is involved. Stepdown fix minimums are often identified by a parallel set of minimums appropriately named by the controlling stepdown fix (Figure 25, position A). The straight-in localizer MDA for Runway 11 is 1,040 feet (Figure 25, position B). If you can identify HASBY (Figure 25, position C) intersection, which is identified by the 063 cross radial from Morro Bay VOR (Figure 25, position D), then you can descend to 540 feet (Figure 25, position E).

The NDB (Non Directional Beacon) Approach

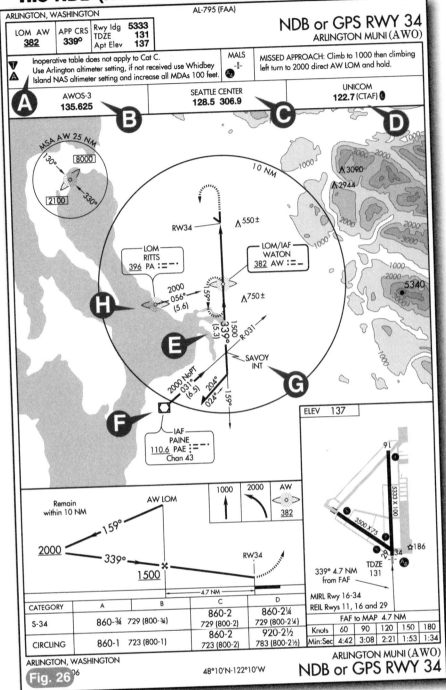

This NDB approach is overlaid with a GPS approach. It can be flown with either ADF or GPS equipment (more on GPS in Chapter 13).

otherwise known as an *overlay approach*. We'll discuss the GPS approach portion of this chart in the next chapter. For now, let's concentrate on the NDB portion by starting at the top of the chart and working our way down.

As with all approaches, you always want to glance over the notes in the briefing area long before you fly the approach. The relevant note here is the one dealing with the altimeter setting (Figure 26, position A). If you don't have the Arlington altimeter setting you must use Whidbey Island's setting and increase all your MDAs by 100 feet. Do we have to raise the MDAs because the folks at Whidbey Island buy their inexpensive pressure measuring equipment from Radio Hut? No. When you're required to use a remote altimeter setting, there's always a chance that it may not reflect the actual pressure at your location. This is the reason an altitude fudge factor is added onto the MDA. Arlington's altimeter setting is provided by the AWOS-3 unit found on or near the field at Arlington (Figure 26, position B). Make sure you use this setting if it's available.

In the lower part of the briefing area, you'll notice that Seattle Center handles approaches into and out of this airport (Figure 26, position C). This should alert you to expect radar coverage beginning at a higher altitude than that of a typical approach/departure control facility. Realistically speaking, the only way you know if radar coverage even exists at an airport is to check the *Airport/Facility Directory* for that airport. If there is an approach and departure control, then it's likely that you'll have radar coverage for the airport. Because Arlington's approach chart lists Seattle Center, you shouldn't expect radar vectoring onto the final approach course here. It's more likely that you'll use your own navigation and fly feeder routes to establish yourself on the approach structure.

It's also important to notice that there is no tower at Arlington. Is that because a student pilot knocked it over with his Cessna? No, the place just doesn't have a tower. It happens. That's why, once you're established on the approach, Seattle Center will turn you over to advisory frequency (CTAF 122.7 as shown in Figure 26, position D), and often expect you to report back to Center or an FSS via radio when you're in a position to cancel your IFR flight plan. Yep, that's right. When landing from an instrument

To Be or To NDB, That is the Question

A friend of mine was a house painter for five years. He thought he'd *never* finish that darn house. And I bet you're thinking that you'll never finish hearing about approaches. Well, there are a few more to do, but the next one is pretty simple. It's an NDB or non-directional beacon approach, as shown in Figure 26. These are, by the way, defined as torture under the Geneva Convention, but are permitted when used by flight instructors on IFR students.

The first thing you'll notice about this chart is that the title shows that it's a combined NDB or GPS approach,

"TERRAIN, TERRAIN - Pull Up!"

A Minimum Safe Altitude (MSA) is defined by FAR Part 91.119(a) as "an altitude allowing, if a power unit fails, an emergency landing without undue hazard to persons or property on the surface."

The minimum altitudes depicted on approach charts provide at least 1,000 feet of obstacle clearance for emergency use within a specified distance from the navigation facility upon which a procedure is based. As a First Officer discovered, a night approach into an airport located in mountainous terrain requires good crew coordination and compliance with charted altitude minimums:

Approach Control cleared us for visual approach approximately 30 nm northwest of the field. We were descending to 6,500 feet on the [STAR] when we received clearance for visual.... The approach controller directed us to "contact tower 11 miles northwest." I looked down, set in the localizer frequency for the ILS and tower frequency in VHF#1 [radio], but did not select tower While I was looking down, the captain selected 4,500 feet in the altitude alerter, and I did not notice that this was well below the MSA of 5800 feet....

Around 15 nm...I selected tower. Shortly thereafter we received an EGPWS alert for terrain. I noticed the black shapes of terrain approximately 3 miles right of us and the captain started a climb out of 5,200 feet to 5,500 feet. Tower contacted us...when Approach Control notified them that he had a low altitude alert on us.

I failed to provide proper back-up by not noticing the new altitude in the alerter, or noting that it was below MSA. I also switched the VHF to Tower prior to 11 miles, which prevented us from hearing Approach Control's warning. Further, while I saw the mountains on the right, I failed to verbalize anything to the captain because I assumed he was lining up on the runway and we would pass well left of them. These mountains rise to 4,687 feet and have no light or beacon on top. At night, with good visibility, it is hard to judge their position.

NASA Callback Report

approach at a tower-controlled field, the tower controller cancels your IFR flight plan for you. When landing at uncontrolled fields, *you* must cancel your IFR flight plan on your own. Here's how you do this.

When Center releases you to contact Arlington Unicom (also referred to as the *advisory frequency*), broadcast your intentions to Arlington traffic on 122.7. I'd say something like, "Arlington traffic, Cessna 2132 Bravo, four miles south, inbound, NDB approach Runway 34." When you're in a position to land, call Seattle Center on Center frequency and cancel your IFR flight plan directly. You can do this while still airborne if you're assured that a landing is assured.

You might also be able to land and call the controller from the ground via radio. If neither of these works for you, then you can call the local FSS and ask the specialist (use proper pronunciation here or they'll give you to the resident spiritualist) to cancel your IFR flight plan for you. You might even be able to do it by phone if you ask for and receive the number before landing. Most often, however, the controller will ask you to return to his frequency and cancel with him when the field is in sight and landing is assured.

It is very important to cancel, by whatever means, because until you do so the controller cannot let another plane into that airspace for landing (or any other purpose, for that matter). Your fellow pilots who are waiting to land or take off under IFR will really not appreciate doing turn time or sitting in the runup area because you forgot to cancel. So be sure to do it.

Looking at the plan view in Figure 26, position E, you can see that the inbound approach course consists of the 339 degree bearing to and from WATON NDB. WATON NDB is also collocated with an outer marker beacon. This provides you with an aural indication and a blue marker beacon light when you're approaching the NDB.

Suppose Seattle Center cleared you direct to Paine VOR (Figure 26, position F) then said, "2132 Bravo, you're cleared for the NDB Runway 34 approach to Arlington via the Paine VOR transition, maintain 3,000 feet until Paine. At WATON, change to advisory frequency, and report canceling your IFR flight plan on this frequency."

Got all that? If you're not experiencing pain yet, you will when you try to copy that clearance in the air.

The big thing here is that you're cleared for the approach from Paine VOR and you're on your own regarding navigation. It's clear that the feeder route from Paine VOR onto the approach structure consists of the 031 degree radial for 6.5 miles with a minimum altitude of 2,000 feet. So you'd maintain 3,000 feet until crossing Paine VOR, turn and track outbound on the 031 degree radial and descend to 2,000 feet after crossing Paine VOR.

SAVOY intersection (Figure 26, position G) is made up of the intersection of the 031 degree radial and the 339 degree inbound course. The feeder route from Paine VOR says *NoPT*, meaning that you're not expected to make a procedure turn when you turn inbound on the approach procedure track at SAVOY.

Is there a time when you might want or need to make a procedure turn when cleared for the approach at Paine VOR? Sure. It's possible (though somewhat unlikely) that you have been dropped from beneath the wing of a B-52 flying overhead and are at 39,000 feet over the VOR. You'd be high and it might be wise to make the procedure turn to lose altitude. Once again, keep in mind that when a route says *NoPT,* it means the controller does not expect you to do one, and you can't do one unless given explicit permission. "No" means no, unless someone other than you says "yes."

If permission is granted, you'd do the procedure turn by flying all the way to WATON, where the procedure turn begins (look in the profile view to see where the procedure turn begins), make a left turn all the way around to intercept the 159 degree NDB bearing outbound and make a 45/180 degree course reversal within 10 miles of AW LOM (WATON). On a few occasions when ATC kept my airplane at a higher altitude than normal, I had to request permission to do the procedure turn just to lose altitude safely.

What happens if ATC told you to proceed direct to RITTS NDB (Figure 26, position H), then cleared you for the approach via the RITTS transition? Is there a feeder route from RITTS onto the approach structure? You bet, mon ami. It's made up of the 056 degree bearing from RITTS to the WATON NDB. Flyable NDB bearings are often *to* some place not *from* some place (I say *usually*, not always. as you'll see shortly). When over RITTS, you'd tune in the WATON NDB and track inbound on the 056 degree bearing and descend to 2,000 feet for 5.6 nautical miles of travel. If you tracked outbound on RITTS NDB to WATON on the 056 degree bearing, you wouldn't know when you arrived at WATON. That's why NDB bearings are often *to*, not *from* in these specific instances.

Since the letters NoPT don't appear on the feeder route from RITTS, the procedure turn is mandatory. You *must* turn outbound on the 159 degree bearing from WATON and fly the procedure turn. You can't just turn inbound from WATON and fly the approach. Sorry. Not on this planet, or on any planet (even UFOs have to do it). It's not legal. There are several reasons for this. First and foremost, because it says so. Remember, controllers *don't like surprises*.

Second, if the turn on the feeder route to the final approach course at the FAF is more than 30 degrees, it is considered an excessive angle for getting safely established on the final approach course. You will find that IFR procedures in general are set up to avoid extreme anything—turns, descent rates, maneuvers. The assumption is always that conditions are challenging, and the pilot needs to move in small, gentle increments. It's aviation ballet, not flamenco.

If the altitude difference between the minimum altitude on the feeder route and the FAF is more than 300 feet above the minimum altitude for crossing the FAF inbound (as seen in the profile view), this would make the required descent for landing too steep for the FAA's taste (on a different note, if you tried this you'd hear gentle pings which

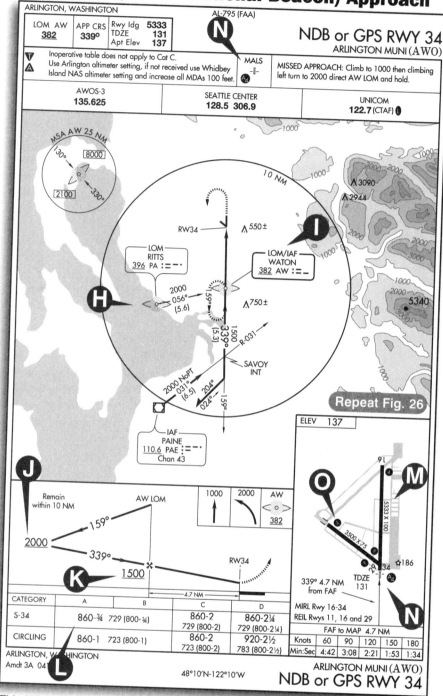

This NDB approach is overlaid with a GPS approach. It can be flown with either ADF or GPS equipment (more on GPS in Chapter 13).

you'd soon recognize as the sound of your passengers' eardrums popping—they wind up going to that infamous eardrum prison, Ping-Ping). For all those reasons, you must do a procedure turn in this situation.

Looking at the profile view of this chart, it's clear that the minimum procedure turn altitude when flying the 45/180 degree leg is 2,000 feet as shown in Figure 26, position J (the line underneath the altitude indicates that it's a minimum altitude). Sure, you can stay higher if you like, since this isn't a mandatory altitude. Yes, there are some mandatory altitudes shown in the profile view (you'll see this shortly with the Burbank Rwy 8 ILS approach) where

What a Difference a Letter Makes

"What a difference a day makes, twenty-four little hours..." So goes the old song. This instructor learned that one little letter--as in assure versus assume—can be important, too.

On a routine training flight to practice instrument approaches, we were given an IFR clearance to "Maintain 5,000, cleared to the [fix] via 12 mile DME arc and inbound on 117 degree radial." We were not cleared for the approach due to company aircraft conducting an approach at the same airport. Immediately after we read the clearance back, the company aircraft reported his missed approach. The student turned onto the arc and began descending.... After he descended to 4,900 feet, I asked him if we were cleared for the approach. He replied that we were. At this point I made several assumptions: 1) We were told to expect approach clearance after company aircraft completed his approach; I heard him call a missed approach and assumed we were cleared. 2) Student said we were cleared and I thought I missed the radio call.... At 4,500 feet, Center asked us to verify our altitude. Busted!

Reasons: Instructor's failure to verify clearance, (you know you're in trouble when you state items such as "student said" and "I thought"), and assuming the student was right. I violated a cardinal credo for instructors here. Corrective action: Increase communication between instructor, student, and controller to assure and not assume critical items are not misunderstood.

NASA Callback Report

you must fly something specific because being higher would create a traffic hazard, most likely from pilots on nearby approaches.

Once you're inbound on the 339 degree bearing, you can descend to 1,500 feet (Figure 26, position K), which I would recommend doing. Remember, descending as soon as possible is almost always a benefit when flying any approach (but let's not send anyone to Ping-Ping, you hear?). This gives you more time to get down to the next minimum altitude or MDA and trim the airplane. That, in turn, gives you more time to look outside for the runway environment.

For instance, if you crossed WATON NDB inbound at 1,500 feet, you'd descend to an MDA of 860 feet for the straight-in Runway 34 NDB approach as shown in Figure 26, position L (Arlington altimeter setting assumed here). Looking at the value of 729 feet after the ¾ mile visibility value, you should recognize this as your HAT or height above the touchdown zone of Runway 34, since this is a straight in approach. Indeed, the airport sketch identifies the TDZE on Runway 34 as 131 feet, which, if added to 729, gives you 860 feet. It's math magic.

If I were flying this approach, I'd descend to 860 feet at about 500 feet per minute (a safe and manageable—non eardrum-busting—descent rate), level off and trim the airplane for level flight. Now I'd have a lot of time to begin searching for the runway environment and perhaps even read a novel (as long as it wasn't titled, *Lost in Space*). It's obvious from the profile view that the missed approach point, which is identified by timing from the FAF (WATON), is at the threshold of Runway 34.

Of course, there's no rule that says you must descend to your lowest permissible MDA (except on your IFR checkride where you're required to), but it makes sense to do so, since this gives you the best chance of seeing the runway environment as well as an easier job of getting down. This is an important point, given that in order to see the runway environment on a non-precision approach you may need to be very near the threshold if the visibility is poor.

Of course, if you're nearly over the runway threshold and 729 feet above it, you'll have to lose at least 729 feet before you can land (we're still talking airplane, here, not helicopter). Is this easy to do in this instance? Think about

it. The runway is 5,333 feet long (Figure 26, position M). That's less than a nautical mile in length. If you're flying at 120 knots, you're covering 2 nautical miles per minute. Just to have your wheels touch down by the end of the runway, you'd have to lose 729 feet in at least one minute, by which time you'd be near if not beyond the end of the runway. The idea of being able to land on a typical runway when you're over its threshold from the typical MDA is pretty risky in most cases.

So, is this some sort of weird *Mission Impossible* deal the FAA has dreamed up? Not really. If you remember from Chapter 8, FAR 91.175, you can depart the MDA for lower ground when you have the required flight visibility and any one of 10 specific runway environment items in sight.

You'll certainly want to leave the MDA when you have the runway environment in sight (3/4 statute mile forward visibility assumed here, too) and the airplane is in a position from which a descent to landing can be made by normal maneuvering while using a normal rate of descent. In other words, you can't descend below your MDA while out near WATON NDB. Doing so wouldn't be smart, and Ned-the-Fed is not buying it if you do. On the other hand, what is a normal rate of descent? It's anything that doesn't cause an accident. Sorry, but that's the only practical definition you'll find anywhere. If you asked my opinion, it's probably a descent that doesn't exceed 1,000 feet per minute (otherwise known as VBurst, maximum descent speed before eardrums sing "ping") since it's hard to arrest an airplane's descent at this rate and above. Fortunately, as you can see in the briefing area and in the airport sketch, Runway 34 has an MIRL system (Figure 26, position N) that is sure to help you find the runway way before you get to it.

Suppose the AWOS system said that the winds at Arlington were from 110 degrees at 20 knots? Would you still attempt to land on Runway 34 in this instance? That wouldn't be too smart would it? With a right quartering tailwind you'd have a challenge getting that airplane down on the runway before you ran out of room. Instead, I hope you'll elect to circle to land on Runway 11. If you elect to land on Runway 11 (because it's election day), then your circling MDA is 860 feet (no change here), and the required flight visibility is now 1 statute mile.

How would you circle in this instance? Well, there are no circling restrictions shown in the briefing area, so it's up to you. You do, however, want to try and make left traffic whenever possible for the simple reason that it gives you the best chance of seeing the runway out your left window while maneuvering.

I'd overfly the threshold of Runway 34, then turn left once I was past the centerline of Runway 11. From there I'd make a left pattern to land on Runway 11. Notice that the airport sketch shows that Runway 11 has a PAPI (Figure 26, position O), given that there's a white P on a black circle (it doesn't have a MOMMY). This is good news, since it will help you decide when to leave the circling MDA. In other words, when turning to align myself with Runway 11, I wouldn't descend for landing until I was nearly aligned with the runway centerline and on the PAPI glideslope. This is especially important if you're circling to land at night. Trust your PAPI not to lead you astray here. Since you're circling above an airport instead of a runway, the 723 foot value next to the 1 mile circling visibility represents your HAA or height above the airport elevation (an elevation of 137 feet MSL plus 723 feet AGL equals 860 feet MSL).

An Approach to an Airport

Figure 27 is the Riverside VOR or GPS-A approach to Riverside Municipal airport. As we've already discussed, this approach doesn't have a runway number associated with it, as do all the other approaches we've covered in this chapter. That's because this is an approach to an airport, not a specific runway. So it gets a letter ("Dear Airport") instead of a number in the title section (Figure 27, position A). An approach to an airport instead of a runway has only circling minimums, as is shown in Figure 27. This is logically consistent, and sensible, since you're not being aligned with any specific runway. The approach circling minimums pertain to a wide area around the runway complex as we've already seen.

There are two main reasons an approach becomes a circling approach instead of one that's straight in to a runway. First, if the final approach course is aligned more than 30 degrees from the runway direction, then it becomes a circling approach (as we discussed in the last chapter). Second, if the descent rate on final from the minimum altitude at the *FAF* to the *runway threshold* is in excess of 400 foot per nautical mile. This violates the "slow and gentle" IFR approach principle.

The Approach to an Airport

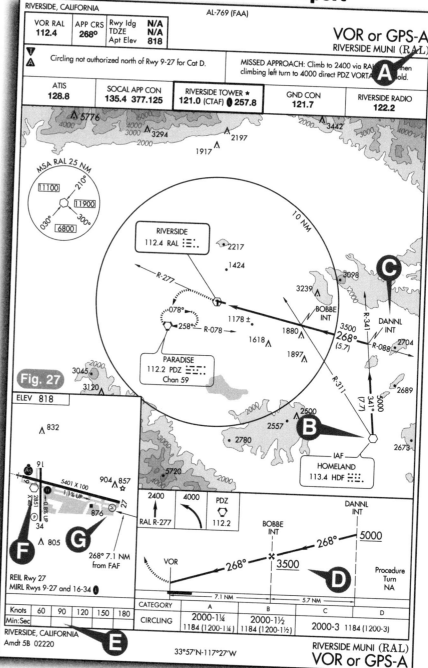

Sometimes an approach will not have runway numbers as is the case above. This indicates it's an approach to an airport with circling minimums and not an approach to a specific runway.

The Riverside approach has a descent rate that exceeds 400 foot per nautical mile. Think about it this way. If you're approaching at 120 knots (2 miles a minute), it would take a descent rate of more than 800 feet per minute to make the runway threshold, assuming you saw the runway from the FAF. This is a steep descent rate for most airplanes. Of course, you're not likely to see the runway from the FAF. Instead, you're more likely to see it when you're closer to the airport. That would make the required descent rate just to land on the runway way in excess of 800 feet per minute (sounds like Ping-Ping time, right?). Circling minimums allow you to maneuver in order to dissipate altitude in preparation for landing.

The IFR Enroute Chart

Riverside VOR is a (T) or terminal class VOR and isn't part of the enroute structure. It is, however, used as the instrument approach aid for the Riverside VOR-A approach.

Just because the controller tells you to circle for landing on a specific runway, it doesn't mean you *can't* land straight in if you're in a position to do so. It's possible that the runway is aligned more than 30 degrees from the final approach course or that the descent rate on final is excessive, but if you're having a great day and are able to spot the runway in time to get properly lined up, set up, and let down, you can land straight-in. As the groundskeeper might say, gopher it. If you can make a straight in approach to a runway safely, you're certainly allowed to do so off a circle-to-land clearance. "Circle to land" is permission to circle *or* land straight-in, depending on how you assess your approach position.

In the plan view of Figure 27, you'll notice that there is no barb symbol indicating that a procedure turn is available. Nor is there a holding pattern course reversal or teardrop procedure turn course reversal. This approach doesn't provide for a procedure turn and it doesn't appear that one is really necessary if you're approaching from the east. It happens that the Riverside VOR is a T class navaid (Figure 28, position A) and this isn't part of the enroute structure (T class navaids are normally used just for instrument approaches at the airport where they live). You aren't likely to be arriving at the RAL VOR via an airway from the west, so there isn't much need for a procedure turn on this approach. More than likely you'll be given radar vectors to the approach structure at Riverside.

If you were approaching from the west, the controller might clear you via an airway to Homeland VOR (Figure 27, position B) and then clear you for the approach. If that happened, you'd track outbound on the 341 degree radial and descend to 5,000 feet. When reaching DANNL intersection (Figure 27, position C) you'd turn inbound on the RAL 088 degree radial (268 degrees inbound) and descend to 3,500 feet (Figure 27, position d). Past BOBBE you'd refer to the minimums section to find that your landing minimums are a circling MDA of 2,000 feet and a visibility of 1¼ miles.

In the time/distance table (Figure 27, position E) you may have noticed that RAL doesn't have time for you. At least there are no times in the time/distance table, much less a defined missed approach point. Is something missing? It's that way because the missed approach point is the VOR, and no timing is needed to identify it. A simple to/from flag flop will do. The profile view makes this quite clear, given that the missed approach climb symbol shows the climb beginning at the VOR, which is 7.1 nautical miles from BOBBE intersection.

When you don't see the listed times of a defined missed approach point in the time/distance table, you'll find the missed approach point in the profile view. It's also important to notice that the VOR's position on the field is shown quite clearly in the airport sketch (Figure 27, position F). The VOR is located near the west end of Runway 27. Sharp instrument pilots will review the airport sketch and get a good idea of where the approach course is as well as the precise location of the missed approach point. Why? On this approach, if you're at the missed approach point the airport is behind you, not ahead of your airplane.

You'll also notice that there's a VASI to the left of Runway 27 (the *V* symbol in a circle in Figure 27, position G). There's also an approach lighting system on the opposite end of the runway. This shouldn't cause you concern, because controllers will often turn off these lights since they aren't useful to you in this instance.

I've seen situations where the controllers haven't turned the lights off and a student has mistaken the far end of the runway for the approach end. No bueno. It's also wise to take note of any airport or city roads that run parallel to the runway. On more than one occasion a pilot has mistaken road lighting for runway lighting and ended up with an Oldsmobile attachment to his landing gear. This is why you should always look over the airport sketch before any approach.

Why CFIs Should Make the Big Bucks!

A student of mine showed me that there are BETTER ways to deal with fast-talking controllers and an over-abundance of communication on the frequency. We were on tower frequency doing touch and go landings at NAS Corpus Christi in a T-28B (this is important because it establishes the fact that I was BEHIND the student and couldn't really see what he was doing!) In any event, NAS Corpus has two parallel runways and on that day we had a full bag of left and right traffic, as well as occasional straight-in instrument approaches to the instrument runway. On the downwind, I could barely hear my student doing his checklist items among all the chatter.

Mercifully, there was a brief pause as we approached the 180 and then I heard, "Delta 685, Corpus Christi Approach, cleared for the ILS 13, contact IFR Tower at the marker". I hollered up front, "What did you do!" The student replied, "Sir, there were too many people talking on that other frequency so I picked one that wasn't as busy". Aaahhhh!   (Submitted by a fellow CFI.)

When Additional Equipment is Required for an Approach

Looking at the title of the El Monte *VOR/DME or GPS-B* approach chart (Figure 29) you might surmise that DME equipment is required to fly this approach. You'd be correct, too. Let's take a look at why this is so.

First, you'll notice that this is a circling approach, given that the letter B exists in place of a runway number. The letter B (Figure 29, position A) indicates that this is the second circling approach published for El Monte. The first would have the letter A as shown in Figure 30. If five circling approaches existed at one airport then the last would have the letter E. Thanks goodness the Japanese don't design approaches. If they did, they wouldn't have circling approaches because they don't have an alphabet.

The profile and plan views show that the fixes used on the final approach structure are defined by DME (Figure 29, position B). Remember that if the plan view shows an intersection being defined by a VOR cross radial or NDB bearing, this method is acceptable for identifying that intersection. It appears that DARTS is the only intersection meeting this criterion (Figure 29, position C). On the other hand, CFCUF, WALLY and MACWO are defined by DME mileage from the PDZ VOR. In fact, the missed approach point for this VOR/DME approach is MACWO, the 27.1 DME reading from PDZ VOR. DME is obviously required for this approach.

In the upper left-hand corner of the airport sketch, take notice of the runway landing information in Figure 29, position D (but don't take anything else if it doesn't belong to you). It appears from the numbers along Runway 1-19 that the runway length is 3,995 feet and the width is 75 feet (it's not 75 feet long and 3,995 feet wide for wide-body aircraft, either).

Required Equipment for the Approach

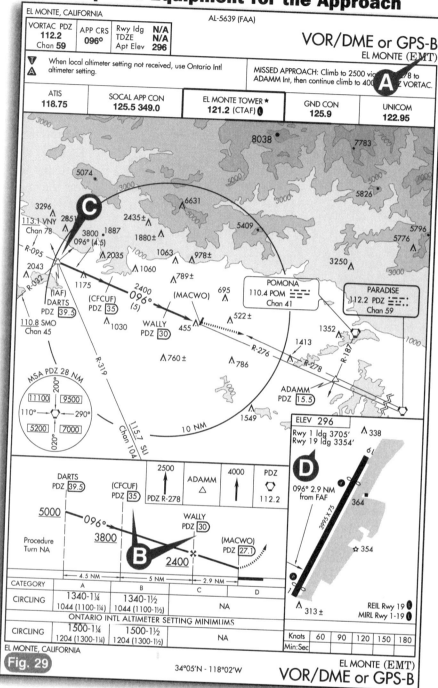

Fig. 29

The title of this procedure indicates that VOR equipment and DME is required to fly the approach (or GPS equipment too, since this is an overlay approach).

But this doesn't mean that this is all available to use for landing. The threshold, for example, might be displaced, which means that it can be used for takeoff or ground rollout but not for touchdown. In the upper left-hand corner of the airport sketch, the useable landing length of the specific runway appears when this is different from the numbers alongside of the runway. Runway 19 has a useable landing length of only 3,354 feet. The two small sunglass-like figures along the runway graphic indicate the displaced thresholds (these symbols don't mean that only Elton John can use the approach).

El Monte's First Circling Approach

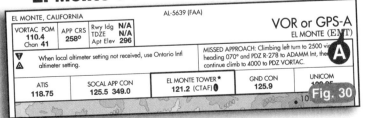

Fig. 30

The first of two circling approach at El Monte is identified by the letter "A" and the second (Figure 29) is identified by the letter "B."

Additional Equipment Needed for the Approach

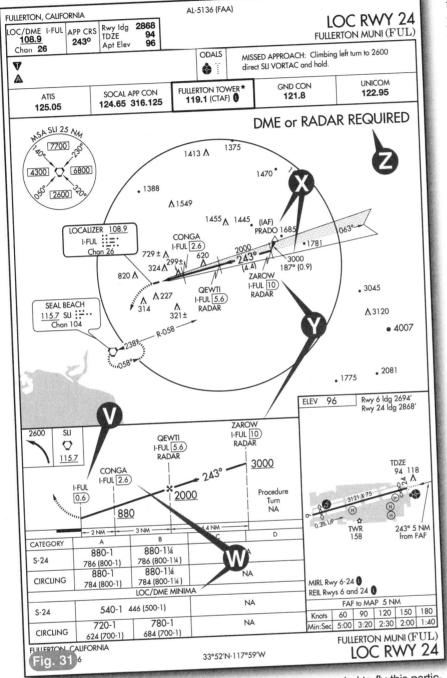

FULLERTON, CALIFORNIA — AL-5136 (FAA)

LOC/DME I-FUL	APP CRS	Rwy Idg	2868
108.9	**243°**	TDZE	94
Chan **26**		Apt Elev	96

LOC RWY 24
FULLERTON MUNI (FUL)

ODALS — MISSED APPROACH: Climbing left turn to 2600 direct SLI VORTAC and hold.

ATIS	SOCAL APP CON	FULLERTON TOWER ★	GND CON	UNICOM
125.05	**124.65 316.125**	**119.1** (CTAF)	**121.8**	**122.95**

DME or RADAR REQUIRED

MSA SLI 25 NM: 040°–230° 7700, 230°–320° 6800, 320°–050° 2600, 4300

LOCALIZER 108.9 I-FUL Chan 26

SEAL BEACH 115.7 SLI Chan 104

CONGA I-FUL 2.6
QEWTI I-FUL 5.6 RADAR
ZAROW I-FUL 10 RADAR

R-058 — 238° — 058°

PRADO 1685 (IAF) — 063°

243° — 2000 (4.4) — 3000 187° (0.9)

ELEV 96 | Rwy 6 ldg 2694' Rwy 24 ldg 2868'

2600	SLI 115.7

ZAROW I-FUL 10 RADAR
QEWTI I-FUL 5.6 RADAR
CONGA I-FUL 2.6
I-FUL 0.6

243° — 3000 — 2000 — 880

Procedure Turn NA

TDZE 94 118
TWR 158
243° 5 NM from FAF
0.3% UP
3121 X 75

MIRL Rwy 6-24
REIL Rwys 6 and 24

2 NM	3 NM	4.4 NM

CATEGORY	A	B	C	D
S-24	880-1 786 (800-1)	880-1¼ 786 (800-1¼)		
CIRCLING	880-1 784 (800-1)	880-1¼ 784 (800-1¼)	NA	
LOC/DME MINIMA				
S-24	540-1 446 (500-1)		NA	
CIRCLING	720-1 624 (700-1)	780-1 684 (700-1)	NA	

FAF to MAP 5 NM

Knots	60	90	120	150	180
Min:Sec	5:00	3:20	2:30	2:00	1:40

FULLERTON, CALIFORNIA — 33°52'N-117°59'W

FULLERTON MUNI (FUL)
LOC RWY 24

Fig. 31

The additional equipment of DME or a controller's radar is needed to fly this particular approach despite the title showing only localizer as the minimum equipment.

There's another way additional equipment required for an approach can be identified on the chart. Figure 31 shows the words *DME or Radar Required* in the plan view (Figure 31, position Z). Just because this additional equipment doesn't appear in the title, that doesn't mean it's not considered part of the approach procedure. It also doesn't mean you can fly the approach without it. If additional equipment is required to get you onto the approach structure or (in rare instances) to fly a missed approach procedure, then this information should be noted somewhere else on the chart. In the case of Fullerton, it's noted in the plan view. So it is mandatory, and you have to have it!

It appears that ZAROW intersection (Figure 31, position Y) can be defined only by the localizer and a reading from its accompanying DME or by a radar callout by the controller. There is no radial or bearing from PRADO intersection to identify ZAROW because the 187 degree routing from PRADO to ZAROW (Figure 31, position X) is based on dead reckoning. Without DME or radar, you wouldn't know precisely when to leave 3,000 feet on final approach. You'd also be unable to tell when you're at QEWTI intersection. If you didn't have DME or radar to help identify ZAROW and QEWTI, you also wouldn't know when to descend to a straight-in MDA of 880 feet. In the minimums section, a lower MDA of 540 feet is allowed if you have DME to help identify CONGA (Figure 31, position W).

Finally, make sure you notice that the missed approach point can be identified in two ways. The first is by DME on the localizer (Figure 31, position V) and the second is timing from the FAF (OK, three ways if your instructor reaches over and points it out to you). Suppose SoCal Approach Control vectored you onto the approach course and called (verbally identified) QEWTI for you. You could now descend to 880 feet, but without DME you couldn't descend to a lower MDA of 540 feet. Why can't SoCal identify CONGA for you, as they did QEWTI? Radar identification of CONGA is not part of this procedure. If it was, you'd see the word RADAR under the intersection as you do with the two previous intersections.

Communications Gone Bad

This happened in 1979. I was working the ground control position at Patrick AFB, Fla.
A flight of two A-4s was parked on the north ramp, preparing to return to Navy JAX.
Lead checked in and requested his clearance be put on request.
I said, "Clearance on request and monitor ATIS 273.5 prior to taxi."
When the flight was ready to taxi he said, "We tried contacting ATIS but couldn't get a word in edgewise."

Source: AvWeb

A No-FAF VOR Approach

For the last approach we'll review here, take a look at the Paso Robles VOR-A approach (Figure 32). The very first thing that may catch your attention on this circling approach is that the plan view doesn't show any way to transition onto the approach structure. In other words, there are no feeder routes to be seen anywhere near PRB VOR (Figure 32, position A). Did the TERPS specialist take a break and forget to do the rest of his job? No. The routes are there in the form of airways leading to and from PRB VOR as seen on the low altitude enroute chart (Figure 33, position A).

Arriving at the VOR from any of these airways is a perfectly acceptable way to begin this approach. Notice that this VOR approach has a procedure turn (Figure 32, position B). If you were cleared for the VOR-A approach on any airway, when you arrive over the VOR you'd turn outbound and fly the 133 degree radial for the procedure turn. The procedure turn is mandatory when approaching the VOR on any airway. That's because there's no reference to *NoPT* anywhere on the chart regarding airways. On some similar charts, there is something known as a *NoPT Arrival Sector* as shown in Figure 34A and 34B.

From the profile view in Figure 32, position C, the procedure turn altitude is 3,600 feet, which is what you should descend to when outbound. As long as you remain within 10 nautical miles of the VOR, you're safe at 3,600 feet. Now here is where things get interesting. As you do the procedure turn and then head inbound, you would normally descend to the intermediate segment altitude from which you'd cross the FAF and prepare for descent to the MDA. This approach, however, has no FAF. There's no Maltese Cross. Not all approaches have a final approach fix. It does have, technically speaking, a FAP or final approach point. This is defined as the point where the final approach descent can be made once the airplane has turn inbound on the approach after completing the procedure turn. So when you're inbound, you may descend to the circling MDA of 2,100 feet (Figure 32, position D).

In this example, it's wise to descend as soon as you can, thus getting the best shot at determining as early as possible if you have landing minimums or better in terms of visibility. The airport sketch shows that the VOR is located *between* the runways (Figure 32, position E). The VOR is also the missed approach point (if you miss it you'll "paso" over Paso Robles and you don't want that, do you?).

Given that Paso Robles doesn't have a tower, you will have already figured out the correct landing runway based on the wind direction offered by the ASOS (Figure 32, position F). Now, you can land on any runway you like, but it makes sense to land into the wind when possible. Take note of the fact that Runways 1-19

The Riverside California Area

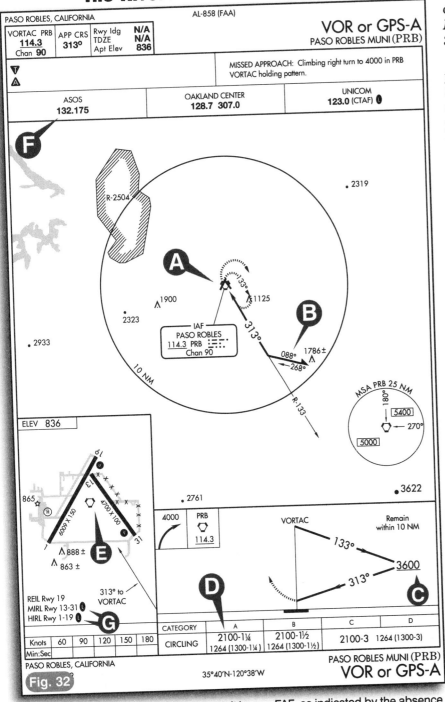

The VOR-A approach to Riverside doesn't have a FAF, as indicated by the absence of a Maltese Cross. It does, however, have a FAP or final approach point which is defined at the point where the final approach descent can be made once the airplane has turn inbound on the approach after completing the procedure turn.

Airways Not Shown on Approach Chart

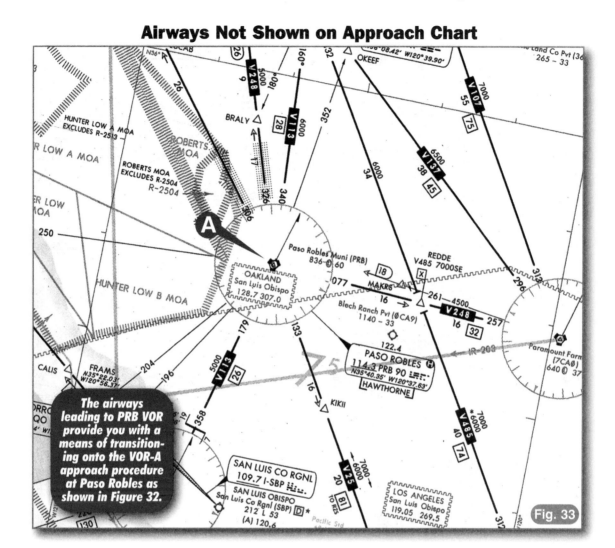

The airways leading to PRB VOR provide you with a means of transitioning onto the VOR-A approach procedure at Paso Robles as shown in Figure 32.

Fig. 33

and 13-31 both have pilot-controlled runway lighting as indicated by the white letters "L" on a black circle (Figure 32, position G). If it's dark and you'd like to light up your life and the runways, do so on the CTAF frequency. When you do, however, *both* runways will light up. This doesn't mean that you should use both runways, or that you have to land twice. It's often just the way the circuits are laid out for multiple runways.

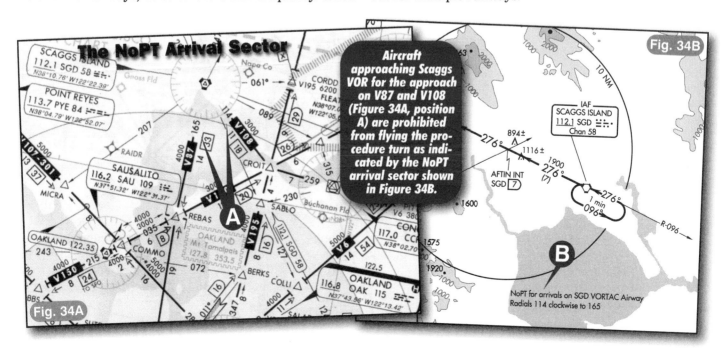

The NoPT Arrival Sector

Aircraft approaching Scaggs VOR for the approach on V87 and V108 (Figure 34A, position A) are prohibited from flying the procedure turn as indicated by the NoPT arrival sector shown in Figure 34B.

Fig. 34B

NoPT for arrivals on SGD VORTAC Airway Radials 114 clockwise to 165

Fig. 34A

VDP or Visual Descent Point

On the animal shows, wranglers often chase down a large animal from a low-flying helicopter, scare it nearly to death, then shoot the critter with 35cc's of soothing narcotics. They then want the animal to go back into the forest and lead a normal life. Right. These animals are now running around the jungle chasing helicopters, hoping to get shot again. "Hey, over here. Shoot me, right here (animal points to arm)." The point? Once you learn about VDPs you'll start looking for them with the same enthusiasm that a once-drugged animal has for overflying helicopters.

The VDP or Visual Descent Point

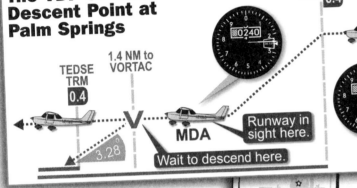

Descents to the MDA can be orderly, progressive, and a prelude to a flawless and well planned landing. Or descents can be fatal. The difference is in understanding how to use the VDP when it is shown on an approach chart.

To help you come somewhere between weed cutting and high altitude fly-bys, procedure designers have established something known as a visual descent point (VDP), as shown for the VOR/DME Runway 30 approach to Palm Springs, CA in Figure 35, position A. The VDP is located along the final approach segment of a straight-in, non-precision approach. The main purpose of the VDP is to prevent a premature descent from the MDA after visual contact with the runway or approach lights has been established. It's also a clue that descents commenced beyond the VDP may require higher than normal descent rates to make the runway. Descents from the VDP provide a descent gradient of 300 to 400 feet per nautical mile (approximately a 3–4 degree angle) to the first 3,000 feet of the landing surface.

The VDP or visual descent point found on non-precision approaches is the point on the final approach course from which normal descents from the MDA to the runway touchdown point may be commenced (assuming you have already met the requirements to descend from the MDA, of course).

VDPs are navigation references that are identified either by marker beacons, DME, or IFR approved GPS readings. When a VDP is established on an approach, and you have the equipment onboard to identify the VDP, you must wait until reaching the VDP before descending from the MDA. You should not descend below the MDA prior to reaching the VDP even if the runway is clearly in sight. If you don't have the equipment to identify the VDP, fly the approach as if no VDP has been provided.

Cleared to Cruise

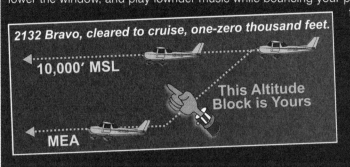

On occasion, ATC may use the term *cruise* and you should know what it means. It does *not* mean you should lower your seat, lower the window, and play lowrider music while bouncing your plane up and down. "Cruise" (in the aviation context) is permission for you to do quite a few things on your own if you choose. For instance, if ATC says, "2132 Bravo, cleared to cruise one zero thousand feet," it means you've been assigned a block of airspace from the minimum IFR altitude up to and including the assigned cruising altitude. If you want, you may climb or descend within that block at your discretion.

However, if you verbally report leaving an altitude in a descent, you may not return to that altitude without specific permission. So don't report leaving an altitude if you plan on returning to it. A cruise clearance is also approval for you to proceed to and make an approach at the destination airport

In the case of Palm Springs, you'd descend from 2,000 feet to an MDA of 240 feet for the straight-in Runway 30 approach (Figure 35, position B). Since the VDP is located 1.4 nm from the VOR (which is on the airport), your DME will eventually count down to 1.4 nm. If you observe the runway environment and have the required visibility for landing prior to a DME reading of 1.4 nm, then you'd maintain an MDA of 240 feet until reaching the VDP. Then you'd descend for landing.

Contact and Visual Approaches

What would you think if I told you there were two types of instrument approaches that don't require use of an instrument approach chart? It's true. One is known as a contact approach; the other is a visual approach.

A contact approach is the instrument pilot's version of special VFR (Figure 36). It's an official IFR approach initiated by a pilot when operating clear of all clouds with at least one-mile flight visibility and believes he can continue to the destination airport in these conditions. Realize that you must be ask for a contact approach. A controller will never offer you a contact approach. They won't even hint at it by saying cute little things like, "So, how are your CONTACTS today?" or "Did you make CONTACT with anyone worth CONTACTING?"

I've used the contact approach option quite frequently over the years when being radar vectored for an approach over an area with which I was familiar. Based on my assessment of the flight conditions, I knew I could follow known landmarks to the airport (it's not necessary to see the airport for a contact approach) so I asked the controller for a contact approach. This meant I could proceed directly to the airport by following landmarks and bypass the time required to be vectored for a published approach then fly that approach. All I had to do was

remain clear of clouds and maintain at least one-mile flight visibility. Of course, just because the approach has the word *contact* in it doesn't mean you should make contact with any obstacles.

Sometimes, when approaching an airport in VFR conditions, the ATIS indicates that the airport (located in Class D airspace) is below VFR minimums with a visibility of two miles. If I can see the airport from above, I call Approach Control and ask for a contact approach. Clearance in hand and airport in sight, I simply circled down from directly over the airport. The advantage? I have priority over all special VFR traffic and I save considerable time over what would be required to fly a full approach. As you can see, contact approaches are sometimes very useful.

For a contact approach to be approved, the reported ground visibility at the airport must be at least one mile and the airport must have a published instrument approach procedure. So don't expect to ask for and receive

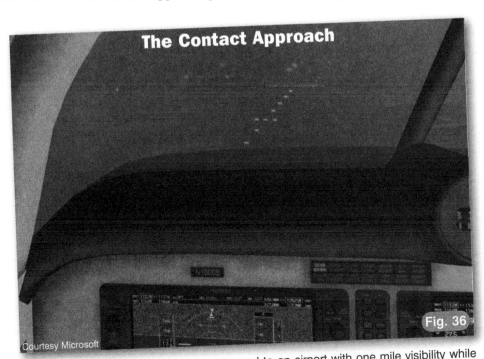

The Contact Approach

Courtesy Microsoft

Fig. 36

The contact approach allows you to proceed to an airport with one mile visibility while remaining clear of clouds and still retain your instrument approach priority. It's especially useful if you are overhead of an airport and don't desire to make a complete instrument approach.

a contact approach to an airport that lacks some form of approved weather reporting service (AWOS, ASOS, human observer, etc.). One reason (and there are several) a published instrument approach is necessary at the airport where the contact approach is made lies with the need to provide a pilot making a contact approach with some means of flying a missed approach in the event the weather and the approach both go south. Granted, the pilot may be nowhere near that approach's missed approach point, but at least he most likely has a chart with information about a proven missed approach procedure as well as other useful information.

A typical contact clearance may sound like this: *2132 Bravo is cleared contact approach at or below 3,000 feet, fly heading 220 degrees and climb and maintain 2,000 feet if approach not possible and advise.* In this instance the controller provided you with a missed approach procedure if you can't complete the approach. Don't expect this every time you receive a contact approach.

Unlike a contact approach, a visual approach can be initiated by the controller. Visual approaches allow you to proceed visually and clear of clouds to the airport. To fly a visual approach, you must have either the airport in sight or an airplane ahead of you that's heading to the airport in sight. The reason a visual approach works here is that the reported weather at the airport must be a ceiling of at least 1,000 feet and visibility of three miles or greater. The reason ATC might want you to fly a visual approach instead of an instrument approach procedure is that it helps them move airplanes more efficiently to the airport.

The interesting thing about a visual approach is that you are not required to maintain normal VFR cloud clearance requirements. There's also no requirement that the airport have weather reporting capability (i.e., ASOS, AWOS or human observer) to receive a visual approach clearance. All the controller needs is some assurance that you can descend and land with at least a 1,000 foot ceiling and three miles visibility (i.e., by use of the area forecast, PIREPS, etc.).

That's the good stuff about the visual approach. Now for the not-so-great stuff. If you accept a visual approach

The Charted Visual Approach Procedure

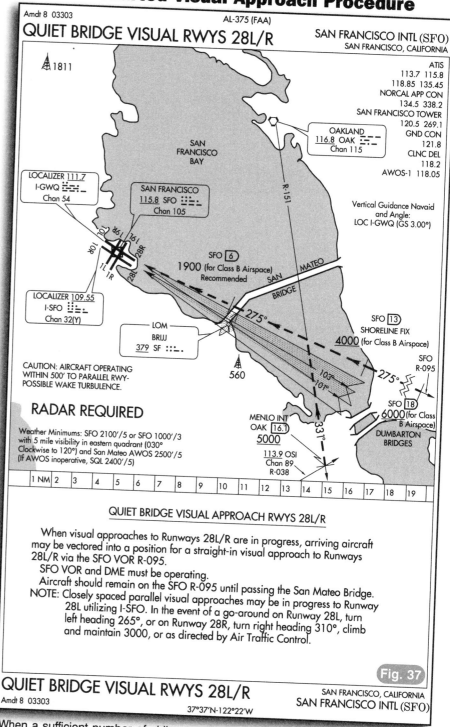

When a sufficient number of airlines use visual approaches to an airport, the FAA may chart a visual approach for that specific airport. The weather requirements for the charted visual are the same as those for a "controller issued" visual approach. The only difference being that the charted visual may require that you adhere to any altitude and geographic restrictions listed on the chart.

and are told to follow another airplane, then you are responsible for maintaining a safe distance behind it to remain free of wake turbulence. Good luck trying to do this at night, even if you're behind a very big airplane. It's hard to judge distances at night. Personally, I'd be reluctant to accept a visual approach like this unless I was absolutely sure I could remain safe at all times. This is especially critical because radar service is terminated

The Standard Terminal Arrival Route - STAR

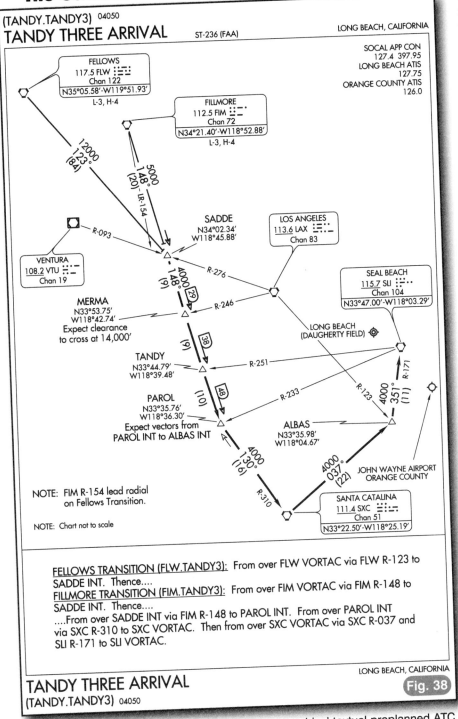

(TANDY.TANDY3) 04050
TANDY THREE ARRIVAL — ST-236 (FAA) — LONG BEACH, CALIFORNIA

SOCAL APP CON
127.4 397.95
LONG BEACH ATIS
127.75
ORANGE COUNTY ATIS
126.0

FELLOWS
117.5 FLW
Chan 122
N35°05.58'-W119°51.93'
L-3, H-4

FILLMORE
112.5 FIM
Chan 72
N34°21.40'-W118°52.88'
L-3, H-4

12000 123° (84)

5000 148° (20) IR-154

R-093

VENTURA
108.2 VTU
Chan 19

SADDE
N34°02.34'
W118°45.88'

R-276

LOS ANGELES
113.6 LAX
Chan 83

SEAL BEACH
115.7 SLI
Chan 104
N33°47.00'-W118°03.29'

4000 148° (9)

29

MERMA
N33°53.75'
W118°42.74'
Expect clearance
to cross at 14,000'

R-246

(9)

38

LONG BEACH
(DAUGHERTY FIELD)

TANDY
N33°44.79'
W118°39.48'

R-251

4000 351° (11) R-171

PAROL
N33°35.76'
W118°36.30'
Expect vectors from
PAROL INT to ALBAS INT

(10)

48

R-233

R-123

4000 351° (11)

ALBAS
N33°35.98'
W118°04.67'

JOHN WAYNE AIRPORT
ORANGE COUNTY

4000 130° (16)

R-310

4000 037° (22)

SANTA CATALINA
111.4 SXC
Chan 51
N33°22.50'-W118°25.19'

NOTE: FIM R-154 lead radial
on Fellows Transition.

NOTE: Chart not to scale

FELLOWS TRANSITION (FLW.TANDY3): From over FLW VORTAC via FLW R-123 to
SADDE INT. Thence....
FILLMORE TRANSITION (FIM.TANDY3): From over FIM VORTAC via FIM R-148 to
SADDE INT. Thence....
....From over SADDE INT via FIM R-148 to PAROL INT. From over PAROL INT
via SXC R-310 to SXC VORTAC. Then from over SXC VORTAC via SXC R-037 and
SLI R-171 to SLI VORTAC.

LONG BEACH, CALIFORNIA

TANDY THREE ARRIVAL
(TANDY.TANDY3) 04050

Fig. 38

The STAR, or standard terminal arrival route, is a graphical textual preplanned ATC procedure that's published by the FAA to provide a transition from the enroute structure to some fix typically found on an instrument approach chart.

approach clearance, then do so VFR, not IFR. If you accept a visual approach to a non-tower airport, you're still required to cancel your IFR flight plan via any of the methods we discussed in Chapter 7.

Some visual approaches are actually charted, as shown in Figure 37. This is the Quiet Bridge approach to San Francisco. No, it's not quiet because you have to fly under the bridge without using full power. These visual approach charts are often named after recognizable landmarks, such as a bridge. With charted visual flight procedures (CVFP), you should follow the special instructions shown on the chart if you're using this specific procedure.

Seeing Stars: Standard Terminal Arrival Routes

Figure 38 is known as a STAR or a *standard terminal arrival route*. Do you use a STAR if you're flying a Constellation or dating someone whose picture has appeared in the National Enquirer? No. A STAR is a graphic or textual preplanned ATC procedure that's published by the FAA to provide a transition from the enroute structure to a fix typically found on an instrument approach chart.

Why would you want to use one of these or why would ATC assign one? It helps simplify the clearance delivery procedure, meaning lower workloads for both you and the controller. For instance, instead of the controller giving you a complex clearance when approaching a busy airport, he or she will just say, "Cleared for the Tandy Three Arrival." That sure beats having to copy the entire textual description shown at the bottom of the STAR and having the bones in your hand disintegrate, doesn't it? It also reduces the risk that you'll stab yourself with your pointy pencil during turbulence while trying to copy the clearance. After all, if you're going to give blood, you'll want to do it at the Red Cross center.

STARs for all airports in the NACO instrument approach booklet are found at the beginning of the booklet in Section P. Now, the graphic presentation of the arrival clearance is sure helpful when it comes to figuring out how to fly this thing. On the other hand, you can use the textual description if you don't have the graphic with you.

when you're instructed to contact the tower. If you're gaining on another airplane and don't notice this, the tower controller might not be able to inform you about this potential problem while you are still right side up.

A visual approach is not an official instrument approach procedure, because it makes no provision for re-entering the IFR system via a missed approach. In other words, ATC does not expect you to make a missed approach if it's VFR at the airport. If you have to go around on a visual

If you'd prefer that ATC not assign you a STAR during your instrument flight plan, you can simply put the words "No STAR" in the remarks section of your flight plan. STARs contain ATC's preferred routings. By having everyone go with the flow, they can make sure the flow goes. Unless you opt out, or conditions are different than normal, you stand a chance of getting a STAR when arriving at busy airports, especially if you're flying a high-performance, turbine or jet powered airplane.

Suppose you were approaching Fellows VOR, as shown in the top left hand corner of Figure 38, position A. If the controller says, "2132 Bravo, you're cleared for the Tandy Three Arrival to Long Beach, cross SADDE at 12,000 feet, descend and maintain 4,000 feet," you'd know you should fly outbound on the Fellows VOR 123 degree radial to SADDE, then to PAROL via the 148 degree radial from Fillmore VOR. According to the note on the STAR (Figure 38, position B), you can expect vectors from PAROL to ALBAS intersection, from which you'll continue the STAR route or the controller will vector you onto the approach course.

The important thing to pay attention to here is that a clearance to fly a STAR is not a clearance for the approach. You must be extremely cautious to fly only the altitudes provided by ATC or to follow the altitude restrictions shown on the chart. For instance, if the controller cleared you for the Tandy Three Arrival from Fillmore VOR and said, "Descend, pilot's discretion, to 4,000 feet," you must level off at 5,000 feet until crossing SADDE intersection because the MEA on that route is 5,000 feet (Figure 38, position C). Doing otherwise would make your instructor SAD, indeed.

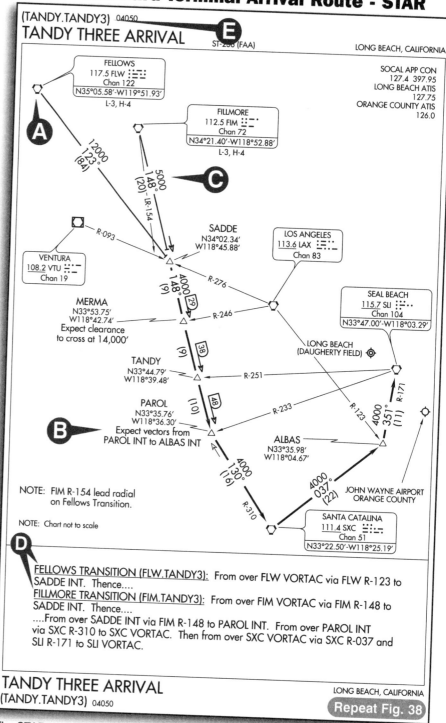

The STAR, or standard terminal arrival route, is a graphical textual preplanned ATC procedure that's published by the FAA to provide a transition from the enroute structure to some fix typically found on an instrument approach chart.

One other note on STARs. There can be several transitions to a single intersection on a STAR. For instance, the Tandy Three Arrival has the Fellows and the Fillmore transitions, both of which take you to SADDE intersection (Figure 38, position D). Depending on your location, the controller might assign you one or the other of these transitions to fly. If you're assigned both, start asking questions.

When filing a flight plan and you want to include a STAR as part of your routing, place the code shown in the title of the chart (TANDY.TANDY3) as shown in Figure 38, position E in the route section of the flight plan. This tells the computer that you'll begin the STAR at TANDY intersection. If you're arriving from over Fellows VOR, instead of describing your airway route to Long Beach from there, you can just use the computer code for the Fellows transition shown at the bottom of the STAR (FLW.TANDY3). This tells the Center computer that the routing you want past FLW is the Fellows transition as described in the STAR.

Return To Land

The pilot of a twin-engine General Aviation aircraft was on an IFR flight plan in instrument conditions when smoke filled the cockpit. Quick thinking and good resource utilization saved the day:

> Pilot and front seat passenger smelled [smoke] and shortly after saw smoke emanating from the instrument panel. I turned off the #2 nav/comm and found that the smoke ceased. I then pulled the circuit breaker and opened the vent window to air out the cabin. I advised ATC of the problem, and requested and received clearance to the departure airport. I asked the front seat passenger to advise the rest of the occupants of the situation, to remain calm, and asked him to retrieve my approach charts. This led to an uneventful landing. I contacted the tower and was told no report was required to be filed.
>
> I have learned to keep handy the plate for the approach in use at the departure airport in the event I ever have to return for landing during IFR conditions.

As a result of this incident, the reporter has adopted a procedure—keeping close at hand the approach plates for the departure airport—that is standard for many commercial operations, and recommended for any pilot flying in actual instrument conditions.

NASA Callback Report

This is a neat thing to know when you think about it. Let's say, for instance, you wanted to file an IFR flight plan from Fellows VOR to Long Beach (this is one where you'll pick up the flight plan in the air with Center on Center frequency). You'd list the departure point in the flight plan as FLW (for Fellows VOR) and the destination as KLGB (not KGB, unless you want to be MIA because you're no good at explaining things to the CIA). For the routing, you'd just list the code FLW.TANDY3 and fill in the rest of the flight plan details as appropriate. The STAR code is interpreted by the Center computer as the routing shown or described by the textual description of the Fellows transition.

By now, you're probably wondering if there's an easier way to absorb all this instrument knowledge. It's kind of like the pastor who invented a drive through church because he wanted to make Sunday mornings easier for his flock. He called it Jack in the Pew and had an express lane for six sins or less. Well, not to worry. It's easier from here on out. While there are many variations in these charts, they all have common elements. If you've understood these basics, you'll have no trouble making sense of these different chart variations.

Postflight Briefing #12-1

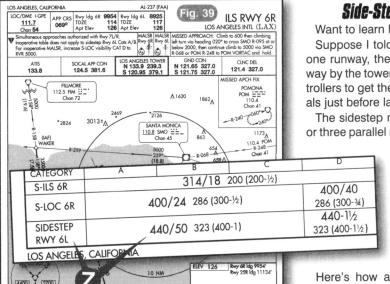

Side-Step Approaches Via the Side-Step Maneuver

Want to learn how to dance the Runway Reggae? Class is in session.

Suppose I told you it was possible to shoot an instrument approach to one runway, then at the last moment, be asked to switch to another runway by the tower controller? It's true and it's not some devious way for controllers to get their kicks by keeping pilots on the edge of their rudder pedals just before landing, either.

The sidestep maneuver allows a pilot, flying an approach to one of two or three parallel runways, to switch to another runway for landing when that maneuver offers an operational advantage. What operational advantage? Sometimes an airplane is taking a little extra time clearing a runway while another airplane is on approach to that same runway. Sidestepping allows the controller to provide the pilot the option of landing without the threat of having to go around. While there are many operational reasons for the sidestep, you should realize that it's only allowed on parallel runways that are separated by 1,200 feet or less.

Here's how a sidestep clearance might sound: *Cessna 2132 Bravo, cleared ILS Runway 6R approach. Sidestep to Runway 6L.*

Since sidestep approaches are all flown to a minimum descent altitude, looking at the chart in Figure 39, you can see that the sidestep MDA for Runway 6L is 440 feet (Figure 39, position Z). This is the altitude you'd descend to if you were cleared by the tower controller for a sidestep approach. In other words, even though you're flying the ILS to Runway 6R, the sidestep clearance automatically turns your precision approach into a non-precision approach. Yes, you can continue on the glideslope to Runway 6L, but you must level off at 440 feet in anticipation of sidestepping.

During the approach you'd descend to no lower than 440 feet and would switch runways as soon as possible after Runway 6L was in sight.

Radar Approaches
Air Route Surveillance Radar (ASR) Approaches

A surveillance approach (sometimes called an ASR approach) is a radar-vectored approach where a controller provides navigation guidance to the runway. Why would you want to fly an approach like this? Well, in an emergency (meaning that you left your approach charts at the flight school before departure or they slid to the back of your airplane on takeoff), an ASR approach would be just what you need (keep those charts on the seat, not on the floor).

An ASR approach is also a simple way for the authorities to establish an instrument approach at an airport when there are no navaids nearby to provide navigational guidance (of course, this was before GPS made it possible to provide many airports with their own approach). If your airport has ASR approach capability and you ask the controller for an ASR approach, you'll be given headings to fly that will align your airplane with the extended centerline of the landing runway.

Unfortunately, because radar information used for a surveillance approach is considerably less precise than that used for a precision approach (think ILS here), the accuracy of the approach will not be as great and higher minimums will apply. Hmmm, what minimums? Well, for an ASR approach to exist, the airport must have published approach minimums that are available in Section N2 of the NACO chart booklet, as shown in Figure 40. These are the minimums you'd use when advised to commence descent to the minimum descent altitude (MDA) or, if appropriate, to an intermediate stepdown fix minimum crossing altitude and subsequently to the prescribed MDA.

RADAR MINIMA										
PAR (c)	10	2.5°/42/1000	ABCDE	**195**/16	100	(100-¼)				Visibility (RVR 100's of feet)
(d)	28	2.5°/48/1068	ABCDE	**187**/16	100	(100-¼)				
ASR	10		ABC	**560**/40	463	(500-¾)	D	**560**/50	463	(500-1)
			E	**580**/60	463	(500-1¼)				
	28		AB	**600**/50	513	(600-1)	C	**600**/60	513	(600-1¼)
			DE	**600**-1½	513	(600-1½)				
CIR (b)	10		AB	**560**-1¼	463	(500-1¼)	C	**560**-1½	463	(500-1½)
	28		AB	**600**-1¼	503	(600-1¼)	C	**600**-1½	503	(600-1½)
	10, 28		DE	**660**-2	563	(600-2)				

All minimums in parentheses not applicable to Civil Pilots. Military Pilots refer to appropriate regulations.

Visibility in Statute Miles

Fig. 40

Radar minimums are published in the NACO chart booklet, Section N2, for airports having ASR and PAR approaches.

You'll also be advised of the location of the missed approach point and the location of the airplane's position each mile on final approach. If you ask, you'll also be given recommended altitudes at each mile on final, based on the descent gradient established for the procedure, down to the last mile that is at or above the MDA. On a really good day, you might also be able to obtain a restaurant recommendation.

A Precision Approach (PAR)

While the ASR approach provides only heading (azimuth) information and recommends altitudes, an approach using precision approach radar (PAR) provides you with highly accurate navigational guidance in azimuth and elevation. They don't call it "precision" for nothing. Along with ASR approaches, PAR approaches are commonly found at military installations. The military favor these types of approaches because they only need radar equipment and a bit of surveying before establishing an approach in enemy territory (or unfriendly territory, which can mean an urban area that doesn't like jet noise).

During a PAR approach, you're given headings to fly that direct you to, and keep your airplane aligned with, the extended centerline of the landing runway. You are told to anticipate glidepath interception approximately 10 to 30 seconds before it occurs and when to start descent to the decision altitude (which is found in the Radar Instrument Approach Minimums, Section N2, of the NACO booklet, as shown in Figure 40.

If the controller observes your airplane deviating above or below the glidepath, you'll be given the relative amount of deviation by use of terms "slightly" or "well." You probably won't hear phrases like, "you're leaving the atmosphere" or "prepare to knock a building over." Upon hearing "slightly" or "well," above or below, you're expected to adjust the aircraft's rate of descent/ascent to return to the glidepath. Trend information is also issued with respect to the elevation of the aircraft and may be modified by the terms "rapidly" and "slowly"; e.g., "well above glidepath, coming down rapidly." Range from touchdown is given at least once each mile.

A No Gyro Approach

A No Gyro approach is available if you suddenly find that your directional gyro or stabilized compass has become inoperative or inaccurate. If this occurs, advise ATC and request a no-gyro vector or approach. When receiving a no-gyro approach, plan on making all turns at standard rate immediately upon receipt of instructions. For example, if the controller says, "Turn right," "Stop turn," then do precisely what the controller says and do it pronto. If you hear the controller say, "Stop it, leave me alone or I'll tell the supervisor," then pay no attention. He's probably talking with the pesky controller sitting next to him. When a surveillance or precision approach is made, after the aircraft has been turned onto final approach you will be advised to make turns at half standard rate.

Chapter 13
GPS Approach Charts

Got GPS?

From the earliest days of flight, pilots have had to confront one of life's most profound mysteries—Where am I? Slowly, over the decades, the methods and means for pilots figuring out an answer to that question have improved, culminating in the Global Positioning System (GPS), which literally shows you where it's at, based on signals from satellites circling the earth. As long as you're close by (to the GPS unit, not the satellites), you know where *you* are at, as well. And like a well-tuned partner, GPS is always ready to help you get where you want to go.

The chances are good that you already have GPS access, in one form or another. Maybe it's an IFR-approved unit built into your panel, or a portable handheld GPS unit to help you navigate. These days, even your average cell phone can have a built-in GPS with a moving map display. When you're talking into a map, there's not much excuse for having to call someone to get directions. Soon, you'll even find GPS units built into hearing aids. A little voice will give you directions and tell you which way to turn, just like mothers-in-law do, though the GPS is more accurate and admits when it makes a mistake. And when it acts up, you can

always remove its batteries. Act like a dolt, lose your volt.

GPS is a true technological marvel. Back when some of us were student pilots, if you'd said that someday soon pilots flying GA airplanes would locate themselves in space by using satellites whose position was interpreted by a panel-mounted computer in a box about the size of two decks of cards, you'd have been injected with Thorazine and removed from the cockpit. Today, this seeming flight fantasy has become reality of flight.

In this chapter we'll examine enough basic information about using GPS and approach charts so that you can successfully fly the incredibly large number of GPS approaches already available (with lots more to follow).

First, we'll examine how GPS approaches differ slightly from the basic approaches we discussed in Chapters 11 and 12. The charting principles are nearly the same, but there are a few exceptions worthy of our attention. Then we'll dive in and look at some GPS approach charts in detail so you can see how to fly these approaches safely, using your eyes in the sky. Let's saddle up and ride.

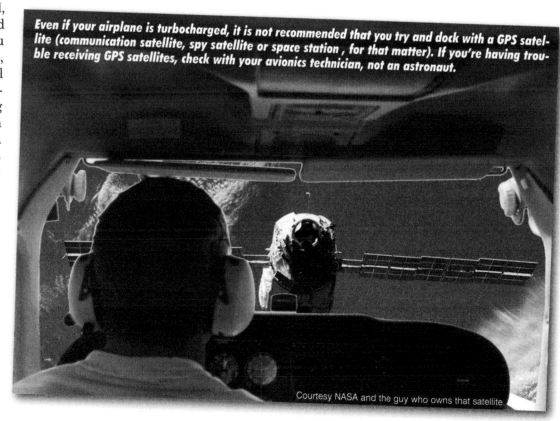

Even if your airplane is turbocharged, it is not recommended that you try and dock with a GPS satellite (communication satellite, spy satellite or space station, for that matter). If you're having trouble receiving GPS satellites, check with your avionics technician, not an astronaut.

Courtesy NASA and the guy who owns that satellite.

About Phases (A Little History Lesson)

GPS is relatively new and evolving rapidly. There's been more flux than you'll find in a bad solder joint as the charting has attempted to keep up with changes in equipment and capabilities of the system.

To date, there have been three distinct phases of GPS approach chart development. Phase one was the earliest or "pioneer" phase, and is no longer of significance to you, so I won't waste your valuable magnum mental power examining the dearly departed.

Phase two is known as a *GPS overlay approach,* and there are still many in existence. This hybrid is a GPS approach built over the underlying structure of a non-precision approach procedure.

Take a look at Figure 1, position A. The "NDB or GPS-A" approach makes it sound like the chart maker couldn't quite make up his or her mind, and said, "Ah, let the pilot decide, I really don't care. Six of one, half a dozen of the other." Which, in a sense, it is. This is both an NDB approach and a GPS approach. The GPS portion follows the same routing as the underlying non-precision approach, but uses a completely different means of navigation.

Instead of NDB combined with GPS in the heading section, you might also see a VOR or VOR/DME as the electronic dance partner. Once again, it's your choice, but you *do* have to choose. You can be slightly poached, but not half approached. You can buy a timeshare, but there are no approach-shares. On any one pass, it's either an NDB, VOR, VOR/DME *or* RNAV approach (typically a GPS approach). Yes, that will be on the final.

Phase three GPS approaches is known as *standalone approaches.* Finally, GPS stands on its own two feet (or five satellites). Figure 1, positions B, C, D and E, show two examples. These approaches are not based on or overlaid on any non-precision approach.

Figure 1, position C shows how all GPS approach chart titles will look after all the approaches are converted to the new terminal arrival area (TAA) format (more on this in a bit). All GPS approaches will also eventually use the title *RNAV (GPS)*, reflecting the fact that a GPS approach is simply area navigation (RNAV) that uses GPS equipment instead of VOR and DME to create waypoints.

While all GPS approaches will eventually be identified as RNAV, not all RNAV is GPS. For instance, the approach

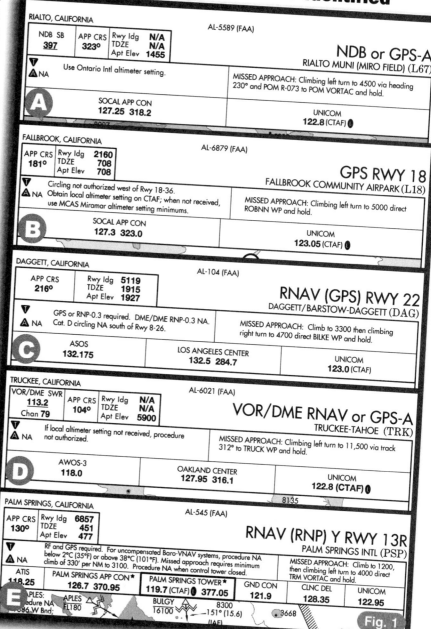

How GPS Approaches are Identified

GPS approaches are identified by the letters "GPS" in the title block of an approach chart. Keep in mind that the term "RNAV" means "area navigation" which is navigation by means of either GPS, VOR/DME RNAV, Loran, FMS, inertial navigation, etc. (or any combination of the above).

for Truckee-Tahoe is a VOR/DME RNAV approach (Figure 1, position D). There are still a few RNAV approaches around based solely on area navigation equipment that uses VOR and DME to create and identify the waypoints.

There's an even less-frequently-seen type of RNAV, used primarily by the heavy metal people. These types of approach are often called *RNP SAAA,* though I don't advise asking for it that way unless you want to be blowing into the Breathalyzer after landing. These approaches require specific equipment that meets required navigational performance specs (that's the RNP part) and they require special aircraft and aircrew authorization (SAAA). These are often approaches with unusual curving feeder routes, as shown in Figure 1, position E, which is the RNAV RNP Y approach into Palm Springs, CA (the letters Z and Y help identify separate GPS approaches that use the same runway).

Just keep in mind that if an RNAV approach doesn't have GPS in parenthesis, then it isn't one that you're likely to fly based on the IFR-certified GPS equipment you have in your airplane. See, this isn't difficult, is it?

GPS Approach Construction: Primary and Secondary Obstacle Protection

Obstacle avoidance is the name of the IFR game. Pilots and their passengers are wrapped in a cocoon of thin aluminum or composite materials that responds adversely to being poked by sharp pointy objects, or brought to an abrupt halt by mountains and other substantial things.

IFR approaches are really the fine art of separating you from what's under you until it's time to land. You've previously learned how that's done for traditional approaches. GPS approach chart segments are similar to those discussed in Chapter 12 for non-GPS approaches (i.e., initial approach segment, intermediate segment, final approach segment, etc.), but the devil's in the details and there are a few differences between the way GPS approaches and non-RNAV type approaches are constructed. In some cases the safety margins are distributed differently.

You should, of course, always strive to keep the CDI needle centered, regardless of the type of approach you're flying. If your CDI indicator looks more like windshield wipers in a rainstorm than an aviation navigation tool, you have work to do. But on a GPS approach, good needleship becomes even more important, because sloppy navigation on a GPS approach with temporary GPS signal integrity problem (more on this later) can expose you to a larger terrain-obstruction collision risk than a wandering needle on a typical VOR approach. Let's see why.

Figure 2 shows the basic architecture upon which GPS approaches are built. All routes within this structure have a primary and secondary area of obstacle protection. The enroute structure (the airway) and feeder routes leading to the initial approach fix (IAF) provide a 1,000 foot obstacle clearance margin (2,000 feet in designated mountainous areas) for four miles on either side of those routes. This is your primary area of protection.

The secondary area of protection offers 500 feet of obstacle clearance beginning at the border of the primary area. This protection *tapers* to zero feet of obstacle protection at a distance of two miles. Just so we're clear on the clearance concept, at 5.5 miles out from the centerline of the airway, you could have as little as 125 feet of guaranteed freedom between you and something that's really going to spoil your day. I've seen people have a bigger vertical twitch than that after having one Starbucks latte. Kind of gives new meaning to the term, "Don't go there," doesn't it?

GPS Approach Chart Protected Airspace

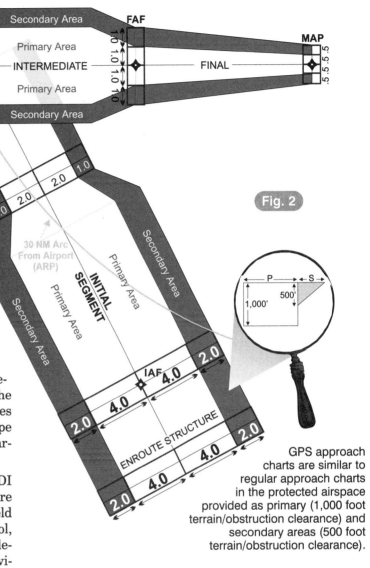

Fig. 2

GPS approach charts are similar to regular approach charts in the protected airspace provided as primary (1,000 foot terrain/obstruction clearance) and secondary areas (500 foot terrain/obstruction clearance).

The magnifying glass insert shows how the obstacle protection looks when viewed as a slice. *S* stands for *secondary* and *P* stands for *primary* areas of protection. For convenience, let's refer to the total width of protection on either side of the airway/feeder route by the number string 2-4-4-2, meaning two nautical miles of secondary protection, four nautical miles of primary protection with these values mirrored on the other side of the airway.

The differences between GPS and non-GPS approaches often begin on the initial approach segment. On non-GPS approaches, the airway, feeder route and initial approach segments provide 2-4-4-2 obstacle protection all the way to the intermediate fix.

Not so on GPS approaches. Here, the 2-4-4-2 protected airspace of the initial approach segment (it begins at the IAF) ramps down to 1-2-2-1 at a point where a 30 nautical mile arc from the airport (airport reference point) intersects that segment (Figure 2). Just for reference, all navigational points on a GPS chart are technically "waypoints" unless the point results from a hole caused by a sharp pencil, in which case it would be called a "waypoke."

It's perfectly accurate, however, to also refer to waypoints as *fixes* (not to suggest that they're broken, of course, or that they have addiction issues). In this chapter I'll refer to them as waypoints.

Back to lower math. On the GPS initial approach segment, you have a *steeper slope* on the secondary protection, because you drop from 1000 feet of protection to zero in the span of just a mile (keep in mind that, at 30 nm from the airport, secondary protection tapers from 1000 feet at its center to ZERO at its periphery). And, you now have two rather than 4 miles of primary protection. So, campers, within 30 miles of the airport, at 2.75 miles from the center of the route you have only 125 feet of clearance that's guaranteed dragon-free. Make mine pure milk, hold the espresso.

The closer this approach brings you to the airport, the smaller the primary and secondary obstacle protection areas become. And this makes sense, since the objective of any instrument approach is to bring you as close to the runway and as low as possible so you'll have the best opportunity of seeing it and landing visually. By ramping down the protected airspace as you approach the runway—this is where you'll typically find fewer and shorter obstacles—chart builders are able to provide you with the lowest minimum descent altitudes in preparation for landing. And the lower the minimum altitudes and required visibilities for the approach, the greater the chance you'll see the runway when the conditions are marginal.

The question is, how does this change in the protective geometry of the primary area affect you and your GPS equipment? Let's see.

Changing CDI Course Sensitivity

While operating in the enroute structure and more than 30 miles from the destination airport, your GPS's course needle (the course deviation indicator or CDI in your VOR omni head that's now slaved to the GPS when flying GPS approaches) has a dot-scale sensitivity of five nautical miles (we call this the GPS's *enroute mode*). This means that for every dot the CDI needle is from the center position, you're off by one nautical mile (there are typically five white dots on either side of center, unless it's snowing in there) as shown in Figure 3, position A. For convenience, I'll refer to this as a CDI scaling of +/– 5 nm. A five-dot deflection puts you five nautical miles off course, and dot's dot. When the CDI is used for VOR navigation, however, each dot of deflection represents two degrees of course deviation.

The moment you are 30 miles from the airport (and have either manually armed or configured the GPS to fly an approach) you'll enter what is known as the *terminal mode* of the approach. If you're thinking that's some sort of sick FAA double entendre, I'm not going to discourage that thinking; it will help you remember that the margin for error just went down drastically. Step back from that

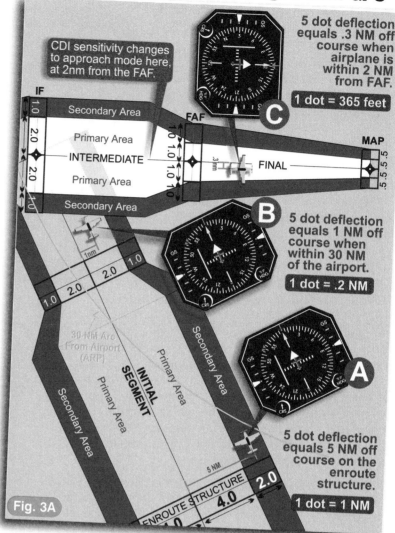

How CDI Sensitivity Changes with GPS

CDI sensitivity changes to approach mode here, at 2nm from the FAF.

5 dot deflection equals .3 NM off course when airplane is within 2 NM from FAF.

1 dot = 365 feet

5 dot deflection equals 1 NM off course when within 30 NM of the airport.

1 dot = .2 NM

5 dot deflection equals 5 NM off course on the enroute structure.

1 dot = 1 NM

IF · Secondary Area · Primary Area · INTERMEDIATE · Primary Area · Secondary Area · FAF · FINAL · MAP · 3nm · 1nm · 30 NM Arc From Airport (ARP) · INITIAL SEGMENT · Primary Area · Secondary Area · Secondary Area · Primary Area · 5 NM · ENROUTE STRUCTURE · Fig. 3A

When flying GPS approaches, CDI sensitivity will automatically change based on the airplane's position from the airport and its position along the approach course.

Starbucks. Steady, Big Boy. At this juncture, the CDI scale scaling automatically changes to +/– 1 nm. Each dot is a 0.2 nm deviation, and at five dots deflection you're a mile off course (Figure 3A, position B).

At two miles from the final approach fix (FAF), you enter the *approach mode* of this approach. The CDI scaling (five dots of deflection) automatically changes to +/– 0.3 nm. That's 0.3 spread over all five dots, not 0.3 per dot (Figure 3A, position C). Each dot now represents approximately 365 feet of course deviation. At this juncture, I'd suggest switching to distilled water.

Because of this increasing CDI sensitivity (and because your GPS unit now enables you to determine your position with great accuracy), the boundaries of protected airspace on GPS approaches can be built to much tighter geometric tolerances (far more tolerance than your geometry teacher had, that's for sure). This is good, because it means you are able to fly approaches with the lowest possible minimums.

Perhaps the biggest difference between RNAV (GPS) and non-RNAV approaches (i.e., VOR, NDB, etc) is in the

"Ever Stop to Think, and Forget to Start Again?"

In a previous issue we published an article titled "Code A/ Alert" that featured a report from a general aviation pilot who had filed an IFR flight plan with the equipment notation *Code /A*. The pilot requested radar vectors for a route short-cut. The Center controller asked whether the aircraft was equipped with GPS, and the pilot replied, "VFR GPS." The pilot was then handed over to another Center controller who rerouted him to a distant VOR fix. Here's what happened next, in the pilot's words...

All was going well until we were handed over to Approach, who complained that we were filed equipment /A but were flying to a distant fix on GPS navigation. He said I should have refused the unsolicited rerouting by Center. I remain confused, as it's my understanding that using any GPS as an adjunct to flying an assigned radar vector to a fix is legal...

(1) There is nothing in the FARs that prevents a pilot from requesting, or a controller from granting, a radar vector routing to any fix, as long as the pilot complies with altitude assignments and other FAR requirements. If ATC grants the request, the controller is responsible for radar monitoring until the pilot is able to proceed direct using the certified navigation equipment on board. In the incident reported to ASRS, the pilot's aircraft was /A equipped, so the primary equipment capability was DME and transponder with Mode C as filed for the flight.

(2) The use of VFR GPS to "aid" navigation to a cleared fix is also not contrary to the FARs, if certain criteria are met. Our FAA headquarters source explained it this way:

Suppose he [the ASRS reporter] had requested and been approved a clearance direct to XYZ and had used a VFR GPS to execute the clearance. Generally, the FARs are permissive, not restrictive, as long as the resulting operation does not reduce the original level of safety. Since the FAA has provided operational approval guidance on the use of VFR RNAV systems in Class A airspace under radar control (see Order 8400.10, Air Transportation Operations Inspectors Handbook, Volume 4, Paragraph 23C(3)(d), using VFR GPS in this case would probably be OK. Additionally, the *Aeronautical Information Manual* seems to provide similar guidance.

Our Headquarters source added that the FAA does not actively promote the use of VFR GPS to comply with IFR clearances, but has initiated a research project to determine the feasibility of this type of operation.   **NASA Callback Report**

final approach course area. At the missed approach point (MAP), the primary area on either side of centerline is 0.5 nm in width. This is approximately 40% less than the primary protected area for many non-precision, non-RNAV approaches.

Enroute CDI Sensitivity with WAAS

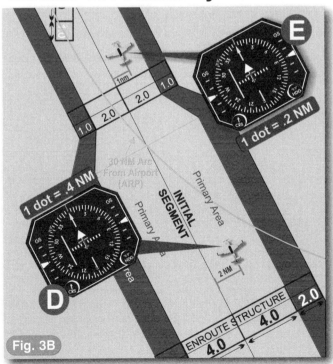

Fig. 3B

When using a WAAS certified IFR receiver (as compared to a regular IFR certified GPS unit), the CDI scaling is much more sensitive in the enroute mode. With a WAAS unit, you can expect your CDI scale scaling to be +/- 2 nm, with five dots representing 2 nm of course deviation (position D). This equates to .2 nm per dot when using a WAAS unit. The terminal mode sensitivity stays the same but the approach mode sensitivity increases similar to that of an ILS approach.

On the other hand, if you're using an IFR certified WAAS unit, then there are two big differences in CDI scaling compared to that of a regular IFR certified GPS. With WAAS, the enroute CDI scaling is +/- 2 nm. Each dot represents 0.4 nm deviation. Five dots represents 2 nm off course as shown in Figure 3B, position D. Terminal mode scaling is the same with WAAS, but approach mode scaling changes to be similar to that of an ILS approach (position E). (See *WAAS Protected Horizontal Limits*, Page 13-20).

As a general comparison, the protected airspace geometry on RNAV (GPS) final approach courses is similar to that found on ILS approaches, albeit not to the same degree, of course. This is especially so on WAAS-based approaches using glideslopes (i.e., LPVs, LNAV/VNAV, etc. See page 13-13 for more info on WAAS). This means that course deviations (and the accompanying rush of adrenaline) on a RNAV (GPS) approach should make you just as nervous as a similar deviation made on an ILS approach. So make sure you keep that needle centered when flying either of these approaches. Of course, I don't want to jelly your brain with minute minutiae here, but good instrument pilot that you are, you'll want to be aware of these things.

Because of the decrease in protected area and the requirement for greater navigational precision, not all RNAV equipment will meet the required navigational performance demanded by the approach design. Here's how to tell if your RNAV equipment makes the grade instead of the grate. We're about to test your GPS' mettle, to avoid tearing your metal.

Required Navigational Performance (RNP)

It makes no sense to have less obstacle-protected airspace without some means of assuring that your area navigation equipment (GPS in this case) is capable of remaining within the area that's without obstacles. So the concept of *required navigational performance* (RNP) was developed to help area navigation equipment designers and chart developers keep pilots safe.

Basically, RNP works like this. An approach chart maker carefully looks at the primary protected airspace throughout an approach. Then a group of engineers (not the kind that play with Legos, either), planners, politicians, managers, and other important folks make a decision about how accurate a navigation system needs to be for pilots to be safe flying a particular type of approach.

Most GPS approaches require an RNP of 0.3 to be allowed to fly today's standard GPS approach. Basically, this means that a pilot tracking a course on final approach with a centered needle can expect to be within 0.3 nm of the centerline 95% of the time. If the primary protected airspace on either side of the course centerline is 0.5 nm (see Figure 2 again), then you have a high probability of really *being* within this primary area if the needle says you're there (if your CDI is centered), despite whatever electronic hiccups, burps or irregularities there are in the navigational equipment.

Once the specific accuracy required of the area navigation equipment is determined, it becomes the required navigational performance value for that equipment. All IFR-certified GPS units in airplanes at the time of this writing meet RNP-0.3 performance standards. Your handheld GPS unit, which is not approved for use as sole means of navigation under IFR conditions, may not meet this RNP requirement. That's one of several reasons that handheld GPS units are not approved for making RNAV (GPS) approaches.

How do you know the required navigational performance of a particular approach? You can assume that the

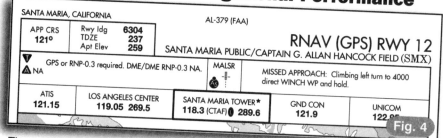

RNP - Required Navigational Performance

The required navigational performance for GPS approaches is 0.3. Other RNAV equipment may require a different value. If that RNAV equipment uses DME and has an RNP value of .5, then the RNAV approach above can't be used.

standard RNP for most GPS approaches is 0.3. If an approach requires a different RNP based on it being flown with area navigation equipment other than GPS, then that RNP value or RNP restriction will we displayed in the briefing area of the chart, as shown in Figure 4. The RNAV (GPS) Runway 12 approach to Santa Maria requires RNAV equipment (remember this can be GPS, inertial nav, VOR/DME RNAV, Loran, etc.) meeting an RNP-0.3 value if used to fly this approach.

Some RNAV units use DME cross referencing, referred to as DME/DME, to help determine the aircraft's position. The note says that you can't fly this approach with a unit based on that type of area navigation, even though the unit itself meets RNP-0.3 limits. One reason for this would be that the airplane could be beyond the service volume limits of one or more of the necessary DME stations at some point in the approach.

Now that you have a basic primer on the workings of GPS, let's take a closer look at GPS approach plates and their symbols.

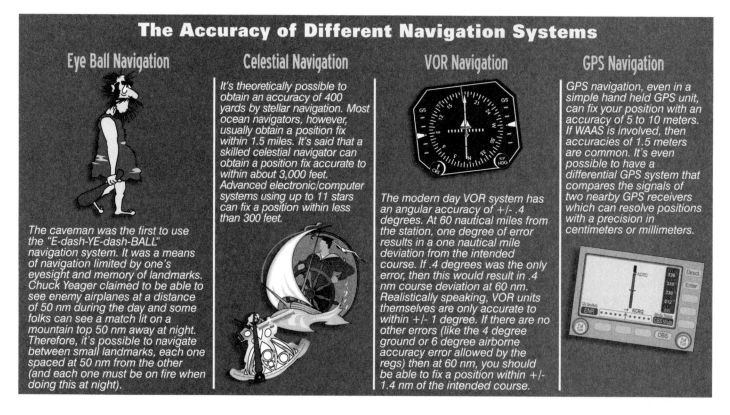

The Accuracy of Different Navigation Systems

Eye Ball Navigation

The caveman was the first to use the "E-dash-YE-dash-BALL" navigation system. It was a means of navigation limited by one's eyesight and memory of landmarks. Chuck Yeager claimed to be able to see enemy airplanes at a distance of 50 nm during the day and some folks can see a match lit on a mountain top 50 nm away at night. Therefore, it's possible to navigate between small landmarks, each one spaced at 50 nm from the other (and each one must be on fire when doing this at night).

Celestial Navigation

It's theoretically possible to obtain an accuracy of 400 yards by stellar navigation. Most ocean navigators, however, usually obtain a position fix within 1.5 miles. It's said that a skilled celestial navigator can obtain a position fix accurate to within about 3,000 feet. Advanced electronic/computer systems using up to 11 stars can fix a position within less than 300 feet.

VOR Navigation

The modern day VOR system has an angular accuracy of +/- .4 degrees. At 60 nautical miles from the station, one degree of error results in a one nautical mile deviation from the intended course. If .4 degrees was the only error, then this would result in .4 nm course deviation at 60 nm. Realistically speaking, VOR units themselves are only accurate to within +/- 1 degree. If there are no other errors (like the 4 degree ground or 6 degree airborne accuracy error allowed by the regs) then at 60 nm, you should be able to fix a position within +/- 1.4 nm of the intended course.

GPS Navigation

GPS navigation, even in a simple hand held GPS unit, can fix your position with an accuracy of 5 to 10 meters. If WAAS is involved, then accuracies of 1.5 meters are common. It's even possible to have a differential GPS system that compares the signals of two nearby GPS receivers which can resolve positions with a precision in centimeters or millimeters.

The Standard I GPS Chart Format

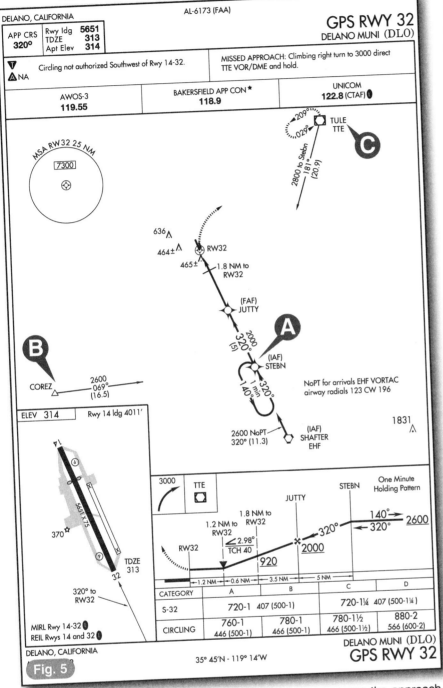

Fig. 5

The "Standard I" GPS approach chart format is named because the approach course appearance is basically a straight line that looks like an "I".

Let's start with the four basic configurations for GPS approach charts: Standard I, Standard T, Modified T and TAA. We'll discuss each of them because, like spinach, it's good for you. We won't, however, discuss GPS overlay approaches since these are slated to disappear soon, leaving only stand-alone approaches standing in their place.

Besides, I know you wouldn't stand for it if I did.

Standard I Chart Format

Figure 5 shows a typical standalone GPS approach, this one to Delano, California. The first thing that stands out on this chart is the four-point waypoint symbol on the plan view, sort of a New Age asterisk, which we quickly see is a waypoint known as STEBN (Figure 5, position A). There's no reason to print DME mileage on the plan view, since GPS doesn't use traditional DME. Instead, GPS is capable of measuring distances between individual waypoints on its own. It neither seeks nor accepts help from other instruments.

The intersection names along the approach procedure track in the plan view are found in the GPS database. Notice the holding pattern course reversal is used in lieu of the standard barb-type procedure turn. This type of approach might require a holding pattern for course reversal, depending on which of the feeder routes you happen to be on when cleared for the approach.

For instance, if you're inbound from COREZ intersection or TTE VOR (Figure 5, position B, C), then a course reversal is mandatory (the routes don't show NoPT). The chart note below and to the right of STEBN says that if you're over EHF VOR and proceeding inbound, no procedure turn is allowed. If you're being radar vectored to final, then it's always understood that there would also be no procedure turn allowed, unless permission is obtained first.

The feeder routes on this chart come from all directions, and they all take you to STEBN intersection. The approach configuration on this chart is known as the *Standard I* because the approach course (the *approach procedure track*) looks straight, like an *I* (stand far away from the chart, use smudgy glasses, squint and use your imagination here, but not someone else's imagination. You'll see it, eventually. If a 3D pattern appears, you looked at it way too long). The minimums section on this chart has the same formatting as that on non-GPS approach charts.

Making Sense of Varying CDI Sensitivity

I'm sure that by now you are definitely getting the picture that the GPS changes CDI sensitivity to match the reduction in the primary protected area along the approach. Much as tolerances tighten as you transition from VOR navigation to an ILS, the navigational sensitivity increases as you get closer to the airport, and so must navigational vigilance. This is neither bad nor dangerous, as long as you don't get sloppy and assume there's a limitless cushion of safety.

How do you spell relief? Keep the needle centered!

Standard T Chart Format

Things get a bit more interesting with the Manassas Regional RNAV (GPS) RWY 16L approach, shown in Figure 6. First, notice that the chart heading uses the title *RNAV (GPS)*. This is the heading format that will eventually be used for all GPS approaches. This is an RNAV approach that uses GPS. As we've discussed before, some RNAV units use VOR/DME while others may use inertial navigation systems and so on.

On the plan view you'll see a major difference, beginning with something known as the *Standard T* approach configuration. This configuration derives its name from the look of the initial approach structure, beginning with corner IAFs at CIDIT and PITIY intersections (Figure 6, position A and B). The approach procedure tracks and the two initial approach routings are perpendicular to each other, creating what appears to be a *T* shape (even if you skipped Alphabet Day at night school, you can easily recognize the T formation here).

The main difference between the Standard T format and other chart formats is that the Standard T doesn't provide a holding pattern for course reversal. In fact, it's the elimination of the course reversal that makes the Standard T format a bit superior to the Standard I format. In lieu of a course reversal, the Standard T allows you to fly direct to either of two (sometimes three) corner IAFs to become established inbound on the approach. These IAFs take you to the intermediate segment waypoint, shown as GIGEY in Figure 6, position C. From here, the approach design attempts to align the runway's centerline with three things: the intermediate segment, the final approach fix (FAF), and the missed approach waypoint. Local conditions don't always permit this alignment (chiropractors are even consulted when there is a misalignment, often to no avail), but the formatting still strives for the basic T formation.

The Standard T format also includes the use of *flyover waypoints* (FOWP) in the plan view (Figure 6, position D

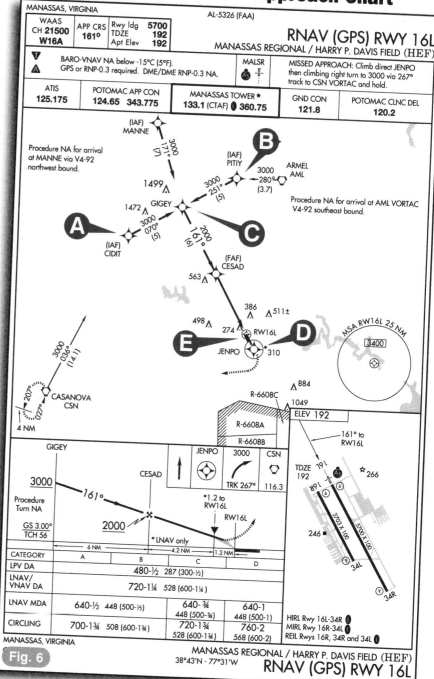

Fig. 6

The "Standard T" GPS approach chart format is so named because the approach course and its initial approach segments give it a "T" shape.

and E). Flyover waypoints shown on an approach chart are identified by the typical four-point waypoint symbol surrounded by a circle, as shown in the RW16L missed approach point and by JENPO (Can't see it? OK, no more arc welding without a helmet for you). Flyover waypoints

The Modified T GPS Approach Chart

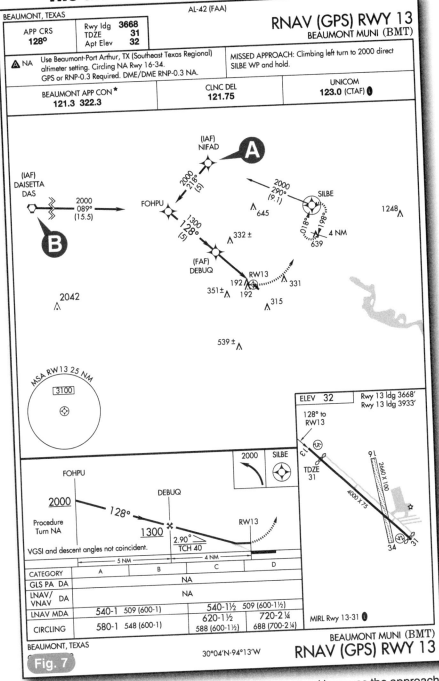

Fig. 7

The "Modified T" GPS approach chart format is so named because the approach course and its single perpendicular initial approach segment (one of two segments possible) give it an almost "T" shape.

either of these intersections can reduce critical terrain and obstruction clearance or prevent your GPS from sequencing between the waypoints necessary to complete a missed approach.

Waypoints made up of four-pointed stars without outside circles are called *flyby* waypoints (FBWP) as shown by NIFAD (Figure 7, position A). These require the use of turn anticipation to avoid overshooting the next flight segment. Fortunately, most GPS units provide you with turn anticipation warnings in the form of flashing lights, arrows or other cues, and this allows you to turn early and end up on the course centerline. And when you're just learning to use GPS, your instructor often provides turn anticipation warnings in the form of waving hands, grunts, and the occasional whack of a WAC chart on the panel. If he whacks you upside the head, this is known as receiving a new heading.

The RNAV (GPS) vs. GPS chart format also includes some major changes in minimums formatting. Let's cover a few more plan view changes before we spend a big chunk of time on the new minimums section found on RNAV approach charts.

Modified T Chart Format

Figure 7 represents the Beaumont Muni RNAV (GPS) Runway 34 Modified T chart format. You usually won't find a holding pattern used for course reversal on Modified T charts, either. Notice that there is only one corner initial approach fix at NIFAD (Figure 7, position A), and it's perpendicular to the approach procedure track.

It's possible that the routes from these corner IAFs will make angles to the approach procedure track that are not perpendicular, thus making a sloppy T formation. If can even begin to look like the letter *P*, creating the tepee formation (OK, there's no such thing).

It's even possible for one or both corner IAFs to be missing, leaving other routes (e.g., from Daisetta VOR, Figure 7, position B) to help establish the airplane on the approach structure. Now that's what you call modified, isn't it?

Yes, it's modified but it still looks T-ish, I didn't lie. I don't want to be like parents who tell their kids never to lie, except at the movies. Then they ask for two adult tickets and one child ticket for their six-foot tall, 250 pound, nine-year-old son. Like the Standard T format, the Modified T format is also designed for approaches to single and multiple runways.

are airspace fixes that your airplane *must cross* before making any turns. This keeps you within the boundaries of the (often small) primary obstacle protection area. An early turn at the missed approach point, for instance, might add a real life treetop-shaped air freshener to your airplane. This, in turn, could cause your insurance company to get treed off at you. When they said they'd insure you against loss of life or limb, this is *not* what they had in mind.

Flyover waypoints are typically found at the missed approach waypoint (MAWP) and the missed approach holding point (MAHP). Making premature turns prior to

TAA Chart Format

Figure 8, the RNAV (GPS) Runway 12 approach, shows the queen bee of them all. This is the last of the RNAV approach configurations, and it's based on the Terminal Arrival Area (TAA) concept. The TAA uses the Standard T approach configuration, but with one distinct difference—it normally includes a holding pattern for course reversal. And the holding pattern, just like the course reversal holding pattern found on non-GPS charts, begins at the fix (waypoint in this case) where the initial approach fix begins, which is the initial approach fix on RNAV charts. The T configuration usually has an IAF at its top center position. This makes for three IAFs on the upper portion of the T formation.

The TAA format is the ideal for RNAV (GPS) approach charts, because it provides for arrivals from all directions without the need for radar vectoring (not that this precludes radar vectoring if it's available). The Standard TAA has three areas: *a straight-in area,* a *left base area,* and a *right base area.* If you are in any one of those areas, ATC can clear you for the approach via the specific intersection identifying these areas and you'll know precisely what to do to complete the approach (or you will in a moment). Let's see how this works.

Area A in Figure 9 is the straight-in area. The upper portion of this area is bounded by a 30 nm arc centered on YBDOR, which is an IAF. The bottom portion of this half-circle shape is bounded by lines perpendicular to the segments extending from the centered fix (YBDOR), through the IAFs, RODBY and MACHO (Hey? I wonder how those neat sounding names managed to get hooked together? That's amazing).

The left base area, area C, (it's to your left as you fly the approach) is bounded by a 30 nm arc centered on the left at MACHO intersection (an IAF). This area shares an upper boundary with the straight-in area (the 218 degree bearing to YBDOR) and is bounded on the side by the inbound approach course segment (the route between YBDOR and ULOST).

The right base area, area B (perhaps not surprisingly, it's on your right as you fly the approach inbound. Who would have thought?), is bounded by a 30 nm arc centered on the right initial approach waypoint, RODBY (an IAF).

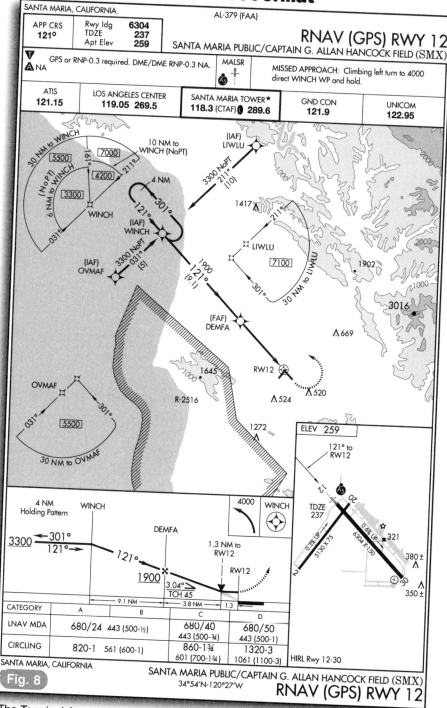

TAA Chart Format

Fig. 8

The Terminal Area Arrival (TAA) chart format is designed to make the transition to the approach structure easy for pilots and controllers. With a clearance to either of the chart's IAFs, a pilot can easily transition onto the approach structure without the aid of a controller. This makes it easy on the pilot because he or she knows what's expected of him and it makes it easy on the controller because she doesn't have to provide vectors to the approach.

This area also shares an upper boundary with the straight-in area (the 038 degree bearing to YBDOR), and is bounded on the side by the inbound approach course segment (the route between YBDOR and ULOST).

The lateral boundaries and minimum altitudes (known as *TAA minimum altitudes*) within each of these three areas are defined by the half or quarter-circle section sym-

TAA Entry Areas

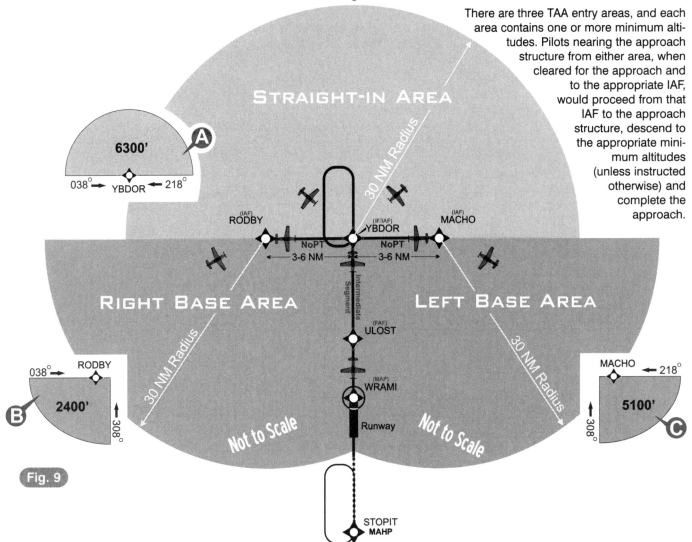

There are three TAA entry areas, and each area contains one or more minimum altitudes. Pilots nearing the approach structure from either area, when cleared for the approach and to the appropriate IAF, would proceed from that IAF to the approach structure, descend to the appropriate minimum altitudes (unless instructed otherwise) and complete the approach.

Fig. 9

bols located within or near each boundary. In the case of the straight-in area (section symbol A), the minimum altitude for the area is 6,300 feet and the lower boundaries to which this altitude applies are made up of the 038 and 218 degree bearings to the center waypoint (YBDOR). When you're within the boundaries of either of these base areas and ATC clears you for the approach, you may proceed to the appropriate IAF and fly the approach.

When Students Don't Read Their GPS Manual

When instructor Dan asks instrument student Bob to check on the number of GPS satellites he is receiving (meaning he wants Bob to access the satellite page on his Garmin GPS), Bob looks up into space in hope of detecting at least a few of these satellites.

For instance, look at airplane #1 in Figure 10. If you're in the right base area heading directly to OVMAF at 7,000 feet, ATC might say, "2132 Bravo, seven miles from OVMAF, cleared RNAV Runway 12 approach." You'll be expected to proceed to OVMAF, descend no lower than 5,500 feet until reaching OVMAF, then complete the approach.

Notice that the route from OVMAF to WINCH is marked *NoPT*. You're not allowed to use the holding pattern for course reversal unless you specifically obtain an ATC clearance to do so. There would be no need to reverse course in the holding pattern when approaching from any of these three areas, since no turn in excess of 90 degrees is required to align you with the intermediate segment. Of course, if you're exceptionally high and need to lose altitude before commencing the approach, then this is a good time to ask for a turn or two in the holding pattern.

Suppose you're 35 miles from OVMAF, heading directly to it at 7,000 feet from the right base area (airplane #2, Figure 10). If ATC clears you for the approach from this position, the clearance will go like this, "2132 Bravo, cleared to OVAMF. Maintain 7,000 feet until entering the TAA, cleared RNAV Runway 12 approach." Since you're beyond the posted altitude limits of the TAA's right base area, ATC issued a minimum altitude restriction to make it clear exactly what you're supposed to do until entering this area. Once you're within 30 miles of OVAMF you may descend to 5,500 feet and fly the approach. Remember, no procedure turn is allowed without permission on this route.

The straight-in area may have additional divisions in the form of pie shaped sectors, or it may have stepdown sections based on lesser arcs from the centered fix (as shown by position D in Figure 10). Suppose you're inbound to WINCH from the northwest and your bearing to the intersection is anywhere between 161 degrees (position E) and 031 degrees (position F). You're also within a range of anywhere from 30 nm to 6 nm of the intersection. The minimum altitude in this instance is 5,500 feet. Once you move to within 6 nm of WINCH, your minimum altitude becomes 3,300 feet.

Once cleared for the approach, you can descend to any of these minimum altitudes, assuming no altitude restrictions were given. No procedure turn is allowed when approaching WINCH from anywhere in the straight-in area. If you were

approaching WINCH between a bearing of 161 degrees and 211 degrees (position E and G), the minimum altitude would be 7,000 feet (between 30 and 10 nm of WINCH) and 4,200 feet anywhere within 10 nm of WINCH.

If, for instance, you're 5 nm northwest of WINCH at 4,000 feet (Figure 10, airplane 3) and ATC clears you for the approach, the clearance should go something like this, "2132 Bravo, you're 5 miles northwest of WINCH, maintain at or above 3,300 until WINCH, cleared RNAV Runway 12 approach." Since the 3,300 foot altitude sector includes a *NoPT* restriction, you are expected to turn straight in at WINCH and fly the approach.

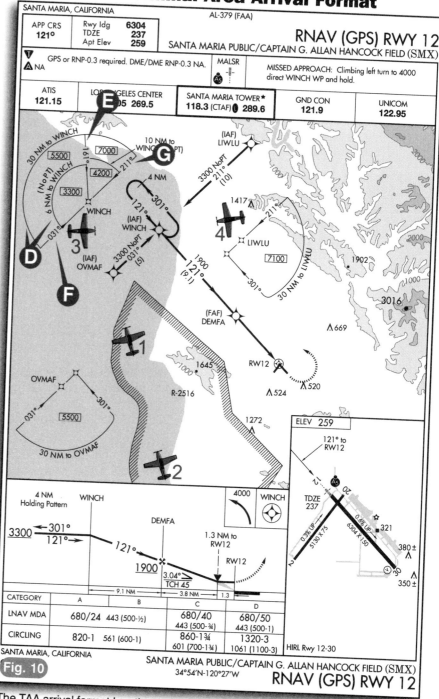

The TAA arrival format has three different arrival areas, all of which are intended to make transitions onto GPS approaches easier for pilots and controllers.

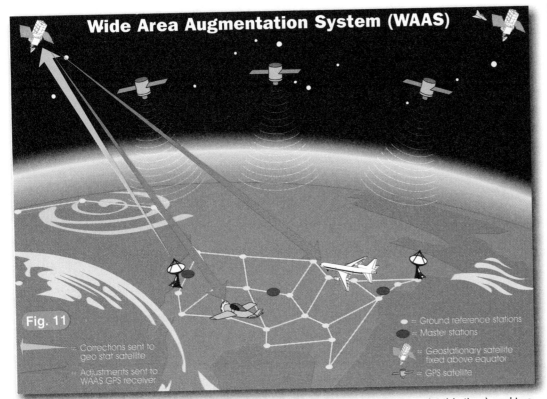

WAAS consists of 25 ground stations (at this time), two master ground stations (at this time) and two geosynchronous communication satellites, all of which improve GPS accuracy.

ing water out of a fire hose, with a fire raging behind you, isn't it? I know you may feel a little awkward here with all these new terms. It's kind of like bringing out your guitar in front of a bunch of professional musicians, playing a bit then having one of them ask, "Do you take requests?" and when you say "yes," the person says, "Can you play somewhere else?" Fret not mon frere. You can always go back over this chapter. These concepts are important for those who want to use their GPS as something more than an enroute entertainment center. So read and re-read if you need to. It's your book.

Now that you understand the basic differences between standard and RNAV charts, let's look at a few additional differences. In particular, I'm speaking of the minimums section. Before we begin dissecting the depiction of the required minimum altitudes and visibilities, we need to first review a few basics of GPS/WAAS.

Now, let's suppose you're in airplane 4, Figure 10, and are 10 nm east of WINCH, heading directly to WINCH at 8,000 feet. If ATC clears you for the approach, the clearance might go like this, "2132 Bravo, you're 10 miles east of WINCH, cleared direct WINCH, maintain at or above 7,100 feet until WINCH, cleared for RNAV Runway 12 approach." In this instance ATC would certainly expect you to enter the holding pattern for course reversal before proceeding inbound on course.

One thing you should have noticed by now is that TAA's don't have MSAs (minimum sector altitudes). Instead, the *TAA minimum altitudes* serve the purpose of providing safe altitudes. But unlike MSAs, TAA minimum altitudes are flyable altitudes that guarantee you at least 1,000 feet of obstacle clearance (or 2,000 feet in mountainous areas) as well as navigation and communication capability.

It's also interesting to note that the distances of the two side IAFs from the center IAF are chosen to accommodate the size and performance of aircraft most likely to use that airport. Typically, the distances between the side and the center IAFs are three to six nautical miles. These distances are carefully chosen to provide you with minimum difficulty when transitioning onto the approach procedure track (no, not you personally. The FAA doesn't show up at your door during approach construction, hold up their mock chart and ask, "Does this look OK to you? What da ya think pal?" But it's a nice thought, eh?). As a general rule, TAAs will be depicted on approach charts with consideration for traffic congestion, obstacle clearance, chart design and airspace restrictions when possible.

Well, how's that for an initial introduction to RNAV (GPS) approach chart construction? It's kind of like drink-

WAAS Up?

While GPS is certainly accurate enough for IFR lateral navigation, it has its ups and downs when it comes to being precisely precise enough for accurate vertical navigation. In other words, you could lose your empennage (or at least grind part of it down) if you relied on GPS to measure your height above sea level and used that measurement to make an instrument descent to an airport. The result could be a *real* letdown. So, the government decided to fix this with a program called Wide Area Augmentation System (WAAS).

No, Wide Area Augmentation is *not* cosmetic surgery. WAAS is a system that improves GPS accuracy dramatically in both the horizontal and vertical dimensions. With WAAS, it's possible to have an accuracy of one to two meters (3-6 feet) horizontally and two to three meters vertically.

As shown in Figure 11, the WAAS hardware, at this time, consists of 25 precisely surveyed wide area ground reference stations (WRS) located around the U.S., including Puerto Rico, Hawaii, and Alaska, two wide area master ground-based stations (WMS), two geosynchronous communication satellites (GEO) and two transponder satellites (Noah must have made the selection and taken two of each kind to keep them from getting lonely. Perhaps the curved path the satellites appear to make in the sky should be known as Noah's Arc.)

Along Track Distance (ATD): Getting the Right Point

Your GPS is not a DME, but sometimes the difference is lost on pilots, who in turn become lost on approaches.

One of the differences of a GPS operating in Leg Mode is that its mileage counter always counts down to the active waypoint. This count is known as ATD or along track distance. Unlike a DME, the GPS is so smart that when it reaches a waypoint, it automatically tees up the next waypoint for you, so it's always counting down a distance to someplace ahead.

The Figure on the right shows the RNAV (GPS) Runway 24 approach into Carlsbad, CA. From the plan view and profile view, it's clear that the missed approach point for the approach is located at the runway threshold (as are most RNAV missed approach points). When you fly the RNAV (GPS) approach, the mileage you see on your GPS unit will be your distance "to" the active waypoint along the final approach course.

If you're on the approach course and inside JABAL intersection (the FAF, position A), your active waypoint will be the next upcoming fix, until reaching the missed approach point (RW24). Your GPS will count down the mileage to each succeeding fix. When reaching ZUXAX, your GPS mileage will read 2.5 miles to the MAP (RW24), eventually reading 0.0 miles at the threshold or MAP. At that point, you'd select the missed approach holding point and fly direct to it. Since this is now the active waypoint, the GPS mileage starts counting down to that intersection. The GPS eventually reads 0.0 miles when you're at the IBUGE.

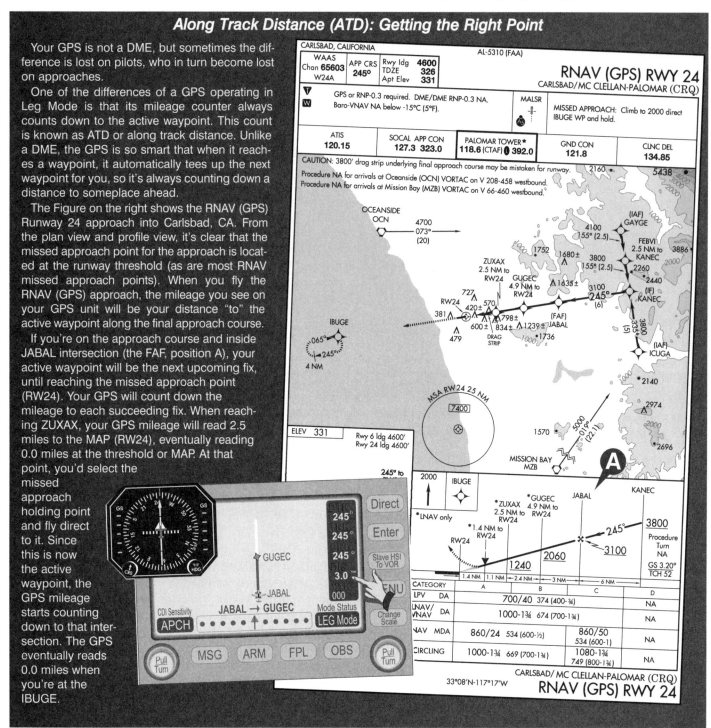

The 25 WRS ground stations receive GPS signals from the regular GPS satellites and look for signal errors. Since the person who planted these 25 ground-based receiving stations knows their precise locations, any GPS error can be immediately detected and a correction sent to your GPS unit (thank goodness we didn't forget to ask him to write down these locations).

Like most pilots, you probably like things precise and consistent, so you're perhaps a bit distressed to find that GPS is less than perfect. Why are there errors in a GPS signal? After all, it's not as if these satellites have to turn to avoid Cessnas. Blame it mostly on nature. It's a long way to outer space, and due to a variety of spacey factors (or Spacely Sprockets), the precise position of each GPS satellite is a plus or minus five meters matter. Not bad, really, when you consider the distance, speed of the satellites, errors in signal propagation, sunspots, moonglow, and heaven (literally) only knows what else.

The timing signal in a satellite's atomic clock is subject to an error of about three meters, and free electrons in the ionosphere produce an uncertainty of eight meters (if there were a charge for those electrons we probably wouldn't have these problems. Oh the *ion-y*). Don't let the stress of your distress at the discovery of a bit of GPS imprecision upset you too much. Raw GPS accuracy is still impressive, despite these small errors. Cooked in WAAS, it's even better.

The 25 ground-based (WRS) stations send their information to the master ground-based station (WMS). Here, corrections are applied to determine the GPS error for a particular part of the country. Yep, different parts of the country might have different GPS errors. After all, the satellites have different positions when seen from different parts of the country, to say nothing of variable atmospheric conditions at different places across the U.S. or electromagnetic interference from who knows what may be on the ground nearby. The correction message is then uplinked to one of the two geosynchronous communications satellites (GEO). We have to hope there isn't a busy signal, because the GEO satellite is responsible for broadcasting the correction on a specific GPS frequency, to be picked up by anyone who has a WAAS-capable receiver. If you're on approach and have one of these receivers, then this would be you, which is really the most important point.

How do you benefit from all these calculational shenanigans? Your WAAS receiver can, with correction, be accurate to within a few meters vertically and horizontally. Of course, WAAS doesn't do you any good if you didn't purchase a WAAS-capable GPS receiver (don't fret over what WAAS, but what can be on your next purchase). Fortunately, WAAS-capable receivers are available for IFR use. There are even handheld GPS units having WAAS capability to assist you in VFR flying. (Remember, there are no IFR certified handheld GPS receivers, WAAS or not, on the market and probably won't be in the future. These units are simply not likely to ever meet the installation standards of Technical Standard Orders 129, governing IFR certified GPS installations or TSO 146, governing GPS units augmented by WAAS.)

Without WAAS, you can still fly GPS approaches on your IFR certified GPS. When you do, you're using what is properly called *lateral navigation (LNAV)*. This is what you've been doing when you've flown regular RNAV (GPS) approaches. With a WAAS-capable IFR certified GPS receiver, you now have the capability of generating a glideslope. This allows you to do something called LNAV/VNAV (sometimes referred to as L/VNAV) approaches which are approaches that use both lateral and vertical navigation. You can also fly something called LPV (Localizer Performance with Vertical guidance) approaches. These are precision approaches that provide horizontal and vertical guidance (through a software generated glideslope) as accurate as any ILS. They can provide decision altitudes as low as 200 feet with touchdown and visibility minimums of ½ mile.

Now that you understand the basics, let's take a look at the minimums section of an RNAV approach chart. This is

The RNAV Chart Minimums Section

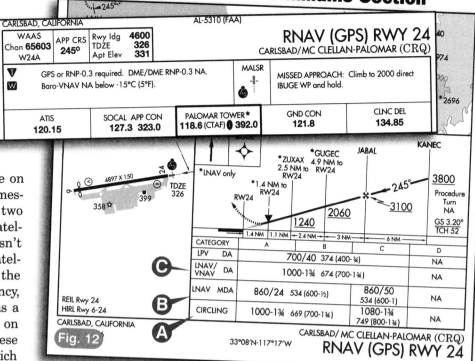

RNAV charts can have four different rows of minimums. LPV with a decision altitude, LNAV/VNAV with a decision altitude, and LNAV with an MDA and a circling MDA.

how we determine where the rubber meets (or at least approaches) the runway.

The RNAV Chart Minimums Section

Figure 12 shows the minimums section for the NACO RNAV (GPS) Runway 24 approach to Carlsbad, California. At first glance, the horizontal minimums equipment section on the left is a little different from the standard format to which you've become accustomed. Let's start at the bottom and work our way up.

The last line (position A) shows the circling minimums for this approach. There's nothing new in this section. The MDAs and required visibilities make their appearance here. You are already familiar with these items.

The next line up lists the LNAV MDA (position B). This is the MDA for lateral navigation. In other words, these are the minimums for flying an ordinary non-precision GPS approach. If you were cleared for the approach and crossed JABAL at 3,100 feet, then you could descend to 2,060 until reaching GUGEC, 1,240 feet until reaching ZUXAX, then 860 feet to the missed approach point (intersections are named after the aliens that crashed at Roswell).

If, on the other hand, you happen to have a WAAS-capable, IFR-certified GPS receiver, you have the option of flying an *approach with vertical guidance (APV)* to this runway (these approaches have decision altitudes but are not technically considered to be precision approaches). APV minima are found in the next two lines up, starting with the letters LNAV/VNAV (Figure 12, position C). If you flew to the LNAV/VNAV minimums your decision altitude (DA) would be 1,000 feet and the required visibility would be 1¾ miles. The slope of the descent path would be

3.20 degrees, as shown in the profile view above the threshold crossing height (TCH) of 52 feet (Figure 12, position D). In short (or in pants), you'd fly a glideslope just as you would on an ILS, except this glideslope is generated by your WAAS–capable, IFR certified GPS receiver. Since your CDI display (your VOR or HSI display) is slaved to your GPS, you'd fly the glideslope down to DA as you would on any ILS approach. You can expect the glideslope to become active near the intermediate fix (IF).

In this instance, you'd probably intersect the glideslope somewhere before JABAL at a minimum of 3,100 feet and fly it down to the DA of 1,000 feet (Figure 12, position B). At DA, if you didn't have the required visibility and/or the runway environment in sight, you'd execute the missed approach.

Keep in mind that, when flying to LNAV/VNAV minimums, you may *not* level off at the DA and continue to the end of the runway in level flight. The DA *is* the point where you must make a decision to land or execute the missed approach, perhaps while singing the line from a 1960s hit, "Did you ever have to finally decide?" As with all approaches having a decision altitude, you're brought in low and dropped off a slight distance from the threshold. If you're on glidepath at DA, you're in a very good configuration for landing. There is usually little or no reconfiguration needed until touchdown. On the other hand, the LNAV/VNAV DA is 140 feet higher than the LNAV MDA here? Isn't a precision approach supposed to get you down lower and put you in a position for landing? What gives?

The RNAV Chart Minimums Section

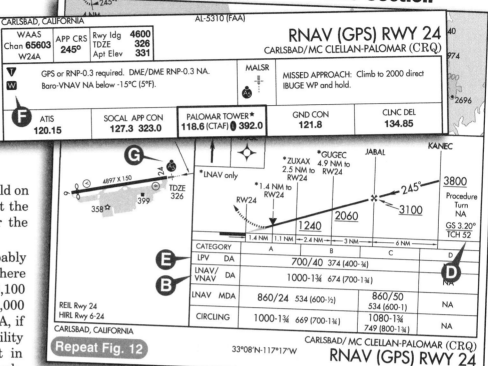

RNAV charts can have four different rows of minimums. LPV with a decision altitude, LNAV/VNAV with a decision altitude, and LNAV with an MDA and a circling MDA.

The answer lies in something called *Baro-VNAV* or *barometric vertical navigation* capability. To fly the glideslope of a LNAV/VNAV approach without a WAAS-capable GPS receiver, you'd need an airplane with Baro-VNAV capability. This is a navigational system with a computer that provides vertical guidance between two waypoints (or a descending angle from a single waypoint) based on barometric altitude, as measured by a special barometric altimeter in your airplane in much the same way an altitude encoder measures pressure. If this is the first time you've heard of this, then there's a good chance that your airplane probably doesn't have Baro-VNAV capability.

Limits of Hand-Held GPS

Many hand-held GPS units have an inherent system limitation, as our reporter discovered.

Flying VFR, I was using a hand-held GPS for navigational reference. While en route, position and status seemed fine. According to the GPS position, a "big airport" was getting closer and closer, but still out of the overlying Class C airspace. From a visual standpoint, the position was definitely in Class C airspace. When I landed at ABC, the GPS indicated the location was XYZ [about 40 nm west]. I turned the unit off, then back on, and the position now indicated ABC.

I called the manufacturer, which had received numerous calls about erroneous positions. A new satellite had been put in orbit; there were now a total of 26 satellites. My unit only showed 25. The manufacturer suggested leaving the GPS on for 45 minutes to acquire the information from the new satellite. I did so, and my unit now shows 26 satellites. The GPS positions seem correct.

Conclusion: use hand-held GPS as a reference only.

According to the reporter's conversation with the manufacturer, hand-held GPS units currently in use do not have the RAIM—Receiver Autonomous Integrity Monitoring—that is built into installed, IFR-certified units. The RAIM monitors the actual navaid signal to assure that there is adequate signal strength for navigation in the selected mode. If the signal is not sufficient, an error message will occur. This is analogous to the 'OFF' flag showing on the VOR receiver when the aircraft is out of range for adequate signal acquisition. Since the reporter's GPS unit did not have RAIM capability, there was no way to know that the unit was providing erroneous information.

Because of the inherent limitations of hand-held units, pilots should carry and use the appropriate charts as cross-reference material, rather than relying solely on GPS.

NASA Callback Report

You Thought You Saw a What?

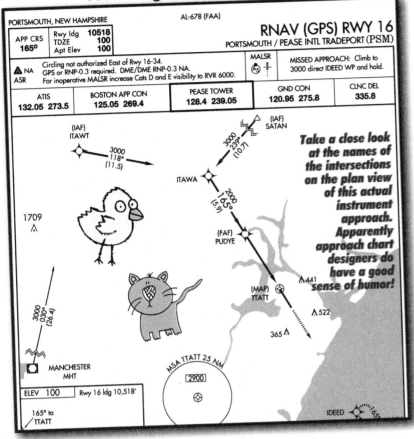

This is equipment normally found in larger corporate aircraft, or combined with fancy airline flight management systems and sophisticated coffee making machines that pilots really like. It's not cheap equipment, either. So don't go to Radio Hut looking for one. The issue here is that Baro-VNAV uses an altimeter, and as with all barometric altimeters, it's affected by extremes in temperature (see *How Cold is Cold: A Temperature Induced Altimeter Error*, page 2-23). Therefore, higher LNAV/VNAV minimums may be a result of compensation for expected temperature errors. Also, LNAV/VNAV approach minimums were created under TSO-c129 specs (before WAAS was in use) and, therefore, they require stricter obstacle clearance criteria which can also result in an unusually high decision altitude (more on this later).

On the other hand, there are minimums that offer near-ILS performance. The very top line in Figure 12, position E, shows the letters *LPV DA* (the next set of APV minima). LPV stands for Localizer Performance with Vertical guidance. LPV minimums require that you have a WAAS capable receiver in your airplane. Just to be clear here, you need a WAAS capable receiver to fly *any* software generated glideslope (except for those with Baro-VNAV who can fly to LNAV/VNAV minimums). An ordinary GPS unit won't do. That's because an ordinary GPS unit can't generate a glideslope, leaving the glideslope needle on your HSI inactive, or off.

If you were cleared for the RNAV Runway 24 approach at Carlsbad and your WAAS receiver indicated that LPV minimums were allowed (more on how you'll know this shortly), you could descend to a DA of 700 feet. The visi-

bility minimums for this approach are 4,000 feet or ¾ mile visibility. This approach brings you 300 feet lower and a lot closer to the threshold than the LNAV/VNAV minimums do. This shows how WAAS was such a big improvement over Baro-VNAV for allowing lower approach minimums.

Keep in mind that to have LPV minimums as low as 200 HAT and ½ mile visibility there must be approach lighting available. Not all RNAV (GPS) approaches are made to runways with approach lights (i.e., MALSR, SSALR, ALSF), despite the fact that they may have LNAV/VNAV or LPV minimums. Even without approach lighting, it's possible to have LNAV/VNAV or LPV minimums of 200 HAT and ¾ mile visibility, and that's not bad at all. Without approach lights, however, it's a lot more difficult to actually identify the runway environment for landing. In the case of Carlsbad, the airport sketch to the left shows that approach lighting does exist on Runway 24 (Figure 12, position G). So, good for you if you're flying this approach into this airport.

There is one additional type of WAAS software-generated glideslope that you many encounter. It's called *LNAV+V*, which is an LNAV approach with *advisory vertical guidance*. This is essentially a non-precision approach (LNAV) with an advisory glideslope (+V) that provides vertical guidance so you don't have to worry about things like stepdown fixes. You fly the glideslope down to an MDA and, if the requirements for landing aren't met, you stop your descent (i.e., level-off or begin a climb) and fly to the missed approach point. If you do meet these requirements, you could remain on the glideslope and ride it all the way to touchdown if it pleases you (and I hope it does). It just so happens that all RNAV (GPS) generated glideslopes take you to a runway intersection point approximately 1,000 feet past the threshold (this distance may vary, however). Of course, you may ignore the vertical guidance if you desire and just descend to the MDA as you would during any non-precision approach. You won't see "LNAV+V" in the minimums section of an approach chart, since these letters don't represent minimums. On your WAAS receiver, however, you should see the letter's "LNAV+V" indicating that an advisory glideslope is available. So use it as a means of enhancing safety.

Finally, notice the white *W* in the black square in the second briefing area in Figure 12, position F. Given that this approach is on the coast of California, and since there are no WAAS WSR ground stations in the ocean (they'd sink, right?), this means that WAAS vertical guidance may not be available all the time at this location. This area may have more unfavorable satellite geometry that can't be compensated for by WRS ground stations that aren't there.

The question is, "How does your WAAS receiver let you know when LPV, L/VNAV, or LNAV minimums or the LNAV+V advisory glideslope are available for use? Let's find out.

Flying the Approach to APV Minimums

Let's say we've elected to fly the RNAV (GPS) Z Rwy 31 approach to Salem's McNary field (Figure 13). Our intent is to fly to the lowest possible minimums on the chart, which happen to be the LPV minimums (Figure 13, position A). We're approximately a mile south of GLORR intersection which is an IAF for this approach (Figure 13, position B). Using our Garmin 500W WAAS certified GPS receiver (Figure 14) we're heading direct to GLORR and have been cleared for the approach. Notice that our GPS is operating in *terminal* mode as shown in (Figure 14, position C) by the letters *TERM* (the GPS enters terminal mode when operating at or within 30 nautical miles of the airport with the airport loaded as the destination).

As we cross GLORR, the intermediate fix (NECIP) becomes the active waypoint (Figure 15, position D). As we continue towards NECIP, our WAAS unit is evaluating its horizontal and vertical accuracy. The WAAS unit is designed to allow the lowest minimums possible based on meeting the required *horizontal position limits* (HPL) and *vertical position limits* (VPL) for those minimums. In most cases, you'll know which minimums are allowed when reaching the intermediate fix (IF). At this point, the approach mode annunciator (Figure 16, position E) will indicate the letters for the lowest minimums allowed. The annunciator may show LPV (for the lowest minimums possible on the RNAV (GPS) 31 approach). If so, then you may use the LPV minimums and descend to a DA of 570 feet (Figure 13, position F). If LPV minimums are allowed, then the glideslope should become active by the time you reach the IF, meaning that the glideslope warning flag will disappear. Now let's examine the other minimums in Figure 13.

If, for any reason, your WAAS unit was unable to meet the HPL/VPL requirements for the LPV minimums, there will be some visual warning on your WAAS unit to alert you, and then the unit will default to LNAV minimums only. In other words, no glideslope is generated for this approach, meaning that no glideslope is available for LNAV/VNAV minimums or for LNAV+V advisory purposes. You are left with flying a non-precision approach. If so, you'll see the letters LNAV in the approach annunciator window as shown in Figure 17, position K. This means you may descend to an MDA of 1,060 feet once you're past

The RNAV Chart Minimums Section

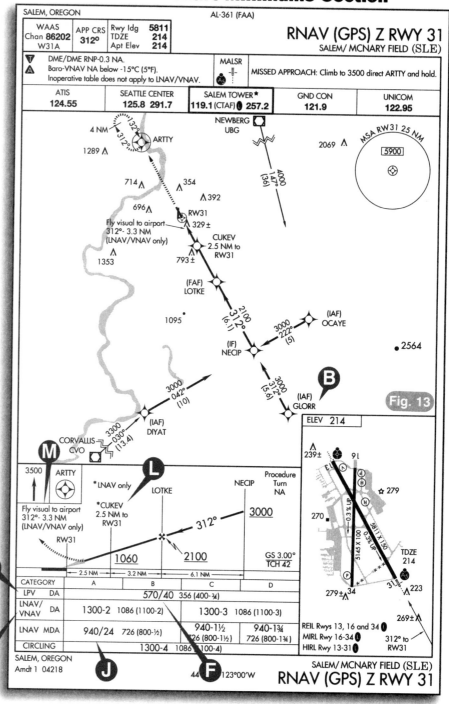

Fig. 13

LOTKE (the FAF) and 940 feet once you're past the stepdown fix at CUKEY (Figure 13, position L). In case you're wondering why the WAAS unit won't default to higher LNAV/VNAV DA minimums if the HPL/VPL requirements aren't met for LPV minimums, there's a good reason. It turns out that the tolerance limits for glideslope generation are basically the same for LPV, LNAV/VNAV and LNAV+V glideslopes. If a glideslope can't be generated for LPV, then it can't be generated for LNAV/VNAV or LNAV+V. The only option left is for LNAV minimums. You get what you get. Get it?

On the other hand, there are approach charts with only one type of APV minima, which is LNAV/VNAV. In other words, LPV minimums aren't shown in the chart's

The Garmin 500W IFR WAAS Certified GPS Receiver in "Terminal" Mode

Heading direct to GLORR, the WAAS unit is in Terminal Mode.

Fig. 14 Courtesy Garmin

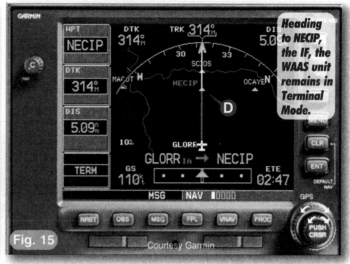

Heading to NECIP, the IF, the WAAS unit remains in Terminal Mode.

Fig. 15 Courtesy Garmin

mimimums section as seen on the Ontario RNAV (GPS) Rwy 26L approach (Figure 18). The LPV minimums are not available at this airport as shown in Figure 18, position O (this chart shows GLS PA [*global navigation system precision approach*] in the LPV section. These letters are the older terms gradually being replaced by the letters LPV). If LNAV/VNAV minimums are available at Ontario, you'll see the letters L/VNAV in your WAAS unit's approach annunciator window as shown in Figure 17, position G. Flying to an LNAV/VNAV DA (Figure 18, position P) is done just like any other precision approach. You descend to 1,405 feet on the glideslope then make a decision either to land or execute the missed approach. No leveling off at an MDA here.

On the other hand, if LNAV/VNAV is available in the approach annunciator window at Ontario, there's nothing that says you can't use the glideslope to descend to the LNAV MDA of 1,540 feet (Figure 18, position Q), level off, and fly to the non-precision missed approach point. Using the glideslope for descent guidance to the MDA would actually be a wise move on your part.

If your WAAS unit provides *advisory vertical guidance* as indicated by the approach annunciator shown in Figure 17, position I,

RNAV With Only LNAV/VNAV Minimums

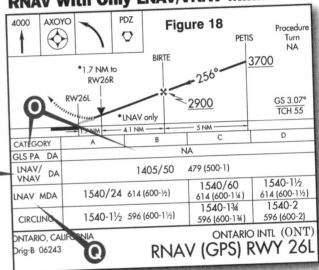

Figure 18

CATEGORY	A	B	C	D
GLS PA DA		NA		
LNAV/VNAV DA	1405/50 479 (500-1)			
LNAV MDA	1540/24 614 (600-½)		1540/60 614 (600-1¼)	1540-1½ 614 (600-1½)
CIRCLING	1540-1½ 596 (600-1½)		1540-1¾ 596 (600-1¾)	1540-2 596 (600-2)

ONTARIO, CALIFORNIA
Orig-B 06243

ONTARIO INTL (ONT)
RNAV (GPS) RWY 26L

The Ontario RNAV (GPS) approach has LNAV/VNAV minimums, but not LPV minimums. If your WAAS unit's approach annunciator indicates "L/VNAV" is available, you may descend to a DA of 1,405 feet.

The Garmin 500W in LPV Approach Mode

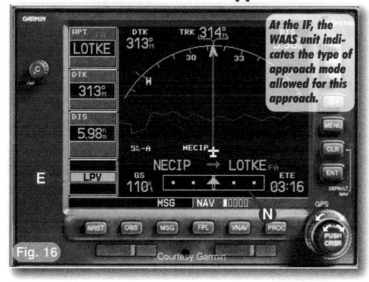

At the IF, the WAAS unit indicates the type of approach mode allowed for this approach.

Fig. 16 Courtesy Garmin

The Four Different Approach Modes in the Garmin 500W

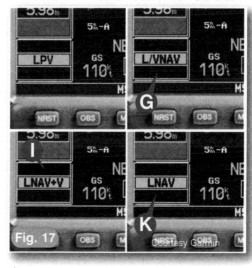

Fig. 17 Courtesy Garmin

you could use the glideslope for descent to the MDA. For instance, suppose you were flying the RNAV (GPS) Rwy 30 approach to Jacqueline Cochran Regional airport (TRM) as shown in Figure 19. If the WAAS HPL and VPL limits are met and a glideslope is generated, the approach annunciator window will indicate LNAV+V as shown in Figure 20, position A (no LPV minimums are available on this approach). You simply follow the glideslope down to the lowest MDA allowed, which is 260 feet at TRM (Figure 19, position B). Following the glideslope allows you to cross FORKI, the stepdown fix (Figure 19, position C), at the appropriate altitude and make an uninterrupted descent to the LNAV MDA of 260 feet. If the requirements for landing aren't met, you stop your descent at 260 feet (i.e., level off or begin a climb) and fly to the missed approach point. If you do meet these requirements, you could remain on the advisory glideslope and ride it all the way to touchdown (and I hope you do because it's obstacle free, meaning it's good for your health and it contains no fat). Remember, all RNAV (GPS) generated glideslopes take you to a runway intersection point approximately 1,000 feet past the threshold. Nevertheless, even though a glideslope exists, you must keep in mind that this is still a non-precision approach. The glideslope is for advisory purposes only. You don't have to follow it to and beyond the MDA, but there's really no good reason not to if you have the required visibility for the approach.

Take note that the glideslope angle is 3.04 degrees and has a threshold crossing height of 45 feet (Figure 19, position D). If, when reaching the MDA, you have

The Advisory Vertical Glideslope: LNAV+V

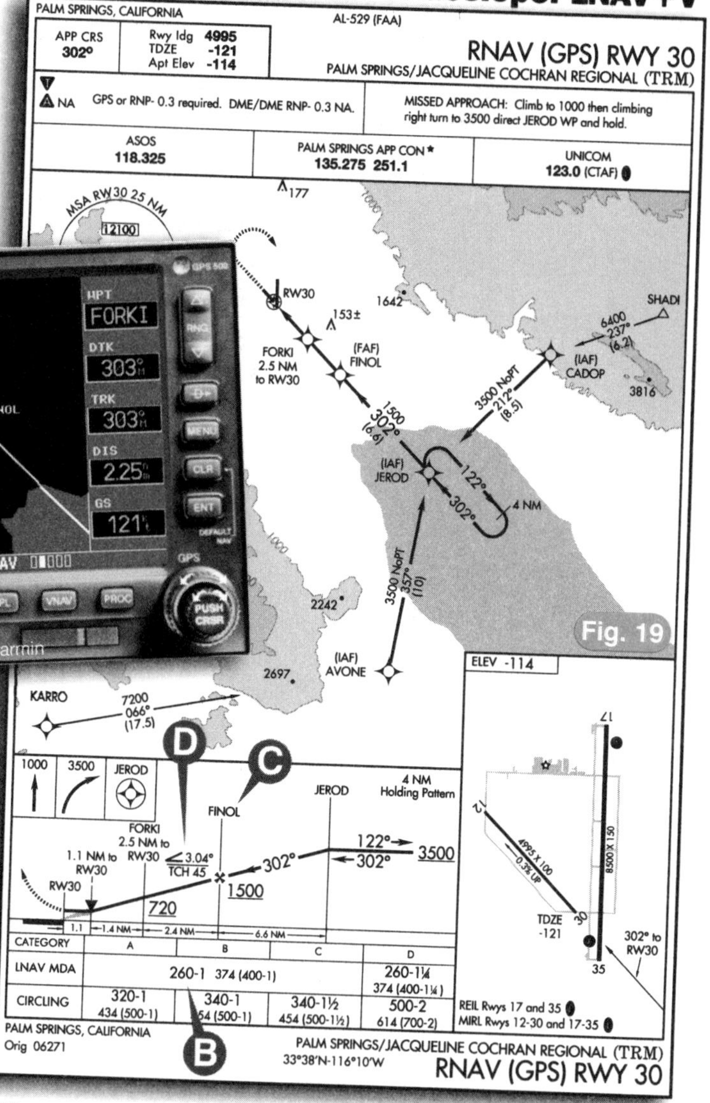

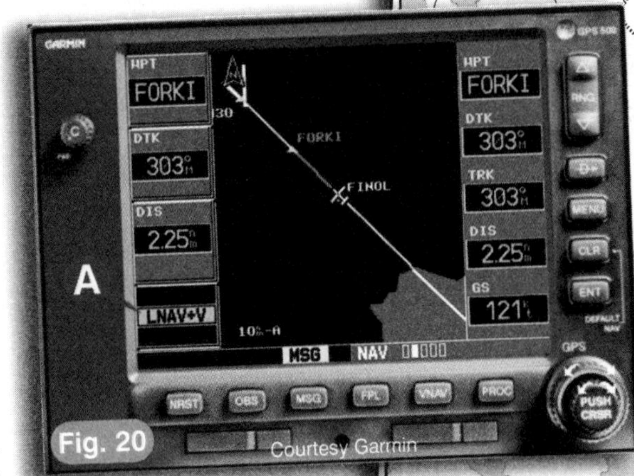

Fig. 20 — Courtesy Garmin

Fig. 19

The approach to TRM has LNAV minimums but provides an advisory vertical glideslope during descent to the MDA.

WAAS Protected Horizontal Limits

When using WAAS for LNAV and LPV approaches, as you approach within two miles of the FAF, your CDI scale gradually transitions from a fixed horizontal distance scale of +/– 1 nm to an angular scale of +/– 2 degrees. In other words, your CDI becomes "localizer like" (thus the reason LPV stands for localizer performance with vertical guidance). At the FAF, your CDI scaling starts somewhere near +/– .3 nm then reduces to a CDI scale of +/– 350 feet (for a five dot deflection, with each dot representing 70 feet displacement from the course centerline) at the missed approach point and remains at +/– 350 feet until a missed approach is initiated. Keep in mind that the CDI shown electronically as the bottom of the Garmin 500W box (Figure 16, position N) only shows two dots for a full scale deflection. This means that each dot deflection at the missed approach point equals 175 feet displacement from the course centerline.

1 dot = 70 feet

On a display with 5 dots, each dot CDI deflection is 70 feet off course.

Ful scale CDI deflection at the MAWP is 350 feet off course.

Sensitivity changes from +/-1 nm full scale deflection to either +/-0.3 nm or +/-2 degrees full scale deflection, whichever is less at the FAF. The change occurs over a 2 nm distance and is completed at the FAF.

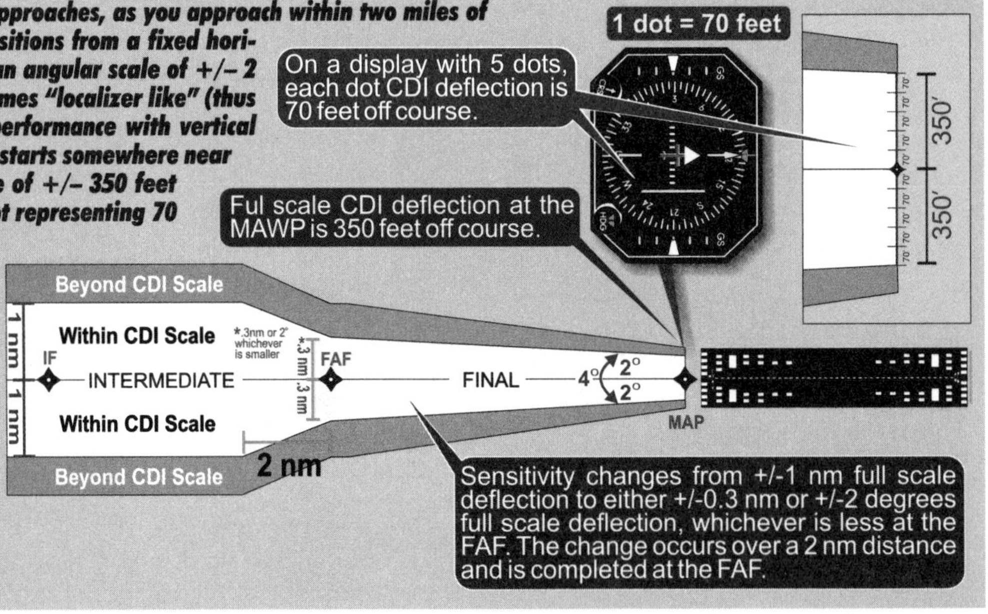

the requirements to descend below it (i.e., visibility and runway environment) you could remain on the glideslope and ride it all the way down to the touchdown zone if you desire.

There are a few additional aspects of the RNAV minimums section that you should pay attention to. Referring to McNary Field (Figure 21), notice that the LNAV/VNAV minimums list a DA of 1,300 feet and a required visibility of 2 miles (Figure 21, position E). Looking at the chart note in the profile section (Figure 21, position F), once you're at the LNAV/VNAV DA and meet the visibility and runway requirements for landing, you fly 3.3 nautical miles

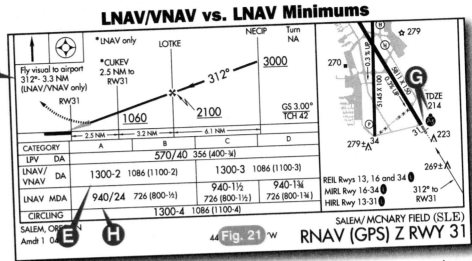

LNAV/VNAV vs. LNAV Minimums

CATEGORY	A	B	C	D
LPV DA		570/40 356 (400-¾)		
LNAV/VNAV DA	1300-2 1086 (1100-2)		1300-3 1086 (1100-3)	
LNAV MDA	940/24 726 (800-½)		940-1½ 726 (800-1½)	940-1¾ 726 (800-1¾)
CIRCLING		1300-4 1086 (1100-4)		

SALEM, OREGON
Amdt 1 04...

Fig. 21

SALEM/ MCNARY FIELD (SLE)
RNAV (GPS) Z RWY 31

The LNAV/VNAV minimums can sometimes be much higher and require a greater flight visibility for landing than the LNAV minimums.

"visually" to reach the runway. In this instance it would be wise to descend the 3.3 miles while remaining on the glideslope. Nevertheless, now you know why the LNAV/VNAV visibility minimum is 2 miles. At DA, if you had 2 miles visibility and you saw the approach lights (which can be 2,400 to 3,000 feet in length), you could legally continue your descent.

In addition to the Baro-VNAV temperature errors we discussed earlier, there's another reason the LNAV/VNAV minimums are so much higher than the LPV minimums (Figure 21, positions E and H). As I've mentioned previously, the LNAV/VNAV minimums were designed with the GPS concept (TSO-c129), not the WAAS concept (TSO 146) in mind. Since plain GPS doesn't offer the same precision and position error correction as WAAS, there is a wider horizontal area of obstacle protection along the final approach segment for approaches using LNAV or LNAV/VNAV minimums, with obstacles on the periphery of the approach course often causing an increase in the DA. This is one of the reasons the LNAV/VNAV DA minimums are so high at McNary. On the other hand, your WAAS unit offers a high degree of horizontal and vertical precision. Since LPV minimums were specifically designed for use with WAAS, and since WAAS allows you to remain confined to a smaller horizontal area along the final approach, this means that chart designers can allow you to descend to a much lower altitude with much less visibility required on many LPV approaches. To learn more about this horizontal protected area, look at the sidebar titled: *WAAS Protected Horizontal Limits*.

An important point to consider here is that until you've reached the intermediate fix on most RNAV (GPS) approaches, you may not have a clear idea of the lowest minimums allowed by your WAAS unit. Remember, the Garmin 500W WAAS unit (and most other WAAS units, too) may not display the type of minimums allowed in the approach annunciator window until the HPL/VPL error checking is accomplished, which normally occurs by the time you reach the IF. Since the IF is often five miles or more from the FAF, you may not know if you can descend

to LPV or LNAV minimums if you're outside the IF. This can be a significant point if you think about it. LPV minimums are substantially lower than the LNAV minimums; therefore, if an airport's weather is below the LNAV minimums but above the LPV minimums, you may have to fly to the IF to find out what your chances are of being able to land. On the other hand, as you'll learn with the detailed operation of your WAAS unit, there is a function called VTF or *vectors to final*, which, when activated, will often show you the lowest minimums available to you in the approach annunciator window regardless of your distance from the IF (the ability to do this may depend on the specific WAAS unit's electronics, however).

Finally, you may have been asking yourself the question, "Why have LNAV/VNAV minimums when LPV minimums are available at the airport? After all, if you can go down to the lowest DA, why stop at the higher one?" Here's why LNAV/VNAV minimums exist on many approach charts.

When the FAA began designing RNAV (GPS) approaches and before WAAS was a viable concept, the airlines wanted a piece of the approach action. So, in addition to the LNAV minimums, the FAA created LNAV/VNAV minimums for use by airlines that have Baro-VNAV equipment. Much of the airline fleet has Baro-VNAV, but you'll be hard pressed to find even one small airplane that does. Baro-VNAV allowed these airlines to fly a pseudo glideslope (not requiring WAAS) down to a DA instead of an MDA. Smaller airplane pilots were stuck with flying LNAV-only approaches since they didn't have Baro-VNAV. That was the case until WAAS arrived.

With a WAAS equipped airplane, you could fly approaches down to LPV minimums, but the airlines typically couldn't. Why? Most airliners don't have GPS, much less WAAS equipment on board. Sure, they may have non-GPS based RNAV (INS, FMS, DME-RNAV, etc.) and Baro-VNAV capability, but they can't fly an approach to LPV minimums unless they have WAAS on board. So now the average general aviation pilot with WAAS has the capability to fly RNAV approaches to lower minimums than most airline pilots.

Postflight Briefing #13-1

RAIM (Receiver Autonomous Integrity Monitoring)

All the GPS gadgets in the world packed into your panel mean nothing if the GPS satellites aren't providing the correct signals. This can happen, and you need to know how to prepare for it. When a VOR stops working because a technician sticks a screwdriver into a wall socket (for fun, of course), then you know about it because of the loss of that station's identification (and possibly the loss of the technician's hair).

How do you know when your GPS isn't working accurately? Sure, if smoke's coming from it, that may signal an onboard problem. But how do you know if the satellites are putting out accurately? The answer is RAIM or *receiver autonomous integrity monitoring*. This is a special program built into your IFR GPS unit's software to warn you when there's a navigational accuracy or reliability problem. Here's the real deal on RAIM, ma'am.

RAIM is internal logic within your GPS unit that verifies two important items. First, it confirms that the signals received from the satellites aren't providing corrupted information. Second, it makes certain that a sufficient number of satellites are being received to check for any transmission errors (also referred to as adequate satellite geometry). Remember high school geometry? It's back, except that the GPS box does the work, and the box instead of Mrs. Whackinback will tell you when you've got bad geometry.

RAIM messages vary somewhat among GPS receivers, but there are generally two types. One type says the RAIM integrity monitor has detected a potential error that exceeds the limit for the current phase of flight. The other tells the tale when there are not enough satellites visible to your GPS receiver to provide RAIM integrity monitoring.

Your GPS knows where all the satellites are supposed to be at any instant (if I told you how it knows this, I'd have to ground you). If things aren't as they should be, and this *pseudo range estimate* doesn't add up, the RAIM in Spain falls mainly in the plane. There's a certain amount of leeway; if there is a discrepancy beyond that, your GPS unit will display a RAIM alert message. This means you can't fly an instrument approach for the duration of the alert.

What could cause the GPS system to RAIM on your parade? A number of things. Satellites sometimes provide incorrect information because of atmospheric disturbances. Good satellites can also go bad and drop out of service. Fortunately, the dropout rate is a lot lower than that of even the best high schools, and they only drop out of service, not out of orbit. But you can imagine how difficult it is trying to get a repairman out there to fix it (the guy with the smoking hair might want to

try it since he's already spaced out). These and other anomalies can cause an erroneous reading in the GPS.

To perform proper RAIM, your GPS unit must be able to spot at least one satellite *in addition* to the minimum of four required for normal nav (four satellites are acceptable if your GPS accepts non-satellite information, such as a current altimeter setting that can be manually entered into the receiver, also known as *baro-aiding*). You'd need six satellites (five, with baro-aiding) in view to actually isolate a corrupt satellite from the navigational program.

The Garmin 530 GPS (Figure 22) shows the number of available satellites and the estimated position error (EPE) on its satellite page. By referring to this page or a similar page on other GPS units, you can see how many satellites are currently available to your GPS unit.

While there are 24 GPS satellites circling the earth, they are not in a geostationary orbit. These satellites circle the earth about two times each day, so they are constantly changing their position relative to each other. Viewed from earth, they appear to rise and set like high-tech planets. Remember Noah's Arc. This creates situations where, at any given moment at a particular location, an insufficient number of satellites may be visible for RAIM, or even for basic nav. The matter is further complicated by the need for a satellite to be at least 7.5 degrees above the horizon to be received by a GPS unit. A combination of these issues increases the chance of having inadequate satellite geometry, meaning that RAIM might not be available when needed.

It's important to note that the term RAIM is used colloquially in several ways. If a pilot says he didn't have RAIM, this means that there weren't a sufficient number of satellites available to fly a GPS approach (or, insufficient satellite geometry is expected between the FAF and the MAP). If a pilot says he received a RAIM alert, this

GPS Satellite Reception

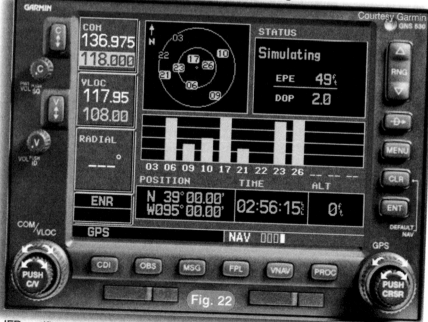

IFR certified GPS units portray satellite reception in different ways. This is how the Garmin 530 GPS unit shows available satellites and their signal strength.

means that he received a RAIM message indicating satellite signal corruption or satellite availability problems.

Fortunately, most GPS units are capable of providing a warning if you don't have a sufficient number of satellites to provide RAIM, as shown in Figure 23. These GPS units have a RAIM page where you can enter your destination and ETA and determine if RAIM will be available to fly a non-precision approach as shown in Figure 24. This prediction applies to the time 15 minutes before and after your ETA. If you don't have RAIM, then you'll need to select another means of navigation to fly the approach.

GPS RAIM Evaluation

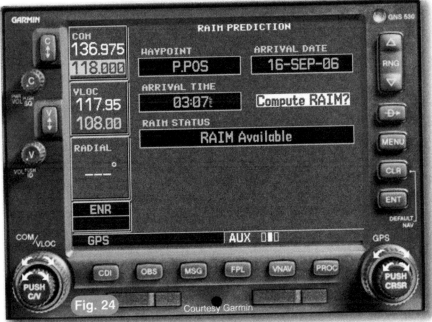

IFR certified GPS units are capable of providing a warning ("INTEG" for example) when there aren't sufficient satellites to provide RAIM.

GPS RAIM Evaluation

GPS units have a RAIM page where you can enter your destination and ETA and determine whether or not you'll have RAIM sufficient to fly an approach on arrival.

This means dusting off that old VOR chart (it should be current, of course) and flying a VOR approach. Ouch.

You can also determine if satellite geometry is sufficient to provide RAIM at your destination by calling the FSS and providing them with your ETA at a specific location. The FSS specialist provides RAIM information which covers a period of three hours: the ETA hour (the hour you'll arrive), and one hour before to one hour after the ETA hour. It can also be provided for a 24-hour time frame at a particular airport. Keep in mind that if you're flying a published GPS departure, then you should also request a RAIM prediction for the departure airport (unless you use your GPS unit to predict RAIM in this instance).

On the other hand, if you have a WAAS-certified IFR GPS, then you want to check the WAAS NOTAMs for *system status* and the *level of service* available at your destination airport. The level of service identifies the type of minimums expected to be available upon arrival (i.e., LPV, LNAV/VNAV or LNAV minimums).

Remember, along with space satellites, WAAS uses ground-based satellites to augment accuracy and reliability. Therefore, it's less likely that any one satellite or ground station that goes bad will affect your ability to navigate. What a signal problem can affect, however, is your ability to fly to the lowest minimums published at the destination airport.

WAAS NOTAMs are available from the FSS or from DUATS (or any other FAA approved vendor). For instance, using DUATS, you might see the following WAAS NOTAM:

EBG 06/036 EBG WAAS LNAV/VNAV AND LPV MNM UNREL WEF 0805041300-0805041700.

Translated, this means that at KEBG, both LNAV/VNAV and LPV minimums are unreliable for use with effect from (WEF) May 5, 2008, at 1300 hours Z until May 5, 2008, 1700 hours Z. This implies that you'll probably have to use LNAV minimums at that airport should you choose to fly a GPS approach.

Let's say, however, that the LPV or LNAV/VNAV minimums are NOTAMed as unreliable, as shown above, and you are approaching the airport while expecting to fly to non-precision (LNAV) minimums. Before you begin the approach you notice that your WAAS unit indicates LPV minimums are available despite the NOTAM (i.e., LPV shown in the approach-mode window. Can you fly to LPV minimums? Yes. If your WAAS unit allows it in this instance, then vertical guidance may be used to complete the approach using the displayed level of service available.

WAAS NOTAMs are are issued as D NOTAMs (see Chapter 16, page 16-27 for D NOTAM information) and it happens that the IFR weather briefing should automatically include D NOTAM information, meaning the FSS specialist should provide you with WAAS reliability information. Don't, however, expect a RAIM prediction here unless you ask the briefer for one.

Keep in mind that a WAAS-certified IFR unit is considered a *stand-alone* navigation unit. That means that with WAAS, you don't need additional navigation equipment to fly IFR. If you don't have a WAAS receiver or if WAAS service isn't available as referenced by NOTAM, then your airplane will need an alternate and approved means of navigation equipment to fly IFR (for all practical purposes this means you need an operational VOR). The FAA trusts your approved GPS equipment and those satellites, but not completely. Now, you don't have to actively monitor that VOR equipment if your GPS receiver uses RAIM for integrity monitoring. Active monitoring of an alternate means of navigation is required when the RAIM capability of the GPS equipment is lost.

Did I ever mention that in America we tell kids to eat their broccoli, and when children ask why, we say, "Because kids in China are starving"? Yet, when the kids in China are told to eat their rice and they ask why, their parents say, "Because the kids in America have got to eat broccoli." The moral is that we often don't realize how good we have it in today's airspace system with RNAV approaches compared to what we had just 10 years ago. It's an amazing time to be a pilot.

Now it's time to take a look at instrument departures and see how to get airborne without knocking things over in the departure path.

Chapter 14
Instrument Departures

When shopping at the market, have you ever seen a cereal named "Ancient Grain of the Aztecs"? The label tells you how healthy this cereal is, and how good it is for you. But did you ever stop and think about the fact that there aren't a lot of Aztecs running around these days? Maybe Cortez was the first cereal killer? Or maybe there's a connection between what the Aztecs ate and their fate?

OK, maybe the connection is a weak link, but there can be little doubt about the strong connection between knowledge and safety when it comes to departing an airport under IMC conditions, when the "see" part of "see and avoid" is inop.

That's where the information in this chapter comes into view. We're going to review all the principles needed for you to depart an airport safely when you can't see what you're doing just by looking out the window.

Let the no-see-'em show begin.

Out of Control

The primary purpose of Air Traffic Control is to provide separation between IFR airplanes operating in *controlled* airspace. As unusual as it may seem, IFR aircraft can and do operate in uncontrolled (Class G) airspace, where they are on their own for terrain avoidance and everything else. That's why they call it *uncon-*

trolled, Captain. It's aviation's version of the wild, wild west, where anything goes, including you (but we're not going to let that happen).

What's a nice IFR pilot doing in uncontrolled airspace?

You'll most often be there because the overlying controlled airspace (Class E) doesn't touch the ground. Short arms. Airports with operating control towers usually have Class B, C and D, surface-based airspace, as shown in Figure 1. Within these areas, the controlled airspace begins at the airport's surface. When you depart a tower-controlled airport under IFR, you are *usually* (but not always) given headings to fly or departure procedures to follow, because you start out in controlled airspace, where ATC has proper jurisdiction.

It's also possible that you might be departing from an airport without an operating tower but which does have surface-based controlled airspace as shown in Figure 2. As you've already learned in private pilot ground school, this Class E surface area is controlled airspace touching the ground.

One of the 12 Early Warning Signs That an IFR Departure Has Gone Bad

Chico's Class D Airspace

Class D (blue cylinder) airspace starts at the surface of an airport with an operating control tower. It extends vertically to approximately 2,500' feet above the airport elevation. During IFR departures when Class D airspace is in effect (when the tower is operating) you'll be departing into controlled airspace.

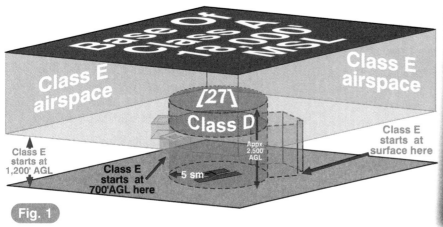

Fig. 1

But what happens when Class B, C or D (controlled) airspace isn't in effect and there isn't any Class E surface area in existence? Suddenly, the alphabet begins with *G*, and a departing IFR flight is forced to ascend through 700 to 1,200 feet (or more) of uncontrolled airspace before reaching Class E (controlled airspace) as shown in Figure 3. This situation demands that you understand your responsibility to avoid obstructions during the transition, because even though the local radar controller (Departure or Center radar in most cases) may be talking to you, he or she is not always responsible for keeping you from following a prairie dog into its house on the side of a hill as you depart. This is the Hobbit Hole One departure, and you should make a habit of avoiding it.

A typical IFR clearance out of a busy controlled airport might read as follows:

2132 Bravo is cleared to San Jose airport as filed. After departure, turn right to a heading of 230 degrees for radar vectors to Seal Beach VOR, climb and maintain 10,000 feet, contact Departure Control on frequency 124.65.

OK, great, that was a nice, neat bundle because you started out in and remained in controlled airspace. Let's un-neaten it by looking at a typical clearance out of a non-towered airport lying in uncontrolled (Class G) airspace. The following clearance (although, ironically, it's not always so clear) leaves it up to you about how you'll depart:

2132 Bravo is cleared to Bigbob airport, via direct Bobette VOR, V135 OLIVE, V334 STARK. Climb and maintain 3,000 feet, contact Departure Control on 127.3 and squawk 1234. Clearance void if not off by 1600 Zulu. If not airborne by 1600 Zulu, contact Bigbob Flight Service Station no later than 1630 Zulu.

Class E Airspace Starting at the Surface

Within the borders of the magenta (red) dashed line, Class E airspace descends all the way to the surface surrounding McComb-Pike airport. Instrument departures from this airport when Class E airspace is in effect will be in controlled airspace. (See Airport/Facillity Directory for Class E airspace effective hours.)

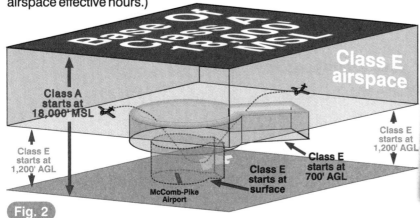

Fig. 2

Class E Airspace at 700' AGL

Within the borders of the magenta faded area surrounding an airport, Class E (controlled) airspace starts at 700 feet above ground level (AGL) instead of the normal 1,200 feet AGL. IFR departures from this airport will be in uncontrolled airpsace until reaching 700 feet AGL within the magenta bordered area or 1,200 feet AGL beyond this border.

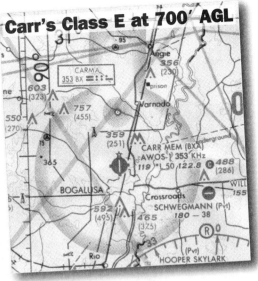

Carr's Class E at 700' AGL

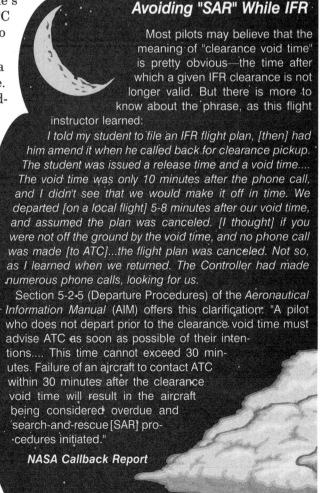

To you, that clearance may sound like Greek, and to a Greek it still sounds like Greek, especially if this Greek doesn't understand Greek. Let's go through each item in this clearance individually, finally working our way up to the point about how you're left to decide how you'll depart safely.

The Void Time

Several items in this clearance are distinctly different from those given during tower-controlled departures. First and foremost, you didn't get this clearance from the clearance delivery position at a tower, because there isn't one (tower or clearance delivery position). You got this clearance either over the phone, from a Flight Service Station, or by radio directly from an ATC facility. Because they aren't on site to see what you're doing, this clearance has a void time. If your airplane's wheels don't *come off the ground* by 1600Z, then the window ATC created for that departure slams shut, and you are instructed to call ATC and tell them you failed to fly.

Don't get your wings caught in the window by attempting a late IFR departure, hoping the controller won't notice or care. She cares. A lot. At one second past 1600Z, the airspace is considered available, and it may very well be occupied. This would seriously defeat the whole point of IFR flight, which is keeping IFR aircraft separated, and would at the very least test the controller's built-in, electric, Radio Hut heart regulating device. You don't want to see one of these things short circuit. You don't have the heart for it.

When delivering a clearance, it's not unusual for controllers to offer an immediate IFR departure window with a lifespan of just a few minutes. Accepting this quickie clearance means that your airplane must be in a position to depart within that timeframe. This could present a problem if ground traffic is present, the runup hasn't been completed, or extra time is needed for take-off because your airplane is so old that it takes several minutes for all its cylinders to synchronize their firing schedule.

Don't accept immediate departure windows unless your airplane is cocked and loaded for departure. Even then, be reluctant. Haste has a strange way of making mistakes happen. If you aren't 100% ready to go instantly, ask for a longer departure window or clearance release at a later time. At least this will allow you to prepare yourself and the airplane for IFR flight.

I've seen pilots depart in such haste that their IFR charts were on the floor between their feet. On takeoff, the charts exe-

Avoiding "SAR" While IFR

Most pilots may believe that the meaning of "clearance void time" is pretty obvious—the time after which a given IFR clearance is not longer valid. But there is more to know about the phrase, as this flight instructor learned:

I told my student to file an IFR flight plan, [then] had him amend it when he called back for clearance pickup. The student was issued a release time and a void time.... The void time was only 10 minutes after the phone call, and I didn't see that we would make it off in time. We departed [on a local flight] 5-8 minutes after our void time, and assumed the plan was canceled. [I thought] if you were not off the ground by the void time, and no phone call was made [to ATC]...the flight plan was canceled. Not so, as I learned when we returned. The Controller had made numerous phone calls, looking for us.

Section 5-2-5 (Departure Procedures) of the *Aeronautical Information Manual* (AIM) offers this clarification: "A pilot who does not depart prior to the clearance void time must advise ATC as soon as possible of their intentions.... This time cannot exceed 30 minutes. Failure of an aircraft to contact ATC within 30 minutes after the clearance void time will result in the aircraft being considered overdue and search-and-rescue [SAR] procedures initiated."

NASA Callback Report

Heeding a Heading

On occasion, ATC will assign you a heading to fly after departure. It's important to understand that sometimes a heading is...well, it's just a heading. Don't invest it with powers it doesn't have by mistaking it for a radar vector, Victor.

Sometimes this heading assignment will happen immediately after departure, and sometimes it will be when reaching the base of the overlying controlled airspace. For instance, your clearance might read, "After departure, fly heading 200 degrees," or it could say, "After departure and when reaching 700 AGL [the base of the overlying controlled airspace], *fly heading* 200 degrees." If you receive either of these instructions, it's very important for you to understand that this heading is *not* a radar vector! It's just a heading.

ATC will not issue radar vectors until your airplane is at or above the Minimum Vectoring Altitude (MVA—a term used by Approach and Departure Control) or the Minimum Instrument Altitude (MIA—a term used by Center), which are depicted on the controller's radar screen.

The only exception to this is when prominent obstructions have been marked on the controller's radar screen, and the aircraft is climbing to an altitude above these obstacles. This vectoring below the MVA can take place only during instrument departures and during missed approaches from an instrument approach procedure. The headings assigned in the clearances above start below the controller's MVA. In these instances, ATC can assign a heading that is *not* a radar vector, below the Minimum Vectoring Altitude, provided the route has

been flight tested and shown to be free of obstructions (the route above, beginning at 700 feet in a direction of 200 degrees, has apparently been flight tested and shown to be safe).

Believing radar guidance is being provided when it is not is a very dangerous situation for instrument pilots. After departure, you may hear the words *radar contact,* and from that conclude that your aircraft is now under radar guidance, and your chosen heading will keep you free from obstructions. Nothing could be further from the tooth (as my dentist used to say)! This is quite similar to believing that if you rent the move Caligula it will improve your handwriting.

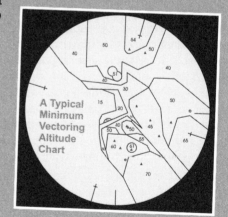

A Typical Minimum Vectoring Altitude Chart

Hearing the words *radar contact* simply means that your airplane has been identified on the controller's radar screen, nothing else. Sure, the controller may provide you with traffic information, but terrain and obstruction clearance is not provided by ATC until the controller begins providing navigational guidance (i.e., radar vectors). In other words, the controller has to tell you to fly in a specific direction before you even begin thinking that your airplane is under radar guidance. So don't mistake heading instructions on paper for those issued verbally by a controller. They aren't the same thing.

cute their own departure procedure, the Slide One, which moves them from between the pilot's feet to the extreme back of the airplane where they are inaccessible until after the next landing. Which isn't a problem, unless of course you need the charts to *make* the next landing.

Let's say that between the time you were given a clearance and the void time, you decided you'd really rather walk to a nearby Starbucks, get a latte, and wait for the airport to go VFR. Now the void time has come and gone, just like the five dollars you spent on that drink. Are you done with ATC? Not quite. Your obligation to ATC is not over if your flight doesn't depart as planned. Remember, your clearance included an instruction to contact ATC if you did *not* get off the ground by the void time.

Since the airspace is available after the void time, why does ATC care what you did? Be aware that *you* are the only one who knows you didn't go; ATC assumes you took off until otherwise informed. The controller has no way of knowing if you departed successfully and then experienced lost communications or had an in-flight emergency after departure and had to force-land in an isolated field. Unless ATC is notified, some form of search and rescue will be undertaken. If they find you at Starbucks, it's not going to be a happy experience for you (someone will think you're a "doppio" and I don't mean the one made with two shots of espresso and one shot of hot water). Phone home.

Since cell phones are so popular and prevalent, you might want to make use of yours as an IFR departure aid.

After filing an IFR flight plan with the FSS, you'll typically be asked to call back in 30 minutes to receive your clearance from the FSS specialist. This procedure is quite common when departing from a non-towered airport. Now, you can sit around a phone booth waiting to call the FSS (and if Superman has to use it, then you're out of there, pal) or you can do the same thing on your cell phone from the runup area.

Of course, you don't want to use an ordinary cell phone in the air. This is against FCC regulations and the fines are pretty steep if you're caught. So don't do it.

Heading Out

Your clearance takes you from your present position direct to Bobette VOR after departure, then via the assigned routing. Does this clearance tell you how to depart the airport safely? No, it doesn't. Does this clearance mean that it's guaranteed safe for you to lift off and immediately turn directly toward Bobette VOR? Absolutely not! And not by any stretch of the imagination, either.

You're more than likely departing into uncontrolled airspace here (at least 700 to 1,200 feet of it initially). That means obstacle avoidance is solely *your* responsibility. Maybe some sole music is in order as you blast off while pondering the fact that nobody's making you any promises. Yes, the controller wants you to go *direct* to the VOR. No, he doesn't want you to bump into anything while doing it. Yes, it's your problem, challenge, and opportunity.

Unless ATC tells you a specific heading to fly immediately after departure (as in the clearance from the tower controlled airport on page 14-2), you're on your own to find a way to depart safely (and that means you also choose your departure runway, too). Think of it as a very personal game of *Survivor,* in which you're the only tribe.

Fortunately, there are three basic do-it-yourself ways of avoiding terrain and obstructions during departure. Let's examine each in detail.

Three Methods of Avoiding the Terror of Terrain

When headed for work, you don't want to miss the train, but when flying, you definitely wish to avoid the terrain. There are at least three ways of avoiding obstructions when departing IFR and ATC isn't providing vectors.

First, you can delay departing until you have sufficient visual minimums to see and avoid obstacles in the vicinity of the airport. With a reasonable amount of forward visibility and cloud clearance, you should easily be able to navigate safely to the enroute structure. This is always a good method if you're unfamiliar with the terrain and know there are obstructions surrounding the airport. Then again, this sort of defeats the purpose of an instrument rating, which is supposed to let you get up and go when visibility is gone. Discretion, however, is the better part of valor, and if you're at an unfamiliar airport high in the mountains, waiting might be a whole lot better strategy than flying into unseen terrain.

Your second option, based on the clearance out of the uncontrolled airport above, is using a sectional chart to decide on an obstruction-free path during an IFR departure in solid IMC. This could, however, make you feel about as comfortable as wearing a toupee that would only look good at a Bigfoot festival. Departing this way is a risky proposition at best. While it's not illegal for a Part 91 operator to take off with zero visibility and self-navigate around obstructions via bearing and radial position fixing or GPS navigation, this action is certainly not very prudent. You just don't have the ability to deal with the unlikely in these instances. After all, it's too easy to become discombobulated, confused, and overwhelmed while trying to navigate and fly. In the process, you could lose your caution cushion and end up with little leeway to handle icing, RAIM errors, engine roughness, spatial disorientation and so on. In short, you increase your workload and reduce your safety options in the process.

Nevertheless, this is still legal to do if you're so inclined and elect not to decline.

Terrain Awareness and Warning System

One of the handy devices available to many pilots nowadays is a GPS moving map display that provides a *terrain awareness warning system (TAWS)*. Simply stated, terrain, obstacle and airport information is stored in a GPS unit's database and used in conjunction with that unit's ability to know where you are both vertically and horizontally. This provides a means of depicting your airplane's position relative to terrain, usually in terms of a color coded system as shown below and to the right. Now you can have a much better idea of your proximity to the terrain and just how to avoid it.

For instance, the Garmin 496 GPS unit (a portable unit) shown to the right has the capability of providing ground proximity information. This requires a subscription to a data service provider such as XM Weather. During an IFR departure, while enroute. or during an instrument approach, you can monitor your terrain proximity simply by looking at the miniature airplane's

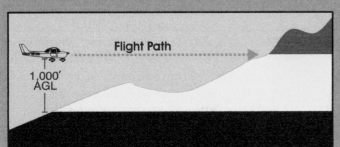

position in relation to the color coded terrain. It's easy to tell if you're heading into higher terrain simply by projecting the airplane ahead of its present flight path. The Garmin 296 unit depicts red terrain when the terrain is or will be within 100 feet of the airplane's altitude and yellow when within 100 to 1,000 feet of the airplane's altitude. Obstacles are also shown symbolically on the map display. This is cheap insurance, considering the relatively small investment.

Don't Stain the Terrain: The ODP or Obstacle Departure Procedure

The last option is the least understood yet probably the best. If the departure airport has an instrument approach, it may also have something known as an *ODP* or *obstacle departure procedure* (something everyone could use when crossing a room at night with the lights out, instead of having to find furniture with one's shins). Figure 4 shows the GPS Runway 18 approach for Fallbrook, California. Let's say we want to depart this airport and do it safely (the alternatives being really unpleasant). If an airport has an instrument approach, examine Section C at the front of the NACO chart booklet and look at the Take-off Minimums and (Obstacle) Departure Procedure information (Figure 5). If an ODP exists for that particular airport, it will be listed alphabetically there. Looking for Fallbrook airport, you see that there is indeed an ODP (Figure 5, position Z).

ODPs are printed either as text or, if the procedure is considered complex due to many turns, routes, altitudes, etc., it will printed in graphical form as a separate chart, located at the end of the approach chart sequence (not Section C) as shown by Figure 6 for Big Bear,

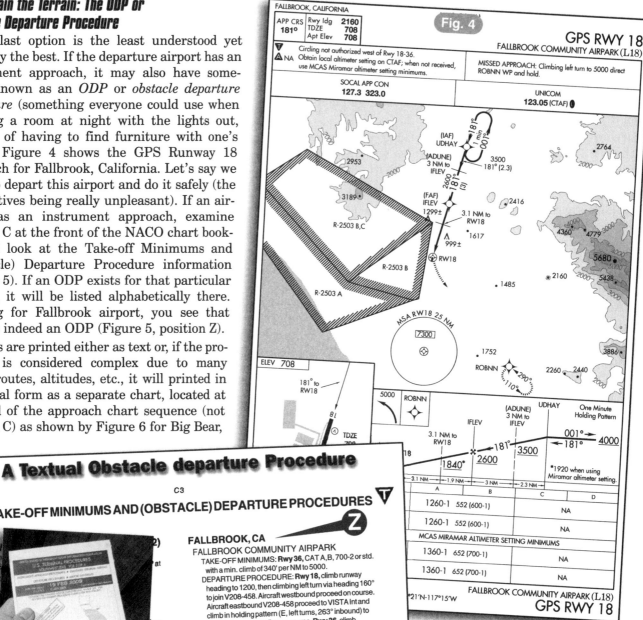

The front of the NACO approach chart booklet (Section C, specifically) contains obstacle departure procedures (ODPs) for airports having instrument approaches. Of course, this assumes that an OPD actually exists for that airport. Airports without obstacles in the departure area won't have a published ODP.

California (if it's an RNAV ODP, it will always be printed graphically). If the ODP is printed graphically, the word "OBSTACLE" will be printed at the top of the chart (Figure 6, position Y).

OK, here's what you've been waiting for. ODPs can be used when ATC doesn't specifically tell you how to depart

the airport. This means at both *towered* as well as *non-towered* airports. Typically, they are used when departing into Class G (uncontrolled) airspace at non-towered airports (places where ATC often doesn't tell you how to depart that airport).

It's important to remember that even at busy airports, Class C, D, and E controlled airspace may not be in operation 24 hours a day (look at the *Airport/Facility Directory* to find the airspace hours of operation). When operating beyond the effective hours of this airspace, you will more than likely be departing into Class G airspace. You have the option of using the ODP, if available, to safely avoid obstructions after takeoff (I recommend that you always use the ODP if one is available and you don't have other guidance).

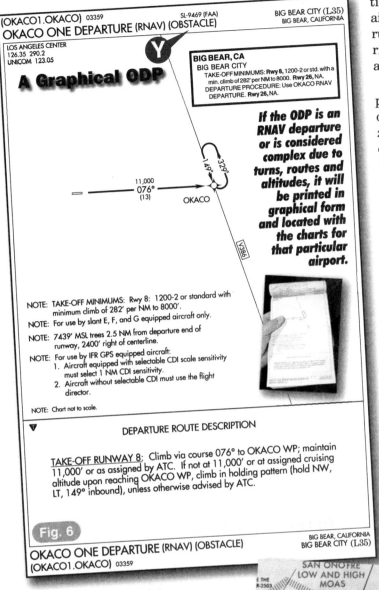

OKACO ONE DEPARTURE (RNAV) (OBSTACLE)

LOS ANGELES CENTER
126.35 290.2
UNICOM 123.05

A Graphical ODP

SL-9469 (FAA)

BIG BEAR CITY (L35)
BIG BEAR, CALIFORNIA

BIG BEAR, CA
BIG BEAR CITY
TAKE-OFF MINIMUMS: Rwy 8, 1200-2 or std. with a
min. climb of 282' per NM to 8000. Rwy 26, NA.
DEPARTURE PROCEDURE: Use OKACO RNAV
DEPARTURE. Rwy 26, NA.

If the ODP is an RNAV departure or is considered complex due to turns, routes and altitudes, it will be printed in graphical form and located with the charts for that particular airport.

11,000
076°
(13)

OKACO

329°
149°

V386

NOTE: TAKE-OFF MINIMUMS: Rwy 8: 1200-2 or standard with
minimum climb of 282' per NM to 8000'.
NOTE: For use by slant E, F, and G equipped aircraft only.
NOTE: 7439' MSL trees 2.5 NM from departure end of
runway, 2400' right of centerline.
NOTE: For use by IFR GPS equipped aircraft:
 1. Aircraft equipped with selectable CDI scale sensitivity
 must select 1 NM CDI sensitivity.
 2. Aircraft without selectable CDI must use the flight
 director.

NOTE: Chart not to scale.

▼ DEPARTURE ROUTE DESCRIPTION

TAKE-OFF RUNWAY 8: Climb via course 076° to OKACO WP; maintain
11,000' or as assigned by ATC. If not at 11,000' or at assigned cruising
altitude upon reaching OKACO WP, climb in holding pattern (hold NW,
LT, 149° inbound), unless otherwise advised by ATC.

Fig. 6

OKACO ONE DEPARTURE (RNAV) (OBSTACLE)
(OKACO1.OKACO) 03359

BIG BEAR, CALIFORNIA
BIG BEAR CITY (L35)

tion. Now, what happens if the prevailing winds at the airport favor Runway 36? Then you should climb on runway heading to 1,500 feet, and then make a climbing right turn to intercept the OCN VOR 027 degree radial to TANNR intersection before proceeding on course.

With higher terrain northwest and east of the airport, this ODP provides you with an excellent means of departing in solid IFR conditions (yes, zero ceiling, zero visibility if you like) and avoiding obstructions during climbout. How's that for service? It's like having your own personal geologist on board telling you which way to go to keep from ruining a rock formation and becoming a rock star while creating a rock stair.

The interesting thing about the Fallbrook departure is that an IFR clearance out of the airport might read, *"2132 Bravo is cleared to John Wayne Pilgrim airport via direct Oceanside (OCN) VOR, V23 John Wayne. Climb and maintain 6,000 feet, squawk 4352 contact Departure Control 127.3 after departure. Clearance void if not off by 1015. Time now, 1005. If not airborne by 1015, contact Riverside FSS no later than 1045."*

Based on that clearance, how would you depart Fallbrook if you were departing to the south? Yes, you'd intercept V208-458, and then fly to OCN on this airway, then as filed to John Wayne. How would you depart to the north? You'd follow the ODP to TANNR, fly V186 to ROBNN, V208-458 to OCN then via the flight planned route. Isn't that out of the way, given your original clearance? Yes. But so what? If ATC doesn't tell you how to depart the airport, then you're perfectly within your legal rights to fly this procedure without telling ATC you're doing it.

In the case of Fallbrook, the ODP says that when departing Runway 18 you should climb on the runway heading to 1,200 feet, and then make a climbing left turn via heading 160 degrees to join V208-458. If you're westbound, you can proceed on course as you intercept the airway. If you're eastbound on this airway, you should proceed to VISTA intersection (position A) and hold east with left turns, 263 degrees inbound, and climb in a holding pattern to 5,000 feet before proceeding on course.

Looking at the IFR enroute chart excerpt (Figure 7) you can see that V208-458 (position B) is south of the airport (position C). Looking at the terrain in the plan view of Figure 4 shows why you're taken this way during departure. There is very little rising terrain in a southerly direc-

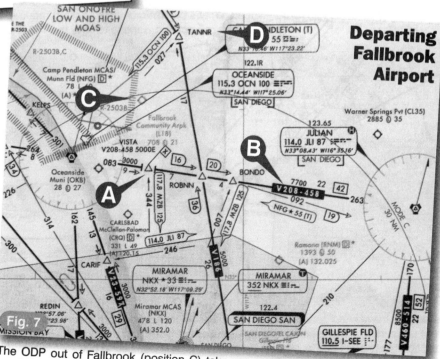

Departing Fallbrook Airport

The ODP out of Fallbrook (position C) takes you to V-208-458 (position B) for a southbound departure and to TANNR intersection (position D) for a northbound departure.

But I do have to be realistic here. Sometimes controllers will ask if you'll be using the IFR ODP for a northerly departure. This lets them know what you're doing when you pop up on their radar heading toward TANNR. I leave nothing to chance. I always put a little note in the flight plan box that says, "Will use Rwy 36 ODP." This lets the controller know what to expect of me, just in case he doesn't know what to expect. I recommend that you always do something similar. Keep in mind the controller's First Principle—controllers don't like surprises. It's not nice to leap out from behind an intersection and yell, "Boo!" Unless, of course, you're angling to be assigned the Hobbit Hole One departure.

It's interesting to note that ODPs are provided at an airport only when there are obstacles in the departure area. What's an "obstacle," and when is it "in the area?" When anything penetrates the 152-foot-per-nautical-mile climb plane (40:1 ratio), starting at 35 feet above the end of the runway, then an ODP will be provided for that airport. This departure gradient is shown in Figure 8. So if I were me, which I am, any time I see an ODP I start looking to see what's poking up around the airport, because I know *something* is out there *somewhere*. It could be an obstruc-

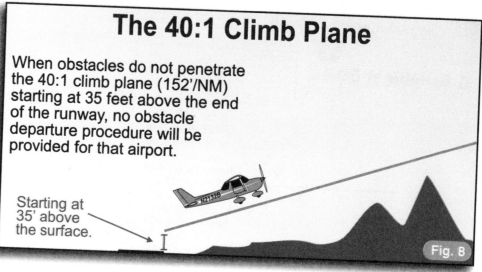

The 40:1 Climb Plane

When obstacles do not penetrate the 40:1 climb plane (152'/NM) starting at 35 feet above the end of the runway, no obstacle departure procedure will be provided for that airport.

Starting at 35' above the surface.

Fig. 8

tion that violates the 152 foot/nm climb plane by only a foot, but it could also be something that could seriously penetrate the other plane—mine. Or yours. Think of an ODP as a big "Flyer beware, dragons lurk out there" sign.

Obstacles penetrating the 152 foot/nm climb plane demand specific avoidance procedures. These will be specified as headings, routes, climb gradients, ceilings or visibilities that assure avoidance of the obstacle. When specific climb gradients are not provided, it's assumed that you will climb at least at 200 foot per-nautical mile to avoid obstacles. This guarantees you an *accumulating* minimum obstacle clearance of 48 feet per nautical mile during the climb.

Determining Climb Rates From Climb Gradients

One easy way to estimate how fast you should climb based on a procedure's nautical mile climb gradient is to use the *Rate of Climb Table* in Section D of your NACO legend shown below. For instance, suppose an ODP requires a 210 foot per nm climb gradient, based on a 140 knot groundspeed. What's the minimum rate of climb required in feet per minute? Looking at the 200 foot per nm column and working over to the 140 knot column, a 467 foot per minute rate of climb is required.

REQUIRED GRADIENT RATE (ft. per NM)	GROUND SPEED (KNOTS)						
	30	60	80	90	100	120	140
200	100	200	267	300	333	400	467
250	125	250	333	375	417	500	583
300	150	300	400	450	500	600	700
350	175	350	467	525	583	700	816
400	200	400	533	600	667	800	933
450	225	450	600	675	750	900	1050
500	250	500	667	750	833	1000	1167
550	275	550	733	825	917	1100	1283
600	300	600	800	900	1000	1200	1400
650	325	650	867	975	1083	1300	1516

FEET PER MINUTE VALUES

But what's the rate for a gradient of 210 feet per nm? You'll have to interpolate here. The easiest way to do this is to notice that there are five divisions of 10 between 200 and 250. So subtract the rate of climb required at 200 foot per nm from that required at 250 foot per nm and you end up with 583-467=116. Now, divide 116 by 5, which equals approximately 23. For each 10 foot per nm increase above 200, you'll need to add a value of 23. Doing this with 467 equals 490. So at 140 knots groundspeed, you'll need to climb at 490 feet per minute on your VSI just to maintain a 210 foot per nm climb gradient.

Now for the truth. The fact is that even well maintained general aviation airplanes might have trouble meeting some of the typical climb requirements in ODPs. A 500 foot per minute climb gradient for most smaller but heavily loaded airplanes on hot days is asking a lot. For the most part, general aviation pilots don't pay all that much attention to how fast their airplanes climb (but we should pay attention to this). We just know that they do and are happy because of it. So the next time you're out flying VFR, take a look at how fast you really climb based on variable density altitude and variable weight conditions. It's best to be aware of your performance so that your performance doesn't make you aware of how little of it there is during an ODP.

Kalispell IFR Departure Accident from the NTSB Files

On January 10, 1980, N3839M, a Piper Arrow aircraft, crashed into a mountain after departing the Kalispell City Airport, Kalispell, Montana. All three persons aboard were killed.

The Safety Board's investigation disclosed that the pilot, who was employed at the Kalispell City Airport as an instrument flight instructor, had been issued, before takeoff, an IFR clearance to the Calgary Airport via direct to the Kalispell VOR, direct to the Calgary VOR. The clearance issued by the Salt Lake City Air Route Traffic Control Center, included a climb to 14,000 feet and a transponder code. After acknowledging the clearance, the pilot asked, "Are we going to get vector northbound?"

The controller replied, "I could vector you to the Canadian border; after that I'm not sure if Canada Can."

The pilot answered, "We'll be receiving Lethbridge by that point."

As the aircraft reached the Kalispell VOR, the controller said, "radar contact" and requested the aircraft's altitude.

After the pilot reported leaving "five point five," the controller made the following transmission: "Three niner mike roger Lethbridge (unintelligible) bearing (unintelligible) five report reaching one four thousand."

About 1 minute later the pilot asked the Center, "...to let us know coming up on some high terrain if you would."

The controller replied, "...are you in the clouds now?" The pilot said he was. There were no more transmissions from N3839M.

The Kalispell Airport has no published instrument approach procedure and, thus, no published IFR departure procedures. An approach by visual reference to the terrain is the only means of access to this airport. However, there are no procedures which prohibit a pilot from filing an IFR flight plan and receiving an IFR clearance for departure from this airport or other airports not having published instrument departure procedures.

Thus, in IFR conditions, such departures involve a hazard because the pilot does not have available any published procedures for instrument flight. Furthermore, he cannot get radar vectors until the aircraft climbs to the minimum vectoring altitude (MVA). The ATC issuance of an IFR clearance for the portion of a flight before it reaches "protected airspace," or airspace that ensures terrain avoidance, gives the pilot implied permission to fly under actual IFR conditions via the IFR flight plan in an area where the flight can only be accomplished safely under VFR.

During the investigation, the controller stated that the MVA for the flight was 12,5000 feet, that radar contact was established as the aircraft left 5,500 feet, that the target was non-mode C, and that the bearing to Lethbridge was an "information only" item.

The Safety Board believes that, in this accident, based on the controller's transmission, the pilot expected radar vectors and was not aware that the controller had no terrain information and therefore was unable to issue vectors until the aircraft was above the MVA.

Heading direct to Kalispell VOR after departure from Kalispell City Airport at 5,500 feet

Courtesy Microsoft

This isn't a great deal of clearance. Most pilots think of this minimum clearance about as positively as they do a root canal. It's also highly possible that departing the airport in a tired, old Cessna 150 freighter will mean difficulty in meeting this climb standard, though most aircraft, under most conditions, will have little or no problem reaching or exceeding this minimum climb gradient. Just make sure the airplane you're flying is one of them.

IFR departure procedures may *require* a turn after departure, as was the case with Fallbrook (a climbing left turn when departing Runway 18). When a turn is required, it's assumed that you will always climb to a minimum of 400 feet above the airport elevation before commencing the turn (unless otherwise stated in the ODP). All climbs should be done at a minimum gradient of 200 feet per nautical mile, unless otherwise noted on the chart. This climb gradient puts the airplane at a minimum of 400 feet AGL within two miles of the departure threshold. This provides you with obstruction clearance during the turning departure.

If ODPs ensure an obstruction-free departure, then why aren't they included in your clearance when departing IFR at any airport, towered or non-towered? The answer is, ATC does assign them when you depart into Class B, C, D or E (controlled) airspace. (Note: at airports without control towers but within a Class E surface area, ATC does have the option of specifying the takeoff/turn or the initial heading to be flown after takeoff, as necessary. ATC will obtain or solicit your concurrence, before takeoff, that these items will allow compliance with traffic patterns, terrain, and avoiding obstruction.)

Keep in mind that ATC has no jurisdiction over the Class G airspace. That's why they don't assign these ODPs. On the other hand, ATC may assign an ODP in Class G (uncontrolled) airspace when it's necessary to prevent a traffic separation problem (such as two airplanes departing IFR at non-towered airports in close proximity to each other).

Unfortunately, ODPs are not available at all airports because not all airports have instrument approaches. That doesn't mean, however, that there aren't other resources available for finding a safe way out. Safe IFR departures can be made if you talk to a few of the airport denizens about airport geography and local departure procedures. Before departure, determine what minimum visibility or ceiling requirements are needed to avoid local obstructions. Professional recommendation (not to mention common sense) has it that there are benefits to taking out a sectional chart and identifying the highest obstacle in the departure path. This becomes your minimum ceiling height for departure. Using a minimum of one mile of visibility for departures, until the aircraft is above or moving away from the referenced obstacle, also provides an excellent safety advantage. The plain fact is that it's easier to avoid an obstacle you can see.

The SID or Standard Instrument Departure Procedure

There is one more type of instrument departure procedure that you're likely to encounter (the ODP and the SID are both technically referred to as a DP or departure procedure). It's a *Standard Instrument Departure*, or SID.

SIDs are developed to easily communicate air traffic control clearances to pilots. SIDs, like STARs, are printed graphically with an accompanying textual description, as shown in Figure 9. SIDs serve the same purpose STARs, but in reverse. SIDs simplify clearance delivery procedures for arriving at an airport.

It's just much easier for a controller to tell you to fly the Musel Six departure than to read you the entire text of the procedure shown on the bottom of the SID. Of course, you don't need the graphic to fly this SID. The textual description will do. If ATC gives you a SID and you don't have a copy of it or elect not to use it, then you can simply refuse the SID and ask for another means of departure in its place. As with STARs, if you know you don't want to use one in advance, then in the remarks section of your flight plan, please put the words, "No SIDs/STARs."

Keep in mind that while Metamucil may be good for you, the Musel departure may not be. Why wouldn't you want a nice, neatly-packaged, pre-approved, and nicely drawn SID? One of the reasons might be that, as is the case at John Wayne airport, it takes you far out over the water. And since you've seen the movies Titanic and Jaws, and you can't swim, you've developed some aversion to the thought of winding up in the water. Fair enough. Your choice. In this instance, if you've listed "No DP" (or you can list "No SIDs," "No STARs," or "No SIDs/STARs," as appropriate, in your flight plan), ATC might assign a different route.

It's important to keep in mind that you can list a SID in the route section of your flight plan using the SID codes, just as you did with STARs. In the case of John Wayne, the basic SID takes you to MUSEL intersection (Figure 9, position A). If this is where you want the SID to end for you, then list (MUSEL6.MUSEL) as the first portion of your route in your flight plan (Figure 9, position B).

If you want the SID to take you all the way to Daggett VOR, then list (MUSEL6.DAG) in the flight plan (Figure 9, position C). Suppose your destination is Daggett airport. If so, then DAG VOR (Figure 9, position D) is probably a fix from which the approach begins (an IAF). You'd want to file the route section in your flight plan to take you to this intersection (more on flight planning in the flight planning chapter). The only thing you have to place in the route section of your flight plan is the code

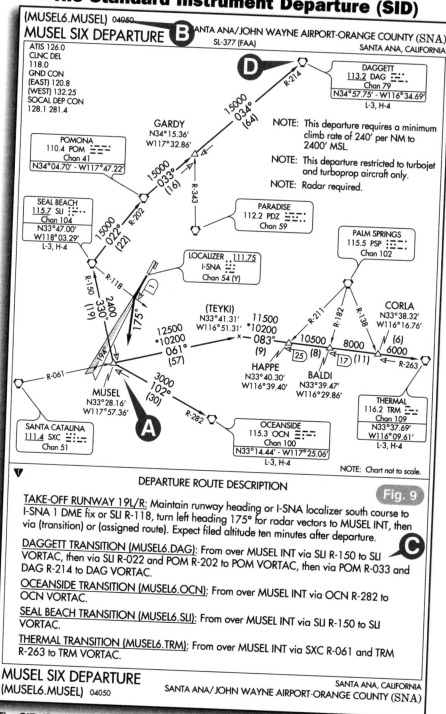

The SID (Standard Instrument Departure) is nothing more than a textually and often graphically depicted departure clearance. The SID makes is easier for the controller to provide a departure clearance (she tells you to fly the specific SID) and makes it easier for you to know how to depart the airport (you look at the paper and do what it says to do).

MUSEL6.DAG. Isn't that neat? You've already listed your departure and destination airport on the flight plan, so this code is all that's needed in the routing section. Wow, this stuff is better than instant cake mix. It makes navigation and flight planning a piece of cake.

As a final note about SIDs, some of them can be complex. Take a look at the Reno Three Departure shown in Figure 10 (the SID probably was named as it is because you've got to read it three times to figure it out). Notice

The Standard Instrument Departure (SID)

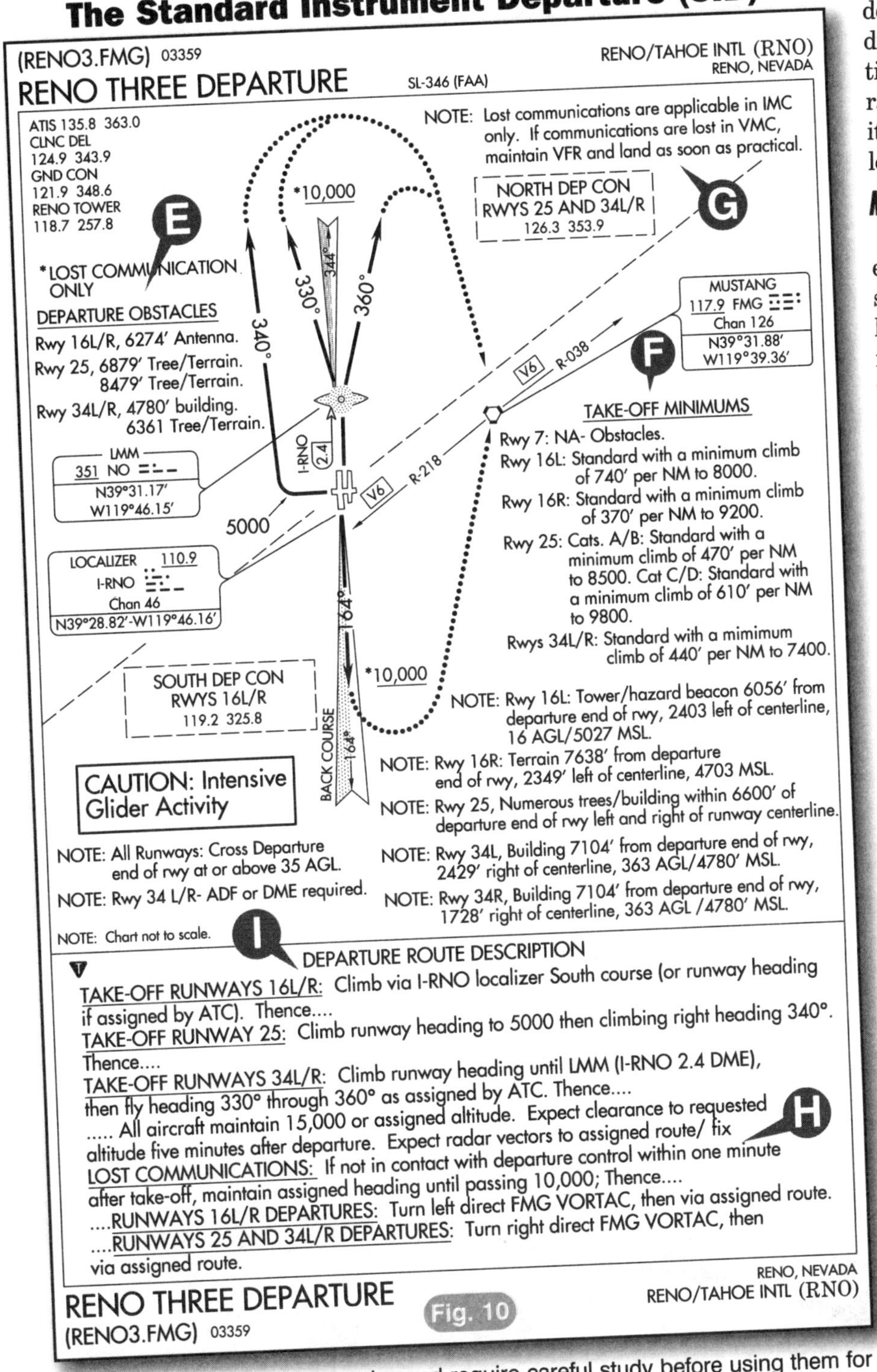

(RENO3.FMG) 03359

RENO THREE DEPARTURE

SL-346 (FAA)

RENO/TAHOE INTL (RNO)
RENO, NEVADA

ATIS 135.8 363.0
CLNC DEL
124.9 343.9
GND CON
121.9 348.6
RENO TOWER
118.7 257.8

E

*LOST COMMUNICATION ONLY

NOTE: Lost communications are applicable in IMC only. If communications are lost in VMC, maintain VFR and land as soon as practical.

NORTH DEP CON
RWYS 25 AND 34L/R
126.3 353.9

G

DEPARTURE OBSTACLES
Rwy 16L/R, 6274' Antenna.
Rwy 25, 6879' Tree/Terrain.
8479' Tree/Terrain.
Rwy 34L/R, 4780' building.
6361 Tree/Terrain.

MUSTANG
117.9 FMG
Chan 126
N39°31.88'
W119°39.36'

F

LMM
351 NO
N39°31.17'
W119°46.15'

*10,000

330° 360° 340°

I-RNO (2.4)

V6 R-038

V6 R-218

5000

LOCALIZER 110.9
I-RNO
Chan 46
N39°28.82'-W119°46.16'

BACK COURSE

164°

164°

SOUTH DEP CON
RWYS 16L/R
119.2 325.8

*10,000

TAKE-OFF MINIMUMS

Rwy 7: NA- Obstacles.
Rwy 16L: Standard with a minimum climb of 740' per NM to 8000.
Rwy 16R: Standard with a minimum climb of 370' per NM to 9200.
Rwy 25: Cats. A/B: Standard with a minimum climb of 470' per NM to 8500. Cat C/D: Standard with a minimum climb of 610' per NM to 9800.
Rwys 34L/R: Standard with a mimimum climb of 440' per NM to 7400.

NOTE: Rwy 16L: Tower/hazard beacon 6056' from departure end of rwy, 2403 left of centerline, 16 AGL/5027 MSL.
NOTE: Rwy 16R: Terrain 7638' from departure end of rwy, 2349' left of centerline, 4703 MSL.
NOTE: Rwy 25, Numerous trees/building within 6600' of departure end of rwy left and right of runway centerline.
NOTE: Rwy 34L, Building 7104' from departure end of rwy, 2429' right of centerline, 363 AGL/4780' MSL.
NOTE: Rwy 34R, Building 7104' from departure end of rwy, 1728' right of centerline, 363 AGL /4780' MSL.

CAUTION: Intensive Glider Activity

NOTE: All Runways: Cross Departure end of rwy at or above 35 AGL.
NOTE: Rwy 34 L/R- ADF or DME required.
NOTE: Chart not to scale.

I

DEPARTURE ROUTE DESCRIPTION

TAKE-OFF RUNWAYS 16L/R: Climb via I-RNO localizer South course (or runway heading if assigned by ATC). Thence....
TAKE-OFF RUNWAY 25: Climb runway heading to 5000 then climbing right heading 340°. Thence....
TAKE-OFF RUNWAYS 34L/R: Climb runway heading until LMM (I-RNO 2.4 DME), then fly heading 330° through 360° as assigned by ATC. Thence....
..... All aircraft maintain 15,000 or assigned altitude. Expect clearance to requested altitude five minutes after departure. Expect radar vectors to assigned route/ fix
LOST COMMUNICATIONS: If not in contact with departure control within one minute after take-off, maintain assigned heading until passing 10,000; Thence....
....RUNWAYS 16L/R DEPARTURES: Turn left direct FMG VORTAC, then via assigned route.
....RUNWAYS 25 AND 34L/R DEPARTURES: Turn right direct FMG VORTAC, then via assigned route.

H

RENO, NEVADA
RENO/TAHOE INTL (RNO)

RENO THREE DEPARTURE

Fig. 10

(RENO3.FMG) 03359

Some SIDs can be rather complex and require careful study before using them for departure. Nevertheless, this SID out of Reno, Nevada is extremely helpful given the high terrain surrounding Reno.

until passing 10,000 feet then, if you departed on Runway 25, you'd turn right direct to FMG VOR. Hopefully, by this time, you'd have figured out where the radio's "off" switch is located and turned it back on. If not, then you'd follow the lost comm procedures set out in the FARs.

Non-Standard Takeoff Minimums

While it's important to know the proper IFR departure path to avoid hitting something, it's equally important to have sufficient visibility and/or ceiling to make this possible. Most of us operate under Part 91 of the regulations and are not required to adhere to any visibility or ceiling requirements during an IFR departure. You have the legal authority to depart with no visibility at all. I'm hoping you have the vision to at least think carefully about opting for that option.

Why aren't Part 91 operators required to adhere to visibility minimums for takeoff? Part 91 tends to see the pilot as the primary person to assume risk, and there's a certain sense that he or she should be restrained only from total foolhardiness. Any passengers on a Part 91 flight are kind of an afterthought.

Commercial carriers, by contrast, are in the business of offering transportation for pay, and the rules for Parts 121, 123, 129, and 135 shift perspective and focus on protecting the presumably innocent passenger who has no idea what risks he or she is assuming by purchasing a ticket.

Commercial operators under Parts 121, 123, 129, and 135 don't have the freedom to depart in zero-zero conditions. This is because these people have a weighty moral responsibility to the paying passengers, who are in no position to assess for themselves the risks the pilot is taking.

Commercial flights must adhere to any visibility and/or ceiling requirement established for the airport and runway (plus their own special, customized rules, provided by the FAA in their operating specifications). So important are these requirements that the FAA has established what is known as standard takeoff minimums for all commercial operators. For instance, standard takeoff minimums require commercial operators having two engines or less to have at least one statute mile of visibility (RVR of 5,000 feet) for takeoff. Those flying planes with more than two engines must have at least one-half statute mile visibility (RVR 2,400 feet).

the departure obstacle information in the top left of the chart (Figure 10, position E); the takeoff minimums information in the right middle (Figure 10, position F); the lost communications information at the top and the bottom of the chart (Figure 10, position G and H), as well as the detailed route descriptions shown in the lower portion of the chart (Figure 10, position I). Yes, SIDs can have specific lost comm procedures printed on them. If you lost communication within one minute after departure, you would be expected to maintain your assigned altitude

There are many airports where the standard takeoff minimums aren't enough to ensure a safe IFR departure. When that's the case, the FAA establishes non-standard takeoff minimums for that airport. How would you know? If you see a black triangle with a white T in it, located in the briefing area (Figure 11, position A), that's your clue.

Of course, you may not care about the Big T, since you're not a commercial operator, but that wouldn't be a wise move on your part. You should care, because these non-standard minimums tell you where you should exercise caution during the IFR departure. Let's return to the Takeoff and ODP section of the NACO booklet, Section C, and take a look at Fallbrook's takeoff minimums (Figure 11, position B).

Takeoffs on Runway 36 (where you're headed in the direction of higher terrain, as shown in Figure 12, positions A and B) require that Category A and B airplanes have a 700-foot ceiling and two miles visibility for takeoff. In addition, a minimum climb gradient of 340 foot per nautical mile is required up to 5,000 feet. This means if you're climbing at 120 knots groundspeed (2 nautical miles per minute), then you'll need to climb at 680 feet per minute.

Are you, as a Part 91 operator, required to honor these takeoff minimums? No. After all, you may fly a lower-performance, less-capable aircraft, which probably couldn't climb at 680 feet per minute at sea level when it was new and toting only eight ounces of fuel. So don't let the T in the black box concern you unless you want to fly with the kind of safety margin the FAA feels is owed to paying passengers. And unless you're convinced you owe your passengers something less. You get the point, right?

It's important to note that a ceiling requirement is normally established a bit higher than the height of the terrain or obstacle you could hit (Figure 13). If you think about

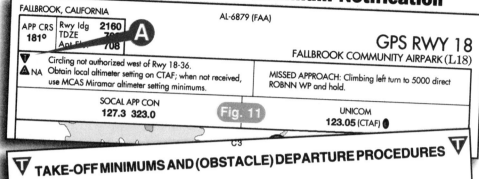

The white "T" in the black triangle (position A) in the briefing area indicates that non standard takeoff minimums apply at this airport for commercial operators (Part 135, 121, etc.). Referring to the ODP in Section C of the NACO book for Fallbrook airport (position B), it appears that a departure on Runway 36 requires both a minimum ceiling and visibility requirement as well as a minimum climb rate requirement. This doesn't apply to Part 91 operators (you), but these requirements are wise to adhere to, nevertheless.

On Runway 36 at Fallbrook

While holding in position on Runway 36 at Fallbrook, you can see the terrain on which the 700 foot ceiling minimum is generated (position A. The terrain here is approximately 1,400 feet MSL, while the airport elevation is 702 feet MSL). Farther north, you can see the terrain on which the 340 foot per nautical climb rate to 5,000 feet requirement is based (position B).

Straight Out From Runway 36 at Fallbrook at 1,400'

After departure from Runway 36 at Fallbrook at 1,402 feet (700 feet AGL above the airport elevation), it appears that you will just clear the terrain ahead. If the ceiling were at 700 feet AGL, you as a commercial operator would (hopefully) be able to keep the terrain in sight and avoid it. This is one of the reasons for establishing a minimum ceiling takeoff requirement for commercial operators (which will hopefully compel you to think about using the same requirement as a Part 91 operator).

the takeoffs minimums in reverse, these values tell you that when departing Runway 36 there's a good chance you'll need a 340 foot per nautical mile climb gradient to avoid a 700 foot obstacle/terrain lurking somewhere north of the airport.

Figure 14 shows the takeoff minimums section for Stockton Metro, California. Notice that the middle briefing area doesn't have the black triangle with the white T inside. That means standard minimums apply to all runways for commercial operators (two engines or less, 1 mile visibility; more than two engines, 1/2 mile visibility). Once again, these standard or nor-standard takeoff minimums don't apply to Part 91 operators, but you should consider them and possibly use them, nevertheless). As an interesting note, when you take a look at Section C of the appropriate NACO booklet, you won't find an ODP for Stockton. This tells

you that no obstacles penetrate the 152 foot/nm climb plane for any departure runway at Stockton as shown in the departure area panorama at the bottom of Figure 14. A departure in any direction is free of obstructions as long as you maintain a 200 foot per nautical mile climb gradient.

It might be worth thinking about what takeoff minimums you will accept on behalf of yourself and your passengers, keeping in mind the commercial standards. After all, if it's good enough for them, why isn't it good enough for you and your passengers? This is especially true if you're interested in maximizing your safety during an IFR departure. Depart in zero-zero conditions and experience an engine failure and you are seriously out of opportunities, Captain. Your landing site and survival chances will be selected entirely by the fickle finger of fate.

Here are a few other points to consider when departing IFR. Most of us fly with some form of GPS moving map display on board our airplane. If you have such a display, then put it to good use. If you are departing IFR and the airport doesn't have an ODP, circle above the airport until you're clear of obstacles before proceeding along your route. You can do this by climbing with a bank sufficient to keep you close to the airport and away from obstructions. You need only look at the moving map display to keep yourself oriented to the runway during a climb. Remember, if the controller doesn't tell you how to depart an airport IFR, then it's up to you to find the safest

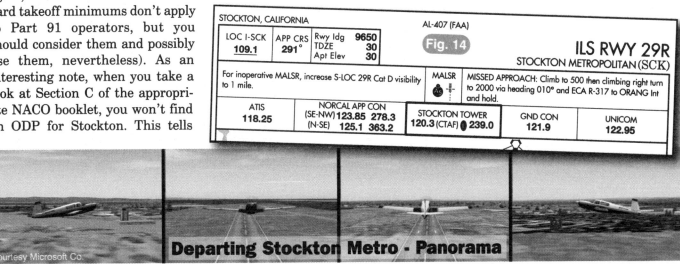

STOCKTON, CALIFORNIA				AL-407 (FAA)	**Fig. 14**		**ILS RWY 29R**
LOC I-SCK **109.1**	APP CRS **291°**	Rwy ldg **9650** TDZE **30** Apt Elev **30**					STOCKTON METROPOLITAN (SCK)

For inoperative MALSR, increase S-LOC 29R Cat D visibility to 1 mile.		MALSR	MISSED APPROACH: Climb to 500 then climbing right turn to 2000 via heading 010° and ECA R-317 to ORANG Int and hold.

ATIS **118.25**	NORCAL APP CON (SE-NW) **123.85 278.3** (N-SE) **125.1 363.2**	STOCKTON TOWER **120.3** (CTAF) **239.0**	GND CON **121.9**	UNICOM **122.95**

Departing Stockton Metro - Panorama

Since Stockton Metro's airport doesn't have an obstacle departure procedure, this means there are no obstacles penetrating the 152 foot per nautical mile climb plane in the immediate vicinity of the airport, as shown in the panorama above. The lack of a reverse bold "T" in the middle briefing area indicates that Stockton has standard IFR takeoff minimums for commercial operators.

method for doing so. Climbing directly above the airport means you won't hit anything, unless you run into some guy on the way down who's using his GPS for an illegal instrument approach. Hopefully this won't happen.

Recently, scientists have discovered how to turn Mexican food into gasoline. Yep. It's true. The only problem is that they don't know if they should call it gasomole or guacohol. Would you like to make some discoveries of your own that don't present a naming challenge? Good. The next chapter involves discovering some pretty interesting things about low altitude IFR enroute charts.

Chapter 15
IFR Enroute Charts

When I was a youngster in Catholic school, the head nun gave me a notebook to keep track of my sins. I was the first kid in my school to go multi-volume. For years, I thought "Last Rites" was the final page in the notebook.

I soon learned shorthand, which meant I could no longer just submit the notebooks in lieu of confession—nobody else could read them. I nearly won a Red Cross blood donation award because of all the paper cuts the notebook gave me as I flipped pages while trying to keep track of those sins.

IFR charts, too, have their secrets but I've never had a blood loss problem with low altitude IFR enroute charts (Figure 1). That's because I don't keep track of my sins on them, and they're made out of softer paper. What's on the charts is certainly no secret, once you learn a bit about how to read chart shorthand. That's why we're here.

Class is in session. Pay attention or someone might rap you on the knuckles, then again, I'll just take the rap for you since I'm used to it.

The High Points of the IFR Low Altitude Enroute Chart

The low altitude enroute chart provides the information you need to fly in the IFR enroute structure below 18,000 feet MSL. Think of this information being all that you need from the time you depart an airport until you arrive at a location covered by an approach chart, at which point you'll begin using that chart. These charts are the peanut butter and jelly of the IFR sandwich. Butter me up and I'll tell you more.

The low altitude enroute chart provides information in four colors (just enough to keep a chameleon interested) and includes things such as airways, navaid information (including frequencies), Morse code identifications, geographic coordinates, obstruction clearance altitudes, airway distances, reporting points, special use airspace and much more (you can swat flies, fan yourself

The Low Altitude IFR Enroute Chart

The NACO low altitude IFR enroute chart provides routes for use in the IFR system below 18,000 feet MSL. It's an essential item for use when operating in the IFR system.

and, on long flights, make a funny hat and force your passengers to wear it for your personal amusement). Basically, it's everything you need to make navigational decisions when flying IFR over long routes.

As you can see from Figure 2, there are 18 double-sided charts (36 sides total) in the low altitude system. In addition, a separate chart, called an Area Chart, is available for 13 high-traffic density areas in the U.S, as shown in Figure 3.

The mileage scales used on low altitude enroute charts vary from 1 inch=8 nautical miles to 1 inch=20 nautical miles. Figure 4 shows the front panel of a low altitude chart with different mileage scales on each of two panels (positions A and B). If you use a "thumb's width" to represent 10 miles on panel 3, you better have someone close the car door on that digit if you want to use it the same way on panel 4. On second thought, forget that idea. It's only a rule of thumb, anyway, and slamming the car door on your finger Hertz.

Unfolded, a low altitude enroute chart measures 55 × 20 inches, about enough to

Low Altitude Enroute Chart U.S. Coverage

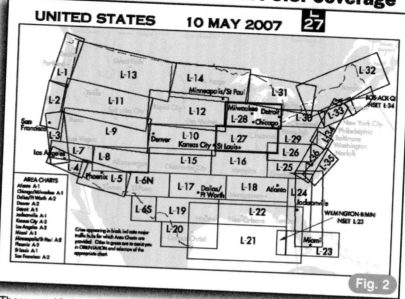

There are 18 double-sided low altitude enroute charts covering the continental United States for operating altitudes below 18,000 foot MSL. When flying IFR between airports you'll use the low altitude enroute chart to identify fly-able airways and routes as well as determine minimum operating altitudes.

cover an entire cockpit. If you weren't IFR before unfolding the chart, you are after. In the hands of an FAA origami master, when folded, these charts scale down to approximately 5 × 10 inches, look rectangular, and have little or no resemblance to a pigeon. Yes, they *can* be

The Area Chart

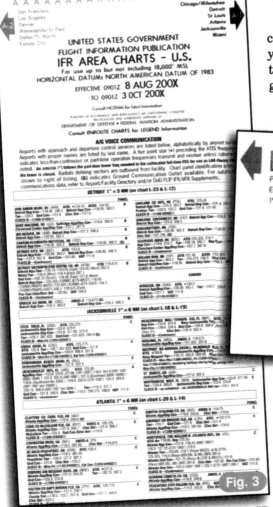

Area charts provided expanded and detailed IFR enroute symbology for areas of high density traffic operations in the U.S. On the single chart shown above you'll find 13 panels, each containing detailed enroute IFR navigation information.

Low Altitude Enroute Chart Scale

The top front header of the low altitude enroute chart contains essential information on chart scale and chart currency.

refolded, and although there are no instructions for this complex maneuver, I know only one or two pilots who can't do it. Like the NACO approach chart booklets, these charts are revised every 56 days. Figure 4 shows an easy way to tell if your chart is current for use in the IFR system. This chart becomes effective on August 5th, 200X beginning at 0901 Zulu and expires on September 30th, 200X at 0901 Zulu.

Area charts (Figure 5) are extremely useful add-ons. The area chart shows a smaller region in greater detail, and in some cases it shows intersections that don't appear on the low altitude

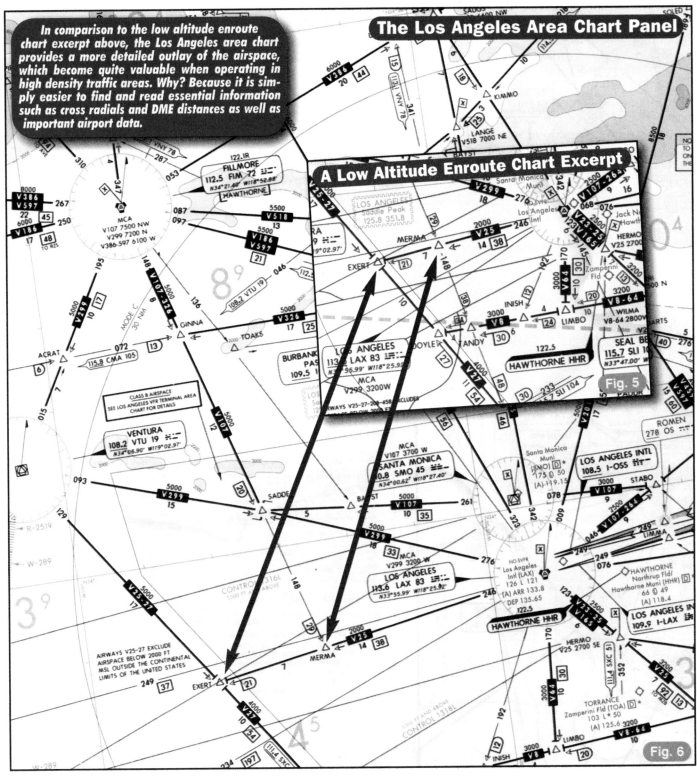

In comparison to the low altitude enroute chart excerpt above, the Los Angeles area chart provides a more detailed outlay of the airspace, which become quite valuable when operating in high density traffic areas. Why? Because it is simply easier to find and read essential information such as cross radials and DME distances as well as important airport data.

The Los Angeles Area Chart Panel

A Low Altitude Enroute Chart Excerpt

Fig. 5

Fig. 6

chart. Area charts help provide guidance in some of the most heavily traveled and complex airspace. If there's an area chart for your departure or destination, make use of it. (A list of the cities that have area charts is shown in black lettering on the chart coverage panel in Figure 2 and tallied at the bottom left corner of the chart panel, too.)

Figure 5 compares a section of the low altitude enroute chart with a comparable section on the LAX IFR area chart (Figure 6). As you can see, the area chart is like having a magnifying glass. If you want to hum a chorus of, "I

Can See Clearly Now," that's fine. Don't forget the line that says, "I can see all obstacles in my way."

Since the low altitude enroute chart is good for altitudes below 18,000 feet MSL, what should you do when flying at and above this altitude? First, make certain your airplane *can* fly at and above that altitude. It's really embarrassing to file for FL240 and run out of steam at 6,000 feet. But assuming you get to 18,000 feet and higher, what do you do for a chart? Just hold the low altitude enroute chart higher, or farther away from your eyeballs? Silly me.

Rod Machado's Instrument Pilot's Handbook

The answer, unremarkably, is to use a different chart. This one is the (roll of drums) *high altitude enroute chart* (Figure 7), for use at (yes, you can guess) high altitudes. Who said IFR is difficult? The high altitude charts show things such as the jet route structure; VHF NAVAIDs with frequency, identification, channel, and geographic coordinates; selected airports; and reporting points. Because of their larger scale (1 inch=18 nautical miles to 1 inch=45 nautical miles), there are only six high altitude charts, totaling 12 chart sides (Figure 8) to cover the conterminous U.S. and two additional charts for Alaska. Because these charts are for altitudes beginning at 18,000 feet, the minimum altitude for operating on any of this chart's jet route structure is 18,000 feet. High altitude charts, like their low altitude brothers, are revised every 56 days.

High Altitude Enroute Chart

High altitude enroute charts provide navigation information for flights at or above 18,000 feet MSL. When climbing to FL 200, you'd use the low altitude enroute chart until reaching 18,000 feet then switch over to the high altitude chart, reversing the process on your way down.

High Altitude Enroute Chart U.S. Coverage

There are only six high altitude charts, each having two sides, for a total of twelve chart sides covering all of the conterminous United States.

You'll notice that IFR charts are revised more frequently than VFR sectional charts (which are revised once every six months). Chart currency is critical for safe IFR operations. As an instrument student, you should purchase either a subscription to NACO approach and enroute charts or at least visit your local pilot supply store once every 56 days and purchase the charts (or their updates) you need to fly IFR (as well as checking the FDC NOTAMS for chart changes).

Looking for Noah's Ark

No, I'm not talking about the ship. I'm speaking of Noah's Ark airport located in Waldron, Missouri. You know how difficult it is to find tiny airports on charts, don't you? Fortunately, the FAA makes the search a lot easier with their *Airport Locations Tab* found on the inside flap of the low altitude enroute chart (Figure 9).

Noah's Ark airport ID is 06MO and it's located on panel *J* of the enroute chart (Figure 9, position Z). Despite the fact that no origami master was involved, low altitude enroute charts expand nicely into individual four individual panels on each side of the two-sided enroute chart as shown in Figure 10. This means there are eight individual panels total, with each panel referenced by letters from A to H (panels A, B, C, and D are on one side of the chart and panels E, F, G and H are on the other) as shown by position Y in Figure 11. Using the Airport Locations Tab, you unfold your chart to the appropriate panel and start looking for the airport. OK, you're on your own from here to find the airport within each panel, but this is sure a lot easier than searching an entire chart for Noah's Ark. Then again, if you're over 40 like me (that's age, not pounds) and are wearing lenses less thick than a big pop bottle, bring along a magnifying glass to read this detailed, small print section.

At one time the FAA had something known as the *Air/Ground Communications* section on the inside panel of the low altitude enroute chart. This section is being removed from chart for two reasons. First, it's always good business to reduce chart clutter. Second, all the air/ground communication information you need can be found in the *Airport/Facility Directory* and, to a limited extent, on the low altitude enroute chart near the airport symbol.

The Communications Section, Panels and Airport Location on Chart

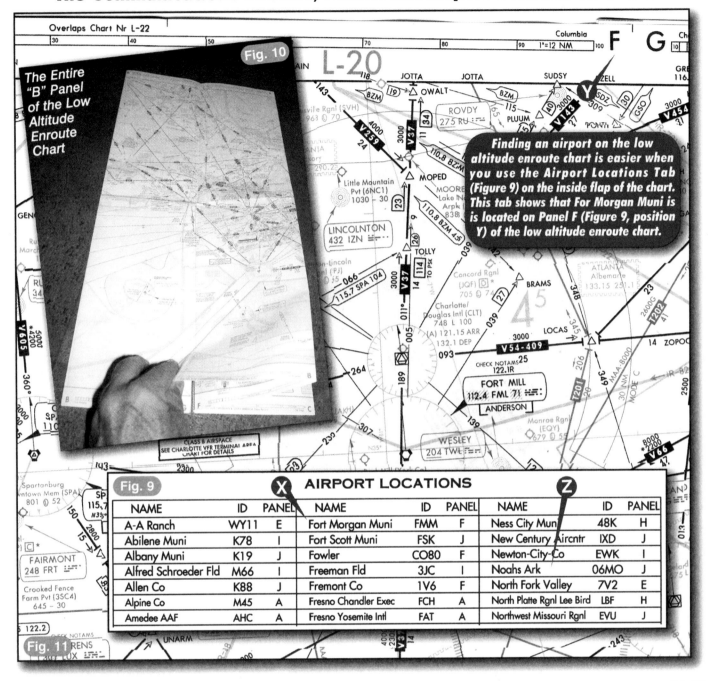

Fig. 10 — The Entire "B" Panel of the Low Altitude Enroute Chart

Finding an airport on the low altitude enroute chart is easier when you use the Airport Locations Tab (Figure 9) on the inside flap of the chart. This tab shows that For Morgan Muni is is located on Panel F (Figure 9, position Y) of the low altitude enroute chart.

Fig. 9 — AIRPORT LOCATIONS

NAME	ID	PANEL	NAME	ID	PANEL	NAME	ID	PANEL
A-A Ranch	WY11	E	Fort Morgan Muni	FMM	F	Ness City Mun	48K	H
Abilene Muni	K78	I	Fort Scott Muni	FSK	J	New Century Aircntr	IXD	J
Albany Muni	K19	J	Fowler	CO80	F	Newton-City-Co	EWK	I
Alfred Schroeder Fld	M66	I	Freeman Fld	3JC	I	Noahs Ark	06MO	J
Allen Co	K88	J	Fremont Co	1V6	F	North Fork Valley	7V2	E
Alpine Co	M45	A	Fresno Chandler Exec	FCH	A	North Platte Rgnl Lee Bird	LBF	H
Amedee AAF	AHC	A	Fresno Yosemite Intl	FAT	A	Northwest Missouri Rgnl	EVU	J

This is just one of the many reasons why you need to know your way around an IFR chart. If you're too busy trying to find the correct enroute chart to use you could stumble into an active MOA. Do that once and you won't do it no-moa!

Military Training Routes (MTRs)

Since NACO charts are also used by the military, they depict military training routes on the front of the chart, as shown in Figure 12 as well as on the chart itself (Figure 13). Route identification and operating altitudes are depicted. If you look closely at the MTRs (they're brown with number IDs on them) you'll notice a slight difference between them (positions A and B). At position A, the IR route is thicker than the one at Position B, as if it's on steroids or something. No, no steroids here. Thicker MTRs represent routes greater than 5 nm on at least one side of the line. Thinner routes are those MTRs that are less than 5 nm on either side of the line.

MTR information isn't of much practical value for flight in the civilian IFR system. Air traffic controllers provide separation between civilian aircraft and military traffic (and, no, they won't let you join up and participate in a bomb drop, not even if you bring your own bombs. Sorry to drop that bomb on you). One circumstance where it might help preserve your bacon is if you're departing through uncontrolled airspace that lies near an active MTR (either an IFR or VFR military training route). While the local controller *should* be advised of any military activity, it wouldn't hurt to double check. Being speared by something would be a bad thing.

Approachable Airports

The low altitude enroute chart shows all airports having hard surface runways of 3,000 feet or longer and/or having an instrument approach procedure (in Alaska, the low altitude charts shows hard or soft runways 3,000 feet or longer). Airports having instrument approach procedures are clearly identifiable. They're shown in blue or green letters, while those without instrument approaches are listed in brown letters. In Figure 14, Needles (position E), Lake Havasu (position D) and Bullhead City (Laughlin, position F) have instrument approaches, while Bullhead City's Sun Valley airport (position G) and Eagle Airpark (position H), Chemehuevi Valley (position J) and Ford Motor Co. Proving Ground (position I) don't.

What's the difference between blue and green airports? At one time, a green airport name indicated that all of the instrument procedures for that airport could be found in the FAA's TPP or *Terminal Procedures Publication* (the NACO chart booklet containing the charts we've

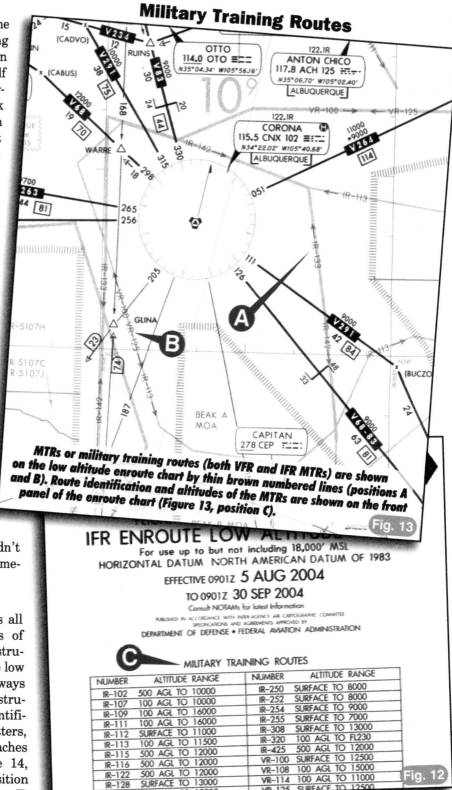

Military Training Routes

MTRs or military training routes (both VFR and IFR MTRs) are shown on the low altitude enroute chart by thin brown numbered lines (positions A and B). Route identification and altitudes of the MTRs are shown on the front panel of the enroute chart (Figure 13, position C).

Fig. 13

IFR ENROUTE LOW ALTITUDE
For use up to but not including 18,000' MSL
HORIZONTAL DATUM NORTH AMERICAN DATUM OF 1983
EFFECTIVE 0901Z 5 AUG 2004
TO 0901Z 30 SEP 2004
Consult NOTAMs for latest information
PUBLISHED IN ACCORDANCE WITH INTER AGENCY AIR CARTOGRAPHIC COMMITTEE
SPECIFICATIONS AND AGREEMENTS APPROVED BY
DEPARTMENT OF DEFENSE ★ FEDERAL AVIATION ADMINISTRATION

MILITARY TRAINING ROUTES

NUMBER	ALTITUDE RANGE	NUMBER	ALTITUDE RANGE
IR-102	500 AGL TO 10000	IR-250	SURFACE TO 8000
IR-107	100 AGL TO 10000	IR-252	SURFACE TO 8000
IR-109	100 AGL TO 16000	IR-254	SURFACE TO 9000
IR-111	100 AGL TO 16000	IR-255	SURFACE TO 7000
IR-112	SURFACE TO 11000	IR-308	SURFACE TO 13000
IR-113	100 AGL TO 11500	IR-320	100 AGL TO FL230
IR-115	500 AGL TO 12000	IR-425	500 AGL TO 12000
IR-116	500 AGL TO 12000	VR-100	SURFACE TO 12500
IR-122	500 AGL TO 12000	VR-108	100 AGL TO 15000
IR-128	SURFACE TO 13000	VR-114	100 AGL TO 11000
IR-130	500 AGL TO 12000	VR-125	SURFACE TO 12500

Fig. 12

discussed in the last few chapters). If the airport name was blue, some or all of those instrument procedures would be found in the separately published DOD FLIP or Department of Defense *Flight Information Publication*. These are the charts that military pilots use to fly instrument approaches.

This green-blue color difference is now irrelevant and will eventually disappear since all of the DOD procedures have been added to the NACO chart booklet. That's why you'll find military approaches mixed in with civilian charts. You are not cleared to land at military airports just because you have their charts, any more than a White House map gives you drop-in privileges! Even in the South, you'll find there isn't a real warm reception waiting at military airports for civilian visitors. By the way, "Follow Me" on the back of a military Jeep sent to meet you is an order, not an invitation.

It's interesting to note that public airports are identified by city name and the associated airport name when the city name is different from the airport name. That's why the names of Eagle Airpark and Sun Valley are listed under the same city name of Bullhead. In Figure 15, position K, you can see that the airport name on the area chart is "Brackett," yet the approach chart and the departure procedure are listed in their respective sections alphabetically under L, for the city name—"La Verne" (on the enroute chart, Figure 15, position M), because, there was no room to place the city name. This is one more

Identifying Airports With and Without Instrument Approaches

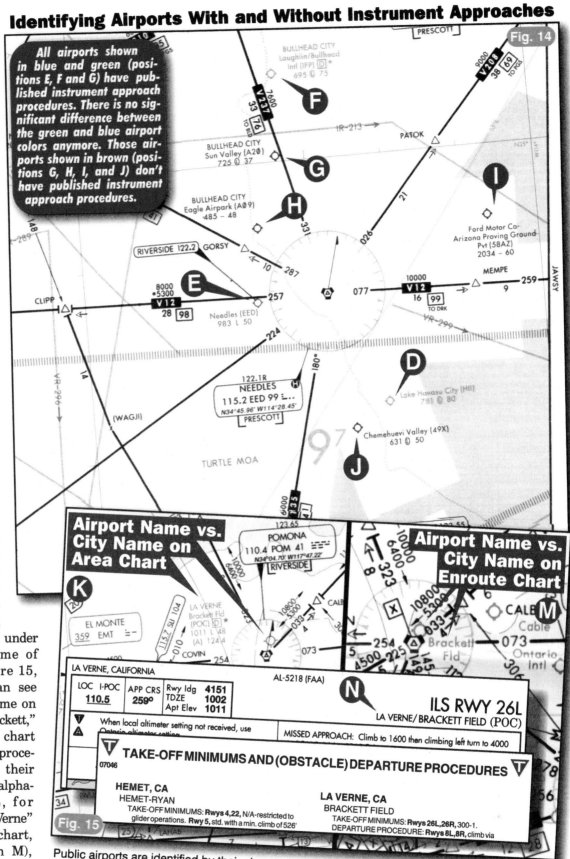

good reason to use the area chart when it exists). If you can't find an instrument approach chart under the name of the airport shown on the low altitude chart, then look for the airport under its city name first. And you thought memorizing the state capitals in fifth grade was hard, huh?

Public airports are identified by their airport name as well as the city in which they're found (position K). When these two names are different, you'll want to look for approach charts, departure charts and other airport information under the city name (position N) as shown above.

Figure 16 shows Camarillo airport on the low altitude enroute chart. A *D* in a box (position Z) next to an asterisk also means that part-time Class D airspace exists at that airport. There are no dashed lines around the airport to indicate the coverage of that airspace, as there would be on a sectional chart. As an IFR pilot, you're expected to know that Class D air is generally a little over 4 nm in radius (this varies considerably, however) and typically extends up to 2,500 feet AGL.

To learn about the operational hours of this airspace, you's need to go to the *Airport/Facility Directory* (an excerpt of which is shown in Figure 16, position Y). There you'll find the effective hours of Class D airspace listed in Zulu (UTC), not local times. In the case of Figure 16, Camarillo's Class D airspace effective hours are 1500–0500Z. If you're having trouble converting Zulu to local time, then do what a friend of mine did. He purchased a spiffy watch to help him. And a great watch it is, having dials for time zones not only on this planet but other planets as well. It's so big that the thing doubles as a dumbbell. Smart, huh?

Use caution when planning an IFR flight to an airport at a time when its surface-based controlled airspace is not in effect. Approach minimums sometimes increase in the absence of surface-based controlled airspace. In fact, some approaches are prohibited unless the Class D or E surface-based airspace is in effect, and some airports are not authorized for filing as alternates unless this controlled airspace is active at the expected time of arrival.

Chart Airspace Designations

Class D airspace exists at Camarillo as is indicated by the box surrounding a "D" (position Z). Tower information can be found in the *Airport/Facility Directory* (excerpt of A/FD shown at position Y).

An example of this is shown in Figure 17, position W for Oxnard, California. You can't list this airport for use as an alternate on the IFR flight plan if you plan on arriving when the tower is closed or when local weather isn't available as shown by the excerpt from Section E of the NACO IFR chart booklet, position V (more on this later). The operating hours for the tower and Class D airspace are shown in the *Airport/Facility Directory* excerpt (position U). As a general rule, the operating hours for Class D or Class E surface-based airspace are usually tied to the operating hours of the tower, FSS, AWOS, AWSS, ASOS or other means of official weather observation.

An official means of weather observation indicates that you'll have essential meteorological

Approach Limitations Based on Airspace Available

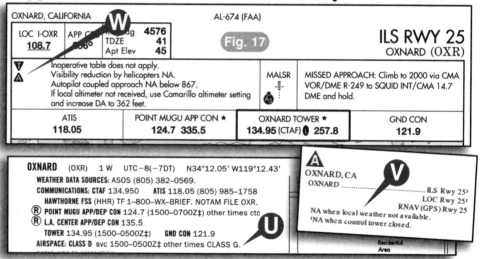

When Oxnard's tower is closed or when local weather isn't available, the airport cannot be listed or used as an alternate on an IFR flight plan. The insert in position V above is taken from the alternate minimums Section E of the NACO chart booklet (more on this Section in the next chapter). Figure 17, position U (above), shows the Class D or tower operating hours in the *Airport/Facility Directory*.

information like the altimeter setting and visibility reports. No weather reporting means no alternative but to find an alternative alternate (this is why I love my job). Of course, you can still list an airport as an alternate—even if it doesn't have an instrument approach—as long as you can descend and land in VFR conditions from the local, appropriate minimum airway altitudes—MEA and/or MOCA (I'll discuss MEAs, MOCAs, MAAs and MCAs at the end of this chapter).

Special Use: Use With Caution

The FAA designates several kinds of *special use* airspace. This is airspace that has something special about it, including a special opportunity ro become an airplane-shish kabob if you're not careful. Much special use airspace involves military or other operations that increase the risks for mere mortals unable to cavort at 1,500 miles an hour.

Special use airspace appears on the low altitude enroute chart. Figure 18 shows the special use airspace around Daggett, California. The closely spaced, brown hatched lines indicate the boundaries of a Military Operations Area or

Special Use Airspace Charting

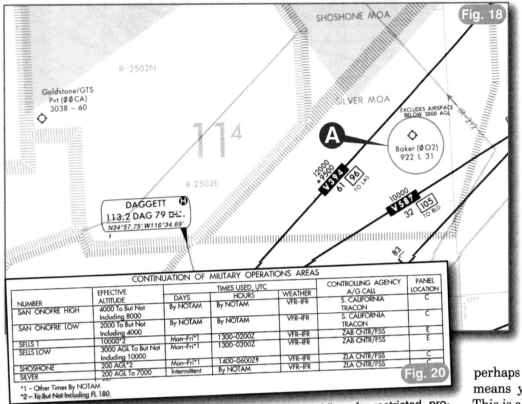

CONTINUATION OF MILITARY OPERATIONS AREAS

NUMBER	EFFECTIVE ALTITUDE	TIMES USED, UTC		WEATHER	CONTROLLING AGENCY A/G CALL	PANEL LOCATION
		DAYS	HOURS			
SAN ONOFRE HIGH	4000 To But Not Including 8000	By NOTAM	By NOTAM	VFR-IFR	S. CALIFORNIA TRACON	C
SAN ONOFRE LOW	2000 To But Not Including 4000	By NOTAM	By NOTAM	VFR-IFR	S. CALIFORNIA TRACON	C
SELLS 1	10000*2	Mon–Fri*1	1300-0200Z	VFR-IFR	ZAB CNTR/FSS	E
SELLS LOW	3000 AGL To But Not Including 10000	Mon–Fri*1	1300-0200Z	VFR-IFR	ZAB CNTR/FSS	E
SHOSHONE	200 AGL*2	Mon–Fri*1	1400-0600Z‡	VFR-IFR	ZLA CNTR/FSS	C
SILVER	200 AGL To 7000	Intermittent	By NOTAM	VFR-IFR	ZLA CNTR/FSS	C

*1 – Other Times By NOTAM
*2 – To But Not Including FL 180

Fig. 20

Special use airspace (Figure18) is defined by blue hatched lines for restricted, prohibited, warning and alert areas. Brown hatched lines identify the boundaries of a military operations area (MOA). Specific information on the MOA is found on the border panel of the low altitude enroute chart (Figure 20).

MOAs are often used by fighter aircraft. The kid who used to race his Corvette up and down the street is now using this airspace to shock and flatten all land- and air-dwelling creatures into submission. And he's probably waiting out there to play with you in his heavily-armed F-16. Unlike restricted airspace, flight through a MOA is not restricted or prohibited, but there *are* parts of you that should be at least somewhat constricted while traversing this territory if it's *hot* (in use).

This is where military pilots go to practice their maneuvers. If they need practice, then maybe they're not all that good at that particular maneuver. And they're always moving fast, perhaps at the speed of sound, which means you can't hear them coming. This is all the more reason to avoid the area. When planning your IFR flight, it's always best to avoid the MOAs. If ATC assigns a route that takes you through special use airspace, it's usually because that airspace isn't active at the time, or because ATC has negotiated a temporary truce for you.

If ATC vectors or routes me through a MOA or restricted area, out of habit I always confirm that the special use airspace is indeed inactive, just in case the controller's brain is temporarily inactive (everybody makes mistakes, controllers too). Remember, they don't call it a MOA for nothing. Go there once and get scared, and you won't want to go back "no moa."

MOA. The blue hatched lines show the boundaries of a restricted area (the same marking is used for prohibited, warning, and alert areas). Shown are restricted areas R-2502N, R-2502E as well as the Shoshone and Silver MOAs.

The special use airspace section of the low altitude enroute chart (Figure 19) shows the variable altitude, times and controlling agencies of these airspace areas. As you can see, R-2502N and R-2502E extend vertically to an unlimited height (UNLTD), which means the next galaxy or someplace just beyond where you can go.

Special Use Airspace Altitudes and Times

P – PROHIBITED, R – RESTRICTED, A – ALERT, W – WARNING AREAS
CANADA: CYA – ADVISORY, CYD – DANGER, CYR – RESTRICTED AREAS

All altitudes are MSL unless otherwise indicated
Days – Sunrise to Sunset except Canada where it means 1/2 hr before sunrise to 1/2 hr after sunset
Nights – Sunset to Sunrise except Canada where it means 1/2 hr after sunset to 1/2 hr before sunrise

Time – Hours shown are UTC unless otherwise indicated
Continuous – 24 hrs a day and/or 7 days a week
Mon–Fri – indicates that area is active every day from Monday through Friday
FL – Flight Level
‡ During periods of Daylight Saving Time (DT) effective hours will be one hour earlier than shown.

NUMBER	EFFECTIVE ALTITUDE	TIMES USED, UTC		WEATHER	CONTROLLING AGENCY A/G CALL	PANEL LOCATION
		DAYS	HOURS			
R-2301E	To FL 800	Cont*1	1330-0700Z	VFR-IFR	ZAB CNTR/FSS	E
R-2301W	To FL 800	Cont	Cont	VFR-IFR	ZLA CNTR/FSS	D,E
R-2302	To 10000	Mon–Sat	1500-0700Z	VFR-IFR	ZAB CNTR/FSS	E
R-2303A	To 15000	Mon–Fri*1	1400-0000Z	VFR-IFR	ZAB CNTR/FSS	F
R-2303B	8000 To FL 300	Mon–Fri*1	1400-0000Z	VFR-IFR	ZAB CNTR/FSS	F
R-2303C	15000 To FL 300	Intermittent	By NOTAM	VFR-IFR	ZAB CNTR/FSS	F
R-2304	To FL 240	Mon–Sat*1	1330-0700Z	VFR-IFR	ZAB CNTR/FSS	E
R-2305	To FL 240	Mon–Sat*1	1330-0700Z	VFR-IFR	ZAB CNTR/FSS	E
R-2501E, N,S,W	UNLTD	Cont	Cont	VFR-IFR	ZLA CNTR/FSS	C
R-2502E, N	UNLTD	Cont	Cont	VFR-IFR	FSS/HI DESERT TRACON	

Fig. 19

Special use airspace times, altitudes and controlling agencies are found on the border panel of the low altitude enroute chart.

Figure 20 shows the MOA information found on the low altitude enroute chart. To the right of Figure 18 at position A, you see Baker airport with a brown circle around it. This is not one of those mysterious crop circles, nor does it mark a UPS sorting facility. The brown circle is called an *aerodrome traffic zone*, and all airspace within this circle that is typically less than 1,500 feet AGL (as identified by the note on the chart) is not part of the MOA. For Baker's aerodrome traffic zone, this airspace exclusion includes the airspace below 3,000 feet AGL. If you are within this circle at less than 3,000 feet AGL, you shouldn't have to worry about military traffic (I'd worry anyway). Military pilots are not supposed to go in this area. However, if you irked one or two of these guys, they might be waiting just outside this circle for you when you attempt your run for home, especially if you once made fun of their Corvette.

Figure 21 shows the symbol for the remote communication outlet (RCO) near the Salt Flat VOR. An RCO is a transmitter and receiver, all by itself, a long way from its home but often connected by a landline. In this case, communication with the Albuquerque FSS can be made on frequency 122.35, thanks to the presence of the RCO. You should address Albuquerque FSS by using something similar to the following phraseology, "Albuquerque Radio, this is Cessna 2132 Bravo, Salt Flat VOR (unless there's a specific name attached to the RCO, then use that name), 122.35, over." The FSS specialist, sitting in Albuquerque, might be controlling a fistful of RCOs. If you don't give him or her an idea of your location and the frequency on which you're calling, the specialist has to play the flick-and-click game. It goes like this. "2132 Bravo?" Click, "2132 Bravo?" Click, "2132 Bravo?" "Goodbye."

The RCO - Remote Communication Outlet

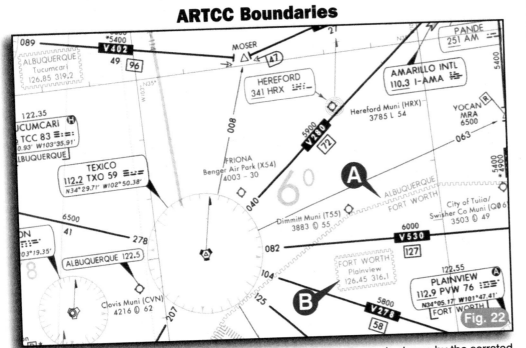

Fig. 21

The RCO or remote communication outlet is both a transmitter and receiver that allows communication via land line with the Flight Service Station. Albuquerque's RCO (position A) on frequency 122.35 allows communication with the Albuquerque FSS.

ATC Boundaries

The boundaries of Air Route Traffic Control Centers (ARTCCs) are depicted by zig-zag lines, as shown in Figure 22, position A. Albuquerque Center lies to the north and Fort Worth to the south. Sector discrete frequencies are shown in each ARTCC box. To contact the Center controller, state the name of the Center and make your request on the frequency shown.

NACO charts show the individual sector names within each sector, as shown in Figure 22, position B. Sector names, for all practical purposes, are meaningless to you as a pilot. If you want to contact Fort Worth Center when in the vicinity of the Planview sector, you wouldn't say, "Forth Worth Center, Planview sector, this is 2132 Bravo, over." The only thing the controller will know when you say this is that you didn't read this book.

ARTCC Boundaries

The boundary separating the Albuquerque and the Fort Worth Center is shown by the serrated line in position A. Individual sector names are shown in the Center identification box (position B). Sector names are no longer used when communicating with the Center controller. You'd simply refer to the Center controller as, "Fort Worth Center."

VOR Station Symbology

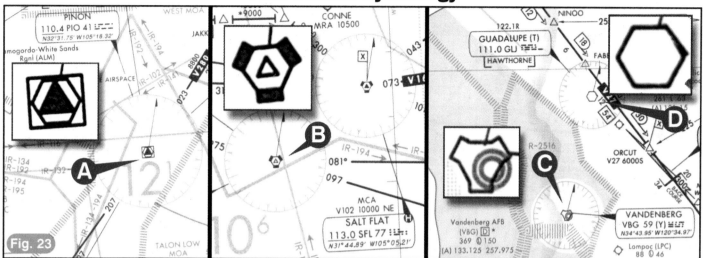

VOR station symbology can tell you about the nav capabilities of a VOR station. The VOR in position A is a VOR/DME facility, the VOR in position B is a VORTAC, the navaid in position C is a TACAN and the VOR in position D is a Terminal class VOR.

If you want to make contact with Fort Worth Center from this location, just tune 126.45 and say, "Fort Worth Center, this is 2132 Bravo, over." The frequency shown is the one on which to make a request for a pop-up IFR clearance or to activate the IFR portion of a composite flight plan. And if you're making a call to Fort Worth, don't use a sentence with the word "less" in it. Don't say, "I decided to call Fort Worth less I miss communicating with you." They're very sensitive about this.

All kidding aside, I always make it a point to listen in on Center frequency, even when I'm VFR and not receiving traffic advisories. You can hear a lot of useful information that way, such as clues about atmospheric turbulence, controller turbulence, winds and other weather observations, and sometimes the scores of the latest games and restaurant recommendations. If you hear American Airlines report that the captain has just jabbed himself with a dinner fork, you know there's turbulence at higher altitude.

Navigational Stations

VORs come in several shapes and sizes. The Pinon VOR (Figure 23, position A) is a combination VOR and DME station. You know this because the six-sided figure that represents a VOR is inside a square that represents DME capability. The UHF TACAN identifier and its two- or three-digit channel number following the NAVAID's VHF identifier (Channel 41 in the Pinon frequency box) also indicates the availability of DME. The black triangle inside the box makes that a compulsory reporting point (see the "Compulsory Reporting Points" sidebar, Page 13).

The Salt Flat VOR (Figure 23, position B) is actually a VORTAC, as indicated by the three black rectangles spaced around the six-sided VOR symbol. The white triangle inside the VORTAC represents a non-compulsory reporting point. (Note: All VORTACs are referred to as VORs here.) Being realistic about it, the most important thing for you to notice here is that all VORTACs have VOR and DME capability. On the other hand, it feels cool to say

the word VORTAC, which is why I try working it into dinner conversations whenever possible. (For example, "I think I shall have another helping of VORTAC, please." Who cares if no one understands you? Who's going to ask? You sound like a Klingon and are now in charge.)

Sometimes an airport will have TACAN (UHF azimuth and DME) capability without any VHF azimuth information. It's sort of a token TACAN. Figure 23, position C shows a TACAN station at Vandenberg AFB. Notice that there is a compass rose; nice, but you won't find it much use unless you're using TACAN equipment, and if you've got an F-16 you can probably skip all the pages in this book.

Note that the Vandenberg frequency box only lists the UHF TACAN frequency. If you want to use the DME at Vandenberg, you would have to know that the paired frequency on Channel 59 is 112.25 MHz. This information is available from NACO in a separate booklet called the *DOD IFR Supplement*. The folks at NACO call it a *DOD IFR Supplement* as a gentle way of letting you know that you probably don't have one unless you specifically ordered it. On the other hand, I don't have one and have never missed it when flying IFR (then again, I eat VORTAC for dinner). And be aware that not every TACAN channel has a paired DME frequency.

Some VOR stations lack DME capability. They really are VOR-only. Look at Figure 23, position D. The six sided VOR symbol for Guadalupe VOR (a *T* or Terminal class VOR) indicates that no DME capability exists at this site. Notice that there is no UHF frequency (i.e., channel) in Guadalupe's VOR frequency box.

Chart Overlap

Think about musicians for a second (this will be music to your ears in a moment). They frantically fiddle or huffingly horn, following the musical notes on a couple of facing pages, until...until they come to the bottom of the right hand page, at which time, somehow, they have to flip the page and keep playing.

You have to do the same thing when flying IFR, so note this. From a chart point of view, you are always flying either up, down, left, or right. Unless you are flying in circles, you *will* eventually come to some edge of the chart. That's when you'll flip.

Figure 24 shows how low altitude chart overlap is shown. The top and right side corners of the chart (positions A and B) tells you which low altitude enroute chart to use if moving off the chart in that direction. These chart overlaps are also shown on the front of the low altitude chart, (see the insert in Figure 24, position C). This information makes it a great deal easier to find the next *correct* chart to use when flying IFR.

It also avoids the disconcerting (for the passengers) situation in which the pilot is frantically whipping the chart around, looking longingly but futilely for navaids and intersections that are on another chart. Of course, the disadvantage of knowing which chart is next is that the passengers are deprived of the cooling, fan-like qualities that waft from frantically rotating paper whose rotational speeds approximate those of the propeller.

Outside the chart border in the lower part of Figure 24, position D, you'll see V530 depart the chart. On the chart border you see the

Low Altitude Chart Overlap Information

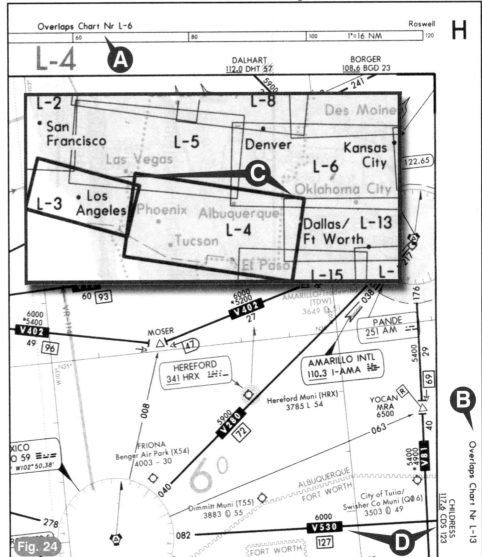

Chart overlap information is provided on the side borders of the low altitude enroute chart (positions A and B), as well as on the front of the low altitude enroute chart (position C).

name of the next VOR supporting V530 (Childress VOR) as well as its frequency and UHF channel. On Figure 25, the next intersection on V198-222 is OZMOS (position E) located on chart L-15 as shown by position F (of course, you've probably already learned this by OZMOSsis).

Low Altitude Chart Overlap Information

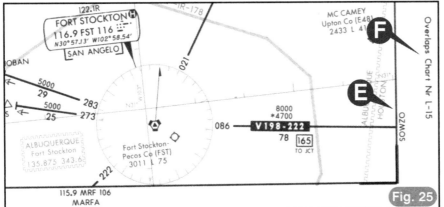

OZMOS intersection (position E) is the next intersection on V198-222 that's found on overlaping chart L-15 (position F).

Compulsory Reporting Points

In the past, before electronics, wheels, and iPods were invented, controllers moved pieces of paper around to try and get a visual sense of where IFR pilots were. These pieces of paper were referred to as "shrimp boats," because they were placed in holders that made the whole thing look (sort of) like a boat. Pilots on IFR flight plans made IFR position reports to ATC at compulsory reporting points shown on their IFR enroute charts, at which time the boat was moved (the controllers ate the shrimp). There are two compulsory reporting points at Pecos and Fort Stockton VOR (shown on the right right by black triangles in the center of the VOR symbol at positions Y and Z). Position X shows an open triangle in the VOR symbol which represents a non-compulsory reporting point.

Position reports include the information represented by the letter sequence PTA-TEN: position, time, altitude, type of flight plan, estimate to the next compulsory reporting point and the next compulsory reporting point after that. Even in today's modern IFR system, paper strips are still kept by controllers (but not moved around a horizontal board like shrimp-boat strips once were) for every airplane that they're controlling.

Wonderful as they are, modern radar systems still break down, which is when the shrimp boats float. Let's say, for instance, that a controller plugged his hair dryer into an outlet on the radar screen (he wants to look good for his shift). Let's also say that the hair dryer is a 500 watt unit the size of typical garden weed blower (he's got thick hair, OK?). If the radar system fries for some reason, pilots on an IFR flight plan are required to resume normal position reporting at compulsory reporting points unless told otherwise by the controller (who, we hope, isn't running around with a prairie fire on his head because his dryer blew up when the circuits fried).

There are other reasons radar contact can be lost, and there are places in the country where there is no radar coverage. If you are IFR and hear the words, "Radar contact lost," the unspoken part is, "Resume position reporting." It's your job, and it should float your boat.

There's another type of compulsory reporting point that's not identified as such on your charts. Anytime you define a direct route of flight in your flight plan between fixes and that route isn't flown on radials or courses of established airways or routes, those fixes become compulsory reporting points when you're not in radar contact.

Chart Niceties and Oddities

Everyone has a crazy uncle or wild aunt in the family who no one talks about (perhaps because of the restraining order). Charts have oddities, too. They're odd because you just don't see these certain things that often. For instance, Figure 26, position W shows that you can identify HITAP intersection in one of two ways. It's identifiable with VOR (the 097 degree radial from HUP VOR) and DME (the 38 DME mileage reading from HUP VOR). You can also identify it with the 097 degree radial from HUP VOR and the 189 degree magnetic bearing to Van Horn NDB.

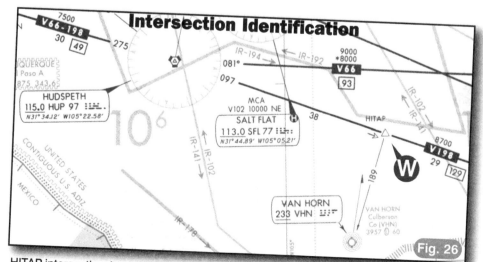

HITAP intersection (positron W) can be identified by either a radial and DME reading from Hudspeth VOR or via cross radial and bearing readings from HUP VOR and VHN NDB.

Looking at Figure 27, you see a lot of strange uncles and aunts, and maybe a mutant cousin or two, too (or in a tutu). Look at the holding pattern located at AXARY intersection, position A. This is a published holding pattern that you'll occasionally find on low altitude enroute charts. It's reasonable to assume that ATC has a need to hold airplanes in this area (not to punish pilots for asking the controller tough questions, either). Suppose you're headed west, enroute to Deming VOR on V94 and ATC asks you to hold as published at

Low Altitude Enroute Holding and Intersection Identification

The published holding pattern at AXARY intersection (position A) indicates that this is a likely area to be held by ATC if holding is in progress. COSES intersection (position B) can be identified by using V94 (from DMN VOR) and the 332 bearing to HAWKE NDB. At position C is an unmanned balloon.

AXARY. Simple, eh? You just make a direct entry into the holding pattern. No muss, no fuss and no complex holding clearance by ATC. And, there's very little way to mess up which would result in ATC saying, "2132 Bravo, are you AXARY going to hold like that?"

Looking further east along V94 at COSES and MOLLY intersections (position B), you see that these two intersections can also be identified by NDB bearings to HAWKE NDB.

In Figure 27, position C, there's a restricted area with an unmanned balloon on a cable extending to 15,000 feet. Apparently it's unmanned because the man wouldn't get in it, and I don't blame him. Actually, it's a balloon with radar equipment to help watch for bad guys crossing the Mexican border without providing a position report.

Looking at Figure 28, position D, you see a black dotted line underneath the portion of V611 penetrating the restricted areas R-5111C and D. The black dotted line represents that portion of an airway penetrating a restricted area. Not to worry, however. If your IFR clearance takes you through this area, then ATC has obtained permission for your passage in advance. The F-16s know you're coming. In fact, they're counting on it. It might be wise to avoid planning your IFR flight through this area if the restricted area (or the restrictions) will be in effect at the time of your passage.

Figure 29, position E show an *A* in brackets underneath the airport information at Meadows Field in the city of Bakersfield. The A indicates that ATIS is available on frequency 118.6 MHz. The *L* within a circle next to the airport elevation (507 feet MSL)

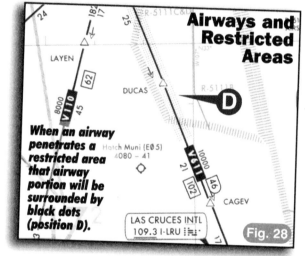

Airways and Restricted Areas

When an airway penetrates a restricted area that airway portion will be surrounded by black dots (position D).

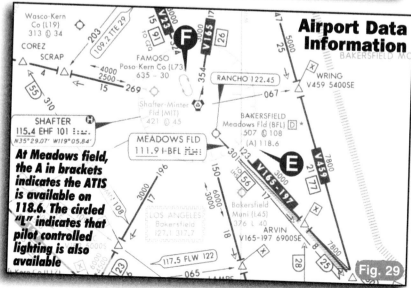

Airport Data Information

At Meadows field, the A in brackets indicates the ATIS is available on 118.6. The circled "L" indicates that pilot controlled lighting is also available

Controlled and Uncontrolled Airspace

The Figure below shows how controlled (Class E, D, etc.) and uncontrolled (Class G) airspace is portrayed on the low altitude enroute chart. The brown areas represent uncontrolled G airspace, extending up to but not including 14,500 feet MSL. The white areas are controlled airspace, usually beginning at 1,200 feet AGL or higher. You'll have to consult a sectional chart to determine the altitude at which any specific controlled airspace begins.

As you can see on V263-611 near CELAV intersection (position A), the controlled airspace typically extends to four nautical miles either side of the airway, and since this airway is in designated mountainous terrain, you're guaranteed a minimum of 2,000 feet of terrain clearance within this area. Sometimes the airway widens (just like aging airline pilots and flight attendants do), as shown near TATKE intersection (position B). In this case the airway terrain clearance applies to this widened area, as well.

Notice that Angel Fire airport, position C, appears to have controlled airspace surrounding it. The white area is Class E airspace beginning at 700 feet AGL around Angel Fire, as shown by the sectional chart excerpt in the lower right corner of the figure. Below 700 feet AGL is Class G, uncontrolled airspace. If you'd like more information on the details of controlled and uncontrolled airspace, you'll find it in Chapter 9 of *Rod Machado's Private Pilot Handbook*.

Why bother showing you where there's uncontrolled airspace like this? As we discussed previously, you might have a short excursion through uncontrolled airspace while on a clearance and enroute to controlled airspace. But wait, there's more. Through some quirky wrinkle in the regulations, it is still legal to fly IFR in uncontrolled airspace *without* an ATC clearance and an IFR flight plan!

Why you or anyone else would do something like this, legal or not, is beyond my imagination. If one of your daredevil friends elects to do this, since the entire area in the Figure above is in a designated mountainous area he'd have to choose a minimum altitude at least 2,000 feet above the ground, as well as meeting the minimum height requirements for VOR navigation (assuming he elects to use VOR as his primary means of navigation here).

and to the left of the longest runway length (10,800 feet) indicates pilot controlled lighting is available. You'll also want to take notice of the published holding pattern located at the Shafter VOR (position F).

In Figure 30, position D, you see a published localizer flag for San Luis Obispo. When a localizer flag is present on the enroute chart, it means that the localizer serves an enroute function, such as identifying CREPE intersection. If you were in the vicinity of Paso Robles VORTAC and wanted to talk to the folks at the FSS, you could call Hawthorne FSS (the controlling FSS as indicated by the name under the PRB VOR box) on 122.4 (in addition to the standard FSS frequencies of 122.2 and 121.5). Your initial call should go some-

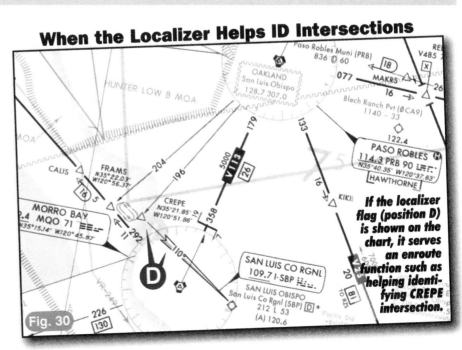

When the Localizer Helps ID Intersections

If the localizer flag (position D) is shown on the chart, it serves an enroute function such as helping identifying CREPE intersection.

Fig. 30

thing like, "Hawthorne Radio, this is Cessna 2132 Bravo, Paso Robles, 122.4, over." Now the FSS specialist knows which transmitter and on what frequency to contact you.

You can find additional information on low altitude enroute chart symbols by looking at the chart legend in Appendix 2.

MEAs, MOCAs and MCAs

A minimum enroute altitude (MEA) is the minimum altitude at which you may fly on any existing airway segment. The MEA gets you two important things—obstruction clearance and reception of navigation stations. You really want these things when flying IFR.

Figure 31, position A, shows V113 from Panoche VOR-TAC to Priest VOR, with 7,000 feet listed above the airway designator. That's the MEA for this section of the airway. The MEA guarantees you 1,000 feet of obstruction clearance in non-mountainous terrain and 2,000 feet of obstruction clearance in mountainous terrain that's officially known as *designated mountainous areas* (Figure 32).

There are times when the MEA must be raised substantially to assure solid reception of navigation stations (lest you run into something solid), or because of precipitous terrain along a portion of the airway. (Precipitous terrain can generate unusual pressure changes, which could dangerously affect the altimeter's accuracy. To a flight inspector, this is known as the *venturi effect*.)

When the MEA is increased because of precipitous terrain (or other reasons besides obstruction clearance), it is sometimes possible to offer an altitude lower than the MEA that can be flown when close to the VOR. At closer range, signal reception is generally not an issue. This lower altitude is called the *minimum obstruction clearance altitude* or MOCA. This is different from the mocha offered by your local *barista,* and you should learn to differentiate the two. An aviation MOCA is shown by an (*) on the chart next to its respective altitude. You'll usually find the MOCA underneath the MEA.

Figure 31, position B, shows a MOCA of *5,500 on V230 between Salinas VORTAC and PANOS intersection, while the MEA for this section is 6,500 feet. The MOCA provides both obstruction clearance and adequate reception within 22 nautical miles (or 25 statute miles) of the VOR. Beyond 22 nautical miles, the MOCA guarantees only obstacle clearance. When only an MEA value is shown on an airway, the MEA is also the MOCA for that route.

When a MOCA is created for a particular route, the airway designers first ask what minimum altitude is necessary along the entire route to provide only the required obstruction clearance of 1,000 or 2,000 feet. Once that's determined, the route is then flight checked to identify any increase in altitude needed to assure navigation reception along the first 22 nautical miles of the route. This minimum altitude then becomes the MOCA. MEAs are created by the same process, except the minimum altitude is increased, if necessary, to enable consistent reception of navigation and communication signals along the entire route.

The OROCA - Off-Route Obstruction Clearance Altitude

There are times during IFR flight, such as during an in-flight emergency, when it's necessary to leave an established airway or route. If and when this ever happens to you, the last thing you need to do is to compound your problems by wondering how high the terrain is below you. That's why the OROCA, shown as 11,000 feet MSL in position A below, is so useful. This is an off-route altitude for the bounded quadrangle (the box made of whole number latitude and longitude lines), which provides obstruction clearance with a 1,000 foot buffer in nonmountainous terrain areas and a 2,000 foot buffer in designated mountainous areas within the U.S. It doesn't necessarily provide signal coverage from ground-based navigational aids, air traffic control radar, or communications coverage, but then again, these things may not be all that important to you at the time, especially when you may be contending with an engine problem or in-flight airframe ice. (And, between you and me, the OROCA also includes the area 4 nm outside the boundary of the quadrangle as well. This will be our little secret, OK?)

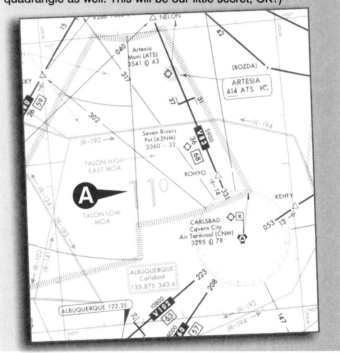

What value is there in having a MOCA beyond 22 nautical miles when it can't be used for navigation with standard VOR equipment? Well, you might have GPS in your airplane. If so, and if you had to descend to stop an ice buildup, you could descend on that airway to the MOCA in an emergency, knowing that this altitude is obstruction free. Remember, the MOCA provides immediate altitude protection of 1,000 or 2,000 feet above obstructions for the entire length of the route.

Mama Mia: MEA Changes

Notice how the airway depictions are interrupted at BASEC intersection, as shown in Figure 31, position C. V230 has an airway line that stops, then continues on the other side of this intersection. On the other hand, V-230 has perpendicular [⊣] barriers, a sort of *T* cap on the break, where the airway breaks and continues at PANOS. So what's the deal, are you supposed to get out and walk at these spots?

Don't get your PANOS in a bind here. These barriers [⊣] exist when there is an MEA, MOCA, or MAA change along

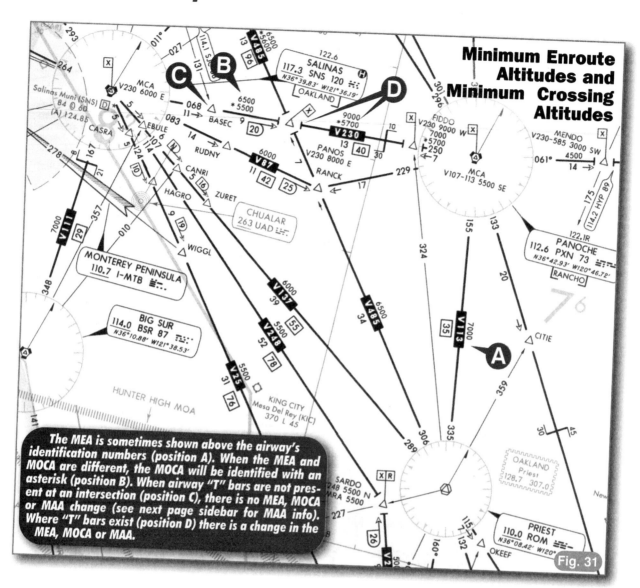

The MEA is sometimes shown above the airway's identification numbers (position A). When the MEA and MOCA are different, the MOCA will be identified with an asterisk (position B). When airway "T" bars are not present at an intersection (position C), there is no MEA, MOCA or MAA change (see next page sidebar for MAA info). Where "T" bars exist (position D) there is a change in the MEA, MOCA or MAA.

Fig. 31

the airway at an intersection. As you can see in Figure 31, position D, both the MEA and MOCA change at PANOS, but these symbolic barriers don't exist at BASEC. From Salinas VOR to PANOS intersection, the MEA is 6,500 feet and the MOCA is 5,500 feet. There is no MEA change at BASEC intersection. At PANOS, the MEA changes on V230 eastbound from 6,500 to 9,000 feet.

The [⊣] barriers become very important during lost communications situations. These symbols alert you to expect a change in the MEA (or MOCA, or MAA). The FARs state that in the event of lost communications, you should maintain your last assigned altitude, or the altitude ATC said to expect in a further clearance, or the MEA, whichever is higher. In the absence of being assigned a higher altitude, you would start a climb to the next MEA at the [⊣] barrier.

Let's assume you lost communications at Salinas VOR and were enroute to Panoche VOR, at an assigned altitude of 7,000 feet. A minimum crossing altitude exists at PANOS intersection and is identified by the presence of an X on a flag pole at the intersection. The X means you should look around, in this case under the letters PANOS, to read *V230 8000 E*. This is your MCA or *minimum cross-*

ing altitude of 8,000 feet if you're eastbound on V230 at PANOS. Because of the MCA, you should start your climb early so you cross PANOS at 8,000 feet or above. You would then continue climbing to the next highest MEA, which is 9,000 feet. When the MEA changes at an intersection, and no MCA is present, start your climb or descent to the next MEA when reaching that intersection.

Designated Mountainous Terrain

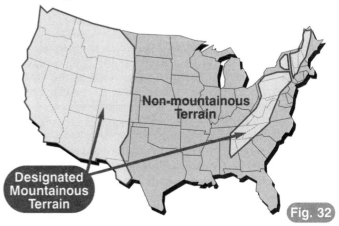

Fig. 32

If an MCA exists at specific intersections, it is shown underneath or near the intersection name. At VORs, where many airways converge, the presence of an MCA is indicated by an "X" located within a flag as we've already mentioned. When several airways converge on a VOR and the VOR has several MCAs for these different airways, you'll find the MCAs listed near the VOR's "X" flag, as shown in Figure 33, position A. To the right of the Palmdale VOR compass rose are all the MCAs for crossing the VOR. For instance, if you are eastbound on V137, your airway MEA past VICKY (position B) is 5,000 feet and you'd need to cross the PMD VOR at 7,000 feet to continue on V137. If you're headed southeast toward PMD VOR on V197, the MEA past FISCH is 5,000 feet and you'd need to cross the VOR at 8,000 feet (in a climb to the MEA of 10,000 feet) if you're continuing southeast bound on V197.

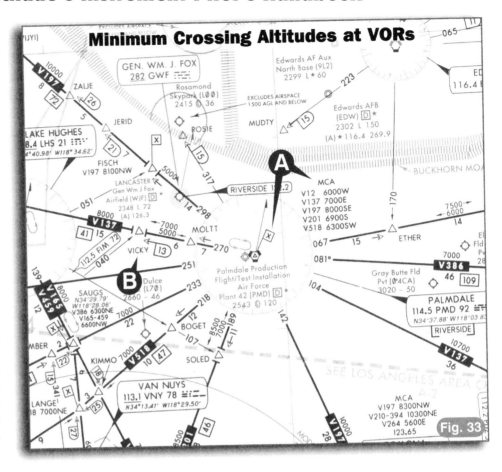

Fig. 33

Climb Incline: Minimum Climb Rates

With every change in MEA or depicted MCA at a particular intersection, a minimum rate of climb is expected beyond that point to keep you clear of obstacles. Assume that you're westbound on V68 from PIZON heading toward ANEEL intersection (position Z). There is an MEA change from 5,000 to 5,200 feet at ANEEL. Since there is no depicted MCA for this intersection, what minimum climb rate is expected of you as you climb from 5,000 to 5,200 feet MSL? The climb rate beyond the MEA or MCA is determined by the altitude at which your aircraft crosses the intersection.

For instance, if the MEA or MCA at an intersection is 5,000 feet or less, a 150 foot per nautical mile or greater rate of climb is required to the next MEA or MCA. If the minimum crossing altitude is greater than 5,000 feet MSL up to 10,000 feet MSL, the minimum rate of climb is 120 feet per nautical mile. If the minimum crossing altitude is greater than 10,000 MSL, the minimum rate of climb is 100 feet per nautical mile. Since the MEA "at" ANEEL is 5,000 feet, you should climb at a minimum rate of 150 foot per nautical mile to reach 5,200 feet.

Suppose you're heading eastbound on V230 and are approaching PANOS intersection (position Y). An MCA of 8,000 feet MSL exists at PANOS. If you're flying at a groundspeed of 120 knots (that's 2nm/min), your aircraft must be able to climb at 240 feet per minute to the next higher MEA of 9,000 feet. This rate of climb allows you to maintain the minimum obstacle clearance height enroute.

This rate of climb, at that altitude, might not be easy to achieve with an aged Cherokee 140 with only three of its four cylinders working. Couple this with a massive tailwind

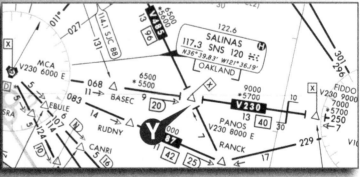

at altitude, and you could end up with less than the best clearance above obstacles. Don't be stingy with altitude gain. Be conservative and, when possible, start the climb well in advance of the intersection when an MEA or MCA is present.

Of course, ATC would normally allow you to climb before reaching the intersection but this knowledge is important when dealing with lost communication problems.

Intersection Identification

Intersection identification is made easy by using the little arrows positioned next to every intersection. REDDE intersection on V248, shown Figure 34, position A, can be identified two ways. Little arrows bordering the intersection are from the facility whose VOR radials (airways) designate that intersection (positions B and C). For instance, Paso Robles and Priest VORs are the facilities used to identify REDDE intersection, because the small arrows originate from these VORs. Avenal VOR shouldn't be used to identify REDDE intersection, even though it is the same distance from the intersection as Paso Robles VOR.

The arrows are very explicit in identifying which navaid should be used for intersection identification. A hollow-tipped arrow next to REDDE from PRB VOR (position B) signals that DME can also be used for intersection identification here. The distance from PRB VOR to REDDE, 16 nautical miles, is shown below the airway and between the VOR and the intersection (position D). This is known as the *route segment distance*. If you elected to use the PRB 077 degree radial (V248) and DME to identify REDDE, you'd know you're at this intersection when your CDI is centered and your DME reads 16 nautical miles from PRB.

There is no hollow-tipped arrow next to the arrow coming from Priest VOR (Figure 34, position C). This is because Priest VOR doesn't have DME capability. The solid arrow only identifies the VOR used to identify the intersection. If you think you are getting a DME signal from Priest, notify the nearest FSS immediately and see if anyone there will hear your confession. You shouldn't be receiving a mileage reading from a facility that doesn't have DME transmitting equipment.

Sometimes DME distances are tallied for ease of identification. SARDO intersection, shown in Figure 34, position E, is identified by the 326 degree radial from Paso Robles VOR at a distance of 26 nautical miles. The *DME thumbnail* containing the number 26 is a DME tally, showing that the cumulative distance between intersections from Paso Robles and SARDO is 26 miles (tally the segment distances between the intersections and you'll find that 9+17=26). This is provided for pilots who didn't have a successful early math experience.

BRALY intersection (position F) is 17 miles from Paso Robles. When no DME thumbnail containing distance values is shown next to an intersection, it is probably the first intersection past the navaid. The route segment distance can be used in identifying the intersection.

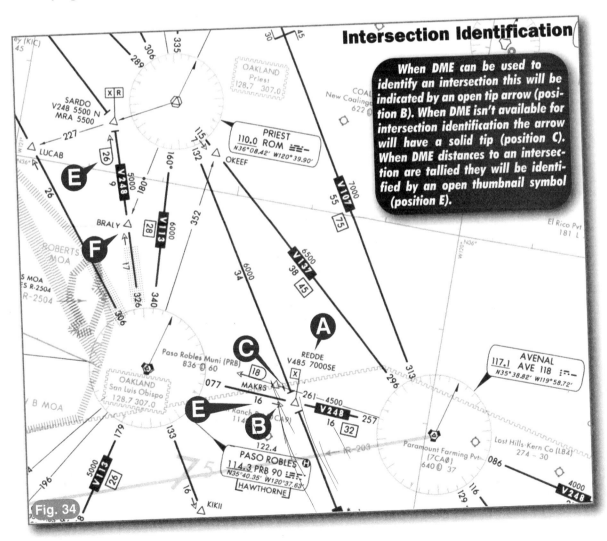

Fig. 34

Here's a trivia tidbit for you. Does the MEA provide obstruction and VOR reception guarantees for *all* nav functions related to the airway? Can you say, "No"? The MEA promises obstruction clearance and navigation reception for the airway itself, but when an intersection is identified by cross radials, the MEA might *not* give you adequate reception of the off-course VOR(s). If that's the case, there will be a *minimum reception altitude* or MRA shown. That's the altitude you have to be at to get a solid signal from everything needed to identify the intersection. Figure 35, position A shows an MRA of 9,000 feet next to OHIGH intersection. The answer to "How high at OHIGH?" is "9,000 feet."

Why so high at OHIGH? Because the intersection is identified either by cross radial identification from the Ventura and Fillmore VORs or radial and DME information from either the Ventura or Fillmore VOR. Aircraft flying westbound on V386 (position B) at the published MEA of 8,000 feet (look above the V386-597 airway box to find the airway's MEA) would be too low to identify V485, which makes up the cross radial identifying OHIGH. In other words, if you're tracking westbound on V386 at

MRA - Minimum Reception Altitude

Fig. 35

The MRA or minimum reception altitude in the figure above is required to identify OHIGH intersection (position A) on V386-597 when using V485 as a cross radial reference.

8,000 feet and tune in the 311 degree radial from Ventura VOR, you're not guaranteed to receive Ventura properly at this altitude. There could be mountains in between, or a UFO service center that's blocking the signal. It doesn't mat-

Hi! MAA or Maximum Authorized Altitude

Position D in the figure below shows how maximum authorized altitudes (MAAs) are portrayed on low altitude enroute charts. South of

Sparta VOR on V213, the MAA is 10,000 feet. This is the highest altitude at which you're allowed to use this airway.

Yes, routes can have height limits, just like buildings. This can happen because of potential conflict with overlying routes, but more frequently it's to keep you from possibly hooking up with the wrong VOR signal. The FAA works hard to keep similar frequencies widely separated geographically, but of course the higher you go, the farther you can "see" electronically. Go too high while tuned to A and you might just receive B and think it's A, which would B A problem.

The FAA really has a tough task trying to balance the implementation of VHF navaids while keeping those on similar frequencies spread far enough apart to prevent frequency overlap. When this can't be done, for whatever reason, the next best solution is an MAA.

Too Short a Cut

It is standard [checklist] procedure to tune and set com and nav radios prior to departure. I reached for the enroute chart [to check frequencies]. My copilot stated that there was no need, as he had made a "cheat sheet." I looked at it briefly and it appeared to match our route. After departing, we were given a vector to join the airway. There were no nav flags and the CDI was full scale to the side. We were just becoming suspicious when Center advised us we had flown through the airway. The "cheat sheet" was correct except for the nav frequency.

Morse Code identification of the navigation frequency is the approved method of verifying correct frequency selection. Cheat sheets can be helpful, but won't do any good if the information is incorrect.

NASA Callback Report

ter. All you need to know is the MRA. Climb to 9,000 feet or above and you'll have no problem receiving Ventura VOR. The reason for all this is that there is an MEA change on the airway from 5,000 feet to 9,000 feet at HENER (Figure 35, position C). If you want to identify an intersection by cross radials, in lieu of DME, you need to be at or above the MRA for that intersection.

Airway Mileage and Changeover Points (COP)

On low altitude enroute charts, the total airway mileage between navaids is shown within a box often located at the midpoint of the airway, as shown in Figure 36, position E. The distance of 42 nm represents the sum of the distances between intersections linking one VOR to the next. In this instance, it's the total distance on V23 between Shafter VOR and Gorman VOR. V165 has a distance of 56 nm between Shafter VOR and its endpoint at Lake Hughes VOR, as is indicated by the "TO LHS" letters next to the total mileage box (Figure 36 position F). An attempt is made to place the distance next to the airway number it represents (Figure 36, position E). That's why the box enclosing the distance of 56 nautical miles is placed under V165 and not the V197 position in this figure.

Airway changeover points are indicated by what appears to be a half swastika. GRAPE intersection, Figure

36, position G, is the changeover point on V23. When tracking northbound on V23, you initially fly outbound on the Gorman 328 degree radial until reaching 10 DME from GMN or when crossing the FLW 083 degree radial, then you switch to the Shafter VOR and track inbound to the VOR on the 150 degree radial. When no changeover point is shown (i.e., no half swastika), the changeover is at the midpoint of the airway segment. Changeover points are in place primarily to assure adequate signal reception, but they can also be located where they are in order to avoid signal interference from another navaid.

It's worth noting that the outbound airway heading from Gorman VOR on V23 is 328 degrees up to GRAPE intersection. After GRAPE, the inbound direction changes to 330 degrees (the reciprocal of 150 degrees). Low altitude airways may look straight, but they can change as much as two degrees in direction at the changeover point. This can be an actual directional change, or a change in the magnetic variation along the route. When the airway changes direction three degrees or more at the changeover point and no intersection designates this spot, a mileage break fix, identified by a small "×", is marked on the airway. Just right of LOPES intersection, on V197 in Figure 36, position H, you can see a mileage breakdown fix. It's at this juncture that you would set the new airway direction in the course selector.

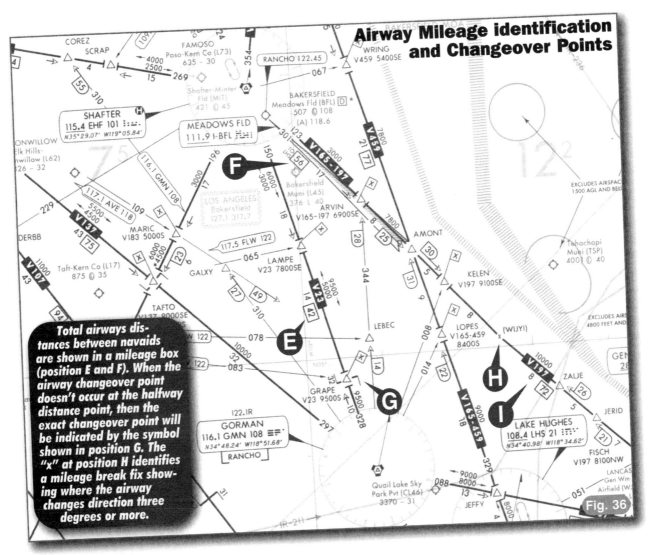

Fig. 36

Notice the letters *WIJYI* in brackets next to the mileage break fix. This is known as a *CNF* or *computer navigation fix*. These letters have value only if the database in your flight management or navigational system uses them to help identify the mileage break. The letters have no other ATC function, nor should they be used when filing flight plans or communicating with ATC. When you're 8 miles northwest of ZALJE intersection on V197 heading northwest bound, you'd change your OBS setting to track inbound on the 301 degree course to Shafter VOR. The mileage to the breakdown fix is indicated by Figure 36, position I.

So, I've done my part to show you the chart. You're now an M.S.–Master of Symbology. You can not only read and understand the most obscure of markings on a low altitude enroute chart but you even know when it's time to switch (rather than swish) charts. So there you stand, chart in hand. Are you ready to take flight? Not quite.

You'll always see IFR pilots armed with charts, plotters, kneeboards, calculators, pens, pencils, magnifiers, pacifiers, and a lot of stuff it's hard to identify. There are military jets with less equipment. These pilots bring what they think they need to get the job of IFR cross country flight planning done. And that just happens to be the topic of the next chapter. So strap in and hold on tight, because I'm going to walk you through an actual IFR flight.

Postflight Briefing #15-1

GPS-only Q and T Routes

Given the popularity of IFR approved GPS units in smaller airplanes, the FAA has started publishing GPS-only low-altitude *T Routes*. These routes are shown in blue (Figure 37, position A). The main purpose of T routes is to provide airplanes with a route around or through congested terminal airspace in the low-altitude enroute system (such as Class B and C airspace, for example). Many VOR airways don't provide the flexibility that RNAV routes can. Therefore, when you file IFR as a /G aircraft, you should be prepared to use these T Routes, (as well as RNAV-Based SIDs, DPs and STARS, too).

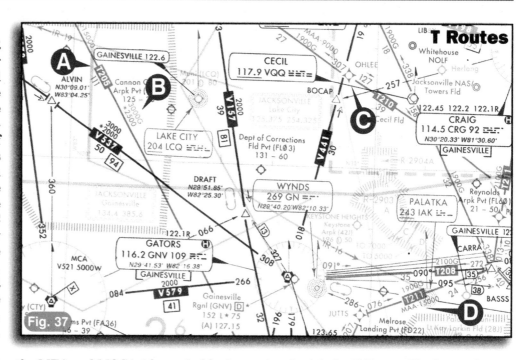

Fig. 37

Figure 37, position B identifies the MEA and MOCA (shown in blue) associated with the T Route. The letter *G* next to the MEA of 3,000 feet indicates that this MEA and MOCA are specifically for airplanes using RNAV that's based on GPS (otherwise referred to as GNSS or Global Navigation Satellite System equipped airplanes).

It's not uncommon to see MEAs associated with T Routes that are lower than the MEAs on traditional VOR-based airways. Remember that both navigation reception and obstruction clearance define the minimum height at which an MEA is established. Since the GPS navigation signal isn't altitude-dependent, the MEAs on T Routes can be lowered based solely on an obstacle clearance requirement.

Figure 37, position C shows a blue-colored waypoint (OHLEE) on the T Route. You'll also notice an MAA associated with the T Route (position D). In this instance, MAAs have nothing to do with navigational signal interference that's often associated with higher altitudes and common with VOR-based airways. More likely, T Route MAAs are established to prevent traffic/airspace conflict with the overlying airspace.

As T Routes apply to the low-altitude airspace system, *Q Routes* (Figure 38, position E) are for use in the high altitude airspace system. These routes are commonly used to alleviate traffic congestion for aircraft flying at or above 18,000 feet MSL.

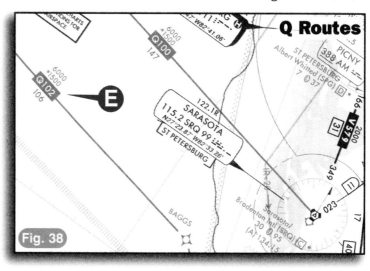

Fig. 38

Chapter 16
IFR Flight Planning

An instrument rating is a license to fly in less than basic VFR conditions when your knowledge, skill, experience, and airplane can do so safely. Which is *not* all the time. Even the biggest of the big boys occasionally face conditions into which they do not knowingly go.

Think about it for a microsecond or three. If the guy in charge of a highly equipped Airbus A320, backed by all kinds of professional support and training, has to "no" sometimes, then what makes *you* think you can blithely fly your Cessna 172 into whatever's out there? You *and* your airplane both have limitations. Knowing and respecting them is probably the most important thing you will do as an instrument rated pilot.

Flying IFR means giving up the margin of safety that comes with being able to see. We accept that tradeoff as a reasonable one. What isn't reasonable is to use your IFR capability to take you, your plane, and your passengers into conditions where there's a high likelihood of trouble.

As a youngster, I liked challenging activities. I remember watching the Lone Ranger on TV as he jumped from a conveniently-high rock onto his horse, Silver. Being a man of action, I once went outside and jumped from the porch onto my Schwinn bicycle. That was the week I got promoted to the "soprano" section in the choir.

Instrument pilots also individuals who like action, especially when the action involves instrument flying. That's why there are few things as frustrating as a ground-bound IFR pilot. You've been very patient so far, and I know you're sitting there with your scratch pad, itching to get into the details of IFR flight planning and then go out and *do it*. But before you bid your chair adieu, there is a bit more we must do.

If Plato Could Fly

If you were lucky enough to have a resident airport philosopher sitting on the FBO porch the day you obtained your instrument rating, this wise sage (whose name could be Rosemary) might offer you a few words of advice.

What would he say? Sure, he might ask you something deeply philosophical such as, "Why is there handicapped parking at the racquetball club?" More likely, he'd sit you down and say, "Just because you've earned your instrument rating, it doesn't mean you can fly IFR any time, anywhere, and in any way you want."

I hear you sputtering. You were under the impression that an IFR rating was practically a guarantee-to-go-at-any-time ticket, weren't you? Lots of pilots, including those who've had their ratings a long time, are still under that impression because they didn't pay attention to the guru who knew. If you paid attention just long enough for the sage's valuable words to sink deep into your cranium, you would achieve IFR nirvana, and a vastly expanded likelihood of living a long and happy pilot life.

Just because you're IFR rated, this doesn't mean you can fly IFR at any time and under any conditions. I know what I'm talking about, just look at the leaves on my forehead.

Wow! Someday I'll have leaves, too.

Ice Isn't Nice - Failure to Flight Plan Properly

Aircraft: Rockwell Aero Commander 500S. Registration: N272BB Category: Private.
Crew: Two.
Number of passengers: None.
Place of accident: 8 nm off the south coast of Iceland, near Date and time: 6 March 2001, at about 08:56 hrs.
Vestmannaeyjar Isles (Last radar plot at 63°32´04´´N 020°39´36´´W)

The accident was notified to the Icelandic Aircraft Accident Investigation Board on 6 March 2001 at 11:35 hrs. The NTSB of the United States, which was the State of Registry, appointed an accredited representative to the investigation. This was a private flight from the United States to London, England, via Greenland, Iceland and Scotland, arriving at Keflavik Airport, Iceland 5 March 2001 where the aircraft stayed overnight. In the morning the two pilots filed a flight plan and prepared their onward flight to Stornoway, Scotland. The take-off from Keflavik was at 08:19 hrs. The departure and communication with the aircraft was normal. The aircraft climbed gradually up to 15,000 feet (Flight level 150), the assigned cruising level, when the radar contact was lost. The crew did not report any difficulties and there was no further communication.

A subsequent replay of the Air Traffic Control (ATC) radar data showed that the aircraft target disappeared from the radar screen at 08:56 hrs.

An extensive search was initiated but only small fragments, personal belongings and human remains were found floating on the ocean, spread in a line north-westwards over a distance of about 5 nm from the point the target disappeared from radar.

A cause of the accident was not positively determined during the investigation. However, the investigation indicates that most probably the aircraft was climbing in icing conditions when it entered into an uncontrolled decent followed by an in-flight break-up during an attempted recovery.

For instance, let's say icing conditions are forecast for your route. Because of the height of the clouds, you can't see a way to remain below them or climb above them. You'd be wise to stay on the ground. Unless your airplane is certified for flight into known icing conditions, you shouldn't be flying in the clouds if the temperatures are at or below freezing.

I know that some people will tell you they've flown in icing conditions and maneuvered to avoid it, or even found it simply didn't appear. Fine. Some folks have special skills, some are just lucky, and others are just so darn macho that if they were a cocktail drink, it would be called *testosterone on the rocks*. The moment you experience any type of ice in a small airplane, you should immediately work to get out of it. And that is often easier said than done, my friend. Just because icing isn't forecast, that doesn't mean you won't get it if you're in visible moisture (i.e., clouds) and are at temperatures of freezing and lower.

What if thunderstorms are forecast for your route and you don't have onboard storm-detection equipment? Are you good to go? It depends on where you expect to wind up. Unless you can remain out of the clouds, you'll have no idea where the thunderstorms are, and your trip could *definitely* have its ups and downs.

Will ATC keep you out of thunderstorms? They'll try to help if they have time, but if you count on ATC to do this for you then you'd better increase your life insurance coverage. Your heirs will certainly appreciate it. And you'll

want to regularly attend a cloud mass, which is a church service for people who do this sort of thing.

No Center has weather radar capability with fidelity comparable to that of airborne radar. Controllers can only offer you macro, and not micro, weather perspectives. You really need the latter to reliably avoid cells. Given that a thunderstorm has more than ample energy to tear your plane apart, can you afford many mistakes?

So when can and should you use your instrument rating in a typical, small general aviation airplane? The answer is when ice, thunderstorms and other serious weather situations can be avoided or aren't an issue.

This almost seems to make an instrument rating useless in small general aviation airplane, doesn't it? Well, your instrument rating isn't useless if you have one of the most important qualities that all safe instrument pilots possess—*patience*. The weather may be bad now, but that doesn't mean it won't be good in an hour, or two, or six from now.

To fly instruments safely, and do so frequently, you must have sufficient patience to wait out the really nasty weather. Of course, the more performance your airplane has, the less often you have to wait. A turbocharged, pressurized airplane with de-ice or anti-ice capability and radar/Sferic (electrical discharge detection) equipment is more capable of dealing with bad weather than one not so equipped. If there's an F-16 parked in your garage, you can fly nearly any time and anywhere you want—who's going to stop you?

So that's what an airport philosopher might say to you if you were lucky enough to hear his words on instrument rating day. Those are wise words, too. They've kept many an instrument pilot safe, and they'll keep you safe, too.

Now, onto the specifics of IFR flight planning.

IFR Pre-flight Planning-Are You Ready? Really?

The very first thing you should think about before planning any instrument flight is whether or not *you* are up to the task. We've already covered many psychological and physiological factors in Chapter Four. Use the I'M SAFE checklist to ensure that you're in good enough mental and physical shape to make this flight safely.

OK, mind and body are accounted for. How about instrument currency and proficiency (they are not the same thing)? Are you instrument current? If you haven't made at least six instrument approaches, and practiced holding procedures, course interception and tracking procedures within the preceding 6 calendar months, you're not current. If your currency has lapsed by an additional six months, then you need to take an IPC (instrument proficiency check) with a CFII.

You can be legally current but not proficient. Some pilots don't fly for six months, then rush out the day before their currency lapses and do the minimum necessary to be technically legal. To a far greater degree than VFR flight, IFR requires the proficiency that comes with frequent practice. If you aren't constantly honing and using your IFR skills, you are probably not *really* ready to meet the challenges an IFR flight can present. Nobody's going to check you on this—until the skills are needed. The problem is, that particular test is pass/fail and while Mother Nature doesn't grade on a curve, on occasion she'll throw you one.

Military pilots must fly at least every 14 days or undergo extensive recurrent training. The military has determined that the loss of that specialized high-performance skill deteriorates sufficiently over a two-week period to necessitate retraining. How sharp do you think your instrument skills will be after a six-month layoff? Or even a two-month gap?

You must decide if you're ready, both legally and in terms of proficiency, to make any instrument flight.

How's the Airplane?

OK, pilot's down and locked. The next item you should consider is whether your airplane is up to the task. In other words, is your machine legal for IFR flight?

1. Do the transponder, altimeter system and altitude reporting equipment have current 24-calendar month inspections?

2. Is the altimeter accurate within 75 feet (based on using the current altimeter setting at a known elevation site on the airport)? (The 75 foot value is a *recommendation* as per AIM section 7-2-3, Altimeter Errors.)

3. Is the GPS database current if you're planning on listing a /G equipment suffix in your IFR flight plan?

4. Have you done a VOR accuracy check within the last 30 days?

5. What about the annual, 100 hour, and ELT inspections and airworthiness directives?

6. Are all the airplane documents in order?

7. Is there any inoperative equipment on the airplane that needs to be placarded? Is the inoperative equipment necessary for VFR or IFR flight? Remember, of the six panel instruments, only the VSI isn't mandatory for IFR flight, but if it's inoperative it still needs to be properly placarded.

8. Finally, based on the amount of passengers, fuel, and baggage you'll carry, is the airplane within its weight and balance limits?

You'll also want to ensure that you have current instrument charts or charts with the most current information on them. That done, you're ready to take a big-picture look at your proposed flight.

A Big Picture Look at the Weather

Of all factors, the one that looms largest in determining whether you go is the weather. There's a place between really good and really bad where you can safely and sanely fly IFR. Finding that place is your assignment.

If I'm planning an instrument flight, I usually begin looking at the weather a few days before the planned departure time. For instance, a Thursday departure will have me watching The Weather Channel by Tuesday to get a big picture feel for what's happening in the atmosphere. Of course, the secret here is not to mistake the SCI FI channel for the weather channel. The last time I did that I canceled

No Flight Plan? I Wonder Why?

Ground, AirBig 216 requesting startup.

Leipzig, as always on Monday.

What? We have the day off on Tuesday!

Sorry AirBig 216, we don't have your flight plan. What is your destination?

But today is Tuesday.

my Seattle trip because I thought aliens had just landed next to the Space Needle and were attempting to communicate by asking, "When did you guys get here?"

I watch The Weather Channel ahead of time for two reasons. First, I want to see if there are any major weather trends that might make the trip so unlikely to happen that I need to make other arrangements. Major flooding, hurricanes, or excessive snowfall might be good examples of such trends. Next, I want to follow the forecasts to see if the weather is happening as predicted. If people did the same with their local TV psychics, there would be fewer psychics on TV but there would be many more public floggings.

The day before the flight, I start taking a closer look at the weather either by calling the FSS and asking for an outlook briefing or logging onto one of the many fine weather services now available by computer. My personal preference is to use a computer to obtain the weather when possible. Why? I can see nearly everything the FSS specialist sees and I can print it, too. Seeing a weather forecast is a whole lot better than just hearing someone talk about it.

There was a time when there were many individual Flight Service Stations located around the country where the briefers had local weather knowledge that was extremely valuable. This made a call or visit to the local FSS very worthwhile. With the consolidation of the FSS system, this just isn't the case now. If you have Internet access, it's usually much more convenient and practical to make your own weather assessment.

While the science of weather prediction has never been more refined, I'm still not able to make a final go/no-go decision 24 hours in advance of my flight, even if the weather seems to be evolving according to the forecasts. But examining the weather several days in advance of a flight allows me to evaluate how the forecasting model is doing when I check the weather just prior to the flight.

We'll talk about the final weather briefing in a bit, but now it's time to take a look at your initial route selection.

An Initial Selection of IFR Routing

After many years of teaching instrument students, I've learned that it's sometimes necessary to let students make several mistakes. One of these just happens to be route selection. No matter how well you plan a flight, you can't always get the IFR route you select. One time I had an instrument student, who was also a professional artist, show up with one of the most elaborately diagrammed and colored flight logs I'd ever seen. She'd spent hours working on route selection and using colored pencils to describe the different airways and altitudes. It was a masterpiece, and Jackson Pollack would have been proud of her offering, and maybe even a bit jealous, too.

Preferred Routes in the A/FD

LOW ALTITUDE

Terminals	Route	Effective Times (UTC)
SAN FRANCISCO/OAKLAND METRO AREA		
From SAN FRANCISCO Area: West Bay Airports		
Los Angeles Area	(70–90–110–130–150–170) V27 VTU V299 SADDE V107 LAX	1400–0800
From OAKLAND Area: East Bay Airports		
Los Angeles Area	(70–90–110–130–150–170) V109 PXN V113 V485 V299 SADDE V107 LAX	1400–0800

HIGH ALTITUDE

Terminals BURBANK	Route	Effective Times (UTC)
Chicago O'Hare	(all B747, B767, B727, DC10, DC87, L1011) DAG LAS BCE MTU OCS J94 ONL J148 MCW JVL–STAR	0000–2359
	or	
	(all other jets) DAG EED DRK J96 IRK BDF–STAR ..	0000–2359

Preferred IFR routes shown in the *Airport/Facility Directory* show you routes that maximize traffic flow and minimize delays in the ATC system.

Unfortunately, it was all for naught when she received her IFR clearance from ATC. She looked as disappointed as the lady whose pooch did the roll-over-and-play-dead trick for her boyfriend, only to have him say, "That's not bad for a dog in his price range." That's why there are always a few things you'll want to do when contemplating an IFR route.

First, check for the existence of any preferred routes covering the area in which you'll fly. The best place to find them, if they exist, is in the rear section of the *Airport/Facility Directory,* as shown in Figure 1. You might be wondering exactly who really prefers these routes. Not necessarily you. ATC defines preferred routes because it enables them to maximize the flow of traffic, minimize delays, and sometimes keep you out of someone else's airspace. In high-volume airspace, if everyone does their own thing, it's not long before nobody can do anything.

It appears that there are two low-altitude preferred routes from the San Francisco and Oakland area into Los Angeles, but no preferred routes going in the opposite direction. Is there a message there? Does the rest of the country prefer L.A. which does not send traffic out of their basin?

The preferred routes shown provide altitudes and a routing, as well as effective times. Preferred IFR routes beginning with a fix indicate that departing airplanes will often be routed to that fix by an instrument departure procedure (DP) or a radar vector. High-altitude preferred routes are also listed in the A/FD when available. If preferred routes are available for your direction of flight, you're likely to receive these routes regardless of what you file in your flight plan (so put those pretty pens and watercolors away, Picasso). It's usually best not to fight City Hall or ATC, so if there are preferred routes, file them. Of course, there are times when you won't want to use a preferred routing and in a while I'll tell you how to fight a bout about a route and (sometimes) get what you want.

TEC - Tower Enroute Control Canned Clearances

TOWER ENROUTE CONTROL | 343

TO: SBA	ROUTE ID CSTM22	ROUTE SXC SXC295R VTU160R VTU VTU282R KWANG	ALTITUDE J100M80 JM50PQ40
NTD CMA OXR (LAXE)	CSTM23	SLI SLI333R V186 FIM	PQ40
NTD OXR CMA	CSTM24	SLI SLI272R SMO125R SMO VNY	M60
NTD OXR CMA	CSTM25	SLI V23 LAX VNY	J80
NRD OXR CMA	CSTM26	SXC SXC295R VTU160R VTU	

FROM: SNA

TO:	ROUTE ID	ROUTE	ALTITUDE
CRQ NFG NKX OKB	CSTM27	V23 OCN	PQ50
MYF NRS NZY SAN SDM SEE	CSTM28	V23 MZB	PQ50
RNM	CSTM29	V23 OCN V208 JLI	PQ50
SAN (SANE)	CSTM30	V23 OCN V165 SARGS	PQ50

FROM: FUL LGB SLI TOA (RWY 11) when SNA South traffic

TO:	ROUTE ID	ROUTE	ALTITUDE
CRQ NFG NKX OKB	CSTM31	SLI V64 V363 V23 OCN	PQ50
RNM	CSTM32	SLI V64 V363 V23 OCN V208 JLI	PQ50
MYF NRS NZY SAN SDM SEE	CSTM33	SLI V64 V363 V23 MZB	PQ50
SAN (SANE)	CSTM34	SLI V64 V363 V165 SARGS	PQ50

FROM: FUL LGB SLI TOA (RWY 11) when SNA North traffic

TO:	ROUTE ID	ROUTE	ALTITUDE
CRQ NFG NKX OKB	CSTM35	V23 OCN	PQ50
MYF NRS NZY SAN SDM SEE	CSTM36	V23 MZB	PQ50
RNM	CSTM37	V23 OCN V208 JLI	PQ50
SAN (SANE)	CSTM38	V23 OCN V165 SARGS	

Fig. 2

The TEC routes listed in the back of the Airport/Facility Directory are canned clearances issued for operating in the local TEC environment.

I'm sure you remember from Chapter 7 on the IFR system that flights within a tower enroute control environment have their own form of preferred routing, known as *TEC* routes (also sometimes known as a tower-to-tower clearance). These are also listed in the back of the A/FD as shown in Figure 2. Make sure you file these routes when operating within a TEC environment (review Chapter 7 to refresh your memory on TEC routings).

There's also one other source for IFR routing that you'll want to consider, though it's neither FAA-approved nor sufficient unto itself. If you're in unfamiliar territory and are filing an IFR flight plan, ask one of the local flight instructors about common routings out of the airport. Local CFIs have route-specific knowledge that could be useful. I'd simply say that I'm planning a flight to a specific destination and ask what route, based on their experience, I might expect. Then, if possible, file this route. It will minimize the amount of clearance copying and revisions you'll have to make. If you ask a local fellow who has a Bowie knife in a hip holster, an eye patch, is missing part of an ear, and all his teeth are even (because 1, 3, 5, and 7 are missing), you might expect him to say something like, "Yeah I fly IFR a lot, which makes me wanna get that instrument rating someday."

Intersection IFR Departures

Did you know that you can file your IFR flight plan to begin at a point other than a departure airport? You can file your IFR flight plan to begin at an intersection, navaid or waypoint in the nearby enroute structure. Suppose you want to depart Dell City Muni (position A), fly VFR to CONNE intersection (position B) and fly V560 to your eventual destination. You'll begin by listing CONNE as the departure point on your IFR flight plan (position C). The airplane is leaving from an airport, but the IFR flight is beginning from an intersection.

That's why item #5 in the flight plan form says *departure point*, not *departure airport*. Your route will be the route from that point to the destination airport (position D). Obviously, you'll need to be VFR from the departure airport to the departure point to be legal using this strategy. You'll call ATC to activate your IFR clearance while in VFR conditions as you approach the departure point. You can determine the proper frequency on which to do this by looking on your IFR enroute chart and selecting the nearest Center frequency (position E). You'll simply call the Center or Approach/Departure controller and say that you've pre-filed IFR from that point to a specific airport and would like to activate your IFR flight plan. The controller will summon your clearance from the Center computer and provide it to you. You'll read it back as before and be on your way on an IFR clearance.

One of the most useful tools in helping you make your initial route selection is NACO's IFR/VFR Low Altitude Flight Planning Chart (Figure 3). Here you'll find all the low altitude airways and important navaids from which to make your initial selection (Figure 4). Airports shown in blue on this chart have instrument approaches, brown airports don't, and airports shown in red are private airports.

One of the other nice things about this chart is the straight-line distance legend, shown in Figure 5. For instance, the nautical mile distance from Houston Hobby airport to Salt Lake City Intl. is 1,055 nautical miles (Figure 5, position A). The total distance from Corpus Christi Intl. to El Paso Intl. is 522 nautical miles (Figure 5, position B). This legend comes in handy when making your initial assessment of the number of stops you will need to make, as well as where you might make them on an IFR flight. Then again, the size of your bladder (not the fuel bladder) often determines the number of stops you'll be making.

Getting Down to Details

You have a rough idea about how the weather is unfolding, the route, the distance, and the number of stops you'll need to make. With that in mind, it's time to deal with the specifics of your flight.

Within six hours of your proposed departure, and based on your latest assessment of the weather, it's time to make your final route selection. While you'd normally want to plan for the most direct route possible, you sometimes need to consider a Warped Triangle (i.e., dog-leg) route. Weather is usually what rains on your go-direct parade, but things such as navaid outages and a desire to avoid terrain can also make the roundabout way the way to go.

If I had an entertainment theme park, I'd create a big tunnel where people rode through

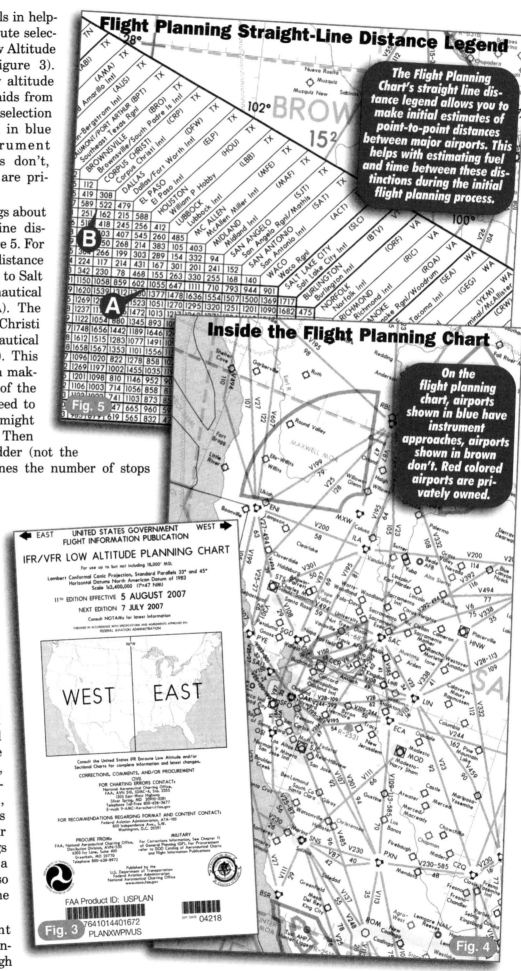

The Flight Planning Chart's straight line distance legend allows you to make initial estimates of point-to-point distances between major airports. This helps with estimating fuel and time between these distinctions during the initial flight planning process.

Fig. 5

On the flight planning chart, airports shown in blue have instrument approaches, airports shown in brown don't. Red colored airports are privately owned.

Fig. 3

Fig. 4

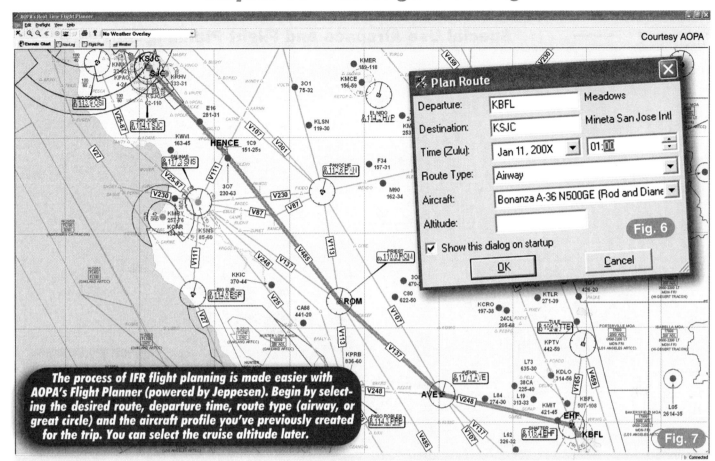

The process of IFR flight planning is made easier with AOPA's Flight Planner (powered by Jeppesen). Begin by selecting the desired route, departure time, route type (airway, or great circle) and the aircraft profile you've previously created for the trip. You can select the cruise altitude later.

in a boat. When they came out the other side, someone would hand them a copy of their home mortgage. I'd call this place, *Reality Land,* which is what I want to welcome you to when considering IFR routes.

I want to be realistic and say that while you may *file* a specific route that avoids an area of thunderstorm activity or nasty terrain, don't expect ATC's computer to always cough up your requested routing on the first pass. ATC has its own issues, and it's *their* computer. And like all computers, if you input the same info and ask the same question, you'll get the same answer. What's needed here is not Divine intervention, but human intervention.

Your best bet is to ask a clearance delivery controller or FSS specialist (the person from whom you obtain your IFR clearance) to intercede on your behalf. These people have bionic implants that enable them to negotiate with ATC computers. As the Rolling Stones said, "You can't always get what you want," but, "If you try, sometime you find you get what you need."

There are times when, depending on conditions and your safety options, you're better off accepting ATC's routing, and then negotiating with the Center controller while aloft for a modified routing. This technique works only if the reason for wanting the alternate routing is something you'd experience somewhere down the air road, and not in the immediate departure area.

For example, part of your departure routing might take you over large bodies of water and you don't want this to happen. If you don't obtain an alternate routing before departure, and if the controller can't provide you with a

different routing pretty darn quickly once aloft, then guess what? You're going over water, so bring that tartar sauce along in hopes of warding off "Jaws."

Bakersfield to San Jose—IFR

Let's say that we want to file an IFR flight plan from Bakersfield, California to San Jose, California. There are two ways to do this. You can do it manually, by tugging out your charts and hand-picking the most direct (or practical) routing possible. Or, if you have a computer with Internet access (and what pilot doesn't?), you can use one of the fine flight planning programs available to you for free to help with the process. Personally, I like to use AOPA's Real-Time Flight Planner (free to all AOPA members) for all my flight planning activities. If you learn how to use any flight-planning program, doing the task manually will be within your grasp, but you'll quickly see why you wouldn't want to use that option. We'll use AOPA's software in this chapter, because I like to play on the computer and I know you do, too. It also does the job faster and in many cases more thoroughly and systematically than many of us would do it by hand.

Let's begin by selecting the departure and destination points and airways for the route type, as shown in Figure 6. Don't worry about the initial altitude selection. If you don't know what altitude you'd like, you can just leave this section blank and fill it in later. When you've listed your date and time of departure (in UTC), click OK and the program uses a sophisticated algorithm (and maybe a little magic, too) to create the most direct airway routing for your direction of flight, as shown in Figure 7.

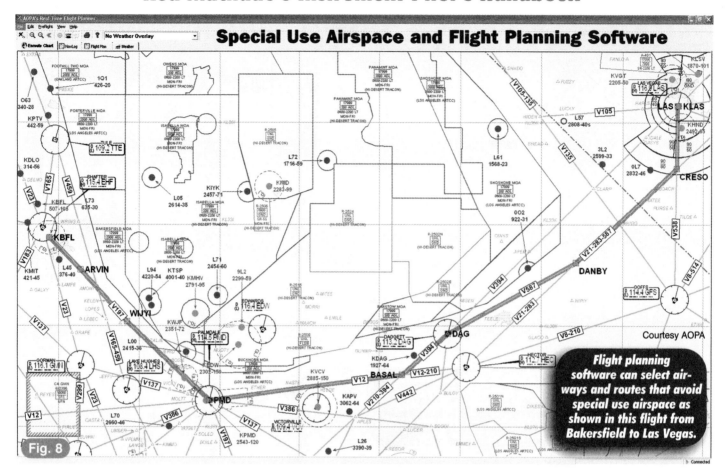

Special Use Airspace and Flight Planning Software

Courtesy AOPA

Flight planning software can select airways and routes that avoid special use airspace as shown in this flight from Bakersfield to Las Vegas.

Fig. 8

With a quick glance, you can see if this routing will take you through any special use airspace like MOAs, or restricted or prohibited areas, which you might prefer to sidestep. Fortunately, many restricted, prohibited and military operation areas (not all, by any means) were built to avoid established airways. This is because airways have been around a lot longer than a lot of the special use airspace. For example, Figure 8 shows a routing from Bakersfield to Las Vegas, heading eastward around the special use airspace. One of the great things about this automated flight planning software is that you can alter your route line by clicking it and dragging and dropping it to any point, navaid, or intersection. This gives you the best of both worlds—the speed and consistency of an automated plan, with the option to tweak to your heart's content. Want to take the scenic route, rather than the most direct route? Just click and drag and drop.

What about altitude selection along the route? By clicking the Nav Log tab, you will see a text list of your routing under the *Filed Route* section as well as the MEAs for the route and a software-selected lowest minimum allowable altitude for that route in the flight log (Figure 9). Since we didn't select an altitude, the software selected 8,000 feet for us, based on the highest MEAs along our route.

We can always change this if we want, by reselecting the route as in Figure 6 and listing a specific altitude. This is important, because we might

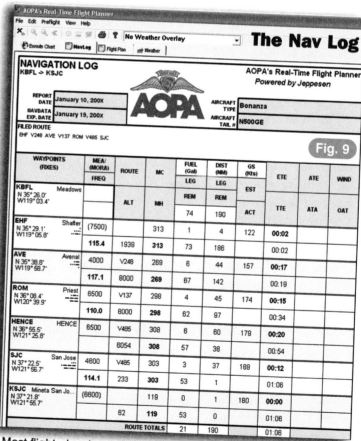

Most flight planning software will provide you with a navigation log of the route and route segments along with the appropriate MEAs and MORAs. Time, distances and fuel estimates are updated when you log on for winds and essential weather information.

Flying Direct Routes

Why would you want to fly airways when you might be able to fly direct from one fix to another? It's often much more efficient to fly a direct routing when you have the equipment (e.g., an IFR approved GPS) and when ATC permits you to do so.

If you only have VOR equipment on your airplane, then you can file from one VOR direct to another even if there are no airways between these VORs. You can do this below 18,000 feet if those VORs are within 80 nautical miles of each other (this is the typical service volume limit of "L" class VORs). What altitude would you choose? You'd have to review your sectional charts and pick an altitude of 1,000 feet (or 2,000 feet in designated mountainous terrain, see page 8-31, Figure 42) above the highest obstacle along the route and within four nautical miles either side of the anticipated course centerline. On the other hand, you can just as easily look at your low altitude enroute chart and pick the highest OROCA (off-route obstruction clearance altitude), which provides terrain clearance of 1,000 and 2,000 feet in non-mountainous and mountainous terrain, respectively (Figure 10, position A). Then you'd want to modify that altitude to fly even or odd thousands based on the magnetic course to be flown.

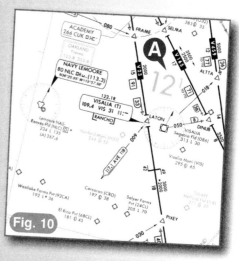

Fig. 10

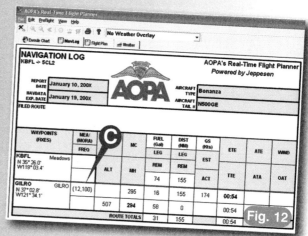

Fig. 11

Most likely you have an IFR certified GPS (or other RNAV unit) on board your airplane and want to file direct without the use of VOR equipment. If so, then you could list a routing direct from the departure airport to an IAF at the destination airport (Figure 11, position B). If this were a flight from Bakersfield to San Jose, you'd simply fly direct to GILRO intersection. The route box in your flight plan would read "DIRECT GILRO." It's a short flight plan, but you're not getting paid by the word. You'd still be required to choose an altitude, based on the terrain you'll overfly. Most flight planning software will provide you with the highest OROCA along the route as shown in Figure 12, position C. If you're not using this software for flight planning, you can often just eyeball an altitude estimate, because the ATC computer will typically assign you an altitude that provides adequate terrain clearance based on the controller's MVA or MIA.

Fig. 12

choose to fly higher or lower due to the wind and weather (i.e., turbulence, freezing level, etc.).

Until now, the software has done everything you would have done if you'd been planning this flight manually. There is, however, one thing you should do when using electronic flight planning software, and that is to make sure the proposed routing comports with the departure and arrival procedures at your airports of choice. This is where you may have to intervene manually and modify the software-generated route. It's your chance to STAR, Sid.

FAA's Method

The following is the FAA's recommended checklist for use when preparing for IFR flight. Look at it carefully and feel free to add and expand it as you gain experience. The most important thing about flight planning is not that you do each thing in a specific order, but that you do all the things that are necessary to ensure that you fly safely.

Preflight Action
• *Plane and pilot fitness*
• *Legal requirements*
• *Preliminary weather check*
Tentative route to destination and alternate
• *Proposed altitude*
• *Route and check points*
• *True or magnetic courses*
• *Distances*
• *Communications/navigation frequencies*
Current instrument approach charts for dest/alt

Where do I start?

Current info on facilities & procedures for flight including:
• *Airport/Facility Directory*
• *Notices to airmen - FDC Notams*
Contact FSS or obtain computer weather briefing
Complete flight log
Compute weight and balance
Complete the flight plan
The IFR Clearance
ATC Communications
Cockpit Organization
Final Go-NoGo decision

Become a Preflight Einstein

Arrival and Departure Procedures

The software selected a route that takes us directly from the airport to EHF VOR (Figure 13, position A). This may or may not be the best way to depart. That's why we look at the DP or *departure procedure* for this airport. It happens that BFL has no SIDs that take you directly to EHF VOR (trust me, I looked). If it did, then you could simply file the SID (or the appropriate SID transition, if necessary) in your flight plan as the initial part of your route.

There is a DP out of BFL, as shown in Figure 14, position B. It appears that the DP requires a direct flight to EHF VOR

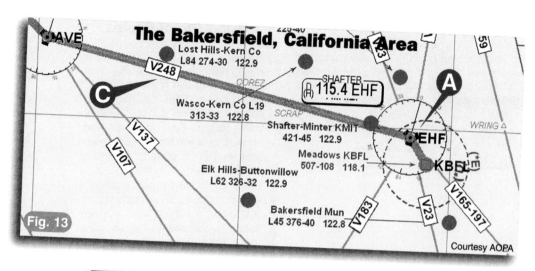

Fig. 13

Courtesy AOPA

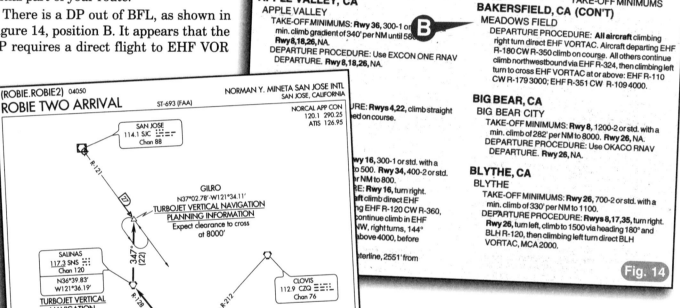

Fig. 14

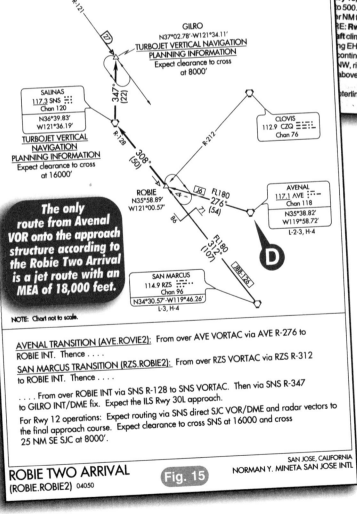

Fig. 15

(Figure 13, position A) and then a climb on course if we're departing northwest on V248 (Figure 13, position C). Since there are no altitude restrictions or depicted climb rates, we can assume that a 200 foot per nautical mile climb gradient will be sufficient to keep us free from obstructions. What about the arrival portion of our flight? This is where we would check for any STARs that apply, based on the direction from which we're arriving.

The closest STAR (and it's not Alpha Centauri, either) that would accommodate you at San Jose is the Robie Two arrival (Figure 15). This arrival has several transitions, one of which is the Avenal Transition (AVE.ROVIE2) that begins over Avenal VOR (Figure 15, position D). The only problem is that the routing from Avenal VOR consists of the jet airway J6, and it has an MEA of FL180 or 18,000 feet. Since you probably don't have a jet, this routing isn't your answer.

Most airports with STARs are also airports that have sufficient commercial traffic to justify the creation of STARs. That usually translates to jet aircraft. Big ones. It's been my experience that smaller general aviation airplanes don't often get to use STARs, even if they file them. ATC usually likes to keep jet traffic on STARs because it's easier to manage these racehorses that way. They really don't want to have a 757 trying to throttle back to follow your Cherokee. That's why smaller general aviation airplanes are usually given local routings to the airport. That keeps them out of harm's way and better manages traffic flow.

Let's assume, for a second, that the Avenal Transition did work for you (let's say you actually have a jet and, because I assumed you didn't, my chances of getting a ride have dropped dramatically). You'd only need to list a routing from BFL to AVE then follow it by the code AVE.ROVIE2. In other words, the routing you'd place in the route section of your flight plan would look like this: *BFL EHF V248 AVE.ROVIE2*. (You are so lucky if you have a jet! I'd really like that ride if you'd find it in your heart to forgive me.)

Tell Them Where to Go

Since there is no STAR you can use (and you probably wouldn't get one anyway), you'll want to look at a San Jose approach chart and pick out a major navaid or intersection from which you can fly the approach without the use of radar vectors. Keep in mind that an instrument clearance is supposed to allow you to fly to an airport and shoot the approach even if you experience communications failure. This means you should find an intersection on an approach chart that has a feeder route leading to the approach structure.

The most effective way to do this is to find an *IAF* and list your routing to this point. From the IAF, the approach chart routing takes you onto the approach structure. There's no need to list a routing beyond the IAF because the ATC computer knows you'll fly the routing on the chart to the airport. Remember, ATC's computer isn't a dual-floppy system. It has a hard drive (most likely, anyway) and is smarter than your new car and me, and your flight instructor (well, certainly smarter than me, any-

The IAF (GILRO) at Our Destination Airport

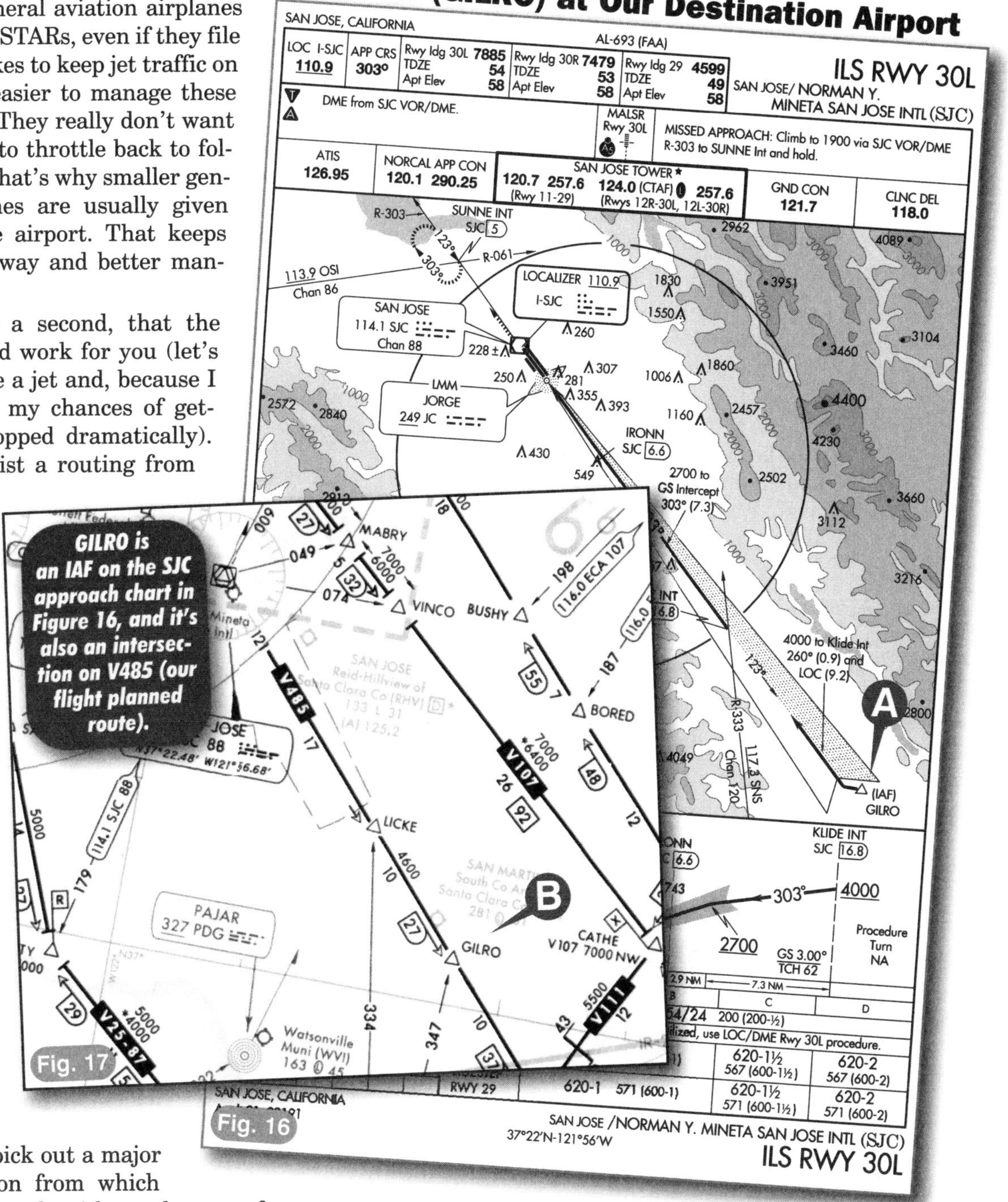

GILRO is an IAF on the SJC approach chart in Figure 16, and it's also an intersection on V485 (our flight planned route).

Fig. 17

Fig. 16

way). My suggestion is to look for an ILS approach, if one is available at that airport, and select the IAF on that chart (or another approach chart) which is located somewhere along your initial routing to the airport.

Why file for an ILS approach (assuming, of course, you have ILS equipment)? Well, if you had communications failure, you'd certainly want to fly the approach that would offer you the best chance of landing in poor weather conditions, which is exactly what an ILS can do. Figure 16 is the ILS 30L approach into San Jose. It appears that GILRO intersection (Figure 16, position A) is an IAF and is southeast of LICKE intersection on V485 (Figure 17, position B). That's what the routing software chose for us. When we file our IFR flight plan, we'll list GILRO as the final intersection/navaid on our selected route.

It's entirely possible that the ILS 30L approach won't be what you wind up flying. The airport's ILS equipment might have gone tubes-up, or the active runway could be different, requiring an entirely different approach to the approach. If this happens, ATC may modify your routing before departure or while enroute.

The principle, however, remains to create a clearance that leaves you with the option of having a flyable, non-radar routing to one of the airport's instrument approaches in the event of communications failure.

Whether the Weather is Together

Now that we've selected our route, let's see if this flight is feasible given the expected weather enroute. If you don't have Internet access, you can call the Flight Service to obtain a weather briefing. Since we're using AOPA's flight planner, we'll go to the weather tab, check the "Standard Wx Route" box (Figure 18, position A), and fill in the relevant data in the popup window that opens (Figure 18, position B). We'll check the NOTAM tab, and list KSAC as our alternate.

I initially listed Sacramento Executive airport (Figure 19, position A) as an alternate because it's a sufficient distance from San Jose that there's a chance of different weather. It's also in a valley behind a few small mountains, which improves the odds of the weather being different and better. If you choose a nearby airport as an alternate, what makes you think its weather will be any better? The objective in having an alternate is to have an alternative!

Selecting WX Briefing and Alternate

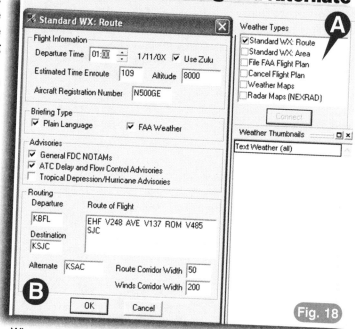

When you select the desired type of weather briefing (i.e., Standard WX Enroute) a popup window opens, allowing you to make a few flight plan modifications, select for FDC NOTAMS and list an alternate airport if one is required.

The situation you *don't* want to be in is missing an approach, knowing the weather at your alternate is zero-zero, and hearing the controller say, "Say your intentions." You are now a man (or woman) without a plan.

I don't want to list an alternate that's too far away, either. For an IFR flight I need to carry enough fuel to fly to the destination, to the alternate, and for an additional 45 minutes at normal cruising speed (FAR 91.167). It all has to fit into one airplane. We'll return to thinking about this alternate shortly.

After completing the route information, select the types of charts you feel are necessary to help you evaluate the weather (Figure 20). My advice is to choose everything you think will be interesting and valuable to you in helping make a go/no-go decision. Figure 21 shows the additional selections I've made for this analysis. When you finish choosing the weather graphics and reports you want to see, download them by clicking the "connect" button.

So, where do we begin analyzing the weather we've collected for our trip? Since we plan to depart at 0100Z (that's 5 p.m. PST, which, for this example, we'll assume is an hour or so away), we need to look at the

The Planned Route to Our Alternate

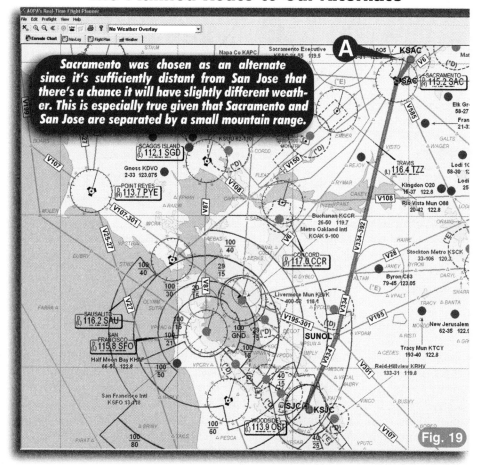

Sacramento was chosen as an alternate since it's sufficiently distant from San Jose that there's a chance it will have slightly different weather. This is especially true given that Sacramento and San Jose are separated by a small mountain range.

Fig. 19

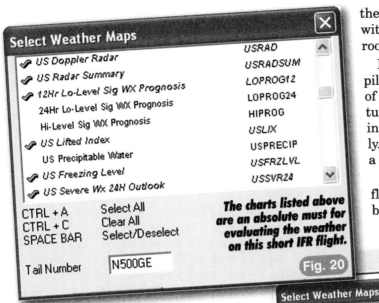

the clouds, then you shouldn't be in those same clouds without storm detection equipment. Period. No wiggle room here.

Icing is the next biggest concern to an instrument pilot. You can often handle icing conditions by getting out of the clouds or heading to an area where the temperatures are above freezing. You can also handle it by avoiding it in the first place. Nevertheless, icing can be deadly. Unlike thunderstorms, however, you frequently have a bit more time to deal with icing.

Often, low visibility conditions can be dealt with by flying an ILS approach, landing at a nearby airport with better visibility or just waiting a bit for the conditions to

weather that exists now as well as at the time we expect to arrive in San Jose. A good initial strategy is to think about the weather that's most likely to make or break a flight plan (or an airplane). I'm specifically thinking about some of aviation's real weather show-stoppers, like thunderstorms.

There are three big weather events that can keep any IFR pilot from starting or completing an IFR flight: *thunderstorms, icing,* and *poor landing visibility,* and they all involve water in the atmosphere.

Convective activity (thunderstorms) is one of your biggest concerns because it involves the most atmospheric water. Remember from Chapter 9 that it takes a lot of energy to suspend the water necessary for the creation of thunderstorms. That energy can be destructive to you and your airplane. The only way you can handle thunderstorms if you don't have onboard storm detection equipment is to circumnavigate them visually. Simply stated, if there are thunderstorms in

improve. For instance, there are times when the approach visibility is below minimums but changes for the better as the sun sets (i.e., the visibility improves because it's often easier to see lighted objects at night).

Given these concerns, let's start by examining the NEXRAD data for our route.

What is Onboard Storm Detection Equipment?

Pilots are often told not to fly in the clouds when thunderstorms are present unless they have *storm detection* equipment. The question is, what constitutes *storm detection* equipment? Is it NEXRAD, ATC's radar, Sferics (Stormscope, StrikeFinder) or onboard weather radar?

While NEXRAD information uplinked to the cockpit is extremely useful, it should be considered a *strategic* tool to flight plan around areas of suspected thunderstorms, not a *tactical* one where you avoid them while in IMC. The problem with NEXRAD information is that it can be as much as 15 minutes old by the time you receive it in the cockpit. Thunderstorms can grow thousands of feet per minute, therefore, it's not reasonable to use this information on a *real time* (tactical) basis when trying to avoid embedded thunderstorms. ATC's weather radar information (i.e. WARP) uses the same NEXRAD information you have in the cockpit, therefore this is still strategic and not tactical information.

Sferics, like Stormscope, detect lightning, and where there's lightning there are thunderstorms. The problem is that pre-thunderstorm clouds can still produce dangerous levels of turbulence. So Sferics alone can't provide a precise picture of where the convective dangers exist.

On board weather radar is the only equipment that can detect suspended water in real time, and it's the amount of suspended water in the air that determines the probability of turbulence. This is why airliners use weather radar in lieu of NEXRAD and Sferics to make tactical weather decisions in flight.

Figure 22, position A, contains the list of charts we've downloaded on the right. By clicking on any chart, you'll bring it into view on the left panel (Figure 22, position B). Our objective is to obtain a big picture understanding of what's happening in the atmosphere along our route. If you'd like to see the NEXRAD weather applied to your entire route, return to the route portion of the program and click the *DTC NEXRAD Mosaic* dropdown tab. Now you have superimposed the NEXRAD chart on top of your route, as shown in Figure 23. This allows you to better understand how this weather would affect you if you were airborne. Keep in mind that the NEXRAD Mosaic doesn't show clouds, it's shows areas where radar energy has reflected off water suspended in the air. You need to look at other charts to determine the extent of the present or expected cloud coverage in this area.

The NEXRAD mosaic (Figure 22, position B) shows a lot of intense weather northwest of the San Francisco Bay area. We know that most frontal systems and wave cyclones move in an easterly direction, so it's likely that this area of weather will move in the direction of our route. We need to check a few other charts to be sure, but that would be a reasonable guess to make. According to the NEXRAD scale at the bottom of the chart (Figure 22, position C), there is weather with a color-coded intensity value between 40 to 50 to the northwest. What do these numbers mean to you? Are they survival odds?

As we previously discussed in *Postflight Briefing #9-3* in Chapter 9, the numerical values on this chart are radar *reflectivity values*. They are also referred to as Z calibrated in decibels (dB), and thus are referred to as *dBZ* or *decibels of Z*. Radar return values represent the amount of water suspended in a cloud. The more water in the cloud,

the stronger the vertical air currents associated with that cloud must be to suspend that water. In other words, more water means there's a probability of greater turbulence associated with that cloud or area of clouds.

How do you interpret the radar reflectivity values (Z)? You have to look at another chart that may not be immediately available to you. That is the National Weather Service's *Storm Level* index (Figure 24). What you need to know here is that airline pilots always avoid Level 3 (and higher) areas. The turbulence associated with a Level 3 storm is that commonly found in thunderstorms, meaning that these areas most likely contain thunderstorms.

These same airline pilots also avoid stand-alone areas of Level 2 returns, because they contain rain and often make for a rough and noisy ride. Level 3 returns are those identified as beginning at 40 dBZ and above. On an airline pilot's radar screen these reflectivity values produce the color red. Unfortunately, there is no standardization in how the makers of NEXRAD charts color-code their products. But that doesn't really matter to you if you know that all areas of 40 dBZ and above need to be avoided.

Keep in mind that the highest level of turbulence associated with the present storm activity in any cloud is assumed to apply statistically throughout the entire mass of clouds containing that storm. Seeing one small 40 dBZ return in a large area of continuous lesser returns means that the 40 dBZ hazard applies to that entire large area, regardless of whether or not that area shows 40 dBZ, 30 dBZ, 20 dBZ, or 10 dBZ (Figure 25). This is one instance where it's good to trust statistics.

There are only a few areas of 40 dBZ returns immediately along our route (Figure 23, position Z), and they may or may not affect our flight. We need much more informa-

NEXRAD Radar Data for Northern California

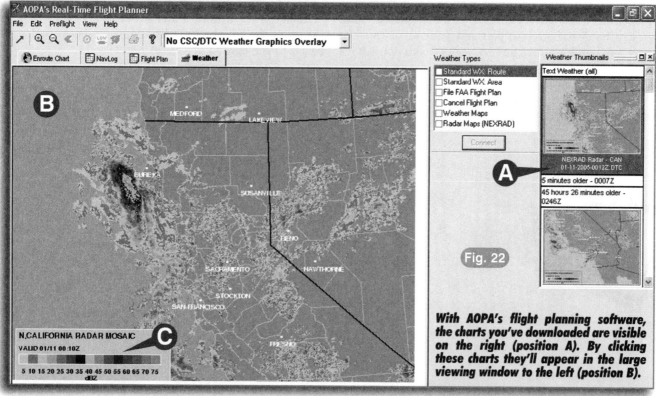

With AOPA's flight planning software, the charts you've downloaded are visible on the right (position A). By clicking these charts they'll appear in the large viewing window to the left (position B).

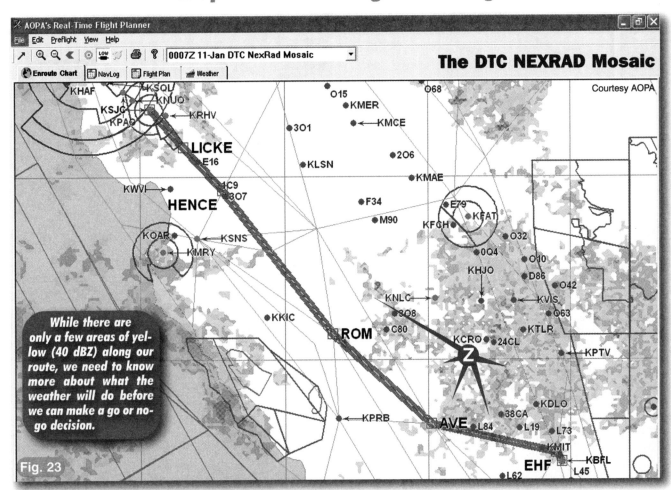

While there are only a few areas of yellow (40 dBZ) along our route, we need to know more about what the weather will do before we can make a go or no-go decision.

Fig. 23

The DTC NEXRAD Mosaic

Courtesy AOPA

tion before we can begin to make a go/no-go decision. Additionally, we need to know where the large Level 3–5 weather system to the northwest of San Francisco is headed. If that weather system is headed southwest, in the direction of San Jose, and if it arrives before we do, then our decision is clear: we don't go. We can either cancel the flight (and that would be no fun) or we can wait for the storm to move out of town (a much better option). Therefore, we need to know where the weather system is heading and how fast it's moving.

National Weather Services Storm Levels

Display Level	VIP Level	dBZ Appx.
Extreme	Level 6	50 to 59 dBZ
	Level 5	
Heavy	Level 4	40 to 49 dBZ
	Level3	
Moderate	Level 2	30 to 39 dBZ
Light	Level 1	16 to 29 dBZ

Fig. 24

Any area of 40 dBZ or higher (shown as yellow on the NEXRAD chart in Figure 22 and 23) represents a Level 3 storm according to the scale above. Airline pilots avoid all weather areas containing Level 3 (40+ dBZ) returns and so should you if they exist along your flight planned route.

Fig. 25

If we assume the yellow area on the NEXRAD return shown above represents a 40 dBZ return and needs to be avoided, then we'd also avoid the entire outlined area. Statistically, the highest level of turbulence associated with 40 dBZ returns applies to the entire area.

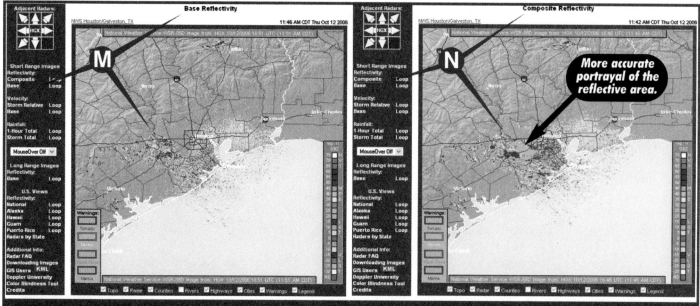

Base Vs. Composite Reflective Imagery

Sometimes you have a choice as to which type of NEXRAD return you can elect to view. Specifically, you often have a choice between *base reflectivity* (position M) and *composite reflectivity* (position N). The base reflectivity image shows only the reflected energy at a single elevation scan of the radar (typically at a lower tilt of the radar antenna). This can be done on either a short range (approximately 124 nm) or long range (approximately 248 nm) basis. Composite reflectivity images, on the other hand, display the highest reflectivity from all elevations within the radar antenna's vertical scan range.

Viewing the base reflectivity image may not reveal the water content in upper portions of the cloud. Heavier precipitation higher in the cloud may not have reached the surface. It is the total water content of any cloud that's important to you as a pilot, because that value represents the potential turbulence within a cloud. That's why the composite reflectivity images are usually more meaningful when trying to understand the turbulence potential of a storm. It's also why many weather uplink providers are now providing pilots with composite reflective imagery in their cockpits.

Since you've learned that the highest level of turbulence associated with a radar return applies to the entire reflective area associated with that return, the composite reflective image (position N) better portrays the entire scope of the affected area.

According to the current surface analysis chart in Figure 26, position R, there's a low-pressure system over Reno, Nevada that's creating a counterclockwise flow. This is likely to cause the convective weather (position S) to move in southeast toward our destination at San Jose, California. This is validated when you refer to the 12- and 24-hour prog charts (Figures 27 and 28, positions A and B). Even if this weather doesn't move directly toward our route, the charts still tell us that Level 3 and 4 weather could develop over the entire area.

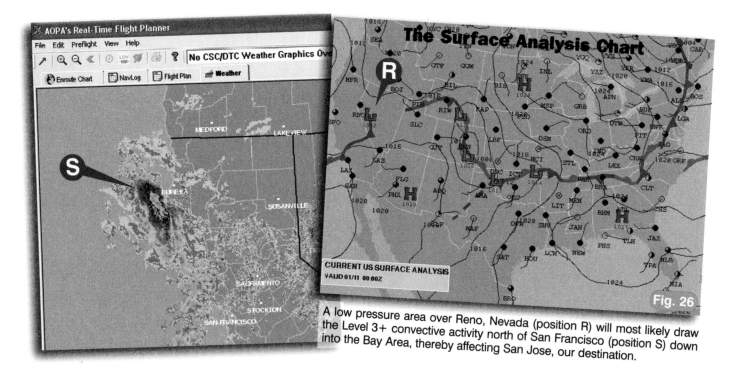

A low pressure area over Reno, Nevada (position R) will most likely draw the Level 3+ convective activity north of San Francisco (position S) down into the Bay Area, thereby affecting San Jose, our destination.

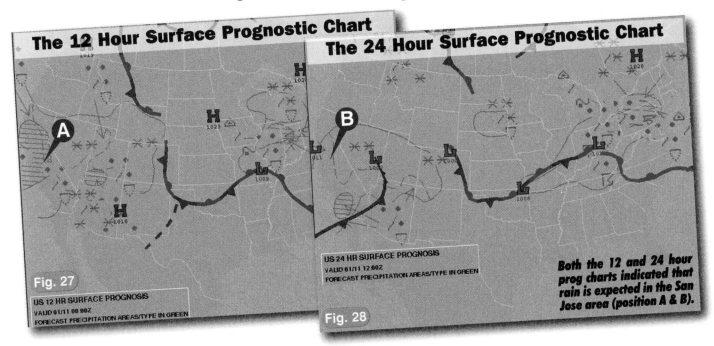

The 12 Hour Surface Prognostic Chart

A

Fig. 27

US 12 HR SURFACE PROGNOSIS
VALID 01/11 00 00Z
FORECAST PRECIPITATION AREAS/TYPE IN GREEN

The 24 Hour Surface Prognostic Chart

B

US 24 HR SURFACE PROGNOSIS
VALID 01/11 12:00Z
FORECAST PRECIPITATION AREAS/TYPE IN GREEN

Both the 12 and 24 hour prog charts indicated that rain is expected in the San Jose area (position A & B).

Fig. 28

Depending on the cloud tops, cloud coverage, and your airplane, it may not be possible to get above the clouds to circumnavigate the convective buildups visually. As a final note of interest. Let's continue to examine some of the other charts we've downloaded.

Figure 29 is the 24-hour severe weather outlook chart. It appears that there is a chance of *non-severe weather* to the right of the green line (as you face its arrow) along the middle California coast (position C). Keep in mind that non-severe weather still means general thunderstorms are forecast to the right of the line. General thunderstorms, relatively speaking, aren't the types of thunderstorms that spawn tornadoes or large hailstones. They have enough energy, however, to make you feel like you're a human piñata in your airplane. The fact is, a thunderstorm is a thunderstorm. It's not something in which you want to fly, and that's that! Period!

Figure 30 is the significant low-level weather prog chart. There is moderate turbulence forecast for the area covered by our route of flight from the surface to 24,000 feet (yellow dashed line, position D). Scalloped lines (position E) predict marginal VFR conditions for nearly all of California, and IFR conditions are forecast for the upper eastern portion of California. The most important forecast here is for the freezing level (green dashed line, position F). It appears that the freezing level over the Bakersfield area is forecast to begin at 8,000 feet (MSL) and slope to 4,000 feet as we approach central Oregon). This is not a good omen for any IFR flight, especially given the amount of moisture present along the route.

Now, I know some folks will tell you that the freezing level is harmless even when clouds are present. In my mind this is just like the dentist who tells you the X-rays are harmless and then puts a lead shield over your reproductive parts and leaves the building before snapping the picture.

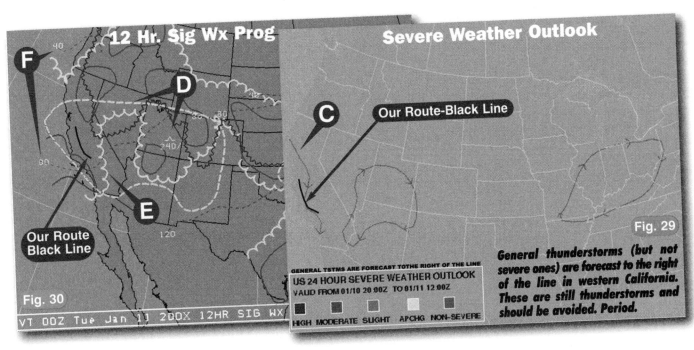

12 Hr. Sig Wx Prog

F

D

E

Our Route
Black Line

Fig. 30

VT 00Z Tue Jan 11 200X 12HR SIG WX

Severe Weather Outlook

C   Our Route-Black Line

Fig. 29

GENERAL TSTMS ARE FORECAST TO THE RIGHT OF THE LINE
US 24 HOUR SEVERE WEATHER OUTLOOK
VALID FROM 01/10 20 00Z TO 01/11 12 00Z

HIGH   MODERATE   SLIGHT   APCHG   NON-SEVERE

General thunderstorms (but not severe ones) are forecast to the right of the line in western California. These are still thunderstorms and should be avoided. Period.

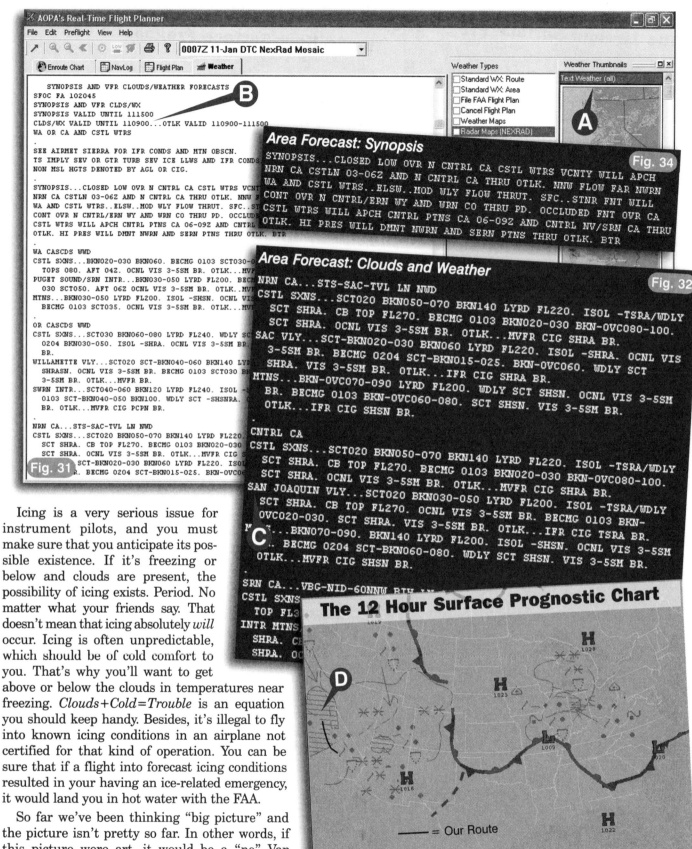

The 12 Hour Surface Prognostic Chart

_____ = Our Route

US 12 HR SURFACE PROGNOSIS
VALID 01/11 00 00Z
FORECAST PRECIPITATION AREAS/TYPE IN GREEN

Fig. 33

Icing is a very serious issue for instrument pilots, and you must make sure that you anticipate its possible existence. If it's freezing or below and clouds are present, the possibility of icing exists. Period. No matter what your friends say. That doesn't mean that icing absolutely *will* occur. Icing is often unpredictable, which should be of cold comfort to you. That's why you'll want to get above or below the clouds in temperatures near freezing. *Clouds+Cold=Trouble* is an equation you should keep handy. Besides, it's illegal to fly into known icing conditions in an airplane not certified for that kind of operation. You can be sure that if a flight into forecast icing conditions resulted in your having an ice-related emergency, it would land you in hot water with the FAA.

So far we've been thinking "big picture" and the picture isn't pretty so far. In other words, if this picture were art, it would be a "no" Van Gogh. The severe weather outlook says there is a chance of thunderstorms along our route and the freezing level exists a little below our initial cruise altitude of 8,000 feet and lowers as we head north. Practically speaking, as it appears now, the only way to make this flight is if you can do it outside the clouds. This strategy allows you to avoid the convective activity and icing. In other words, it seems that we'd have to look at more charts to see if it were possible to climb above the clouds or at least spend a great deal of time out of them. And all this assumes that the weather at San Jose

Aviation Weather Center's CIP or Current Icing Potential Plot

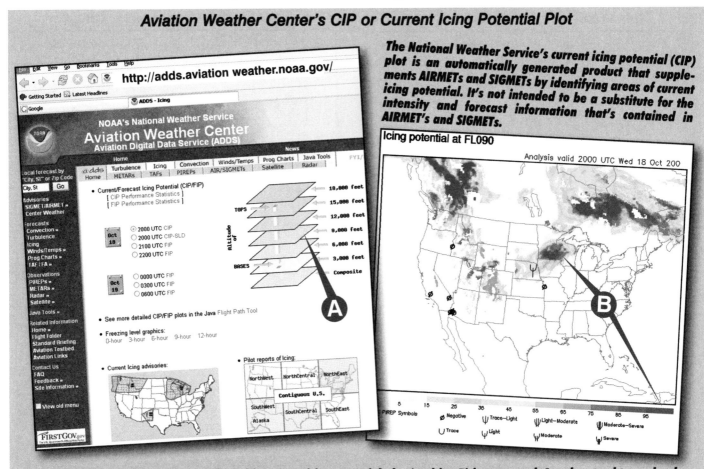

The National Weather Service's current icing potential (CIP) plot is an automatically generated product that supplements AIRMETs and SIGMETs by identifying areas of current icing potential. It's not intended to be a substitute for the intensity and forecast information that's contained in AIRMET's and SIGMETs.

By clicking the 9,000 foot base level (position A), an icing potential plot (position B) is generated. As colors tend toward red, the icing potential increases. This information, coupled with AIRMET and SIGMET icing intensity and forecast data, allows you to obtain a three dimensional idea about the likelihood of icing along your route of flight.

won't get much worse given the convective activity to the northwest. We need more information.

The Details

It's time to get a little more specific by checking the area forecast for more details and any AIRMETs and SIGMETs of interest. AIRMETs and SIGMETs essentially amend the area forecast. This is why we look at the area forecast first, and then see if, when, and how it has been amended. This sequence gives us a better idea of how the weather's evolving. We can check for the downloaded textual weather by clicking the textual weather tab above our downloaded charts (Figure 31, position A). The textual weather is now shown to the left.

Let's begin with the area forecast first. The *synopsis* section (Figure 31, position B and Figure 32) is valid until 1500Z on the 11th and it indicates that there's a large, closed low pressure center on its way bringing a lot of moisture to our destination area. A stationary and occluded front are expected, too. OK, that's good to know. Let's continue with the *clouds and weather* section (Figure 31, position B), which is valid until 0900Z. Keep in mind that our expected departure time is 0100Z.

The clouds and weather forecast for central and northern California (Figure 33, position C) shows that the San Joaquin valley of central California (where Bakersfield is located) will have scattered clouds at 2,000 feet MSL, a broken cloud layer from 3,000 to 5,000 feet MSL with layers up to FL 200. There will also be isolated thunderstorms (single cells) with light rain showers with widely scattered light rain showers (over less than 25% of the area) in the region. Cumulonimbus tops will rise to FL270.

By 0100Z to 0300Z, approximately the time that we expect to be airborne, the clouds are forecast to become an overcast condition between 2,000 and 3,000 feet MSL. This doesn't inspire confidence that we can make any portion of this flight above the clouds to circumnavigate the convective weather. Nor does it offer a lot of hope that we could remain clear of the clouds, and minimize our chances of encountering icing along our route.

Remembering my recommendation from an earlier chapter, we'll want to compare the area forecast to the prog chart (Figure 33). Evaluating these charts together helps us to develop a three-dimensional idea of where the cloud coverage might be changing. The shape marked by a green hatched line (Figure 33, position D) indicates moderate rain covers more than half the circled area. That circle shows the extent of the affected area, as indicated by the area forecast's synopsis (Figure 32).

We still need more information about the cloud coverage along our route so let's examine the weather depiction chart excerpt taken from the National Weather Service's

The Weather Depiction Chart   ## The Radar Summary Chart

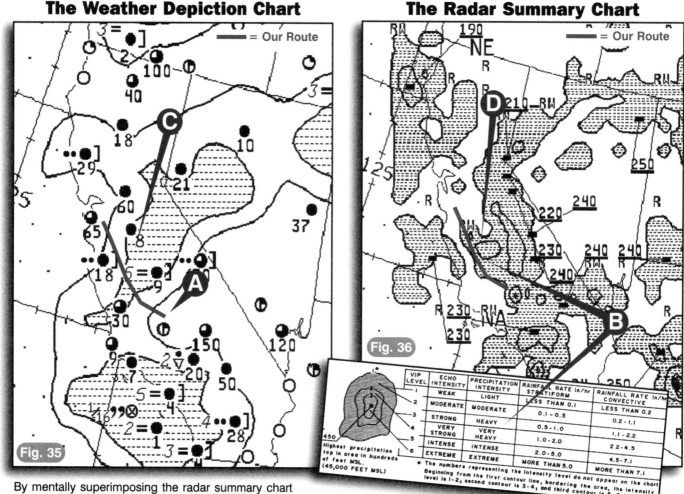

By mentally superimposing the radar summary chart
onto the weather depiction chart you're able to obtain a three dimensional idea
of how the atmosphere looks. It appears that our flight (the red line), while heading northward, will take us
over an area of decreasing ceilings (as shown on the weather depiction chart). This appears to coincide with the increasing
radar return levels shown on the radar summary chart indicating that the radar returns are sources of precipitation.

site (Figure 35). The station models along the route show that most of central California has broken-to-overcast cloud coverage, with ceilings ranging from 800 to 2,000 feet AGL. This chart also shows you some areas of VFR weather. This is always a good thing to know in case you experienced a complete electrical failure and had to make your way on your own for a letdown through the clouds to VFR Weather. Flying IFR is about knowing your options, and creating them when necessary. If you don't have some options in your bag when you get ready to depart, don't depart. The good news here is that we appear to begin our flight in one of those VFR areas (Figure 35, position A). This implies that we might be able to depart with sufficient cloud clearance to take a look at the weather and evaluate whether or not we can visually avoid those isolated thunderstorms and remain out of clouds while operating at or below the freezing level. The bad news is that the cloud coverage appears to increase and the ceilings appear to decrease as we head north. To better understand what we see on rod weather depiction chart we should compare it with the radar summary chart.

Figure 36 is a radar summary chart excerpt for the same area. There is an extensive area of echoes (not

canyon echoes, either...either...either) in the central portion of California. According to the radar summary chart legend, at least some portion of our planned flight will be in close proximity to Level 3 or 4 weather activity (Figure 36, position C). While the radar summary chart can be an hour or more old, it does tell you about the present convective potential of the air.

The secret to obtaining a three-dimensional image of how the atmosphere looks is to mentally superimpose the radar summary chart on top of the weather depiction chart on the left (if you've spent too much time watching TV you may not be able to imagine any more and will be forced to hold one chart slightly above the other to see the comparison). Doing this allows you to have a rough idea of how extensive the cloud coverage is horizontally and how extensive the water is vertically. It does appear that the middle portion of our route will be in the clouds and through at least Level 1 and 2 weather while closely skirting Levels 3 and 4 weather located to the east. It's also appears that the areas with the lowest ceilings (Figure 35, position C) on the weather depiction chart are co-located with the increasing storm levels on the radar summary chart (Figure 36, position D). Now let's take a look at the potential for icing along our route.

AIRMET Coverage Area

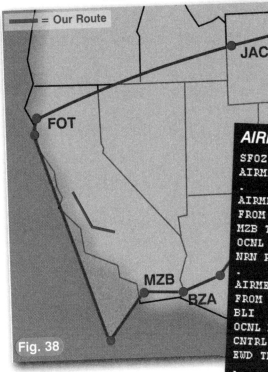

= Our Route

RAP
JAC
BFF
FOT
MZB
BZA

Fig. 38

Figure 37 is AIRMET Zulu for ice and freezing levels. There is an extensive area of moderate rime or mixed icing in clouds and precipitation forecast between the freezing level and FL220. The area where this is expected to occur is roughly depicted in Figure 38 by the area within the brown line that connects the defining VOR

stations. According to Figure 37, position E, the freezing level in central California is from the surface to 7,000 feet MSL. This alone makes our instrument flight a bad proposition if we don't have an airplane certified for flight into known icing conditions (this means the airplane is equipped with anti- or de-ice equipment and has been flight tested in known icing conditions).

AIRMET Zulu: Freezing and Ice

Fig. 37

```
SF0Z WA 102045
AIRMET ZULU UPDT 3 FOR ICE AND FRZLVL VALID UNTIL 110300

AIRMET ICE...CA AND CSTL WTRS ID WY NV UT CO AZ NM
FROM 70NNW RAP TO BFF TO GLD TO 50W LBL TO FMN TO PHX TO BZA TO
MZB TO 210SW MZB TO 130WSW FOT TO 130WNW FOT TO JAC TO 70NNW RAP
OCNL MOD RIME OR MXD ICGICIP BTN FRZLVL AND FL220. FRZLVL SFC-080
NRN PTN..RSG 080-110 SRN PTN. CONDS CONTG BYD 03Z THRU 09Z.

AIRMET ICE...WA OR AND CSTL WTRS ID MT
FROM BLI TO 30N FCA TO JAC TO 130WNW FOT TO 100WNW ONP TO TOU TO
BLI
OCNL MOD RIME OR MXD ICGICIP BTN FRZLVL AND 160. FRZLVL SFC-070
CNTRL AND ERN PTN..030-050 WRN PTN. CONDS CONTG BYD 03Z SPRDG
EWD THRU 09Z.
.
FRZLVL...WA..020-035 W OF CASCDS SFC-030 ELSW.
    OR..025-045 W OF CASCDS SFC-050 ELSW.
    NRN CA..WRN 040-050 ERN SFC-050.
    CNTRL CA..SIERNEV SFC-070 ELSW 050 NRN TO 090 SRN.
    SRN CA..085-115.
```

E

An AIRMET is a significant weather addition to the area forecast. It's issued for a maximum six hour period and you should always compare it with the area forecast to obtain a better understanding of the overall weather picture. The AIRMET above indicates that icing exists both in the clouds and in precipitation all along our route.

The National Weather Service's ADDS Flight Path Tool

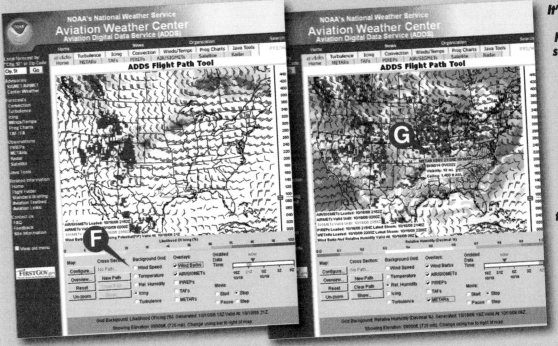

It's hard to find any weather source that rivals the NWS's *Flight Path Tool*. By selecting the turbulence or icing tabs, you'll have a choice to choose the Java *Flight Path Tool*. This allows you to overlay the atmospheric conditions selected by the bottom buttons (position F) on your flight path to better understand how the weather will affect you. For instance, by selecting the relative humidity button and the wind barb, AIRMET, SIGMET and METAR buttons, you'll be able to see how areas of high humidity are related to the weather at any location over which you move your mouse cursor (position G).

At this point we just don't have enough information to decide if it would even be possible to depart on an IFR flight plan and climb above or fly between layers in VMC conditions. Doing so would allow us to visually avoid convective buildups and possibly avoid icing. On the other hand, there is *icing in precipitation* and this is technically defined as a possible encounter with supercooled rain drops inside or outside of a cloud. The only way to handle this problem is to have sufficient horizontal cloud clearance so as to avoid rain showers. It certainly doesn't look good for the home team here but let's continue with our analysis.

According to AIRMET Tango (Figure 39), we can expect occasional moderate turbulence below 12,000 feet MSL in the area shown in Figure 40. This just happens to cover the entire route we're expecting to fly. Moderate turbulence isn't necessarily a show-stopper for most instrument pilots. This type of turbulence isn't risky in the sense that it could destroy an airplane. It just doesn't make flying very comfortable. On the other hand, the forecast for moderate turbulence doesn't apply to the inside of any thunderstorm that we might run into. Elvis must have been in a thunderstorm when he penned the words for "All Shook Up."

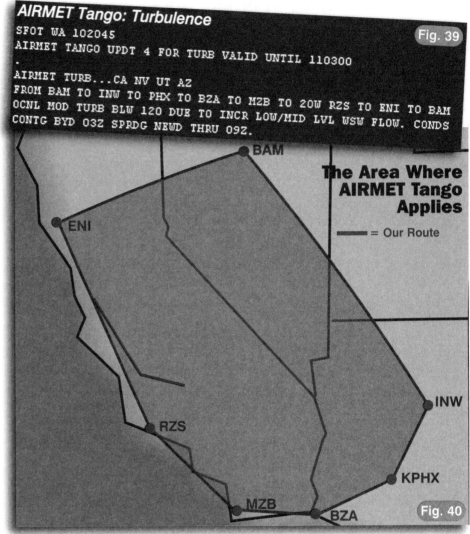

AIRMET Tango: Turbulence

Fig. 39

```
SFOT WA 102045
AIRMET TANGO UPDT 4 FOR TURB VALID UNTIL 110300
.
AIRMET TURB...CA NV UT AZ
FROM BAM TO INW TO PHX TO BZA TO MZB TO 20W RZS TO ENI TO BAM
OCNL MOD TURB BLW 120 DUE TO INCR LOW/MID LVL WSW FLOW. CONDS
CONTG BYD 03Z SPRDG NEWD THRU 09Z.
```

The Area Where AIRMET Tango Applies

═══ = Our Route

Fig. 40

The area within the brown line is the affected area where occasional moderate turbulence may be found below 12,000 feet MSL until 0300Z.

Inside one of those monsters you're sure to experience a lot worse than moderate turbulence. That's why I avoid these weather beasts by *at least 20 nm* and recommend that you do the same.

At this point, if you really want to know wazzup in the atmosphere, you need to check for pilot reports. PIREPS can tell you very important things, such as if anyone is actually flying in the weather, which might mean that this person is very brave, very ignorant, or knows something that you don't

NOAA's National Weather Service
Aviation Weather Center
Aviation Digital Data Service (ADDS)

Home

Local forecast by "City, St" or Zip Code
City, St Go

@dds | Turbulence | Icing | Convecti
Home | METARs | TAFs | PIREPs

Advisories
SIGMET/AIRMET »
Center Weather

Forecasts
Convection »
Turbulence
Icing
Winds/Temps »
Prog Charts »
TAF / FA »

Observations
PIREPs »
METARs »
Radar »
Satellite »

Java Tools »

Related Information
Home »
Flight Folder
Standard Briefing
Aviation Testbed
Aviation Links

Contact Us
FAQ
Feedback »

• Interactive PIREPs Java Tool

• Plot of PIREPs:
  ○ Icing
  ⊙ Turbulence
  ○ Weather/Sky

Northwest | NorthCentral | NorthEast
Contiguous U.S.
SouthWest | SouthCentral | SouthEast
Alaska

Fig. 41

Pilot Reports (PIREPs) of Icing

═══ = Our Route

There are no pilot reports along our route in western California. Either none have been offered or no pilots are flying in that area.

Fig. 42

ICE TYPE: ∨ = RIME   + = CLEAR   — = MIXED
∅ NEG   ∨ TRACE-LGT   ✦ LGT-MOD   ∨ MOD-SEV
∪ TRACE   ∪ LGT   ∨ MOD   ∨ SEV

Clear form

about the weather (such as it not being as bad as forecast).

One of my favorite places to go for PIREPS is the NWS's *Aviation Digital Data Service* site (Figure 41). By clicking the PIREPs tab, you can select a visual representation of PIREPS for turbulence, sky conditions, weather, and icing. Figure 42 will show any icing PIREPS for the western half of the United States. From the looks of it, there aren't any PIREPS available. This is a case where no news isn't necessarily good news. My conclusion would be that nobody's up there to make a pilot report.

Realistically speaking, if you're an instrument rated pilot and refuse to fly at the mere mention of thunderstorms or icing, then you'll probably need to hangar your airplane for at least six or seven months out of every year. That's the typical length of thunderstorm and icing season in many parts of the country. This certainly isn't a way to make that investment in training or in an airplane pay off. The fact is that there's nothing wrong with flying when thunderstorms and ice are predicted as long as you can *avoid* those bad boys.

Since most folks don't have weather radar or deicing equipment on their airplanes, the only option is to fly IFR in such a way that you limit your exposure to these weather conditions. That means you must get out of the clouds to see the thunderstorms and avoid the ice. If there is no convective activity near the airport and you can climb above the clouds, then you can fly to your destination using your eyeballs as storm detection equipment. Even if there is a thin layer of potentially ice-laden clouds above you and the cloud base is high enough, it may be reasonable to climb above those clouds to the clear air where ice won't form. In some parts of the northwest United States where icing is a serious problem, ATC allows pilots to climb in holding patterns to VMC above the clouds. If the pilot feels the icing is serious before he gets on top, he can descend in the pattern to VMC below. Keep in mind that this isn't for everyone and it takes experience and good judgment to use these types of procedures. You'll have to make this call but at least it's nice to know that you may have options when the weather forecast seems stingy in offering them.

It's time to look at the terminal forecast and see whether or not a climb to visual conditions is even possible at Bakersfield.

The Forecast Weather at 0100Z for BFL

This is what the forecast weather at 0100Z might look like at Bakersfield.

Photos courtesy of Microsoft Flight Simulator X

Bakersfield's Terminal Forecast

```
TERMINAL FORECASTS
TAF KBFL 102320Z 110024 VRB03KT P6SM SCT020 BKN040 OVC200
   FM0800 03007KT 5SM -RA BR SCT020 OVC040 PROB30 0915 2SM RA BR
OVC020
   FM1600 36008KT 6SM -SHRA BR OVC030
   FM1800 36008KT P6SM SCT020 BKN030 PROB30 2124 2SM TSRA
BKN020CB
```

Fig. 43

The terminal forecast for Bakersfield indicates that, at 0100Z, our proposed departure time, the 2,000 foot AGL scattered and 4,000 foot AGL broken cloud layer might make it difficult to fly our route in VMC conditions (remember, our cruising altitude is 8,000 feet minimum and Bakersfield's elevation is 507 feet MSL).

According to the terminal forecast for Bakersfield (Figure 43), broken clouds are expected at 4,000 feet AGL from 0000Z to 0800Z. After 0800Z, there should be an overcast condition at 4,000 feet AGL. We still won't have sufficient working room to allow us to climb on top of the clouds and circumnavigate any convective activity visually, while avoiding the potential for icing.

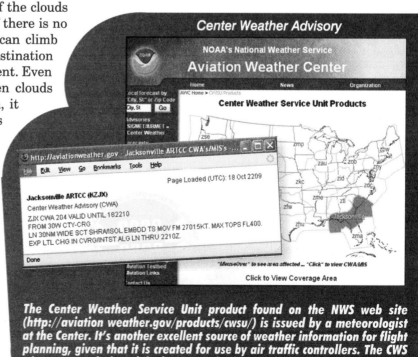

The Center Weather Service Unit product found on the NWS web site (http://aviation weather.gov/products/cwsu/) is issued by a meteorologist at the Center. It's another excellent source of weather information for flight planning, given that it is created for use by air traffic controllers. The CWS is an accumulation of the latest monitoring, analysis and interpretation of real time weather. It just doesn't get much better than this. Use it!

What about the forecast weather in the San Jose area? From the terminal forecast in Figure 44, it appears that San Jose will have broken clouds at 4,000 feet AGL and overcast clouds at 6,000 feet AGL until 0500Z, when the broken ceilings will lower to 3,000 feet AGL (the authorities are not working to fix those broken clouds ASAP, either). Once again, you can't find too much hope that the weather is going to improve enough in the near term to consider actually making this IFR flight.

Conservatively speaking, it's fairly clear that this flight just isn't going to depart at 0100Z. Although we've collected a great deal of data, there just isn't enough information for us to know that we could remain clear of clouds to avoid the isolated thunderstorms and the icing that's forecast in both the clouds and in precipitation. Now, I'm all for going ahead and taking a look as long as you have a guaranteed way out of trouble and are willing to divert if you come across impenetrable weather. But there's no evidence that you have those options at this time. So I've concluded (your mileage may vary, of course) that this flight is a no go at 0100Z.

Of course, I chose to flight plan during a time when the thunderstorm and icing potential made this flight unreasonable. Despite that fact, the entire process of flight planning and weather analysis so far is the same for any IFR flight you'll make, even when the weather is much better. Nevertheless, you'll often find that there will be times when you just don't have enough information to make an informed go/no-go decision. Welcome to the real world. Now you have a few of your own leaves on your forehead like the cartoon guy from the first page of this chapter.

Perhaps the best question to ask now is when will it be a good time to fly this trip? To find out, we need to look at an extended forecast for the area.

The Forecast Weather at 0206Z for SJC

This is what the forecast weather at 0206Z might look like at San Jose.

Photos courtesy of Microsoft Flight Simulator X

San Jose's Terminal Forecast

```
TAF KSJC 102354Z 110024 17010KT P6SM SCT025 BKN040 OVC060 TEMPO
    0105 5SM RA BKN030 BKN040
    FM0500 21010KT 6SM -RA BKN030 OVC060
    FM2100 31008KT P6SM -RA BKN030 OVC060
TAF KSAC 102343Z 110024 15008KT P6SM SCT018 BKN050 TEMPO 0002
    BKN018
    FM0200 17010G20KT 5SM -RA BR OVC030 TEMPO 0408 2SM RA BR
    OVC018
    FM0800 16010KT 6SM -RA OVC040
    FM1400 15006KT 5SM BR OVC040 TEMPO 1418 2SM -RA BR
    BKN020
    FM1800 19005KT P6SM -SHRA SCT010 BKN060
```
Fig. 44

The terminal forecast for San Jose indicates that at 0206Z, our proposed arrival time, there will be a 3,000 foot broken ceiling and a 4,000 foot broken ceiling with more than six miles visibility. This is excellent weather at the destination (if we could just get there).

The 24-hour surface prog that we downloaded previously is shown in Figure 45. The valid time for this chart is 1200Z and we were originally planning a 0100Z departure. It appears that there is still an area of continuous rain covering less than half the area in the middle portion of California (the green line in Figure 45, position A, isn't shaded, meaning the precipitation is expected to cover less than half the area). It looks like the low pressure system will most likely propel a cold frontal system through the area (even though fronts don't have propellers). With the movement of the weather to the east, it's possible that the freezing level and thunderstorms

Weather: Bones About It?

The crowd on the porch is discussing whether or not the weather is going to stay good enough for cross-country flying, as there are many towering cumulus clouds building. They'd consulted the NEXRAD in the school's weather room. They'd called the FSS. They'd solicited PIREPs from returning pilots.

Grandma, hearing all this, decides to put her opinion into the mix.

"It's not going to rain," she announces. "My bones aren't hurting."

Whereupon all the pilots on the porch immediately decide to go flying.

The 24 Hour Surface Prog Chart

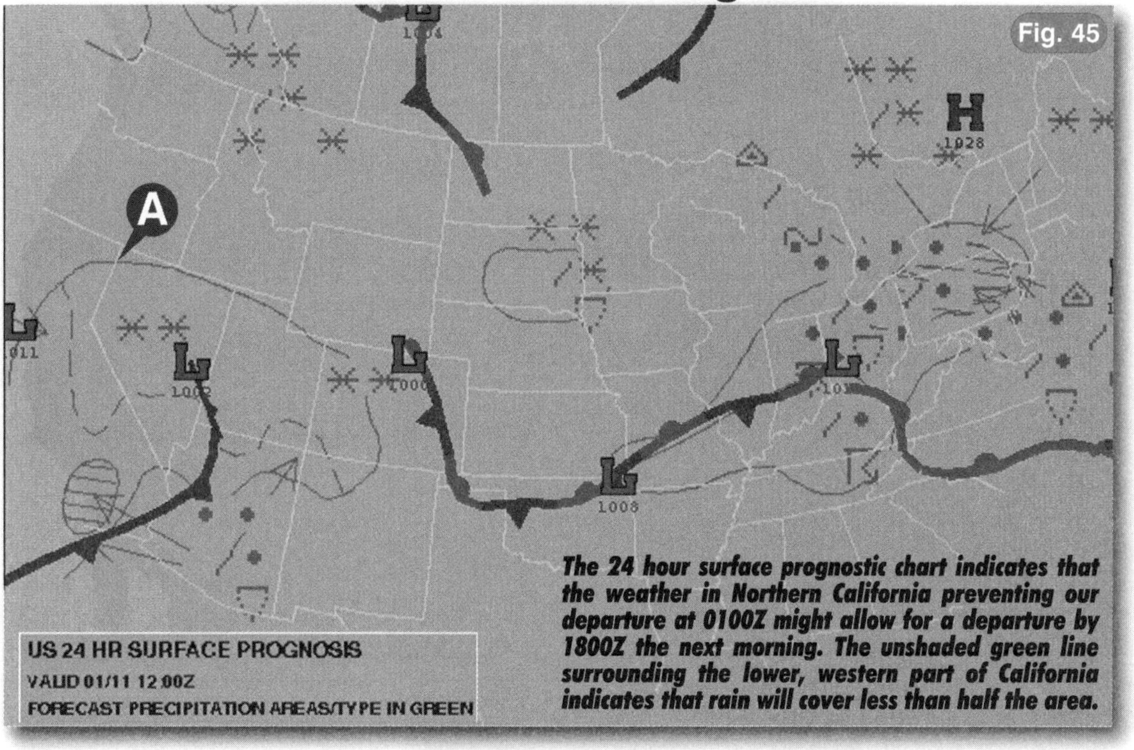

Fig. 45

US 24 HR SURFACE PROGNOSIS
VALID 01/11 12:00Z
FORECAST PRECIPITATION AREAS/TYPE IN GREEN

The 24 hour surface prognostic chart indicates that the weather in Northern California preventing our departure at 0100Z might allow for a departure by 1800Z the next morning. The unshaded green line surrounding the lower, western part of California indicates that rain will cover less than half the area.

won't be a problem and we might be able to make this flight by 1200Z. Then again, that's 4 a.m. local time. I'm normally in my Spiderman pajamas by this time, and since it's illegal to fly in superhero pajamas (it intimidates other pilots), it might be best to delay the flight until the next day.

What if?

Of course, we could stop our flight planning here but we'd have to forgo a lot of useful information about flight planning. This is, after all, what this chapter is all about. What if we assume, for the purposes of continuity in completing the flight planning process, that, while IFR conditions persist enroute, there were no thunderstorms and no icing forecast that would prevent this flight? Given this new assumption, let's plan on departing at our original time of 0100Z.

We should then consider checking all the appropriate NOTAMs for our route of flight. Remember, we're doing this as an exercise to learn about flight planning. We really wouldn't make the flight under the previously discussed weather conditions. Figure 46 is the list of NOTAMs received when we downloaded the weather. Looking them over carefully, there doesn't appear to be any item on the list that would affect our flight.

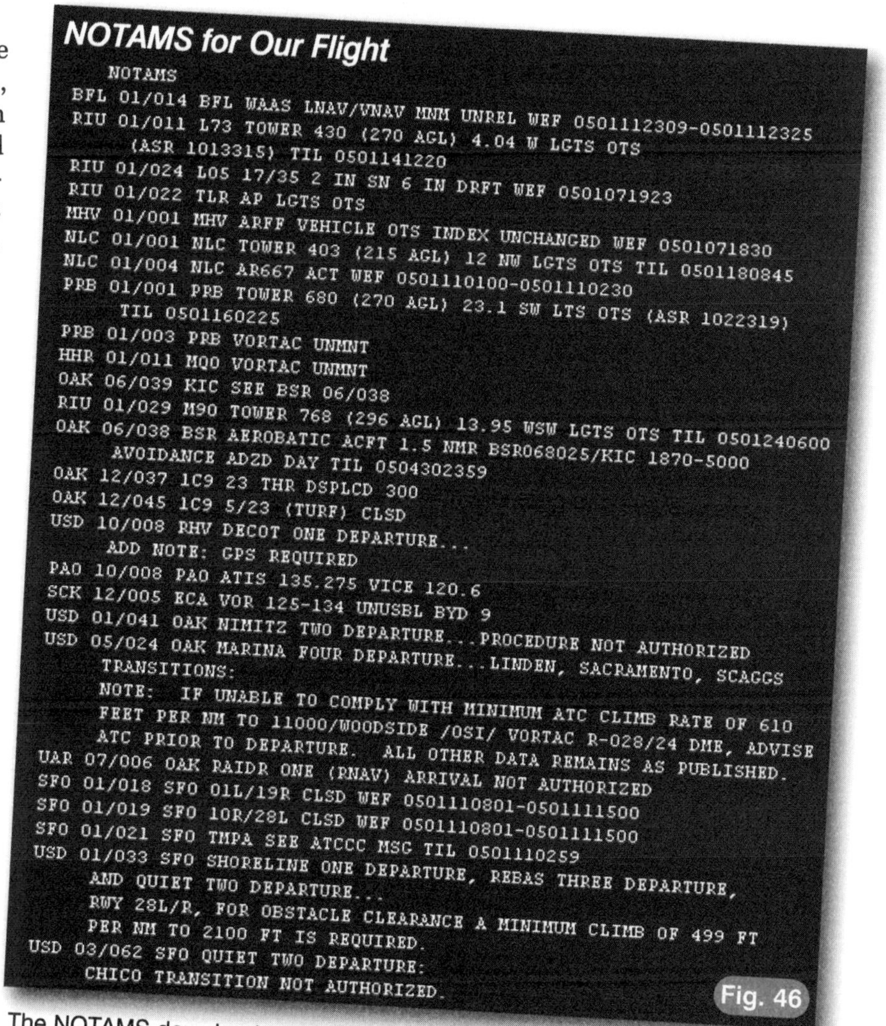

NOTAMS for Our Flight

```
NOTAMS
BFL 01/014 BFL WAAS LNAV/VNAV MNM UNREL WEF 0501112309-0501112325
RIU 01/011 L73 TOWER 430 (270 AGL) 4.04 W LGTS OTS
    (ASR 1013315) TIL 0501141220
RIU 01/024 LO5 17/35 2 IN SN 6 IN DRFT WEF 0501071923
RIU 01/022 TLR AP LGTS OTS
MHV 01/001 MHV ARFF VEHICLE OTS INDEX UNCHANGED WEF 0501071830
NLC 01/001 NLC TOWER 403 (215 AGL) 12 NW LGTS OTS TIL 0501180845
NLC 01/004 NLC AR667 ACT WEF 0501110100-0501110230
PRB 01/001 PRB TOWER 680 (270 AGL) 23.1 SW LTS OTS (ASR 1022319)
    TIL 0501160225
PRB 01/003 PRB VORTAC UNMNT
HHR 01/011 MQO VORTAC UNMNT
OAK 06/039 KIC SEE BSR 06/038
RIU 01/029 M90 TOWER 768 (296 AGL) 13.95 WSW LGTS OTS TIL 0501240600
OAK 06/038 BSR AEROBATIC ACFT 1.5 NMR BSR068025/KIC 1870-5000
    AVOIDANCE ADZD DAY TIL 0504302359
OAK 12/037 1C9 23 THR DSPLCD 300
OAK 12/045 1C9 5/23 (TURF) CLSD
USD 10/008 RHV DECOT ONE DEPARTURE...
    ADD NOTE: GPS REQUIRED
PAO 10/008 PAO ATIS 135.275 VICE 120.6
SCK 12/005 ECA VOR 125-134 UNUSBL BYD 9
USD 01/041 OAK NIMITZ TWO DEPARTURE...PROCEDURE NOT AUTHORIZED
USD 05/024 OAK MARINA FOUR DEPARTURE...LINDEN, SACRAMENTO, SCAGGS
    TRANSITIONS:
    NOTE: IF UNABLE TO COMPLY WITH MINIMUM ATC CLIMB RATE OF 610
    FEET PER NM TO 11000/WOODSIDE /OSI/ VORTAC R-028/24 DME, ADVISE
    ATC PRIOR TO DEPARTURE. ALL OTHER DATA REMAINS AS PUBLISHED.
UAR 07/006 OAK RAIDR ONE (RNAV) ARRIVAL NOT AUTHORIZED
SFO 01/018 SFO 01L/19R CLSD WEF 0501110801-0501111500
SFO 01/019 SFO 10R/28L CLSD WEF 0501110801-0501111500
SFO 01/021 SFO TMPA SEE ATCCC MSG TIL 0501110259
USD 01/033 SFO SHORELINE ONE DEPARTURE, REBAS THREE DEPARTURE,
    AND QUIET TWO DEPARTURE...
    RWY 28L/R, FOR OBSTACLE CLEARANCE A MINIMUM CLIMB OF 499 FT
    PER NM TO 2100 FT IS REQUIRED.
USD 03/062 SFO QUIET TWO DEPARTURE:
    CHICO TRANSITION NOT AUTHORIZED.
```

Fig. 46

The NOTAMS downloaded during our weather briefing don't list any airport or navaid that will affect our flight plan.

Figure 47 lists the FDC NOTAMs for our flight. If we assume that our airplane has an IFR certified GPS on board as well as ADF and DME, then there are two FDC NOTAM that pertain to us.

The FDC NOTAM that's relevant to us references the sixth amendment of the approach chart (Figure 47, position A), and when we look at the bottom left hand corner of the actual NDB/DME Rwy 30L approach, we see that it lists amendment number 5A (Figure 48, position C). Therefore, this chart has not been updated yet, making this FDC NOTAM relevant to us. We want to make a note on the chart of the increase in MDAs to 780 feet as shown. This suffices to meet our obligation of having current charts (of course, when a new chart is issued, that works even better).

Note that the rest of this NOTAM references Category C and D minimums. You're a big boy, but that's probably not you unless mom and dad bought you that Boeing 777 you saw in the magazine for your birthday. Lucky you!

We should also update the RNAV (GPS) Rwy 11 approach, too (Figure 49). Notice that the FDC NOTAM amendment version (Figure 49, position B) is the same as that shown on the RNAV chart (Figure 49, position D) or *Orig-A*. This means that the NOTAM may be temporary and doesn't justify a new issuance of an approach chart. Looking at the San Jose FDC NOTAMS, there's a temporary crane in the vicinity and this may be the reason for the circling MDA increase to 700 feet as I've drawn in the minimums section of Figure 33D.

There are other NOTAMs you should also pay attention to that might be important. Please read the Notices to Airmen (NOTAMs) sidebar to refresh your knowledge on the subject.

FDC NOTAMS for San Jose

```
FDC 4/0435 SJC FI/T NORMAN Y. MINETA SAN JOSE INTL,
    SAN JOSE, CA.
    NDB/DME RWY 30L, AMDT 6.                                 A
    S-30L MDA 780/HAT 723 ALL CATS.  VIS CAT C 1 1/2, CAT D 2.
    SIDESTEP RWY 29 MDA 780/HAT 728 ALL CATS.  VIS CAT C 2,
    CAT D 2 1/4.
    SIDESTEP RWY 30R MDA 780/HAT 725 ALL CATS.  VIS CAT C 2,
    CAT D 2 1/4.
    TEMPORARY CRANE 426 FT MSL 1.62 NM EAST OF RWY 30R.
FDC 4/1053 SJC FI/T NORMAN Y. MINETA SAN JOSE INTL, SAN JOSE, CA.
    RNAV (GPS) RWY 11, ORIG-A...
    LNAV MDA 480/HAT 433 ALL CATS VIS CAT D 1 1/2.             B
    CIRCLING CAT A MDA 700/HAA 641, CAT D MDA 780/HAA 721. VIS
    CAT C 2, CAT D 2 1/4.
```
Fig. 47

FDC (National Flight Data Center) NOTAMS are regulatory changes affecting instrument charts. Despite planning to fly the ILS Runway 30 approach to San Jose, we should still ensure the other approach charts are updated with appropriate FDC NOTAMS. There's always a possibility that we might be required to fly a different approach upon our arrival. The crane at 426 feet MSL located 1.62 miles east of Runway 30R is noteworthy, too.

Amendment to the SJC NDB/DME 30L Approach

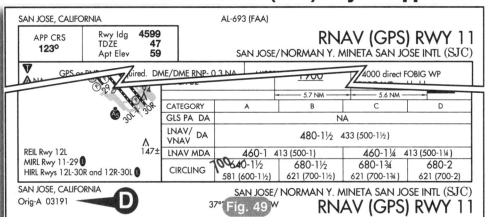

The FDC NOTAM above (Figure 47, position A), is the 6th amendment to the SJC NDB/DME Rwy 30L approach. The NDB/DME approach chart (Figure 48, position C), indicates a lesser number, meaning that we need to make a note of these changes on the chart.

Amendment to the SJC RNAV (GPS) Rwy 11 Approach

The FDC NOTAM above (Figure 47, position B), is the "Orig-A" or *original* issuance of this chart. The chart above (Figure 49, position D) shows the same Amendment value. Therefore, this NOTAM is probably temporary and doesn't justify a new issuance of the approach chart. Nevertheless, you need to make note of the MDA change.

Notices To Airmen (NOTAMs)

When there are significant and important changes in aeronautical information, you need to know about them. This becomes especially important when that information might affect the safety of your flight. Such safety-of-flight information is conveyed to pilots as Notices to Airmen (NOTAMs).

NOTAMs contain information such as airport or primary runway closures, changes in the status of navigational aids, radar service availability and other information essential to planned enroute, terminal or landing operations. When such information is not known far enough in advance to be included in the *Airport/Facility Directory*, it's likely to have at least a brief career as a NOTAM.

There are three types of NOTAMs you should be familiar with: NOTAM D, NOTAM L, and FDC NOTAMs. Let's examine all three.

NOTAM D–NOTAM D is information that is given distant (D) distribution from its generating source. In other words, any aviation information relating to and affecting IFR operations (i.e., approach light outages, navigation facilities, frequency changes, etc.) as well as public use airports listed in the *A/FD* is distributed via this distant NOTAM service.

All this information is kept in a big computer (a little bigger than the one you have at home) in Atlanta, GA and is distributed automatically via several sources. The FSS has the capability of providing you with these NOTAMs during your weather briefing.

FDC NOTAMs–Occasionally, it becomes necessary to issue information on changes that are regulatory in nature. A regulatory change might be an amendment to an instrument chart used by IFR pilots or the issuance of a temporary flight restriction (like prohibition of flight over a natural disaster area). When such an action is necessary, the National Flight Data Center (NFDC) will issue an FDC NOTAM (See Figure 47).

FDC NOTAMs are issued once and kept on file at the FSS until published (like NOTAM Ds) or canceled. FSSs are responsible for maintaining a file of current, unpublished FDC NOTAMs concerning conditions within 400 miles of their facilities. FDC NOTAM information concerning conditions that are more than 400 miles from the FSS, or that are already published, is given to a pilot only on request. During your weather briefing, make sure you also ask the FSS specialist for any pertinent FDC NOTAM information concerning your flight. If you use a computer vendor for your official weather briefing, you must (as we did in Figure 18), check to ensure you download the FDC NOTAMs.

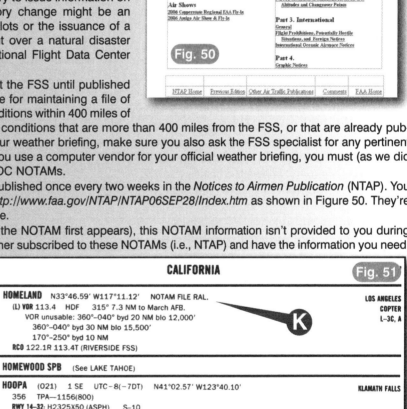

Fig. 50

Keep in mind that both D and FDC NOTAMs are published once every two weeks in the *Notices to Airmen Publication* (NTAP). You can view these NOTAMS on the FAA's web site at *http://www.faa.gov/NTAP/NTAP06SEP28/Index.htm* as shown in Figure 50. They're also available at a FSS if you happen to be near one.

Once published (generally about two weeks after the NOTAM first appears), this NOTAM information isn't provided to you during your weather briefing. It's assumed that you have either subscribed to these NOTAMs (i.e., NTAP) and have the information you need, or that you have acquired the information from some other source. The problem is that some of these NOTAMs remain in effect for extended periods of time (e.g., a VOR you want to use may be down for several weeks). If you want to know about any published NOTAMs, and don't have internet access (because electricity and wires scare you), then you must specifically ask the FSS specialist for the published NOTAMs that affect your flight.

NOTAM L–NOTAM L provides you with information on a local (L) level. This information consists of taxiway closures, personnel and equipment near or crossing runways, airport rotating beacons outages and airport lighting aids that do not affect IFR operations (such as a VASI outage). When you call your local AFSS, you'll receive L NOTAMS for only the area covered by that specific FSS. In other words, you won't find NOTAM L information at FSS locations beyond the local area. A separate file of NOTAM L information is maintained at each FSS for facilities in their service area only. If you want the local NOTAMs for the area you'll visit, you have to call the FSS having responsibility for that area ahead of time (DUATS doesn't provide NOTAM L information). How do you know what the AFSS number is? Simply call the local FSS on (800) WX-BRIEF and ask. Another way to identify the FSS having jurisdiction over your destination airport is to look at the *Airport/Facility Directory*. Figure 51 shows that the NOTAM files for Homeland (position K) and Hoopa (position L) airports are located at the Riverside (RAL) and Arcata (ACV) FSS respectively.

GPS NOTAMs can also be had by calling your local FSS. GPS NOTAMs essentially consist of satellite outages that prevent you from having sufficient RAIM coverage at your destination ETA to legally fly the approach. No, the FAA specialist won't tell you where the satellites are, either (OK, look up and to your left. Can you see it?)

Our next consideration would be selecting an alternate airport. According to our flight log (Figure 52), a rough estimate for time enroute is one hour and six minutes. (Once of the very nice features of AOPA's flight planner is that it automatically calculates the headings and groundspeeds based on an initial assessment of the current winds. If you download the winds aloft, the flight planner will automatically update the heading and groundspeeds for you in the flight log.) We anticipate arriving at San Jose at 0209Z. The question is, are we required to have an alternate for this flight?

Do you remember our 1-2-3 rule regarding alternate airport requirements from our discussion on regulations? If our destination airport, one hour before and one hour after our anticipated arrival, is expected to have a ceiling less than 2,000 feet or a visibility of less than 3 miles, then we're required to list an alternate on our flight plan.

What's the weather we can expect at San Jose between 0109Z and 0309Z? Looking at the terminal forecast again (see Figure 44, page 16-24) for San Jose, it appears that between 0100Z and 0500Z there's a temporary condition expected where the ceilings will be 3,000 feet broken with a visibility of 5 miles. According to this report, we don't need to list an alternate on our flight plan. But let's assume we did need to include an alternate. How do we know if Sacramento Executive would be a legitimate choice for an alternate?

To find out, we must look at the approach chart we'll use for Sacramento Executive and see if non-standard alternate minimums apply, or if the airport is even available to be listed as an alternate. Figure 53 shows the briefing strips for the three approaches into Sacramento Executive. Two of the approaches show a black triangle with the white letter "A" inside (see sidebar *Alternate Not Authorized* to find out how to tell when an airport or approach can't be used as an alternate). This means that some form of non-standard alternate minimums apply at this airport. To find out

Our completed Nav Log to San Jose

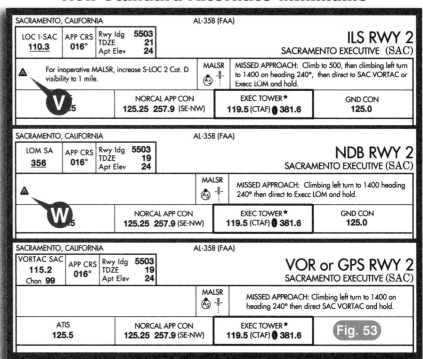

When the weather reports are downloaded, the flight planner applies the actual winds aloft and calculates your ETE.

Section E-NACO Booklet

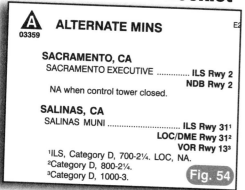

If your alternate ETA occurs when the tower is closed at Sacramento, neither the ILS Rwy 2 or the NDB Rwy 2 approach can be used to evaluate the suitability of Sacramento's weather for listing Sacramento as an alternate on your flight plan.

Non-Standard Alternate Minimums

The "A" in the black triangle indicates that non-standard alternate minimums apply for these approaches in evaluating Sacramento's alternate suitability.

Alternate Not Authorized

Suppose you were checking to see if an instrument approach at an airport was allowed to be used as an alternate and saw the letter "A" in a triangle with the letters "NA" next to it as shown in Figure 55, position Z below. The letters "NA" mean that this approach is not authorized as an alternate. It's possible that another approach at the same airport could be allowed as an alternate. Or not.

In the case of Marina, no approach at the airport is valid as an alternate. Why? Most likely because there isn't an official weather reporting service at the airport to help you determine the weather at critical times, such as when you're low on fuel and must decide if there's a good chance of getting into the airport. So be careful not to assume that just because an instrument approach exists at an airport that this airport or approach is legal to use as an alternate.

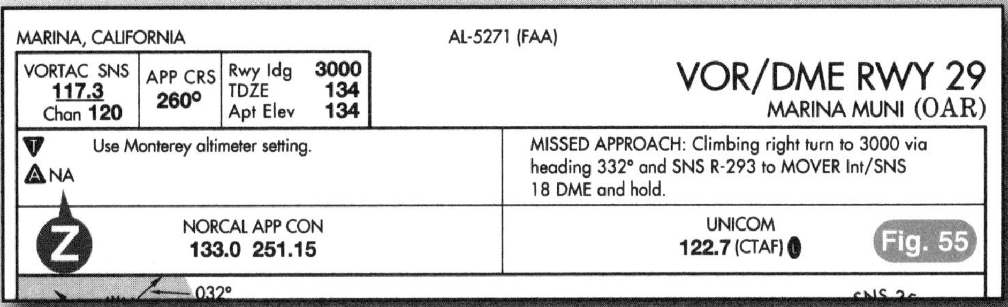

You might be thinking, "What happens if there's no viable alternate within range?" Well, that makes you the Lone Ranger without his horse, because without an alternate (assuming one is required), you have no alternative but to cancel or wait for the weather to change.

Here's one that will win you a round or two in the hangar trivia game. True

Fig. 55

or false, an airport has to have *some* instrument approach in order to be used as an alternate? And your final answer is? False, true? Yes, it's true that it's false. You can list an airport as an alternate even if it doesn't have an instrument approach. You must, however, be able to descend from the airway MEA and land in VFR conditions. This is obviously a much more stringent weather requirement than 600-2 and 800-2. Many times, though, airports just a few miles apart can have very different weather conditions. This is particularly true where you have an airport near an ocean, and a nearby airport in an inland valley. The former can be closed by fog while the sun's shining at the latter.

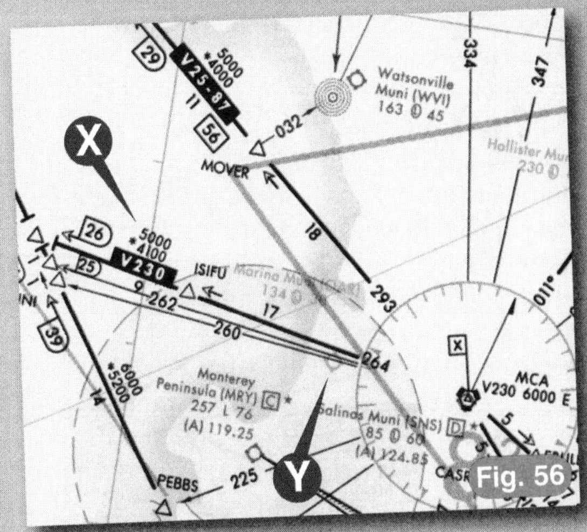

Suppose you still wanted to list Marina Muni (Figure 56, position Y) as an alternate. If so, you'd need to look at the MEA on the closest airway to begin your assessment. It appears that the MEA of 5,000 feet on V230 closest to Marina Muni would be the best choice here (Figure 56, position X). The big question is, "If you wanted to list an airport that doesn't have an instrument approach as an alternate, how do you know if the weather will allow a descent and landing under VFR conditions from the MEA? The answer is that you need to look at the area forecast to find out. The area forecast is the only forecast that provides information on cloud heights between reporting stations and this is just what you need to know when contemplating a VFR descent and landing from the MEA on V230. Of course, if there is a TAF for the airport then you should also consult it to ensure a VFR landing can be made. In the case of Marina, we could list it as an alternate on the flight plan despite the approach chart saying that its use as an alternate is NA. That's because we won't be flying Marina's instrument approach. Instead, we'll be landing VFR from V230.

Fig. 56

To descend and land in VFR conditions at Marina you'd need clouds forecast at no lower than 500 feet above V230's MEA of 5,000 feet or 5,500 feet MSL (you must be 500 feet below any clouds at this altitude for VFR flight) and you'd need 3 miles visibility (the required visibility in controlled airspace at this altitude). If the area forecast indicated at least these conditions, then you could list Marina as an alternate on your flight plan.

Suppose you made a missed approach at your destination and headed off to Marina, your alternate. Upon arriving at V230 over Marina you coordinated with ATC for a descent to 5,000 feet and found that you were still in the clouds. There's no way you're going to descend to Marina in VFR conditions if you're still in the clouds. A pilot report, however, indicates that the cloud bases are 4,600 feet. Now you're in luck. Why? Because the MOCA is 4,100 feet and it's useable within 22 nm of the VOR. If you can coordinate with ATC to descend to the MOCA (or even the controller's lowest MIA) and find yourself in VFR conditions (i.e., 500 feet below and 3 miles visibility), then you can cancel your IFR flight plan and land at Marina. Keep in mind that the regulations require the MEA to be used in evaluating Marina as an alternate, they don't require you to use it in lieu of the MOCA (within 22 nm, of course) or controller's MIA upon your arrival over the area.

Keep in mind that when using GPS for navigation and instrument approaches, any required alternate airport that you choose for your flight plan must have an approved operational instrument approach procedure *other* than GPS. Why? The GPS is subject to a few more vagaries than other guidance equipment. Remember our discussion of the RAIM alert, the need for sufficient satellites "in sight," etc.? Given that the alternate is quite possibly your last chance, the FAA wants to make pretty sure you've got a good shot at getting from air to there (this doesn't apply to an IFR certified WAAS GPS receiver since it certified as a "sole source" navigation device).

what these non-standard alternate minimums are, we need to consult Section E of the NACO booklet (see Figure 54).

Section E shows that the ILS and NDB approaches can't be used in evaluating Sacramento Executive for use as an alternate if you plan to arrive when the tower is closed. On the other hand, the VOR or GPS Rwy 2 approach can be used in this evaluation, regardless of whether the tower is closed. To find out if the tower will be open or closed when we arrive at the alternate, we need to see how long it would take to get to Sacramento Executive airport from San Jose.

Returning to our flight planning software, we can make a quick calculation to find the routing, airway distance and time to KSAC, as shown in Figure 57, position A. The estimate has it taking us 27 minutes to get to Sacramento Executive if we had to make a missed approach at San Jose. This would put us at KSAC at 0209Z+27=0236Z. According to the A/FD excerpt in Figure 58, the tower at Sacramento Executive operates from 1400Z to 0500Z, so we can indeed plan on having a precision and non-precision approach available at the alternate. Let's use the ILS approach in our alternate calculations.

Since a precision approach exists at Sacramento and can be used at this alternate airport, and since standard alternate minimums apply here, a ceiling of 600 feet and 2 miles visibility must be forecast at our alternate ETA. Since we expect to arrive at KSAC at 0236Z, let's take a look at the terminal forecast (Figure 44-Repeat) to see what the weather is expected to be at this time. (Keep in mind that terminal forecasts are issued once every six hours beginning at 0000Z. If you're on the cusp of a new issuance you might want to wait a bit to ensure you have the latest forecast.)

According to the TAF, the weather from 0200-0400Z is expected to be a 3,000 foot overcast with 5 miles visibility. From the looks of it, we're legal to list KSAC as an alternate on our flight plan. Of course, if we had to fly to Sacramento Executive, then we'd fly the approach and use the minimums shown on the approach chart we happen to be using. The 600-2 (for a precision approach) and 800-2 (for a non-precision approach) weather requirements are only for deciding whether you can list a specific airport as an alternate.

Figure 59 represents the actual IFR flight plan we'd file for this trip.

From San Jose to Sacramento, Our Alternate

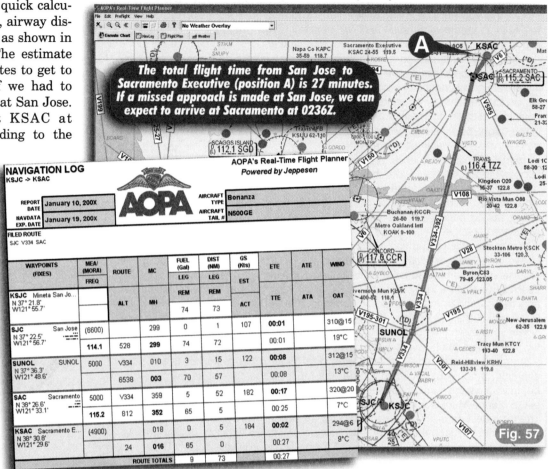

The total flight time from San Jose to Sacramento Executive (position A) is 27 minutes. If a missed approach is made at San Jose, we can expect to arrive at Sacramento at 0236Z.

AOPA's Real-Time Flight Planner
Powered by Jeppesen

NAVIGATION LOG
KSJC → KSAC

WAYPOINTS (FIXES)	MEA/(MORA) FREQ	ROUTE ALT	MC MH	FUEL (Gal) LEG REM	DIST (NM) LEG REM	GS (Kts) EST ACT	ETE TTE	ATE ATA	WIND OAT
KSJC Mineta San Jo... N 37° 21.8' W121° 55.7'				74	73				
SJC San Jose N 37° 22.5' W121° 56.7'	(6600) 114.1	299 528	299	0 74	1 72	107	00:01 00:01		310@15 19°C
SUNOL SUNOL N 37° 36.3' W121° 48.6'	5000 6538	V334	010 003	3 70	15 57	122	00:08 00:08		312@15 13°C
SAC Sacramento N 38° 26.6' W121° 33.1'	5000 115.2	V334 812	359 352	5 65	52 0	182	00:17 00:25		320@20 7°C
KSAC Sacramento E... N 38° 30.8' W121° 29.6'	(4900) 24		018 016	0 65	5 0	184	00:02 00:27		294@6 9°C
	ROUTE TOTALS			9	73		00:27		

AIRCRAFT TYPE: Bonanza
AIRCRAFT TAIL #: N500GE
REPORT DATE: January 10, 200X
NAVDATA EXP. DATE: January 19, 200X
FILED ROUTE: SJC V334 SAC

Fig. 57

Sacramento's A/FD Excerpt   Fig. 58

SACRAMENTO EXECUTIVE (SAC) 3 SW UTC−8(−7DT) N38°30.75' W121°29.61' SAN FRANCISCO
24 B S4 FUEL 100LL, JET A OX 1, 2, 3, 4 TPA—See Remarks H−3B, L−2G
RWY 02−20: H5503X150 (ASPH) S−60, D−130, DT−210 MIRL IAP, AD
  RWY 02: MALSR. Tree.
  RWY 20: REIL. VASI(V4L)—GA 3.0° TCH 52'. Tree.
RWY 12−30: H3836X100 (ASPH) S−30, D−43, DT−67 MIRL
  RWY 12: REIL. VASI(V2L)—GA 3.0° TCH 58'. Trees.
  RWY 30: REIL. VASI(V2L)—GA 3.5° TCH 26'. Tree.
RWY 16−34: H3485X150 (ASPH) S−60, D−85, DT−90
  RWY 16: Tree.   RWY 34: Tree.
AIRPORT REMARKS: Attended 1400−0500Z‡. Arpt restricted by arpt operator to acft with maximum tkf weight of 50,000 pounds or more as listed in FAA Advisory Circulars 36−1 and 36−2. Rwy 16 CLOSED to takeoffs of turbo−jet acft. Jets use Rwy 02−20. No touch and go landings or low approaches between hrs 0400−1300Z‡. No mid−field departures. Rwy 16 blast pad from Rwy 12−30 intersection to north hangers clsd permanently to acft taxi tfc. Rwy 20 calm wind rwy. Golf course lights shine across Rwy 02 final apch from right to left beginning approximately 1500' from rwy thld from dusk to 0800Z‡. TPA—1024(1000), turbine and large aircraft 1524(1500). Acft are prohibited by county code if tkf noise level listed in FAA Advisory Ci...

Sacramento is attended daily from 1400Z to 0500Z.

Sacramento's Terminal Forecast

```
TAF KSAC 102343Z 110024 15008KT P6SM SCT018 BKN050 TEMPO 0002
     BKN018
     FM0200 17010G20KT 5SM -RA BR OVC030 TEMPO 0408 2SM RA BR
     OVC018
     FM0800 16010KT 6SM -RA OVC040
     FM1400 15006KT 5SM BR OVC040 TEMPO 1418 2SM -RA BR
     BKN020
     FM1800 19005KT P6SM -SHRA SCT010 BKN060
```

Fig. 44 Repeat

The terminal forecast for Sacramento Executive indicates that, at 0236Z (between 0200Z and 0400Z), we can expect a 3,000 foot overcast ceiling and five miles visibility.

Flight Plan Items

IFR flight plans require some very specific information for them to make it to the Air Route Traffic Control Center's computer. The following is a list of each flight plan item required for filing an IFR flight plan:

Block 1. Check the type flight plan. Check both the VFR and IFR blocks if composite VFR/IFR (see sidebar, page 16-33).

Block 2. Enter your complete aircraft identification including the prefix "N" if applicable.

Block 3. Enter the designator for the aircraft, followed by a slant(/), and the transponder or DME equipment code letter; e.g., C-182/U. Heavy aircraft, add prefix "H" to aircraft type; example: H/DC10/U. Consult an FSS briefer for any unknown elements (no, not like *airplanium*).

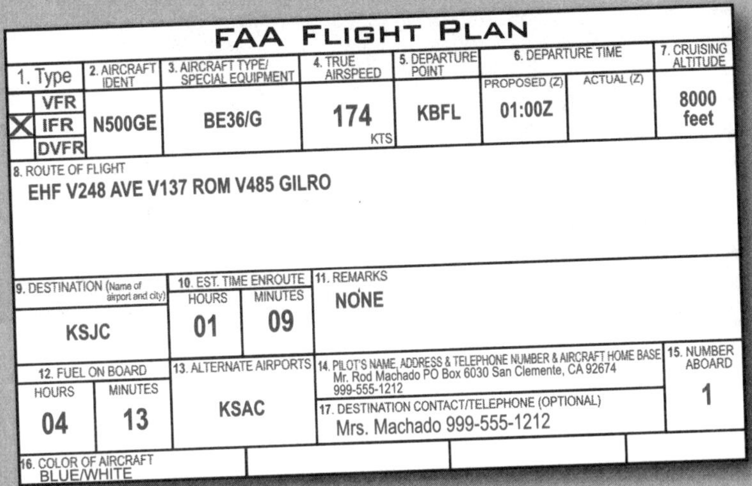

Block 4. Enter your computed true airspeed (TAS).

NOTE: If the average TAS changes plus or minus 5 percent or 10 knots, whichever is greater, advise ATC.

Block 5. Enter the departure airport identifier code (or the name if the identifier is unknown). NOTE: Use of identifier codes will expedite the processing of your flight plan.

Block 6. Enter the proposed departure time in Coordinated Universal Time (UTC) (Z). If airborne, specify the actual or proposed departure time as appropriate.

Block 7. Enter the requested enroute altitude or flight level. NOTE: Enter only the initial requested altitude in this block. When you want more than one IFR altitude or flight level along the route of flight, it is best to make a subsequent request directly to the controller.

Block 8. Define the route of flight by using NAVAID identifier codes (or names if the code is unknown), airways, jet routes, and waypoints (for RNAV). NOTE: Use NAVAIDs or waypoints to define direct routes and radials/bearings to define other unpublished routes.

Block 9. Enter the destination airport identifier code (or name if the identifier is unknown).

Block 10. Enter your estimated time enroute based on latest forecast winds.

Block 11. Enter only those remarks pertinent to ATC or to the clarification of other flight plan information, such as the appropriate radiotelephony (call sign) associated with the designator filed in Block 2. Items of a personal nature are not accepted. Do not assume that remarks will be automatically transmitted to every controller. Specific ATC or enroute requests should be made directly to the appropriate controller.

Block 12. Specify the fuel on board, in hours and minutes, computed from the departure point.

Block 13. Specify an alternate airport if desired or required, but do not include routing to the alternate airport.

Block 14. Enter the complete name, address, and telephone number of pilot-in-command, or in the case of a formation flight, the formation commander (no, you can't be a commander if you're the only guy and don't have a formation). Enter sufficient information to identify home base, airport, or operator. NOTE: This information would be essential in the event of a search and rescue operation.

Block 15. Enter the total number of persons on board, including crew.

Block 16. Enter the predominant colors. NOTE: Close IFR flight plans with tower, Approach Control, or ARTCC, or if unable, with FSS. When landing at an airport with a functioning control tower, IFR flight plans are automatically canceled. The information transmitted to the ARTCC for IFR flight plans will consist of only flight plan blocks 2, 3, 4, 5, 6, 7, 8, 9, 10, and 11.

As you can see, I've changed the route of flight section (Box #8) to end at GILRO, where we'll begin using the approach chart for navigation. Of course, this doesn't mean we've filed GILRO as the destination; KSJC is still listed as the destination (Box No. 5). For this flight you don't want to list an intersection in space as your destination unless you have a spaceship, which I know you don't have (and, unlike my earlier F-16 joke, you can't be mad at me for this assumption). The ATC computer assumes that you'll file to a point where you can begin the approach, which is usually an IAF on an approach chart for the destination airport. To learn about the specifics of completing the flight plan form, read the accompanying sidebar, *Flight Plan Items*.

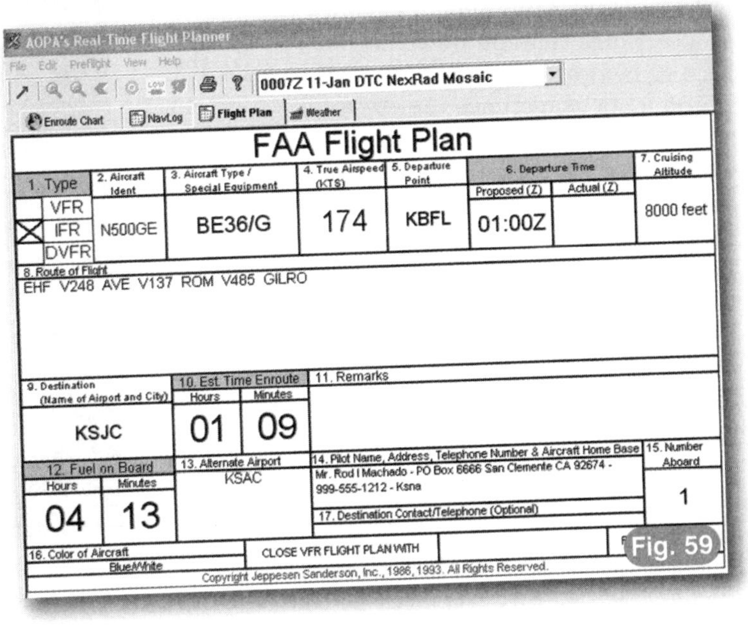

At this point, if we're going to make flight, we would file the flight plan at least 30 minutes ahead of the proposed departure time. Then we'd do the

Fig. 59

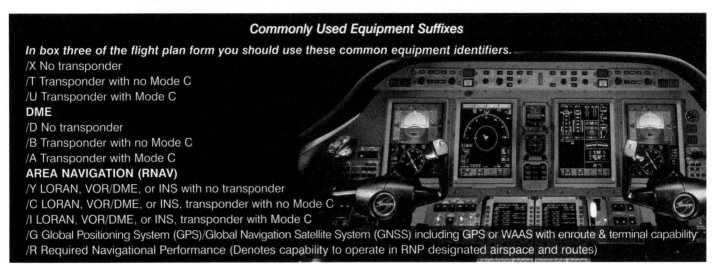

Commonly Used Equipment Suffixes

In box three of the flight plan form you should use these common equipment identifiers.

/X No transponder
/T Transponder with no Mode C
/U Transponder with Mode C

DME

/D No transponder
/B Transponder with no Mode C
/A Transponder with Mode C

AREA NAVIGATION (RNAV)

/Y LORAN, VOR/DME, or INS with no transponder
/C LORAN, VOR/DME, or INS, transponder with no Mode C
/I LORAN, VOR/DME, or INS, transponder with Mode C
/G Global Positioning System (GPS)/Global Navigation Satellite System (GNSS) including GPS or WAAS with enroute & terminal capability
/R Required Navigational Performance (Denotes capability to operate in RNP designated airspace and routes)

necessary weight and balance computations, as well as work any performance charts necessary to ensure we'd have the takeoff and landing performance necessary to operate at both our destination and alternate airports. If you've read my *Private Pilot Handbook,* then you're certainly familiar with how to make these computations. If it's been a while, you might want to consult that book or another source and review how to make these important calculations.

It's time to head to the airplane for a preflight, a final check of all the required documents (and I don't mean *Field & Stream,* either) as well as to do a little cockpit organization.

In the chapter on FARs, we discussed the required instruments for IFR flight. While it's possible to placard some instruments as inoperative and be legal (not the engine, of course), you must make sure that all those required for IFR flight are in good working order. It's also assumed that the airplane you'll use will have all the required inspections, including the pitot-static inspection and the transponder inspection, and a logged VOR check within the previous 30 days.

Cockpit Organization

As an instrument pilot, flexibility is an asset because things can and do change on a moment's notice. Sometimes it's weather, sometimes it's ATC requirements, sometimes it's an in-flight problem (mechanical or physiological). There can be lots of causes, but the result is the same—a change to your carefully plotted plan.

One sign that this is about to happen is a call from the controller that begins, "2132 Bravo, I have an amendment to your clearance. Ready to copy?" It is, I can tell you, futile to respond with things such as, "Do you have any idea how long I worked on that flight plan? I've now got carpal tunnel problems." or "Look at this masterpiece. How can anyone ruin this beauty?" Sorry Picasso. You can't change planes, but you can change plans.

This is just one of the many good reasons for keeping your cockpit organized so that you can

find what you need quickly. This is especially important in terms of your instrument approach charts. I knew one fellow who placed his approach chart binder on the floor. When he accelerated on takeoff, the charts slid to the back of the cockpit. That's bad, sad, and an expensive way to find out that your engine produces thrust. Even sadder, he was on his instrument checkride at the time. The FAA examiner looked over at him and asked, "OK, what do you need that you don't have now?" The pilot replied, "Ahhh, a shorter airplane?" Of course, he ended up with a pink license (also known as a *pink slip*). Ouch!

When setting up your cockpit for departure, I recommend that in addition to the IFR enroute chart and any DPs you'll use, you also keep the approach charts for the departure airport handy. Why? There might be an occasion when you'll have to return to the airport quickly and an instrument approach could be in order. Remember, you wouldn't be the first person to have a door pop open on liftoff (that's when they normally pop open), and in many high-performance airplanes you can't shut doors when you're airborne. At such times you

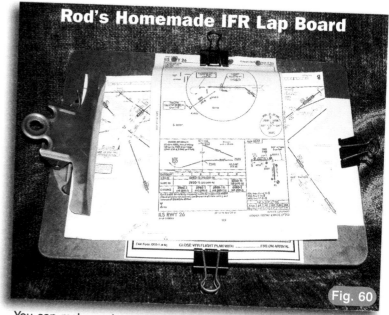

Rod's Homemade IFR Lap Board

You can make an impressive IFR lapboard with just a clipboard and three extra clips.

Fig. 60

Composite Flight Plans

The *Aeronautical Information Manual* has a provision for filing what is known as a *composite* VFR/IFR flight plan. When you file a composite VFR/IFR flight plan, the FSS specialist actually fills out two separate flight plans for you (and this is the way you'd need to do it if you were to file a composite flight plan via DUAT or any other computer based flight plan filing system). One flight plan contains the necessary information for the VFR portion of your flight, the other for the IFR portion.

Suppose I want to file VFR for the first portion of my flight and IFR for the next over the Internet via DUAT? To do this, file a VFR flight plan from a departure point to a navaid or fix enroute. Then file an IFR flight plan from this specific intersection or navaid to a destination airport.

Upon reaching the intersection or navaid, you cancel your VFR flight plan via radio with the local FSS and open the IFR flight plan with the Center controller. It's important to understand that you must cancel the VFR portion of the flight plan with the FSS. The Center controller won't do this for you when you activate your IFR flight plan. He or she hasn't a clue that you were on a VFR flight plan for the first portion of the flight. This information is not shown on your data strip.

The IFR flight plan can be activated by calling Center on the local sector frequency, which is shown on the low altitude IFR enroute chart (see Albuquerque Center insert below). This method is also an excellent way to ensure that you will have a way into the system, if things get busy.

Filing both a VFR and an IFR flight plan is useful when you want to fly IFR for the route, yet anticipate departure delays. If it's VFR in the departure area, you simply file the VFR flight plan to end at an intersection outside the area of delays, which will be FLYME intersection in the accompanying figure. At FLYME, we would cancel our VFR flight plan with the local FSS and open our IFR flight plan with Albuquerque on 128.2.

Here's how you'd fill out the flight plan form. You'd file a VFR flight plan with a destination of FLYME intersection and fill out the form with the altitude, route (BRD V247 FLYME), destination (FLYME), ETE (the time to FLYME) and the fuel on board (the fuel to FLYME).

The IFR flight plan from FLYME to Ducklips airport would list the departure point as FLYME, the departure time as the time you'd expect to arrive over FLYME intersection, the IFR cruising altitude of your choice, the route of flight as V456 DLP, the destination as Ducklips airport, the ETE as the time from FLYME to Ducklips airport, the fuel on board is the fuel remaining after flying VFR to FLYME intersection and an alternate airport if required.

The VFR/IFR method comes in handy when you're planning a departure during times when major air carriers arrive and depart the airport. At least you can depart the area if it's VFR and pick up your IFR flight plan enroute.

Of course, you may elect to forgo the VFR flight plan altogether. If you do, then file an IFR flight plan to be picked up at some enroute point such as FLYME intersection (or any navaid or waypoint where the IFR flight will begin).

You can also file IFR for the first portion of the route and VFR for the latter portion. This allows you to exit an area of bad weather to an area of VFR weather. The IFR flight plan is filed to an intersection, navaid or waypoint (FLYME, in this instance), then cancelled with the controller and the VFR flight plan (from FLYME to Ducklips airport) is activated with the local FSS.

I find filing an IFR/VFR flight plan useful when I am departing an area in which it's difficult to navigate VFR, such as an area near complex Class B airspace. There are certain areas of the country where you might like to have a pre-programmed route out of the busy terminal area (an IFR route), then continue the flight VFR under the protection of a VFR flight plan.

do *not* want to be sifting through your book looking for the approach chart.

I'm a big fan of having sectional or WAC charts handy for all departures and arrivals. I think it's a very good idea to review the local terrain before every departure, just in case ATC asks you to move mountains by accidentally turning you toward higher terrain. Remember, we're only human, and controllers make mistakes, too. Of course, if you have a spaceship you might have some non-humans aboard and this wouldn't apply. But since you don't have a spaceship (and I know you don't), it applies.

How you organize your charts is your business, but I teach my students a method that has proved successful over the years. The best solution to the chart folding challenge is to purchase an 11×14 inch clipboard and three strong clips. Place the clips in the middle of three sides of the clipboard, as shown in Figure 60. This is a ready-made cockpit organizer.

Place the enroute chart under the big clip, on the left side of the board. The enroute chart should be folded so that it can be pulled out to examine the route, then released to compress back into the folded position. The approach chart is at the top of the clipboard, and the flight planning information and other charts are clipped to the bottom of the board. The clearance-copying and doodling paper is on the far right hand side of the board. If you are left-handed, put the clearance paper on the left side. If you're ambidextrous, I have to hand it to you. Do whatever you want.

What's both unique and useful about this setup is that each chart can be raised and lowered over any other chart at any time. It's the Jack in the Box approach. Pop goes the chart. You will never have to remove any chart at any point in the flight, making you an instant master of the art of the chart. It's often a good idea to glue a little strip of foam rubber or Velcro under the clipboard to keep it from sliding off your lap. This sure beats the old gladiator-style kneeboard that straps to your thigh, which was often useful only if you accidentally found yourself in a Thai boxing ring. If you really like the kneeboard, then stick with one board. I don't think you really need to "Thai" on three or four of them, unless you plan on eating at a Thai restaurant and not paying your bill.

Obtaining Your IFR Clearance

With the flight planned filed and the cockpit organized, you're ready to obtain your IFR clearance. Remember, you don't have to rush here, even if you're from Russia. ATC will keep your IFR flight plan on file for at least one hour after your proposed departure time. If you're running late, make a call to the local FSS and give the specialist a new departure time.

Before starting your engine at busy tower controlled airports, listen to the ATIS. In many cases you'll be instructed to call Clearance Delivery on a specific frequency to obtain your IFR clearance. Since Bakersfield doesn't have a Clearance Delivery frequency listed in the *A/FD* (Figure 61, position A), you obtain your clearance from Ground Control before starting your engine. Some airports have what is known as pre-taxi clearance procedures (Figure 62, position B). When this is available, it's recommended that you call no more than 10 minutes before the proposed departure time. That way, the controller who provides you with a clearance knows you'll be leaving within 10 minutes of your request and can better coordinate your departure with Departure Control.

When you call for your clearance, it will often go something like the following:

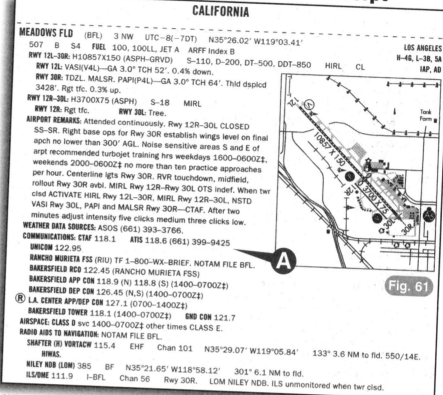

Bakersfield Meadows A/FD Excerpt

Fig. 61

Without a dedicated Clearance Delivery frequency at Bakersfield, you should call Ground Control to obtain your IFR clearance before departure.

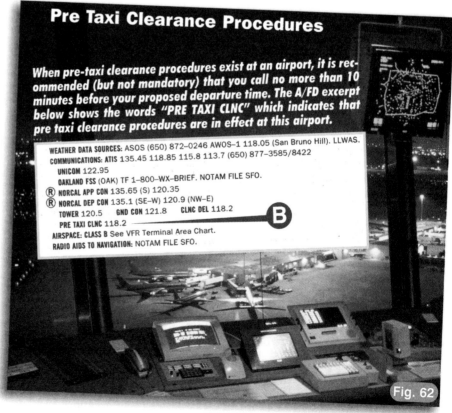

Pre Taxi Clearance Procedures

When pre-taxi clearance procedures exist at an airport, it is recommended (but not mandatory) that you call no more than 10 minutes before your proposed departure time. The A/FD excerpt below shows the words "PRE TAXI CLNC" which indicates that pre taxi clearance procedures are in effect at this airport.

Fig. 62

VFR On Top

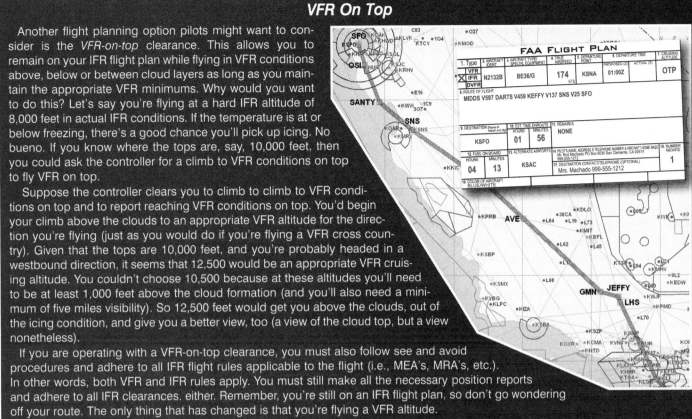

Another flight planning option pilots might want to consider is the *VFR-on-top* clearance. This allows you to remain on your IFR flight plan while flying in VFR conditions above, below or between cloud layers as long as you maintain the appropriate VFR minimums. Why would you want to do this? Let's say you're flying at a hard IFR altitude of 8,000 feet in actual IFR conditions. If the temperature is at or below freezing, there's a good chance you'll pick up icing. No bueno. If you know where the tops are, say, 10,000 feet, then you could ask the controller for a climb to VFR conditions on top to fly VFR on top.

Suppose the controller clears you to climb to climb to VFR conditions on top and to report reaching VFR conditions on top. You'd begin your climb above the clouds to an appropriate VFR altitude for the direction you're flying (just as you would do if you're flying a VFR cross country). Given that the tops are 10,000 feet, and you're probably headed in a westbound direction, it seems that 12,500 would be an appropriate VFR cruising altitude. You couldn't choose 10,500 because at these altitudes you'll need to be at least 1,000 feet above the cloud formation (and you'll also need a minimum of five miles visibility). So 12,500 feet would get you above the clouds, out of the icing condition, and give you a better view, too (a view of the cloud top, but a view nonetheless).

If you are operating with a VFR-on-top clearance, you must also follow see and avoid procedures and adhere to all IFR flight rules applicable to the flight (i.e., MEA's, MRA's, etc.). In other words, both VFR and IFR rules apply. You must still make all the necessary position reports and adhere to all IFR clearances. either. Remember, you're still on an IFR flight plan, so don't go wondering off your route. The only thing that has changed is that you're flying a VFR altitude.

While you can change VFR altitudes at your whim, you should always advise ATC prior to any altitude change to ensure the exchange of accurate traffic information. The unique thing about the VFR-on-top clearance is that it's relatively easy to obtain a hard IFR altitude if the weather conditions deteriorate. Simply ask the controller for an IFR altitude. Of course, providing adequate lead time will keep you from being caught in a tight predicament.

Instead of asking for VFR conditions on top when aloft, you can file for this condition just as you would any other IFR flight plan, with one exception. Instead of a hard IFR altitude being listed in block 7 of the flight plan, the letters "OTP" are substituted as shown in the figure above. This informs the controller that a climb to *VFR conditions on top* is requested for the route.

You'll receive your IFR clearance with an altitude authorization similar to the following: *2132 Bravo, climb to and maintain VFR conditions on top. If not on top by (altitude), maintain (altitude) and advise*. The on-top clearance allows you to climb through cloud layers to VFR conditions on top while remaining in the IFR system. The neat thing about it is that you get to choose your own VFR cruising altitude.

Don't ask for VFR on top when flying in Class A airspace. It isn't allowed. Do it and everyone on the radio will know you didn't do too well on your FAA instrument knowledge exam.

"Bakersfield Ground Control, this is Cessna 2132 Bravo, request pre-filed IFR clearance to San Jose, over."

Sometimes the controller will come back with, "Roger 2132 Bravo, clearance on request."

Now, if you say, "OK, I'm requesting it," then everyone will know that you don't have your instrument rating (or spaceship) yet. Clearances are like Chinese food. You have to send out for them. What the controller means here is that he's either called the local departure controller and requested your clearance or he has typed your request into his computer and is awaiting the arrival of your clearance.

When the controller obtains your clearance he or she will call you back, saying "2132 Bravo, clearance." He's really saying, "I've got it, are you ready to write?" The polite response to this invitation is "2132 Bravo, ready to copy." Unless, of course, you are *not* ready, in which case tell the controller, "Stand by." Then let him know when you *are* ready to copy.

Your clearance will normally contain several specific items. First, it will clear you to a particular airport, or an intersection or navaid short of that airport. This is the *clearance limit*. Sometimes the computer can't clear you all the way to the destination airport because of traffic or other issues, which I guess it figures it will figure out later. This means you'll typically be given a clearance to an intersection or navaid short of the destination field. Farther along the route, ATC will clear you to the destination airport.

Next, the controller will state the name of the SID if one is issued for your flight, the route of flight, the altitude to maintain, any holding instructions or special information and finally the Departure Control frequency and a transponder code.

When copying a clearance, don't worry about analyzing it. Just get it down on paper. I've had students who were so enamored of hearing their call sign that they never got past that! Write it down. Once copied, you can review it in detail.

The first time you hear a clearance, you will probably be stunned, thinking it is one long word of Martian. After a few rounds, you'll see that like a carefully choreographed dance, the clearance has parts that are very predictable. Once you know what's coming, you'll hear it a lot better.

What type of special shorthand script/code should you use to copy that clearance? The big fact is that it doesn't matter one small bit. There are several recommended shorthand alphabets you can memorize and I've provided one on page 18-32 in the Glossary. On the other hand, I love to foster creativity. If a small upward arrow that morphs into an "M" works as "Climb and maintain" for you, do it. A half circle with the arrow pointing right, for right turn, vice versa for left? Be my guest. Nobody is going to check your homework. Only you need to be able to read what you're writing. Make up symbols, doodles, and noodles. You'll soon see that the vocabulary of a clearance is fairly limited; only the names change, probably to protect the guilty.

If you don't get it right the first time, you can always have the controller read it again. And if you're one of the people who said, "I'm requesting it," when the controller said, "Clearance on request," then the controller will know you don't have your instrument rating yet and will probably expect to read your clearance a few times before you get it right.

You are not legally *required* to read back your clearance, but I do not know of many IFR pilots who'd pass on a chance to make sure they heard what they thought they heard. If the controller said "left" and you wrote "right," now would be a far better time to surface the disagreement than in solid IFR when you've pointed yourself in the wrong direction. Think of the clearance as a contract between you and ATC, in which you're promising to do what's in the clearance. Make sure you know what that is. Always read back a clearance, Clarence, to make sure controller Victor gave you the right vector. Roger? Over!

OK, you've heard it, you've written it, and now you're really looking at it for the first time and you don't like everything you see. Maybe you've been given a routing that has an MEA too high for you or your airplane. If so, speak now or forever hold your oxygen bottle. Call the controller, tell him what routing you'd really like to have, and see if he or she can work this out with the facility responsible for departure control.

In some instances, when ATC reads you your clearance, the controller will say, "2132 Bravo, cleared to San Jose International airport, as filed, maintain one zero thousand, contact Bakersfield Departure on 126.45, squawk 4632, over." This is known as an *abbreviated IFR departure clearance*. It means that the route you filed in your flight plan

has been approved, as is. You, bright and shining IFR star you are, of course have a copy of what you filed. You *can* ask for a reading of the full clearance, but it's kind of like announcing to everyone, "I wasn't on top of things enough to bring along a copy of the flight plan I filed." I suggest starting any such request with "My dog ate my flight plan."

An abbreviated clearance does not, however, mean that the altitude you filed for has been approved. That's why an abbreviated IFR departure clearance will always contain an ATC-assigned altitude. The only exception to this is when a DP such as a SID has assigned altitudes as part of the procedure. If you filed to use a SID for departure (and I don't mean a pilot named Sid, either), then ATC is required to state the name of that SID. The controller might not say the assigned altitude if it's part of the SID and is listed in the procedure.

More often than not, the route you selected will be modified by ATC, depending on how busy the airspace is at the time. If you receive an amended routing, now is the time to make sure you can fly it safely. It's up to you to check the route thoroughly. Don't let anyone rush you in this process. If the controller wants to know when you'll be ready for departure, tell him that you'll be a few minutes checking the route. If the controller presses you, then tell him to standby. Yes, this works and I've done it on many an occasion. Most controllers are pretty good about not pressing pilots. They're typically not as good at pressing shirts or pants.

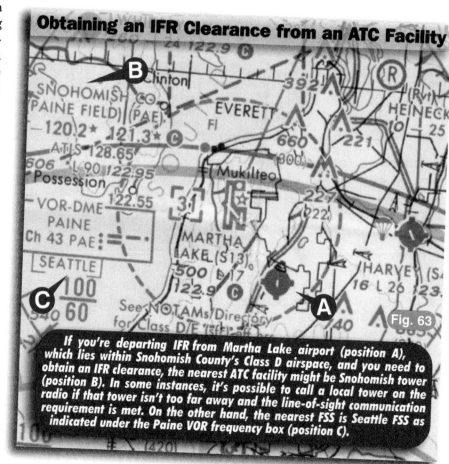

Obtaining an IFR Clearance from an ATC Facility

If you're departing IFR from Martha Lake airport (position A), which lies within Snohomish County's Class D airspace, and you need to obtain an IFR clearance, the nearest ATC facility might be Snohomish tower (position B). In some instances, it's possible to call a local tower on the radio if that tower isn't too far away and the line-of-sight communication requirement is met. On the other hand, the nearest FSS is Seattle FSS as indicated under the Paine VOR frequency box (position C).

Fig. 63

There are occasions when you'll be departing IFR from a non-towered airport. Who you gonna call? You have the option of obtaining your clearance from the nearest ATC facility, which normally means the nearest Flight Service Station (Figure 63). This typically means calling the FSS via phone, obtaining the clearance and a void time, going to the airplane, and departing before your clearance void time is up. Cell phones are a great help here, for obvious reasons. I've discussed this in an earlier chapter, so I won't revisit it any further.

OK, you've got your clearance, checked it, done your runup, and are ready to blast off. Before you launch (I say this just in case you've gotten a spaceship since the last few paragraphs), you'll want to consider how to set up your radios. Hear me out.

Suppose your routing takes you direct to a VOR station and you have dual VOR equipment on the airplane. Should you tune one radio to the first VOR and the second to the next VOR you'll use? This isn't always a good idea, even though I know your CFIs have drilled into your head the necessity of staying ahead of the airplane. But after many years of training instrument students, I've found that it's easy for someone to mistake the VOR equipment in use or inadvertently place the right frequency in the wrong nav radio, or the wrong nav frequency in either radio. I like to set both VOR nav radios to the same frequency, unless there's a good reason to have the second VOR set to a different station (such as if I need to identify an intersection on the first VOR course with a cross radial and don't have DME with which to do this).

Cross Checking With Your Nav Equipment

Photos courtesy of Microsoft Flight Simulator X

Fig. 64

It's often best to set both VOR receivers to the same station when it's not necessary to have each one set on separate frequencies. In the example above, we desire to track to the Oceanside VOR whose frequency is 115.3. If we accidentally set the number one nav radio to 115.7, we might easily detect the error since both CDIs don't read the same course deviation. Using your nav equipment to back up other nav equipment is often very wise. DME, for instance, can often be used as check on your GPS unit. After all, if you neglect a RAIM warning and see the GPS distance indicator reading something dramatically different from the DME (both assumed to reference the same location), then you have probable cause to check for the source of the error.

With two VORs set to the same frequency, you've created your own nav equipment backup check. If the two VOR units disagree in presentation, the most likely reason is that you've got the wrong frequency set or one unit has failed (Figure 64). Remember, you're seldom using two VORs to navigate at the same time. So it makes sense to use one to check the other. I do the same when making instrument approaches. I try and keep both VOR nav radios tuned to the same station as a means of checking for failures (both my own and the equipment's).

When you're ready to go, remember the catchy phrase, "Lights, camera, and action." This means, when you taxi onto the runway, you want to turn on the strobes and landing light, if available; turn on the transponder (the "camera" from ATC's perspective); and take action, meaning to take off. Before applying full throttle, you should always make note of the time in your flight log. You'll want to know this to keep track of your progress and, most important, your fuel consumption.

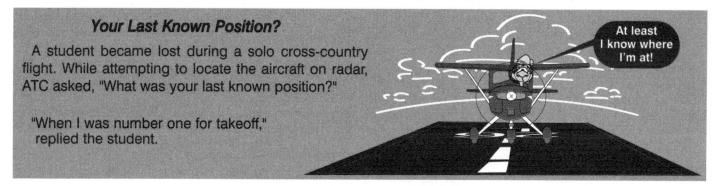

Your Last Known Position?

A student became lost during a solo cross-country flight. While attempting to locate the aircraft on radar, ATC asked, "What was your last known position?"

"When I was number one for takeoff," replied the student.

At least I know where I'm at!

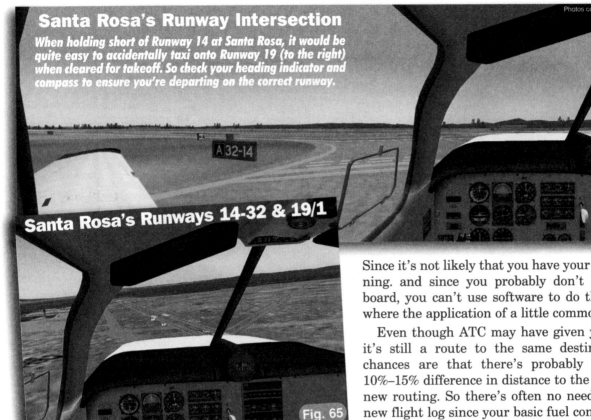

Photos courtesy of Microsoft Flight Simulator X

Santa Rosa's Runway Intersection
When holding short of Runway 14 at Santa Rosa, it would be quite easy to accidentally taxi onto Runway 19 (to the right) when cleared for takeoff. So check your heading indicator and compass to ensure you're departing on the correct runway.

Santa Rosa's Runways 14-32 & 19/1

Fig. 66

Fig. 65

The tragic crash of a commuter airliner in Kentucky in late 2006, was a reminder of the importance of taking a moment to glance at your compass or heading indicator after rolling onto the runway, to confirm you're on the runway you were cleared onto. In low visibility, at an airport with multiple runways, such as at Santa Rosa, California (Figure 65), it's easier than you might think to wind up on the wrong runway, especially if it's an airport you're not familiar with. When holding in position at the intersection of Runway's 14-32 and 19-1 (Figure 66), it's easy to mistake one for the other. So let the numbers in the transponder be a reminder to check the other camera—the compass—to make certain you are where you should be.

Do you really need to keep a flight log when flying IFR cross country? You'd better believe you do! Now, this may not be the same type of flight log you used as a student pilot, where you went from one cross country checkpoint to another. After all, even though AOPA's software created a flight "nav" log for you, this doesn't mean ATC won't give you an entirely different clearance from the one you filed, which would make the flight planning log generated by the software useful only as scratch paper.

You should keep some organized tally of your progress during your flight. I use a 5x7 inch tablet mounted on my airplane's yoke (Figure 67. I can tell to the minute how much fuel I have left and how much is left in any tank. But what about the planned total trip time found in the original flight log? Given a route change by ATC, won't you need to calculate a new total trip time, specifically, the total time between navaids found on the new routing?

Since it's not likely that you have your laptop up and running, and since you probably don't have a printer on board, you can't use software to do this for you. That's where the application of a little common sense can help.

Even though ATC may have given you a new routing, it's still a route to the same destination, right? The chances are that there's probably not more than a 10%–15% difference in distance to the destination via the new routing. So there's often no need to create a whole new flight log since your basic fuel consumption is probably about the same or hasn't changed significantly. On the other hand, if your previous flight planning had you landing at the alternate with exactly 45 minutes of "barely legal" cruise fuel left in the tanks, you might want to reconsider recalibrating the estimated fuel use for your new routing. You have to be pragmatic in these instances. Some people get so caught up with the most minute of minutiae that they forget the flying. Aviate first, calculate later.

When I roll out onto the runway for departure (or leave a space dock—I say that to kiss up just in case you do have a spaceship and are planning on giving me a ride) I note the time in the flight log, then think, "Lights, camera and

My In-flight Paper Fuel Log

	L.T.	TOTAL	R.T.
✓NFO JULIET – RW19R/2995/900-15/CLR 121.85			
START 10:05			
LIFTOFF 10:20	③	③	
327/GPH 10:35	6.8	9.8	
176 GPH 10:40	1.4	11.2	
176th 11:10		19.7	8.5
176th 11:40	8.5	28.2	
DESCENT 11:55 LAND		30.2	2.0

Fig. 67

There are many ways to keep track of your fuel when flying. You can use a flight log or a paper fuel log as shown above. LT and RT represent the fuel drained from each tank and the values in the center are fuel use totals.

When Cross Country Flight Planning Goes Bad

You've heard of the Air Force's ultra-high-security, super-secret base in Nevada, known simply as Area 51? Well, late one afternoon, the Air Force folks out at Area 51 were surprised to see a single-engine Cessna 172 landing at their "secret" base. They immediately impounded the aircraft and hauled the pilot into an interrogation room. The pilot's story was that he took off from Las Vegas, got lost, and spotted the base just as he was about to run out of fuel. The Air Force started a full FBI background check on the pilot and held him overnight during the investigation. By the next day, they were convinced the non-instrument rated private pilot really was lost and wasn't a spy. They gassed up his airplane, gave him a terrifying "you-did-not-see-a-base" briefing, complete with threats of spending the rest of his life in prison, told him Las Vegas was that-a-way on such-and-such a heading, and sent him on his way. The next day, to the disbelief of the Air Force, the same single-engine Cessna 172 showed up again. Once again, the MP's surrounded the plane... only this time there were two people in the plane. The same pilot jumped out and said, "Do anything you want to me, but my wife is in the plane and you have to tell her where I was last night!"

action." Since this is an IFR flight, I'm especially careful to ensure that the engine gauges are all in the green, that the instruments are working properly (e.g., the airspeed is alive and none of the gyro instruments are reading erroneously) and that nothing is leaving my airplane. In other words, I look to the right and left to see if fuel is leaking out of the tank, if a pitot tube cover is on, or if the baggage door is flapping. Considering that you might soon be entering the clouds; if anything looks unusual (and I don't mean if Sid, your copilot, looks unusual, either), now is the time to bring the airplane to a stop.

Once airborne, I follow the directions given in the clearance. As you remember from the chapter on departure procedures, if your clearance calls for a turn after departure, climb to at least 400 feet, *then* make the turn. Unless your clearance instructs otherwise or unless the tower controller instructs you differently, this turn altitude applies to any "DP required" turn at an airport.

When departing a tower controlled airport, some pilots will fly straight ahead until the tower instructs them to contact Departure Control (or they hit a tower). This may take the airplane beyond the obstacle-protected area created for the turn and put the airplane perilously close to obstructions when departing IFR. Remember your priorities. They are to, *aviate, navigate,* and *communicate,* in that order. Unless something says otherwise, you don't need the tower controller's permission to make the turn required as part of your IFR clearance.

When making your initial call to the departure controller (or to whoever is controlling the departure), it should sound something like this: "Bakersfield Departure, Cessna 2132 Bravo, leaving 800 feet, climbing to 4,000 feet." You always want to state your full call sign on initial contact. Since this is the initial contact with the controller, you want to state your present altitude so the controller has some way of knowing that your Mode C altitude reporting equipment is operating properly. Then you want to tell the controller what altitude you're climbing to. Check? Double check.

While enroute, flying from one sector to another, you'll be asked to contact the next controller on a specific frequency.

I've always made it a point to write down the newest frequency on my pad, just in case I became distracted (such as if Sid magically turned into Nicole Kidman).

I tune in the new frequency, but keep my lips locked for at least a few seconds. Nothing drives controllers and fellow pilots nuts more than having someone come on frequency and walk all over a transmission just because the controller stopped to take a breath and there were two microseconds of silence. You don't have anything to report that's all *that* urgent. Before you were handed off, the prior controller notified the new controller (verbally or electronically) and told him you were coming, so you're not exactly hot news. Listen for a few seconds to make sure no one is talking before reporting in on the new frequency. It's good airtiquette.

Whatever you do, don't say, "Oakland Center, 2132 Bravo is *with you.*" If you want to be with him/her, ask for a date. The proper phraseology is, "Oakland Center, Cessna 2132 Bravo, level one-zero-thousand." Or, if you're climbing or descending, you'd say, "Oakland Center, Cessna 2132 Bravo, climbing (or descending) to one-two-thousand." You aren't with someone unless you're sitting right next to them.

Let me say a word here about the words you say. Learn to make it short and sweet. In IFR conditions, the ability to be in touch with the controller is crucial. If you're hogging the frequency, others can't communicate. Learn to say what you have to say concisely and clearly, with a minimum of fluff. If you're an "Um" and "Ahhh" and "Like, you know" person on the ground, train yourself to be spare in the air. The proper order of things is think, press the button, speak.

On occasion, you'll need to go off Center frequency to talk to the FSS or Flight Watch. If so, say something such as, "Oakland Center, this is 2132 Bravo, request frequency change to Flight Watch, will report back on frequency." I've never been refused a request to do this, although I have on occasion been asked to delay it a bit because the controller knew he'd need to talk to me in the next couple of moments (handoff, traffic point out, etc.).

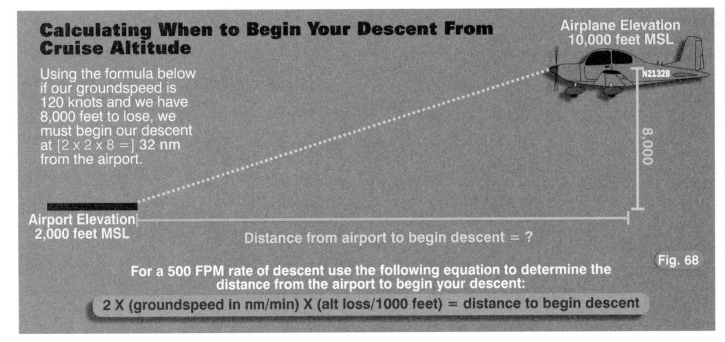

Calculating When to Begin Your Descent From Cruise Altitude

Using the formula below if our groundspeed is 120 knots and we have 8,000 feet to lose, we must begin our descent at [2 x 2 x 8 =] **32 nm** from the airport.

Airplane Elevation **10,000 feet MSL**

N2132B

8,000

Airport Elevation **2,000 feet MSL**

Distance from airport to begin descent = ?

Fig. 68

For a 500 FPM rate of descent use the following equation to determine the distance from the airport to begin your descent:

2 X (groundspeed in nm/min) X (alt loss/1000 feet) = distance to begin descent

On occasion a Center controller will have a new clearance for you or will ask you a question that demands a certain amount of your time (such as, "Why does Sid's voice sound so different?") It's important to keep in mind that the difference between you and the controller is that you're moving and he isn't. If you're not ready to copy a clearance or answer a question, just say the magic words, "Standby." Controllers understand this, and unless a specific issue needs immediate attention, they'll work with you at your pace (or the pace of your pacemaker).

While enroute, always want to keep track of your fuel consumption (Figure 68). The fuel in your tanks directly represents the flyable distance from your present position. This is important when the weather is going sour and you need to know where to go and if you can make it. That's why I make it a point to switch tanks (which does not involve moving the tanks to different wings) every 30 minutes. I don't like waiting longer to switch tanks because it creates a lateral fuel imbalance that needs correcting either by the autopilot, meaning the autopilot works harder, or by the pilot, which means I work harder (and Sid's not much of a help now, since he's doing his nails).

It's possible for the average pilot, if he knows his airplane and even if that airplane doesn't have a fuel totalizer, to keep track of his fuel consumption within a range of +/– 2 gallons. Fuel is life when flying VFR, IFR (or any other "R"), so get good at predicting and tracking its usage.

Descent planning is another thing you'll want to get good at when flying IFR, especially if you're flying high-performance airplanes. Let's assume that ATC will let you descend so that you aren't forced to arrive over the IAF and drop like the stock market after bad news. What strategy do you have for planning your descent? There are many strategies used by pilots. I have a simple one that works quite well. It's based on descending at a comfortable rate of 500 feet per minute (Figure 68). The rule is, *The distance from which to begin a 500 FPM descent*

equals two times the groundspeed (in miles per minute), times the altitude to lose (in thousands of feet).

First, let's take the difference in thousands of feet between the altitude you're at and the one to which you want to descend. Let's say that this is 10,000 feet – 2,000 feet=8,000 feet. The nautical mile/per minute coverage of the airplane during descent at 120 knots is 2 nautical miles per minute. To find our distance to begin our descent from the airport, we multiply 2×2×8=32 nautical miles. If ATC allows, we'd begin our 500 FPM descent 32 nautical miles from the point at which we'd like to arrive at 2,000 feet. Whether or not ATC will allow you to begin your descent this far out from the airport is based on his or her traffic concerns as well as minimum allowable altitudes, among other things. But it's a good bit of knowledge to have. If your descent is delayed, you know you have to get down at faster than 500 feet/minute.

That's our journey through the flight planning jungle. Yes, there's much more to cover, but this is enough to get you started as an instrument pilot. As you make more IFR cross-country flights, you'll find your own methods for doing things. And more power to you if you do.

Always remember that the secret to safe IFR flying begins, and is heavily dependent on, the flight planning stage of the flight. So don't skimp there.

Do I get my leaves now?

Not yet grasshopper. We have one more chapter to go.

Chapter 17
IFR Pilot Potpourri

Some towns are so small that they don't give you a new phone book every year. Instead, the operator calls up and says, "OK, now scratch Bob's number off the list..." If IFR flying were like small towns, this book might consist of just this page.

Well, IFR flying isn't like that, which is why we need to connect the dots with a lot of ancillary but very important information that gets lost among lofty concepts like ILS approaches, GPS navigation, and convective weather analysis. In this chapter we'll connect those dots with information that you, as an instrument pilot, will definitely find useful.

Runway—Not the Type for Models, Either

Did you know that there are three different types of runway markings? They're called *visual*, *non-precision instrument* and *precision instrument* runway markings as shown in Figure 1. They're all used for takeoff and landings, and they all have several things in common, including a centerline, a threshold and designations (i.e., runway numbers, not big words saying, "land here"). However, there are some subtle differences that separate them.

A non-precision instrument runway is one established for an airport with an instrument approach that doesn't have vertical guidance (such as a VOR, Localizer, NDB, or GPS [LNAV] approach). A non-precision instrument runway is different from a visual runway in that it has something known as an *aiming point marking* (sometimes referred to as the *fixed distance markers*) which look like two large while rectangles (Figure 1). They don't add the words "aiming point" to these markings because nobody ever flies toward them (as you'll soon see we do). In fact, the beginning of these markings is 1,000 feet from the runway threshold (note: a visual runway can have aiming point markings if it's at least 4,000 feet long and is used by jet aircraft). To understand the aiming point markings, you have to understand the precision instrument runway.

The precision instrument runway is associated with instrument approaches at airports having a glidepath

(PAR) or glideslope (ILS). The aiming point markings represent the location on the runway where the glideslope or path would theoretically intersect the runway. I say "theoretically" because the glideslope on an ILS approach flares electronically about 25 feet above the runway itself. Your mileage may vary. If you're on an ILS approach, these markings represent the place where the airplane's glideslope antenna would touch down, assuming the glideslope antenna had landing gear, of course. If you flare your airplane as most pilots do (because they don't like to see their insurance rates increase), you'll probably touch down a little farther down the runway.

Runway Markings

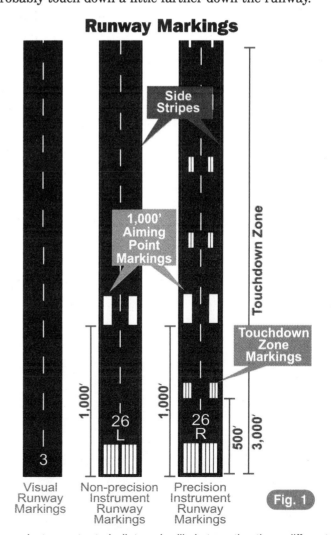

Fig. 1

As an instrument rated pilot you're likely to notice three different types of runway markings when using the IFR system.

One of the most important concepts behind these aiming point markings is that they give a pilot a place to aim for on the runway (even if no glideslope is available) or when transitioning from IMC to VMC while flying an approach. And that's why they're painted even on non-precision instrument runways. A precision instrument runway is also different from its non-precision brother by virtue of having touchdown zone markings as shown in Figure 1.

The touchdown zone is the first 3,000 feet of the runway, measured from the runway threshold. The touchdown zone markings are white stripes, each spaced to provide distance information, at 500-foot intervals on the runway. If you told someone you landed within the runway's touchdown zone, then you've basically said that you've landed somewhere within the first 3,000 feet of the runway.

If, however, you told someone you landed on a touchdown zone marking, then you could have landed anywhere on the runway at 500-foot increments, which could mean you're a bouncer and bounced your way down the runway (at least you did precision bouncing). Why are 500 foot markings important? They provide you with one means of estimating how much runway remains. This assumes, of course, that you did a proper preflight briefing, know the full length of the runway, and can count fast as the stripes go by.

Runway side stripes provide contrast between the landing surface and the dirt (or whatever else is beyond the edge). Venture outside the sidelines and you might just turn your airplane into a dirt bike or Jet Ski (even if your airplane's not a jet). Believe me when I say that on rainy nights, it's sometimes hard to tell where the side of the runway ends and dirt bike mania begins. I know that runway edge lighting should help here, but these lights are sometimes hard to see when rain obscures your forward view. Side stripes are just one more bit of information to help you, the pilot, keep your airplane on the straight and narrow.

There's a lot of intelligence behind runway design. Not the CIA kind. Keep in mind that, to descend below DA or MDA and land, the regulations require you to have the required visibility and one of the nine items associated

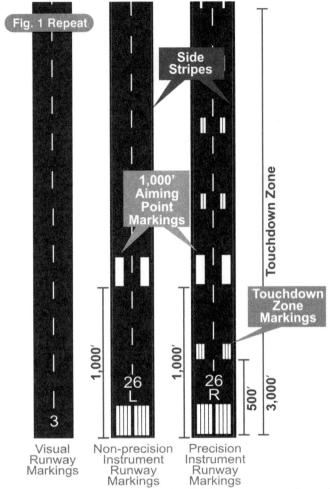

As an instrument rated pilot you're likely to encounter three different types of runways when using the IFR system.

with the landing side of the runway. It happens that the touchdown zone or touchdown zone markings are on the list. Given the detail, complexity, and size of these white markings, if you can see them while on the approach then there's a good chance that you'll be able to keep those markings in sight all the way to landing.

As a final note, if an airport has a precision instrument runway, any associated approach lighting system will be 2,400 to 3,000 feet long. Non-precision instrument runways typically have approach lighting systems that are 1,400 to 1,500 feet long.

Taxi to, Not Through

ASRS frequently receives reports of runway incursion incidents attributed to the forgetting of taxi rules, faulty crew coordination, and unmet expectations. Our first reporter belatedly remembered the basic rule of taxiing—proceed only as far as instructed, and never onto the assigned takeoff runway without specific permission.

We were cleared to taxi to 16L. As we approached 16L, I looked for traffic, saw none, and continued across. As the nose of the aircraft entered the runway area, I saw a small airplane on final. It was too late to stop, so I sped up to cross faster. The other airplane landed without incident.

Listening to Ground earlier, I had heard him give, "Taxi 16L via...hold short of 16L," [to another aircraft]. Because I did not get the "hold short," I was in the mind set that I was cleared to cross, forgetting the old basic that "taxi to" is permission to cross all runways except the active. We get so used to being told where to hold short that, when it is not said, we forget about this exception to the basic rule of taxiing. **NASA Callback Report**

Runway Lighting

Runway edge lighting, shown in Figure 2, position A, borders both sides of the runway. You don't have to be edgy to use it. These lights are normally white and are spaced 200 feet apart. I say these lights are normally white because on an instrument runway, they turn yellow on the last 2,000 feet or half of the runway length, whichever is less (Figure 2, position B). This is also known as the runway caution zone. Guess why the lights are yellow? First, yellow is more easily seen in fog. Second, yellow should be the color of your spine if you're still moving fast and haven't yet applied the brakes, anchor, and anything else needed to make you stop moving.

The beginning of the runway is announced with green threshold lights, while the far end of the runway is lit in red (Figure 2, position C). Red is an appropriate color to indicate you are running out of usable landing surface. These lights lead a dual life. On one side they're green; on the other, red. Think about it for a second. The beginning (or threshold) of one runway is the end of another. The lights on the threshold of Runway 8 (not shown in Figure 2, position C) are also at the terminus of Runway 26. One man's ceiling is another man's floor. You're also likely to find blue taxiway edge lighting as shown in Figure 2, position D.

What I've described so far is the basics of runway lighting, which you will encounter at almost any airport that supports night operations. It can and does get a lot fancier. For instance, on a precision instrument runway you're likely to find these additional types of lighting:

Green, in-pavement taxiway centerline lighting (Figure 2, position E). These lights are useful in assisting your ground movement during low visibility conditions.

Flashing yellow runway guard lighting (Figure 2, position F). These lights are used to identify an active runway, and location of the runway hold position.

In-pavement clearance bar lights (Figure 2, position G). These consist of three yellow lights used to denote a hold position for airplanes and ground vehicles. In this instance, they're located prior to the yellow-dashed taxiway holding lines.

Geographic position markings, or pink spots (Figure 2, position H), denote places used either as holding points or for position reporting while on the taxiway.

ILS critical areas (Figure 2, position I). See the "ILS Critical Area" sidebar, page 17-6.

In-pavement red stop bar lights (Figure 2, position J). These lights are used at intersections of illuminated taxiways and active runways for operations when the RVR is less than 6 (600 feet RVR). When you see these lights on a taxiway you should stop and never cross them until instructed to do so by ATC (the controller will usually turn them off when it's OK to continue taxiing).

Sometimes where one-way taxiways exist or where surface roads for automobiles exist that can are easily confused with taxiways, a "no entry" sign (Figure 2, position K) is installed.

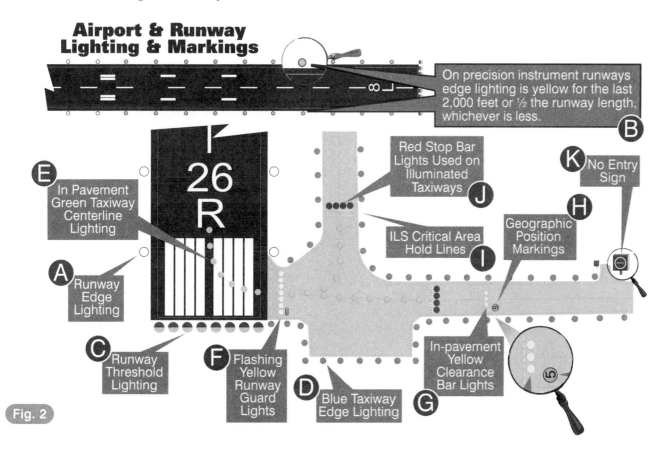

Fig. 2

Runway Surface Lighting

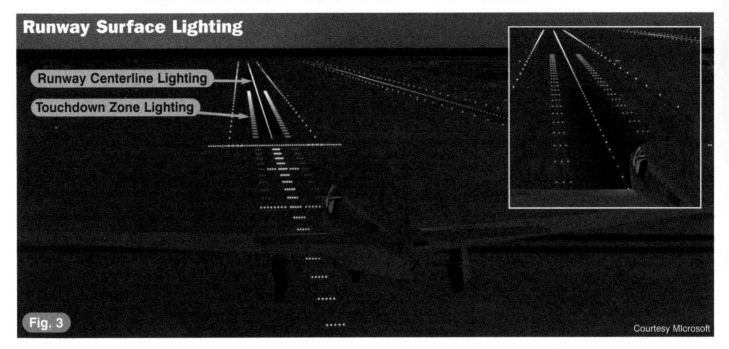

Runway Centerline Lighting

Touchdown Zone Lighting

Fig. 3

Courtesy MIcrosoft

Figure 3 shows the additional runway lighting you're apt to see on a precision instrument runway. Runway centerline lighting (RCLS) is installed to help you find the runway centerline in poor weather. These lights, flush with the pavement, are spaced at 50-foot intervals beginning 75 feet from the landing threshold. If you land off center you can't use the old, "I couldn't see the centerline" excuse when you land on a runway with RCLS.

Touchdown zone lights (TDZL, Figure 3) are installed on some precision instrument runways to help pilots, well, find the touchdown zone. There's a move to install them in NFL stadiums, as well. TDZLs consist of two rows of transverse light bars situated symmetrically about the runway centerline. Expect to see steady-illuminated white light that starts 100 feet beyond the landing threshold and extend the width of the touchdown zone, or 3,000 feet beyond the landing threshold, or to the midpoint of the runway, whichever is less. And don't worry about these lights. You won't hurt them if you land on them. That's what they're designed for. In fact, I have it on good word that the lights actually like it.

Taxi Way Lead Off Lights

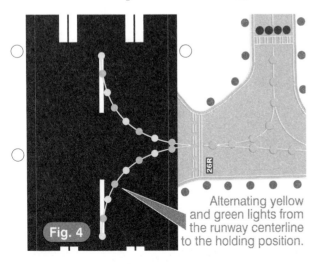

Fig. 4

Alternating yellow and green lights from the runway centerline to the holding position.

Expect to see taxiway leadoff lights on some runways, too. These lights extend from the runway centerline to a spot on an exit taxiway (Figure 4). The intention here is to help move traffic off the runway, a runway that other pilots want to use. A pilot who has managed to find the runway and land from an ILS under low visibility conditions will often not be able to figure out how to get off that same runway. Alternating green and yellow lights are the path to safety.

Taxiway Markings

Figure 5 shows a drawing of taxiway markings from an airport chart. Taxiway D (Delta) parallels the north side of Runway 8L-26R and Taxiway C (Charlie) parallels the northwest side of Runway 3-21. There are several intersecting taxiways with individual phonetic names.

Taxiways are identified by a continuous yellow line with parallel double yellow lines on the outer edges of the taxi surface (Figure 6). Taxiway names are shown by small signs (Figure 6). If you've ever heard someone say, "Give me a sign," well, here it is.

The taxiway you're on is indicated by a sign at the side of the taxiway, with yellow lettering on a black background. Signs containing black lettering on a yellow background indicate intersecting taxiways. Arrows indicate the relative direction of these intersecting taxiways. You might also see taxiway and runway signs painted on the taxiway. These are equivalent to a raised sign. Think of them as being flattened by a big jet with fat tires and you'll interpret them properly.

As an instrument pilot, you must be able to identify the point where the taxiway ends and the runway begins. This is one of those places where precision matters. One toke over the line and you could have some explaining to do. The taxiway/runway transition is identified by four yellow lines—two solid and two dashed—perpendicular to the taxiway and running parallel to the runway (Figure 7). These markings are known as runway hold markings.

Taxiways at a Typical Airport

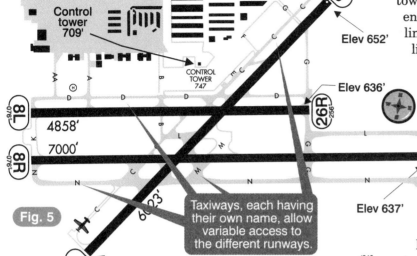

Fig. 5

Control tower 709'

CONTROL TOWER 747

Elev 652'

Elev 636'

Elev 637'

Elev 600'

4858'
7000'

Taxiways, each having their own name, allow variable access to the different runways.

Taxiway Markings

All taxiway markings are in yellow.

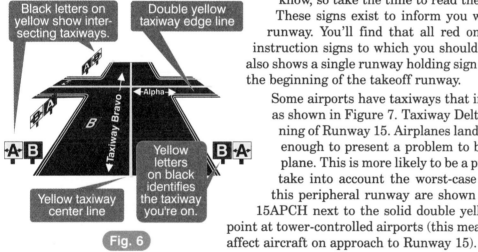

Black letters on yellow show intersecting taxiways.

Double yellow taxiway edge line

Yellow taxiway center line

Yellow letters on black identifies the taxiway you're on.

Fig. 6

They don't look big enough to hold an entire runway, but they do.

If the two solid lines are on your side, then at a tower-controlled airport a clearance is required to enter the runway. If the double broken dashed lines are on your side, then you should cross those lines to clear the runway and enter the taxiway. (From now on we'll assume that a controlled airport is one having an "operating" control tower.)

Assuming you have just landed and are taxiing off the runway. In this instance, taxi across the double broken dashed lines and clear the runway. The FAA says that your airplane hasn't cleared the runway until the entire airplane (down to the last rivet) is on the other side of those broken double yellow lines. This is to prevent the tails of long airplanes (like a stretched DC-8) from poking out onto the runway.

Another way to identify where the runway begins is with a white-on-red sign located next to the dashed and solid double yellow lines (Figure 7). These information billboards are called runway holding signs, though they don't actually hold anything. They also indicate the runway direction. This is important news that you need to know, so take the time to read the whole thing—it's only two numbers. These signs exist to inform you when you're about to enter an active runway. You'll find that all red on white signs are mandatory airport instruction signs to which you should always pay close attention. Figure 7 also shows a single runway holding sign indicating that the taxiway intersects the beginning of the takeoff runway.

Some airports have taxiways that interfere with the runway safety area, as shown in Figure 7. Taxiway Delta is located directly behind the beginning of Runway 15. Airplanes landing on Runway 15 could approach low enough to present a problem to both the approaching and taxiing airplane. This is more likely to be a problem for big airplanes, but the rules take into account the worst-case scenario. Holding position signs for this peripheral runway are shown by white on red lettering. The term 15APCH next to the solid double yellow lines indicates a mandatory hold point at tower-controlled airports (this means any aircraft on this taxiway might affect aircraft on approach to Runway 15).

Additional Runway Markings

Protection of the runway safety area prevents collisions between taxiing and landing airplanes.

Taxiway holding lines.

Fig. 7

On reverse side of this sign

RUNWAY SAFETY AREA

Ouch! I've been rabbit punched.

Thump!

You should cross the broken double-yellow lines when they're on your side so as to clear the runway safety area.

This is a holding position sign for the runway safety area. An ATC clearance is required to cross the solid yellow hold lines when you're at an airport with an operating control tower.

This is a holding position sign for Runway 15.

Runway Markings

Taxiway Lighting

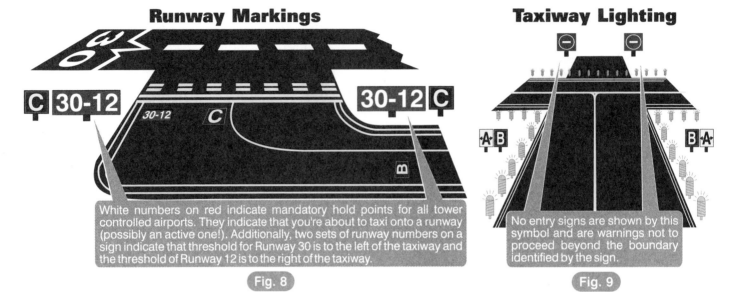

White numbers on red indicate mandatory hold points for all tower controlled airports. They indicate that you're about to taxi onto a runway (possibly an active one!). Additionally, two sets of runway numbers on a sign indicate that threshold for Runway 30 is to the left of the taxiway and the threshold of Runway 12 is to the right of the taxiway.

Fig. 8

No entry signs are shown by this symbol and are warnings not to proceed beyond the boundary identified by the sign.

Fig. 9

On the opposite side of the runway, on taxiway Delta, on the back side of the runway hold sign, is a runway safety area sign (normally found at only tower controlled airports). This consists of the same marking shown on the taxiway (double solid and dashed lines). These signs can be used as a guide in deciding when to report back to a controller that you are clear of the runway.

In Figure 8, the white numbers *30–12* on red background indicate that the beginning of Runway 30 is to the left and the beginning of Runway 12 is to the right. At controlled airports, these signs are your cue to hold your position, unless a clearance has been given to enter or cross the runway.

On some runways and taxiways you may have seen a no entry sign, as shown in Figure 9. Hopefully you didn't see it go by as you taxied past it. This sign means you can't enter the area beyond the sign. This sign is usually used for one-way taxiways or places where pilots may mistake a road for a runway or taxiway. You can imagine what a surprise your airplane would be for someone in a Ford Cricket, or at the drive-through at a Jack in the Box.

Additional Runway Markings

Just because you see concrete or asphalt in the shape of a runway doesn't mean that it can be used for landing. Some runways have yellow chevrons painted on them (Figure 10, position A). That doesn't make it a Chevron gas station. It signals that the surface is unsuitable for taxiing, taking off, or landing. It's basically an airplane no-man's land. Don't use any portion of this area. It might be off limits because the surface won't support the weight of an airplane even for taxiing, let alone landing, or because the surface is otherwise unsuitable. Maybe it's a seasonal swamp with quicksand. Whatever it is, there's no guarantee it will hold water or your airplane. Planes that venture onto chevrons can find themselves up to their axles in asphalt, trapped like a gigantic fly on a No-Pest Strip.

White arrows pointing in one direction form what is called a displaced threshold (Figure 10, position B). This is a runway area that is not to be used for landing, but which is available for taxi, takeoff, or roll out after landing. Displaced thresholds often exist as part of a noise abatement effort. By forcing you to land farther down the run-

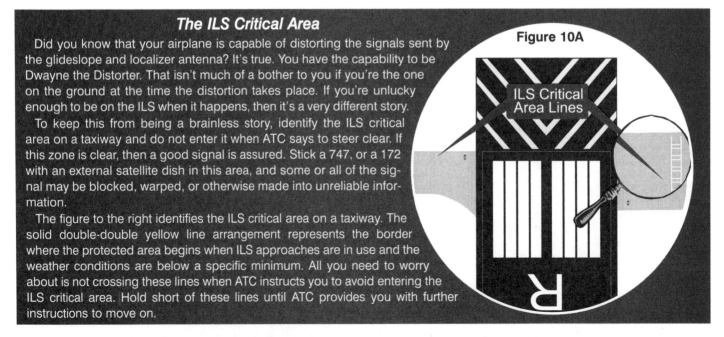

The ILS Critical Area

Did you know that your airplane is capable of distorting the signals sent by the glideslope and localizer antenna? It's true. You have the capability to be Dwayne the Distorter. That isn't much of a bother to you if you're the one on the ground at the time the distortion takes place. If you're unlucky enough to be on the ILS when it happens, then it's a very different story.

To keep this from being a brainless story, identify the ILS critical area on a taxiway and do not enter it when ATC says to steer clear. If this zone is clear, then a good signal is assured. Stick a 747, or a 172 with an external satellite dish in this area, and some or all of the signal may be blocked, warped, or otherwise made into unreliable information.

The figure to the right identifies the ILS critical area on a taxiway. The solid double-double yellow line arrangement represents the border where the protected area begins when ILS approaches are in use and the weather conditions are below a specific minimum. All you need to worry about is not crossing these lines when ATC instructs you to avoid entering the ILS critical area. Hold short of these lines until ATC provides you with further instructions to move on.

Figure 10A

ILS Critical Area Lines

Additional Runway Markings

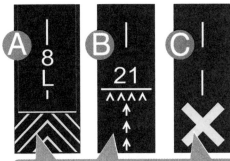

Yellow chevrons (A) are areas on which you can't land, takeoff or taxi. White arrows (B) indicated a displaced threshold and a yellow X (C) indicates a closed or temporarily closed runway or taxiway.

Fig. 10

way, you maintain a higher glidepath than you would if landing at the very beginning of the runway.

A displaced threshold can exist for other reasons, such as the presence of a surface that will support the weight of an airplane, but not the impact of an airplane landing. (There's a big difference. I know this since one of my instructors used to call out Richter scale values following my touchdowns.)

A runway or taxiway with a large yellow X painted on it (Figure 10, position C) means this is a closed or temporarily closed surface. Land there and you wind up in the X Files. The runway could be under repair, torn up, trenched, non-existent, or in the process of being converted to a housing tract. Treat it like a wall socket and don't let any part of your airplane touch it.

Pilot Control of Airport Lighting

As a private pilot, you've probably turned on airport lighting via your radio many times. Fun, isn't it? Now that's what I call a real in-command sort of maneuver. A few clicks and the whole airport lights up. Power to the rabbit.

Now that you're an instrument pilot, the fun doesn't have to stop. You'll still be turning the lights on for yourself, especially at airports without a control tower or at one where the control tower has shut down for the evening. To see what's watt, you only need a short thumb; the lights are activated by keying your mic button.

Three different intensities of runway edge lighting (high, medium and low) are available at many airports. To activate runway lighting from the cockpit, key (click) the microphone button on the appropriate CTAF frequency. How many times should you click it? If all three intensities of lighting exist at an airport, click the mic 7 times within 5 seconds for the high intensity runway lighting

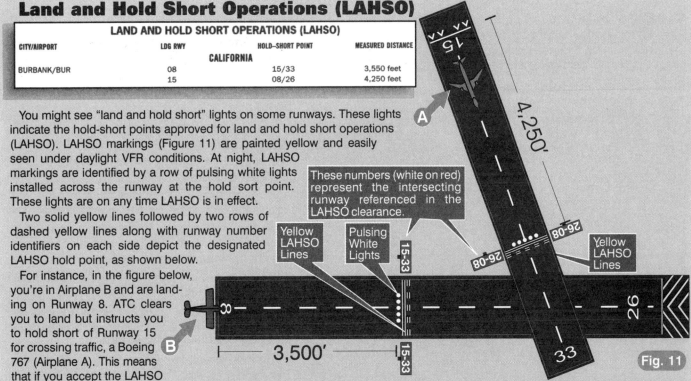

Land and Hold Short Operations (LAHSO)

LAND AND HOLD SHORT OPERATIONS (LAHSO)

CITY/AIRPORT	LDG RWY	HOLD–SHORT POINT	MEASURED DISTANCE
		CALIFORNIA	
BURBANK/BUR	08	15/33	3,550 feet
	15	08/26	4,250 feet

You might see "land and hold short" lights on some runways. These lights indicate the hold-short points approved for land and hold short operations (LAHSO). LAHSO markings (Figure 11) are painted yellow and easily seen under daylight VFR conditions. At night, LAHSO markings are identified by a row of pulsing white lights installed across the runway at the hold sort point. These lights are on any time LAHSO is in effect.

Two solid yellow lines followed by two rows of dashed yellow lines along with runway number identifiers on each side depict the designated LAHSO hold point, as shown below.

For instance, in the figure below, you're in Airplane B and are landing on Runway 8. ATC clears you to land but instructs you to hold short of Runway 15 for crossing traffic, a Boeing 767 (Airplane A). This means that if you accept the LAHSO

These numbers (white on red) represent the intersecting runway referenced in the LAHSO clearance.

Yellow LAHSO Lines

Pulsing White Lights

Yellow LAHSO Lines

Fig. 11

clearance, you can't use the full length of Runway 8. You should land and exit by the first convenient taxiway short of the LAHSO hold lines. If you can't exit the runway, then hold at the LAHSO hold lines.

A LAHSO clearance doesn't preclude a rejected landing (a go-around). If this is necessary, then go around, but maintain safe separation from other traffic and promptly notify the controller. A ceiling of 1000 feet and 3 miles visibility is required for a LAHSO clearance. Student pilots should not participate in the LAHSO program.

The available landing distance on a LAHSO runway is found in the A/FD. It's very important that you give the controller a full readback of the LAHSO clearance. This lets the controller know that you know what's expected of you. And, if you need the full length of the runway, don't accept the LAHSO clearance. Remember, you're the PIC!

(HIRL), 5 times within 5 seconds for the medium intensity runway lighting (MIRL) and 3 times in 5 seconds for the low intensity runway lighting (LIRL). Once activated, the lights stay on for 15 minutes. It's on a timer, like the heat lamp in the bathroom at the Leastdusted Motel and Spa, where you've got a room booked.

If you're approaching the airport at night and it's been about 15 minutes since you've last activated the lights, click the mic again the appropriate number of times to reactivate the glowing globes for an additional 15 minutes. Personally, I re-key the microphone the appropriate number of times when I'm on final approach just to make sure the lights don't go off by surprise. Imagine being on short final when the airport disappears. Not only will this leave you in the dark about where to land, it will also upset your passengers. Runway hide-and-seek is not a game that should be played using an airplane.

The FAA suggests that when approaching an airport, you should key the microphone 7 times in 5 seconds to activate all

Pilot Controlled Lighting

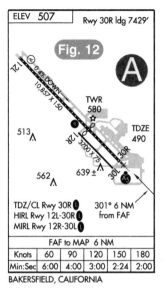
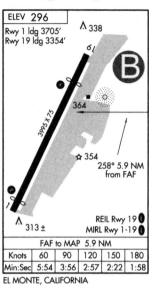

At Bakersfield airport, pilot controlled lighting is available for the PAPI, the MALSR, the HIRL and MIRL on Runway 30R as well as the touchdown zone and centerline lights. At El Monte, the PAPI on Runway 1-19, the REIL on Runway 19 and the MIRL on Runway 1-19 are all pilot controlled.

NACO Chart Lighting Legend

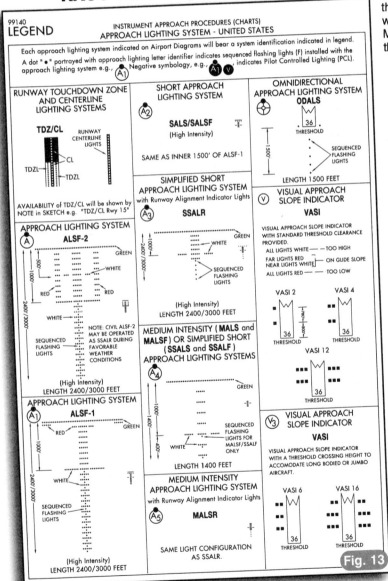

NACO's legend for airport lighting says that "white on black lettering" (i.e., negative symbology) indicates that this lighting system is pilot controlled.

the airport's controlled lighting. After this, you can key the mic and lower the lighting intensity (if MIRL or HIRL are installed) or deactivate other lighting systems (VASI, REIL, PAPI, approach lights) that may be wired into the control system (more on these other lighting systems shortly).

There may be several different lighting systems under the control of the pilot, as shown on approach charts in Figure 12. This figure depicts an airport with circle/ellipse symbols having white on black (called *negative symbology*) lettering. This type of reverse bold symbol indicates that pilot controlled lighting exists at Bakersfield airport and specifically exists for those lighting features symbolized. Not only is the approach lighting system controlled by the pilot (shown by the *A5* in the black circle), but so are the touchdown zone and centerline lighting, the high intensity and the medium intensity runway lighting (indicated by the small black circle on top of the bigger black circle), and probably the lights for any McDonald's within 5 miles of the airport. Figure 13 shows the NACO chart legend describing the different types of airport lighting.

How do you control this lighting? Well, in many instances you must look at the *Airport/Facility Directory* to find out. Figure 14 shows the AF/D excerpt for Bakersfield airport. In the remarks section it says that you must activate all the lights by clicking the mic as discussed above on the CTAF or common traffic advisory frequency. After turning on the lights, wait two minutes and then you can adjust the intensity of these lights to medium with five clicks and to low with three clicks.

Runway End Identifier Lights

A REIL Strobe Light

Fig. 15

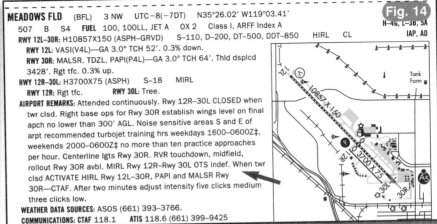

Fig. 14

MEADOWS FLD (BFL) 3 NW UTC−8(−7DT) N35°26.02' W119°03.41' H−4G, L−3B, 5A
507 B S4 FUEL 100, 100LL, JET A OX 2 Class I, ARFF Index A IAP, AD
RWY 12L−30R: H10857X150 (ASPH−GRVD) S−110, D−200, DT−500, DDT−850 HIRL CL
  RWY 12L: VASI(V4L)—GA 3.0° TCH 52'. 0.3% down.
  RWY 30R: MALSR. TDZL. PAPI(P4L)—GA 3.0° TCH 64'. Thld dsplcd
  3428'. Rgt tfc. 0.3% up.
RWY 12R−30L: H3700X75 (ASPH) S−18 MIRL
  RWY 12R: Rgt tfc. RWY 30L: Tree.
AIRPORT REMARKS: Attended continuously. Rwy 12R−30L CLOSED when
  twr clsd. Right base ops for Rwy 30R establish wings level on final
  apch no lower than 300' AGL. Noise sensitive areas S and E of
  arpt recommended turbojet training hrs weekdays 1600−0600Z‡,
  weekends 2000−0600Z‡ no more than ten practice approaches
  per hour. Centerline lgts Rwy 30R. RVR touchdown, midfield,
  rollout Rwy 30R avbl. MIRL Rwy 12R−Rwy 30L OTS indef. When twr
  clsd ACTIVATE HIRL Rwy 12L−30R, PAPI and MALSR Rwy
  30R—CTAF. After two minutes adjust intensity five clicks medium
  three clicks low.
WEATHER DATA SOURCES: ASOS (661) 393−3766.
COMMUNICATIONS: CTAF 118.1 ATIS 118.6 (661) 399−9425

The Airport Remarks section indicates that you must activate all lighting. Then, after waiting two minutes, you can adjust the lighting intensity with additional mic clicks.

At some airports there are two small stroboscopic lights (Figure 15 near the runway's threshold. These are not disco balls, they're REIL or *Runway End Identifier Lights* (Figure 16). REIL is pronounced like the word *real*. Now you know why pilots are sometimes confused if someone tells them to "get real." REIL lights provide for the rapid and positive identification of a runway that's surrounded by other lighting and lacks contrast with the surrounding terrain (Figure 16).

REILs also help identify a runway in reduced visibility conditions. The AF/D excerpt (Figure 14) says that the REIL flights

Runway End Identification Lights (REIL) identify the runway threshold.

REIL (White)

Fig. 16

are also under the control of the pilot on the CTAF. Notice that El Monte also has a PAPI or Precision Approach Path Indicator that's wired into the pilot controlled lighting system (Figure 12B).

Pilot Controlled Lighting Systems

All lighting systems that are radio controlled at an airport, whether on a single runway or multiple runways, operate on the same radio frequency.

On runways having both approach lighting and runway lighting (runway edge lights, taxiway lights, etc.) systems, the approach lighting system takes precedence for air-to-ground radio control over the runway lighting system which is set at a predetermined intensity step, based on expected visibility conditions.

Runways without approach lighting may provide radio controlled intensity adjustments of runway edge lights. Other lighting systems, including VASI, REIL, and taxiway lights may be either controlled with the runway edge lights or controlled independently of the runway edge lights. Your *A/FD* will tell you.

Runways With Approach Lights

Lighting System	No. of Steps	Status (Non Use Period)	Intensity Step Selected Per No. of Mic Clicks		
			3 Clicks	5 Clicks	7 Clicks
Approach Lights (Med. Int.)	2	Off	Low	Low	High
Approach Lights (Med. Int.)	3	Off	Low	Med	High
MIRILS	3	Off or Low	◆	◆	◆
LIRLS	5	Off or Low	◆	◆	◆
VASI	2	Off	*	*	*

Note: ◆ Identifies a predetermined intensity step.
      * Low intensity for night use. High Intensity for day use as determined by photocell control.

Runways Without Approach Lights

Lighting System	No. of Steps	Status (Non Use Period)	Intensity Step Selected Per No. of Mic Clicks		
			3 Clicks	5 Clicks	7 Clicks
MIRILS	3	Off or Low	Low	Med	High
HIRLS	5	Off or Low	Step 1 or 2	Step 3	Step 5
LIRL	1	Off	On	On	On
VASI*	2	Off	◆	◆	◆
REIL*	1	Off	Off	On/Off	On
REIL*	3	Off	Low	Med	High

Note: ◆ Low intensity for night use. High intensity for day use as determined by photocell control.
      * The Control of VASI and/or REIL may be independent of other lighting systems.

Visual Approach Slope Indicator [VASI]

Under poor visibility conditions or at night, the lack of outside visual clues sometimes makes determining the proper landing glidepath difficult. Fortunately there is something known as a Visual Approach Slope Indicator (VASI) that provides you with a visual clue as to the proper glidepath to fly.

A VASI is any of several combinations of light bars located alongside the runway, although the term usually refers to the model consisting of two lightbars (it's often called a two-bar VASI. These are the types of definitions I like. No confusion here). The two VASI bars are usually 500–1,000 feet from the approach threshold (Figure 17). These lights project either a red or white color, depending on your altitude. The colors are constant and don't actually change within the box. What changes is your height, which allows you to look at the VASI from different angles and see different colors. The choice is limited to red or white, though, so please don't go underground looking for something that matches your interior.

When you are below the proper glidepath, both VASI bars show red. Some pilots remember that this signals trouble by thinking of it as "red over red, you'll conk your head." If the VASI bars appear red as you reach the MDA, level off until you see red over white, meaning you've intercepted the proper glidepath.

Red over white means that you're above the glidepath for the bar closest to you and below the glidepath for the bar farther away. This is a complicated way of saying you're on the glidepath that will plunk you down on the runway at a position halfway between the two light bars (minimal flaring assumed). A good way to remember this is "red over white, you're all right."

Of course, if you're too high, both bars will show white. A good memory aid for this is "white over white, you're out of sight." Increase the descent rate until the upwind bar turns red. You can expect the VASI's red and white bars to transition through a pink color as your altitude in relation to the proper glidepath changes. Either there's a salmon stuck in the box, or you're in between red and white.

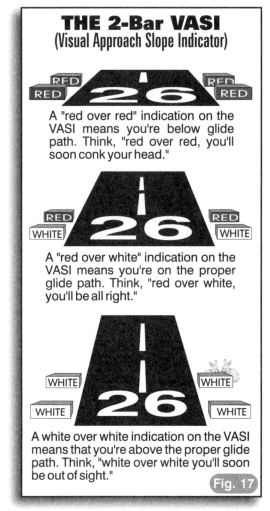

THE 2-Bar VASI
(Visual Approach Slope Indicator)

A "red over red" indication on the VASI means you're below glide path. Think, "red over red, you'll soon conk your head."

A "red over white" indication on the VASI means you're on the proper glide path. Think, "red over white, you'll be all right."

A white over white indication on the VASI means that you're above the proper glide path. Think, "white over white you'll soon be out of sight."

Fig. 17

If you see flashing red over flashing white, then you're making an approach to a police car. Now you're in really big trouble.

VASIs are visible from 3–5 miles during the day and 20 miles or more at night. You can count on safe obstruction clearance for 10° either side of the runway centerline when using the VASI. Obstruction clearance is guaranteed for a distance up to four miles out along the centerline of the runway (Figure 18).

If you're nearing your a turn onto final approach, it's best not to start a descent using the VASI until you are aligned with the runway. Personally, I wouldn't start my descent until aligned with the runway even if I were within 10° of the

VASI Protected Area

Fig. 18

4 nm

10°   10°

The VASI provides you with obstacle clearance for plus or minus 10 degrees either side of the runway centerline for 4 nautical miles.

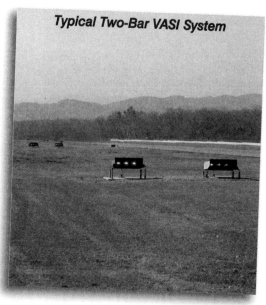

Typical Two-Bar VASI System

Sighting Range of Lighting Systems

A key factor in being able to land successfully when flying a non-precision approach is your ability to identify the runway early enough to allow a reasonable descent for landing. If you see the runway (or its environment) only when you're near the approach threshold at a typical MDA, it's unlikely that you'll be able to descend and land using a normal or reasonably safe rate of descent. Being able to identify the runway/airport lighting as soon as possible after leaving the final approach fix inbound is essential for a safe landing. While flight visibility is the most significant factor in your ability to identify the runway environment, not all runway/airport lighting systems have the same sighting distances (distances from the runway at which they can be seen and identified).

For instance, the chart in Figure 19 shows the sighting distances for runway/airport lights during an overcast day in fog. At an MDA of 700 feet AGL (position A) with a visibility of one mile (position B), REIL lights can typically be seen at maximum distance of 1.4 or 1.2 miles. The PAPI can only be seen at 700 feet AGL if you're a bit closer at .9 miles (position D) and to see the

Sighting Range of Lighting Systems Past Threshold
Overcast Day Fog Visible Range of Lights
Non-precision Minimums — Fig. 19

Altitude (MDA)	700 feet (AGL)	400 feet (AGL)	400 feet (AGL)	400 feet (AGL)
Visibility	1 mile	1 mile	1.2 miles	1.5 miles
Transmissivity	0.156	.030	.066	0.112
REILS(a)	1.4 miles	1.4 miles	1.6 miles	1.8 miles
REILS(b)	1.2 miles	1.2 miles	1.3 miles	1.5 miles
MIRILS	.6 miles	.6 mile	.7 miles	.75 miles
LIRLS	.4 miles	.4 mile	.4 miles	.5 miles
PAPI	.9 miles	1.5 miles	1.75 miles	2 miles
HIRLS	.3 miles	1.3 miles	1.5 miles	1.7 miles
ODALS	1.5 miles	1.5 miles	1.6 miles	1.8 miles

1. The minimum sighting distance from the runway to make a 5 degree descent from an MDA of 700 feet AGL to the touchdown zone is 1.5 miles and .9 miles from an MDA of 400 feet.
2. The minimum sighting distance from the runway to make a 3 degree descent from an MDA of 700 feet AGL to the touchdown zone is 2.3 miles and 1.6 miles from an MDA of 400 feet.
REILS(a) 15,000 candela Uni-Directional REILS(b) 5,000 candela Omni-Directional

HIRLS you'll need to be with .3 miles of the runway. On the other hand, the ODALS can be seen at a distance of 1.5 miles from the runway threshold (position E). The important thing to notice here is that the greater the mileage value, the greater the distance from the runway at which these lights can be seen, thus triggering a chorus of, "I see the lights. . ."

Now look what happens to some of these sight distance values when the airplane descends to an MDA of 400 feet AGL (position F). The sight distances remain the same for the REILS, MIRLS, LIRLS and ODALS but change with the PAPI and HIRLS. In fact, the sighting distances increase as the airplane gets lower for these two lighting systems. Why? Because at 400 feet AGL the airplane is making a shallower approach to the runway (perhaps 3 degrees vs. 5 degrees) and the HIRLS and PAPI project their maximum lighting intensity at 3.5 degrees and 3 degrees, respectively. If you're too high on approach, these two lighting systems won't be as visually distinct to you.

Figure 20 shows airport/runway lighting sighting distances for lights in night fog or snow conditions. As common sense suggests, airport/runway lighting is easier to detect at night, which explains why the sight distance values are larger than those in Figure 19.

Looking at Figure 21, we see an airplane at an MDA of 400 feet

Sighting Range of Lighting Systems Past Threshold
Night Fog or Snow Visible Range of Lights
Non-precision Minimums

Altitude (MDA)	700 feet (AGL)	400 feet (AGL)	400 feet (AGL)	400 feet (AGL)
Visibility	1 mile	1 mile	1.2 miles	1.5 miles
Transmissivity	0.156	.030	.066	0.112
REILS(a)	1.5 miles	1.4 miles	1.7 miles	2 miles
REILS(b)	1.4 miles	1.3 miles	1.6 miles	1.9 miles
MIRILS	1.2 miles	1.1 miles	1.4 miles	1.7 miles
LIRLS	1 mile	1 mile	1.3 miles	1.5 miles
PAPI(a)	1.1 miles	1.2 miles	1.5 miles	1.8 miles
PAPI(b)	1 mile	1.1 miles	1.4 miles	1.7 miles
HIRLS	1.2 miles	1.3 miles	1.6 miles	1.8 miles
ODALS	1.7 miles	1.6 miles	1.9 miles	2.2 miles

1. The minimum sighting distance from the runway to make a 5 degree descent from an MDA of 700 feet AGL to the touchdown zone is 1.5 miles and .9 miles from an MDA of 400 feet.
2. The minimum sighting distance from the runway to make a 3 degree descent from an MDA of 700 feet AGL to the touchdown zone is 2.3 miles and 1.6 miles from an MDA of 400 feet.
REILS(a) 15,000 candela Uni-Directional PAPI(a) 20% of day maximum
REILS(b) 5,000 candela Omni-Directional PAPI(b) 5% of day maximum — Fig. 20

AGL, in a position from which to make a five degree (position Z) and three degree (position Y) descent to the runway. Descending from either of two points will land the airplane somewhere within the runway's touchdown zone. The question is, what airport/runway lighting will be visible if and when the airplane is ready to begin its descent?

It's clear that the position for a five degree descent (position Z) puts the airplane at .9 miles from the runway or 1.5 miles from the runway for a three degree descent (position X). Using the Overcast Day Fog chart (Figure 19), it appears that when you're at the position to begin a five degree descent at an MDA of 400 feet AGL, you may not be able to see the MIRLS or LIRLS (Figure 19, positron G), even if you have a flight visibility of one mile. The same applies even if you have 1.2 or even 1.5 miles flight visibility. So, if this airport has nothing more than MIRLS or LIRLS, you'll most likely have to move closer to the airport before sighting these lighting systems or detecting other parts of the runway environment.

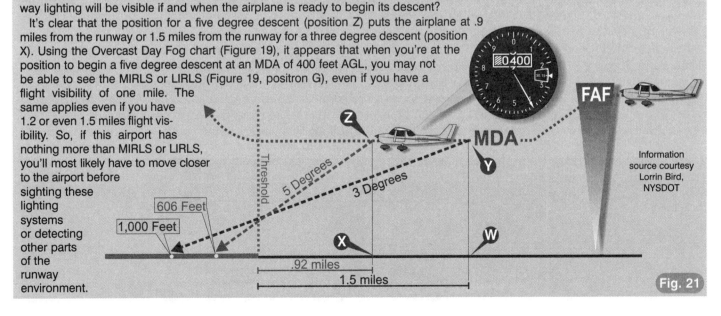

Information source courtesy Lorrin Bird, NYSDOT

Fig. 21

runway centerline. You never know what's out there, and I'm not about to turn my airplane into a probe whose mission it is to find a newly installed obstruction.

Regulations require that you fly at or above the glideslope when approaching a runway equipped with a VASI in Class B, C, and D airspace. Be cautious about making premature descents below the glideslope. In addition to safety, VASIs aid in keeping pilots from descending early into noise-sensitive areas along the flight path.

Precision Approach Path Indicator [PAPI]

A PAPI (pronounced PAP-pee) is another type of a visual glidepath indicator, as shown in Figure 22 (no, it's not that nice guy who's paying for your flying lessons either—that's your pappy). The PAPI uses red and white signaling colors in an arrangement of four horizontal lights to identify the correct glidepath. It's kind of like a double VASI turned on its side. The four horizontal light units appear to change color as your glidepath varies (Figure 23). If you're above a 3.5° glidepath, the PAPI shows all four light units as white. If you're slightly high (on a 3.2° glidepath), you'll see three white lights on the left and one red light on the right.

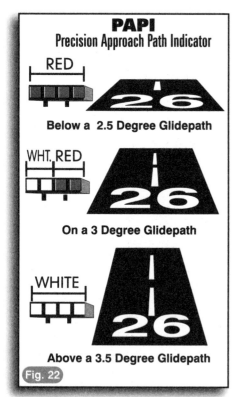

When on an ideal 3° glidepath, the right two lights are red and the left two lights are white. Being slightly below or on a 2.8° glidepath means you'll see one white light on the left and three red lights on the right. When below a 2.5° glidepath, all four light units show red. A pink transition between lights doesn't exist as it does with a two- or three-bar VASI.

Tricolor VASI

A tricolor VASI is not the national flag of any nation, nor is it as common as the two- and three-bar VASIs. It normally consists of a single light unit projecting a three-color visual approach path into the final approach area of the runway, as shown in Figure 24. Red is the below glidepath indication. The above glidespath indication is amber, and the on glidepath indication is green. When the airplane descends from green to red the pilot may see a dark amber color during the transition. Tricolor VASIs have a useful range of one-half to one mile during the day and up to five miles at night.

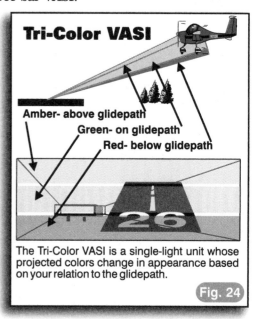

The Tri-Color VASI is a single-light unit whose projected colors change in appearance based on your relation to the glidepath.

3-Bar VASI

Some of the larger air carrier airports have a 3-bar VASI. This exists to serve the jumbo jet crowd, as shown in Figure 25. Problems arise in long-bodied aircraft when the captain is on a safe glidepath but the passengers behind him or her are not, as shown in Figure 26. If pilots of jumbo jets landed this way, obstructions in the flight path might intrude on passengers seated in row 38 through AL, or aft lavatory.

Three-bar VASI's have two glidepaths. One is angled at 3° and is identified by a bar combination of red/red over white as shown in Figure 27. The higher glidepath is angled at approximately 3.25° (1/4° steeper than the lower glidepath). Long bodied aircraft use this and see a color combination of red/white over white. VASI glideslope angles vary depending on the obstructions located along the approach path. It's possible to have VASI glidepaths as high as 4.5°. Even if you're in a Cessna 152 pretending to be a Boeing 747, it's best to use the lower glidepath to avoid steep descents. Look for red/red over white as the appropriate on-glidepath indication for this lower (3°) glidepath.

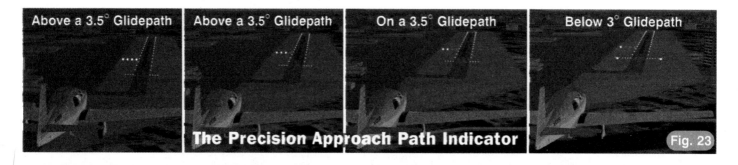

The Precision Approach Path Indicator

THE 3-BAR VASI
(Visual Approach Slope Indicator)

Smaller aircraft use the lower glide path giving them a 3 degree glidepath.

Figure 25

Larger aircraft use the higher glide path giving them a 3.25 degree (or higher) glidepath.

THE 3-BAR VASI

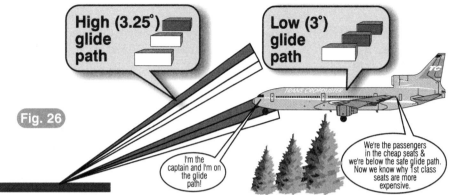

High (3.25°) glide path

Low (3°) glide path

Fig. 26

I'm the captain and I'm on the glide path!

We're the passengers in the cheap seats & we're below the safe glide path. Now we know why 1st class seats are more expensive.

When flying the lower glidepath (he should be on the upper one), the captain of this airliner is on glidepath while the rest of his long-bodied airplane is below glidepath. This is why many large aircraft use the high glidepath for landing.

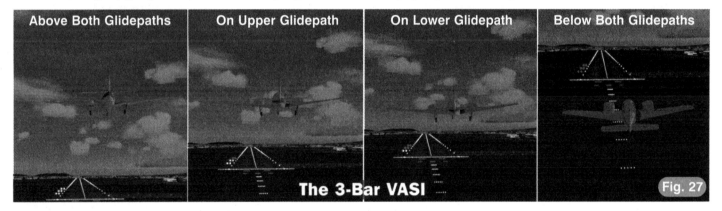

Above Both Glidepaths | On Upper Glidepath | On Lower Glidepath | Below Both Glidepaths

The 3-Bar VASI — Fig. 27

Wake Turbulence

Wake turbulence sounds like some personal trauma that causes loss of sleep, and in a way, it is. Wake turbulence is one of the unseen but very serious hazards of flight. Wake turbulence can be any form of airplane-generated disturbance of the atmosphere. The most common and hazardous type of wake turbulence is *wingtip vortices*. Wingtip vortices pose quite a hazard to other airplanes. An airplane caught in these vortices can experience a rolling motion so severe that there isn't enough control capacity to fight it. They can also roll a small plane inverted and, quite frankly, passengers often become very upset when suddenly and unexpectedly placed upside down in an airplane. Playing rock and roll music during such an event will not help, according to recent studies.

If that's not enough, the rolling motions and turbulence produced by the vortices can damage aircraft components. This doesn't mean that your airplane is necessarily going to go to pieces upon encountering vortices, but it's a risk that's not worth the gamble.

Wingtip vortices come not from somebody's shoes, but as an unwanted byproduct of lift. Wingtip vortices are a byproduct of the differential pressure over and under a wing's surfaces (Figure 28). High pressure air under the wing attempts to sneak over the tip of the wing, toward the low pressure air above. The vortex starts from under the wing, moves outward, then upward and inward toward the fuselage. The vortex appears to coil or rotate while trailing behind the wing of a moving airplane.

Wingtip Vortices

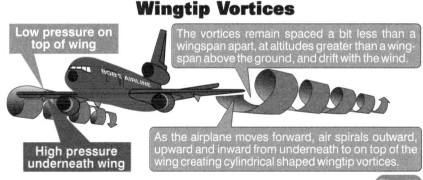

Low pressure on top of wing

High pressure underneath wing

The vortices remain spaced a bit less than a wingspan apart, at altitudes greater than a wingspan above the ground, and drift with the wind.

As the airplane moves forward, air spirals outward, upward and inward from underneath to on top of the wing creating cylindrical shaped wingtip vortices.

Fig. 28

Generally, the heavier the airplane, the stronger the wingtip vortex (there are a few exceptions to this that aren't worth discussing here, over there, or anywhere for that matter). The vortices produced by a fully loaded Boeing 747 are a lot stronger than those of a fully loaded Cessna 152. The reason is that heavier airplanes must produce more lift and more lift means greater vortex strength. This is why the strength of wing tip vortices increases with an increase in airplane weight (more weight means more lift).

When an airplane's gear and flaps are retracted, there is a tendency to produce stronger vortices. An airplane in this no-gear-and-flap configuration is said to be clean (this isn't a newly washed airplane). Couple a cleanly-configured airplane with slow airspeed and you've got a condition that produces the strongest wingtip vortices. Slow speed means a higher angle of attack, which results in a greater pressure differential between the bottom and the top of the wing. Any large airplane that's flying heavy, clean and slow can produce more serious wingtip vortices.

As a small-airplane pilot, you must watch out for airplanes that produce hazardous wingtip vortices. Some are famous—or infamous—as generators of these horizontal tornadoes. Beware of Boeing 747s, 757s and 767s, and DC-10s. Even other large airplanes try to avoid the vortices of these mammoth jumbos. But more than size matters here. Learjets, although small in size, can produce serious wingtip vortices.

Always remember that wingtip vortices are a byproduct of lift. The moment an airplane's wheels leave the ground, lift is being generated and vortices are produced (Figure 29, position A). So expect vortices at and beyond the point of airplane rotation, as shown in Figure 29, position B. Likewise, as soon as the airplane's wheels touch down, production of wingtip vortices stops (Figure 29, position C).

If you are departing behind a larger airplane, it's best to lift off before the point where that airplane raised its nose (rotated) and commenced climbing. Once off the ground, avoid flying into the flight path of the departing airplane (Figure 29, position B). In a small airplane with limited performance, it's unlikely you will have the oomph to climb above the glidepath of the larger airplane, so the answer is to turn right or left to avoid climbing into the larger airplane's departure path (and its vortices), as shown in Figure 29, position B. Let the tower controller know what you're doing (if departing a controlled field).

Once free of the wing, vortices lead a life of their own. The unique thing about wingtip vortices is that they tend to descend at a rate of several hundred feet per minute and normally level off at 500–1,000 feet below the generating airplane (Figure 30). They also tend to remain a little less than a wingspan apart, and drift with the wind. They must have read *Gone with the Wind*. It's always wise to avoid the area 1,000 feet below any large airplane. Maneuver laterally (preferably upwind) to avoid flying below and behind these large aircraft.

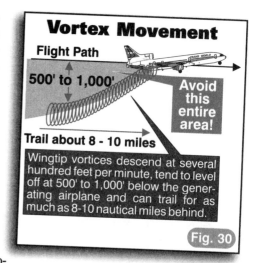

Vortex Movement

Flight Path

500' to 1,000'

Avoid this entire area!

Trail about 8 - 10 miles

Wingtip vortices descend at several hundred feet per minute, tend to level off at 500' to 1,000' below the generating airplane and can trail for as much as 8-10 nautical miles behind.

Fig. 30

Wingtip Vortice Production

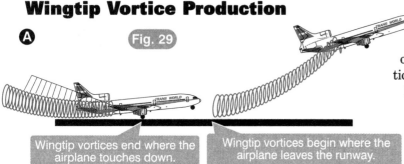

Ⓐ Fig. 29

Wingtip vortices end where the airplane touches down.

Wingtip vortices begin where the airplane leaves the runway.

Ⓑ

Plan to lift off before this point where the jet lifted off the runway.

Vortex production stars here.

Wingtip vortices begin at the point where the heavier airplane lifts off the runway (to be precise, vortices begin when the nose wheel lifts off the runway). Make sure you lift off long before reaching this point and avoid flying directly into the path of the vortices. In other words, you may need to turn left or right to avoid the vortices.

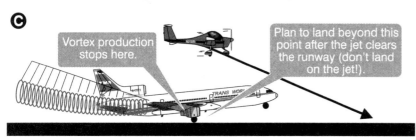

Ⓒ

Vortex production stops here.

Plan to land beyond this point after the jet clears the runway (don't land on the jet!).

When landing behind a heavier airplane, plan to land beyond the point where the airplane touched down. And make sure you don't sink into the the vortices while on the approach.

While vortices diminish with time as well as with atmospheric turbulence (this helps chop them up and disrupt their rotational energy), they remain a threat for many minutes after the passage of a large airplane. Vertical separation of at least 1,000 feet below the airplane can be considered safe. Personally, I'd recommend you avoid flying directly beneath and parallel to the flight path of a large transport airplane even if you're more than 1,000 feet below it (vortices can persist 8–10 nautical miles behind an airplane). It never makes sense to thumb your nose at any in-flight hazard, especially one you can't see.

Be prepared for vortices to drift when crosswinds exist at the airport. Figure 31, position A shows the typical behavior of a drifting vortex near the surface.

Chapter 17 - IFR Pilot Potpourri

When vortices sink to 100 to 200 feet above the ground, they tend to move sideways at a speed of 2 to 3 knots. A crosswind will decrease the sideways movement of the upwind vortex and increase the movement of the downwind vortex as shown in Figure 31, position B. Expect the upwind vortex to remain over or near the touchdown zone if a light crosswind component of 1 to 5 knots exists.

A light quartering tailwind can move the vortices forward into the touchdown zone (Figure 31, position C). You must be especially cautious because this increases the possibility of lingering vortices in the touchdown area. Be especially alert when departing on close, parallel runways when a large airplane is upwind of your runway (Figure 31, position D). The vortices can drift directly into your flight path.

Another area of concern is when a larger airplane makes a low approach, missed approach, or a go-around and flies directly over (or near) your airplane during the climbout. This is most common on parallel, closely spaced runways. It's also a problem on runways that intersect at a small angle. If you experience such an event and feel the airplane will pass less than 1,000 feet over your airplane during the go-around, move out from under the airplane's flight path. Your job is to protect you and your passengers. Call the tower and explain that you'd like to turn right or left in the interest of wake turbulence avoidance (if it's critical, turn first, talk later). I have never been refused a request to do something in the interest of safety.

In many cases ATC will issue a "caution wake turbulence" warning when such a hazard presents itself. Even if ATC issues no warning, adjust your flight path as necessary to prevent encountering these dangerous wingtip vortices.

And always be prepared for the unexpected. A fellow pilot (so the story goes) in a Cessna 421 (a twin-engine airplane) was cleared for takeoff when a small rabbit pulled out on the runway. He radioed the tower that he couldn't take off until the rabbit moved. The tower replied, "The rabbit on the runway is now cleared for takeoff. And Cessna 421, you're cleared for takeoff too, caution wake turbulence from the departing rabbit." This is what happens when tower controllers have a lot of free time on their hands.

ATC Wake Turbulence Separation Requirements

For the purposes of wake turbulence separation minimums, ATC classifies aircraft as heavy, large, and small.

Heavy aircraft are aircraft capable of takeoff weights greater than 255,000 pounds regardless of their weight during any particular phase of flight. Large aircraft are aircraft of more than 41,000 pounds maximum certified takeoff weight, up to 255,000 pounds. Small

Wingtip Vortice Drift

When the vortices of larger aircraft sink close to the ground (within 100 to 200 feet), they tend to move sideways over the ground at a speed of 2 or 3 knots if no wind is present.

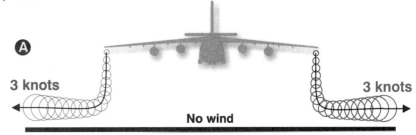

Vortex movement near ground - no wind present

A crosswind will decrease the sideways movement of the upwind vortex and increase the movement of the downwind vortex. Thus a light wind with a cross- runway component of 1 to 5 knots could result in the upwind vortex remaining in the touchdown zone for a period of time and hasten the drift of the downwind vortex toward another runway.

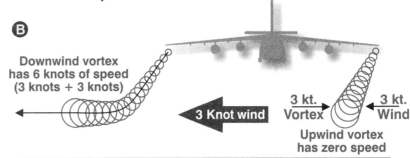

Vortex movement near ground - with crosswind

Similarly, a tailwind condition can move the vortices of the preceding aircraft forward into the touchdown zone. The light quartering tailwind requires maximum caution. Pilots should be alert to large aircraft upwind from their approach and takeoff flight paths (especially when the runways are closer than 2,500 feet).

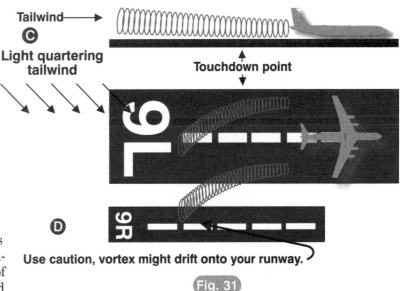

Use caution, vortex might drift onto your runway.

Fig. 31

Wake Vortex Hazard at Cruise Altitude

Wake turbulence is commonly associated with Terminal Area arrival and departure operations. However, ASRS has received several recent reports that describe wake vortex incidents at cruise altitudes, with 10 miles or more in-trail separation between the involved aircraft. All the incidents appeared to occur in smooth air with little or no wind. More from the flight crew of a Fokker-100:

Just prior to leveling off at FL330—at about FL32.7 we encountered moderate to severe rapid and instantaneous roll reversals and turbulence. We were in perfectly smooth air with no [FMS] wind and not anywhere near the jet stream as forecasted. We were about 17 nm in trail with a Heavy B-767 that had previously overflown us in his faster climbout and speed capability. We immediately requested and received clearance to FL290. All systems and controls were normal. We strongly...suspect that in the calm air, this heavy aircraft's vortices do not descend very fast—if at all—and at 17 miles in trail are only about one and on-half minutes behind.

I recommend that all Operator's Manuals be updated to reflect this wake vortex behavior at altitude in smooth air, which is very similar to their behavior in smooth air at low altitude with anticipated separation.... **NASA Callback**

Courtesy NASA Collection

aircraft are aircraft of 41,000 pounds or less maximum certified takeoff weight. (For purposes of an aircraft type rating, a large aircraft is one weighing more than 12,500 pounds. See Chapter 6 of *Rod Machado's Private Pilot Handbook*, page F3.)

Be especially alert to the word *heavy* when used by transport-type airplanes. This means the airplane can weigh a quarter of a million pounds or more. And don't be fooled by the words "small aircraft," either. A Falcon 50 jet is a three-engine business jet that packs a tremendous wake turbulence wallop, and it is classified as a small aircraft by these definitions.

If you're landing your small airplane behind a heavy jet, ATC will provide at least a six-mile separation between you and that airplane by the time it crosses the runway threshold. If you're following (not landing behind) a heavy jet, ATC will keep you either 1,000 feet below or at least 5 miles behind the big fellow. These distances tell you a lot about how smaller airplanes are affected by wingtip vortices.

When departing directly behind a heavy jet or when your projected flight paths will cross, ATC provides a two-minute wait for wake turbulence (or the five mile separation mentioned above). ATC may state, "2132 Bravo, hold for wake turbulence avoidance."

As the pilot in command you can opt to waive the wait. To do this, you do not wave at the tower. In fact, my recommendation is that you neither wave nor waive. Do something a little less risky, like honking your horn behind a Hell's Angels motorcycle gang on the freeway. Just remember, "fools rush in where angels fear to tread." If you don't want to be meeting angels, don't be a fool. Take two.

Taking off from a runway intersection poses very significant hazards if a large or heavy aircraft has just

departed. Your departure path could put you directly into this airplane's descending vortices. Controllers provide a three-minute wait for wake turbulence separation in these instances (if it's a heavy aircraft, ATC won't let you waive the hold time. Ask and they'll say "No way, Jose").

ATC Communication Procedures

Let's face it, there's no possible way to fly IFR in today's airspace system without talking to ATC. Yes, we do have lost communication procedures to handle communications failure, but as you've probably already noticed in the regulations section, these procedures are pretty complex. Perhaps this is a not-so-subtle indication of just how important it is to keep in touch with ATC when flying IFR. Comm is so important, in fact, that I'm going to direct your attention to some specific IFR communication procedures.

When the ATC tower is in operation and you're preparing to taxi, always state your position on the airport to the controller (that's not your position at work, either—they don't care if you're the CEO). This minimizes the chances the controller will not understand your location and give you a clearance to go where no person should ever go—like on a taxiway heading toward another airplane.

When ATC gives you a clearance to "taxi to" an assigned takeoff runway, the absence of holding instructions authorizes you to cross all runways that the taxi route intersects except the assigned takeoff runway. Be very clear that "taxi to" is not an authorization to taxi onto or cross the assigned takeoff runway at any point. To prevent a misunderstanding here, ATC will not use the word "cleared" in conjunction with authorization for aircraft to taxi.

When arriving at a runway intersection (as opposed to departure end) for takeoff, state your position again. This is another check and balance to prevent the controller

ATIS—Automatic Terminal Information Service

© Santino Ambrogio - FOTOLIA

When you ask someone of they've got the ATIS, it sounds like you're asking them if they've got a skin disease that might best be cured by calamine lotion or something really nasty smelling whipped up by Aunt Bessy. Well, it isn't a skin disease, and it's good to have the ATIS, since it's the continuous broadcast of recorded non-control information in selected high activity terminal areas.

This recording helps makes life easier on the controller and relieves frequency congestion by automating the repetitive transmission of essential but routine information. The ATIS is continuously broadcast over a discrete VHF radio frequency or the voice portion of a local NAVAID. It's a transmission that's engineered to be receivable to a maximum of 60 nm from the ATIS site and a maximum altitude of 25,000 feet AGL (just in case your throttle got stuck in your Cessna 152 turbo-JATO bottle model). You can also receive the ATIS almost anywhere on the ground at airports with ATIS service. The A/FD identifies airports for which ATIS is available.

ATIS information includes the time of the latest weather sequence, ceiling, visibility, obstructions to visibility, temperature, dew point (if available), wind direction (magnetic), and velocity, altimeter, other pertinent remarks, instrument approach and runway in use. The ceiling/sky condition, visibility, and obstructions to vision may be omitted from the ATIS broadcast if the ceiling is above 5,000 feet and the visibility is more than 5 miles.

The departure runway will only be given if different from the landing runway, except at locations having a separate ATIS for departure. The broadcast may include the appropriate frequency and instructions for VFR arrivals to make initial contact with approach control.

If you are arriving or departing the terminal, you can receive the continuous ATIS broadcast at times when cockpit duties are least pressing and listen to as many repeats as desired (make a recording to take home if you enjoy these kinds of things. You make the call). ATIS broadcasts are updated upon receipt of any official hourly and special weather. A new recording will also be made when there is a change in other pertinent data such as runway change, instrument approach in use, etc.

from mistaking your position and clearing you for takeoff when another airplane might still be using your runway (which means it's not quite yours yet).

Of course, you're always required to remain in communication with ATC while on the ground or in the air. That means you must use your radio (no cans or string, either). A common communication problem occurs when pilots turn down the volume on the comm unit with ATC in order to call Flight Watch or another facility on the second radio. If you want to do this, just ask the controller for permission to be off frequency for a minute or two. I can't remember an instance where I wasn't allowed to do this, although for traffic or tactical reasons, a controller may ask that you wait a bit before switching.

Instrument students often have trouble obtaining the ATIS before entering the airport environment. That's a bit odd, since the ATIS is there for the listening, all the time, and it can be heard far from the airport. The problem is not radio reception, it's failure to use their head to think ahead. Get the ATIS early. The closer to the airport you get, the busier you will be.

Another advantage to getting the ATIS early is the edge it gives you in figuring out what ATC is likely to order up as your approach routing. The ATIS tells you which runway is in use and if there are any special activities of which you should be aware.

I'm speaking of activities such as a runway being closed for snow removal.

As mentioned in the ATIS sidebar, you can plan to listen to the ATIS as far as 60 nautical miles from the airport. If you feel shy about asking the controller to be off frequency for a short time, then flip the switch and listen to the ATIS over your cockpit speaker while listening to ATC through the headphones. The difference in sound between the two is often sufficient to keep you from confusing ATC with the ATIS recording. Either way works in my book, which is what you're reading at the moment.

I've noticed that IFR students also have trouble handling traffic advisories when flying VFR or IFR. If you're in solid IMC conditions and ATC calls out traffic for you (and I don't mean freeway traffic... "Look out for that Malibu on I-95"), just say, "2132 Bravo, unable." The controller knows what that means. You don't have to tell

When the ATIS is Misunderstood

This is Broadview tower information Mike, altimeter is...

2132 Bravo, do you have Mike?

No. Mike couldn't make it today.

him you're in the clouds. He knows you're on an IFR flight plan.

Suppose you're VFR or in VMC on an IFR flight plan and ATC calls traffic for you. If you don't see the traffic, acknowledge the call by saying, "2132 Bravo, no contact." If you see the traffic, say that it's in sight. If you don't see the traffic and it seems uncomfortably close or closing, ask ATC for an avoidance vector around traffic.

Keep in mind that controllers can't see which way your airplane is crabbing into the wind (Figure 32). It's a radar screen, not a movie screen. The controller only sees the airplane's direction of travel. If your radar blip is heading directly toward another blip but your airplane is crabbing 20 degrees to the left, the target called by ATC will be at 1 o'clock, not 12 o'clock.

You will sometimes be told to, "Resume own navigation." This usually happens when ATC was temporarily providing vectors to another location, or to get you clear of conflicting traffic. After the need for assistance is over, you're back on your own—you resume you own navigation, meaning you are to use the navigation equipment in your airplane to fly the route shown in your last ATC clearance. You are still in radar contact with ATC, so you don't need to make those non-radar contact position reports we previously discussed.

Sometimes you will have been in perfectly fine radar contact that suddenly goes bye-bye for some reason (jelly sandwich splotches on the screen, radar outage, no coverage where you are, pulsating UFO signals). How will you know when this happens? ATC will say, "Radar contact lost," or "Radar service terminated."

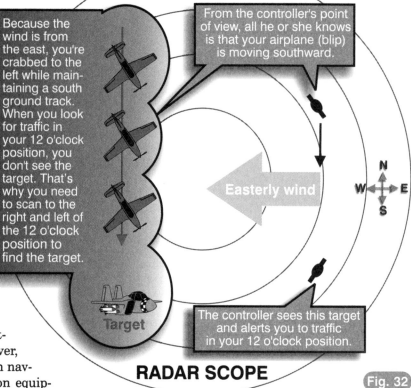

Wind Effect on Traffic Calls

Because the wind is from the east, you're crabbed to the left while maintaining a south ground track. When you look for traffic in your 12 o'clock position, you don't see the target. That's why you need to scan to the right and left of the 12 o'clock position to find the target.

From the controller's point of view, all he or she knows is that your airplane (blip) is moving southward.

Easterly wind

The controller sees this target and alerts you to traffic in your 12 o'clock position.

Target

RADAR SCOPE   Fig. 32

If you hear these words, you are no longer under ATC radar surveillance and must resume position reports at compulsory reporting points. It won't happen very often, especially due to lack of coverage or jelly sandwich splotches. On the other hand, equipment failures do happen. There was recently a major outage at a Southern California ARTCC caused by a car accident that took out a power pole. ATC's 100% "sure-thing, can't miss," backup generators failed to generate, and it was time for the Shrimp Boat Song to be sung, and position reports to be made.

On another occasion, when a portion of a Center's radar facility went blank and controllers resorted to separation based on airplane position reports, the controller told me that my radar service was terminated. I told him I wasn't at the terminal yet, and asked if he could unterminate it. Negative. Apparently a vacuum tube failed somewhere and radar was out (OK, they probably don't use tubes anymore. Just kidding).

Talking the Talk

Doctors sound like doctors; lawyers sound like lawyers; and pilots sound like pilots. As an instrument pilot, you'll want to be sure to talk the talk correctly when flying IFR. It won't do much in terms of providing a lift for the airplane, but it will provide considerable lift for you.

Avspeak consists of acronyms, special vocabulary, and particular shorthand ways of saying things. Much of this has evolved because of the need to communicate on the radio, where it's essential to communicate a lot while saying little. Especially important is the concept of ensuring both you and the controller know what to expect from each other. Imagine the discomfort you'll feel if the controller asks you to descend to "one point five thousand."

Be Brief and Happy on the Radio

Yes, it's even all right to sound happy on the radio if it pleases you. Just be sure to think about brevity in communication, and think carefully before you speak. And you might want to take the earrings off when wearing the headset (this applies to the ladies, too).

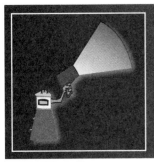

Radio Volume Training 101

In a radio-related report, an introduction to instrument training turned into a lesson in priorities and cockpit discipline. A private pilot reports:

After a briefing on the ground, we took off. Runway 35 was in use and we were to fly the ILS 17 approach. I was wearing a hood, and the CFI was coaching me through the turns and timing. Intercom between headsets was in use. At some point, the CFI turned down the radio volume because traffic between Tower and other aircraft was conflicting with his instructions. I removed the hood at decision altitude, noted a flashing red light signal from the Tower cab, and immediately initiated a missed approach. My first thought was that the Tower had lost their radio. Then I was shocked to see our radio volume turned down. The CFI admitted that he had forgotten to turn it back up. **NASA**

Does he mean 1,500 feet? 150 feet? 15,000 feet? This is why speaking properly is essential when flying IFR.

The first and most important item is identifying yourself. Suppose your aircraft number is N794CT and you want to call an ATC facility. Using the phonetic alphabet (yes, I know we don't have many Phonecians flying nowadays, but the alphabet they developed is a good one, right?), your call would be:

"SoCal Approach, this is Cessna seven niner four Charlie Tango."

The prefix *N* is dropped when the aircraft manufacturer's name or model number is stated. After initial communication is established, ATC may use an abbreviated call sign and refer to your aircraft by the prefix N and your last three digits or letter. In the above example, ATC may refer to you as *November four Charlie Tango,* or more commonly just *four Charlie Tango.*

When informing ATC of your altitude, aviation phraseology should be used in the following manner (I'll assume that you are flying below 18,000 feet MSL):

If your altitude is 6,500 feet state this as *six thousand five hundred.*

If your altitude is 10,500 feet state this as *one zero thousand five hundred.* It's not *ten thousand five hundred.*

If you're referring to a frequency like 125.6 MHz, it's properly stated as *one two five point six.* Decimals are identified by the word *point.*

Over is often used at the end of a transmission, although it is not essential if the context and pattern of your communication makes it obvious when you're done talking. When you use *over* at the end of your statements, it means that a reply is expected. It's also an effective way of telling the receiving party that you're done talking. If we were to use such language at a cocktail party, there would be much less confusion about who's still talking. "Well Bob, how are you doing, over?" "To tell you the truth Frank, I'm not sure, over."

The word *roger* is used to let the transmitting party know their transmission has been received. It should not be used to answer a question requiring a *yes* or *no* answer. Speaking of *yes* and *no,* these become *affirmative* and *negative* in avspeak. Once again, the goal is to create clarity and eliminate (as much as possible) any chance of confusion. *No* can sound like too many other words when said over an aviation radio, which degrades speech considerably (no matter how silver-tongued you are). *Yes* could be *I guess,* or *what a mess.*

When the tower says to do something and you agree that you can and will accept the instruction, the proper response is *wilco,* which means you have received the message, understand it, and will comply. Sometimes pilots are a little lazy and use *roger* instead of *wilco.* I can assure you that the words *roger dodger* are not part of the aviation communication lingo, so please don't use them. If you're carrying around any leftover CB lingo, get your ears on for a second good buddy, and listen up. Drop it, lest you become the laughingstock of the aviation airwaves.

Flight Service Station is a nice name, but a bit long for throwing around on the radio. That's why we call a Flight Service Station *radio.* Hawthorne FSS becomes *Hawthorn Radio* on a radio call.

Other ground stations have their own nomenclature:

Airport unicom ..... *Corona Unicom.*

EFAS - Enroute flight Advisory Service (Flight Watch) ..... *Hawthorne Flight Watch.*

Air Traffic Control Tower ..... *Lambert Tower.*

Ground Control ..... *Boise Ground.*

Clearance Delivery ..... *Ontario Clearance Delivery.*

Approach Control ..... *New York Approach.*

Departure Control .... *St. Louis Departure.*

Air Route Traffic Control Center ..... *Miami Center.*

Then there's the matter of time. Pilots have lots of it. *Zulu* or *UTC (coordinated universal time)* time is the time in Greenwich, England. Who cares? You do, because many aviation times are stated as Zulu (or Z) times. Weather reports are stated in Zulu time, and the flight plans you file will give departure and arrival times in Zulu time. By using a clock in one place, pilots who sometimes cross large amounts of space in a relatively brief period don't wrestle with local time zones and conversions. When it's 0300 Zulu, it's 0300 Zulu *everywhere in the world,* although what it comes out to be in *local time* varies.

Another type of pilot time is the 24-hour clock (like that used in the military). In this system, the hours of the day are numbered from 1 to 24; 1:00 a.m. is 0100 hours, and 1:00 p.m. is 1300 hours. Local time is expressed on the 24 hour clock in aviation. Of course, this can be a bit of a mystery to non-aviators. One time I was on my way out of a parking garage. The young attendant looked at my ticket, subtracted 1300 (1:00 p.m., when I'd entered) from 1500 (3:00 p.m., when I was leaving) and announced the bill as 200 hours times $3/hour, for a total of $600. No checks or credit cards accepted (ouch!).

There's lots more avtalk to learn, but this will get you started.

Self-Announce Position and/or Intentions at Non-tower Airports

Here's a chance to talk about yourself. Need I say more?

Self-announce is a procedure where you broadcast your position and intentions on the airport's common traffic advisory frequency (CTAF) as shown in Figure 33. This is a procedure used primarily at airports that do not have an operating control tower. The self-announce procedure is particularly applicable to you as an instrument pilot, since you'll fly instrument approaches instead of making the typical traffic pattern entry. In other words, you will make be making a straight-in or circling approach under marginal weather conditions, when a few hardy VFR pilots may still be operating in the traffic pattern. It's entirely possible to find yourself on final approach at a non-tower airport staring straight into the spinner of another airplane that's taking off. It's enough to make your prop stop.

That's why you should be particularly alert when conducting an instrument approach to one of these airports. When flying any actual or practice instrument approach, regardless of its direction relative to other airport operations, make a good entrance by announcing the following on the airport's CTAF:

1. Announce when you are departing the final approach fix, inbound on a non-precision approach, or departing the outer marker or fix used in lieu of the outer marker, inbound on a precision approach (it's often best to use distances and directions instead of less-well-recognized fix names);

2. Announce when you are established on the final approach segment or immediately upon being advised by ATC to contact the local advisory frequency;

3. Announce when you're making a missed approach.

On the other hand, please don't announce something like, "Who is the greatest plot and why am I?"

Keep in mind that when ATC allows you to switch to advisory frequency, you're still obligated to cancel your IFR flight plan if you haven't already done so. On many occasions when flying an instrument approach during VFR conditions to a now-towered airport, I've cancelled IFR when asked to switch to the CTAF. On other occasions, I've had to make a radio or phone call from the ground after arrival to cancel my IFR flight plan. Sometimes

Self Announce on the CTAF

When flying an instrument approach to a non-tower airport or an airport where the tower is closed, self-announce your position on the Common Traffic Advisory Frequency (position A) when ATC allows a frequency change.

you can do this with your VHF radio. At other times you'll need to call the local FSS and have the specialist forward your request to cancel to the appropriate controller.

When the controller switches you to the advisory frequency, ask if radio communication from the ground is possible at this airport. The controller working the local area will usually know. If not, ask for their local phone number and call via cell phone or landline after landing. I've done this on few occasions, and it works quite well.

The following is an example of self-announce phraseology:

Inbound

Corona traffic, Cessna Two One Three Two Bravo, (say position), (say altitude), (descending) or entering downwind/base/final (as appropriate) Runway two-four (full stop or touch-and-go), Corona.

Corona traffic, Cessna Two One Three Two Bravo clear of Runway two-four, Corona.

Outbound

Corona traffic, Cessna Two One Three Two Bravo (say location on airport) taxiing to Runway two-four, Corona.

Corona traffic, Cessna Two One Three Two Bravo departing Runway six. Departing the pattern to the (say direction), climbing to (say altitude), Corona.

Practice Instrument Approach

Corona traffic, Cessna Two One Three Two Bravo (say position from airport) inbound descending through (say altitude) practice (say name of approach) approach Runway six, Corona.

Corona traffic, Cessna Two One Three Two Bravo practice (say type) approach completed or terminated, Runway six, Corona

Why Self Announcing on the CTAF is Important

Near Miss Bliss

An airport that normally has an operating control tower becomes an uncontrolled airport when the tower closes for the night. Pilots then use the tower frequency as a Common Traffic Advisory Frequency (CTAF). At least some pilots do. An air carrier captain reports:

We transmitted our intentions on CTAF and proceeded to Runway 20. During taxi, we heard no other radio calls. We announced on CTAF that we were taxiing onto Runway 20. We had still heard no calls from any other aircraft. I was about to advance the throttles, when to our total astonishment, we saw a light aircraft lifting off, coming straight at us on Runway 2. Due to the lay of the land, we were unable to see him until he lifted off. He flew overhead and finally broke the silence by announcing that he was turning downwind. After he was well clear, we departed uneventfully. It was just luck and fortunate timing that we did not meet head-on at high speed at mid-field.

The preceding reports emphasize the importance of vigilance and radio communications at uncontrolled fields.

NASA Callback Report

Practice Instrument Approaches

There are times when a pilot needs to practice flying instrument approaches but isn't IFR current, and thus can't legally file an IFR flight plan. Fortunately, there's a provision in the ATC system that allows you to fly an instrument approach in VFR conditions without having to file IFR. It's called a *practice instrument approach*, which is technically a VFR activity.

To practice instrument approaches in VFR conditions, just ask the controller for a practice instrument approach. Use that specific phrase, and both you and the controller will know that this will be a VFR operation conducted in VFR conditions. Sure, the controller will still provide separation between you and other airplanes. How much separation? In addition to the normal horizontal IFR separation minimums, 500 feet vertical separation may be applied between VFR aircraft and between a VFR and IFR aircraft.

Just to be double clear here, a practice instrument approach is not in any way, shape, or form an IFR clearance. If at some point along the way you want to really conduct IFR operations (perhaps it's no longer possible to maintain VFR), you must specifically request and obtain an IFR clearance from the controller.

Controllers are usually quite willing to let you practice approaches, on a workload-permitting basis. When requesting a practice instrument approach, let the approach control facility or the tower know the type of practice approach you want to make and how you intend to terminate it, (i.e., full-stop landing, touch-and-go, or missed or low approach maneuver). I even make it a point to let the controller know that I'm aware of how busy he or she can be when making this request by stating, "Approach, 2132 Bravo, workload permitting, request practice ILS to Long Beach followed by a low approach." Sometimes I'll even say, "...and perhaps I'll use the afterburner on departure for your amusement." This always gets their attention, especially when you're flying a Cessna 152 (OK, don't say the last part).

The controller's job is to integrate these approaches so they do not disrupt the flow of arriving and departing IFR or VFR aircraft. Sometimes that simply isn't possible, due to the number of people wanting to take off and land. Because few controllers know how important you are, you'll have to be a bit flexible, just like the wings are.

I remember a Goodyear blimp flying a practice ILS approach to Long Beach, California (yes, the blimp actually flies instrument approaches. Instead of a stopwatch for timing from the FAF, the pilot uses a calendar). The controller was in a pickle when a Boeing 727 jet suddenly showed up to use the same ILS approach. The controller informed the 727 that there would be a bit of a delay. Hearing this, the blimp pilot offered to slide over to the right of the localizer, stop in mid air, and let the jet go by. The controller agreed, and the jet flew the ILS and landed. The controller thanked the blimp pilot and instructed him to cancel his "side bag" maneuver and rejoin the localizer for the approach. It's nice when pilots work together, right?

VFR aircraft practicing instrument approaches are not automatically authorized to execute the missed approach procedure. If you want to do a missed, then you must specifically request and receive permission from the controller (either the tower or the approach controller) to do so. Aircraft separation will not be provided unless the missed approach has been approved by ATC.

When flying a practice instrument approach you must not, except in an emergency, deviate from the approved procedure until cleared to do so by the controller. Hopefully you won't have trouble remaining on the approach course, even if you're really out of practice. If you're so rusty that your ILS approach needles look like two Samurai warriors in a sword fight, grab an instructor to help smooth things out.

Shogun a' Need More Practice

Hopefully, when flying an ILS approach, the localizer and glideslope needles in your omni display won't look two Samurai warriors challenging each other. On the other hand, if you hear an embarrassing clicking noise coming from your panel, you can always tell your passengers that you left your airplane's turn signal on.

It's also important to remember to keep your eyes looking outside the airplane during practice instrument approaches, especially when approaching the airport. Of course, if you're wearing a view limiting device, this will be difficult. It would also be cheating. Naturally, if you're wearing one of these things you'll have a safety pilot with you. So instruct this person to remain sharp and aware. Even so, if traffic becomes too heavy, pull off those Foggles to assist in traffic avoidance.

As a final note, it's not at all unreasonable to ask a controller to practice other aspects of IFR under VFR conditions. For instance, you might want to practice holding in VFR conditions. If so, ask the Approach or Center controller to provide you with a few holding clearances at local intersections. Most controllers are not only willing to help, they're pleased to do so since they don't often get a chance to issue these clearances. They need the practice, too.

Traffic Alerting/Avoidance Systems

Not too long ago, it was only a dream that pilots would fly with onboard equipment that alerted them to the location of airborne traffic, then provided the proper resolution for avoiding an unwanted encounter. Things have changed. There are now four common categories of traffic alerting or collision-avoidance systems you're likely to encounter. Before I explain each one, let me provide you with an overview of the three categories of traffic alerting/avoidance system by explaining the service each provides.

Category 1. This system detects a target's distance and altitude, but provides no bearing and target direction information. This system is called a TCAD.

Category 2. These systems detect a target's distance, bearing, direction of flight, altitude and whether that target is climbing or descending. These systems are called either, TAS, TIS, ADS-B, or TIS-B.

Category 3. This system is called TCAS and has three different variations.

A TCAS I system can detect a target's distance, bearing, direction of flight and altitude.

A TCAS II system has TCAS I capabilities and it can tell whether a target is climbing or descending as well as telling you to climb or descend to resolve the conflict, thus providing what is known as "resolution advisories."

A TCAS III system does all that a TCAS II system can do as well as providing resolution advisories in the horizontal direction, too.

Let's examine each system in detail.

TCAS

Most of today's modern airliners are equipped with TCAS or *traffic alert and collision avoidance system*. This is a high tech and very expensive piece of equipment that provides a proximity warning of other aircraft. There are three versions of TCAS.

A "TCAS I" system provides a proximity warning in the form of a target's distance, bearing, direction of flight and altitude. This system doesn't provide a means of resolving the traffic conflict, also known as *resolution advisories*. In other words, it doesn't tell you to climb, descend, turn

How TCAS Presents Traffic Alert and Avoidance Information

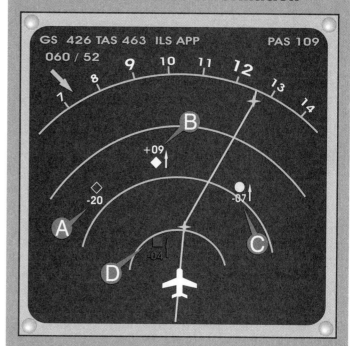

The movement behind the development of the modern TCAS system was the result of two airliners colliding over the Grand Canyon on June 30th, 1956. The aviation industry understood that, at the speeds modern airliners fly, pilots needed a system that would help them avoid collisions.

In 1974 the MITRE Corporation's Center for Advanced Aviation System Development (CAASD) proposed using the transponders that were already on modern airplanes in development of an *alerting and collision avoidance* device. This proposal led to the development of an onboard system that sent transponder interrogation signals to nearby aircraft. These interrogated transponders then sent reply signals that were received by the original sending aircraft. Through this exchange, it was possible to determine the location, the speed and the direction of flight for each target and present this data to a pilot for collision avoidance.

In 1981 the FAA elected to pursue MITRE's concept in lieu of a ground based system collision avoidance system that was concurrently under consideration. Many other companies were involved in the development of what has become known as TCAS.

Here's what the typical symbols on TCAS indicate. Keep in mind that different TCAS units can be set up to display information in different ways. Target A indicates other traffic in level flight 2,000 feet below. Target B indicates proximate traffic 900 feet above climbing at 500 ft/min or greater. Target C indicates a *Traffic Advisory* or TA with the traffic shown in yellow at 700 feet below climbing at 500 ft/min or greater. A Traffic Advisory is indicated by the accompanying aural warning of "TRAFFIC, TRAFFIC," which sounds once and then is reset until the next TA occurs. Target D indicates a TCAS *Resolution Advisory* (RA) with traffic shown in red and 400 feet below climbing at 500 ft/min or greater. RAs are indicated by one or more aural warnings that offer guidance in avoiding the target aircraft. This may include warnings like, 'Climb-Climb Now, Increase Descent, Descend-Descend Now," etc.

A TA or RA message followed by the traffic's range, altitude and (if applicable) vertical motion arrow appear on the display if TCAS cannot determine the other aircraft's bearing.

The Original Traffic Alert and Collision Avoidance System

right or left. You have to figure out how to avoid traffic on your own, but at least you have help in finding it.

A "TCAS II" system provides traffic advisories and single-axis vertical resolution advisories. You are given a recommended maneuver in a vertical direction (climb or descend only) to avoid exchanging paint with the other aircraft. TCAS II is usually intended for airliners and larger commuter and business aircraft that carry many passengers. You won't typically find these systems on smaller airplanes, because most private pilots find the cost of $150,000-$200,000 a bit steep for equipping a 172.

TCAS III is similar to TCAS II, but the system also provides resolution advisories in the horizontal direction. You'll be instructed to go right or left as well as up or down, to avoid traffic. These systems are even more expensive, and thus even less likely to be seen on anything that doesn't have "jet" as part of its name.

TCAS works through the magic of an antenna (and fancy circuitry, too) that sends and receives transponder interrogation signals. After an interrogating pulse is sent to another airplane's transponder by the antenna, the target airplane's transponder receives and returns the signal (it has been interrogated, so to speak). The return signal is received by the TCAS antenna in such a way that the target airplane's direction can be identified. While a technical description of how this works is beyond the scope of this book, it's safe to say that an antenna laid out in two dimensions (similar to an ADF loop antenna) will receive different parts of the signal at different times. This is essentially how the TCAS antenna works its magic. Then, through some incredibly sophisticated electronics (about $200,000 worth), calculations are made that determine the target's direction and distance along with the target's altitude from its Mode C/S transponder. The key point here is that a target airplane without an operating transponder won't show up on anyone's TCAS. If the target airplane's pilot is operating in Mode A only (because he doesn't have his transponder set to ALT) then his altitude won't be shown on a TCAS unit.

TAS

TAS or *traffic advisory system* is very similar to TCAS in that it is an active system that interrogates the transponders of other aircraft and provides information on a target's distance, bearing and altitude. But no resolution advisories are provided, making this unit similar to a TCAS I system in its capabilities. The difference between TAS and TCAS is cost. Avidyne's TAS-600 traffic advisory system and the Goodrich SkyWatch HP Traffic Alerting System are good examples of traffic advisory systems (Figure 34). These systems cost around $14,000 and $20,000–$25,000 respectively. Like TCAS, these systems actively interrogate the transponders of other aircraft. They just happen to do so at much less cost to you, the pilot.

Avidyne/Ryan TAS-600

The TAS-600 system is similar to TCAS in that it provides realtime traffic monitoring and advisories and is not dependent on radar coverage ground-based transmitters. As with TCAS, this system independently interrogates the transponders of nearby aircraft up to a range of seven nautical miles with a 3,500 foot vertical separation. The TAS600 provides three levels of alert, so pilots can monitor traffic before it ever becomes a threat. The first level of alert is indicated on the display as an open diamond shape (Figure 34, position A), with the altitude separation indicated between the host and threat aircraft and an arrow indicating if the threat aircraft is climbing, descending, or at the same altitude (as shown in position A). This is referred to as Other Traffic (OT). OT is not an immediate threat but is within the surveillance area and the pilot should be aware of existing traffic.

The second level of alert is Proximity Alert (PA) and is displayed with the same information as OT, with the exception that the diamond shape is now a solid shape on the traffic display (Figure 34, position B and C). The target in Position B is 300 feet below you and descending while the target in position C is 500 feet below you and climbing. Both OT and PA alerts are white on a color display or are not highlighted on a monochromatic display.

Traffic with a calculated intercept course for altitude and direction become a Traffic Alert (TA). When a TA is encountered, the intruder traffic is indicated as an yellow circle (Figure 34, position D). The target is position D is 200 feet above you in level flight. When a traffic conflict is eminent, pilots need the right information in real time. Avidyne's heads-up audible system tells you the target's bearing, range and relative altitude for rapid visual acquisition of traffic.

Fig. 34

TCAD

TCAD or *traffic and collision alerting device* is a phrase that is becoming less common. These systems are often referred to as "passive" or "listening" systems in that they listen for a transponder that's already being interrogated. For systems like this to work, you must be in an area where the transponders on aircraft are being interrogated by ATC radar or by the TCAS/TAS systems on other aircraft (remember, TCAS/TAS interrogate transponders on their own). Leave radar coverage (or be beyond the TCAS/TAS coverage from other airplanes) and your TCAD system stops showing traffic.

The ATD-300 Traffic-Watch is a passive receiver capable of detecting transponder replies from nearby aircraft and displaying their range and altitude

Once the TCAD identifies a target airplane's transponder reply to someone else's interrogation, it typically displays the target's altitude and distance from your airplane. It doesn't display target bearing and direction of flight. There is also no "avoidance" information provided as there is with a TCAS II or III system.

Sometimes manufacturers use the term TAS for their TCAD devices. This can be a bit confusing but that's the way aviation is sometimes. TCAD devices are relatively inexpensive and serve a good purpose in aviation. For instance, the Monroy TrafficWatch ATD-300 (Figure 35) unit sells for less than $650. These units are small, fit easily on the top of your panel and provide target distance and altitude information. You shouldn't, however, wear them on top your headset. If you're like me, you've probably already glued a small, spinning propeller up there.

TIS

TIS or *traffic information service* provides traffic information in terms of distance, bearing, direction of flight, and altitude. It doesn't provide resolution advisories. TIS requires that your airplane have a Mode S transponder, like Garmin's GTX330 (Figure 36), and some means of presenting target information visually, such as a moving map display. TIS also requires that your aircraft be within range of a ground station (Figure 37). A Mode S transponder does the same thing as a Mode A and C transponder, and a bit more. It has the capability of uplinking the transponder data from other airplanes to your cockpit via the ground station I

Garmin's Mode S Transponder

Garmin's GTX330 is a Mode S transponder (retailing for about $5,000) that allows data uplinking/downlinking from ground based transmitters (GBTs) to your airplane. The Mode S transponder is an essential part of TIS (traffic information service).

just mentioned. This is how you get all that traffic information in your cockpit.

Here's how TIS works. The ground based stations (Figure 38) collect information on all transponder equipped aircraft (operating in Modes A, C or S) and uplink this information to your airplane's Mode S transponder (the GTX330

How Traffic Information Service (TIS) Works

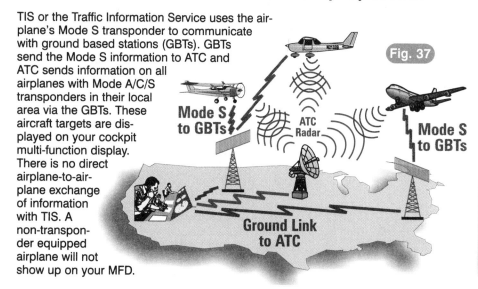

TIS or the Traffic Information Service uses the airplane's Mode S transponder to communicate with ground based stations (GBTs). GBTs send the Mode S information to ATC and ATC sends information on all airplanes with Mode A/C/S transponders in their local area via the GBTs. These aircraft targets are displayed on your cockpit multi-function display. There is no direct airplane-to-airplane exchange of information with TIS. A non-transponder equipped airplane will not show up on your MFD.

A TIS Ground Based Transmitter (GBT)

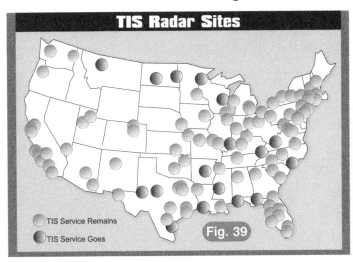

TIS Radar Sites

○ TIS Service Remains
● TIS Service Goes

Fig. 39

Less than 25% of the continental U.S. has TIS ground based stations (GBTs). GBTs are often associated with approach ASR 7/8/9 radar sites. As these sites are upgraded to ASR 11 status, they are not being given TIS functionality. It's possible that ADS-B will eventually replace TIS as a means of controlling traffic and for traffic awareness and collision avoidance.

from Garmin that I just mentioned). This information can then be displayed on certain moving map displays, such as Garmin's 400/500/1000 series GPS units. Not only can you see altitude, direction and distance of the target aircraft, but it's possible on Garmin's unit to see a target aircraft's vector line (its direction of flight). Keep in mind that all this occurs without your airplane having to actively interrogate or even passively identify another aircraft's transponder. That's because the TIS ground station is doing all the work. Your Mode S transponder is providing the means of data uplink and your moving map display is electronically displaying the information received.

What you get with a Mode S transponder and a moving map display is the ability to do what the Avidyne/Ryan TAS-600 or Goodyear's SkyWatch system does, but at a price that might be affordable even if you're not a publicly held company. A Mode S transponder typically sells for less than $5,000 (if you purchase it from the back of a van in a parking lot, it probably costs a lot less and probably belonged to someone else, too. So don't do this).

Unfortunately, as of this writing, less than 25% of the continental United States has TIS ground station coverage and this number appears to be decreasing (Figure 39). TIS is currently available from 107 Mode S terminal radars, which were the older ASR7/8/9 units. During facility upgrades to ASR II facilities, the FAA failed to require TIS functionality, so these newer facilities don't have TIS capability. Whether or not TIS will be made available at these newer facilities is not clear. It appears, however, that the FAA has become more interested in our next system, known as *ADS-B*.

ADS-B and TIS-B

ADS-B or *automatic dependent surveillance broadcast* is cutting edge technology that is already present in the cockpit of many airplanes. It's a revolutionary new way of identifying and controlling air traffic. The concept is simple. Here's how it works.

Unlike radar, which bounces radio waves from ground-based antennas off airborne targets and then captures the reflected signals for interpretation, ADS-B uses conventional *Global Navigation Satellite System* (GNSS) technology and a relatively simple broadcast communications link as its fundamental components. It does this with a UAT or *universal access transceiver* (Garmin's GDL 90 is a UAT that interfaces with a multi-function cockpit display). This UAT is remotely mounted in your airplane and is designed to transmit, receive, and decode ADS-B messages sent from other airplanes and from ADS-B ground stations (called GBTs). This data link broadcasts your aircraft's position, velocity, projected track (all derived from GPS) and flight identification to other ADS-B equipped aircraft in your area, as well as to GBTs (Figure 40).

It's important to remember that ADS-B allows airplane-to-airplane information exchange. No GBTs are required for ADS-B equipped airplanes to talk (exchange data) with each other. This is what allows ADS-B equipped airplanes to identify each other's position, direction of flight, speed and altitude. Unfortunately, resolution advisories are not provided by ADS-B units at this time.

The interesting thing about the GBTs is that they can uplink to your airplane the traffic information shown on

ADS-B - Automatic Dependent Surveillance Broadcast

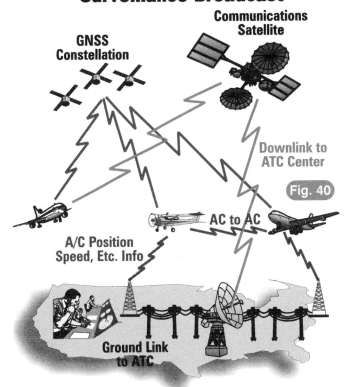

GNSS Constellation

Communications Satellite

Downlink to ATC Center

Fig. 40

A/C Position Speed, Etc. Info

AC to AC

Ground Link to ATC

ADS-B or Automatic Dependent Surveillance Broadcast is the latest cutting edge technology for controlling traffic and collision awareness. It uses a UAT or Universal Access Transmitter to send and receive data between other airplanes and ground based stations (GBTs). In this way there is airplane-to-airplane data exchange and airplane to GBTs data exchange (which means airplane-to-airplane data exchange with ATC via the GBTs). Airplanes don't have to be within range of a GBT to have a traffic information exchange.

ADS-B Presentation on Garmin's MX 20 Multi-Function Display

ADS-B displays traffic information using the same convention we've already seen with TCAS and TAS. Target position and direction of flight are identified by blue symbols (position A). Next to each target is an altitude reference (position B) indicating whether the airplane is above (a + sign) or below (a - sign) your airplane and the amount of altitude difference in hundreds of feet. Your airplane is centered in the display (position C). At present, it costs approximately $8,000 to equip an airplane with ADS-B equipment. The cost should dramatically decrease in the next few years.

Picture Courtesy Jim Cieplak MX 20

Fig. 41

ATC's secondary surveillance radar. This means that, in addition to identifying other ADS-B equipped airplane, you can see the Mode A/C/S targets that the controller sees on his or her radar screen. In fact, there is a special name for this very specific uplink activity. It' called TIS-B or *traffic information service-broadcast.*

So, if you're asked what TIS-B is, you should say that it's nothing more than the reception of GBT uplinked secondary surveillance radar traffic information to your ADS-B equipped airplane. Figure 41 shows how TIS-B information is typically presented on a cockpit multi-function display. You can remember this by thinking of the Christmas song that includes the words, "Do you see what I see?"

ADS-B accuracy does not seriously degrade with range, atmospheric conditions, or target altitude. And update intervals do not depend on the rotational speed or reliability of mechanical antennas. It is also a relatively simple, cost effective technology that works well at low altitudes and on the ground. It's completely effective in remote areas or in mountainous terrain where there is either no radar coverage, or where radar coverage is restricted by problems with elevation, or line of sight. In fact, ADS-B proved itself successful during its early tests conducted in Alaska. Now that's mountainous and isolated terrain.

What TCAS/TCAD/TAS/TIS/ADS-B or TIS-B Allows You to Do

Be aware that the information provided by TIS-B or any other traffic system (other than TCAS II and III, as you'll see shortly) is for pilot situational awareness (since they don't provide resolution advisories). These units are not collision avoidance systems, they're traffic alerting or information type systems only. These units most definitely do not relieve you of the responsibility to see and avoid.

Unless there's an imminent conflict requiring immediate action, any deviation from an air traffic control clearance based on an electronically displayed target must be approved by ATC prior to commencing the maneuver. A deviation made on your own without informing ATC could place your airplane in close proximity to another aircraft under ATC control (one that you can't or didn't see on your airborne traffic equipment). This could result in a pilot deviation action, since you're expected to maintain your assigned altitude within +/- 300 feet while flying IFR. It could also result in a crash, which is even worse. Exceeding these limits as a response to an alert without visually identifying a real collision threat is in violation of the regulations.

If you are alerted to the presence of a target you should search for it visually and quickly. Set aside your tuna sandwich for a moment. If you spot the traffic and there's a problem, the ideal strategy is to ask for permission to maneuver. But it's entirely possible that you will see a critical intruder target on your TIS unit before the controller does. You are not expected to swallow a 747 (or your tuna sandwich) while waiting for permission to deviate. Implied in the regulations is your right to do what's necessary to stay alive. If, in your judgment, there's no time to ask, then act. Period.

Avoiding a potential target is an entirely different matter if you're using a TCAS II or III unit. If you're equipped with either of these units, then you're expected to maneuver to avoid a collision based on their *resolution advisories* (see TCAS sidebar, page 17-22). Once that's done, you're expected to notify ATC of that deviation ASAP, and then return to your assigned altitude, heading and/or route. Unless the controller is on a break, it's highly likely he or she will notice if your plane suddenly plummets or climbs a few hundred feet, which should be enough to get the dialog going. TCAS units are sophisticated enough to minimize the chance that a false or erroneous target might generate an avoidance maneuver in the form of a resolution advisory.

Minimum Fuel Advisory

There comes a time in every pilot's experience where he or she, somehow, for some reason, manages to get low on fuel or at least thinks he's low on fuel. Regardless of the reason, there is a procedure for alerting the controller to this situation without actually having to declare an emergency or obtain priority handling. It's called a *minimum fuel advisory*, which just happen to be the words you'd utter to the controller to convey the urgency of your situation. Here's how it works.

When it dawns on you that the fuel on board will permit approximately zero delay after reaching your destination, tell the nice controller that you have "minimum fuel." This isn't quite a declaration of an emergency, but merely an advisory that if there's any undue delay along the way, it could become an emergency, which would raise the adrenaline level for everyone, and we don't really want that, do we, ma'am?

The proper way to inform the controller is to use the phraseology, "Bay Approach, this is 2132 Bravo, minimum fuel." You may deliver the phrase an octave or two above your normal range, but at least the controller will know of your situation and assist you during arrival.

Now You Have Leaves

Congratulations. You've been through a lot and now it's graduation time. You've made it this far and deserve a full set of leaves for your noggin. The instrument rating is something that you'll use for a long time. Even if you never fly instruments, you'll find comfort in knowing that you know a lot more about the IFR systems that your non-instrument rated fellow pilots. It's a real confidence booster to have that rating in your back pocket.

Then again, as with any skill, if you want the instrument rating as a backup plan for bad weather, you need to practice your IFR flying skills, even when the weather is VFR. How? When taking trips normally flown VFR, try filing an IFR flight plan. If you have a safety pilot, then fly using a view limiting device. If not, then fly the trip on an IFR flight plan for no other reason than increased exposure to the IFR system. It's amazing how confidence building the experience will be. Confidence at instrument flying is as much a matter of feeling comfort working in the IFR system as it is feeling capable on the gauges. Given the proliferation of GPS and glass cockpit displays, maintaining your confidence and fidelity with the equipment in your airplane is now more important than ever. Good flying to you!

The Fellow With the Tough Job

Brian Weiss is the owner of WORD'SWORTH, a marketing communications and design company. WORD'SWORTH provides services for all forms and formats of communications materials. Capabilities include the creation of brochures, books, newsletters, direct response letters, advertising, catalog sheets, slide shows and videos.

WORD'SWORTH clients have included Bank of America, Xerox Corporation, the National Childhood Cancer Foundation, Childrens Hospital (Los Angeles), the University of California (Irvine and Los Angeles campuses), Health Valley Foods, McGraw-Hill/CRM Films, Saint Joseph Hospital, *American Health* magazine, *Psychology Today* magazine, *Equity Quarterly*, Saint John's Hospital, *Aviation Safety* magazine, Long Beach and Santa Monica airports, and many others in a wide variety of fields.

In addition to general business expertise, WORD'SWORTH provides specialized background and knowledge in the areas of medicine and health care, science and technology, aviation and fundraising.

WORD'SWORTH also offers consulting on marketing strategies, direct mail campaigns, and fundraising proposals.

A little about Brian Weiss:

Founder (1977) and owner, WORD'SWORTH
Former editor, *Baja Explorer* magazine
Former associate editor, *Psychology Today* magazine
Served on the faculties of UCLA and the University of Michigan teaching introductory courses and advanced seminars in departments of human behavior, geography, and journalism.
Author for six years of a nationally syndicated consumer newspaper column (*FREEBIES*), and creator of a national magazine of the same name
Former medical/science editor, *Aviation Safety* magazine
Member (and former Board of Directors member), of Angel Flight, a not-for-profit community service organization.
Brian has been a pilot since 1980. He packs a private pilot certificate with an instrument rating and is the proud owner of a Cessna 172. He's one of the organizers of Flight Log, a group which provides information for pilots flying in Baja and throughout Mexico.

Brian Weiss

"Brian is one of the most talented, energetic and intelligent people with whom I've had the pleasure of working. His advice and dedication to this project were simply invaluable!"
Rod Machado

WORD'SWORTH

626-510-9180

bweiss@aol.com

The Gal With Talent and a Lot of Patience

The Aviation Speakers Bureau
Providing Quality Aviation Speakers Since 1986

The Aviation Speakers Bureau features speakers for your banquet, educational seminar, safety standdown, convention, conference, forum, trade show, keynote, corporate training, airshow, safety program or association meeting. We guarantee a perfect match for your needs and objectives, and recommend only the very best in speakers. Our professionals shine and make YOU look good every time!

"We will help you find the perfect speaker for your budget and there is <u>never</u> a charge for our service."

Presentation and Topics

Safety, Weather, Instrument Flying, Inspirational, Cockpit Resource Management, Aviation Humor, Understanding Airspace, Test Pilots, Teamwork, Stress, Fighter Pilots and Aces, Weather Radar, In-flight Emergencies, Multi-engine Procedures, Celebrities and Heroes, Vietnam Pilots, Aviation Management, Interpreting Instrument Charts, Comedy, Air Racers, Policies and Politics of Aviation, Motivational, Industry Specific Training, Maneuvers, Success, Patriotic, Aviation Firsts, Stunt Flying, Air Combat, Aviation Psychology, Survival, Aviation Careers, Jeppesen Charts, Aerobatic Pilots, Wright Brothers, Accident Investigations, Survival and much more.

For information on our speakers call
800-247-1215
For all other calls 949-498-2498

P.O. Box 6030
San Clemente, CA 92674-6030

Read speaker biographies and view video clips:
www.aviationspeakers.com

Charter Member

Learning to fly in 1973, Diane holds a commercial certificate with an instrument rating. Her logbook is a Heinz 57 mixture of different makes and models. Flights include ferrying aircraft from the factory, flying fire patrol and a number of air races. Until 1981, she worked as a radar qualified air traffic controller on the high/low sectors at Houston Center. Diane has been a passenger on a carrier landing and takeoff, flown a T-38, rode dozens of airline jumpseats and logged a few blimp flights.

Diane Titterington

The Ongoing Editor: Diane Titterington

Her father, who worked at WPAFB, told tales of test pilots Bob Hoover, Scott Crossfield and Chuck Yeager when she was young. Diane never dreamed that she would later work with such aviation greats. As the President of The Aviation Speakers Bureau, Diane supplies speakers for hundreds of safety seminars, banquets and conventions. She places aviation speakers, celebrities and specialists at events across the United States, Canada and other countries.

"It is a pure pleasure to work with dozens of brilliant and gifted individuals such as Jim Tucker, Bob Hoover, Col. Joe Kittinger, Brian Udell, Al Haynes, Dave Gwinn, Dr. Jerry Cockrell and Ralph Hood. With their unusual experiences, unique delivery styles, and vast knowledge of aviation, our speakers are the most sought after in the business. By providing inspiring speakers for aviation events, we help motivate and educate. And we help to keep the skies safe too." Visit our web site: www.aviationspeakers.com

Diane has been the ongoing editor of *Rod Machado's Private Pilot Handbook* and *Rod Machado's Instrument Pilot's Survival Manual*. She is the designer, compiler, managing editor and producer of *Speaking of Flying*, a book of stories from 44 aviation speakers.

"As if your instructor is explaining everything in *PLANE* English."

Rod Machado's Private Pilot Handbook is a serious text written in a fun and witty style. With more than 1,100 illustrations and photos and 64 pages in full color, this 572 page manual makes preparation for the FAA private pilot oral and knowledge exams (flight reviews too) a pleasant and enjoyable experience. Here's some of what's inside:

- Easy to understand analogies and examples for technical subjects such as engines, aerodynamics, flight instruments and the airplane's electrical system.

- New weather codes: METAR 8 TAF

- Alphabet airspace made E-Z with 3-D color illustrations

- Step-by-step procedures for planning a cross country

- Clear, down-to-earth explanations of pertinent FARs –Part 61 & 91

- Easy to apply navigation methods for VOR, GPS and ADF

- Practical tips and techniques for ensuring safe and enjoyable flight

$34.95

Rod Machado's Private Pilot Handbook 572 pages 8-3/8 x 10-7/8, perfect bound, ISBN 0-9631229-9-1

Visit our web site at: *www.rodmachado.com*

Rod Machado's Private Pilot Workbook

The new *Rod Machado's Private Pilot Workbook* is now available. As a programmed learning guide, this book will help prepare you for the FAA Private Pilot Knowledge Exam. The questions are organized to follow the presentation of material, section for section, as found in the *Handbook*. Not only will this book prepare you for the Private Pilot Knowledge Exam, it will help you understand and absorb the knowledge necessary for you to fly safely. You can test your knowledge and comprehension in each subject area with numerous weight and balance, performance, and flight planning problems.

This valuable one-stop workbook contains:

● An excellent, thorough and complete self-study system when used with *Rod Machado's Private Pilot Handbook*.
● 1,811 FAA Private Pilot Knowledge Exam and general aviation knowledge questions.
● Questions organized to follow the layout of *Rod Machado's Private Pilot Handbook* so you can test your knowledge and comprehension in each subject area.
● Color navigation charts & numerous weight-and-balance, performance, and flight planning problems.
● An FAA approved, Part 141 ground training syllabus for use in an FAA approved Part 141 ground school.

$24.95

Speaking of Flying

This wonderful 438 page hardbound book was written by 44 pilots who are speakers with The Aviation Speakers Bureau. These funny, dramatic, and inspiring stories are some of aviation's finest tales. You would expect nothing less from aviation's celebrities, experts and specialists.

Our flight plan sees us barnstorming in the U.S., flying aerial combat missions in World War II and Vietnam, test piloting new aircraft, performing air rescue, winging to exotic places, and flying to historically important aviation places from Kitty Hawk to the moon. You will go along as history is being made and hear the pilot's perspective on some of these aviation firsts. You will find ACES and true heroes within these pages. *Speaking of Flying* is your ticket to adventure. Step aboard, and be prepared to laugh, cry, and feel the excitement.

$29.95

Rod Machado's DVDs

Defensive Flying Video/DVD

Watch with over 300 pilots in this live, entertaining and educational video presentation as Rod Machado discusses how pilots can learn to think defensively. As Bill Wagstaff from *Aviation International News* says, "... Machado's humor serves as the glue that keeps his message together. Source for most of his guiles are real-world incidents, the essence of hangar-flying tales told with style by Machado. ...he makes us smile while we learn, a rare ability. *Defensive Flying* is an excellent tape for pilots to share." Learn about acknowledging your own limitations and a pilot's psychological predators as well as never underestimating aerial enemies. Listen to an actual, hair-raising, in-flight emergency as two professional pilots exercise one of the most important skills in Defensive Flying. This presentation contains many new stories and humor not previously heard on Rod's audio tapes.

Defensive Flying - $ 29.95   Approximate Length 1:45

Aviation Humor Video/DVD

Laugh along with over 2,000 pilots as Rod delights and entertains his audience with some of the best of his aviation stories. As a professional humorist, Rod has always been known for his ability to move people off the edge of their seats and onto the floor with his fast paced, humorous presentations. As Scott Spangler, Editor of *Flight Training* magazine says, ".. Get a copy of Aviation Humor. It's Rod Machado at his best. His humor is effective and funny because it strikes at the truth pilots seldom admit, such as the pride a new pilot feels when he uses his certificate as identification when cashing a check and the clerk asks, 'What is that?' If you're in need of a good laugh, get this video. You won't regret it. "After so many requests for a video version of his very popular audio tapes, this video of Rod's is sure to be a popular addition to your library. Funny, Funny stuff!

Aviation Humor - $29.95   Approximate Length 1:00

Rod Machado's Instrument Pilot's Survival Manual

Rod Machado's *Instrument Pilot's Survival Manual* is written to answer the instrument pilot's most important and frequently unanswered questions. For the price of one hour's worth of dual you will learn the following:

1. How GPS approaches are constructed and how to fly them.
2. How to differentiate between benign cumulus clouds and those that can damage an airplane.
3. How to measure flight visibility at DA & MDA.
4. A unique three-step method of scanning your instruments.
5. Secrets of using Jeppesen and NACO charts.
6. Using Center radar, ASR-9 radar, NEXRAD and Stormscope (sferics) to avoid thunderstorm and icing conditions.
7. New ways of thinking about the IFR system and managing cockpit resources and much more!

Instrument Pilot's Survival Manual (424 pages) $34.95

IFR Flying *Tips & Techniques* Video/DVD

If you've enjoyed Rod's presentation in the *ABC's Wide World of Flying* and *Wonderful World of Flying* video magazine, you're sure to enjoy this tape. Rod has incorporated six of his most popular IFR segments into this educational video and interspersed live, humorous clips from one of his popular seminars between each story segment.

Rod shows you:
1. *A unique, multi-step instrument scan*
2. *Single pilot IFR cockpit management*
3. *How to really use the approach lighting system*
4. *Techniques to make safe IFR departures*
5. *A two step method for flying NDB approaches*
6. *What maneuvering speed means and how to use it*

IFR Flying Tips & Techniques - $29.95   Appx. Length 1:30

Rod Machado's Plane Talk
The Mental Art of Flying an Airplane
You'll Learn, You'll Laugh, You'll Remember!

Welcome to a collection of Rod Machado's most popular aviation articles and stories from the last 15 years. *Rod Machado's Plane Talk* contains nearly 100 flights of fun and knowledge that will stimulate your aviation brain and tickle your funny bone. In addition to the educational topics listed below, you'll read about higher learning, the value of aviation history, aviation literature, aviation art and how an artist's perspective can help you better understand weather. You'll also find more than a few articles written just to make you laugh.

In this book you'll discover...

How to Assess and Manage Aviation Risks
Learn how safe pilots think, how to apply the safety strategy used by General Jimmy Doolittle (known as the master of the calculated risk), how famed gunfighter Wyatt Earp can help you cope with aviation's risks, how misleading aviation statistics can be and why flying isn't as dangerous as some folks say it is.

Several Techniques for Making Better Cockpit Decisions
Discover how to use your inner copilot in the cockpit and the value of one good question asked upside down.

New Ways to Help You Cope With Temptation
Fly safer by developing an aviation code of ethics, understand how human nature can trick you into flying beyond your limits, why good pilots are prejudiced and how a concept like honor will protect you while aloft.

How to Use Your Brain for a Change
You can learn faster by understanding how the learning curve—the brain's performance chart—is affected by the little lies we tell ourselves, the mistakes we need to make, our need to please our instructors, and simulator and memory training.

The Truth About Flying, Anxiety and Fear
Learn why it's often the safest of pilots that make excuses instead of flights, why anxiety should be treated as a normal part of flying, and a three-step process to avoiding panic in the cockpit.

How to Handle First Time Flyers and Anxious Passengers
Discover how to behave around new passengers, how to avoid most common mistakes that scare passengers in airplanes and how to reduce the cockpit stress between pilot and spouse.

Favorite Skills Used By Good Pilots
Learn why good pilots scan behind an airplane as well as ahead of it, are sometimes rough and bully-like on the flight controls, occasionally fly without using any of the airplane's electronic navigation equipment, don't worry about turbulence breaking their airplanes, master airspeed control as a means of making better landings and much more.

$29.95

Rod Machado's 14 Audio CD Set/Order Form

The Best of Rod Machado Live on 14 Audio CDs

These unique audio CDs contain 12.5 hours of aviation material recorded live before pilot groups across the country with Machado at his best. Using his trademark "Laugh & Learn" style, Rod entertains his audience as he teaches. Originally recorded as two "six-cassette" tape volumes, Rod has combined 10 of the best live recordings from the original "Laugh and Learn" series and added four additional live recordings to produce this exciting 14 CD album. These recordings include CDs from Rod's popular seminar on *handling in-flight emergencies,* as well as his latest programs on *defensive flying, the art of flying* and *the nonpilot's guide to landing an airplane.* And if you like to laugh then you'll find three CDs containing Rod's funniest standup aviation humor. Now you can laugh and learn while driving in your car or sitting in your lounge chair in the comfort of your own home. What else will you learn? Take a look at the CD disc contents below.

CONTENTS

$99.95

CD-1 Laugh Your Empennage Off (95/5)*
CD-2 Samurai Airmanship (30/70)*
CD-3 Reducing Cockpit Stress Between the Sexes (60/40)*
CD-4 Cockpit Management (40/60)*
CD-5 An Aviation Sense of Humor (95/5)*
CD-6 Creative Solutions to Common Problems (40/60)*
CD-7 Handling In-flight Emergencies 1 (10/90)*

CD-8 Handling In-flight Emergencies 2 (10/90)*
CD-9 Handling In-flight Emergencies 3 (10/90)*
CD-10 Handling In-flight Emergencies 4 (10/90)*
CD-11 The Nonpilot's Guide to Landing an Airplane (30/70)*
CD-12 Aviation Humor: The Light Stuff (95/5)*
CD-13 Yoke and Pedal: The Art of Flying (10/90)*
CD-14 More Defensive Flying (10/90)*

*(% Humor content / % Information content)

"Rod has a wonderful sense of humor that will keep you in stitches and when you're done laughing, you'll be amazed at how much you've learned."
John & Martha King, King Video

"Mary Poppins once sang, 'A spoon full of sugar helps the medicine go down.' Rod Machado goes one step further by sugar coating invaluable aeronautical wisdom with entertaining wit and humor."
Barry Schiff, TWA Captain/Noted Author

How to Order

Free Samples! Go to: www.rodmachado.com for page and CD samples

COPY & MAIL COMPLETED FORM TO: THE AVIATION SPEAKERS BUREAU, P.O. BOX 6030 SAN CLEMENTE, CA 92674-6030

Order Form

Credit card ordering 24 hours - 7 days a week
Call: **(800) 437-7080** for ordering only

Title		Quantity	X	=	Total
Defensive Flying Video or DVD (circle one)			$29.95		
Aviation Humor Video or DVD (circle one)			$29.95		
Instrument Flying Tips (circle one)			$29.95		
Rod Machado Live on 14 Audio CDs			$99.95		
Instrument Pilot's Survival Manual			$34.95		
Rod Machado's Instrument Pilot's Handbook			$59.95		
Rod Machado's Private Pilot Handbook			$34.95		
Rod Machado's Private Pilot Workbook			$24.95		
Rod Machado's Private Pilot Audiobook 30CDs			$149.95		
Rod Machado's Plane Talk			$29.95		
Speaking of Flying			$29.95		
		Product Subtotal			
Sales Tax - CA Residents only		Product Subtotal x .0775			
Product shipping & handling (US)		—	—	$3.00	
International shipping: $10 surface $27 air ($5 each add. item) Canada: $6 surface $10 air ($5 each add. item) Please indicate if ordering PAL videos					
			Total		

For more information and secure internet ordering visit *www.rodmachado.com*
Questions: Email us from web site.
FAX: (888) MACHADO (622-4236)

Name _____

Address _____

City _____ State _____

Zip _____

Phone (____) _____

Check # _____ or:

We accept checks, money orders, MasterCard, VISA, American Express and Discover.

Credit Card # _____

Expiration Date: _____

Authorized Signature _____

A

ABBREVIATED IFR FLIGHT PLANS- An authorization by ATC requiring pilots to submit only that information needed for the purpose of ATC. It includes only a small portion of the usual IFR flight plan information. In certain instances, this may be only aircraft identification, location, and pilot request. Other information may be requested if needed by ATC for separation/control purposes. It is frequently used by aircraft which are airborne and desire an instrument approach or by aircraft which are on the ground and desire a climb to VFR-on-top.

ACKNOWLEDGE - Let me know that you have received my message.

ADVISE INTENTIONS - Tell me what you plan to do.

ADVISORY - Advice and information provided to assist pilots in the safe conduct of flight and aircraft movement.

ADVISORY FREQUENCY - The appropriate frequency to be used for Airport Advisory Service.

ADVISORY SERVICE - Advice and information provided by a facility to assist pilots in the safe conduct of flight and aircraft movement.

AERODROME - A defined area on land or water (including any buildings, installations and equipment) intended to be used either wholly or in part for the arrival, departure, and movement of aircraft.

AERONAUTICAL BEACON - A visual NAVAID displaying flashes of white and/or colored light to indicate the location of an airport, a heliport, a landmark, a certain point of a Federal airway in mountainous terrain, or an obstruction.

AERONAUTICAL CHART - A map used in air navigation containing all or part of the following: topographic features, hazards and obstructions, navigation aids, navigation routes, designated airspace, and airports. Commonly used aeronautical charts are:

a. Sectional Aeronautical Charts (1:500,000)- Designed for visual navigation of slow or medium speed aircraft. Topographic information on these charts features the portrayal of relief and a judicious selection of visual check points for VFR flight. Aeronautical information includes visual and radio aids to navigation, airports, controlled airspace, restricted areas, obstructions, and related data.

b. VFR Terminal Area Charts (1:250,000)- Depict Class B airspace which provides for the control or segregation of all the aircraft within Class B airspace. The chart depicts topographic information and aeronautical information which includes visual and radio aids to navigation, airports, controlled airspace, restricted areas, obstructions, and related data.

c. World Aeronautical Charts (WAC) (1:1,000,000)- Provide a standard series of aeronautical charts covering land areas of the world at a size and scale convenient for navigation by moderate speed aircraft. Topographic information includes cities and towns, principal roads, railroads, distinctive landmarks, drainage, and relief. Aeronautical information includes visual and radio aids to navigation, airports, airways, restricted areas, obstructions, and other pertinent data.

d. En Route Low Altitude Charts- Provide aeronautical information for en route instrument navigation (IFR) in the low altitude stratum. Information includes the portrayal of airways, limits of controlled airspace, position identification and frequencies of radio aids, selected airports, minimum en route and minimum obstruction clearance altitudes, airway distances, reporting points, restricted areas, and related data. Area charts, which are a part of this series, furnish terminal data at a larger scale in congested areas.

e. En Route High Altitude Charts - Provide aeronautical information for en route instrument navigation (IFR) in the high altitude stratum. Information includes the portrayal of jet routes, identification and frequencies of radio aids, selected airports, distances, time zones, special use airspace, and related information.

f. Instrument Approach Procedures (IAP) Charts- Portray the aeronautical data which is required to execute an instrument approach to an airport. These charts depict the procedures, including all related data, and the airport diagram. Each procedure is designated for use with a specific type of electronic navigation system including NDB, TACAN, VOR, ILS/MLS, and RNAV. These charts are identified by the type of navigational aid(s) which provide final approach guidance.

g. Instrument Departure Procedure (DP) Charts- Designed to expedite clearance delivery and to facilitate transition between takeoff and en route operations. Each DP is presented as a separate chart and may serve a single airport or more than one airport in a given geographical location.

h. Standard Terminal Arrival (STAR) Charts- Designed to expedite air traffic control arrival procedures and to facilitate transition between en route and instrument approach operations. Each STAR procedure is presented as a separate chart and may serve a single airport or more than one airport in a given geographical location.

i. Airport Taxi Charts- Designed to expedite the efficient and safe flow of ground traffic at an airport. These charts are identified by the official airport name; e.g., Ronald Reagan Washington National Airport.

AIR DEFENSE IDENTIFICATION ZONE (ADIZ) - The area of airspace over land or water, extending upward from the surface, within which the ready identification, the location, and the control of aircraft are required in the interest of national security.

a. Domestic Air Defense Identification Zone. An ADIZ within the United States along an international boundary of the United States.

b. Coastal Air Defense Identification Zone. An ADIZ over the coastal waters of the United States.

c. Distant Early Warning Identification Zone (DEWIZ). An ADIZ over the coastal waters of the State of Alaska.

d. Land-Based Air Defense Identification Zone. An ADIZ over U.S. metropolitan areas, which is activated and deactivated as needed, with dimensions, activation dates and other relevant information disseminated via NOTAM.

AIR ROUTE SURVEILLANCE RADAR - Air route traffic control center (ARTCC) radar used primarily to detect and display an aircraft's position while en route between terminal areas. The ARSR enables controllers to provide radar air traffic control service when aircraft are within the ARSR coverage. In some instances, ARSR may enable an ARTCC to provide terminal radar services similar to but usually more limited than those provided by a radar approach control.

AIR ROUTE TRAFFIC CONTROL CENTER - A facility established to provide air traffic control service to aircraft operating on IFR flight plans within controlled airspace and principally during the en route phase of flight. When equipment capabilities and controller workload permit, certain advisory/assistance services may be provided to VFR aircraft.

AIRCRAFT APPROACH CATEGORY - A grouping of aircraft based on a speed of 1.3 times the stall speed in the landing configuration at maximum gross landing weight. An aircraft must fit in only one category. If it is necessary to maneuver at speeds in excess of the upper limit of a speed range for a category, the minimums for the category for that speed must be used. For example, an aircraft which falls in Category A, but is circling to land at a speed in excess of 91 knots, must use the approach Category B minimums when circling to land. The categories are as follows:

a. Category A - Speed less than 91 knots.

b. Category B - Speed 91 knots or more but less than 121 knots.

c. Category C - Speed 121 knots or more but less than 141 knots.

d. Category D - Speed 141 knots or more but less than 166 knots.

e. Category E- Speed 166 knots or more.

AIRCRAFT CLASSES - For the purposes of Wake Turbulence Separation Minima, ATC classifies aircraft as Heavy, Large, and Small as follows:

a. Heavy- Aircraft capable of takeoff weights of more than 255,000 pounds whether or not they are operating at this weight during a particular phase of flight.

b. Large- Aircraft of more than 41,000 pounds, maximum certificated takeoff weight, up to 255,000 pounds.

c. Small- Aircraft of 41,000 pounds or less maximum certificated takeoff weight.

AIRMET - In-flight weather advisories issued only to amend the area forecast concerning weather phenomena which are of operational interest to all aircraft and potentially hazardous to aircraft having limited capability because of lack of equipment, instrumentation, or pilot qualifications. AIRMETs concern weather of less severity than that covered by SIGMETs or Convective SIGMETs. AIRMETs cover moderate icing, moderate turbulence, sustained winds of 30 knots or more at the surface, widespread areas of ceilings less than 1,000 feet and/or visibility less than 3 miles, and extensive mountain obscurement.

AIRPORT ADVISORY AREA - The area within ten miles of an airport without a control tower or where the tower is not in operation, and on which a Flight Service Station is located.

AIRPORT/FACILITY DIRECTORY - A publication designed primarily as a pilot's operational manual containing all airports, seaplane bases, and heliports open to the public including communications data, navigational facilities, and certain special notices and procedures. This publication is issued in seven volumes according to geographical area.

AIRPORT LIGHTING - Various lighting aids that may be installed on an airport. Types of airport lighting include:

a. Approach Light System (ALS) - An airport lighting facility which provides visual guidance to landing aircraft by radiating light beams in a directional pattern by which the pilot aligns the aircraft with the extended centerline of the runway on his/her final approach for landing. Condenser-Discharge Sequential Flashing Lights/Sequenced Flashing Lights may be installed in conjunction with the ALS at some airports. Types of Approach Light Systems are:

1. ALSF-1 - Approach Light System with Sequenced Flashing Lights in ILS Cat-I configuration.

2. ALSF-2 - Approach Light System with Sequenced Flashing Lights in ILS Cat-II configuration. The ALSF-2 may operate as an SSALR when weather conditions permit.

3. SSALF - Simplified Short Approach Light System with Sequenced Flashing Lights.

4. SSALR - Simplified Short Approach Light System with Runway Alignment Indicator Lights.

5. MALSF - Medium Intensity Approach Light System with Sequenced Flashing Lights.

6. MALSR - Medium Intensity Approach Light System with Runway Alignment Indicator Lights.

7. LDIN - Lead-in-light system- Consists of one or more series of flashing lights installed at or near ground level that provides positive visual guidance along an approach path, either curving or straight, where special problems exist with hazardous terrain, obstructions, or noise abatement procedures.

8. RAIL - Runway Alignment Indicator Lights-Sequenced Flashing Lights which are installed only in combination with other light systems.

9. ODALS - Omnidirectional Approach Lighting System consists of seven omnidirectional flashing lights located in the approach area of a non-precision runway. Five lights are located on the runway centerline extended with the first light located 300 feet from the threshold and extending at equal intervals up to 1,500 feet from the threshold. The other two lights are located, one on each side of the runway threshold, at a lateral distance of 40 feet from the runway edge, or 75 feet from the runway edge when installed on a runway equipped with a VASI.

b. Runway Lights/Runway Edge Lights - Lights having a prescribed angle of emission used to define the lateral limits of a runway. Runway lights are uniformly spaced at intervals of approximately 200 feet, and the intensity may be controlled or preset.

c. Touchdown Zone Lighting - Two rows of transverse light bars located symmetrically about the runway centerline normally at 100 foot intervals. The basic system extends 3,000 feet along the runway.

d. Runway Centerline Lighting - Flush centerline lights spaced at 50-foot intervals beginning 75 feet from the landing threshold and extending to within 75 feet of the opposite end of the runway.

e. Threshold Lights - Fixed green lights arranged symmetrically left and right of the runway centerline, identifying the runway threshold.

f. Runway End Identifier Lights (REIL) - Two synchronized flashing lights, one on each side of the runway threshold, which provide rapid and positive identification of the approach end of a particular runway.

g. Visual Approach Slope Indicator (VASI) - An airport lighting facility providing vertical visual approach slope guidance to aircraft during approach to landing by radiating a directional pattern of high intensity red and white focused light beams which indicate to the pilot that he/she is "on path" if he/she sees red/white, "above path" if white/white, and "below path" if red/red. Some airports serving large aircraft have three-bar VASIs which provide two visual glide paths to the same runway.

h. Precision Approach Path Indicator (PAPI) - An airport lighting facility, similar to VASI, providing vertical approach slope guidance to aircraft during approach to landing. PAPIs consist of a single row of either two or four lights, normally installed on the left side of the runway, and have an effective visual range of about 5 miles during the day and up to 20 miles at night. PAPIs radiate a directional pattern of high intensity red and white focused light beams which indicate that the pilot is "on path" if the pilot sees an equal number of white lights and red lights, with white to the left of the red; "above path" if the pilot sees more white than red lights; and "below path" if the pilot sees more red than white lights.

i. Boundary Lights - Lights defining the perimeter of an airport or landing area.

AIRPORT MARKING AIDS - Markings used on runway and taxiway surfaces to identify a specific runway, a runway threshold, a centerline, a hold line, etc. A runway should be marked in accordance with its present usage such as:

a. Visual.

b. Nonprecision instrument.

c. Precision instrument.

AIRPORT REFERENCE POINT (ARP) - The approximate geometric center of all usable runway surfaces.

ALONG TRACK DISTANCE (ATD) - The distance measured from a point-in-space by systems using area navigation reference capabilities that are not subject to slant range errors.

ALTERNATE AIRPORT - An airport at which an aircraft may land if a landing at the intended airport becomes inadvisable.

ALTIMETER SETTING - The barometric pressure reading used to adjust a pressure altimeter for variations in existing atmospheric pressure or to the standard altimeter setting (29.92).

ALTITUDE - The height of a level, point, or object measured in feet Above Ground Level (AGL) or from Mean Sea Level (MSL).

a. MSL Altitude- Altitude expressed in feet measured from mean sea level.

b. AGL Altitude- Altitude expressed in feet measured above ground level.

c. Indicated Altitude- The altitude as shown by an altimeter. On a pressure or barometric altimeter it is altitude as shown uncorrected for instrument error and uncompensated for varia-

tion from standard atmospheric conditions.

ALTITUDE READOUT - An aircraft's altitude, transmitted via the Mode C transponder feature, that is visually displayed in 100-foot increments on a radar scope having readout capability.

ALTITUDE RESTRICTION - An altitude or altitudes, stated in the order flown, which are to be maintained until reaching a specific point or time. Altitude restrictions may be issued by ATC due to traffic, terrain, or other airspace considerations.

ALTITUDE RESTRICTIONS ARE CANCELED - Adherence to previously imposed altitude restrictions is no longer required during a climb or descent.

APPROACH CONTROL FACILITY - A terminal ATC facility that provides approach control service in a terminal area.

APPROACH GATE - An imaginary point used within ATC as a basis for vectoring aircraft to the final approach course. The gate will be established along the final approach course 1 mile from the final approach fix on the side away from the airport and will be no closer than 5 miles from the landing threshold.

APPROACH SPEED - The recommended speed contained in aircraft manuals used by pilots when making an approach to landing. This speed will vary for different segments of an approach as well as for aircraft weight and configuration.

ARC - The track over the ground of an aircraft flying at a constant distance from a navigational aid by reference to distance measuring equipment (DME).

AREA NAVIGATION - Area Navigation (RNAV) provides enhanced navigational capability to the pilot. RNAV equipment can compute the airplane position, actual track and ground speed and then provide meaningful information relative to a route of flight selected by the pilot. Typical equipment will provide the pilot with distance, time, bearing and crosstrack error relative to the selected "TO" or "active" waypoint and the selected route. Several distinctly different navigational systems with different navigational performance characteristics are capable of providing area navigational functions. Present day RNAV includes INS, LORAN, VOR/DME, and GPS systems. Modern multisensor systems can integrate one or more of the above systems to provide a more accurate and reliable navigational system. Due to the different levels of performance, area navigational capabilities can satisfy different levels of required navigational performance (RNP). The major types of equipment are:

a. VORTAC referenced or Course Line Computer (CLC) systems, which account for the greatest number of RNAV units in use. To function, the CLC must be within the service range of a VORTAC.

b. OMEGA/VLF, although two separate systems, can be considered as one operationally. A long-range navigation system based upon Very Low Frequency radio signals transmitted from a total of 17 stations worldwide.

c. Inertial (INS) systems, which are totally self-contained and require no information from external references. They provide aircraft position and navigation information in response to signals resulting from inertial effects on components within the system.

d. MLS Area Navigation (MLS/RNAV), which provides area navigation with reference to an MLS ground facility.

e. LORAN-C is a long-range radio navigation system that uses ground waves transmitted at low frequency to provide user position information at ranges of up to 600 to 1,200 nautical miles at both en route and approach altitudes. The usable signal coverage areas are determined by the signal-to-noise ratio, the envelope-to-cycle difference, and the geometric relationship between the positions of the user and the transmitting stations.

f. GPS is a space-base radio positioning, navigation, and time-transfer system. The system provides highly accurate position and velocity information, and precise time, on a continuous global basis, to an unlimited number of properly equipped users. The system is unaffected by weather, and provides a worldwide common grid reference system.

AREA NAVIGATION [ICAO] - A method of navigation which permits aircraft operation on any desired flight path within the coverage of station-referenced navigation aids or within the limits of the capability of self-contained aids, or a combination of these.

AREA NAVIGATION (RNAV) APPROACH CONFIGURATION:

a. STANDARD T - An RNAV approach whose design allows direct flight to any one of three initial approach fixes (IAF) and eliminates the need for procedure turns. The standard design is to align the procedure on the extended centerline with the missed approach point (MAP) at the runway threshold, the final approach fix (FAF), and the initial approach/intermediate fix (IAF/IF). The other two IAFs will be established perpendicular to the IF.

b. MODIFIED T - An RNAV approach design for single or multiple runways where terrain or operational constraints do not allow for the standard T. The "T" may be modified by increasing or decreasing the angle from the corner IAF(s) to the IF or by eliminating one or both corner IAFs.

c. STANDARD I - An RNAV approach design for a single runway with both corner IAFs eliminated. Course reversal or radar vectoring may be required at busy terminals with multiple runways.

d. TERMINAL ARRIVAL AREA (TAA) - The TAA is controlled airspace established in conjunction with the Standard or Modified T and I RNAV approach configurations. In the standard TAA, there are three areas: straight-in, left base, and right base. The arc boundaries of the three areas of the TAA are published portions of the approach and allow aircraft to transition from the en route structure direct to the nearest IAF. TAAs will also eliminate or reduce feeder routes, departure extensions, and procedure turns or course reversal.

1. STRAIGHT-IN AREA - A 30NM arc centered on the IF bounded by a straight line extending through the IF perpendicular to the intermediate course.

2. LEFT BASE AREA - A 30NM arc centered on the right corner IAF. The area shares a boundary with the straight-in area except that it extends out for 30NM from the IAF and is bounded on the other side by a line extending from the IF through the FAF to the arc.

3. RIGHT BASE AREA - A 30NM arc centered on the left corner IAF. The area shares a boundary with the straight-in area except that it extends out for 30NM from the IAF and is bounded on the other side by a line extending from the IF through the FAF to the arc.

ARINC - An acronym for Aeronautical Radio, Inc., a corporation largely owned by a group of airlines. ARINC is licensed by the FCC as an aeronautical station and contracted by the FAA to provide communications support for air traffic control and meteorological services in portions of international airspace.

ATC ADVISES - Used to prefix a message of noncontrol information when it is relayed to an aircraft by other than an air traffic controller.

ATC CLEARS - Used to prefix an ATC clearance when it is relayed to an aircraft by other than an air traffic controller.

ATC INSTRUCTIONS - Directives issued by air traffic control for the purpose of requiring a pilot to take specific actions; e.g., "Turn left heading two five zero," "Go around," "Clear the runway."

ATC PREFERRED ROUTE NOTIFICATION - URET notification to the appropriate controller of the need to determine if an ATC preferred route needs to be applied, based on destination airport.

AUTOMATED RADAR TERMINAL SYSTEMS - The generic term for the ultimate in functional capability afforded by several automation systems. Each differs in functional capabilities and equipment. ARTS plus a suffix roman numeral denotes a specific system. A following letter indicates a major modification to that system. In general, an ARTS displays for the terminal controller aircraft identification, flight plan data, other flight associated information; e.g., altitude, speed, and aircraft position symbols in conjunction with his/her radar presentation. Normal radar co-exists with the alphanumeric display. In addition to enhancing visualization of the air traffic situation, ARTS facilitate intra/interfacility transfer and coordination of flight information. These capabilities are enabled by specially designed computers and subsystems tailored to the radar and communications equipments and operational requirements of each automated facility. Modular design permits adoption of improvements in computer software and electronic technologies as they become available while retaining the characteristics unique to each system.

a. ARTS II. A programmable nontracking, computer-aided display subsystem capable of modular expansion. ARTS II systems provide a level of automated air traffic control capability at terminals having low to medium activity. Flight identification and altitude may be associated with the display of secondary radar targets. The system has the capability of communicating with ARTCCs and other ARTS II, IIA, III, and IIIA facilities.

b. ARTS IIA. A programmable radar-tracking computer subsystem capable of modular expansion. The ARTS IIA detects, tracks, and predicts secondary radar targets. The targets are displayed by means of computer-generated symbols, ground speed, and flight plan data. Although it does not track primary radar targets, they are displayed coincident with the sec-

ondary radar as well as the symbols and alphanumerics. The system has the capability of communicating with ARTCCs and other ARTS II, IIA, III, and IIIA facilities.

c. ARTS III. The Beacon Tracking Level of the modular programmable automated radar terminal system in use at medium to high activity terminals. ARTS III detects, tracks, and predicts secondary radar-derived aircraft targets. These are displayed by means of computer-generated symbols and alphanumeric characters depicting flight identification, aircraft altitude, ground speed, and flight plan data. Although it does not track primary targets, they are displayed coincident with the secondary radar as well as the symbols and alphanumerics. The system has the capability of communicating with ARTCCs and other ARTS III facilities.

d. ARTS IIIA. The Radar Tracking and Beacon Tracking Level (RT&BTL) of the modular, programmable automated radar terminal system. ARTS IIIA detects, tracks, and predicts primary as well as secondary radar-derived aircraft targets. This more sophisticated computer-driven system upgrades the existing ARTS III system by providing improved tracking, continuous data recording, and fail-soft capabilities.

AUTOMATED TERMINAL TRACKING SYSTEM (ATTS) - ATTS is used to identify the numerous tracking systems including ARTS IIA, ARTS IIE, ARTS IIIA, ARTS IIIE, STARS, and M-EARTS.

AUTOMATED UNICOM - Provides completely automated weather, radio check capability and airport advisory information on an Automated UNICOM system. These systems offer a variety of features, typically selectable by microphone clicks, on the UNICOM frequency. Availability will be published in the Airport/Facility Directory and approach charts.

AUTOMATIC ALTITUDE REPORTING - That function of a transponder which responds to Mode C interrogations by transmitting the aircraft's altitude in 100-foot increments.

AUTOMATIC CARRIER LANDING SYSTEM - U.S. Navy final approach equipment

AUTOMATIC DEPENDENT SURVEILLANCE-BROADCAST (ADS-B) - A surveillance system in which an aircraft or vehicle to be detected is fitted with cooperative equipment in the form of a data link transmitter. The aircraft or vehicle periodically broadcasts its GPS-derived position and other information such as velocity over the data link, which is received by a ground-based transmitter/receiver (transceiver) for processing and display at an air traffic control facility.

AUTOMATIC TERMINAL INFORMATION SERVICE - The continuous broadcast of recorded noncontrol information in selected terminal areas. Its purpose is to improve controller effectiveness and to relieve frequency congestion by automating the repetitive transmission of essential but routine information; e.g., "Los Angeles information Alfa. One three zero zero Coordinated Universal Time. Weather, measured ceiling two thousand overcast, visibility three, haze, smoke, temperature seven one, dew point five seven, wind two five zero at five, altimeter two niner niner six. I-L-S Runway Two Five Left approach in use, Runway Two Five Right closed, advise you have Alfa."

AUTOMATIC TERMINAL INFORMATION SERVICE [ICAO] - The provision of current, routine information to arriving and departing aircraft by means of continuous and repetitive broadcasts throughout the day or a specified portion of the day.

AZIMUTH (MLS) - A magnetic bearing extending from an MLS navigation facility.

Note: Azimuth bearings are described as magnetic and are referred to as "azimuth" in radio telephone communications.stop

B

BEARING - The horizontal direction to or from any point, usually measured clockwise from true north, magnetic north, or some other reference point through 360 degrees.

BELOW MINIMUMS - Weather conditions below the minimums prescribed by regulation for the particular action involved; e.g., landing minimums, takeoff minimums.

C

CALL UP - Initial voice contact between a facility and an aircraft, using the identification of the unit being called and the unit initiating the call.

CEILING - The heights above the earth's surface of the lowest layer of clouds or obscuring phenomena that is reported as "broken," "overcast," or "obscuration," and not classified as "thin" or "partial."

CENTER'S AREA - The specified airspace within which an air route traffic control center (ARTCC) provides air traffic control and advisory service.

CENTER WEATHER ADVISORY - An unscheduled weather advisory issued by Center Weather Service Unit meteorologists for ATC use to alert pilots of existing or anticipated adverse weather conditions within the next 2 hours. A CWA may modify or redefine a SIGMET.

CERTIFIED TOWER RADAR DISPLAY (CTRD) - A radar display that provides a

CHARTED VISUAL FLIGHT PROCEDURE APPROACH - An approach conducted while operating on an instrument flight rules (IFR) flight plan which authorizes the pilot of an aircraft to proceed visually and clear of clouds to the airport via visual landmarks and other information depicted on a charted visual flight procedure. This approach must be authorized and under the control of the appropriate air traffic control facility. Weather minimums required are depicted on the chart.

CIRCLE-TO-LAND MANEUVER - A maneuver initiated by the pilot to align the aircraft with a runway for landing when a straight-in landing from an instrument approach is not possible or is not desirable. At tower controlled airports, this maneuver is made only after ATC authorization has been obtained and the pilot has established required visual reference to the airport.

CIRCLE TO RUNWAY (RUNWAY NUMBER) - Used by ATC to inform the pilot that he/she must circle to land because the runway in use is other than the runway aligned with the instrument approach procedure. When the direction of the circling maneuver in relation to the airport/runway is required, the controller will state the direction (eight cardinal compass points) and specify a left or right downwind or base leg as appropriate; e.g., "Cleared VOR Runway Three Six Approach circle to Runway Two Two," or "Circle northwest of the airport for a right downwind to Runway Two Two."

CLASS G AIRSPACE - That airspace not designated as Class A, B, C, D or E.

CLEAR AIR TURBULENCE (CAT) - Turbulence encountered in air where no clouds are present. This term is commonly applied to high-level turbulence associated with wind shear. CAT is often encountered in the vicinity of the jet stream.

CLEAR OF THE RUNWAY -

a. Taxiing aircraft, which is approaching a runway, is clear of the runway when all parts of the aircraft are held short of the applicable runway holding position marking.

b. A pilot or controller may consider an aircraft, which is exiting or crossing a runway, to be clear of the runway when all parts of the aircraft are beyond the runway edge and there are no restrictions to its continued movement beyond the applicable runway holding position marking.

c. Pilots and controllers shall exercise good judgement to ensure that adequate separation exists between all aircraft on runways and taxiways at airports with inadequate runway edge lines or holding position markings.

CLEARANCE LIMIT - The fix, point, or location to which an aircraft is cleared when issued an air traffic clearance.

CLEARANCE VOID IF NOT OFF BY (TIME) - Used by ATC to advise an aircraft that the departure clearance is automatically canceled if takeoff is not made prior to a specified time. The pilot must obtain a new clearance or cancel his/her IFR flight plan if not off by the specified time.

CLEARED APPROACH - ATC authorization for an aircraft to execute any standard or special instrument approach procedure for that airport. Normally, an aircraft will be cleared for a specific instrument approach procedure.

CLEARED (Type of) APPROACH - ATC authorization for an aircraft to execute a specific instrument approach procedure to an airport; e.g., "Cleared ILS Runway Three Six Approach."

CLEARED AS FILED - Means the aircraft is cleared to proceed in accordance with the route of flight filed in the flight plan. This clearance does not include the altitude, DP, or DP Transition.

CLEARED FOR THE OPTION - ATC authorization for an aircraft to make a touch-and-go, low approach, missed approach, stop and go, or full stop landing at the discretion of the pilot. It is normally used in training so that an instructor can evaluate a student's performance under changing situations.

CLEARED THROUGH - ATC authorization for an aircraft to make intermediate stops at specified airports without refiling a flight plan while en route to the clearance limit.

CLEARED TO LAND - ATC authorization for an aircraft to land. It is predicated on known traffic and known physical airport conditions.

CLIMB TO VFR - ATC authorization for an aircraft to climb to VFR conditions within Class B, C, D, and E surface areas when the only weather limitation is restricted visibility. The aircraft must remain clear of clouds while climbing to VFR.

CLOUD - A cloud is a visible accumulation of minute water droplets and/or ice particles in the

atmosphere above the Earth's surface. Cloud differs from ground fog, fog, or ice fog only in that the latter are, by definition, in contact with the Earth's surface.

CLUTTER - In radar operations, clutter refers to the reception and visual display of radar returns caused by precipitation, chaff, terrain, numerous aircraft targets, or other phenomena. Such returns may limit or preclude ATC from providing services based on radar.

CODES - The number assigned to a particular multiple pulse reply signal transmitted by a transponder.

COMMON TRAFFIC ADVISORY FREQUENCY (CTAF) - A frequency designed for the purpose of carrying out airport advisory practices while operating to or from an airport without an operating control tower. The CTAF may be a UNICOM, Multicom, FSS, or tower frequency and is identified in appropriate aeronautical publications.

COMPASS LOCATOR - A low power, low or medium frequency (L/MF) radio beacon installed at the site of the outer or middle marker of an instrument landing system (ILS). It can be used for navigation at distances of approximately 15 miles or as authorized in the approach procedure.

a. Outer Compass Locator (LOM) - A compass locator installed at the site of the outer marker of an instrument landing system.

b. Middle Compass Locator (LMM) - A compass locator installed at the site of the middle marker of an instrument landing system.

COMPOSITE FLIGHT PLAN - A flight plan which specifies VFR operation for one portion of flight and IFR for another portion. It is used primarily in military operations.

COMPULSORY REPORTING POINTS - Reporting points which must be reported to ATC. They are designated on aeronautical charts by solid triangles or filed in a flight plan as fixes selected to define direct routes. These points are geographical locations which are defined by navigation aids/fixes. Pilots should discontinue position reporting over compulsory reporting points when informed by ATC that their aircraft is in "radar contact."

CONTACT APPROACH - An approach wherein an aircraft on an IFR flight plan, having an air traffic control authorization, operating clear of clouds with at least 1 mile flight visibility and a reasonable expectation of continuing to the destination airport in those conditions, may deviate from the instrument approach procedure and proceed to the destination airport by visual reference to the surface. This approach will only be authorized when requested by the pilot and the reported ground visibility at the destination airport is at least 1 statute mile.

CONTERMINOUS U.S. - The 48 adjoining States and the District of Columbia.

CONTINENTAL UNITED STATES - The 49 States located on the continent of North America and the District of Columbia.

CONTINUE - When used as a control instruction should be followed by another word or words clarifying what is expected of the pilot. Example: "continue taxi", "continue descent", "continue inbound" etc.

CONTROL SECTOR - An airspace area of defined horizontal and vertical dimensions for which a controller or group of controllers has air traffic control responsibility, normally within an air route traffic control center or an approach control facility. Sectors are established based on predominant traffic flows, altitude strata, and controller workload. Pilot-communications during operations within a sector are normally maintained on discrete frequencies assigned to the sector.

CONTROLLED AIRSPACE - An airspace of defined dimensions within which air traffic control service is provided to IFR flights and to VFR flights in accordance with the airspace classification.

a. Controlled airspace is a generic term that covers Class A, Class B, Class C, Class D, and Class E airspace.

b. Controlled airspace is also that airspace within which all aircraft operators are subject to certain pilot qualifications, operating rules, and equipment requirements in 14 CFR Part 91 (for specific operating requirements, please refer to 14 CFR Part 91). For IFR operations in any class of controlled airspace, a pilot must file an IFR flight plan and receive an appropriate ATC clearance. Each Class B, Class C, and Class D airspace area designated for an airport contains at least one primary airport around which the airspace is designated (for specific designations and descriptions of the airspace classes, please refer to 14 CFR Part 71).

c. Controlled airspace in the United States is designated as follows:

1. CLASS A - Generally, that airspace from 18,000 feet MSL up to and including FL 600, including the airspace overlying the waters within 12 nautical miles of the coast of the 48 contiguous States and Alaska. Unless otherwise authorized, all persons must operate their aircraft under IFR.

2. CLASS B - Generally, that airspace from the surface to 10,000 feet MSL surrounding the nation's busiest airports in terms of airport operations or passenger enplanements. The configuration of each Class B airspace area is individually tailored and consists of a surface area and two or more layers (some Class B airspaces areas resemble upside-down wedding cakes), and is designed to contain all published instrument procedures once an aircraft enters the airspace. An ATC clearance is required for all aircraft to operate in the area, and all aircraft that are so cleared receive separation services within the airspace. The cloud clearance requirement for VFR operations is "clear of clouds."

3. CLASS C - Generally, that airspace from the surface to 4,000 feet above the airport elevation (charted in MSL) surrounding those airports that have an operational control tower, are serviced by a radar approach control, and have a certain number of IFR operations or passenger enplanements. Although the configuration of each Class C area is individually tailored, the airspace usually consists of a surface area with a 5 nautical mile (NM) radius, a circle with a 10 NM radius that extends no lower than 1,200 feet up to 4,000 feet above the airport elevation and an outer area that is not charted. Each person must establish two-way radio communications with the ATC facility providing air traffic services prior to entering the airspace and thereafter maintain those communications while within the airspace. VFR aircraft are only separated from IFR aircraft within the airspace.

4. CLASS D - Generally, that airspace from the surface to 2,500 feet above the airport elevation (charted in MSL) surrounding those airports that have an operational control tower. The configuration of each Class D airspace area is individually tailored and when instrument procedures are published, the airspace will normally be designed to contain the procedures. Arrival extensions for instrument approach procedures may be Class D or Class E airspace. Unless otherwise authorized, each person must establish two-way radio communications with the ATC facility providing air traffic services prior to entering the airspace and thereafter maintain those communications while in the airspace. No separation services are provided to VFR aircraft.

5. CLASS E - Generally, if the airspace is not Class A, Class B, Class C, or Class D, and it is controlled airspace, it is Class E airspace. Class E airspace extends upward from either the surface or a designated altitude to the overlying or adjacent controlled airspace. When designated as a surface area, the airspace will be configured to contain all instrument procedures. Also in this class are Federal airways, airspace beginning at either 700 or 1,200 feet AGL used to transition to/from the terminal or en route environment, en route domestic, and offshore airspace areas designated below 18,000 feet MSL. Unless designated at a lower altitude, Class E airspace begins at 14,500 MSL over the United States, including that airspace overlying the waters within 12 nautical miles of the coast of the 48 contiguous States and Alaska, up to, but not including 18,000 feet MSL, and the airspace above FL 600.

CONVECTIVE SIGMET - A weather advisory concerning convective weather significant to the safety of all aircraft. Convective SIGMETs are issued for tornadoes, lines of thunderstorms, embedded thunderstorms of any intensity level, areas of thunderstorms greater than or equal to VIP level 4 with an area coverage of 4/10 (40%) or more, and hail 3/4 inch or greater.

COORDINATES - The intersection of lines of reference, usually expressed in degrees/minutes/seconds of latitude and longitude, used to determine position or location.

COUPLED APPROACH - A coupled approach is an instrument approach performed by the aircraft autopilot which is receiving position information and/or steering commands from onboard navigation equipment. In general, coupled nonprecision approaches must be discontinued and flown manually at altitudes lower than 50 feet below the minimum descent altitude, and coupled precision approaches must be flown manually below 50 feet AGL.

Note: Coupled and autoland approaches are flown in VFR and IFR. It is common for carriers to require their crews to fly coupled approaches and autoland approaches (if certified) when the weather conditions are less than approximately 4,000 RVR.

COURSE -

a. The intended direction of flight in the horizontal plane measured in degrees from north.

b. The ILS localizer signal pattern usually specified as the front course or the back course.

c. The intended track along a straight, curved, or segmented MLS path.

CROSS (FIX) AT (ALTITUDE) - Used by ATC when a specific altitude restriction at a specified fix is required.

CROSS (FIX) AT OR ABOVE (ALTITUDE) - Used by ATC when an altitude restriction at a specified fix is required. It does not prohibit the aircraft from crossing the fix at a higher altitude than specified; however, the higher altitude may not be one that will violate a succeeding altitude restriction or altitude assignment.

CROSS (FIX) AT OR BELOW (ALTITUDE) - Used by ATC when a maximum crossing altitude at a specific fix is required. It does not prohibit the aircraft from crossing the fix at a lower altitude; however, it must be at or above the minimum IFR altitude.

CRUISE - Used in an ATC clearance to authorize a pilot to conduct flight at any altitude from the minimum IFR altitude up to and including the altitude specified in the clearance. The pilot may level off at any intermediate altitude within this block of airspace. Climb/descent within the block is to be made at the discretion of the pilot. However, once the pilot starts descent and verbally reports leaving an altitude in the block, he/she may not return to that altitude without additional ATC clearance. Further, it is approval for the pilot to proceed to and make an approach at destination airport and can be used in conjunction with:

a. An airport clearance limit at locations with a standard/special instrument approach procedure. The CFRs require that if an instrument letdown to an airport is necessary, the pilot shall make the letdown in accordance with a standard/special instrument approach procedure for that airport, or

b. An airport clearance limit at locations that are within/below/outside controlled airspace and without a standard/special instrument approach procedure. Such a clearance is NOT AUTHORIZATION for the pilot to descend under IFR conditions below the applicable minimum IFR altitude nor does it imply that ATC is exercising control over aircraft in Class G airspace; however, it provides a means for the aircraft to proceed to destination airport, descend, and land in accordance with applicable CFRs governing VFR flight operations. Also, this provides search and rescue protection until such time as the IFR flight plan is closed.

CRUISE CLIMB - A climb technique employed by aircraft, usually at a constant power setting, resulting in an increase of altitude as the aircraft weight decreases.

CRUISING ALTITUDE - An altitude or flight level maintained during en route level flight. This is a constant altitude and should not be confused with a cruise clearance.

D

DEAD RECKONING - Dead reckoning, as applied to flying, is the navigation of an airplane solely by means of computations based on airspeed, course, heading, wind direction, and speed, groundspeed, and elapsed time.

DECISION HEIGHT - With respect to the operation of aircraft, means the height at which a decision must be made during an ILS, MLS, or PAR instrument approach to either continue the approach or to execute a missed approach.

DEFENSE VISUAL FLIGHT RULES - Rules applicable to flights within an ADIZ conducted under the visual flight rules in 14 CFR Part 91.

DELAY INDEFINITE (REASON IF KNOWN) EXPECT FURTHER CLEARANCE (TIME) - Used by ATC to inform a pilot when an accurate estimate of the delay time and the reason for the delay cannot immediately be determined; e.g., a disabled aircraft on the runway, terminal or center area saturation, weather below landing minimums, etc.

DEPARTURE CONTROL - A function of an approach control facility providing air traffic control service for departing IFR and, under certain conditions, VFR aircraft.

DEPARTURE TIME - The time an aircraft becomes airborne.

DESIRED COURSE-

a. True- A predetermined desired course direction to be followed (measured in degrees from true north).

b. Magnetic- A predetermined desired course direction to be followed (measured in degrees from local magnetic north).

DESIRED TRACK - The planned or intended track between two waypoints. It is measured in degrees from either magnetic or true north. The instantaneous angle may change from point to point along the great circle track between waypoints.

DEVIATIONS-

a. A departure from a current clearance, such as an off course maneuver to avoid weather or turbulence.

b. Where specifically authorized in the CFRs and requested by the pilot, ATC may permit pilots to deviate from certain regulations.

DIGITAL-AUTOMATIC TERMINAL INFORMATION SERVICE (D-ATIS) - The service provides text messages to aircraft, airlines, and other users outside the standard reception range of conventional ATIS via landline and data link communications to the cockpit. Also, the service provides a computer-synthesized voice message that can be transmitted to all aircraft within range of existing transmitters. The Terminal Data Link System (TDLS) D-ATIS application uses weather inputs from local automated weather sources or manually entered meteorological data together with preprogrammed menus to provide standard information to users. Airports with D-ATIS capability are listed in the Airport/Facility Directory.

DIGITAL TERMINAL AUTOMATION SYSTEM (DTAS) - A system where digital radar and beacon data is presented on digital displays and the operational program monitors the system performance on a real-time basis.

DIRECT - Straight line flight between two navigational aids, fixes, points, or any combination thereof. When used by pilots in describing off-airway routes, points defining direct route segments become compulsory reporting points unless the aircraft is under radar contact.

DISCRETE CODE - As used in the Air Traffic Control Radar Beacon System (ATCRBS), any one of the 4096 selectable Mode 3/A aircraft transponder codes except those ending in zero; e.g., discrete codes: 0010, 1201, 2317, 7777; nondiscrete codes: 0100, 1200, 7700. Nondiscrete codes are normally reserved for radar facilities that are not equipped with discrete decoding capability and for other purposes such as emergencies (7700), VFR aircraft (1200), etc.

DISCRETE FREQUENCY - A separate radio frequency for use in direct pilot-controller communications in air traffic control which reduces frequency congestion by controlling the number of aircraft operating on a particular frequency at one time. Discrete frequencies are normally designated for each control sector in en route/terminal ATC facilities. Discrete frequencies are listed in the Airport/Facility Directory and the DOD FLIP IFR En Route Supplement.

DISPLACED THRESHOLD - A threshold that is located at a point on the runway other than the designated beginning of the runway.

DISTANCE MEASURING EQUIPMENT - Equipment (airborne and ground) used to measure, in nautical miles, the slant range distance of an aircraft from the DME navigational aid.

DISTRESS - A condition of being threatened by serious and/or imminent danger and of requiring immediate assistance.

DIVERSE VECTOR AREA - In a radar environment, that area in which a prescribed departure route is not required as the only suitable route to avoid obstacles. The area in which random radar vectors below the MVA/MIA, established in accordance with the TERPS criteria for diverse departures, obstacles and terrain avoidance, may be issued to departing aircraft.

DME FIX - A geographical position determined by reference to a navigational aid which provides distance and azimuth information. It is defined by a specific distance in nautical miles and a radial, azimuth, or course (i.e., localizer) in degrees magnetic from that aid.

DME SEPARATION - Spacing of aircraft in terms of distances (nautical miles) determined by reference to distance measuring equipment (DME).

DOD FLIP - Department of Defense Flight Information Publications used for flight planning, en route, and terminal operations. FLIP is produced by the National Imagery and Mapping Agency (NIMA) for world-wide use. United States Government Flight Information Publications (en route charts and instrument approach procedure charts) are incorporated in DOD FLIP for use in the National Airspace System (NAS).

DOWNBURST - A strong downdraft which induces an outburst of damaging winds on or near the ground. Damaging winds, either straight or curved, are highly divergent. The sizes of downbursts vary from 1/2 mile or less to more than 10 miles. An intense downburst often causes widespread damage. Damaging winds, lasting 5 to 30 minutes, could reach speeds as high as 120 knots.

DVFR FLIGHT PLAN - A flight plan filed for a VFR aircraft which intends to operate in airspace within which the ready identification, location, and control of aircraft are required in the interest of national security.

E

EMERGENCY - A distress or an urgency condition.

EMERGENCY LOCATOR TRANSMITTER - A radio transmitter attached to the aircraft structure which operates from its own power source on 121.5 MHz and 243.0 MHz. It aids in locating downed aircraft by radiating a downward sweeping audio tone, 2-4 times per second. It is designed to function without human action after an accident.

EN ROUTE AIR TRAFFIC CONTROL SERVICES - Air traffic control service provided aircraft on IFR flight plans, generally by centers, when these aircraft are operating between departure and destination terminal areas. When equipment, capabilities, and controller workload permit, certain advisory/assistance services may be provided to VFR aircraft.

EN ROUTE AUTOMATION SYSTEM (EAS) - The complex integrated environment consisting of situation display systems, surveillance systems and flight data processing, remote devices, decision support tools, and the related communications equipment that form the heart of the automated IFR air traffic control system. It interfaces with automated terminal systems and is used in the control of en route IFR aircraft.

EN ROUTE FLIGHT ADVISORY SERVICE - A service specifically designed to provide, upon pilot request, timely weather information pertinent to his/her type of flight, intended route of flight, and altitude. The FSSs providing this service are listed in the Airport/Facility Directory.

EN ROUTE MINIMUM SAFE ALTITUDE WARNING - A function of the EAS that aids the controller by providing an alert when a tracked aircraft is below or predicted by the computer to go below a predetermined minimum IFR altitude (MIA).

EN ROUTE TRANSITION -

a. Conventional STARs/SIDs. The portion of a SID/STAR that connects to one or more en route airway/jet route.

b. RNAV STARs/SIDs. The portion of a STAR preceding the common route or point, or for a SID the portion following, that is coded for a specific en route fix, airway or jet route.

ESTABLISHED - To be stable or fixed on a route, route segment, altitude, heading, etc.

ESTIMATED TIME OF ARRIVAL - The time the flight is estimated to arrive at the gate (scheduled operators) or the actual runway on times for nonscheduled operators.

ESTIMATED TIME EN ROUTE - The estimated flying time from departure point to destination (lift-off to touchdown).

EXECUTE MISSED APPROACH - Instructions issued to a pilot making an instrument approach which means continue inbound to the missed approach point and execute the missed approach procedure as described on the Instrument Approach Procedure Chart or as previously assigned by ATC. The pilot may climb immediately to the altitude specified in the missed approach procedure upon making a missed approach. No turns should be initiated prior to reaching the missed approach point. When conducting an ASR or PAR approach, execute the assigned missed approach procedure immediately upon receiving instructions to "execute missed approach."

EXPECT (ALTITUDE) AT (TIME) or (FIX) - Used under certain conditions to provide a pilot with an altitude to be used in the event of two-way communications failure. It also provides altitude information to assist the pilot in planning.

EXPECT DEPARTURE CLEARANCE TIME - The runway release time assigned to an aircraft in a traffic management program and shown on the flight progress strip as an

EXPECT FURTHER CLEARANCE (TIME) - The time a pilot can expect to receive clearance beyond a clearance limit.

EXPECT FURTHER CLEARANCE VIA (AIRWAYS, ROUTES OR FIXES) - Used to inform a pilot of the routing he/she can expect if any part of the route beyond a short range clearance limit differs from that filed.

EXPEDITE - Used by ATC when prompt compliance is required to avoid the development of an imminent situation. Expedite climb/descent normally indicates to a pilot that the approximate best rate of climb/descent should be used without requiring an exceptional change in aircraft handling characteristics.

F

FAST FILE - A system whereby a pilot files a flight plan via telephone that is tape recorded and then transcribed for transmission to the appropriate air traffic facility. Locations having a fast file capability are contained in the Airport/Facility Directory.

FEEDER FIX - The fix depicted on Instrument Approach Procedure Charts which establishes the starting point of the feeder route.

FEEDER ROUTE - A route depicted on instrument approach procedure charts to designate routes for aircraft to proceed from the en route structure to the initial approach fix (IAF).

FILED - Normally used in conjunction with flight plans, meaning a flight plan has been submitted to ATC.

FILED FLIGHT PLAN - The flight plan as filed with an ATS unit by the pilot or his/her designated representative without any subsequent changes or clearances.

FINAL - Commonly used to mean that an aircraft is on the final approach course or is aligned with a landing area.

FINAL APPROACH COURSE - A bearing/radial/track of an instrument approach leading to a runway or an extended runway centerline all without regard to distance.

FINAL APPROACH FIX - The fix from which the final approach (IFR) to an airport is executed and which identifies the beginning of the final approach segment. It is designated on Government charts by the Maltese Cross symbol for nonprecision approaches and the lightning bolt symbol for precision approaches; or when ATC directs a lower-than-published glideslope/path intercept altitude, it is the resultant actual point of the glideslope/path intercept.

FINAL APPROACH-IFR - The flight path of an aircraft which is inbound to an airport on a final instrument approach course, beginning at the final approach fix or point and extending to the airport or the point where a circle-to-land maneuver or a missed approach is executed.

FINAL APPROACH POINT - The point, applicable only to a nonprecision approach with no depicted FAF (such as an on airport VOR), where the aircraft is established inbound on the final approach course from the procedure turn and where the final approach descent may be commenced. The FAP serves as the FAF and identifies the beginning of the final approach segment.

FINAL CONTROLLER - The controller providing information and final approach guidance during PAR and ASR approaches utilizing radar equipment.

FLIGHT LEVEL - A level of constant atmospheric pressure related to a reference datum of 29.92 inches of mercury. Each is stated in three digits that represent hundreds of feet. For example, flight level (FL) 250 represents a barometric altimeter indication of 25,000 feet; FL 255, an indication of 25,500 feet.

FLIGHT MANAGEMENT SYSTEMS - A computer system that uses a large data base to allow routes to be preprogrammed and fed into the system by means of a data loader. The system is constantly updated with respect to position accuracy by reference to conventional navigation aids. The sophisticated program and its associated data base insures that the most appropriate aids are automatically selected during the information update cycle.

FLIGHT PATH - A line, course, or track along which an aircraft is flying or intended to be flown.

FLIGHT PLAN - Specified information relating to the intended flight of an aircraft that is filed orally or in writing with an FSS or an ATC facility.

FLIGHT WATCH - A shortened term for use in air-ground contacts to identify the flight service station providing En Route Flight Advisory Service; e.g., "Oakland Flight Watch."

FLY HEADING (DEGREES) - Informs the pilot of the heading he/she should fly. The pilot may have to turn to, or continue on, a specific compass direction in order to comply with the instructions. The pilot is expected to turn in the shorter direction to the heading unless otherwise instructed by ATC.

FLY-BY WAYPOINT - A fly-by waypoint requires the use of turn anticipation to avoid overshoot of the next flight segment.

FLY-OVER WAYPOINT - A fly-over waypoint precludes any turn until the waypoint is overflown and is followed by an intercept maneuver of the next flight segment.

FUEL REMAINING - A phrase used by either pilots or controllers when relating to the fuel remaining on board until actual fuel exhaustion. When transmitting such information in response to either a controller question or pilot initiated cautionary advisory to air traffic control, pilots will state the APPROXIMATE NUMBER OF MINUTES the flight can continue with the fuel remaining. All reserve fuel SHOULD BE INCLUDED in the time stated, as should an allowance for established fuel gauge system error.

G

GATE HOLD PROCEDURES - Procedures at selected airports to hold aircraft at the gate or other ground location whenever departure delays exceed or are anticipated to exceed 15 minutes. The sequence for departure will be maintained in accordance with initial call-up unless modified by flow control restrictions. Pilots should monitor the ground control/clear-

ance delivery frequency for engine start/taxi advisories or new proposed start/taxi time if the delay changes.

GLIDESLOPE - Provides vertical guidance for aircraft during approach and landing. The glideslope/glidepath is based on the following:

a. Electronic components emitting signals which provide vertical guidance by reference to airborne instruments during instrument approaches such as ILS/MLS, or

b. Visual ground aids, such as VASI, which provide vertical guidance for a VFR approach or for the visual portion of an instrument approach and landing.

c. PAR. Used by ATC to inform an aircraft making a PAR approach of its vertical position (elevation) relative to the descent profile.

GLIDESLOPE INTERCEPT ALTITUDE - The minimum altitude to intercept the glideslope/path on a precision approach. The intersection of the published intercept altitude with the glideslope/path, designated on Government charts by the lightning bolt symbol, is the precision FAF; however, when the approach chart shows an alternative lower glideslope intercept altitude, and ATC directs a lower altitude, the resultant lower intercept position is then the FAF.

GLOBAL POSITIONING SYSTEM (GPS) - A space-base radio positioning, navigation, and time-transfer system. The system provides highly accurate position and velocity information, and precise time, on a continuous global basis, to an unlimited number of properly equipped users. The system is unaffected by weather, and provides a worldwide common grid reference system. The GPS concept is predicated upon accurate and continuous knowledge of the spatial position of each satellite in the system with respect to time and distance from a transmitting satellite to the user. The GPS receiver automatically selects appropriate signals from the satellites in view and translates these into three-dimensional position, velocity, and time. System accuracy for civil users is normally 100 meters horizontally.

GO AHEAD - Proceed with your message. Not to be used for any other purpose.

GO AROUND - Instructions for a pilot to abandon his/her approach to landing. Additional instructions may follow. Unless otherwise advised by ATC, a VFR aircraft or an aircraft conducting visual approach should overfly the runway while climbing to traffic pattern altitude and enter the traffic pattern via the crosswind leg. A pilot on an IFR flight plan making an instrument approach should execute the published missed approach procedure or proceed as instructed by ATC; e.g., "Go around" (additional instructions if required).

GROUND-BASED TRANSCEIVER (GBT)- The ground-based transmitter/receiver (transceiver) receives automatic dependent surveillance-broadcast messages, which are forwarded to an air traffic control facility for processing and display with other radar targets on the plan position indicator (radar display).

GROUND COMMUNICATION OUTLET (GCO) - An unstaffed, remotely controlled, ground-ground communications facility. Pilots at uncontrolled airports may contact ATC and FSS via VHF to a telephone connection to obtain an instrument clearance or close a VFR or IFR flight plan. They may also get an updated weather briefing prior to takeoff. Pilots will use four "key clicks" on the VHF radio to contact the appropriate ATC facility or six "key clicks" to contact the FSS. The GCO system is intended to be used only on the ground.

H

HAVE NUMBERS - Used by pilots to inform ATC that they have received runway, wind, and altimeter information only.

HAZARDOUS INFLIGHT WEATHER ADVISORY SERVICE - Continuous recorded hazardous inflight weather forecasts broadcasted to airborne pilots over selected VOR outlets defined as an HIWAS BROADCAST AREA.

HAZARDOUS WEATHER INFORMATION - Summary of significant meteorological information (SIGMET/WS), convective significant meteorological information (convective SIGMET/WST), urgent pilot weather reports (urgent PIREP/UUA), center weather advisories (CWA), airmen's meteorological information (AIRMET/WA) and any other weather such as isolated thunderstorms that are rapidly developing and increasing in intensity, or low ceilings and visibilities that are becoming widespread which is considered significant and are not included in a current hazardous weather advisory.

HEIGHT ABOVE AIRPORT - The height of the Minimum Descent Altitude above the published airport elevation. This is published in conjunction with circling minimums.

HEIGHT ABOVE TOUCHDOWN - The height of the Decision Height or Minimum Descent Altitude above the highest runway elevation in the touchdown zone (first 3,000 feet of the runway). HAT is published on instrument approach charts in conjunction with all straight-in minimums.

HERTZ - The standard radio equivalent of frequency in cycles per second of an electromagnetic wave. Kilohertz (KHz) is a frequency of one thousand cycles per second. Megahertz (MHz) is a frequency of one million cycles per second.

HIGH FREQUENCY - The frequency band between 3 and 30 MHz.

HIGH FREQUENCY COMMUNICATIONS - High radio frequencies (HF) between 3 and 30 MHz used for air-to-ground voice communication in overseas operations.

HIGH SPEED TAXIWAY - A long radius taxiway designed and provided with lighting or marking to define the path of aircraft, traveling at high speed (up to 60 knots), from the runway center to a point on the center of a taxiway. Also referred to as long radius exit or turn-off taxiway. The high speed taxiway is designed to expedite aircraft turning off the runway after landing, thus reducing runway occupancy time.

HOLD FOR RELEASE - Used by ATC to delay an aircraft for traffic management reasons; i.e., weather, traffic volume, etc. Hold for release instructions (including departure delay information) are used to inform a pilot or a controller (either directly or through an authorized relay) that an IFR departure clearance is not valid until a release time or additional instructions have been received.

HOLD PROCEDURE - A predetermined maneuver which keeps aircraft within a specified airspace while awaiting further clearance from air traffic control. Also used during ground operations to keep aircraft within a specified area or at a specified point while awaiting further clearance from air traffic control.

HOLDING FIX - A specified fix identifiable to a pilot by NAVAIDs or visual reference to the ground used as a reference point in establishing and maintaining the position of an aircraft while holding.

HOLD-SHORT POINT - A point on the runway beyond which a landing aircraft with a LAHSO clearance is not authorized to proceed. This point may be located prior to an intersecting runway, taxiway, predetermined point, or approach/departure flight path.

HOLD-SHORT POSITION LIGHTS - Flashing in-pavement white lights located at specified hold-short points.

HOLD-SHORT POSITION MARKING - The painted runway marking located at the hold-short point on all LAHSO runways.

HOLD-SHORT POSITION SIGNS - Red and white holding position signs located alongside the hold-short point.

HOMING - Flight toward a NAVAID, without correcting for wind, by adjusting the aircraft heading to maintain a relative bearing of zero degrees.

HOW DO YOU HEAR ME? - A question relating to the quality of the transmission or to determine how well the transmission is being received.

I

I SAY AGAIN - The message will be repeated.

IAWP - Initial Approach Waypoint

ICING - The accumulation of airframe ice. Types of icing are:

a. Rime Ice - Rough, milky, opaque ice formed by the instantaneous freezing of small supercooled water droplets.

b. Clear Ice - A glossy, clear, or translucent ice formed by the relatively slow freezing or large supercooled water droplets.

c. Mixed - A mixture of clear ice and rime ice.

Intensity of icing:

a. Trace - Ice becomes perceptible. Rate of accumulation is slightly greater than the rate of sublimation. Deicing/anti-icing equipment is not utilized unless encountered for an extended period of time (over 1 hour).

b. Light - The rate of accumulation may create a problem if flight is prolonged in this environment (over 1 hour). Occasional use of deicing/anti-icing equipment removes/prevents accumulation. It does not present a problem if the deicing/anti-icing equipment is used.

c. Moderate - The rate of accumulation is such that even short encounters become potentially hazardous and use of deicing/anti-icing equipment or flight diversion is necessary.

d. Severe - The rate of accumulation is such that deicing/anti-icing equipment fails to reduce or control the hazard. Immediate flight diversion is necessary.

IDENT - A request for a pilot to activate the aircraft transponder identification feature. This will help the controller to confirm an aircraft identity or to identify an aircraft.

IF NO TRANSMISSION RECEIVED FOR (TIME) - Used by ATC in radar approaches to prefix procedures which should be followed by the pilot in event of lost communications.

IFR AIRCRAFT - An aircraft conducting flight in accordance with instrument flight rules.

IFR CONDITIONS - Weather conditions below the minimum for flight under visual flight rules.

IFR MILITARY TRAINING ROUTES (IR) - Routes used by the Department of Defense and associated Reserve and Air Guard units for the purpose of conducting low-altitude navigation and tactical training in both IFR and VFR weather conditions below 10,000 feet MSL at airspeeds in excess of 250 knots IAS.

IFR TAKEOFF MINIMUMS AND DEPARTURE PROCEDURES - Title 14 Code of Federal Regulations Part 91, prescribes standard takeoff rules for certain civil users. At some airports, obstructions or other factors require the establishment of nonstandard takeoff minimums, departure procedures, or both to assist pilots in avoiding obstacles during climb to the minimum en route altitude. Those airports are listed in FAA/DOD Instrument Approach Procedures (IAPs) Charts under a section entitled "IFR Takeoff Minimums and Departure Procedures." The FAA/DOD IAP chart legend illustrates the symbol used to alert the pilot to nonstandard takeoff minimums and departure procedures. When departing IFR from such airports or from any airports where there are no departure procedures, DPs, or ATC facilities available, pilots should advise ATC of any departure limitations. Controllers may query a pilot to determine acceptable departure directions, turns, or headings after takeoff. Pilots should be familiar with the departure procedures and must assure that their aircraft can meet or exceed any specified climb gradients.

IF/IAWP - Intermediate Fix/Initial Approach Waypoint. The waypoint where the final approach course of a T approach meets the crossbar of the T. When designated (in conjunction with a TAA) this waypoint will be used as an IAWP when approaching the airport from certain directions, and as an IFWP when beginning the approach from another IAWP.

IFWP - Intermediate Fix Waypoint

ILS CATEGORIES - 1. ILS Category I. An ILS approach procedure which provides for approach to a height above touchdown of not less than 200 feet and with runway visual range of not less than 1,800 feet. - 2. ILS Category II. An ILS approach procedure which provides for approach to a height above touchdown of not less than 100 feet and with runway visual range of not less than 1,200 feet. - 3. ILS Category III:

a. IIIA. - An ILS approach procedure which provides for approach without a decision height minimum and with runway visual range of not less than 700 feet.

b. IIIB. - An ILS approach procedure which provides for approach without a decision height minimum and with runway visual range of not less than 150 feet.

c. IIIC. - An ILS approach procedure which provides for approach without a decision height minimum and without runway visual range minimum.

ILS PRM APPROACH - An instrument landing system (ILS) approach conducted to parallel runways whose extended centerlines are separated by less than 4,300 feet and the parallel runways have a Precision Runway Monitoring (PRM) system that permits simultaneous independent ILS approaches.

IMMEDIATELY - Used by ATC or pilots when such action compliance is required to avoid an imminent situation.

INFORMATION REQUEST - A request originated by an FSS for information concerning an overdue VFR aircraft.

INITIAL APPROACH FIX - The fixes depicted on instrument approach procedure charts that identify the beginning of the initial approach segment(s).

INSTRUMENT APPROACH PROCEDURE - A series of predetermined maneuvers for the orderly transfer of an aircraft under instrument flight conditions from the beginning of the initial approach to a landing or to a point from which a landing may be made visually. It is prescribed and approved for a specific airport by competent authority.

a. U.S. civil standard instrument approach procedures are approved by the FAA as prescribed under 14 CFR Part 97 and are available for public use.

b. U.S. military standard instrument approach procedures are approved and published by the Department of Defense.

c. Special instrument approach procedures are approved by the FAA for individual operators but are not published in 14 CFR Part 97 for public use.

INSTRUMENT DEPARTURE PROCEDURE (DP) - A preplanned instrument flight rule (IFR) departure procedure published for pilot use, in graphic or textual format, that provides obstruction clearance from the terminal area to the appropriate en route structure. There are two types of DP, Obstacle Departure Procedure (ODP), printed either textually or graphically, and, Standard Instrument Departure (SID), which is always printed graphically.

INSTRUMENT FLIGHT RULES - Rules governing the procedures for conducting instrument flight. Also a term used by pilots and controllers to indicate type of flight plan.

INSTRUMENT LANDING SYSTEM - A precision instrument approach system which normally consists of the following electronic components and visual aids:

a. Localizer.
b. Glideslope.
c. Outer Marker.
d. Middle Marker.
e. Approach Lights.

INSTRUMENT METEOROLOGICAL CONDITIONS - Meteorological conditions expressed in terms of visibility, distance from cloud, and ceiling less than the minima specified for visual meteorological conditions.

INSTRUMENT RUNWAY - A runway equipped with electronic and visual navigation aids for which a precision or nonprecision approach procedure having straight-in landing minimums has been approved.

INSTRUMENT RUNWAY [ICAO] - One of the following types of runways intended for the opera-

tion of aircraft using instrument approach procedures:

a. Nonprecision Approach Runway - An instrument runway served by visual aids and a nonvisual aid providing at least directional guidance adequate for a straight-in approach.

b. Precision Approach Runway, Category I - An instrument runway served by ILS and visual aids intended for operations down to 60 m (200 feet) decision height and down to an RVR of the order of 800 m.

c. Precision Approach Runway, Category II - An instrument runway served by ILS and visual aids intended for operations down to 30 m (100 feet) decision height and down to an RVR of the order of 400 m.

d. Precision Approach Runway, Category III - An instrument runway served by ILS to and along the surface of the runway and:

1. Intended for operations down to an RVR of the order of 200 m (no decision height being applicable) using visual aids during the final phase of landing;

2. Intended for operations down to an RVR of the order of 50 m (no decision height being applicable) using visual aids for taxiing;

3. Intended for operations without reliance on visual reference for landing or taxiing.

Note 1: See Annex 10 Volume I, Part I, Chapter 3, for related ILS specifications.

Note 2: Visual aids need not necessarily be matched to the scale of nonvisual aids provided. The criterion for the selection of visual aids is the conditions in which operations are intended to be conducted.

INTERMEDIATE FIX - The fix that identifies the beginning of the intermediate approach segment of an instrument approach procedure. The fix is not normally identified on the instrument approach chart as an intermediate fix (IF).

INTERNATIONAL AIRPORT - Relating to international flight, it means:

a. An airport of entry which has been designated by the Secretary of Treasury or Commissioner of Customs as an international airport for customs service.

b. A landing rights airport at which specific permission to land must be obtained from customs authorities in advance of contemplated use.

c. Airports designated under the Convention on International Civil Aviation as an airport for use by international commercial air transport and/or international general aviation.

INTERROGATOR - The ground-based surveillance radar beacon transmitter-receiver, which normally scans in synchronism with a primary radar, transmitting discrete radio signals which repetitiously request all transponders on the mode being used to reply. The replies received are mixed with the primary radar returns and displayed on the same plan position indicator (radar scope). Also, refers to the airborne element of the TACAN/DME system.

INTERSECTION -

a. A point defined by any combination of courses, radials, or bearings of two or more navigational aids.

b. Used to describe the point where two runways, a runway and a taxiway, or two taxiways cross or meet.

INTERSECTION DEPARTURE - A departure from any runway intersection except the end of the runway.

J

JET ROUTE - A route designed to serve aircraft operations from 18,000 feet MSL up to and including flight level 450. The routes are referred to as "J" routes with numbering to identify the designated route; e.g., J105.

JET STREAM - A migrating stream of high-speed winds present at high altitudes.

K

KNOWN TRAFFIC - With respect to ATC clearances, means aircraft whose altitude, position, and intentions are known to ATC.

L

LAHSO - An acronym for "Land and Hold Short Operation." These operations include landing and holding short of an intersecting runway, a taxiway, a predetermined point, or an approach/departure flightpath.

LAHSO-DRY - Land and hold short operations on runways that are dry.

LAHSO-WET - Land and hold short operations on runways that are wet (but not contaminated).

LAND AND HOLD SHORT OPERATIONS - Operations which include simultaneous takeoffs and landings and/or simultaneous landings when a landing aircraft is able and is instructed by the controller to hold-short of the intersecting runway/taxiway or designated hold-short point. Pilots are expected to promptly inform the controller if the hold short clearance cannot be accepted.

LANDING MINIMUMS - The minimum visibility prescribed for landing a civil aircraft while using an instrument approach procedure. The minimum applies with other limitations set forth in 14 CFR Part 91 with respect to the Minimum Descent Altitude (MDA) or Decision Height (DH) prescribed in the instrument approach procedures as follows:

a. Straight-in landing minimums. A statement of MDA and visibility, or DH and visibility, required for a straight-in landing on a specified runway, or

b. Circling minimums. A statement of MDA and visibility required for the circle-to-land maneuver.

Note: Descent below the established MDA or DH is not authorized during an approach unless the aircraft is in a position from which a normal approach to the runway of intended landing can be made and adequate visual reference to required visual cues is maintained.

LAST ASSIGNED ALTITUDE - The last altitude/flight level assigned by ATC and acknowledged by the pilot.

LATERAL NAVIGATION (LNAV) - A function of area navigation (RNAV) equipment which calculates, displays, and provides lateral guidance to a profile or path.

LATERAL SEPARATION - The lateral spacing of aircraft at the same altitude by requiring operation on different routes or in different geographical locations.

LOCAL AIRPORT ADVISORY [LAA] - A service provided by facilities, which are located on the landing airport, have a discrete ground-to-air communication frequency or the tower frequency when the tower is closed, automated weather reporting with voice broadcasting, and a continuous ASOS/AWOS data display, other continuous direct reading instruments, or manual observations available to the specialist.

LOCALIZER - The component of an ILS which provides course guidance to the runway.

LOCALIZER OFFSET - An angular offset of the localizer from the runway extended centerline in a direction away from the no transgression zone (NTZ) that increases the normal operating zone (NOZ) width. An offset requires a 50 foot increase in DH and is not authorized for CAT II and CAT III approaches.

LOCALIZER TYPE DIRECTIONAL AID - A NAVAID used for nonprecision instrument approaches with utility and accuracy comparable to a localizer but which is not a part of a complete ILS and is not aligned with the runway.

LOCALIZER USABLE DISTANCE - The maximum distance from the localizer transmitter at a specified altitude, as verified by flight inspection, at which reliable course information is continuously received.

LONGITUDINAL SEPARATION - The longitudinal spacing of aircraft at the same altitude by a minimum distance expressed in units of time or miles.

LORAN - An electronic navigational system by which hyperbolic lines of position are determined by measuring the difference in the time of reception of synchronized pulse signals from two fixed transmitters. Loran A operates in the 1750-1950 KHz frequency band. Loran C and D operate in the 100-110 KHz frequency band.

LOST COMMUNICATIONS - Loss of the ability to communicate by radio. Aircraft are sometimes referred to as NORDO (No Radio). Standard pilot procedures are specified in 14 CFR Part 91. Radar controllers issue procedures for pilots to follow in the event of lost communications during a radar approach when weather reports indicate that an aircraft will likely encounter IFR weather conditions during the approach.

LOW ALTITUDE AIRWAY STRUCTURE - The network of airways serving aircraft operations up to but not including 18,000 feet MSL.

LOW ALTITUDE ALERT SYSTEM - An automated function of the TPX-42 that alerts the controller when a Mode C transponder equipped aircraft on an IFR flight plan is below a predetermined minimum safe altitude. If requested by the pilot, Low Altitude Alert System monitoring is also available to VFR Mode C transponder equipped aircraft.

LOW APPROACH - An approach over an airport or runway following an instrument approach or a VFR approach including the go-around maneuver where the pilot intentionally does not make contact with the runway.

LOW FREQUENCY - The frequency band between 30 and 300 KHz.

LPV- A type of approach with vertical guidance (APV) based on WAAS, published on RNAV (GPS) approach charts. This procedure takes advantage of the precise lateral guidance available from WAAS. The minima is published as a decision altitude (DA).

M

MACH NUMBER - The ratio of true airspeed to the speed of sound; e.g., MACH .82, MACH 1.6.

a. Concerning altitude/flight level, the term means to remain at the altitude/flight level specified. The phrase "climb and" or "descend and" normally precedes "maintain" and the altitude assignment; e.g., "descend and maintain 5,000."

b. Concerning other ATC instructions, the term is used in its literal sense; e.g., maintain VFR.

MANDATORY ALTITUDE - An altitude depicted on an instrument Approach Procedure Chart requiring the aircraft to maintain altitude at the depicted value.

MARKER BEACON - An electronic navigation facility transmitting a 75 MHz vertical fan or boneshaped radiation pattern. Marker beacons are identified by their modulation frequency and keying code, and when received by compatible airborne equipment, indicate to the pilot, both aurally and visually, that he/she is passing over the facility.

MAWP - Missed Approach Waypoint

MAXIMUM AUTHORIZED ALTITUDE - A published altitude representing the maximum usable altitude or flight level for an airspace structure or route segment. It is the highest altitude on a Federal airway, jet route, area navigation low or high route, or other direct route for which an MEA is designated in 14 CFR Part 95 at which adequate reception of navigation aid signals is assured.

MAYDAY - The international radiotelephony distress signal. When repeated three times, it indicates imminent and grave danger and that immediate assistance is requested.

MICROBURST - A small downburst with outbursts of damaging winds extending 2.5 miles or less. In spite of its small horizontal scale, an intense microburst could induce wind speeds as high as 150 knots

MICROWAVE LANDING SYSTEM - A precision instrument approach system operating in the microwave spectrum which normally consists of the following components:

a. Azimuth Station.

b. Elevation Station.

c. Precision Distance Measuring Equipment.

MIDDLE MARKER - A marker beacon that defines a point along the glideslope of an ILS normally located at or near the point of decision height (ILS Category I). It is keyed to transmit alternate dots and dashes, with the alternate dots and dashes keyed at the rate of 95 dot/dash combinations per minute on a 1300 Hz tone, which is received aurally and visually by compatible airborne equipment.

MILITARY TRAINING ROUTES - Airspace of defined vertical and lateral dimensions established for the conduct of military flight training at airspeeds in excess of 250 knots IAS.

MINIMUM CROSSING ALTITUDE - The lowest altitude at certain fixes at which an aircraft must cross when proceeding in the direction of a higher minimum en route IFR altitude (MEA).

MINIMUM DESCENT ALTITUDE - The lowest altitude, expressed in feet above mean sea level, to which descent is authorized on final approach or during circle-to-land maneuvering in execution of a standard instrument approach procedure where no electronic glideslope is provided.

MINIMUM EN ROUTE IFR ALTITUDE - The lowest published altitude between radio fixes which assures acceptable navigational signal coverage and meets obstacle clearance requirements between those fixes. The MEA prescribed for a Federal airway or segment thereof, area navigation low or high route, or other direct route applies to the entire width of the airway, segment, or route between the radio fixes defining the airway, segment, or route.

MINIMUM FUEL - Indicates that an aircraft's fuel supply has reached a state where, upon reaching the destination, it can accept little or no delay. This is not an emergency situation but merely indicates an emergency situation is possible should any undue delay occur.

MINIMUM HOLDING ALTITUDE - The lowest altitude prescribed for a holding pattern which assures navigational signal coverage, communications, and meets obstacle clearance requirements.

MINIMUM IFR ALTITUDES - Minimum altitudes for IFR operations as prescribed in 14 CFR Part 91. These altitudes are published on aeronautical charts and prescribed in 14 CFR Part 95 for airways and routes, and in 14 CFR Part 97 for standard instrument approach procedures. If no applicable minimum altitude is prescribed in 14 CFR Part 95 or 14 CFR Part 97, the following minimum IFR altitude applies:

a. In designated mountainous areas, 2,000 feet above the highest obstacle within a horizontal distance of 4 nautical miles from the course to be flown; or

b. Other than mountainous areas, 1,000 feet above the highest obstacle within a horizontal distance of 4 nautical miles from the course to be flown; or

c. As otherwise authorized by the Administrator or assigned by ATC.

MINIMUM OBSTRUCTION CLEARANCE ALTITUDE - The lowest published altitude in effect between radio fixes on VOR airways, off-airway routes, or route segments which meets obstacle clearance requirements for the entire route segment and which assures acceptable navigational signal coverage only within 25 statute (22 nautical) miles of a VOR.

MINIMUM RECEPTION ALTITUDE - The lowest altitude at which an intersection can be determined.

MINIMUM SAFE ALTITUDE -

a. The minimum altitude specified in 14 CFR Part 91 for various aircraft operations.

b. Altitudes depicted on approach charts which provide at least 1,000 feet of obstacle clearance for emergency use within a specified distance from the navigation facility upon which a procedure is predicated. These altitudes will be identified as Minimum Sector Altitudes or Emergency Safe Altitudes and are established as follows:

1. Minimum Sector Altitudes. Altitudes depicted on approach charts which provide at least 1,000 feet of obstacle clearance within a 25-mile radius of the navigation facility upon which the procedure is predicated. Sectors depicted on approach charts must be at least 90 degrees in scope. These altitudes are for emergency use only and do not necessarily assure acceptable navigational signal coverage.

2. Emergency Safe Altitudes. Altitudes depicted on approach charts which provide at least 1,000 feet of obstacle clearance in nonmountainous areas and 2,000 feet of obstacle clearance in designated mountainous areas within a 100-mile radius of the navigation facility upon which the procedure is predicated and normally used only in military procedures. These altitudes are identified on published procedures as "Emergency Safe Altitudes."

MINIMUM SAFE ALTITUDE WARNING - A function of the ARTS III computer that aids the controller by alerting him/her when a tracked Mode C equipped aircraft is below or is predicted by the computer to go below a predetermined minimum safe altitude.

MINIMUMS - Weather condition requirements established for a particular operation or type of operation; e.g., IFR takeoff or landing, alternate airport for IFR flight plans, VFR flight, etc.

MINIMUM VECTORING ALTITUDE - The lowest MSL altitude at which an IFR aircraft will be vectored by a radar controller, except as otherwise authorized for radar approaches, departures, and missed approaches. The altitude meets IFR obstacle clearance criteria. It may be lower than the published MEA along an airway or J-route segment. It may be utilized for radar vectoring only upon the controller's determination that an adequate radar return is being received from the aircraft being controlled. Charts depicting minimum vectoring altitudes are normally available only to the controllers and not to pilots.

MISSED APPROACH -

a. A maneuver conducted by a pilot when an instrument approach cannot be completed to a landing. The route of flight and altitude are shown on instrument approach procedure charts. A pilot executing a missed approach prior to the Missed Approach Point (MAP) must continue along the final approach to the MAP.

b. A term used by the pilot to inform ATC that he/she is executing the missed approach.

c. At locations where ATC radar service is provided, the pilot should conform to radar vectors when provided by ATC in lieu of the published missed approach procedure.

MISSED APPROACH POINT - A point prescribed in each instrument approach procedure at which a missed approach procedure shall be executed if the required visual reference does not exist.

MULTICOM - A mobile service not open to public correspondence used to provide communications essential to conduct the activities being performed by or directed from private aircraft.

N

NATIONAL FLIGHT DATA CENTER - A facility in Washington D.C., established by FAA to operate a central aeronautical information service for the collection, validation, and dissemination of aeronautical data in support of the activities of government, industry, and the aviation community. The information is published in the National Flight Data Digest.

NAVAID CLASSES - VOR, VORTAC, and TACAN aids are classed according to their operational use. The three classes of NAVAIDs are:

a. T- Terminal.

b. L- Low altitude.

c. H- High altitude.

Note: The normal service range for T, L, and H class aids is found in the AIM. Certain operational requirements make it necessary to use some of these aids at greater service ranges than specified. Extended range is made possible through flight inspection determinations. Some aids also have lesser service range due to location, terrain, frequency protection, etc. Restrictions to service range are listed in Airport/Facility Directory.

NEGATIVE - "No," or "permission not granted," or "that is not correct."

NEGATIVE CONTACT - Used by pilots to inform ATC that:

a. Previously issued traffic is not in sight. It may be followed by the pilot's request for the controller to provide assistance in avoiding the traffic.

b. They were unable to contact ATC on a particular frequency.

NIGHT - The time between the end of evening civil twilight and the beginning of morning civil twilight, as published in the American Air Almanac, converted to local time.

NO GYRO APPROACH - A radar approach/vector provided in case of a malfunctioning gyro-compass or directional gyro. Instead of providing the pilot with headings to be flown, the controller observes the radar track and issues control instructions "turn right/left" or "stop turn" as appropriate.

NONAPPROACH CONTROL TOWER - Authorizes aircraft to land or takeoff at the airport controlled by the tower or to transit the Class D airspace. The primary function of a nonapproach control tower is the sequencing of aircraft in the traffic pattern and on the landing area. Nonapproach control towers also separate aircraft operating under instrument flight rules clearances from approach controls and centers. They provide ground control services to aircraft, vehicles, personnel, and equipment on the airport movement area.

NONDIRECTIONAL BEACON - An L/MF or UHF radio beacon transmitting nondirectional signals whereby the pilot of an aircraft equipped with direction finding equipment can determine his/her bearing to or from the radio beacon and "home" on or track to or from the station. When the radio beacon is installed in conjunction with the Instrument Landing System marker, it is normally called a Compass Locator.

NONPRECISION APPROACH PROCEDURE - A standard instrument approach procedure in which no electronic glideslope is provided; e.g., VOR, TACAN, NDB, LOC, ASR, LDA, or SDF approaches.

NONRADAR - Precedes other terms and generally means without the use of radar, such as:

a. Nonradar Approach. Used to describe instrument approaches for which course guidance on final approach is not provided by ground-based precision or surveillance radar. Radar vectors to the final approach course may or may not be provided by ATC. Examples of nonradar approaches are VOR, NDB, TACAN, and ILS/MLS approaches.

b. Nonradar Approach Control. An ATC facility providing approach control service without the use of radar.

c. Nonradar Arrival. An aircraft arriving at an airport without radar service or at an airport served

by a radar facility and radar contact has not been established or has been terminated due to a lack of radar service to the airport.

d. Nonradar Route. A flight path or route over which the pilot is performing his/her own navigation. The pilot may be receiving radar separation, radar monitoring, or other ATC services while on a nonradar route.

e. Nonradar Separation. The spacing of aircraft in accordance with established minima without the use of radar; e.g., vertical, lateral, or longitudinal separation.

NOTICE TO AIRMEN - A notice containing information (not known sufficiently in advance to publicize by other means) concerning the establishment, condition, or change in any component (facility, service, or procedure of, or hazard in the National Airspace System) the timely knowledge of which is essential to personnel concerned with flight operations.

a. NOTAM(D)- A NOTAM given (in addition to local dissemination) distant dissemination beyond the area of responsibility of the Flight Service Station. These NOTAMs will be stored and available until canceled.

b. NOTAM(L)- A NOTAM given local dissemination by voice and other means, such as telautograph and telephone, to satisfy local user requirements.

c. FDC NOTAM- A NOTAM regulatory in nature, transmitted by USNOF and given system wide dissemination.

NOTICES TO AIRMEN PUBLICATION - A publication issued every 28 days, designed primarily for the pilot, which contains current NOTAM information considered essential to the safety of flight as well as supplemental data to other aeronautical publications. The contraction NTAP is used in NOTAM text.

O

OBSTACLE - An existing object, object of natural growth, or terrain at a fixed geographical location or which may be expected at a fixed location within a prescribed area with reference to which vertical clearance is or must be provided during flight operation.

OBSTACLE DEPARTURE PROCEDURE (ODP)- A preplanned instrument flight rule (IFR) departure procedure printed for pilot use in textual or graphic form to provide obstruction clearance via the least onerous route from the terminal area to the appropriate en route structure. ODPs are recommended for obstruction clearance and may be flown without ATC clearance unless an alternate departure procedure (SID or radar vector) has been specifically assigned by ATC.

OBSTACLE FREE ZONE - The OFZ is a three dimensional volume of airspace which

OFF-ROUTE VECTOR - A vector by ATC which takes an aircraft off a previously assigned route. Altitudes assigned by ATC during such vectors provide required obstacle clearance.

OFFSET PARALLEL RUNWAYS - Staggered runways having centerlines which are parallel.

OMEGA - An RNAV system designed for long-range navigation based upon ground-based electronic navigational aid signals.

ON COURSE -

a. Used to indicate that an aircraft is established on the route centerline.

b. Used by ATC to advise a pilot making a radar approach that his/her aircraft is lined up on the final approach course.

ONE-MINUTE WEATHER - The most recent one minute updated weather broadcast received by a pilot from an uncontrolled airport ASOS/AWOS.

OPTION APPROACH - An approach requested and conducted by a pilot which will result in either a touch-and-go, missed approach, low approach, stop-and-go, or full stop landing.

OUTER AREA (associated with Class C airspace) - Nonregulatory airspace surrounding designated Class C airspace airports wherein ATC provides radar vectoring and sequencing on a full-time basis for all IFR and participating VFR aircraft. The service provided in the outer area is called Class C service which includes: IFR/IFR-standard IFR separation; IFR/VFR-traffic advisories and conflict resolution; and VFR/VFR-traffic advisories and, as appropriate, safety alerts. The normal radius will be 20 nautical miles with some variations based on site-specific requirements. The outer area extends outward from the primary Class C airspace airport and extends from the lower limits of radar/radio coverage up to the ceiling of the approach control's delegated airspace excluding the Class C charted area and other airspace as appropriate.

OUTER MARKER - A marker beacon at or near the glideslope intercept altitude of an ILS approach. It is keyed to transmit two dashes per second on a 400 Hz tone, which is received aurally and visually by compatible airborne equipment. The OM is normally located four to seven miles from the runway threshold on the extended centerline of the runway.

P

PARALLEL ILS APPROACHES - Approaches to parallel runways by IFR aircraft which, when established inbound toward the airport on the adjacent final approach courses, are radar-separated by at least 2 miles.

PILOT BRIEFING - A service provided by the FSS to assist pilots in flight planning. Briefing items may include weather information, NOTAMS, military activities, flow control information, and other items as requested.

PILOT IN COMMAND - The pilot responsible for the operation and safety of an aircraft during flight time.

PILOT WEATHER REPORT - A report of meteorological phenomena encountered by aircraft in flight.

PILOT'S DISCRETION - When used in conjunction with altitude assignments, means that ATC has offered the pilot the option of starting climb or descent whenever he/she wishes and conducting the climb or descent at any rate he/she wishes. He/she may temporarily level off at any intermediate altitude. However, once he/she has vacated an altitude, he/she may not return to that altitude.

POSITION AND HOLD - Used by ATC to inform a pilot to taxi onto the departure runway in takeoff position and hold. It is not authorization for takeoff. It is used when takeoff clearance cannot immediately be issued because of traffic or other reasons.

POSITION REPORT - A report over a known location as transmitted by an aircraft to ATC.

POSITIVE CONTROL - The separation of all air traffic within designated airspace by air traffic control.

PRACTICE INSTRUMENT APPROACH - An instrument approach procedure conducted by a VFR or an IFR aircraft for the purpose of pilot training or proficiency demonstrations.

PRECIPITATION - Any or all forms of water particles (rain, sleet, hail, or snow) that fall from the atmosphere and reach the surface.

PRECIPITATION RADAR WEATHER DESCRIPTIONS - Existing radar systems cannot detect turbulence. However, there is a direct correlation between the degree of turbulence and other weather features associated with thunderstorms and the weather radar precipitation intensity. Controllers will issue (where capable) precipitation intensity as observed by radar when using weather and radar processor (WARP) or NAS ground based digital radars with weather capabilities. When precipitation intensity information is not available, the intensity will be described as UNKNOWN. When intensity levels can be determined, they shall be described as:

a. LIGHT (< 30 dBZ)

b. MODERATE (30 to 40 dBZ)

c. HEAVY (> 40 to 50 dBZ)

d. EXTREME (> 50 dBZ)

PRECISION APPROACH PROCEDURE - A standard instrument approach procedure in which an electronic glideslope/glidepath is provided; e.g., ILS, MLS, and PAR.

PRECISION APPROACH RADAR - Radar equipment in some ATC facilities operated by the FAA and/or the military services at joint-use civil/military locations and separate military installations to detect and display azimuth, elevation, and range of aircraft on the final approach course to a runway. This equipment may be used to monitor certain nonradar approaches, but is primarily used to conduct a precision instrument approach (PAR) wherein the controller issues guidance instructions to the pilot based on the aircraft's position in relation to the final approach course (azimuth), the glidepath (elevation), and the distance (range) from the touchdown point on the runway as displayed on the radar scope.

Note: The abbreviation "PAR" is also used to denote preferential arrival routes in ARTCC computers.

PREFERENTIAL ROUTES - Preferential routes (PDRs, PARs, and PDARs) are adapted in ARTCC computers to accomplish inter/intrafacility controller coordination and to assure that flight data is posted at the proper control positions. Locations having a need for these specific inbound and outbound routes normally publish such routes in local facility bulletins, and their use by pilots minimizes flight plan route amendments. When the workload or traffic situation permits, controllers normally provide radar vectors or assign requested routes to minimize circuitous routing. Preferential routes are usually confined to one ARTCC's area and are referred to by the following names or acronyms:

a. Preferential Departure Route (PDR). A specific departure route from an airport or terminal area to an en route point where there is no further need for flow control. It may be included in

an Instrument Departure Procedure (DP) or a Preferred IFR Route.

b. Preferential Arrival Route (PAR). A specific arrival route from an appropriate en route point to an airport or terminal area. It may be included in a Standard Terminal Arrival (STAR) or a Preferred IFR Route. The abbreviation "PAR" is used primarily within the ARTCC and should not be confused with the abbreviation for Precision Approach Radar.

c. Preferential Departure and Arrival Route (PDAR). A route between two terminals which are within or immediately adjacent to one ARTCC's area. PDARs are not synonymous with Preferred IFR Routes but may be listed as such as they do accomplish essentially the same purpose.

PREFERRED IFR ROUTES - Routes established between busier airports to increase system efficiency and capacity. They normally extend through one or more ARTCC areas and are designed to achieve balanced traffic flows among high density terminals. IFR clearances are issued on the basis of these routes except when severe weather avoidance procedures or other factors dictate otherwise. Preferred IFR Routes are listed in the Airport/Facility Directory. If a flight is planned to or from an area having such routes but the departure or arrival point is not listed in the Airport/Facility Directory, pilots may use that part of a Preferred IFR Route which is appropriate for the departure or arrival point that is listed. Preferred IFR Routes are correlated with DPs and STARs and may be defined by airways, jet routes, direct routes between NAVAIDs, Waypoints, NAVAID radials/DME, or any combinations thereof.

PROCEDURE TURN - The maneuver prescribed when it is necessary to reverse direction to establish an aircraft on the intermediate approach segment or final approach course. The outbound course, direction of turn, distance within which the turn must be completed, and minimum altitude are specified in the procedure. However, unless otherwise restricted, the point at which the turn may be commenced and the type and rate of turn are left to the discretion of the pilot.

PROCEDURE TURN INBOUND - That point of a procedure turn maneuver where course reversal has been completed and an aircraft is established inbound on the intermediate approach segment or final approach course. A report of "procedure turn inbound" is normally used by ATC as a position report for separation purposes.

PROFILE DESCENT - An uninterrupted descent (except where level flight is required for speed adjustment; e.g., 250 knots at 10,000 feet MSL) from cruising altitude/level to interception of a glideslope or to a minimum altitude specified for the initial or intermediate approach segment of a nonprecision instrument approach. The profile descent normally terminates at the approach gate or where the glideslope or other appropriate minimum altitude is intercepted.

PROGRESSIVE TAXI - Precise taxi instructions given to a pilot unfamiliar with the airport or issued in stages as the aircraft proceeds along the taxi route.

PROPOSED DEPARTURE TIME - The time that the aircraft expects to become airborne.

PROTECTED AIRSPACE - The airspace on either side of an oceanic route/track that is equal to one-half the lateral separation minimum except where reduction of protected airspace has been authorized.

PUBLISHED ROUTE - A route for which an IFR altitude has been established and published; e.g., Federal Airways, Jet Routes, Area Navigation Routes, Specified Direct Routes.

Q

Q ROUTE - 'Q' is the designator assigned to published RNAV routes used by the United States.

QNE - The barometric pressure used for the standard altimeter setting (29.92 inches Hg.).

QNH - The barometric pressure as reported by a particular station.

QUADRANT - A quarter part of a circle, centered on a NAVAID, oriented clockwise from magnetic north as follows: NE quadrant 000-089, SE quadrant 090-179, SW quadrant 180-269, NW quadrant 270-359.

QUICK LOOK - A feature of the EAS and ARTS which provides the controller the capability to display full data blocks of tracked aircraft from other control positions.

R

RADAR ADVISORY - The provision of advice and information based on radar observations.

RADAR APPROACH CONTROL FACILITY - A terminal ATC facility that uses radar and non-radar capabilities to provide approach control services to aircraft arriving, departing, or transiting airspace controlled by the facility.

a. Provides radar ATC services to aircraft operating in the vicinity of one or more civil and/or military airports in a terminal area. The facility may provide services of a ground controlled approach (GCA); i.e., ASR and PAR approaches. A radar approach control facility may be operated by FAA, USAF, US Army, USN, USMC, or jointly by FAA and a military service. Specific facility nomenclatures are used for administrative purposes only and are related to the physical location of the facility and the operating service generally as follows:

1. Army Radar Approach Control (ARAC) (Army).

2. Radar Air Traffic Control Facility (RATCF) (Navy/FAA).

3. Radar Approach Control (RAPCON) (Air Force/FAA).

4. Terminal Radar Approach Control (TRACON) (FAA).

5. Air Traffic Control Tower (ATCT) (FAA). (Only those towers delegated approach control authority).

RADAR ARRIVAL - An aircraft arriving at an airport served by a radar facility and in radar contact with the facility.

RADAR CONTACT -

a. Used by ATC to inform an aircraft that it is identified on the radar display and radar flight following will be provided until radar identification is terminated. Radar service may also be provided within the limits of necessity and capability. When a pilot is informed of "radar contact," he/she automatically discontinues reporting over compulsory reporting points.

RADAR CONTACT LOST - Used by ATC to inform a pilot that radar data used to determine the aircraft's position is no longer being received, or is no longer reliable and radar service is no longer being provided. The loss may be attributed to several factors including the aircraft merging with weather or ground clutter, the aircraft operating below radar line of sight coverage, the aircraft entering an area of poor radar return, failure of the aircraft transponder, or failure of the ground radar equipment.

RADAR IDENTIFICATION - The process of ascertaining that an observed radar target is the radar return from a particular aircraft.

RADAR REQUIRED - A term displayed on charts and approach plates and included in FDC NOTAMs to alert pilots that segments of either an instrument approach procedure or a route are not navigable because of either the absence or unusability of a NAVAID. The pilot can expect to be provided radar navigational guidance while transiting segments labeled with this term.

RADAR ROUTE - A flight path or route over which an aircraft is vectored. Navigational guidance and altitude assignments are provided by ATC.

RADAR SERVICE - A term which encompasses one or more of the following services based on the use of radar which can be provided by a controller to a pilot of a radar identified aircraft.

a. Radar Monitoring - The radar flight-following of aircraft, whose primary navigation is being performed by the pilot, to observe and note deviations from its authorized flight path, airway, or route. When being applied specifically to radar monitoring of instrument approaches; i.e., with precision approach radar (PAR) or radar monitoring of simultaneous ILS/MLS approaches, it includes advice and instructions whenever an aircraft nears or exceeds the prescribed PAR safety limit or simultaneous ILS/MLS no transgression zone.

b. Radar Navigational Guidance - Vectoring aircraft to provide course guidance.

c. Radar Separation - Radar spacing of aircraft in accordance with established minima. of radar.

RADAR SERVICE TERMINATED - Used by ATC to inform a pilot that he/she will no longer be provided any of the services that could be received while in radar contact. Radar service is automatically terminated, and the pilot is not advised in the following cases:

a. An aircraft cancels its IFR flight plan, except within Class B airspace, Class C airspace, a TRSA, or where Basic Radar service is provided.

b. An aircraft conducting an instrument, visual, or contact approach has landed or has been instructed to change to advisory frequency.

c. An arriving VFR aircraft, receiving radar service to a tower-controlled airport within Class B airspace, Class C airspace, a TRSA, or where sequencing service is provided, has landed; or to all other airports, is instructed to change to tower or advisory frequency.

d. An aircraft completes a radar approach.

RADAR SURVEILLANCE - The radar observation of a given geographical area for the purpose of performing some radar function.

RADAR TRAFFIC ADVISORIES - Advisories issued to alert pilots to known or observed radar traffic which may affect the intended route of flight of their aircraft.

RADAR TRAFFIC INFORMATION SERVICE -

RADIAL - A magnetic bearing extending from a VOR/VORTAC/TACAN navigation facility.

RADIO ALTIMETER - Aircraft equipment which makes use of the reflection of radio waves from the ground to determine the height of the aircraft above the surface.

RADIO MAGNETIC INDICATOR - An aircraft navigational instrument coupled with a gyro compass or similar compass that indicates the direction of a selected NAVAID and indicates bearing with respect to the heading of the aircraft.

RANDOM ALTITUDE - An altitude inappropriate for direction of flight and/or not in accordance with FAAO 7110.65, Para 4-5-1, VERTICAL SEPARATION MINIMA.

RANDOM ROUTE - Any route not established or charted/published or not otherwise available to all users.

READ BACK - Repeat my message back to me.

RECEIVER AUTONOMOUS INTEGRITY MONITORING (RAIM) - A technique whereby a civil GNSS receiver/processor determines the integrity of the GNSS navigation signals without reference to sensors or non-DoD integrity systems other than the receiver itself. This determination is achieved by a consistency check among redundant pseudorange measurements.

REMOTE AIRPORT ADVISORY (RAA) - A remote service which may be provided by facilities, which are not located on the landing airport, but have a discrete ground-to-air communication frequency or tower frequency when the tower is closed, automated weather reporting with voice available to the pilot at the landing airport, and a continuous ASOS/AWOS data display, other direct reading instruments, or manual observation is available to the AFSS specialist.

REMOTE AIRPORT INFORMATION SERVICE (RAIS) - A temporary service provided by facilities, which are not located on the landing airport, but have communication capability and automated weather reporting available to the pilot at the landing airport.

REMOTE COMMUNICATIONS AIR/GROUND FACILITY - An unmanned VHF/UHF transmitter/receiver facility which is used to expand ARTCC air/ground communications coverage and to facilitate direct contact between pilots and controllers. RCAG facilities are sometimes not equipped with emergency frequencies 121.5 MHz and 243.0 MHz.

REMOTE COMMUNICATIONS OUTLET - An unmanned communications facility remotely controlled by air traffic personnel. RCOs serve FSSs. RTRs serve terminal ATC facilities. An RCO or RTR may be UHF or VHF and will extend the communication range of the air traffic facility. There are several classes of RCOs and RTRs. The class is determined by the number of transmitters or receivers. Classes A through G are used primarily for air/ground purposes. RCO and RTR class O facilities are non-protected outlets subject to undetected and prolonged outages. RCO (O's) and RTR (O's)

Glossary

were established for the express purpose of providing ground-to-ground communications between air traffic control specialists and pilots located at a satellite airport for delivering en route clearances, issuing departure authorizations, and acknowledging instrument flight rules cancellations or departure/landing times. As a secondary function, they may be used for advisory purposes whenever the aircraft is below the coverage of the primary air/ground frequency.

EPORT - Used to instruct pilots to advise ATC of specified information; e.g., "Report passing Hamilton VOR."

REQUEST FULL ROUTE CLEARANCE - Used by pilots to request that the entire route of flight be read verbatim in an ATC clearance. Such request should be made to preclude receiving an ATC clearance based on the original filed flight plan when a filed IFR flight plan has been revised by the pilot, company, or operations prior to departure.

REQUIRED NAVIGATION PERFORMANCE (RNP) - A statement of the navigational performance necessary for operation within a defined airspace. The following terms are commonly associated with RNP:

a. Required Navigation Performance Level or Type (RNP-X). A value, in nautical miles (NM), from the intended horizontal position within which an aircraft would be at least 95-percent of the total flying time.

b. Required Navigation Performance (RNP) Airspace. A generic term designating airspace, route (s), leg (s), operation (s), or procedure (s) where minimum required navigational performance (RNP) have been established.

c. Actual Navigation Performance (ANP). A measure of the current estimated navigational performance. Also referred to as Estimated Position Error (EPE).

d. Estimated Position Error (EPE). A measure of the current estimated navigational performance. Also referred to as Actual Navigation Performance (ANP).

e. Lateral Navigation (LNAV). A function of area navigation (RNAV) equipment which calculates, displays, and provides lateral guidance to a profile or path.

f. Vertical Navigation (VNAV). A function of area navigation (RNAV) equipment which calculates, displays, and provides vertical guidance to a profile or path.

RESOLUTION ADVISORY - A display indication given to the pilot by the traffic alert and collision avoidance systems (TCAS II) recommending a maneuver to increase vertical separation relative to an intruding aircraft. Positive, negative, and vertical speed limit (VSL) advisories constitute the resolution advisories. A resolution advisory is also classified as corrective or preventive

RESUME NORMAL SPEED - Used by ATC to advise a pilot that previously issued speed control restrictions are deleted. An instruction to "resume normal speed" does not delete speed restrictions that are applicable to published procedures of upcoming segments of flight, unless specifically stated by ATC. This does not relieve the pilot of those speed restrictions which are applicable to 14 CFR Section 91.117.

RESUME OWN NAVIGATION - Used by ATC to advise a pilot to resume his/her own navigation-

al responsibility. It is issued after completion of a radar vector or when radar contact is lost while the aircraft is being radar vectored.

ROGER - I have received all of your last transmission. It should not be used to answer a question requiring a yes or a no answer.

ROUTE - A defined path, consisting of one or more courses in a horizontal plane, which aircraft traverse over the surface of the earth.

ROUTE SEGMENT - As used in Air Traffic Control, a part of a route that can be defined by two navigational fixes, two NAVAIDs, or a fix and a NAVAID.

RUNWAY GRADIENT - The average slope, measured in percent, between two ends or points on a runway. Runway gradient is depicted on Government aerodrome sketches when total runway gradient exceeds 0.3%.

RUNWAY HEADING - The magnetic direction that corresponds with the runway centerline extended, not the painted runway number. When cleared to "fly or maintain runway heading," pilots are expected to fly or maintain the heading that corresponds with the extended centerline of the departure runway. Drift correction shall not be applied; e.g., Runway 4, actual magnetic heading of the runway centerline 044, fly 044.

RUNWAY IN USE/ACTIVE RUNWAY/DUTY RUNWAY - Any runway or runways currently being used for takeoff or landing. When multiple runways are used, they are all considered active runways. In the metering sense, a selectable adapted item which specifies the landing runway configuration or direction of traffic flow. The adapted optimum flight plan from each transition fix to the vertex is determined by the runway configuration for arrival metering processing purposes.

RUNWAY OVERRUN - In military aviation exclusively, a stabilized or paved area beyond the end of a runway, of the same width as the runway plus shoulders, centered on the extended runway centerline.

RUNWAY PROFILE DESCENT - An instrument flight rules (IFR) air traffic control arrival procedure to a runway published for pilot use in graphic and/or textual form and may be associated with a STAR. Runway Profile Descents provide routing and may depict crossing altitudes, speed restrictions, and headings to be flown from the en route structure to the point where the pilot will receive clearance for and execute an instrument approach procedure. A Runway Profile Descent may apply to more than one runway if so stated on the chart.

RUNWAY TRANSITION-

a. Conventional STARs/SIDs. The portion of a STAR/SID that serves a particular runway or runways at an airport.

b. RNAV STARs/SIDs. Defines a path(s) from the common route to the final point(s) on a STAR. For a SID, the common route that serves a particular runway or runways at an airport.

S

SAFETY ALERT - A safety alert issued by ATC to aircraft under their control if ATC is aware the aircraft is at an altitude which, in the controller's judgment, places the aircraft in unsafe proximity to terrain, obstructions, or other aircraft. The controller may discontinue the issuance of fur-

ther alerts if the pilot advises he/she is taking action to correct the situation or has the other aircraft in sight.

a. Terrain/Obstruction Alert - A safety alert issued by ATC to aircraft under their control if ATC is aware the aircraft is at an altitude which, in the controller's judgment, places the aircraft in unsafe proximity to terrain/obstructions; e.g., "Low Altitude Alert, check your altitude immediately."

b. Aircraft Conflict Alert - A safety alert issued by ATC to aircraft under their control if ATC is aware of an aircraft that is not under their control at an altitude which, in the controller's judgment, places both aircraft in unsafe proximity to each other. With the alert, ATC will offer the pilot an alternate course of action when feasible; e.g., "Traffic Alert, advise you turn right heading zero niner zero or climb to eight thousand immediately."

Note: The issuance of a safety alert is contingent upon the capability of the controller to have an awareness of an unsafe condition. The course of action provided will be predicated on other traffic under ATC control. Once the alert is issued, it is solely the pilot's prerogative to determine what course of action, if any, he/she will take.

SAY AGAIN - Used to request a repeat of the last transmission. Usually specifies transmission or portion thereof not understood or received; e.g., "Say again all after ABRAM VOR."

SAY ALTITUDE - Used by ATC to ascertain an aircraft's specific altitude/flight level. When the aircraft is climbing or descending, the pilot should state the indicated altitude rounded to the nearest 100 feet.

SAY HEADING - Used by ATC to request an aircraft heading. The pilot should state the actual heading of the aircraft.

SCHEDULED TIME OF ARRIVAL (STA) - A STA is the desired time that an aircraft should cross a certain point (landing or metering fix). It takes other traffic and airspace configuration into account. A STA time shows the results of the TMA scheduler that has calculated an arrival time according to parameters such as optimized spacing, aircraft performance, and weather.

SDF -

SEGMENTED CIRCLE - A system of visual indicators designed to provide traffic pattern information at airports without operating control towers.

SEGMENTS OF AN INSTRUMENT APPROACH PROCEDURE - An instrument approach procedure may have as many as four separate segments depending on how the approach procedure is structured.

a. Initial Approach - The segment between the initial approach fix and the intermediate fix or the point where the aircraft is established on the intermediate course or final approach course.

b. Intermediate Approach - The segment between the intermediate fix or point and the final approach fix.

c. Final Approach - The segment between the final approach fix or point and the runway, airport, or missed approach point.

d. Missed Approach - The segment between the missed approach point or the point of arrival at decision height and the missed approach fix at the prescribed altitude.

SEVERE WEATHER AVOIDANCE PLAN - An approved plan to minimize the affect of severe weather on traffic flows in impacted terminal and/or ARTCC areas. SWAP is normally implemented to provide the least disruption to the ATC system when flight through portions of airspace is difficult or impossible due to severe weather.

SEVERE WEATHER FORECAST ALERTS - Preliminary messages issued in order to alert users that a Severe Weather Watch Bulletin (WW) is being issued. These messages define areas of possible severe thunderstorms or tornado activity. The messages are unscheduled and issued as required by the National Severe Storm Forecast Center at Kansas City, Missouri.

SHORT RANGE CLEARANCE - A clearance issued to a departing IFR flight which authorizes IFR flight to a specific fix short of the destination while air traffic control facilities are coordinating and obtaining the complete clearance.

SIDESTEP MANEUVER - A visual maneuver accomplished by a pilot at the completion of an instrument approach to permit a straight-in landing on a parallel runway not more than 1,200 feet to either side of the runway to which the instrument approach was conducted.

SIGMET - A weather advisory issued concerning weather significant to the safety of all aircraft. SIGMET advisories cover severe and extreme turbulence, severe icing, and widespread dust or sandstorms that reduce visibility to less than 3 miles.

SIMPLIFIED DIRECTIONAL FACILITY - A NAVAID used for nonprecision instrument approaches. The final approach course is similar to that of an ILS localizer except that the SDF course may be offset from the runway, generally not more than 3 degrees, and the course may be wider than the localizer, resulting in a lower degree of accuracy.

SIMULTANEOUS ILS APPROACHES - An approach system permitting simultaneous ILS/MLS approaches to airports having parallel runways separated by at least 4,300 feet between centerlines. Integral parts of a total system are ILS/MLS, radar, communications, ATC procedures, and appropriate airborne equipment.

FLIP IFR Supplement under "Communications" indicates this service is available at an aerodrome.

SQUAWK (Mode, Code, Function) - Activate specific modes/codes/functions on the aircraft transponder; e.g., "Squawk three/alpha, two one zero five, low."

STAND BY - Means the controller or pilot must pause for a few seconds, usually to attend to other duties of a higher priority. Also means to wait as in "stand by for clearance." The caller should reestablish contact if a delay is lengthy. "Stand by" is not an approval or denial.

STANDARD INSTRUMENT DEPARTURE (SID)- A preplanned instrument flight rule (IFR) air traffic control (ATC) departure procedure printed for pilot/controller use in graphic form to provide obstacle clearance and a transition from the terminal area to the appropriate en route structure. SIDs are primarily designed for system enhancement to expedite traffic flow and to reduce pilot/controller workload. ATC clearance must always be received prior to flying a SID.

STANDARD RATE TURN - A turn of three degrees per second.

STANDARD TERMINAL ARRIVAL - A preplanned instrument flight rule (IFR) air traffic control arrival procedure published for pilot use in graphic and/or textual form. STARs provide transition from the en route structure to an outer fix or an instrument approach fix/arrival waypoint in the terminal area.

STEP TURN - A maneuver used to put a float plane in a planing configuration prior to entering an active sea lane for takeoff. The STEP TURN maneuver should only be used upon pilot request.

STEPDOWN FIX - A fix permitting additional descent within a segment of an instrument approach procedure by identifying a point at which a controlling obstacle has been safely overflown.

STOP ALTITUDE SQUAWK - Used by ATC to inform an aircraft to turn-off the automatic altitude reporting feature of its transponder. It is issued when the verbally reported altitude varies 300 feet or more from the automatic altitude report.

STOP SQUAWK (Mode or Code) - Used by ATC to tell the pilot to turn specified functions of the aircraft transponder off.

STRAIGHT-IN APPROACH IFR - An instrument approach wherein final approach is begun without first having executed a procedure turn, not necessarily completed with a straight-in landing or made to straight-in landing minimums.

STRAIGHT-IN APPROACH VFR - Entry into the traffic pattern by interception of the extended runway centerline (final approach course) without executing any other portion of the traffic pattern.

STRAIGHT-IN LANDING - A landing made on a runway aligned within 30° of the final approach course following completion of an instrument approach.

SUNSET AND SUNRISE - The mean solar times of sunset and sunrise as published in the Nautical Almanac, converted to local standard time for the locality concerned. Within Alaska, the end of evening civil twilight and the beginning of morning civil twilight, as deflned for each locality.

SUPER HIGH FREQUENCY - The frequency band between 3 and 30 gigahertz (GHz). The elevation and azimuth stations of the microwave landing system operate from 5031 MHz to 5091 MHz in this spectrum.

SURVEILLANCE APPROACH - An instrument approach wherein the air traffic controller issues instructions, for pilot compliance, based on aircraft position in relation to the final approach course (azimuth), and the distance (range) from the end of the runway as displayed on the controller's radar scope. The controller will provide recommended altitudes on final approach if requested by the pilot.

T

TACTICAL AIR NAVIGATION - An ultra-high frequency electronic rho-theta air navigation aid which provides suitably equipped aircraft a continuous indication of bearing and distance to the TACAN station.

TERMINAL AREA - A general term used to describe airspace in which approach control service or airport traffic control service is provided.

TERMINAL AREA FACILITY - A facility providing air traffic control service for arriving and departing IFR, VFR, Special VFR, and on occasion en route aircraft.

TERMINAL DATA LINK SYSTEM (TDLS) - A system that provides Digital Automatic Terminal Information Service (D-ATIS) both on a specified radio frequency and also, for subscribers, in a text message via data link to the cockpit or to a gate printer. TDLS also provides Pre-departure Clearances (PDC), at selected airports, to subscribers, through a service provider, in text to the cockpit or to a gate printer. In addition, TDLS will emulate the Flight Data Input/Output (FDIO) information within the control tower.

TERMINAL RADAR SERVICE AREA - Airspace surrounding designated airports wherein ATC provides radar vectoring, sequencing, and separation on a full-time basis for all IFR and participating VFR aircraft. The AIM contains an explanation of TRSA. TRSAs are depicted on VFR aeronautical charts. Pilot participation is urged but is not mandatory.

TERRAIN FOLLOWING - The flight of a military aircraft maintaining a constant AGL altitude above the terrain or the highest obstruction. The altitude of the aircraft will constantly change with the varying terrain and/or obstruction.

THAT IS CORRECT - The understanding you have is right.

360 OVERHEAD-

THRESHOLD - The beginning of that portion of the runway usable for landing.

THRESHOLD CROSSING HEIGHT - The theoretical height above the runway threshold at which the aircraft's glideslope antenna would be if the aircraft maintains the trajectory established by the mean ILS glideslope or MLS glidepath.

TOUCHDOWN ZONE - The first 3,000 feet of the runway beginning at the threshold. The area is used for determination of Touchdown Zone Elevation in the development of straight-in landing minimums for instrument approaches.

TOUCHDOWN ZONE ELEVATION - The highest elevation in the first 3,000 feet of the landing surface. TDZE is indicated on the instrument approach procedure chart when straight-in landing minimums are authorized.

TOWER EN ROUTE CONTROL SERVICE - The control of IFR en route traffic within delegated airspace between two or more adjacent approach control facilities. This service is designed to expedite traffic and reduce control and pilot communication requirements.

TRACK - The actual flight path of an aircraft over the surface of the earth.

TRAFFIC ADVISORIES - Advisories issued to alert pilots to other known or observed air traffic which may be in such proximity to the position or intended route of flight of their aircraft to warrant their attention. Such advisories may be based on:

a. Visual observation.

b. Observation of radar identified and nonidentified aircraft targets on an ATC radar display, or

c. Verbal reports from pilots or other facilities.

Note 1: The word "traffic" followed by additional information, if known, is used to provide such advisories; e.g., "Traffic, 2 o'clock, one zero miles, southbound, eight thousand."

Note 2: Traffic advisory service will be provided to the extent possible depending on higher priority duties of the controller or other limitations; e.g., radar limitations, volume of traffic, frequency congestion, or controller workload. Radar/nonradar traffic advisories do not relieve the pilot of his/her responsibility to see and avoid other aircraft. Pilots are cautioned that there are many times when the controller is not able to give traffic advisories concerning all traffic in the aircraft's proximity; in other words, when a pilot requests or is receiving traffic advisories, he/she should not assume that all traffic will be issued.

TRAFFIC ALERT AND COLLISION AVOIDANCE SYSTEM - An airborne collision avoidance system based on radar beacon signals which operates independent of ground-based equipment. TCAS-I generates traffic advisories only. TCAS-II generates traffic advisories, and resolution (collision avoidance) advisories in the vertical plane.

TRAFFIC IN SIGHT - Used by pilots to inform a controller that previously issued traffic is in sight.

TRAFFIC NO FACTOR - Indicates that the traffic described in a previously issued traffic advisory is no factor.

TRANSITION -

a. The general term that describes the change from one phase of flight or flight condition to another; e.g., transition from en route flight to the approach or transition from instrument flight to visual flight.

b. A published procedure (DP Transition) used to connect the basic DP to one of several en route airways/jet routes, or a published procedure (STAR Transition) used to connect one of several en route airways/jet routes to the basic STAR.

TRANSITION POINT - A point at an adapted number of miles from the vertex at which an arrival aircraft would normally commence descent from its en route altitude. This is the first fix adapted on the arrival speed segments.

TRANSITION WAYPOINT - The waypoint that defines the beginning of a runway or en route transition on an RNAV SID or STAR.

TRANSITIONAL AIRSPACE - That portion of controlled airspace wherein aircraft change from one phase of flight or flight condition to another.

TRANSMISSOMETER - An apparatus used to determine visibility by measuring the transmission of light through the atmosphere. It is the measurement source for determining runway visual range (RVR) and runway visibility value (RVV).

TURN ANTICIPATION - (maneuver anticipation).

U

ULTRAHIGH FREQUENCY - The frequency band between 300 and 3,000 MHz. The bank of radio frequencies used for military air/ground voice communications. In some instances this may go as low as 225 MHz and still be referred to as UHF.

UNABLE - Indicates inability to comply with a specific instruction, request, or clearance.

UNDER THE HOOD - Indicates that the pilot is using a hood to restrict visibility outside the cockpit while simulating instrument flight. An appropriately rated pilot is required in the other control seat while this operation is being conducted.

UNPUBLISHED ROUTE - A route for which no minimum altitude is published or charted for pilot use. It may include a direct route between NAVAIDs, a radial, a radar vector, or a final approach course beyond the segments of an instrument approach procedure.

UNRELIABLE (GPS/WAAS) - An advisory to pilots indicating the expected level of service of the GPS and/or WAAS may not be available. Pilots must then determine the adequacy of the signal for desired use.

URGENCY - A condition of being concerned about safety and of requiring timely but not immediate assistance; a potential distress condition.

V

VERIFY SPECIFIC DIRECTION OF TAKEOFF (OR TURNS AFTER TAKEOFF) - Used by ATC to ascertain an aircraft's direction of takeoff and/or direction of turn after takeoff. It is normally used for IFR departures from an airport not having a control tower. When direct communication with the pilot is not possible, the request and information may be relayed through an FSS, dispatcher, or by other means.

VERTICAL NAVIGATION (VNAV) - A function of area navigation (RNAV) equipment which calculates, displays, and provides vertical guidance to a profile or path.

VERTICAL SEPARATION - Separation established by assignment of different altitudes or flight levels.

VERY HIGH FREQUENCY - The frequency band between 30 and 300 MHz. Portions of this band, 108 to 118 MHz, are used for certain NAVAIDs; 118 to 136 MHz are used for civil air/ground voice communications. Other frequencies in this band are used for purposes not related to air traffic control.

VFR CONDITIONS - Weather conditions equal to or better than the minimum for flight under visual flight rules. The term may be used as an ATC clearance/instruction only when:

a. An IFR aircraft requests a climb/descent in VFR conditions.

b. The clearance will result in noise abatement benefits where part of the IFR departure route does not conform to an FAA approved noise abatement route or altitude.

c. A pilot has requested a practice instrument approach and is not on an IFR flight plan.

Note: All pilots receiving this authorization must comply with the VFR visibility and distance from cloud criteria in 14 CFR Part 91. Use of the term does not relieve controllers of their responsibility to separate aircraft in Class B and Class C airspace or TRSAs as required by FAAO 7110.65. When used as an ATC clearance/instruction, the term may be abbreviated "VFR;" e.g., "MAINTAIN VFR," "CLIMB/DESCEND VFR," etc.

VFR NOT RECOMMENDED - An advisory provided by a flight service station to a pilot during a preflight or inflight weather briefing that flight under visual flight rules is not recommended. To be given when the current and/or forecast weather conditions are at or below VFR minimums. It does not abrogate the pilot's authority to make his/her own decision.

VFR-ON-TOP - ATC authorization for an IFR aircraft to operate in VFR conditions at any appropriate VFR altitude (as specified in 14 CFR and as restricted by ATC). A pilot receiving this authorization must comply with the VFR visibility, distance from cloud criteria, and the minimum IFR altitudes specified in 14 CFR Part 91. The use of this term does not relieve controllers of their responsibility to separate aircraft in Class B and Class C airspace or TRSAs as required by FAAO 7110.65.

VISIBILITY - The ability, as determined by atmospheric conditions and expressed in units of distance, to see and identify prominent unlighted objects by day and prominent lighted objects by night. Visibility is reported as statute miles, hundreds of feet or meters.

a. Flight Visibility - The average forward horizontal distance, from the cockpit of an aircraft in flight, at which prominent unlighted objects may be seen and identified by day and prominent lighted objects may be seen and identified by night.

b. Ground Visibility - Prevailing horizontal visibility near the earth's surface as reported by the United States National Weather Service or an accredited observer.

c. Prevailing Visibility - The greatest horizontal visibility equaled or exceeded throughout at least half the horizon circle which need not necessarily be continuous.

d. Runway Visibility Value (RVV) - The visibility determined for a particular runway by a transmissometer. A meter provides a continuous indication of the visibility (reported in miles or fractions of miles) for the runway. RVV is used in lieu of prevailing visibility in determining minimums for a particular runway.

e. Runway Visual Range (RVR) - An instrumentally derived value, based on standard calibrations, that represents the horizontal distance a pilot will see down the runway from the approach end. It is based on the sighting of either high intensity runway lights or on the visual contrast of other targets whichever yields the greater visual range. RVR, in contrast to prevailing or runway visibility, is based on what a pilot in a moving aircraft should see looking down the runway. RVR is horizontal visual range, not slant visual range. It is based on the measurement of a transmissometer made near the touchdown point of the instrument runway and is reported in hundreds of feet. RVR is used in lieu of RVV and/or prevailing visibility in determining minimums for a particular runway.

1. Touchdown RVR - The RVR visibility readout values obtained from RVR equipment serving the runway touchdown zone.

2. Mid-RVR - The RVR readout values obtained from RVR equipment located midfield of the runway.

3. Rollout RVR - The RVR readout values obtained from RVR equipment located nearest the rollout end of the runway.

VISUAL DESCENT POINT - A defined point on the final approach course of a nonprecision straight-in approach procedure from which normal descent from the MDA to the runway touchdown point may be commenced, provided the approach threshold of that runway, or approach lights, or other markings identifiable with the approach end of that runway are clearly visible to the pilot.

VISUAL FLIGHT RULES - Rules that govern the procedures for conducting flight under visual conditions. The term "VFR" is also used in the United States to indicate weather conditions that are equal to or greater than minimum VFR requirements. In addition, it is used by pilots and controllers to indicate type of flight plan.

VISUAL HOLDING - The holding of aircraft at selected, prominent geographical fixes which can be easily recognized from the air.

VISUAL METEOROLOGICAL CONDITIONS - Meteorological conditions expressed in terms of visibility, distance from cloud, and ceiling equal to or better than specified minima.

VISUAL SEPARATION - A means employed by ATC to separate aircraft in terminal areas and en route airspace in the NAS. There are two ways to effect this separation:

a. The tower controller sees the aircraft involved and issues instructions, as necessary, to ensure that the aircraft avoid each other.

b. A pilot sees the other aircraft involved and upon instructions from the controller provides his/her own separation by maneuvering his/her aircraft as necessary to avoid it. This may involve following another aircraft or keeping it in sight until it is no longer a factor.

VOT - A ground facility which emits a test signal to check VOR receiver accuracy. Some VOTs are available to the user while airborne, and others are limited to ground use only.

W

WAYPOINT - A predetermined geographical position used for route/instrument approach definition, progress reports, published VFR routes, visual reporting points or points for transitioning and/or circumnavigating controlled and/or special use airspace, that is defined relative to a VORTAC station or in terms of latitude/longitude coordinates.

WEATHER ADVISORY - In aviation weather forecast practice, an expression of hazardous weather conditions not predicted in the area forecast, as they affect the operation of air traffic and as prepared by the NWS.

WHEN ABLE - When used in conjunction with ATC instructions, gives the pilot the latitude to delay compliance until a condition or event has been reconciled. Unlike "pilot discretion," when instructions are prefaced "when able," the pilot is expected to seek the first opportunity to comply. Once a maneuver has been initiated, the pilot is expected to continue until the specifications of the instructions have been met. "When

able," should not be used when expeditious compliance is required.

WIDE-AREA AUGMENTATION SYSTEM (WAAS) - The WAAS is a satellite navigation system consisting of the equipment and software which augments the GPS Standard Positioning Service (SPS). The WAAS provides enhanced integrity, accuracy, availability, and continuity over and above GPS SPS. The differential correction function provides improved accuracy required for precision approach.

WILCO - I have received your message, understand it, and will comply with it.

WIND SHEAR - A change in wind speed and/or wind direction in a short distance resulting in a tearing or shearing effect. It can exist in a horizontal or vertical direction and occasionally in both.

WORDS TWICE -

a. As a request: "Communication is difficult. Please say every phrase twice."

b. As information: "Since communications are difficult, every phrase in this message will be spoken twice."

The FAA's Suggested IFR Clearance Shorthand

Above	ABV	Delay Indefinite	DLI	Outer Marker	OM
Above (Altitude, Hundreds of Feet	70	Depart (direction, if specified)	T→ ( )	Over (Station)	OKC
Adjust speed to 250 knots	250 K	Departure Control	DPC	On Course	OC
Advise	ADZ	Descend To (Altitude, Hundreds of Feet)	↓70	Precision Approach Radar	PAR
After (Passing	<	Direct	DR	Procedure Turn	PT
Airway (Designation)	V26	Direction: Eastbound (EB), Westbound (WB),		Radar Vector	RV
Airport	A	Northbound (NB), Southbound (SB) Inbound		Radial (080° Radial)	080R
Alternate Instructions	( )	(IB), Outbound (OB)		Reduce Speed 20 Knots	-20 K
Altitude 6,000-17,000	60-170	DME Fix (Mile)	21	Remain This Frequency	RTF
And	&	Each	EA	Remain Well to Left Side	LS
Approach	AP	Enter Control Area	⌂	Remain Well to Right Side	RS
Approach Control	APC	Estimated Time of Arrival	ETA	Report Crossing	RX
Area Navigation	RNAV	Expect	EX	Report Departing	RD
Arriving	↓	Expect-Further-Clearance	EFC	Report Leaving	RL
At	@	Fan Marker	FM	Report on Course	R-CRS
At or Above	↥	Final	F	Report Over	RO
At or Below	↧	Final Approach	FA	Report Passing	RP
(ATC) Advises	CA	Flight Level	FL	Report Reaching	RR
(ATC) Clears or Cleared	C	Flight Planned Route	FPR	Report Starting Procedure Turn	RSPT
(ATC) Requests	CR	For Further Clearance	FFC	Reverse Course	RC
Back Course	BC	For Further Headings	FFH	Right Turn After Takeoff	↻
Bearing	BR	From	FM	Runway Heading	RH
Before (Reaching, Passing)	>	Ground	GND	Runway (Number)	RY18
Below	BLO	GPS Approach	GPS	Squawk	SQ
Below (Altitude, Hundreds of Feet)	70	Heading	HDG	Standby	STBY
Center	CTR	Hold (Direction	H-W	Straight-in Approach	SI
Clearance Void if Not Off By (time)	v<	Holding Pattern	⬯	Surveillance Radar Approach	ASR
Cleared as Filed	CAF	ILS Approach	ILS	Takeoff (Direction)	T N
Cleared to Airport	A	Increase Speed 30 Knots	+30 K	Tower	→Z
Cleared to Climb/Descend at Pilot's Discretion	PD	Initial Approach	I	Turn Left	TL
Cleared to Cross	X	Instrument Departure Procedure	DP	Turn Right	TR
Cleared to Depart From the Fix	D	Intersection	XN	Until	/
Cleared to the Fix	F	Join or Intercept Airway/Jet Route/Track or		Until Advised (By)	UA
Cleared to Hold and Instructions Issued	H	CourseLeft Turn After Takeoff	↗	Until Further Advised	UFA
Cleared to Land	L	Locator Outer Marker	LOM	VFR Conditions On Top	OTP
Cleared to the Outer Marker	O	Magnetic	M	Via	VIA
Climb to (Altitude, Hundreds of Feet)	↑70	Maintain	↦	Victor (Airway Number)	V14
Contact Approach	CT	Maintain VFR Conditions On Top	VFR	Visual Approach	VA
Contact (Denver) Approach Control	(den	Middle Compass Locator	ML	VOR	⊙
Contact (Denver) Center	DEN	Middle Marker	MM	VOR Approach	VR
Course	CRS	Missed Approach	MA	VORTAC	Ⓣ
Cross	X	Nondirectional Beacon Approach	NDB		
Cruise	→	Out of (Leave) Control Area	⌂		